C0-ADX-180

IDENTIFICATION OF PURE ORGANIC COMPOUNDS

IDENTIFICATION OF PURE ORGANIC COMPOUNDS

Tables of Data on Selected Compounds of Order I

(Compounds of carbon with hydrogen or with hydrogen and oxygen)

BY

ERNEST HAMLIN HUNTRESS, Ph.D.

Associate Professor of Organic Chemistry
Massachusetts Institute of Technology

AND

SAMUEL PARSONS MULLIKEN, Ph.D.

Late Professor of Organic Chemistry
Massachusetts Institute of Technology

NEW YORK
JOHN WILEY & SONS, Inc.
London: CHAPMAN & HALL, Limited
1941

Printed in U. S. A.

Printing
F. H. GILSON CO.
BOSTON

Composition
TECHNICAL COMPOSITION CO.
BOSTON

Binding
STANHOPE BINDERY
BOSTON

PREFACE

This volume presents in organized and accessible form a summary of data on a selected list of organic compounds containing carbon and hydrogen, or carbon, hydrogen, and oxygen. It will be found useful not only to students engaged with courses in organic qualitative analysis but also to all chemists who have occasion to utilize any of the compounds herein considered. Users of this volume should not construe its approach as indissolubly connected with or restricted to a particular scheme of analysis, but rather recognize that its data will provide valuable guidance irrespective of the particular avenue by which the analyst may elect to undertake the identification of an unknown.

Because the scope of this volume is restricted to compounds containing only carbon and hydrogen, either with or without oxygen, as was the first volume of Mulliken's *Identification of Pure Organic Compounds* of 1904, and because the primary form of classification is similar to that employed in that work, a merely superficial inspection might lead to the misconception that the present volume represents merely a revision or rewritten second edition of that work. Careful examination will quickly disclose, however, that on the contrary it constitutes an entirely new contribution. Evidence for this view may readily be obtained by comparing with the appropriate entry of the earlier book the corresponding treatment of the same compound in the present volume.

In 1929 the undersigned was invited by the late Professor Samuel P. Mulliken to collaborate in the preparation of a manual of organic qualitative analysis. This joint effort was intended to coordinate and modernize the most important general procedures of the three-volume work of the then senior author, and to integrate the somewhat scattered directions of the larger work into a compact form suitable in magnitude and arrangement for constant use by individual students in large laboratory classes. It presently became increasingly evident, however, that such an undertaking would require the preparation of entirely new tables of data on the properties of individual compounds, especially the uniquely important substances comprising Order I. The execution of this very considerable enterprise has been carried out exclusively by the undersigned.

It should therefore be pointed out that there are two distinct new works in which the names of Professor Mulliken and the undersigned are associated. One of these, designated *A Manual for the Systematic Identification of Organic Compounds*, is generally referred to as Mulliken and Huntress, or simply as the *Manual*. In several mimeographed or planographed editions the *Manual* has been for a number of years in constant use, not only by students in the Massachusetts Institute of Technology, but also by those in many other laboratories. The other book is the present volume of *Tables of Data on Selected Compounds of Order I,* conveniently distinguished from the *Manual* by referring to it as Huntress and Mulliken, or simply as the *Tables.* The preparation of these two books has proceeded concurrently for more than eleven years. The present volume is published at this time in order to make generally available without further delay the considerable amount of data which has been assembled and organized and so to facilitate, expedite, and stimulate further development of a most important branch of organic chemistry. Although closely correlated with and containing many cross references to the *Manual,* this volume has been so constructed as to be independent of it and thus to serve the adherents of any scheme of analysis whatever. Publication of the *Manual* is, however, expected in the near future.

Unusual care has been given to the selection of the 1364 compounds whose characteristics are listed in this volume. Many of these represent materials now of common occurrence and greatest practical importance but not even known forty years ago. Conversely, many of the 2300 individuals mentioned in the precursor of this book have here been excluded as of but slight interest. Since this book may perhaps find use in courses of instruction, only those materials have generally been included which are commercially available or which can be prepared with ease from accessible materials. Some deviations from this principle have been made when it was deemed advisable to have conveniently available data for groups of closely related substances. The catalogues of Eastman Organic Chemicals and the first twenty volumes of *Organic Syntheses* have given some indication of the existence of interest in particular compounds within the scope of this volume. Special effort has been made to include compounds of current industrial importance as well as many which seem likely to develop into commercial chemicals in the near future.

In preparing these *Tables* many valuable data obtained in this Laboratory over a long period of years have been utilized. In addition the chemical literature of each and every compound has been systematically and painstakingly searched, particularly over the period 1920–1940. The author holds the view that the all too common practice of writing textbooks without supplying any guide by which their users may amplify the information given retards the progress of knowledge, and has therefore endeavored to document this volume with particular thoroughness. With few exceptions each reference which has been retained in this text has personally been examined in the original by the undersigned author and represents a critical selection of those most likely to be of help to users of the book. Of approximately 7200 citations included, about 70 per cent represent material published since 1920.

The author has long placed great emphasis upon the preparation of numerous derivatives not only as a means assuring the unequivocal identification of an unknown sample, but also as an important tool in broadening the acquaintance of the student with the behavior of organic compounds in general and the principles of organic qualitative analysis in particular. For this reason the author has indicated in the text a generous selection of derivatives critically chosen from the great number of possibilities. All the reactions cited have actually been carried out, most of them many times, and the precise literature reference to details of procedure is given for the guidance of those who may require additional assistance.

For a more extended explanation of the general principles which have guided the selection and organization of the substance of the text, reference should be made to the introduction comprising Chapter I. Even in this Preface, however, attention should be called to two especially novel features which in this Laboratory have demonstrated their utility. The first is the inclusion of an index of chemical types, located at the beginning of the descriptive tables of aldehydes, acids, phenols, esters, ketones, alcohols, and hydrocarbons and designed to facilitate the rapid location of particular forms of combinations of groups. The second is the organization of tables of melting-point sequences of certain important families of derivatives which comprises Chapter XIII. Neither of these features is available in any other book.

The author is keenly aware that he cannot hope to satisfy in full the particular interests of every user. There must necessarily exist differences of opinion on the relative importance of this or that compound, reaction, or derivative. However, if all possible objections were first to be overcome nothing would ever be accomplished, and the author hopes that any deficiencies of this volume may to some extent be compensated by its merits.

Furthermore, in a work of this kind and magnitude it is inevitable that, despite every good intention and every earnest and painstaking effort, actual errors of fact will still have escaped detection and correction. The author invites the friendly cooperation of all who discover any such flaws, meanwhile being consoled by the view expressed by the ancient Chinese writer Tai T'ung, who, some seven hundred years ago, issued his *History of Chinese Writing* with this statement: " Were I to await perfection my book would never be finished . . . The book awaits a wise and lofty spirit to correct and suppress where the text is in error, to add where it is defective, and to supply new facts where it is altogether silent."

Ernest Hamlin Huntress

Research Laboratory of Organic Chemistry
Massachusetts Institute of Technology
Dec. 29, 1940

CONTENTS

CHAPTER VI

CHAPTER VII

CHAPTER VIII

CHAPTER IX

CHAPTER X

CHAPTER XI

CHAPTER XII

CHAPTER XIII

CHAPTER XIV

ABBREVIATIONS

A

$[\alpha]_D^{20}$	specific rotation at 20° for D line
$\bar{A}$	represents acid residue in whose description it occurs
abs.	absolute; absolutely
abt.	about
abund.	abundant
abv.	above
Ac	acetyl radical, i.e., $CH_3.CO—$
AcOEt	ethyl acetate
AcOH	acetic acid (glacial acetic acid when unmodified)
Ac_2O	acetic anhydride
ac.	acid
acc.	according
acid.	acidify, acidified, acidification
act.	active
addn.(l)	addition (additional)
adj.	adjacent (e.g., 1,2,3)
alc.	alcohol (95% unless otherwise stated); alcoholic
ald.	aldehyde
alk.(y)	alkali; alkaline; (alkalinity)
alm.	almost
Am	amyl
ammon.	ammoniacal
amorph.	amorphous
amt.(s)	amount(s)
anal.	analysis; analyses
anhyd.	anhydrous
anti-	anti (stereomeric opposite of *syn-*)
apprec.	appreciable; appreciably
approx.	approximate; approximately
aq.	water or aqueous
arom.	aromatic
assoc.(d) (n)	associate(s) (associated) (association)

B

$\bar{B}$	represents a molecule of the " basic " salt-forming compound in whose description it occurs
B.B.No.	bromide-bromate number
bibl.	bibliography
bkn.	" broken " (cf. color terminology)
boilg.	boiling
b.p.	boiling point (at atm. pressure unless specified)
Bu	*n*-butyl
bril.	brilliant
brn.	brown
Bz	benzoyl, i.e., $C_6H_5.CO—$
BzOH	benzoic acid

C

C	Centigrade degrees
$\bar{C}$	used to designate the compound in whose description it occurs
calc.(d) (n)	calculate(d) (calculation)
cap.	capillary
cat.	catalyst; catalytic; catalyzed
cc.	cubic centimeter(s)
cf.	compare
cg.	centigram(s)
charac.	characteristic
chem.	chemical
cis-	stereochemical opposite of *trans-*
cm.	centimeter(s)

coeff.	coefficient
col.(n)	color (coloration)
comb.(d) (n) (g)	combine(d) (combination) (combining)
comml.	commercial
compd.	compound
compn.	composition
conc.(d) (n)	concentrate(d) (concentration)
condens.	condensation
cond.	condition(s)
confrm.(n)	confirm; confirmatory (confirmation)
const.	constant
cont.(s) (g)	contain(s) (containing)
conv.(n)	convert (conversion)
cor.	corrected
corresp.	corresponding
C.P.	chemically pure
cpd.	compound
crit.	critical
cryst.(n) (d)	crystal(s); crystallize(s) (d); crystalline (crystallization)
C.S.T.	critical solubility temperature

D

Ⓓ	derivative (used to introduce important derivatives for specific characterizations)
(D)	dark (following name of a broken color)
D_4^{20}	density at 20° referred to water at 4°
d-	dextrorotatory
dec.(d) (n)	decompose(s) (decomposed) (decomposition)
deliq.	deliquesce(s), deliquescent
depolym.(d) (n)	depolymerize(s) (depolymerized) (depolymerization)
deriv.(s) (d) (n)	derivative(s) (derived) (derivation)
desic.	desiccator; desiccated
detectn.	detection
detn.(d)	determine; determination (determined)
diam.	diameter
dif.	different; difference; difficultly
dil.(td) (tg) (n)	dilute (diluted) (diluting) (dilution)
dimin.	diminish; diminishing; diminished; diminutive
dis.(lvd)	dissolve (dissolved)
dissoc.(d) (g) (n)	dissociate(d) (dissociating) (dissociation)
dist.(d) (g) (n)	distil(led) (distilling) (distillation)
distrib.(n)	distribute (distribution)
div.(n)	divide (division)
dk.	dark
d,l-	racemic (by external compensation as contrasted with *meso*)
D.V.	Duclaux Value

E

eas.	easily
efferv.	effervesce(s); effervescent
equiv.	equivalent
espec.	especially
est.(d) (g) (n)	estimate(s) (estimated) (estimating) (estimation)
Et	ethyl, i.e., $CH_3.CH_2$—
EtOH	ethyl alcohol (generally refers to 95% if unmodified)
eth.	ether (generally means ordinary diethyl ether)
evap.(d) (g) (n)	evaporate(d) (evaporating) (evaporation)
evol.(n)	evolve(s) (evolution)
exam.(d) (n)	examine(d) (examination)
expt.(l)	experiment(al)
ext.(d) (g) (n)	extract(s) (extracted) (extracting) (extraction)

F

filt.(n)	filter(s); filtrate (filtration)
floc.	flocculate; flocculent
fluores.	fluoresce(s); fluorescent

f.p.	freezing point
freq.	frequently
fract.(n) (nl)	fraction; fractionate (fractionation) (fractional)
fum.	fumaroid (stereochemical opposite of *maleinoid*)
fumg.	fuming
fus.(n)	fuse(s), melt(s); fusible; fusing (fusion)

G

g.	gram(s)
gem.	geminate (said of two like groups attached to same atom)
geom.	geometrical
glac.	glacial
gr.	green
grad.	graduate; graduated; gradually
gran.	granular; granulated

H

H.E.	hydrolysis equivalent
hexag.	hexagon; hexagonal
hr.(s)	hour(s)
ht.(d) (g)	heat(ed) (heating)
hydrol.(g) (zd)	hydrolyze; hydrolysis; (hydrolyzing) (hydrolyzed)
hygros.	hygroscopic

I

ibid.	in the same place
ident.	identical; identity
identif.(d) (n)	identify (identified) (identification)
i.e.	that is
immed.	immediate; immediately
impt.	important
inact.	inactive; inactivated
indef.	indefinite
indic.	indicate; indicator; indicated
inf.	infinite
inorg.	inorganic
insol.(y)	insoluble (insolubility)
irreg.	irregular
irrit.(n)	irritating (irritation)
isom.(d) (n)	isomer; isomerize (isomerized) (isomerization)

K

k	ionization constant

L

(L)	Light (modifying name of a broken color)
l-	laevorotatory
l.	liter(s)
lft(s).	leaflet(s)
lgr.	ligroin
liq.	liquid; liquefy
lt.	light (of a color)

M

(M)	medium (modifying name of a broken color)
m.	melt(s)
m-	meta
mal.	maleinoid (stereochemical opposite of *fumaroid*)
max.	maximum
Me	methyl, i.e., CH_3—
MeOH	methanol, i.e., CH_3OH
m.e.	milliequivalent
mg.	milligram(s)
mic.	micro
microcryst.	microcrystalline
min.	minute(s); minimum
minl.	mineral
misc.	miscellaneous; miscible
mixt.	mixture(s)
mod.	moderate
modifn.	modification
mol.	molecular
monoclin.	monoclinic
ml.	milliliter
mm.	millimeter
m.p.	melting point
ms	meso-

N

N	normal (equivalents per liter)
n	normal
n_D^{20}	refractive index at 20° for D line of sodium
ndl.(s)	needle(s)
neg.	negative
Neut. Eq.	neutralization equivalent
neut.(zd)	neutral (neutralized)
no.	number
non-fus.	non-fusible
non-vol.	non-volatile

O

o-	ortho
obs.(d) (n)	observe(d) (observation)
obt.(d)	obtain(ed)
opt.	optical
optim.	optimum
or.	orange
ord.	ordinary
orig.	original; originally
org.	organic
oxid.(g) (n)	oxidize(s) (oxidizing) (oxidation)

P

Ⓟ	preliminary test
p-	para
perm.	permanent
pet.	petroleum
Ph	phenyl, i.e., C_6H_5—
phys.	physical
physiol.	physiological
Pk	picryl, i.e., 2,4,6-trinitrophenyl-
PkOH	picric acid
pl.	plate(s)
polym.(n)	polymer; polymerize; polymerized (polymerization)
pos.	positive
powd.	powder; powdered
ppt.(d) (g) (n)	precipitate(d) (precipitating) (precipitation)
Pr	propyl
pr.	prism(s)
pract.	practically
prep.(d) (g) (n)	prepare(d) (preparing) (preparation)
pres.	presence
press.	pressure
prim.	primary
prin.	principal
prismat.	prismatic
prob.	probably
proc.	procedure
prod.	product; produce; produced
prop.	property; properties
pt.(s)	part(s)
pulv.(d)	pulverize(d)
pung.	pungent
purif.(d) (g) (n)	purify (purified) (purifying) (purification)

Q

quad.	quadratic
qual.	qualitative; qualitatively
quant.	quantity; quantitative; quantitatively
quat.	quaternary
q.v.	quod vide (which see)

R

rac.	racemic
rap.	rapid; rapidly
reactn.	reaction(s)
reagt.(s)	reagent(s)
rearr.	rearrange(s); rearrangement
recommd.	recommend; recommended
recryst.(d) (g) (n)	recrystallize(d) (recrystallizing) (recrystallization)
rect.	rectangular
redis.	redissolve
reduc.(d) (g) (n)	reduce(d) (reducing) (reduction)
ref.	reference
reminis.	reminiscent
reppt.(d) (g) (tn)	reprecipitate(d) (reprecipitating) (reprecipitation)

resid.	residue; residual
resin.	resinify; resinification
resp.	respectively
rhomb.	rhombic

S

Sap. Eq.	saponification equivalent
sapon.(d) (g) (n)	saponify (saponified) (saponifying) (saponification)
sat.(d) (g) (n)	saturate(d) (saturating) (saturation)
sec.	second(s)
sec.	secondary
sect.	section
sep.(d) (g) (n)	separate(d) (separating) (separation)
sft.(n)(s)	soft; soften(s)
shak.(g) (n)	shake (shaking) (shaken)
sint.(d)	sinter(s) (sintered)
sl.	slightly
sld. cap.	sealed capillary
S.N.	system number (Beilstein)
spar.	sparing; sparingly
sol.(n) (y)	soluble (solution) (solubility)
solv.	solvent(s)
sp.gr.	specific gravity
sq.	square
subl.(g)	sublimes; sublimate; subliming; sublimation
subl. w.m.	sublimes without melting
subseq.	subsequent
subst.	substance; substantially; substituted
suff.	suffices; sufficient
supersat.(d)(g)(n)	supersaturate(d)(supersaturating) (supersaturation)
st.	steam
s.t.	sealed tube
stdg.	standing
sym.	symmetrical
syn-	stereochemical opposite of *anti-*
syst.	system; systematic; systematically

T

T	Numbered Test
tbl.(s)	tablet(s); tabular
tech.	technical
temp.	temperature
theor.	theoretical
therm.	thermometer
T.N.B.	1,3,5-trinitrobenzene
T.N.T.	2,4,6-trinitrotoluene
ter-	tertiary
trans-	stereochemical opposite of *cis-*
transf.	transfer; transform
tt.	test tube

U

u.c.	uncorrected
undec.	undecomposed
undislvd.	undissolved
unoxid.	unoxidized
unsat.	unsaturated
unsym.	unsymmetrical
U.S.P.	United States Pharmacopœia
u.v.	ultra violet

V

vac.	vacuum
vap.	vapor; vaporize
var.	variable
vic.	vicinal (adjacent)
vig.	vigorous; vigorously
viol.	violent; violently; violet
visc.	viscous
volat.(g) (n)	volatile (volatilizing) (volatilization)
volumin.	voluminous

W

warm.	warming
wh.	white
wt.	weight

Y

yel.	yellow

CHAPTER I

INTRODUCTION

1. Classification of compounds

The identification of organic compounds is much facilitated by classification into some systematic sequence. Such a sequence is employed in this book.

The *order* of a compound is established by its qualitative elementary composition. Compounds containing the same elements belong to the same order. Compounds of carbon with hydrogen, or of carbon with both hydrogen and oxygen, constitute Order I and are the only ones described in this volume. When other elements are also present, a compound is said to belong to a higher order; data on these are available in Volumes II and IV of Mulliken's *Identification of Pure Organic Compounds.*

Order I is divided into two *suborders:* Suborder I, comprising colorless compounds; and Suborder II, colored compounds. In this volume Suborder I is very large compared with Suborder II, since the majority of compounds of Order I are colorless.

A *genus* is a group of individual compounds characterized by a common behavior in certain prescribed and carefully defined *generic* tests. With few exceptions generic tests are based on chemical reactions rather than differences in physical properties. The nine genera comprising Suborder I of Order I are arranged in a sequence such that no compound shall give the generic test for any genus preceding it.

Each genus is further arranged in two *divisions* according to the normal physical condition of the pure compound. Division A contains the solid and Division B the liquid compounds of a particular genus. Gaseous compounds are not included in these tables. Abundant cross references are provided in the tables for solid compounds which for various reasons are most frequently met in liquid form or which, because of the presence of more than a single type of functional group, share the characteristics of more than one genus.

Certain genera containing a large number of individuals are further subdivided into *sections*. Such sections are usually established according to solubility or density.

The individual compounds which form the fundamental units in this classification are arranged within their respective genus, division, or section in a sequence corresponding to the increasing numerical magnitude of their melting points if they are solids, or of their boiling points (under standard conditions) if they are liquids.

2. Brief synopsis of general procedure

The fundamental operations to be carried out in the course of identification of every specimen are briefly summarized in the following paragraphs.

A. Establish the homogeneity of the sample.

Establish a presumption that the unknown substance is really a pure compound before attempting to identify it. If it is not homogeneous, purify it, for the constituents of an unknown organic mixture cannot be satisfactorily identified previous to their separation. The homogeneity of compounds which exist only in the form of uncrystallizable sirups that cannot be distilled without serious decomposition is so difficult to establish that such species are generally excluded from these tables.

B. Determine the physical properties of the specimen.

If the sample is a solid and appears to melt when heated, determine its melting point accurately as described elsewhere. If the sample is a liquid, determine its boiling point and its specific gravity at 20° referred to water at 4°. In either case note its odor, color, and other salient characteristics, and determine its approximate solubility in water. These tests consume little or no material which cannot be recovered, and the information which they furnish is sure to be required at some later period of the study.

C. Determine the Order and Suborder to which the compound belongs.

This is accomplished by carrying out systematic tests for the component elements (Ordinal Tests). At this point always make use of any information concerning the origin or history of the compound, for to undervalue such evidence is to accept an unnecessary handicap. Even an incomplete acquaintance with the materials and reactions that have led to its production, or with the treatment to which it may have been subjected, or of the uses for which it is intended, deserves serious consideration. Such collateral information may quickly eliminate otherwise plausible hypotheses or furnish the lacking clue with less effort and greater certainty than a long series of more pretentious tests and reactions.

If the compound contains no other elements save carbon and hydrogen, or carbon, hydrogen, and oxygen, it belongs to Order I and should be sought in this volume. If it contains any elements other than carbon, hydrogen, or oxygen, it does not fall within the scope of this book.

If the purified compound belongs to Order I and is colorless, it should be sought in Suborder I. If, after purification, it is still definitely colored, however, it belongs in Suborder II. It should be remembered that many very light straw-colored materials become white after exhaustive purification.

D. Determine the genus to which the compound belongs.

If the compound has been found to belong to Order I and is colorless, apply Generic Tests 1–8 successively until its genus is ascertained. Do not vary the sequence of the tests or omit any unless from circumstances surrounding the origin of the sample they are known to be definitely unnecessary.

E. Determine the division and section to which the compound belongs.

Assignment to a division is determined by the solid or liquid character of the compound. Assignment to a section must be made in the light of data on the solubility or specific gravity, or in a few instances by special indicated tests.

F. Location of the individual description

The order, suborder, genus, and (if necessary) section of the compound having been located, reference should then be made to the tables of data.

The properties of the sample are compared with the properties of all individuals that melt or boil within 5–10° of the observed melting or boiling point, and are described in the subdivision of the genus to which it has been found to belong. If there are numerous compounds which closely resemble it, time will be saved by directing attention next to preliminary tests marked Ⓟ. After such preliminary tests have further limited the range of possibilities, preparation of several particularly characteristic derivatives and determination of their physical constants usually leads to satisfactory identification. Suggestions for such derivatives are indicated by Ⓓ.

Color reactions, though often useful as preliminary indications, are not in general suitable for use as confirmatory tests. Frequently, the determination of some quantitative characteristic such as neutralization equivalent, saponification equivalent, Duclaux Value, or refractive index will serve as satisfactorily as a derivative.

3. The arrangement of data on individual compounds

The data given for each compound are arranged in a standard form. This form may be construed as made up of the following parts:

A. The heading.
B. General information on the properties and reactions.
C. Designation of derivatives.
D. References to the chemical literature for further information or substantiation of the data given.

The relative amount of space devoted to these four aspects varies from one genus to another according to circumstances. Each of these aspects will be discussed in full detail below.

A. The heading (first line)

The heading for each compound may be construed to contain two principal parts, representing two horizontal lines of data. The upper line is usually divided into five parts; the lower into four parts.

The five components of the upper line of the heading always occur in the following sequence from left to right, viz.:

(1) Location number of compound in this book.	(2) Name.	(3) Structural formula.	(4) Empirical formula.	(5) Beilstein reference.

(1) *The location number.* Each compound for which data are given in this book has been assigned an arbitrary number to facilitate frequent cross reference in the descriptive tables. This number consists of a digit representing the order of the compound (thus all compounds in this volume have location numbers beginning with 1), followed by a colon, and then a four-digit arbitrary number. The system is, therefore, entirely comparable to a telephone number, the initial digit before the colon corresponding to the exchange, the four digits following the colon corresponding to the individual line. The spread of numbers thus assigned is summarized as follows:

Order I: Suborder I
Genus 1. Aldehydes
Division A. Solids 1:0002–1:0080
Division B. Liquids 1:0100–1:0285

Genus 2. Carbohydrates
  Division A. Solids
    Section 1
      Subsection A 1:0300
      Subsection B 1:0305–1:0330
      Subsection C 1:0350–1:0370
    Section 2 . . . . 1:0375–1:0345

Genus 3. Acids
  Division A. Solids
    Section 1. "Soluble" 1:0399–1:0559
    Section 2. "Insoluble" 1:0560–1:0910
  Division B. Liquids
    Section 1. "Soluble" 1:1000–1:1070
    Section 2. "Insoluble" 1:1100–1:1175

Genus 4. Phenolic compounds
  Division A. Solids 1:1400–1:1640
  Division B. Liquids 1:1700–1:1840

Genus 5. Esters
  Division A. Solids 1:2005–1:2590
  Division B. Liquids 1:3000–1:4570

Genus 6. Anhydrides, lactones, etc.
  Division A. Solids 1:4905–1:4970
  Division B. Liquids 1:5070–1:5080

Genus 7. Ketones
  Division A. Solids 1:5111–1:5215
  Division B. Liquids 1:5400–1:5600

Genus 8. Alcohols
  Division A. Solids
    Section 1. "Soluble" 1:5805–1:5850
    Section 2. "Insoluble" 1:5890–1:5990
  Division B. Liquids
    Section 1. $D_4^{20} < 0.90$ 1:6100–1:6300
    Section 2. $D_4^{20} > 0.90$ 1:6400–1:6720

Genus 9. Hydrocarbons, ethers, etc.
  Division A. Solids
    Section 1. "Non-aromatics" 1:7000–1:7090
    Section 2. "Aromatics" 1:7115–1:7285
  Division B. Liquids
    Section 1. "Aromatics" 1:7400–1:7645
    Section 2. Acyclic ethers 1:7800–1:7990
    Section 3. Dienes, alkynes, cyclenes,
      terpenes, etc. 1:8000–1:8175
    Section 4. Alkenes 1:8200–1:8385
    Section 5. Naphthenes 1:8400–1:8490
    Section 6. Alkanes 1:8499–1:8900

ORDER I: SUBORDER II
  Division A. Solids 1:9000–1:9115
  Division B. Liquids 1:9500

For each compound the full descriptive data are given only in one place. Whenever it is desirable to be reminded in more than one place of a particular compound, the heading only is repeated, a cross reference to the detailed description is given, but the place ordinarily occupied by the location number is indicated merely by a dash.

(2) *The name of the compound.* The second element of the upper line of the heading is devoted to the name of the compound. Out of all possible names, one has been selected and printed in bold-face capitals in this top line. The general principles which have been used in selecting this " principal name " are more fully explained below under nomenclature. In many instances, however, there are several other names which are in common use and which might occur to users of this book. A selection of such names is printed in ordinary type just below the principal name. The subject index of this book contains both the principal name and subsidiary name (or names) together with the corresponding location number.

(3) *The structural formula of the compound.* Since it is frequently easier to interpret the chemical reactions of a compound by consideration of its structural formula rather than its name, such structural pictures are given for most of the compounds in this book. There are two exceptions to this practice. The structural formulas of esters are not given since too much space would be required and since the formula is readily deducible from those of the component acids and alcohols to which cross reference is made in each ester description. The second exception is in the small group of carbohydrates constituting Genus 2. Although such structural formulas are construed as the third element of the heading of each compound, it frequently happens, owing to practical considerations, that the formula is not actually printed as part of the top line but depressed somewhat below it.

(4) *The empirical formula.* The fourth element of the top line of the heading is the empirical formula. This will be found exceedingly useful in many ways, particularly in suggesting isomeric compounds (via the formula index) from which distinction must be made, and in searching the abstract periodicals for data which are later than the publication of this book.

(5) *The Beilstein reference.* Each compound listed in these *Tables* bears in the upper right-hand corner of its heading a reference to Beilstein's *Handbuch der organischen Chemie.* All such references designate the fourth edition of this important tool.

Such Beilstein references belong invariably to one or the other of two types. The first type is that of specific reference to a particular volume and page, e.g., Beil. VIII-123. The other type is that in which merely the Beilstein system number of the compound is given, e.g., Beil. S.N. 644. This second form is used only when the compound in question is of such recent origin that Beilstein's *Handbuch* contains no reference to it, either in the main or first supplementary series. The designation of system number (rather than specific volume and page), therefore, immediately indicates that no reference to the substance is contained in those volumes of Beilstein published up to the end of 1940. Whenever the second supplementary series of Beilstein becomes available, however, the system number will indicate within reasonable limits just where the compound will be found.

One further important aspect of the specific form of Beilstein reference must also be mentioned. It frequently happens that a particular compound is described in the first supplementary series of Beilstein volumes but not in the main edition. In such a case the Beilstein reference is of this form: Beil. VIII_1-(225). This indicates Volume VIII of the *first supplementary* series of the fourth edition of Beilstein and refers to the regular pagination of that supplementary volume.

It is imperative to keep in mind that the proper use of Beilstein's *Handbuch* invariably involves reference to two places, viz., the indicated page of the proper volume of the main series (covering the literature up to 1910), and *also* the corresponding volume and page of the supplementary series (covering the literature from 1910 to 1920). For convenience in using the supplementary volumes, Beilstein carries the page numbers of the corresponding main volume (in heavy type) at the top center of the corresponding pages of the supplementary series. This means that a reference to a particular volume and page of the main series automatically locates the corresponding material in the first (or any subsequent) supplementary series. When a compound was not known in time to be included in the main series of Beilstein, however, there can be no page number to transfer to the supplementary series, and the regular independent book pagination of the supplementary volume is then employed. To avoid confusion such " absolute " pagination is printed in this book with parentheses around the page number.

It should be clearly understood that these references to Beilstein's *Handbuch* are included here only for the convenience of the users of these *Tables*. This book is wholly independent of Beilstein, and those users to whom Beilstein may be inaccessible need feel no concern that the value of these *Tables* to them is in any way impaired.

B. The heading (second line)

The second line of the standard heading contains four elements always presented in the same sequence as follows:

1. Melting point or boiling point.
2. Neutralization equivalent (for acids) or saponification equivalent (for esters).
3. Density (in the case of liquids).
4. Refractive index.

(1) *The melting or boiling point.* In choosing the values cited for these constants, particular effort has been made to obtain those values representing

the purest possible material which has been reported. (See comments elsewhere on literature references.) In some instances where it has been impossible to determine which of several divergent values is most reliable several are given. Boiling points are given for pressures of 760 mm. unless otherwise designated. Whenever very precise determinations have been reported, the values are often given in that form since this in no way impairs their value for ordinary work and may be very important to workers in specialized fields. On the other hand, data are often given for constants over a range of degrees, indicating that precise data were not available.

In recent times much information has been obtained regarding the melting points of liquids at very low temperatures. When the melting point of a compound is given much below 0° it is rarely feasible to use the low melting point as a means of identification. It is, however, included for comparison and, since most such cases occur in genera which do not have neutralization or saponification equivalents, is often printed in the location otherwise left blank.

(2) *Neutralization or saponification equivalents.* These values possess particular significance for acids and esters, respectively, and should invariably be determined in the identification of every compound to which they apply.

(3) *Densities.* Wherever possible data for this constant are given in the form D_4^{20}, i.e., the density of the substance at 20° C. referred to water at 4° C. There are many compounds for which data at these temperatures are not available and in such instances other temperatures are given on the ground that some idea is better than none. For some very important compounds density data are also given at one or more additional temperatures such as D_4^{15} or D_4^{25}, since this supplies information on the rate of change of density with temperature.

(4) *Refractive indices.* These are usually given in the form n_D^{20}, i.e., the refractive index taken at 20° with the D line of sodium light. In some instances other lines of the spectrum have been employed where no data on the D line were available. As with density, refractive index data are sometimes given at several other temperatures.

C. General information on properties and reactions

The second part of the description of each compound is concerned with those properties and reactions which are of interest and have bearing of one kind or another upon its identification. The nature of the treatment varies somewhat from one genus to another, as will be appreciated by inspection of typical cases. It should be understood, however, that it is not the intention to include in this part of the description all the possible reactions of the material (since those may be found in Beilstein) but rather only those reactions or properties which may have bearing upon the identification of the material.

When a method of synthesis for a compound has been particularly well studied, reference to the method is frequently cited, partly to afford some evidence as to the ease of accessibility of the material and partly to indicate how an authentic sample can best be prepared for comparison.

The reactions cited in this part of the description often lead to materials which contain elements other than carbon, hydrogen, and oxygen and are therefore not themselves treated in detail in this volume. For such reaction products the corresponding Beilstein reference is often given in brackets for convenience should further information be desired. Whenever the product of a reaction is itself treated in full in this volume, however, its location number is given.

Frequently it happens that, within a family of derivatives most of whose members are solids well suited for confirmation of the identity of an unknown, particular individuals are liquids or very low-melting solids not so convenient for this purpose as solid members of some other series. These *Tables* often call attention to cases of this kind.

More than one value for the melting point of a particular product derived from a numbered compound, or conversely several citations for the same constant, will often be noted in the *Tables.* In the latter case this serves to draw attention to the concordance of results of several different workers; in the former, attention is directed to the very fact that not all results agree.

The constants of racemic compounds are often quite different from those of the component optical enantiomorphs; wherever possible data of this kind have been included.

In the case of compounds with multiple functions of the same kind, such as dibasic acids, dihydric phenols, dihydric alcohols, and diketones, it often happens that during the preparation of derivatives involving both functions some of the mono derivative is isolated. For this reason particular care has been taken to supplement the data on the normal reaction product by including the constants on the mono reaction products. A low melting sample of a product intended to be a bis derivative often is found to contain small amounts of the mono reaction product, after whose removal the desired product is entirely satisfactory.

Although the analyst is expected to use his knowledge of organic chemistry to anticipate possible impurities in commercial samples attributable to the method by which they were or might have been prepared, attention is frequently drawn in the *Tables* to unconventional contaminants of sufficient importance to have been reported in the literature. Hydrates or other combinations with solvents, polymers, or other reaction products which may be formed in small amounts during the treatment of the sample are also mentioned.

Although the primary interest of this book is directed to the identification of compounds by qualitative means, the *Tables* contain many references to studies on the application of these methods to the quantitative determination of the compounds.

Inasmuch as it is often necessary to characterize particular compounds subsequent to their isolation from mixtures, many data of assistance in this connection have been included. Many references will be found on the formation of azeotropic (constant-boiling) mixtures with one or more other components. Occasionally deliberate preparation of such mixtures and determinations of their significant properties, such as boiling point or refractive index of the azeotrope, will serve to characterize the individual.

D. *Preliminary tests*

For many of the most common of the compounds included in these *Tables*, there exist specific or semi-specific color tests. These are generally simple to execute, may often be applied satisfactorily to minute amounts of material, and when positive are so significant that they should invariably precede the preparation and characterization of derivatives. Such tests are indicated by the symbol Ⓟ. They should be regarded as merely preliminary in character and not always carrying the same weight of conviction as the derivatives.

E. *Derivatives*

After the data comprised in the nine component parts of the heading, and in the main text descriptive of the behavior of each compound, there usually follows a section of derivatives. Each recommended derivative is preceded by the symbol Ⓓ, but occasionally in this section (to complete a family) data are inserted for products related to the parent numbered compound but not advised as derivatives for identification purposes. In such cases a dash replaces the usual symbol.

The sequence in which these derivatives are listed has no relation to their respective merits as derivatives for the particular parent. Within a given genus the particular sequence is arbitrary but standard in form and sequence in order to facilitate intercomparison and reference. In addition to the types of derivatives common to all conventional numbers of the genus, there are sometimes interpolated specific derivatives which are applicable to particular compounds but not general in type for all members of the group.

The sequence of generic derivatives naturally varies from one genus to another, but for the very important type of carbonyl compounds, acids, and hydroxy compounds the sequence employed will be outlined below.

For aldehydes the standard sequence is as follows: oximes, semicarbazones, phenylhydrazones, *p*-nitrophenylhydrazones, 2,4-dinitrophenylhydrazones, dimethones.

For ketones the standard sequence is as follows: oximes, phenylhydrazones, *p*-nitrophenylhydrazones, 2,4-dinitrophenylhydrazones, semicarbazones.

For phenols the standard sequence is as follows: acetates, benzoates, *p*-nitrobenzoates, 3,5-dinitrobenzoates, benzenesulfonates, *p*-toluenesulfonates, *p*-nitrobenzyl ethers, 2,4-dinitrophenyl ethers, aryloxyacetic acids, *N*-phenylcarbamates, *N*-(α-naphthyl)carbamates, *N*-(*p*-xenyl)carbamates, *N*,*N*-(diphenyl)carbamates.

For alcohols the standard sequence is as follows: acetates, benzoates, *p*-nitrobenzoates, 3,5-dinitrobenzoates, acid phthalates, acid 3-nitrophthalates, *N*-phenylcarbamates, *N*-(*p*-nitrophenyl)carbamates, *N*-(α-naphthyl)-carbamates, *N*-(*p*-xenyl)carbamates, *N*,*N*-(diphenyl)carbamates.

For acids the standard sequence is as follows: *p*-nitrobenzyl esters, phenacyl esters, *p*-chlorophenacyl esters, *p*-bromophenacyl esters, *p*-iodophenacyl esters, *p*-phenylphenacyl esters, amides, anilides, *p*-toluidides, benzimidazoles, *S*-benzylthiuronium salts, piperazonium salts.

Before proceeding to the actual preparation of derivatives the analyst will often find advisable reference to the tables of sequence of melting points comprising Chapter XIII. The form of the data there presented readily enables the experimenter to determine whether or not a particular derivative will possess real value in distinguishing his unknown from other suspects.

F. Literature references

The fifth and final section of the descriptive material for each serially numbered compound comprises the corresponding references to the chemical literature. These are associated with the corresponding portions of the descriptive text by arbitrary numbers set in bold-face carets, e.g., **⟨5⟩**.

The cardinal principle which has guided the selection of literature citations has been that of greatest utility to users of this book. The references cited have been selected so as to assist the analyst in difficulty by guiding him directly to much more detailed information than can possibly be included in a book of this kind.

In general no literature reference has been cited unless it has actually been consulted in the original by the author and found important. When the literature source of descriptive data would be evident from an examination of Beilstein's *Handbuch,* reference has often been omitted, but material which would not be found in this manner has been appropriately documented. In the preparation of these tables the chemical literature of each and every compound has been systematically searched, particularly over the period 1920–1940, inclusive, not covered by the fourth edition of Beilstein. This is reflected by the fact that, of the more than 7000 citations, approximately 70 per cent represent work reported since the period covered by Beilstein.

Association of the references with the descriptive material has been arranged for the convenience of the users. It must not be construed as suggesting that reference to the original is imperative for the successful execution of any given procedure. Whenever difficulties or abnormalities arise, however, those who will take the trouble to examine the original papers will find their effort well recompensed.

4. Nomenclature

Unusually careful attention has been given in this book to precision of the nomenclature. Although absolute consistency is perhaps an unattainable ideal, it has been pursued with vigor. Some aspects of the problem deserve particular mention.

Where the name of a compound contains several different radicals, these have been arranged in alphabetical sequence irrespective of their size or nature; e.g., ethyl methyl ketone, isobutyl methyl ketone, 5-isopropyl-2-methylacetophenone, methyl phenyl ether, phenyl *p*-tolyl ketone.

Esters are named from the radical of alcohol or phenol together with that of the acid which they contain. Neutral esters of polybasic acids, however, invariably contain the syllable di-, tri-, etc., as part of the main name and not as a prefix; e.g., ethyl acetate, diisobutyl oxalate, trimethyl citrate, tetraethyl pyromellitate. The normal ester of adipic acid is thus listed as diethyl adipate, the half ester as ethyl hydrogen adipate. Esters (or ethers) of polyhydric alcohols include a syllable emphasizing the number of acid radicals involved; e.g., ethylene glycol dibenzoate, ethylene glycol diphenyl ether, ethylene glycol monoformate.

In a few types of compounds, particularly with branched-chain alcohols, alkenes, and alkynes, the numbering of the prefixes representing substituents of the main chain varies according to whether the standard Geneva nomenclature used by Beilstein or the modification employed by *Chemical Abstracts* is employed. For such compounds both names are given and indexed.

5. Abbreviations

Necessity for economy of space has required in this book unusually extensive employment of abbreviations. Many of these used are already familiar from contemporary abstract journals. Those which may be peculiar to this book have generally been chosen so as to suggest the full word, particularly when assisted by the context in which they occur. No attempt has been made to enslave the text to the abbreviations, however, and the full word is frequently used even though an abbreviation for it is included in the list.

6. Indexes

This book contains four different types of indexes. Two of these are distinctly novel and two are conventional, as is explained below.

A. Chemical type index

Seven of the nine genera comprising this book are immediately preceded by a special type of listing designated as an index of chemical types. In this type of index the compounds of the particular genus are so arranged as to clarify certain important aspects of their structure. The precise sequence is arbitrary and varies from one genus to another according to the nature of the compounds, but the principle underlying each will be evident upon inspection. For example, in that for Genus 8, Alcohols, the individual compounds for which descriptions occur in the *Tables* are classified according to their mono-, di-, or polyhydric character; according to whether they are primary, secondary, or tertiary alcohols; etc. In Genus 5, Esters, the individual compounds are classified according to the nature of the acid radical which they contain, etc. Users of this book should take pains to examine these type indexes since they often prove a most useful accessory tool in suggesting ideas and possible procedures.

B. Index of melting-point sequence of derivatives

The second novel type of index in this book constitutes Chapter XIII. The individual members of a number of important families of derivatives have here been arranged in the sequence of increasing numerical magnitude of their melting points. For each individual substance whose derivative is thus classified the location number is given in order to facilitate the examination of the details of the descriptive text without the necessity for intermediate consultation of the alphabetical index.

Consultation of this index should invariably precede the preparation of a particular derivative in order to afford assurance that its characteristics will really be of diagnostic value. The chapter is also useful in suggesting to the analyst individual compounds corresponding to the melting point of a derivative which he may already have prepared. By comparison of the melting-point values for two or more derivatives of different families, it is often possible to restrict to a conveniently small list the number of structural possibilities for a given original unknown.

C. Empirical formula index

This is arranged in the conventional familiar form, first according to the number of carbon atoms, and then according to increasing numbers of atoms of hydrogen and oxygen. Not only does this index serve to suggest to the analyst groups of isomers of the compound whose identity he has been led to suspect, and to facilitate literature searches for material published subsequent to the appearance of this book, but it also occasionally may serve as a final verification of the presence in or absence of a particular compound from the *Tables*, in any instances where the names which occur to the analyst do not appear in the alphabetical index.

D. Alphabetical index

This conventional type of index includes not only the " principal " name, but also all the subsidiary names given in the *Tables* for every numbered compound in this book. It cannot, of course, guarantee to contain every name which might conceivably be applied, since for the field of organic chemistry such names are legion. However, with every name which is listed is associated the corresponding location number, so that use of the index is perfectly straightforward and requires no cross referencing within itself. The first letter of the first syllable establishes the alphabetical position of each name, irrespective of any literal or numerical prefix such as *o*-, *m*-, *p*-, *sec*-, *ter*-, *cis*-, *trans*-, α-, β-, *d*-, *l*-, *d,l*-, *meso*-, or 1,3,5-. Within a particular group of isomers with the same name, however, the sequence is *o*-, *m*-, *p*-; or *sec*-, *ter*-; or α-, β-, γ-, as the case may be. *Iso* is not construed in this book as a prefix but as part of the main root.

CHAPTER II

THE GENERIC TESTS OF ORDER I

GENUS 1. ALDEHYDES

Generic Test 1

Add 0.05 g. of the finely powdered substance (if a solid) or 1 drop (if it is a liquid) to 5 ml. of fuchsin-aldehyde reagent (Note 1). If the substance dissolves, allow the solution to stand *two minutes*, and then observe the color. If the substance does not dissolve, shake the test tube containing it gently for *two minutes* and then observe the color. Never apply heat (Note 2).

The appearance of a distinct pink, red, purple, or blue coloration in the solution within two minutes indicates that the compound tested should be sought in the tables of Genus 1, Order I (pages 30–76) (cf. Note 3).

If the substance is a solid and no coloration is obtained, pass on to Generic Test 2 (page 16); if a liquid, to Generic Test 3 (page 17).

Notes on Generic Test I

1. *Fuchsin-aldehyde reagent.* Dissolve 0.2 g. certified basic fuchsin in 10 ml. of a freshly prepared cold saturated aqueous solution of sulfur dioxide. Allow the solution to stand for several hours until all pink color disappears and it becomes colorless or pale yellow. Then dilute with water to 200 ml. and preserve in a tightly stoppered bottle. Note that "Acid Fuchsin" may *not* be used in the preparation of this reagent.

The reagent keeps well if not unnecessarily exposed to air and light and should always be kept on hand. The directions for its preparation should be followed with care since any large increase of sulfurous acid above the quantity specified diminishes its sensitiveness and may lead to failure to detect the less reactive aromatic aldehydes such as salicylaldehyde and vanillin. A reagent which has been used for many months and is found to have lost sensitiveness may be revivified by cautious addition of sodium acetate, stopping at the moment when a faint pink coloration begins to appear, and discharging this color by a few drops of the oxidized solution held in reserve for the purpose.

2. It should be noted that the fuchsin-aldehyde reagent is turned red by free alkali or by any substances whose solutions are alkaline by hydrolysis (such as the alkali salts of any weak acid), or by organic bases. It is also reddened by heating or by exposure in small quantities to the air at ordinary temperatures.

3. Soluble aldehydes usually color the fuchsin reagent within a few seconds; those which are difficultly soluble and of high molecular weight sometimes require the full two minutes. Substances of aromatic, fruity, or pungent odor which have failed to give color in this test may be acetals or polymerized aldehydes and should be boiled with 5 ml. of water containing 1 drop of concentrated hydrochloric acid, a few drops of the cooled solution then being added to the fuchsin-aldehyde reagent. Enough of the compound may thus be hydrolyzed or depolymerized to give a good reaction.

4. In addition to true aldehydes this test admits to the genus those acetals and aldehyde polymers which are either partially hydrolyzed to aldehydes under the conditions of the experiment or by treatment according to Note 3, but excludes the aldose carbohydrates. Commercial acetone and some other soluble ketones prepared by destructive distillation gradually redden the reagent if added to it in large quantity, but the color is due chiefly if not wholly to the presence of traces of aldehydes or acetals. The limits set upon the quantity of material used, and the time allowed for the development of a distinct coloration, are both conditions which must not be disregarded.

GENUS 2. CARBOHYDRATES

Generic Test 2

This test consists of two parts: the Molisch carbohydrate reaction and three supplementary tests. Apply the Molisch reaction first; then, if the result should be negative, omit the supplementary tests (Note 1) and pass on to Generic Test 3 (page 17).

The Molisch Carbohydrate Reaction

Place about 5 mg. of the substance with 10 drops of water in a 3-inch test tube, and mix with 2 drops of a 10% chloroform solution of α-naphthol. Allow 1 ml. of pure concentrated sulfuric acid to flow slowly from a pipet down the lower inclined side of the tube, so that the acid may form a layer beneath the aqueous one without mixing with it. If a carbohydrate is present, a red ring will appear within a few seconds at the interface. The color soon changes on standing or shaking, a dark purple solution being formed. Shake, and allow to stand for one or two minutes; then dilute with 5 ml. of cold water. In the presence of a carbohydrate, a dull violet precipitate will immediately appear. Addition of an excess of strong ammonia will change the color to a rusty yellowish-brown. Any substance that gives the dull violet and rusty brown precipitate as well as the purple coloration, under the circumstances described, may be a carbohydrate (Note 2).

The Supplementary Tests

1. Dissolve or suspend a little of the powdered substance in a few drops of water and test the reaction with litmus; if it is distinctly acid the compound is not a carbohydrate.

2. Place about 5 mg. of the substance in a 3-inch test tube, cover with 10 drops of water, and then mix with 1 ml. of pure concentrated sulfuric acid. If a red or purple coloration, or indeed any coloration other than a yellow brown to black, makes its appearance, the compound is not to be sought among the carbohydrates (Note 1).

3. Add 1 drop of 0.1% ferric chloride solution to 1 ml. of a 1% aqueous solution of the substance, or if the latter is very insoluble to its cold saturated solution. Unless the solution remains colorless, or at the most shows a pale yellow or orange-yellow coloration, the compound is not to be looked for in this genus (Note 1).

Notes on Generic Test 2

1. The reason for applying the supplementary tests after a positive Molisch reaction is to exclude certain species of other genera which give coloration and might otherwise be mistaken for carbohydrates. Supplementary test 2 is required to exclude several glucosides such as salicin and esculin.

2. On account of the delicacy of the Molisch reaction it is very essential that the substance examined shall be free from all traces of filter paper, particles of woody fiber, or dust. The purity of the reagents employed should also be placed beyond question. The presence of nitrous acid in the sulfuric acid is particularly objectionable. The reagents may be tested by shaking 1 drop of the α-naphthol solution with 10 drops of water and 1 ml. of concentrated sulfuric acid. The mixture should be golden-yellow in color; if it is dark green the reagents are not sufficiently pure. The α-naphthol solution does not keep well and should not be prepared in large quantities. The coloration observed in the Molisch reaction is supposed to be due to an unstable condensation product of furfural and α-naphthol.

GENUS 3. ACIDS

Generic Test 3

This test consists of two parts: (*A*) titration in water; and (*B*) titration in alcohol. Apply procedure *A* to every solid or liquid specimen regardless of solubility. Apply procedure *B* only to those solid compounds which are insoluble in water and fail to titrate as acids in procedure *A*. If either procedure *A* or *B* is positive see Note 8; if both procedures are negative pass on to Generic Test 4 (page 19).

Procedure A. Titration in water (Note 1). Weigh out accurately about 0.10 g. of substance into a 50-ml. beaker. Solids must be finely powdered before weighing (Note 2). Add 10–15 ml. of distilled water and 1 drop of phenolphthalein indicator solution (Note 3). Place the beaker on a sheet of white paper and titrate with $N/10$ alkali until the pink color produced by an excess of 1 drop of reagent over that required for exact neutralization persists for more than one minute (Note 4) even when the solution is constantly stirred.

Procedure B. Titration in alcohol. If less than 2 ml. of alkali were required for neutralization in procedure A, and if the solid substance did not go into solution, repeat the titration, substituting for the water about 25 ml. of alcohol, using 3–4 drops of phenolphthalein solution instead of 1, and disregarding any precipitate which may form. If the alcohol has an acid reaction, add the indicator to it and bring the mixture to neutrality before adding the sample.

Definition of positive test. Any compound that consumes more than 2 ml. of $N/10$ alkali in either titration and that also gives a sharp and normal color transition at the end point should be sought in the tables of Genus 3 (pages 84–200). The sharpness of the color transition and the alkali consumption are phenomena of coordinate importance. The color transition is defined as " sharp " when a single drop of $N/10$ alkali, added at the moment when the solution is exactly neutral but still colorless, suffices to develop a full strong pink color which is not greatly intensified when the quantity of free alkali is increased (Note 5). Any compound which after titration yields a solution that has a pronounced color other than a full pink is likely to be a species of Genus 4 (Phenols). Never titrate hot solutions or substitute any other indicator for phenolphthalein.

Notes on Generic Test 3

1. Whenever the available quantity of substance will permit, it is allowable to make a preliminary titration upon a small unweighed pinch of solid (about 0.1 g.) or on 3 drops of liquid. If not more than 3–4 drops of $N/10$ alkali are neutralized, or if the color transition at the end is not " sharp," the accurate titration may be omitted and time saved.

2. Always grind a solid to a uniformly fine powder before beginning a titration unless it is known in advance that it dissolves readily in cold water. If this injunction is observed, and the suspended powder is persistently stirred, all but the weakest and most insoluble acids may, with a little patience, be successfully titrated without the use of alcohol. If, however, an acid is both very weak and almost absolutely insoluble (e.g., stearic acid), an aqueous suspension will not neutralize the alkali and the use of alcohol becomes indispensable.

3. The phenolphthalein indicator solution is prepared by dissolving 1 part of phenolphthalein in 300 parts of 50% alcohol.

4. This one-minute time limit is imposed to avoid the gradual fading of the end point because of absorption of carbon dioxide from the air or because of gradual hydrolysis of esters by the alkali. With nearly insoluble acids, neutralization of the dilute alkali is very slow toward the end of the titration when the quantity in

suspension is small. If stirring were unduly prolonged the end color would gradually disappear owing to carbon dioxide in the air. A few esters (e.g., methyl formate, dimethyl oxalate, and some esters of hydroxy acids) do neutralize $N/10$ alkali within the time limit selected and are consequently described in Genus 3, but this behavior is exceptional.

5. The quantity of alkali consumed in titrating from colorlessness to a full pink diminishes as the strength of the acid increases, the limits varying from a fraction of a drop to several milliliters. The presence of carbonate in the alkali or of carbon dioxide in the water increases the transition interval and is very detrimental to sharpness if the impurity is at all considerable. For ordinary work, however, standard solutions prepared from the purest reagent caustic and ordinary distilled water will give satisfactory results. The condition of any doubtful alkali solution can quickly be determined by a blank titration of 2–3 drops of acetic acid.

6. This large and important genus includes all colorless non-aldehydic carboxylic acids of Order I together with a few acid anhydrides and easily saponified esters which respond to the generic test. Many compounds popularly known as acids, and whose water or alcohol solutions will redden blue litmus, are too feebly acidic to respond to this generic test. Some phenols, beta diketones, and similar compounds consume more than 2 ml. of alkali before the appearance of a pink color, but these may be distinguished from the members of Genus 3 by the lack of sharpness of their end reactions.

7. In titrating anhydrides a very characteristic phenomenon will often be observed. Instead of becoming pink when the neutral point is passed and alkali is present in excess, the solution remains colorless, but gradually becomes pink after standing for some time. The explanation seems to be that the anhydride acylates the hydroxyl groups of the indicator so that the power to form colored salts is lost. The colorless reaction product is gradually saponified, however, by the excess of alkali present after the titration, and the colored indicator salt is again formed. Confirmation of this hypothesis is found in the fact that direct titrations of acid anhydrides may be made successfully by testing the neutrality of the solution from time to time with fresh pieces of phenolphthalein paper. Under these conditions the indicator is always present in the free state and so performs its proper function.

8. In Genus 3 both the solid and liquid divisions are further subdivided into sections: Section 1 comprising those individuals which are soluble in less than 50 parts of cold water, Section 2 those which are not. To determine the solubility approximately, weigh out 0.2 g. of sample (if it is solid it must be in the form of an impalpable powder) into a small test tube, and add cold water in small measured portions from a small graduate or pipet, shaking persistently after each addition. If complete solution is effected by 10 ml. of water the compound should be sought in Section 1; if much more than this amount is required, in Section 2. Borderline cases are generally cross referenced in the *Tables*.

GENUS 4. PHENOLIC COMPOUNDS

Generic Test 4

This generic test includes two procedures: 4-*A*, the ferric chloride test; and 4-*B*, the alkali test. Apply procedure 4-*A* of this test to every compound whether solid or liquid. Apply procedure 4-*B* to every solid compound that fails to give a coloration in procedure 4-*A*, *but not to liquids*. Compounds that show a phenolic behavior in the first part of the generic test are classified as phenols irrespective of their behavior in procedure 4-*B*. If either procedure 4-*A* or 4-*B* is positive, the compound should be sought in the tables of Genus 4 (pages 201–272); if both are negative, pass on to Generic Test 5 (page 21).

Procedure 4-*A*. *The ferric chloride test.* Dissolve about 0.05 g. of the substance in 1 ml. of cold water; or, if the material is difficultly soluble, prepare a hot saturated aqueous solution, cool, filter, and use 1 ml. of the cold filtrate. To this solution in a 3-inch test tube held in front of a sheet of white paper, add 3 drops of a reagent prepared by diluting 3 drops of 10% ferric chloride solution with 1 ml. of water. Pause for a few seconds after the addition of each drop to note whether any color change occurs. If no coloration is noticed, repeat the test as before, substituting alcohol for water as the solvent. If any transient or permanent coloration other than a yellow (Y) or orange-yellow (OY) is observed, the substance is probably a phenol or an enol.

Procedure 4-*B*. *The alkali test.* (*a*) Place 0.10 g. of the finely powdered substance in a 3-inch test tube with 1 ml. of cold water, shake or stir vigorously for a few moments, and observe whether it dissolves. If complete solution occurs in the cold and no significant coloration was observed with ferric chloride in procedure 4-*A*, the substance is not a phenol.

(*b*) If the substance did not dissolve appreciably in (*a*), add 1 ml. of cold aqueous 10% sodium hydroxide to the mixture. Shake or stir well for about one minute, and notice whether solution is effected or any strong coloration produced. If the compound now dissolves completely, or if it dissolves completely after diluting the alkaline mixture with an additional milliliter of cold water, the compound should be sought among the phenols of Genus 4. The appearance of any pronounced coloration in the alkaline solution also shows the compound to be a phenol.

Notes on Generic Test 4

1. *The ferric chloride test.* Yellow and orange-yellow colorations developed in this test have to be disregarded because tones of these hues are produced by many polyhydric alcohols belonging to subsequent genera. A strong yellow also appears whenever alcohol is substituted for water as the solvent. The colorations given by phenols, although varying widely in hue, intensity, and permanence, are fortunately not often yellow. The colorations characteristic of some appear in extremely dilute solutions; others only in concentrated solutions. Some remain unchanged in quality for many hours; others appear and disappear within a second. A trifling excess of reagent is sometimes sufficient to destroy the color; in other cases it is beneficial or necessary. For these reasons it is desirable to observe the color after the addition of each drop of ferric chloride reagent. The test is applicable only to cold solutions. The cause of the color has been determined in but few cases and probably varies.

2. *The alkali test.* Several distinct principles are involved in the formulated procedure. The first and most important is that, with the exception of some polyhydric phenols like resorcinol and pyrogallol, the members of this genus are not easily soluble in cold water although they dissolve readily in cold sodium hydroxide solutions of appropriate concentrations. In most cases 1 N alkali has been found to serve best, but since the sodium salts of some (e.g., sodium methyl salicylate) are much less soluble in alkali than in water, they occasionally precipitate even with 1 N alkali. It is to provide for this contingency that it is directed in (*b*) to dilute with about 1 volume of water. The use of a weaker alkali at the start is inadvisable because the salts of many phenols are so completely hydrolyzed in solution, unless a considerable excess of alkali is present, that their solubility in $N/10$ sodium hydroxide may appear to be no greater than in pure water. Finally, it should be noted that some compounds having phenolic structure will not dissolve in normal alkali. It has seemed wiser to treat such compounds as exceptions than to complicate the generic test.

3. It is necessary to restrict the alkali test of procedure 4-*B* to solid phenols because a considerable number of liquid compounds of the subsequent genera 5 and 6, which react neutral in the generic titration test of Genus 3, are saponified by short shaking with 5% aqueous alkali. Since, as far as is known, all the liquid phenols give at least transient colorations with ferric chloride, this limitation of the alkali test entails no serious disadvantage.

4. The production of a colored solution in the test with alkali is not a general reaction of the phenols, but whenever a coloration does appear at this point or in the titration of Generic Test 3 it is very significant and alone suffices to indicate that the compound should be sought among the phenols in Genus 4. The colors are sometimes very brilliant (the phthaleins), but are often yellow or dark brown. Brown colorations appearing gradually on stirring are characteristic of phenols like pyrogallol, the alkaline solution being rapidly oxidized by absorption of atmospheric oxygen.

GENUS 5. ESTERS

Generic Test 5

Weigh out accurately into a 3-inch test tube about 0.1 g. of the substance. Add 2 ml. of an approximately normal solution of alkali in methanol from a thin-stemmed pipet. The pipet need not be accurately calibrated but must be used with such precautions to insure uniformity of delivery that the volume of liquid discharged in successive experiments shall not differ by more than about 0.005 ml. Stopper the test tube tightly with a sound soft cork, and wire the stopper down. Prepare also a second exactly similar test tube, containing a similar 2-ml. sample of the standard alkali solution, to serve as a blank. Hang the tubes side by side in a beaker of boiling water for thirty minutes. Then rinse out the contents of each tube into separate small beakers and titrate carefully with $N/10$ acid using phenolphthalein as indicator.

From the results of these two titrations calculate the "saponification equivalent" of the compound, i.e., the number of grams which would be required to react with 1000 ml. (1 equivalent) of normal alkali. This may readily be done by means of the following formula:

$$\text{Sap. Eq.} = \frac{1000 \times \text{grams of substance}}{\text{normality of } \textit{acid} \times (\text{ml. acid neutralized by blank minus ml. acid neutralized by tube with sample})}$$

If the saponification equivalent found is greater than 510, pass on to Generic Test 7 (page 23), for the compound cannot be a species described in either Genus 5 or Genus 6. If, however, the value obtained is less than 510 a search must be made through the appropriate divisions of the tables of Genera 5 and 6 for a compound whose physical constants and saponification equivalent correspond to those found for the substance. If this search suggests a material which not only corresponds to the data obtained but also has some especially salient characteristics, these characteristics may suffice for the specific identification. Usually, however, it is necessary to saponify a larger quantity of the unknown with aqueous alkali (Note 3), isolating and identifying its component alcohol (or phenol) and acid or both. (See T 1.51 of the *Manual.*)

Notes on Generic Test 5

1. In binding down the stoppers, the wire, after first being doubled, is twisted so as to form a small eye. It is then drawn tightly around the tube by twisting with pliers, after which the free ends are passed over the cork and through the eye. They are then seized with the pliers and drawn back with sufficient force to imbed the wire slightly into the edges of the cork. If the wire is now bent sharply back upon itself the stopper will be held securely during the subsequent heating.

2. The tables of Genus 5 contain only the most important esters derived from common alcohols or phenols. Other esters must be characterized by means of their alcohol (or phenol) and acid saponification products. Esters that are readily saponified by cold alkali, ester-acids, ester-phenols, and the enolic esters show a behavior with reagents which places them in Genus 3 (Acids) or Genus 4 (Phenols). Among the liquid esters there are some slightly soluble compounds (e.g., diethyl succinate) which appear perfectly neutral in the titration test for acids, but which are dissolved with saponification when shaken with cold aqueous normal alkali. Compounds of this class escape classification with the phenols only because of the provision that Generic Test 4-*B* shall not be applied to liquids. On the other hand, a few esters which offer extraordinary resistance to the action of hot alkali fall into later genera.

3. For esters very difficultly soluble in aqueous alkali this saponification with alcoholic alkali is indispensable to proper classification. The most serious limitation of the test is that the use of methanol as a solvent renders impracticable the direct identification of the lower-boiling alcohols when they are formed as saponification products. Inasmuch as this test is merely used to establish generic classification, however, and a separate aqueous alkali hydrolysis on a larger sample (*Manual* T 1.51) is almost always used for the isolation of the ester or anhydride

components, this limitation is unimportant. Occasionally replacement of the methanol by a higher-boiling alcohol, such as diethylene glycol, facilitates the saponification of esters which hydrolyze slowly. Cf. Redemann, Lucas, *Ind. Eng. Chem., Anal. Ed.* **9**, 521–522 (1937); Shaefer, Piccard, *Ind. Eng. Chem., Anal. Ed.* **10**, 515–517 (1938).

4. The possibilities for experimental error in the determination of saponification equivalent as a generic test are more numerous than in the determination of the neutralization equivalents for acids. Differences of 5% between experimental and theoretical values should not be considered serious discrepancies. The main object of the procedure is to ascertain quickly whether or not the compound belongs in Genus 5 or Genus 6.

GENUS 6. ACID ANHYDRIDES AND LACTONES

Generic Test 6

No independent Generic Test 6 exists, the claim of any compounds to membership in the genus being settled by the outcome of Generic Test 5, and by the examination of the saponification products. Those compounds should be sought in Genus 6 which, although not rapidly enough attacked by cold alkali to respond to the generic tests for acids or phenols, yield a saponification equivalent of less than 510 in Generic Test 5, and form the sodium salt of an acid as their sole saponification product.

Notes on Generic Test 6

1. The number of compounds described in the tables of Genus 6 is smaller than for any other genus in Order I. This is partly due to the fact that many of the simpler and more important anhydrides (e.g., acetic anhydride, succinic anhydride, benzoic anhydride), are sufficiently reactive towards either cold $N/10$ or 1 N alkali to be classified with the acids or phenols.

GENUS 7. KETONES

Generic Test 7

This test consists of two parts: part (A) conducted at room temperature; and part (B) at 80°C. Part (B) is employed only if part (A) gives negative results. If either is positive the compound should be sought in the tables of Genus 7 (pages 354–397); if both are negative, pass on to Generic Test 8 (page 24).

Procedure 7-A. To 3 ml. of the special phenylhydrazine reagent (Note 1) in a dry 6-inch test tube add 1 drop of the compound if it is a liquid, or 0.05 g. in finely powdered form if it is a solid. Suspend the test tube by its lip between the thumb and middle finger, and sway it with a gentle pendulous motion (one vibration per second) for five minutes. Violent shaking must be carefully avoided since it will obscure observation by the formation of opaque emulsions or suspensions of merely mechanical origin. If the foregoing experiment performed at room temperature produces neither a creamy or opaque mixture, nor the appearance of a definite precipitate, proceed at once to part 7-*B*.

Procedure 7-*B*. Stand the loosely stoppered tube in a 500-ml. beaker containing a thermometer and a 3-cm. layer of water already heated to a nearly constant temperature of 80° C. Maintain this temperature, making frequent observations of the phenomena, for 15 minutes.

If the originally clear liquid above or surrounding the drops or suspended particles of the compound being tested becomes creamy or opaque from the formation of an emulsion or precipitate during the prescribed period, it is to be sought in Genus 7. In doubtful cases the test for opacity is to hold the test tube against a piece of white paper on which a small black cross has been drawn with ink lines 1 mm. in width. If the cross is not visible on looking horizontally through the solution with a good light falling upon it from behind the observer, the mixture is opaque. In making this test for opacity in part (*B*) of the experiment, the tube is first removed from the bath and quickly wiped dry, but it must not be allowed to stand or cool down before making the observation.

Notes on Generic Test 7

1. *The Special Phenylhydrazine Reagent.* This is prepared by mixing 1 ml. of pure phenylhydrazine, 7.5 ml. of 95% ethyl alcohol, and 2.5 ml. of glacial acetic acid, and diluting with distilled water to a total volume of 25 ml. This reagent keeps fairly well in a dark place, but it should not be prepared in large quantities, or used in testing if it has become turbid or dark colored.

2. Since many aldehydic and ketonic compounds of the lower genera also give a positive reaction in the foregoing test it is particularly important that the specimen tested shall give no color reaction with the fuchsin-aldehyde reagent in Generic Test 1. Slightly oxidized alcohols and unsaturated hydrocarbons may also lead to error for a similar reason.

3. The test gives satisfactory positive results with all the ketones included in the tables of Genus 7, but fails with a few unreactive compounds which if examined by it will appear to belong to Genera 8 or 9. These exceptions are in part provided for in the *Tables* by cross reference. Ketones which are unreactive in this test will generally have a carbonyl group that is joined to two alkyl radicals higher than hexyl, to any aryl radical and an alkyl higher than $C_{11}H_{23}$, to any two tertiary alkyl radicals, or to any carbocyclic radical containing two substituents in ortho position to its point of attachment to the carbonyl group. Isocyclic ketones such as fenchone, having an esocyclic carbonyl lying immediately between two ortho substituents, are likewise unreactive.

GENUS 8. ALCOHOLS

Generic Test 8

This test comprises two parts, *A* and *B*, as follows:

Procedure 8-*A*. If the compound under examination is completely soluble in less than 50 parts of water at 20° C. (see Note 8 under Generic Test 3, page

19), and has failed to give the preceding generic tests, it should be sought in the tables of Genus 8 (pages 398–481).

Procedure 8-B. If the compound does not dissolve in 50 parts of water at 20° C. (see above) and is a liquid at 75° C. (see Note 4 below), apply the sodium test which follows.

The sodium test for alcohols. Place 5 drops of the liquid in a 3-inch test tube which has been dried carefully just before use. Support the tube in a vertical position by thrusting it through a perforated cork held in a clamp. Obtain a piece of clean crust-free sodium from the stock bottle, and preserve it in a small porcelain dish under dry kerosene. Grasping the sodium with forceps under the surface of the hydrocarbon, use a sharp knife to cut off a bright piece of metal approximately equivalent to a 2-mm. cube. Seize the fragment with the forceps, touch it quickly to a piece of soft filter paper to remove adhering oil, and without delay drop it into the liquid in the test tube. Allow it to stand at room temperature (Note 3) for two minutes, and observe any evolution of gas or change in the appearance of the metal.

At the end of this time, if the sodium has not disappeared, arrange the clamp holding the test tube so that the tube dips into a small beaker of concentrated sulfuric acid previously brought to a temperature of 75° C. Maintain this temperature for about five minutes.

If a brisk effervescence takes place in either part of this test the compound is an alcohol. If the gas evolution is rather slow, but is nevertheless well sustained after the first minute, the compound is probably described in the tables of Genus 8. If there is no effervescence and the sodium remains unattacked during both parts of the test the compound is not an alcohol.

Notes on Generic Test 8

1. Correct interpretation of the phenomena requires good judgment and some experience on the part of the observer. Very few commercial specimens belonging to Genus 9 are so free from moisture as to give off no gas at all. Ability to make the right decision is most quickly gained by examining the behavior of a few representative compounds.

2. Heat is employed in the second part of the test to increase the number of compounds to which it is applicable and to make the result more decisive where reaction is slow. At the prescribed temperature of 75° C. no compound of the succeeding genus is known to be decomposed by sodium. At higher temperatures, however, sodium attacks some hydrocarbons, e.g., melted anthracene, with considerable violence.

3. Substances which melt between room temperature and 75° C. are to be tested only in the melted state.

4. Examination of the tables will show a few compounds included in this genus which (since they are not soluble in 50 parts of water and are still solid at 75° C.) are not covered by the provisions of the generic test. These are as follows: 1:5961 Decanediol-1,10; 1:5965 Terpin hydrate; 1:5970 Diphenyl-α-naphthyl-

carbinol; 1:5975 Cholesterol; 1:5980 Ergosterol; 1:5985 Triphenylcarbinol; and 1:5990 *d*-Borneol. However, most of these substances exhibit in other ways chemical behavior so characteristic as to make unwarranted any extension of the generic test merely to include these cases.

GENUS 9. HYDROCARBONS, ETHERS, ETC.

This final genus of Suborder I consists mainly of hydrocarbons but also contains some ethers as well as a few unreactive ketones and esters which have not responded to earlier generic tests. There is no special Generic Test 9.

Within the solid and liquid divisions of this genus the several compounds are arranged by sections, all of which should be examined in establishing the identity of any unknown which appears not to have reacted to any of the preceding generic tests and thus presumably belongs to Genus 9.

CHAPTER III

GENUS 1. ALDEHYDES

1. Alphabetical Name Index*

* For complete alphabetical name index covering all listed names of all numbered compounds in this book see the main alphabetical index.

2. Chemical Type Index

(Names used here are not necessarily same as subject index names.)

Cinnamaldehyde......... **1:0245**
α-*n*-Amylcinnamaldehyde.. **1:0285**

Hexahydrobenzaldehyde... **1:0186**

C. *Phenolic aldehydes*

o-Hydroxybenzaldehyde... **1:0205**
m-Hydroxybenzaldehyde.. **1:0055**
p-Hydroxybenzaldehyde... **1:0060**
2-Hydroxy-5-methylbenzaldehyde.............. **1:0030**
2,4-Dihydroxybenzaldehyde.................. **1:0065**
3,4-Dihydroxybenzaldehyde.................. **1:0073**

D. *Ethers of phenolic aldehydes*

o-Methoxybenzaldehyde... **1:0235**
m-Methoxybenzaldehyde.. **1:0232**
p-Methoxybenzaldehyde... **1:0240**
o-Ethoxybenzaldehyde.... **1:0242**
m-Ethoxybenzaldehyde.... **1:0238**
p-Ethoxybenzaldehyde.... **1:0251**

2,4-Dimethoxybenzaldehyde.................. **1:0040**
3,4-Dimethoxybenzaldehyde.................. **1:0015**
3,4-Diethoxybenzaldehyde. **1:0261**
3,4-Methylenedioxybenzaldehyde.............. **1:0010**

Protocatechualdehyde-3-methyl ether........... **1:0050**
Protocatechualdehyde-3-ethyl ether............ **1:0045**

III. Miscellaneous

Furfural diacetate........ **1:0020**

ORDER I: SUBORDER I: GENUS 1: ALDEHYDES

Division A, Solid Aldehydes

1:0002 ***n*-UNDECYLALDEHYDE** $CH_3.(CH_2)_9.CHO$ $C_{11}H_{22}O$ **Beil. I-712**
(Undecanal)

M.P. −4° ⟨1⟩ D_4^{23} = **0.8251 ⟨1⟩** n_D^{23} = **1.4322 ⟨1⟩**

Polymerizes spontaneously, or alm. instantly with few drops of H_2SO_4 to a trimer [Beil. XIX-392], ndls. or lfts. from ether, m.p. 47–48°; eas. sol. C_6H_6, dif. sol. AcOH. Above b.p. partially depolymerizes and condenses ⟨1⟩.

$\bar{C}$ oxidizes in air to undecylic acid (1:0573) — Reduces Tollens' soln. (T 1.11) — Treatment with $NaHSO_3$ soln. transforms $\bar{C}$ to the trimer; addn. does not occur ⟨1⟩.

Reduction with Zn dust + AcOH yields *n*-undecyl alc. (1:5890) ⟨1⟩.

Ⓓ **Undecylaldoxime:** white ndls. from MeOH, m.p. 72° ⟨1⟩.
Ⓓ **Undecylaldehyde semicarbazone:** ndls. from MeOH, m.p. 103° ⟨1⟩.
Ⓓ **Undecylaldehyde 2,4-dinitrophenylhydrazone:** yellow, m.p. 104° ⟨2⟩.

1:0002 ⟨1⟩ Blaise, Guerin, *Bull. soc. chim.* (3) **29,** 1203–1207 (1903). ⟨2⟩ Allen, *J. Am. Chem. Soc.* **52,** 2958 (1930).

—— ***p*-METHOXYBENZALDEHYDE** $CH_3O.C_6H_4.CHO$ $C_8H_8O_2$ **Beil. VIII-67**

M.P. 0°

See 1:0240. Genus 1: Aldehydes. B.P. 248°.

—— ***o*-METHOXYBENZALDEHYDE** $CH_3O.C_6H_4.CHO$ $C_8H_8O_2$ **Beil. VIII-43**

M.P. 2.7-3.0° (m.p. after fusion of 35° form).

See 1:0235. Genus 1: Aldehydes. B.P. 243–244°.

—— **LAURALDEHYDE** (isomeric form) $CH_3.(CH_2)_{10}.CHO$ $C_{12}H_{24}O$ **Beil. I-714**

M.P. +11.1°

See 1:0017. Genus 1: Aldehydes (later in this section).

—— **PARALDEHYDE** (Acetaldehyde trimer) $C_6H_{12}O_3$ **Beil. XIX-395**

M.P. +12.6

See 1:0170. Genus 1: Aldehydes. B.P. 124°.

—— ***p*-ETHOXYBENZALDEHYDE** $C_2H_5.O.C_6H_4.CHO$ $C_9H_{10}O_2$ **Beil. VIII-73**

M.P. 13-14°

See 1:0251. Genus 1: Aldehydes. B.P. 255°.

1:0003 ***n*-TRIDECYLALDEHYDE** $CH_3.(CH_2)_{11}.CHO$ $C_{13}H_{26}O$ **Beil. I-715**
(Tridecanal)

M.P. 14° ⟨1⟩

Readily sol. org. solv.

On stdg. polymerizes grad. to a trimer [Beil. XIX-392], ndls. from ether, m.p. 61.5°; dif. sol. alc. or ether, eas. sol. C_6H_6, $CHCl_3$. The trimer does not reduce $KMnO_4$ in acetone. On slow distn. it is reconverted to monomer ⟨1⟩.

C̄ in acetone soln. reduces $KMnO_4$ yielding tridecylic ac. (1:0600) ⟨1⟩.

C̄ in ether soln., shaken with satd. aq. $NaHSO_3$ (cf. T 1.12) yields a crystn. $NaHSO_3$ cpd. ⟨1⟩.

Ⓓ **Tridecylaldoxime:** ndls. from dil. alc., m.p. 80.5° ⟨1⟩.
Ⓓ **Tridecylaldehyde semicarbazone:** pl. from alc., m.p. 106° ⟨1⟩.

1:0003 ⟨1⟩ Le Sueur, *J. Chem. Soc.* **87,** 1903–1905 (1905).

1:0004 ***n*-MYRISTALDEHYDE** $CH_3.(CH_2)_{12}.CHO$ $C_{14}H_{28}O$ **Beil. I-716**
(Tetradecylaldehyde; tetradecanal)

M.P. 23.0° ⟨1⟩ ⟨2⟩
22.5° ⟨3⟩

On stdg. polymerizes gradually to a trimer [Beil. XIX-392], ndls. from ether, m.p. 65.5°, insol. cold alc., ether, or acetone. The trimer does not reduce $KMnO_4$ in acetone even on boiling. On slow distn. at reduced press. it is quant. reconverted to monomer, m.p. 23.5° ⟨2⟩.

C̄ in acetone soln. slowly reduces $KMnO_4$ in cold; very readily on warming, yielding myristic acid (1:0630) ⟨2⟩.

C̄ in ether soln., shaken with satd. aq. $NaHSO_3$ (cf. T 1.12), yields a crystn. $NaHSO_3$ cpd. ⟨2⟩ ⟨4⟩.

Ⓓ **Myristaldoxime:** ndls. from dil. alc. or from MeOH, m.p. 82.5° ⟨1⟩ ⟨4⟩, 82.5–83.5° ⟨3⟩.
Ⓓ **Myristaldehyde semicarbazone:** ndls. from dil. alc. or from MeOH, m.p. 106.5° ⟨1⟩.
Ⓓ **Myristaldehyde *p*-nitrophenylhydrazone:** bright yel. cryst. pdr., m.p. 95° ⟨1⟩.

1:0004 ⟨1⟩ Stephen, *J. Chem. Soc.* **127,** 1876 (1925). ⟨2⟩ Le Sueur, *J. Chem. Soc.* **87,** 1900–1902 (1905). ⟨3⟩ Uhl, *J. Am. Pharm. Assoc.* **24,** 382 (1935). ⟨4⟩ Krafft, *Ber.* **23,** 2361 (1890).

1:0005 ***n*-PENTADECYLALDEHYDE** $CH_3.(CH_2)_{13}.CHO$ $C_{15}H_{30}O$ **Beil. I-716**
(Pentadecanal)

M.P. 24-25° ⟨1⟩ ⟨2⟩

On stdg. polymerizes grad. to a trimer [Beil. XIX-392], ndls. (from ether), m.p. 69–70° ⟨1⟩, insol. cold alc., ether, acetone, or AcOEt. The trimer does not reduce $KMnO_4$ in acetone even on boiling. On slow distn. under reduced press. the trimer is quant. reconverted to monomer, m.p. 24–25° ⟨1⟩.

C̄ in acetone soln. slowly reduces $KMnO_4$ in cold, very readily on warming, yielding pentadecylic acid (1:0620) ⟨1⟩.

C̄ in ether soln., shaken with satd. aq. $NaHSO_3$ (cf. T 1.12), yields cryst. $NaHSO_3$ cpd. ⟨1⟩.

Ⓓ **Pentadecylaldoxime:** ndls. from dil. alc., m.p. 86° ⟨1⟩.
Ⓓ **Pentadecylaldehyde semicarbazone:** ndls. from alc., m.p. 106.5° ⟨1⟩.
Ⓓ **Pentadecylaldehyde *p*-nitrophenylhydrazone:** yel. scales from alc., m.p. 94–95° ⟨2⟩.
Ⓓ **Pentadecylaldehyde 2,4-dinitrophenylhydrazone:** m.p. 107.5° ⟨2⟩; yel. pr. from pyridine + alc., m.p. 106–107° ⟨3⟩.
Ⓓ **Pentadecylaldehyde thiosemicarbazone:** cryst. from ether, m.p. 95–96.5° ⟨2⟩.

1:0005 ⟨1⟩ Le Sueur, *J. Chem. Soc.* **87,** 1896–1898 (1905). ⟨2⟩ Landa, *Bull. soc. chim.* (4) **37** 1236–1237 (1925). ⟨3⟩ Newman, *J. Am. Chem. Soc.* **57,** 734 (1935).

1:0007 PALMITALDEHYDE $CH_3.(CH_2)_{14}.CHO$ $C_{16}H_{32}O$ **Beil. I-717**
(*n*-Hexadecylaldehyde; hexadecanal)

M.P. 34° ⟨1⟩ ⟨2⟩.

Thin pl. with nacreous luster (from ether) — Insol. aq., sol. org. solv.

On stdg. polymerizes (incompletely) to a trimer [Beil. XIX-392], ndls. (from ether), m.p. 73° ⟨1⟩ ⟨2⟩, insol. alc., ether, or lt. pet. The trimer does not reduce $KMnO_4$ in acetone even on long boilg., nor form a $NaHSO_3$ cpd. — On htg. under reduced press. ⟨1⟩ or at 150° with trace of $ZnCl_2$ ⟨3⟩ the trimer is reconverted to monomer.

$\bar{C}$ in acetone soln. is oxid. by $KMnO_4$ to palmitic ac. (1:0650) ⟨1⟩.

$\bar{C}$ in ether soln., shaken with satd. aq. $NaHSO_3$ (cf. T 1.12), yields crystn. $NaHSO_3$ cpd. accompanied by trace of trimer.

Ⓓ **Palmitaldoxime:** ndls. from dil. alc., m.p. 88° ⟨1⟩ ⟨2⟩.

Ⓓ **Palmitaldehyde semicarbazone:** pl. from dil. alc., m.p. 107° ⟨1⟩; 108–109° ⟨2⟩.

Ⓓ **Palmitaldehyde *p*-nitrophenylhydrazone:** yel. ndls. from alc., m.p. 96.5° ⟨2⟩.

Ⓓ **Palmitaldehyde thiosemicarbazone:** m.p. 109° ⟨4⟩. [For m.p.s. of mixtures with corresp. deriv. of stearaldehyde (1:0012) see ⟨5⟩.]

1:0007 ⟨1⟩ Le Sueur, *J. Chem. Soc.* **87,** 1892–1894 (1905). ⟨2⟩ Stephen, *J. Chem. Soc.* **127,** 1876 (1925). ⟨3⟩ Gottfried, Ulzer, *Cent.* **1928,** I, 1193. ⟨4⟩ Feulgen, Behrens, *Z. physiol. Chem.* **177,** 229 (1928). ⟨5⟩ Feulgen, Imhauser, Behrens, *Z. physiol. Chem.* **180,** 170 (1929).

—— ***o*-METHOXYBENZALDEHYDE** $CH_3O.C_6H_4.CHO$ $C_8H_8O_2$ **Beil. VIII-43**

M.P. 35°

See 1:0235. Division B. Liquid aldehydes. B.P. 243–244°.

1:0009 MARGARALDEHYDE $CH_3.(CH_2)_{15}.CHO$ $C_{17}H_{34}O$ **Beil. I-717**
(*n*-Heptadecylaldehyde; heptadecanal)

M.P. 35-36°

Ndls. (from pet. ether) — Odor like paraffin — Very sol. cold ether, $CHCl_3$, C_6H_6, or lt. pet.; not readily sol. alc., acetone, or EtOAc in cold, but easily on htg.

From hot abs. alc. cryst. with 1 mole EtOH in ndls., m.p. 52° — Alc. of crystn. lost on stdg. in vac. over conc. H_2SO_4.

$\bar{C}$ in acetone soln. reduces $KMnO_4$ in cold yielding margaric ac. (1:0635).

On stdg. $\bar{C}$ slowly polymerizes to a trimer [Beil. XIX-392], ndls. from lt. pet., m.p. 77–78°, which does not reduce $KMnO_4$ in acetone, nor combine with $NaHSO_3$ or NH_2OH — On htg. at 245–250° the trimer is alm. quant. reconverted to monomer, m.p. 35–36°.

$\bar{C}$ in ether soln., shaken with satd. aq. $NaHSO_3$ (cf. T 1.12), yields crystn. $NaHSO_3$ cpd. accompanied by trace of trimer.

Ⓓ **Margaraldoxime:** pl. from AcOEt, m.p. 89.5° ⟨1⟩.

Ⓓ **Margaraldehyde semicarbazone:** ndls. from alc., m.p. 107–108° ⟨1⟩.

1:0009 ⟨1⟩ Le Sueur, *J. Chem. Soc.* **85,** 833–835 (1904).

1:0010 PIPERONAL $C_8H_6O_3$ **Beil. XIX-115**
(Heliotropin; 3,4-methylene-dioxybenzaldehyde)

H_2C——O
O—⟨benzene ring⟩—CHO

M.P. 37° **B.P. 263°**

Ndls. from hot aq.; sol. in 500–600 pts. cold aq. — Heliotrope odor. Gives cryst. $NaHSO_3$ compd. (T 1.12) dif. sol. aq. or alc. — Eas. volat. with steam.

Oxidn. with aq. $KMnO_4$ at 70–80° ⟨1⟩ ⟨2⟩, or with hot KOBr (quant. yield) [NaOCl does not work] ⟨3⟩, or with alk. H_2O_2 (quant. yield in 30 min.) ⟨4⟩, yields piperonylic ac. (1:0865), m.p. 228°.

Ⓓ **6-Nitropiperonal:** Warm 0.1 g. $\bar{C}$ gently with HNO_3 (D = 1.4); ppt. solid with cold aq.; cryst. from hot aq.; pale yel. silky ndls., m.p. 95.5°. ⟨6.⟩ — Salway ⟨7⟩ recommends extn. crude with $NaHSO_3$ soln. to dis. 6-nitro prod., later pptg. by addn. of alk.; material insol. in $NaHSO_3$ is $CH_2{<}^{O}_{O}{>}C_6H_3.NO_2$(1,2,4), m.p. 145°.

Ⓓ **Piperonaldoxime** (***anti***)**:** ndls. from hot aq., m.p. 110° ⟨8⟩.

Ⓓ **Piperonal semicarbazone:** m.p. 234° ⟨9⟩.

Ⓓ **Piperonal phenylhydrazone:** yel. ndls. from alc., m.p. 102–103° ⟨8⟩.

Ⓓ **Piperonal *p*-nitrophenylhydrazone:** red cryst., m.p. 199–200° (Heilbron).

Ⓓ **Piperonal 2,4-dinitrophenylhydrazone:** red cryst. from AcOH, m.p. 266° dec. ⟨10⟩, from xylene, m.p. 265° dec. ⟨11⟩. [Cf. T 1.14.] [Use in detn. of $\bar{C}$ ⟨14⟩.]

Ⓓ **Piperonal dimethone:** yel. cryst. from alc., m.p. 193° ⟨12⟩; 177–178° ⟨13⟩; corresp. anhydride; m.p. 219 220 cor. ⟨13⟩. [Cf. T 1.13.]

1:0010 ⟨1⟩ Cattelain, *Bull. soc. chim.* (4) **39,** 1188 (1926). ⟨2⟩ Shriner, Kleiderer, *Organic Syntheses* **10,** 82–83 (1930). ⟨3⟩ Van Linge, *Rec. trav. chim.* **16,** 45 (1897). ⟨4⟩ Slotta, Nold, *Ber.* **68,** 2227 (1935). ⟨6⟩ Mulliken, " Method " I, 17. ⟨7⟩ Salway, *J. Chem. Soc.* **95,** 1163 (1908). ⟨8⟩ Marcus, *Ber.* **24,** 3656 (1891). ⟨9⟩ Wilson, Keenan, *J. Assoc. Official Agr. Chem.* **13,** 390, 395 (1931). ⟨10⟩ Campbell, *Analyst* **61,** 392 (1936).

⟨11⟩ Brady, *J. Chem. Soc.* **1931,** 758. ⟨12⟩ Bernardi, Tartarini, *Ann. chim. applicata* **16,** 133 (1926). ⟨13⟩ Vorländer, *Z. anal. Chem.* **77,** 266 (1929). ⟨14⟩ Iddles, Low, Rosen, Hart, *Ind. Eng. Chem., Anal. Ed.* **11,** 102–103 (1939).

1:0012 STEARALDEHYDE $CH_3.(CH_2)_{15}.CH_2.CHO$ $C_{18}H_{36}O$ Beil I-718

(*n*-Octadecylaldehyde; octadecanal)

M.P. 38° ⟨1⟩

Rapidly polymerizes to a white solid, m.p. 80° ⟨1⟩.

Ether soln. of $\bar{C}$ shaken for a long time with satd. aq. $NaHSO_3$ gives white lfts. of $NaHSO_3$ cpd. which begin to decompose at 143° ⟨2⟩.

Oxidn. with $KMnO_4$ in AcOH at 100° gives stearic ac. (1:0660) ⟨3⟩; reduction with Na + AmOH gives stearyl alcohol (1:5953) ⟨3⟩.

Ⓓ **Stearaldoxime:** ndls., m.p. 89° ⟨1⟩.

Ⓓ **Stearaldehyde semicarbazone:** ndls., m.p. 108–109° ⟨1⟩.

Ⓓ **Stearaldehyde *p*-nitrophenylhydrazone:** yel. ndls. from MeOH, m.p. 101° ⟨1⟩.

Ⓓ **Stearaldehyde thiosemicarbazone:** m.p. 111° ⟨4⟩. [For melting points of mixtures with corresp. deriv. of palmitaldehyde (1:0007) see ⟨5⟩.]

1:0012 ⟨1⟩ Stephen, *J. Chem. Soc.* **127,** 1876 (1925). ⟨2⟩ Rosenmund, *Ber.* **51,** 592 (1918). ⟨3⟩ Grün, *Ber.* **53,** 995 (1920). ⟨4⟩ Feulgen, Behrens, *Z. physiol. Chem.* **177,** 227–228 (1928). ⟨5⟩ Feulgen, Imhauser, Behrens, *Z. physiol. Chem.* **180,** 170 (1929).

1:0015 VERATRALDEHYDE $(CH_3O)_2.C_6H_3.CHO$ $C_9H_{10}O_3$ Beil. VIII-255

(3,4-Dimethoxybenzaldehyde; protocatechualdehyde dimethyl ether)
(Van llin methyl ether)

M.P. 44° (58°) **B.P. 285°**

Alm. insol. cold aq.; more sol. hot aq.; eas. sol. alc., ether; only very sl. volat. with steam — Yields cryst. $NaHSO_3$ cpd. (cf. T 1.12).

[For prepn. from vanillin (1:0050) + dimethyl sulfate (95% yield) ⟨1⟩ ⟨2⟩ ⟨9⟩.]

Oxidn. with $K_2Cr_2O_7$ + H_2SO_4, or with KOBr ⟨3⟩ or with alk. H_2O_2 (90% yield) ⟨4⟩, gives veratric acid [Beil. X-393], m.p. 181° when anhydrous.

Boiling with 15 pts. 48% HBr for 3 hrs. splits one methoxy group yielding 3-hydroxy-4-methoxybenzaldehyde (isovanillin) [Beil. VIII-254], m.p. 116° ⟨5⟩.

Ⓓ **Veratraldoxime:** cryst. from lgr., m.p. 94–95° ⟨6⟩.
Ⓓ **Veratraldehyde phenylhydrazone:** cryst. from alc., m.p. 121° ⟨7⟩.
Ⓓ **Veratraldehyde 2,4-dinitrophenylhydrazone:** or. pr. from nitrobenzene, m.p. 261–263° cor. ⟨8⟩ [cf. T 1.14].

1:0015 ⟨1⟩ Barger, Silberschmidt, *J. Chem. Soc.* **1928,** 2924. ⟨2⟩ Buck, Perkin, *J. Chem. Soc.* **125,** 1678 (1924). ⟨3⟩ von Kostanecki, Tambor, *Ber.* **39,** 4022 (1906). ⟨4⟩ Slotta, Nold, *Ber.* **68,** 2227 (1935). ⟨5⟩ Lovecy, Robinson, Sugasawa, *J. Chem. Soc.* **1930,** 818. ⟨6⟩ Fulda, *Monatsh.* **23,** 913 Note (1902). ⟨7⟩ Juliusberg, *Ber.* **40,** 119 (1907). ⟨8⟩ Strain, *J. Am. Chem. Soc.* **57,** 760 (1935). ⟨9⟩ Buck, *Organic Syntheses* **13,** 102–104 (1933).

1:0017 LAURALDEHYDE $CH_3(CH_2)_{10}.CHO$ $C_{12}H_{24}O$ **Beil. I-714**
(*n*-Dodecylaldehyde; dodecanal)

M.P. 445° ⟨1⟩ ⟨2⟩
42-43° ⟨3⟩

C̄ in air, or more rapidly in pres. of traces of mineral acids, polymerizes to a dimer (?) cryst. from 50 pts. alc. or 10 pts. ether, m.p. 57° ⟨4⟩. This polymer is very stable and not depolymerized by htg., steam distn., or even warm. with dil. or conc. H_2SO_4 ⟨4⟩.

[A 2nd form of C̄, m.p. +11.1°, definitely monomolecular and giving same derivs. as the 44.5° form, has been reported ⟨2⟩. With dil. aq. H_2SO_3 the liq. is conv. to the polymer, m.p. 57° ⟨2⟩.]

C̄ fused with lauryl alc. (1:5900) forms a mol. cpd., m.p. 44.5–45.5°, definitely distinct from C̄ itself ⟨5⟩.

C̄ yields $NaHSO_3$ cpd. [cf. T 1.12].

Ⓓ **Lauraldoxime:** lfts. from pet. ether, m.p. 76–77° ⟨4⟩; ndls. from MeOH, m.p. 77.5–78° ⟨2⟩.
Ⓓ **Lauraldehyde semicarbazone:** m.p. 102.5–103.5° ⟨4⟩; 105.5–106.5° ⟨2⟩.
Ⓓ **Lauraldehyde *p*-nitrophenylhydrazone:** m.p. 90° ⟨4⟩.
Ⓓ **Lauraldehyde 2,4-dinitrophenylhydrazone:** yel. cryst., m.p. 106° ⟨6⟩ [cf. T 1.14].
Ⓓ **Lauraldehyde thiosemicarbazone:** m.p. 100–100.5° ⟨3⟩.

1:0017 ⟨1⟩ Krafft, *Ber.* **13,** 1415 (1880). ⟨2⟩ Zaar, *J. prakt. Chem.* (2) **132,** 169–171 (1931). ⟨3⟩ Uhl, *J. Am. Pharm. Assoc.* **24,** 381 (1935). ⟨4⟩ Mannich, Nadelmann, *Ber.* **63,** 798–799 (1930). ⟨5⟩ Zaar, *J. prakt. Chem.* (2), **132,** 168 (1931). ⟨6⟩ Allen, *J. Am. Chem. Soc.* **52,** 2958 (1930).

1:0020 FURFURAL DIACETATE $C_9H_{10}O_5$ **Beil. XVII-278**
(Fural diacetate; furfurylidene diacetate)

```
H—C——C—H
  ‖     ‖
H—C     C—CH(O.CO.CH3)2
   \   /
     O
```

M.P. 52° **B.P. 220°**

Tbls. from ether, pet. ether, or lgr. on slow cooling; ndls. from pet. ether on rapid cooling — Dif. sol. aq., pet. eth., eas. sol. ether, C_6H_6.

[For prepn. from furfural + Ac_2O + $SnCl_2.2H_2O$ see ⟨1⟩.] Abs. pure material is entirely stable.

On boilg. with aq., acids, or alk., hydrolyzes to furfural (1:0185) and acetic acid (1:1010), q.v.

1:0020 ⟨1⟩ Gilman, Wright, *Rec. trav. chim.* **50,** 833–835 (1931).

1:0025 **β-(α-FURYL)ACROLEIN** $C_7H_6O_2$ **Beil. XVII-305**

```
H—C——C—H
  ‖    ‖
H—C    C—CH=CH.CHO
   \  /
    O
```

M.P. 54° (51°)

Ndls. from lgr. — Eas. sol. hot aq., alc., ether; dif. sol. cold aq.

Eas. volat. with steam — Cinnamonlike odor.

[For prepn. from furfural + acetaldehyde + aq. NaOH (54% yield) see ⟨3⟩.]

Reduces Tollens' reagt. (T 1.11) — Yields $NaHSO_3$ cpd. (cf. T 1.12), gives green color with aniline acetate (T 1.23).

Sol. in conc. H_2SO_4 with brown red color changing to green on addn. of trace of HNO_3.

Ⓓ β-(α-**Furyl)acrolein oxime:** ndls., m.p. 110–111° ⟨1⟩.

Ⓓ β-(α-**Furyl)acrolein phenylhydrazone:** cryst. from pet. ether, m.p. 132° ⟨2⟩.

Ⓓ β-(α-**Furyl)acrolein semicarbazone:** m.p. 219.5° (Maquenne block) ⟨1⟩.

1:0025 ⟨1⟩ Ivanoff, *Bull. soc. chim.* (4) **35,** 1661 (1924). ⟨2⟩ König, *J. prakt. Chem.* (2) **88,** 211 (1913). ⟨3⟩ Burdick, Adkins, *J. Am. Chem. Soc.* **56,** 441 (1934).

1:0030 ***p*-HOMOSALICYLALDEHYDE** $C_8H_8O_2$ **Beil. VIII-100**

(2-Hydroxy-5-methylbenzaldehyde; 6-hydroxy-3-methylbenzaldehyde) (Not to be confused with *o*-hydroxyphenylacetaldehyde, sometimes called homosalicylaldehyde)

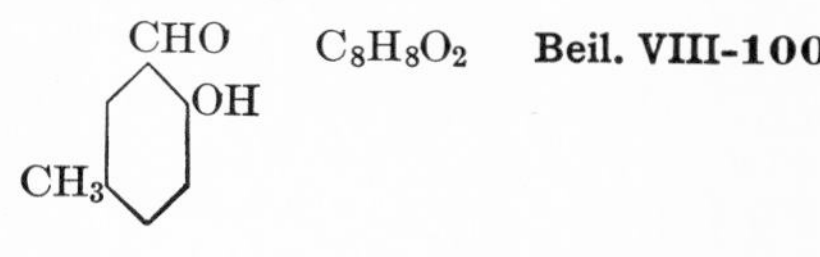

M.P. 56° **B.P. 217-218°**

Lfts. from dil. alc. — Dif. sol. aq.; eas. sol. alc., ether, $CHCl_3$ — Volat. with steam.

Yields a $NaHSO_3$ cpd. (cf. T 1.12) — Under cert. conditions gives yel. ppt. with fuchsin-ald. reagt. ⟨7⟩.

Colored deep yel. by NH_4OH or aq. alk.; with $FeCl_3$ (T 1.41) gives deep blue color [dif. from *o*-homosalicylaldehyde [Beil. VIII-98], which gives only bluish color; dif. from α-*m*-homosalicylaldehyde [Beil. VIII-101], which gives violet color ⟨1⟩].

Gives red coloration with acetone + NaOH.

Dry K salt of $\bar{C}$ (from evapn. of neut. soln.) + Ac_2O in ether yields 2-acetoxy-5-methylbenzaldehyde, ndls. from dil. alc., m.p. 57° ⟨2⟩. [Gives no $FeCl_3$ color, no $NaHSO_3$ cpd., not volat. with steam.]

$\bar{C}$ refluxed several hrs. with 3 pts. Ac_2O yields 2-acetoxy-5-methylbenzaldiacetate, cryst. from alc., m.p. 94° ⟨2⟩.

[For 12 dif. variously subst. arylhydrazones of $\bar{C}$ see ⟨3⟩.]

Ⓓ ***p*-Homosalicylaldoxime:** cryst. from hot aq., m.p. 105° ⟨4⟩.

Ⓓ ***p*-Homosalicylaldehyde phenylhydrazone:** straw yel. ndls. from alc., m.p. 149° ⟨5⟩ ⟨3⟩.

Ⓓ ***p*-Homosalicyloxyacetic acid:** lfts. from hot aq., m.p. 182–183° ⟨6⟩ [cf. T 1.46].

1:0030 ⟨1⟩ Tiemann, Schotten, *Ber.* **11,** 774 (1878). ⟨2⟩ Schotten, *Ber.* **11,** 786 (1878). ⟨3⟩ Chang, Sah, *J. Chinese Chem. Soc.* **4,** 80–81 (1936). ⟨4⟩ Goldbeck, *Ber.* **24,** 3658 (1891). ⟨5⟩ Anselmino, *Ber.* **35,** 4105 (1902). ⟨6⟩ von Auwers, *Ann.* **393,** 365 (1912). ⟨7⟩ Shoesmith, Sosson, Hetherington, *J. Chem. Soc.* **1927,** 2222.

1:0035 **PARAISOBUTYRALDEHYDE** $(C_4H_8O)_3$ $C_{12}H_{24}O_3$ **Beil. XIX-390**

(2,4,6-Tri-isopropyl-1,3,5-trioxan)

M.P. 59-60° **B.P. 195°** cor., sl. depolym.

Ndls. from alc. — Insol. aq., sol. alc., eas. sol. ether — Subl. even at 70°. Volat. with steam.

Does not combine with satd. aq. $NaHSO_3$.
Htd. with dil. or conc. H_2SO_4 depolymerizes to isobutyraldehyde, b.p. 64° (1:0120), q.v.

1:0036 β-NAPHTHALDEHYDE $C_{11}H_8O$ Beil. VII-401

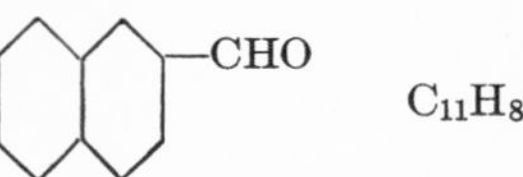

M.P. 60°

Lfts. from boilg. aq.; insol. cold aq.; somewhat sol. hot aq.; very eas. sol. alc., ether. Eas. volat. with steam.

[For prepn.: from β-naphthonitrile + HCl + $SnCl_2$ + ether (76% yield ⟨1⟩, 91% yield ⟨8⟩) see ⟨1⟩ ⟨8⟩; from β-naphthylmethyl bromide + hexamethylenetetramine (70–80% yield) see ⟨2⟩.]

C̄ forms $NaHSO_3$ cpd. with excess satd. aq. $NaHSO_3$ soln. (cf. T 1.12) ⟨3⟩ — C̄ reduces Tollens' reagt. (T 1.11).

Oxidn. with $KMnO_4$ yields β-naphthoic ac. (1:0800), m.p. 184° — C̄ in 8 pts. 80% alc. refluxed ½ hr. with 0.1 pt. KCN in 1 pt. aq. gives 78% yield β-naphthoin, rhomb. pl. from alc., m.p. 125–126° ⟨1⟩.

Ⓓ **β-Naphthaldoxime:** ndls. from dil. alc., m.p. 156° ⟨4⟩.

Ⓓ **β-Naphthaldehyde semicarbazone:** ndls. from alc., m.p. 245° ⟨3⟩ ⟨5⟩.

Ⓓ **β-Naphthaldehyde phenylhydrazone:** lfts. from alc., m.p. 205–206° dec. ⟨3⟩ ⟨5⟩; 217–218° ⟨6⟩.

Ⓓ **β-Naphthaldehyde *p*-nitrophenylhydrazone:** m.p. 230° ⟨7⟩.

Ⓓ **β-Naphthaldehyde 2,4-dinitrophenylhydrazone:** red ndls. from AcOH, m.p. 270° (Campbell) [cf. T 1.14].

1:0036 ⟨1⟩ Fulton, Robinson, *J. Chem. Soc.* **1939,** 200. ⟨2⟩ Mayer, Sieglitz, *Ber.* **55,** 1857 (1922). ⟨3⟩ Monier-Williams, *J. Chem. Soc.* **89,** 276 (1906). ⟨4⟩ Wuyts, Koeck, *Bull. soc. chim. Belg.* **41,** 201 (1932). ⟨5⟩ Gattermann, *Ann.* **393,** 228 (1912). ⟨6⟩ Weil, Ostermeier, *Ber.* **54,** 3217 (1921). ⟨7⟩ Shoppee, *J. Chem. Soc.* **1933,** 41. ⟨8⟩ Williams, *J. Am. Chem. Soc.* **61,** 2248–2249 (1939).

1:0040 β-RESORCYLALDEHYDE DIMETHYL ETHER $C_9H_{10}O_3$ Beil. VIII-242

(2,4-Dimethoxybenzaldehyde)

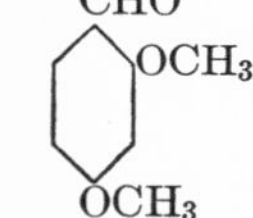

M.P. 71°

Ndls. from dil. alc. or lgr. — Insol. aq.; eas. sol. alc., ether, C_6H_6, lgr. Volat. with steam.

[Prepn. from Na salt of 2-hydroxy-4-methoxybenzaldehyde via dimethyl sulfate in toluene ⟨1⟩: from β-resorcylaldehyde (2,4-dihydroxybenzaldehyde) (1:0065) with 50% KOH + dimethyl sulfate ⟨2⟩ ⟨3⟩.]

Gives no coloration with $FeCl_3$ (T 1.41).

Oxidn. with $KMnO_4$ yields 2,4-dimethoxybenzoic ac. [Beil. X-379], ndls. from aq., m.p. 110° ⟨4⟩ — Nitration with conc. HNO_3 in AcOH gives (on stdg. in cold 12 hrs.) 75–80% yield 5-nitro-2,4-dimethoxybenzaldehyde, cryst. from MeOH, m.p. 188–189° ⟨5⟩.

Ⓓ **2,4-Dimethoxybenzaldoxime:** ndls. from aq., 106° ⟨4⟩.

1:0040 ⟨1⟩ Ott, Nauen, *Ber.* **55,** 925 (1922). ⟨2⟩ Cullinane, Philpott, *J. Chem. Soc.* **1929,** 1764. ⟨3⟩ Reimer, Tobin, *J. Am. Chem. Soc.* **52,** 343 (1930). ⟨4⟩ Gattermann, *Ann.* **357,** 369 (1907). ⟨5⟩ Rao, Srikantia, Iyengar, *J. Chem. Soc.* **127,** 558 (1925).

1:0045 PROTOCATECHUALDEHYDE 3-ETHYL ETHER $C_9H_{10}O_3$ **Beil. VIII-256**

(" Bourbonal "; " Ethylvanillin ")

CHO

OC_2H_5

OH

M.P. 77°

Scales from aq. — Odor like vanillin — A mixt. of 10% $\bar{C}$ + 90% vanillin (1:0050) melts at 77° ⟨1⟩.

[For studies of methods of detect. of $\bar{C}$ by itself or in presence of vanillin see ⟨2⟩ ⟨3⟩ ⟨4⟩ ⟨5⟩ ⟨6⟩ ⟨7⟩.]

1:0045 ⟨1⟩ Lockwood, *Analyst* **59,** 730–732 (1934). ⟨2⟩ Stadler, Wagner, *Z. anal. Chem.* **108,** 161–167 (1937). ⟨3⟩ Stadler, Wagner, *Z. anal. Chem.* **111,** 391–393 (1938). ⟨4⟩ Fuchs, Mayrhofer, *Mikrochemie, Pregl Festschrift* **1929,** 109–116. ⟨5⟩ Klotz, *Am. J. Pharm.* **101** 442–447 (1929). ⟨6⟩ Hoeke, *Chem. Weekblad* **35,** 316–319; 364–365 (1938). ⟨7⟩ Chenoweth, *Ind. Eng. Chem., Anal. Ed.* **12,** 98–99 (1940).

1:0050 VANILLIN $C_8H_8O_3$ **Beil. VIII-247**

(4-Hydroxy-3-methoxybenzaldehyde; protocatechualdehyde-3-methyl ether)

CHO

$-OCH_3$

OH

M.P. 80-81° **B.P. 285°**

Strong vanilla odor — Taste first burning, then like vanilla.

Ndls. from hot aq. — Sol. 90–100 pts. cold aq., 20 pts. hot aq. — Eas. sol. in alc., ether, $CHCl_3$, CS_2, AcOH, pyridine, or hot lgr.; insol. cold lgr. — Subl. undecomposed.

Aq. soln. reacts acidic, decomposing $NaHCO_3$ soln., but $\bar{C}$ gives slightly low values when titrated — $FeCl_3$ on 1:200 aq. soln. gives immed. blue color (T 1.41) — $\bar{C}$ is completely extd. from ether soln. by satd. $NaHSO_3$ (cf. T 1.12) but $NaHSO_3$ cpd. is quite sol. — $\bar{C}$ gives only feeble fuchsin-aldehyde react. [For study see ⟨1⟩.]

Long exposure of powdered $\bar{C}$ to air and light gives vanillic acid [Beil. X-392] but with most oxidg. agts. $\bar{C}$ is either unattacked or completely destroyed ⟨2⟩ — $\bar{C}$ with Br_2 in AcOH yields 5-bromovanillin (5-bromo-4-hydroxy-3-methoxybenzaldehyde), cryst. from alc., m.p. 164° ⟨3⟩ ⟨4⟩.

$\bar{C}$ with equiv. 1 *N* aq. KOH shaken with 1 equiv. Ac_2O gives 95% vanillin (mono)acetate, ndls. from dil. alc., m.p. 78° ⟨5⟩ — $\bar{C}$, htd. several hrs. with excess Ac_2O + trace $SnCl_2.2H_2O$ gives (87% yield) vanillin triacetate, cryst. from alc., m.p. 90° ⟨6⟩ — $\bar{C}$ in aq. NaOH shaken with BzCl ⟨7⟩ or with excess pyridine in ether ⟨8⟩ [cf. T 1.47] gives vanillin (mono)benzoate, pr. from alc., m.p. 78° — $\bar{C}$ with *p*-nitrobenzyl bromide + alk. (T 1.44) gives vanillin *p*-nitrobenzyl ether, m.p. 124.5° ⟨9⟩ — $\bar{C}$ with chloroacetic ac. + alk. (T 1.46) yields 2-methoxy-4-formylphenoxyacetic ac., ndls. from aq., m.p. 189° ⟨10⟩.

Ⓓ **Dehydrodivanillin** [Beil. VIII-542]: Dissolve 0.05 g. $\bar{C}$ in 10 ml. aq. Add 2 drops conc. HCl and 2 drops 10% $FeCl_3$. Boil 1 min., filter hot, wash. Boil residue with 5 ml. alc., filter, dry at 100°. Prod. forms slender nearly colorless silky microcryst. ndls. melting with dec. at abt. 304° u.c. ⟨11⟩.

Ⓓ **Vanillin oxime:** in quant. yield as tbls. from aq., m.p. 117° ⟨12⟩.

Ⓓ **Vanillin semicarbazone:** m.p. 230° ⟨13⟩. [Ref. also gives photomicrograph.]

Ⓓ **Vanillin phenylhydrazone:** lfts. from C_6H_6 + lgr., m.p. 105° ⟨14⟩.

Ⓓ **Vanillin *p*-nitrophenylhydrazone:** lfts. from AcOH, m.p. 227° ⟨15⟩; m.p. 223° ⟨16⟩.

Ⓓ **Vanillin 2,4-dinitrophenylhydrazone:** red cryst. from AcOH, m.p. 271° cor., dec. ⟨17⟩; 270° ⟨18⟩ (cf. T 1.14). [For use in quant. detn. of C̄ see ⟨19⟩.]

Ⓓ **Vanillin dimethone:** tbls. from alc., m.p. 196–198° cor. ⟨21⟩; corresp. anhydride (cf. T 1.13), m.p. 227–228° cor. ⟨21⟩.

1:0050 ⟨1⟩ Shoesmith, Sosson, Hetherington, *J. Chem. Soc.* **1927**, 2222. ⟨2⟩ Tiemann, *Ber.* **9,** 415 (1876). ⟨3⟩ Dakin, *Am. Chem. J.* **42,** 493 (1909). ⟨4⟩ Raiford, Hilman, *J. Am. Chem. Soc.* **49,** 1572 (1927). ⟨5⟩ Pschorr, Sumuleanu, *Ber.* **32,** 3407 (1899). ⟨6⟩ Knoevenagel, *Ann.* **402,** 121 (1914). ⟨7⟩ Popovici, *Ber.* **40,** 3505 (1907). ⟨8⟩ Rosenmund, *Ber.* **46,** 1041 (1913). ⟨9⟩ Reid, *J. Am. Chem. Soc.* **39,** 307 (1917). ⟨10⟩ Elkan, *Ber.* **19,** 3055 (1886).

⟨11⟩ Mulliken, " Method " I, 17. ⟨12⟩ Hoesch, Zarzecki, *Ber.* **50,** 463 (1917). ⟨13⟩ Wilson, Keenan, *J. Assoc. Official Agr. Chem.* **13,** 390, 396 (1930). ⟨14⟩ Tiemann, Kees, *Ber.* **18,** 1662 (1885). ⟨15⟩ Biltz, Sieden, *Ann.* **324,** 323 (1902). ⟨16⟩ Phillips, *Analyst* **48,** 367 (1923). ⟨17⟩ Campbell, *Analyst* **61,** 392 (1936). ⟨18⟩ Blanksma, Wackers, *Rec. trav. chim.* **55,** 658 (1936). ⟨19⟩ Rubin, Bloom, *Am. J. Pharm.* **108,** 387–388 (1936). ⟨20⟩ Iddles, Jackson, *Ind. Eng. Chem., Anal. Ed.* **6,** 455 (1934).

⟨21⟩ Vorländer, *Z. anal. Chem.* **77,** 266 (1929).

1:0053 PHENYLGLYOXAL HYDRATE $C_8H_8O_3$ Beil. VII-671

(Benzoylformaldehyde hydrate) —CO.CH(OH)$_2$

M.P. 91° ⟨1⟩ ⟨2⟩; **93-94°** ⟨3⟩

Ndls. from aq., $CHCl_3$, CS_2, alc. or ether + lgr. — Sol. in 35 parts aq. at 20°. M.p.'s recorded vary from 73–94° prob. due to varying degrees of dryness.

On htg. above m.p. loses aq. and yields phenylglyoxal (1:0278).

C̄ in even very dil. aq. soln. gives on addn. of a few drops of NH_4OH finely divided white flocks which coalesce on acidifn. ⟨4⟩. [For discussion of structure of products see Beil. XXIV 224–225.]

1:0053 ⟨1⟩ Pinner, *Ber.* **38,** 1532, Note 1 (1905). ⟨2⟩ Riley, Morley, Friend, *J. Chem. Soc.* **1932,** 1877. ⟨3⟩ von Auwers, Ludewig, Müller, *Ann.* **526,** 171 (1936). ⟨4⟩ Müller, von Pechmann, *Ber.* **22,** 2557 (1889).

1:0055 *m*-HYDROXYBENZALDEHYDE $C_7H_6O_2$ Beil. VIII-58

(*m*-Aldehydophenol; *m*-formylphenol)

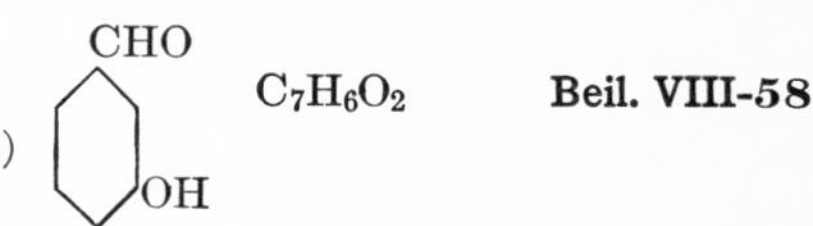

M.P. 104° (108° cor.) **B.P. abt. 240°**

Ndls. from hot aq. — Fairly eas. sol. hot aq.; eas. sol. alc., ether, C_6H_6; insol. lgr. Not volatile with steam.

C̄, although too weakly acidic to titrate, dis. in aq. KOH or NH_4OH yielding yel. solns.; solid salts, however, are colorless.

C̄ in aq. soln. gives violet color with $FeCl_3$ (T 1.41) — Forms $NaHSO_3$ cpd. (cf. T 1.12) but latter is eas. sol. aq. ⟨1⟩.

C̄, htd. at 190–240° with powdered KOH + few drops aq. gives H_2 + 91% yield of *m*-hydroxybenzoic acid (1:0825), m.p. 202° cor. ⟨2⟩ — C̄ at 50–60° for 1 hr. with 2 pts. KOH + 2 pts. aq. gives 94% yield each of *m*-hydroxybenzyl alc., cryst. from C_6H_6, m.p. 73° cor., and *m*-hydroxybenzoic ac. (1:0825), cryst. from boil aq., m.p. 202° cor. ⟨2⟩ — C̄, shaken with aq. aniline 2 hrs. at 35–40°, stood overnight, gives quant. yield *m*-hydroxybenzalaniline, cryst. from C_6H_6, m.p. 91° ⟨3⟩.

C̄ with chloroacetic ac. + alk. (cf. T 1.46) yields 3-formylphenoxyacetic ac., ndls. from warm aq., m.p. 148° ⟨4⟩ — C̄ in ether with phenylisocyanate yields on stdg. 3-formylphenyl *N*-phenylcarbamate, ndls. from C_6H_6, m.p. 158–160° ⟨5⟩. C̄ refluxed with excess Ac_2O 3–4 hrs., poured into aq., oil allowed to cryst., solid pressed between papers, then recrystd.

from dil. alc., yields *m*-acetoxybenzaldiacetate, white lfts., m.p. 76° ⟨1⟩ [*m*-acetoxybenzaldehyde (mono-acetylation prod.) is an oil]. C̄ with BzCl + pyridine gives 65% yield *m*-benzoxybenzaldehyde, m.p. 37–38° ⟨11⟩.

Ⓓ ***m*-Hydroxybenzaldehyde phenylhydrazone:** cryst. from toluene, m.p. 130–131.5° ⟨6⟩; after recrystn. from C_6H_6 or directly from C̄ + phenylhydrazine in AcOH, m.p. **147°** cor. ⟨7⟩.

Ⓓ ***m*-Hydroxybenzaldehyde *p*-nitrophenylhydrazone:** cryst. from dil. AcOH, m.p. 221–222° ⟨8⟩.

Ⓓ ***m*-Hydroxybenzaldehyde 2,4-dinitrophenylhydrazone:** red cryst. from alc., m.p. 260° dec. ⟨9⟩; scarlet pr. from xylene, m.p. 259° ⟨10⟩ (cf. T 1.14).

1:0055 ⟨1⟩ Tiemann, Ludwig, *Ber.* **15,** 2047 (1882). ⟨2⟩ Lock, *Ber.* **62,** 1182–1183 (1929). ⟨3⟩ Bamberger, Müller, *Ann.* **313,** 112 (1900). ⟨4⟩ Elkan, *Ber.* **19,** 3043 (1896). ⟨5⟩ Brady, Dunn, *J. Chem. Soc.* **109,** 676 (1916). ⟨6⟩ Rudolph, *Ann.* **248,** 102 (1888). ⟨7⟩ Jowett, *J. Chem. Soc.* **77,** 710 (1900). ⟨8⟩ Hodgson, Beard, *J. Soc. Chem. Ind.* **45T,** 93 (1926). ⟨9⟩ Campbell, *Analyst* **61,** 392 (1936). ⟨10⟩ Brady, *J. Chem. Soc.* **1931,** 758.
⟨11⟩ Russell, Clark, *J. Am. Chem. Soc.* **61,** 2655 (1939).

1:0060 ***p*-HYDROXYBENZALDEHYDE** (*p*-Aldehydophenol; *p*-formylphenol) $C_7H_6O_2$ **Beil. VIII-64**

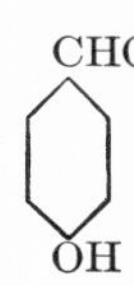

M.P. 116–117°

Subl. undecd.; not volat. with steam — Dif. sol. cold aq.; cryst. in ndls. from hot aq.

Aq. soln. gives fuchsin-ald. test only faintly, but undislvd. solid turns red with fresh reagent — [For study of reaction see ⟨1⟩.] — $FeCl_3$ soln. gives pale violet color (T 1.41) — Although sol. in alk. fails to give sharp end point with phenolphthalein and cannot be titrated; neutral to methyl orange — C̄.$NaHSO_3$ is eas. sol. and does not sep., yet C̄ is completely extd. from ether soln. by $NaHSO_3$; repptd. by acid.

C̄ htd. 1 hr. at 140–210° with 10 pts. powdered KOH + few drops aq. gives H_2 (90% theor.) + 87% theor. of *p*-hydroxybenzoic ac. (1:0840), cryst. from boilg. aq., m.p. 210° cor. ⟨13⟩ — C̄, dislvd. in 5 pts. AcOH and slowly treated with 2 moles Br_2 in AcOH with cooling, poured into aq., ppt. recrystd. from dil. alc., gives ndls. of 3,5-dibromo-4-hydroxybenzaldehyde, m.p. 178–179° ⟨2⟩. [Note: excess Br_2 gives much tribromophenol.] — 2 pts. C̄ + 3 pts. fused AcONa + 5 pts. Ac_2O, htd. 8–10 hrs. at 175–180°, yields acetate, which after boiling 1 hr. with excess alk., filtering, and acidif., gives on cooling 80% yield of *p*-hydroxycinnamic ac., cryst. from aq., m.p. 206–207° ⟨3⟩.

C̄ with chloroacetic ac. + alk. (cf. T 1.46) yields 4-formylphenoxyacetic acid, lfts. from hot aq., m.p. 198° ⟨11⟩.

C̄ in ether with phenylisocyanate yields 4-formylphenyl *N*-phenylcarbamate, ndls. from C_6H_6, m.p. 136° ⟨12⟩.

Ⓓ ***p*-Benzoxybenzaldehyde:** from C̄ + BzCl + aq. alk., ndls. from alc., m.p. 72° ⟨4⟩; 89° ⟨14⟩; 90° ⟨15⟩.

Ⓓ ***p*-Hydroxybenzaldehyde phenylhydrazone:** ndls. from alc., m.p. 177–178° ⟨5⟩; 184° slow htg. ⟨6⟩.

Ⓓ ***p*-Hydroxybenzaldehyde 2,4-dinitrophenylhydrazone:** red cryst. (with 1 H_2O) m.p. 260° ⟨7⟩; purple red cryst. from AcOH, m.p. 280° dec. ⟨8⟩. [Use in quant. detn. of C̄ ⟨9⟩ ⟨16⟩.] [Cf. T 1.14.]

Ⓓ ***p*-Hydroxybenzaldehyde dimethone:** m.p. 188–190° cor. ⟨9⟩, 184° ⟨10⟩; corresp. anhydride [cf. T 1.13], m.p. 246° ⟨9⟩; 208–209° ⟨10⟩.

1:0060 ⟨1⟩ Shoesmith, Sosson, Hetherington, *J. Chem. Soc.* **1927,** 2222. ⟨2⟩ Paal, *Ber.* **28,** 2408 (1895). ⟨3⟩ Sonn, *Ber.* **46,** 4052 (1913). ⟨4⟩ Kopp, *Ann.* **277,** 350 (1893). ⟨5⟩ Rudolph, *Ann.* **248,** 102 (1888). ⟨6⟩ Anselmino, *Ber.* **36,** 3974 (1903). ⟨7⟩ Blanksma, Wackers, *Rec. trav. chim.* **55,** 658 (1936). ⟨8⟩ Campbell, *Analyst* **61,** 392 (1936). ⟨9⟩ Vorländer, *Z. anal. Chem.* **77,** 263 (1929). ⟨10⟩ Chakravarti, Chattopadhyaya, Ghosh, *Cent.* **1932,** I, 2330.

⟨11⟩ Elkan, *Ber.* **19,** 3041 (1886). ⟨12⟩ Brady, Dunn, *J. Chem. Soc.* **109,** 676 (1916). ⟨13⟩ Lock, *Ber.* **62,** 1186 (1929). ⟨14⟩ Russell, Clark, *J. Am. Chem. Soc.* **61,** 2655 (1939). ⟨15⟩ Raiford, Milbury, *J. Am. Chem. Soc.* **56,** 2728 (1934). ⟨16⟩ Iddles, Low, Rosen, Hart, *Ind. Eng. Chem., Anal. Ed.* **11,** 102–103 (1939).

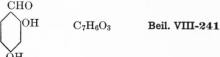

1:0065 β-RESORCYLALDEHYDE (2,4-Dihydroxybenzaldehyde) — [structure: benzene ring with CHO, OH (ortho), OH (para)] — $C_7H_6O_3$ — **Beil. VIII-241**

M.P. 135-136°

Yellowish ndls. from aq.; alm. colorless ndls. from ether + lgr. — Eas. sol. aq., alc., ether, $CHCl_3$, AcOH; spar. sol. C_6H_6.

Gives Generic Test 1 (fuchsin-aldehyde reagt.) only feebly, sometimes accompanied by yel. ppt. [For study of this see ⟨1⟩.]

In 20% alc. ⟨2⟩ ⟨3⟩ titrates with NaOH + phenolphthalein as a monobasic acid (Neut. Eq. = 138) — C̄ in alc. soln. (without indicator) gives no color on addn. of NaOH [dif. from 2,3- or 2,5-dihydroxybenzaldehydes] ⟨4⟩.

Gives deep brown color with $FeCl_3$ (T 1.41).

Reduction with amalgamated Zn + dil. HCl yields 2,4-dihydroxytoluene (cresorcinol) (1:1521), cryst. from C_6H_6, m.p. 104–105° ⟨5⟩ ⟨6⟩.

C̄, with excess dimethyl sulfate + 50% aq. KOH yields 2,4-dimethoxybenzaldehyde. (1:0040), cryst. from alc., m.p. 71° ⟨7⟩ — C̄ in dry ether + K_2CO_3, shaken 30 min. with Ac_2O, gives 76% yield diacetyl-β-resorcylaldehyde, ndls. from abs. alc., m.p. 69° ⟨12⟩ — C̄ with BzCl + pyridine gives (85% yield) resorcylaldehyde dibenzoate, ndls. from alc., m.p. 98° ⟨13⟩.

Htg. for 1 hr. at 250–270° with 10 pts. pdr. KOH gives (72% yield) resorcinol (1:1530) + K_2CO_3 + H_2 ⟨14⟩.

[For prepn. of C̄ from resorcinol + formanilide + aq. NaOH see ⟨7⟩ ⟨6⟩; from resorcinol + HCN + HCl in ether see ⟨8⟩.]

Ⓓ **2,4-Dihydroxybenzaldoxime:** ndls. from aq., m.p. 191° ⟨9⟩ [cf. comments on oximation of alk. sensitive phenolic aldehydes ⟨10⟩].

Ⓓ **2,4-Dihydroxybenzaldehyde phenylhydrazone:** ndls. from alc., m.p. 159° ⟨11⟩ [cf. T 1.14].

Ⓓ **2,4-Dihydroxybenzaldehyde 2,4-dinitrophenylhydrazone:** bright red cryst. from hot AmOH (87% yield ⟨15⟩), m.p. 286° dec. ⟨15⟩ [cf. T 1.14].

1:0065 ⟨1⟩ Shoesmith, Sosson, Hetherington, *J. Chem. Soc.* **1927,** 2221–2230. ⟨2⟩ Pauly, Schübel, Lockemann, *Ann.* **383,** 311 (1911). ⟨3⟩ Ref. 1, page 2226. ⟨4⟩ Ref. 2, page 304. ⟨5⟩ Bell, Bridge, Robertson, *J. Chem. Soc.* **1937,** 1543. ⟨6⟩ Johnson, Lane, *J. Am. Chem. Soc.* **43,** 355 (1921). ⟨7⟩ Cullinane, Philpott, *J. Chem. Soc.* **1929,** 1763–1764. ⟨8⟩ Hinkel, Ayling, Morgan, *J. Chem. Soc.* **1932,** 2796, 2798. ⟨9⟩ Marcus, *Ber.* **24,** 3651 (1891). ⟨10⟩ Ott, Nauen, *Ber.* **55,** 926–927 (1922).

⟨11⟩ Knöpfer, *Monatsh.* **31,** 102 (1910). ⟨12⟩ Malkin, Nierenstein, *J. Am. Chem. Soc.* **53,** 241 (1931). ⟨13⟩ Russell, Clark, *J. Am. Chem. Soc.* **61,** 2655 (1939). ⟨14⟩ Lock, *Ber.* **66,** 1762 (1933). ⟨15⟩ Scott, Burns, *J. Am. Chem. Soc.* **62,** 3522 (1940).

1:0070 *d,l*-GLYCERALDEHYDE (dimer) $[CH_2OH-CH(O)-CH-OH]_2$ $C_6H_{12}O_6$ (dimer) **Beil. I-845**

M.P. 138.5° ⟨1⟩
142° ⟨2⟩ ⟨7⟩

[For comprehensive review of prop. + derivs. see ⟨3⟩.] [For prepn. (80% yield) via hydrolysis of *d,l*-glyceraldehyde diethylacetal (1:0280) see ⟨4⟩ ⟨1⟩.]

Solid *d,l*-glyceraldehyde is a dimer; white non-hygroscopic sl. sweet pdr.; ndls. from 40% MeOH ⟨1⟩ — Sol. in aq. (3%); spar. sol., alc., ether; insol. C_6H_6, pet.

In aq. soln. the dimer is grad. converted to monomeric form ⟨5⟩. The aq. soln. reduces Fehling's solution (T 1.22) at ord. temp. ⟨5⟩.

$\bar{C}$ on distillation with dil. H_2SO_4 gives (in dist.) methylglyoxal [Beil. I-762] ⟨9⟩.

$\bar{C}$ with Ac_2O + pyridine 24 hrs. at room temp. gives (58% yield) dimolecular *d,l*-glyceraldehyde diacetate, ndls. from much abs. alc., m.p. 154° ⟨6⟩ ⟨7⟩; with BzCl + pyridine at 0° (quant. yield) gives dimeric *d,l*-glyceraldehyde dibenzoate, cryst. from toluene, m.p. 231° ⟨6⟩; with *p*-nitrobenzoyl chloride + pyridine + $CHCl_3$ gives (quant. yield) dimeric *d,l*-glyceraldehyde *p*-nitrobenzoate, cryst. from toluene, m.p. 247° ⟨6⟩.

With dimethyldihydroresorcinol (T 1.13) aq. solns. of $\bar{C}$ (i.e. monomer) yield *d,l*-glyceraldehyde dimethone (poor yield, 38% in 3 days), cryst. from 50% alc., m.p. 197° cor. ⟨8⟩, 203° ⟨7⟩; corresp. anhydride by further action of Ac_2O, ndls. from 50% alc., m.p. 172° cor. ⟨8⟩.

***d,l*-Glyceraldehyde 2,4-dinitrophenylhydrazone:** From either $\bar{C}$ or its aq. soln.; recryst. from 50% MeOH to remove traces of corresp. osazone, m.p. 166–167° cor. ⟨9⟩ [cf. T 1.14].

1:0070 ⟨1⟩ Reeves, *J. Chem. Soc.* **1927,** 2481–2483. ⟨2⟩ Witzemann, *J. Am. Chem. Soc.* **36,** 1913–1916 (1914). ⟨3⟩ Abderhalden, "Biochemisches Handlexikon" **13,** 271 (1931). ⟨4⟩ Witzemann, Evans, Hass, Schroeder, *Organic Syntheses* **11,** 50–51 (1931). ⟨5⟩ Wohl, *Ber.* **31,** 2394–2395 (1898). ⟨6⟩ Fischer, Taube, Baer, *Ber.* **60,** 483 (1927). ⟨7⟩ Fischer, Ahlstrom, Richter, *Ber.* **64,** 613 (1931). ⟨8⟩ Vorländer, *Z. anal. Chem.* **77,** 256–257 (1929). ⟨9⟩ Neuberg, *Biochem. Z.* **255,** 11 (1932).

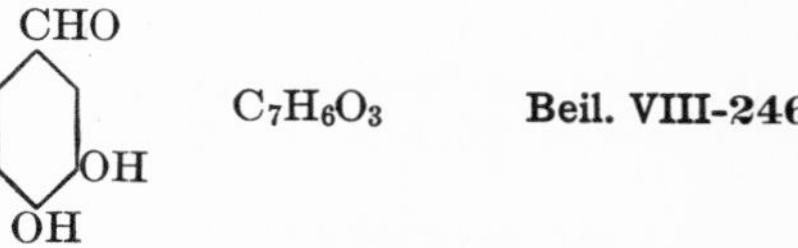

1:0073 PROTOCATECHUALDEHYDE (3,4-Dihydroxybenzaldehyde) $C_7H_6O_3$ **Beil. VIII-246**

M.P. 153-154° dec.

Cryst. from aq. or toluene — [For prepn. (62% yield) from piperonal (1:0010) with PCl_5 see ⟨1⟩.]

With $FeCl_3$ (T 1.41) aq. soln. of $\bar{C}$ becomes green, on addition of Na_2CO_3 soln. turns violet, then red — In 20% alc. $\bar{C}$ titrates with 0.1 *N* NaOH quant. as a monobasic ac. (Neut. Eq. 138) ⟨2⟩.

$\bar{C}$ htd. with powd. KOH 1 hr. at 150–190° under H_2 yielded H_2 (91%) and protocatechuic acid (1:0545) (91%) ⟨3⟩.

$\bar{C}$ + Ac_2O + trace $FeCl_3$ soon solidifies yielding 3,4-diacetoxybenzal diacetate, cryst. from alc., m.p. 131° ⟨4⟩ — $\bar{C}$ in cold alc. shaken with equiv. amt. alc. KOH + BzCl yields protocatechualdehyde dibenzoate, ndls. from alc., m.p. 96–97° ⟨5⟩ ⟨6⟩.

Ⓓ **Protocatechualdoxime:** from $\bar{C}$ + $NH_2OH.HCl$ + excess 2 *N* NaOH (93% yield), ndls. from xylene, m.p. 157° ⟨7⟩.

Ⓓ **Protocatechualdehyde phenylhydrazone:** α-form (together with some β) obtd. on stdg. C̄ with equal wt. phenylhydrazine in alc., cryst. from aq., m.p. 175–176° dec. ⟨8⟩.

Ⓓ **Protocatechualdehyde 2,4-dinitrophenylhydrazone:** dark red cryst. from MeOH, m.p. 275° dec. [cf. T 1.14].

Ⓓ **Protocatechualdehyde dimethone:** pr. from alc., m.p. 145° dec. ⟨9⟩.

1:0073 ⟨1⟩ Buck, Zimmermann, *Organic Syntheses* **18,** 75–76 (1938). ⟨2⟩ Pauly, Schübel, Lockemann, *Ann.* **383,** 311 (1911). ⟨3⟩ Lock, *Ber.* **62,** 1186 (1929). ⟨4⟩ Knoevenagel, *Ann.* **402,** 126 (1914). ⟨5⟩ Rosenmund, *Ber.* **46,** 1043 (1913). ⟨6⟩ Hayduck, *Ber.* **36,** 2930 (1903). ⟨7⟩ Hoesch, von Zarzecki, *Ber.* **50,** 465 (1917). ⟨8⟩ Wegscheider, *Monatsh.* **17,** 245 (1896). ⟨9⟩ Chakravarti, Chattopadhyaya, Ghosh, *Cent.* **1932,** I, 2330.

1:0075 METALDEHYDE $(C_2H_4O)_n$ Beil. I-602

M.P. 246° (sealed cap. tube)

A polymer of acetaldehyde; value of *n* varies from 4 (in phenol) or gas ⟨4⟩ to 6 (in thymol) ⟨1⟩. [For prepn. from acetaldehyde with HCl gas see ⟨3⟩.]

Ndls. or pr. insol. aq., acetone, CS_2, AcOH; spar. sol. alc., ether, C_6H_6, cold $CHCl_3$; sol. hot $CHCl_3$.

On htg. in open tube subl. 112–115° with partial depolymerization to acetaldehyde (1:0100) — On long stdg. even at room temp. C̄ begins to decomp. into acetaldehyde (1:0100), paraldehyde (1:0170), and other products ⟨2⟩. [For study of microchem. ident. see ⟨5⟩.]

When pure, C̄ does not react with fuchsin-ald. reagt., Fehling's soln., $KMnO_4$, or CrO_3.

Ⓓ **Conversion to acetaldehyde:** boil C̄ with dil. H_2SO_4 and in distillate identify the acetaldehyde (1:0100).

1:0075 ⟨1⟩ Hantzsch, Oechslin, *Ber.* **40,** 4341–4344 (1907). ⟨2⟩ Troeger, *Ber.* **25,** 3316–3317 (1902). ⟨3⟩ Patterson, Holmes, *J. Chem. Soc.* **1937,** 904. ⟨4⟩ Volmer, *Z. physik. Chem., Bodenstein Festband* **1931,** 870–871. ⟨5⟩ Denigès, *Bull. soc. chim. pharm. Bordeaux* **63,** 207–212 (1925); *Chem. Abs.* **20,** 1043 (1926).

1:0080 PARAFORMALDEHYDE $(CH_2O)_nH_2O$ Beil. I-566

(Also incorrectly called " trioxymethylene " ⟨1⟩)

M.P. abt. 120–130° s.t.⟨1⟩

This name applied to a mixt. of polymethylene glycols having general formula above where *n* varies from 6 to 50. The amt. of H_2O also varies.

Ord. prepd. by evapn. of 30–40% aq. HCHO soln. — White amorph. pdr. with strong HCHO odor — Dis. slowly in cold, rapidly in hot aq. — At room temp. forms 20–30% aq. solns. which behave like formaldehyde solns. (1:0145) — Insol. alc., ether.

On htg. or on distn. with dil. H_2SO_4 C̄ depolymerizes to HCHO (1:0145). C̄ htd. in a s.t. 20 min. at 178° has its m.p. changed to 175–178° and its rate of soln. in aq. greatly decreased ⟨2⟩.

[For impt. review of properties and relationships of formaldehyde polymers see ⟨1⟩.]

1:0080 ⟨1⟩ Walker, *Ind. Eng. Chem.* **23,** 1220–1222 (1931). ⟨2⟩ Walker, *J. Am. Chem. Soc.* **55,** 2823 (1933).

ORDER I: SUBORDER I: GENUS 1: ALDEHYDES

Division B, Liquid Aldehydes

1:0100 ACETALDEHYDE $CH_3.CHO$ C_2H_4O **Beil. I-594**

B.P. 20.2° **M.P. −123°** D^0_4 = **0.8050** n^{18}_D = **1.3392**

Odor, when dil. agreeable; when concd. produces respiratory cramp — Misc. with aq., but salted out by $CaCl_2$; misc. with alc., ether — Eas. volat. with steam.

Reduces Tollens' reagt. (T 1.11) and Fehling's soln. (T 1.22) — With NaOH + I_2 (T 1.81) yields CHI_3. [For study of sensitivity see ⟨1⟩.] — Oxidizes even in air to acetic acid (1:1010).

With drop of conc. H_2SO_4 polymerizes alm. explosively to trimeric paraldehyde (1:0170). [For anal. of mixts. of C̄, paraldehyde + aq. by use of density + n^{20}_D, see ⟨2⟩.] — With HCl gas in cold C̄ polymerizes to metaldehyde (1:0075) ⟨3⟩.

With $NH_2OH.HCl$ C̄ yields acetaldoxime, m.p. 47°, b.p. 114–115°; with phenylhydrazine C̄ yields 2 (presumably stereoisomeric) acetaldehyde phenylhydrazones, m.p. 98–100° and m.p. 57° (cf. Beil. XV-127); with semicarbazide C̄ yields acetaldehyde semicarbazone, ndls. from aq. or alc., m.p. 163° ⟨4⟩.

Ⓟ **Aldehyde resin formation:** Boil 1 ml. clear strong aq. soln. of C̄ with 5 ml. 10% NaOH for 1–2 min. The soln. first turns yel., then becomes turbid, opaque, and yel.-or. from sepn. of resin, a peculiar penetrating and persistent odor being evolved. [Propionaldehyde solns. give similar results, but the turbidity is less, is nearly white instead of yel., and entirely disappears on contd. boilg. ⟨5⟩.]

Ⓟ **Simon's test:** C̄ + 10% sodium nitroprusside soln. + piperidine gives deep blue color (cf. T 2.25-B). [Also given by acrolein or propionaldehyde, but not by formaldehyde ⟨6⟩.]

Ⓓ **Ethylidene di-β-naphthyloxide:** 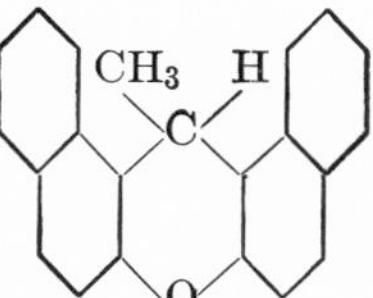

[Beil. XVII-991]. In a 3-in. tt. shake, 0.2 g. β-naphthol with 2 drops conc. HCl and 2 ml. AcOH until solid is nearly dislvd., then add 1 drop C̄ and shake again. Heat at 50–60° for 1 min.; then boil 1 min. Cool and shake vig. until cryst. ppt. seps.; allow to settle, filter through small filter, wash with 1 ml. cold AcOH. Ext. the solid by boilg. with mixt. of 3 ml. alc. + 1 ml. aq. for $\frac{1}{2}$ min., most of ppt. remaining undislvd. Cool thoroughly, shake, filter, wash with 1 ml. cold 50% alc., and dry at 100°. M.p. 173° ⟨5⟩. [This test is not applicable to very dil. C̄ solns. but may be used directly on paraldehyde ⟨7⟩ or acetal ⟨8⟩. The by-product, m.p. 201°, is ethylidene di-β-naphthylacetal [Beil. VI-643].]

Ⓓ **Acetaldehyde *p*-nitrophenylhydrazone:** m.p. 128.5° ⟨9⟩. [For photomicrographs see ⟨10⟩.]

Ⓓ **Acetaldehyde 2,4-dinitrophenylhydrazone** [cf. T 1.14]: exists in two dif. crystn. modifications; ord. "stable" form, cryst. from alc., m.p. 168.5° cor. ⟨11⟩ ⟨12⟩, and

" metastable form " (obtd. by subl. of first), m.p. 157°; crystn. of the melt produces a mixt. of both (probably an equil. mixt.) melting near 148° ⟨11⟩. [For use of this deriv. in quant. detn. of $\bar{C}$ see ⟨13⟩.]

Ⓓ **Acetaldehyde dimethone** [cf. T 1.13]: cryst. from MeOH, m.p. 139° ⟨14⟩ ⟨15⟩; 140° ⟨16⟩; 141° ⟨17⟩; corresp. anhydride, lfts. from alc., m.p. 173–174° ⟨14⟩⟨ 15⟩, 175.5–176.5° cor. ⟨17⟩. [For use of this deriv. for sepn. and detn. of formaldehyde (1:0145) and acetaldehyde see ⟨18⟩ ⟨19⟩.]

1:0100 ⟨1⟩ Korenman, *Z. anal. Chem.* **93,** 340 (1933). ⟨2⟩ Strada, Macri, *Giorn. chim. ind. applicata* **16,** 335–341 (1934). ⟨3⟩ Patterson, Holmes, *J. Chem. Soc.* **1935,** 905. ⟨4⟩ Michael, *J. Am. Chem. Soc.* **41,** 421 (1919). ⟨5⟩ Mulliken, " Method " I, 22–23 (1904). ⟨6⟩ Lewin, *Ber.* **32,** 3388–3389 (1898). ⟨7⟩ Claisen, *Ann.* **237,** 270–271 (1887). ⟨8⟩ Delépine, *Bull. soc. chim.* (3) **25,** 578–579 (1901). ⟨9⟩ Hyde, *Ber.* **32,** 1813 (1898). ⟨10⟩ Griebel, Weiss, *Z. Untersuch. Lebensm.* **56,** 160–161 (1928).

⟨11⟩ Bryant, *J. Am. Chem. Soc.* **60,** 2815 (1938). ⟨12⟩ Campbell, *Analyst* **61,** 392 (1936). ⟨13⟩ Iddles, Jackson, *Ind. Eng. Chem., Anal. Ed.* **6,** 454–456 (1934). ⟨14⟩ Vorländer, *Z. anal. Chem.* **77,** 249–251 (1927). ⟨15⟩ Klein, Linser, *Mikrochemie, Pregl Festschrift* **1929,** 226. ⟨16⟩ Kao, Yen, *Science Repts. Natl. Tsing Hua Univ.*, Ser. **A-1,** 187 (1932). ⟨17⟩ Gee, Chaikoff, *J. Biol. Chem.* **70,** 154–157 (1926). ⟨18⟩ Vorländer, *Z. anal. Chem.* **77,** 321–327 (1929). ⟨19⟩ Ionescu, Slusanchi, *Bull. soc. chim.* (4) **53,** 909–918 (1933).

1:0105 METHYLAL $CH_2(OCH_3)_2$ $C_3H_8O_2$ Beil. I-574

(Formaldehyde dimethylacetal; methylene dimethyl ether)

B.P. 42.3° ⟨1⟩ ⟨2⟩ **F.P. −104.0°** ⟨1⟩ D_4^{20} = **0.86012** ⟨1⟩ n_D^{20} = **1.35335** ⟨2⟩
D_4^{15} = **0.86645** ⟨1⟩ n_D^{15} = **1.35626** ⟨1⟩

Odor alcoholic — Dis. in 3 vols. aq.; const.-boilg. mixt. with aq. conts. 98.6% $\bar{C}$ and boils 42.05°; with CH_3OH conts. 92.15% $\bar{C}$ and boils 41.82° ⟨3⟩; treatment with $CaCl_2$ then Na_2CO_3 gives pure $\bar{C}$ in quant. yield ⟨2⟩ — No ternary mixt. ⟨3⟩. [For sepn. from acetone by minim. const.-boilg. mixt. with CS_2 see ⟨4⟩.]

When absolutely pure $\bar{C}$ does not give fuchsin-ald. react. (Generic Test 1) but does so after boilg. for a moment with a drop of minl. acid — Boilg. with HCl yields H.CHO (1:0145) + CH_3OH (1:6120); with H_2SO_4 yields HCHO (1:0145) + $CH_3O.SO_2.OH$.

Ⓟ Distil $\bar{C}$ with dil. H_2SO_4 and test distillate as for formaldehyde (1:0145).

1:0105 ⟨1⟩ Timmermans, Martin, *J. chim. phys.* **25,** 438–439 (1928). ⟨2⟩ Palomaa, Honkanen, *Ber.* **70,** 2200–2201 (1937). ⟨3⟩ Ghysels, *Bull. soc. chim. Belg.* **33,** 61 (1924). ⟨4⟩ Duclaux, Lanzenburg, *Bull. soc. chim.* (4) **27,** 781 (1920).

1:0110 PROPIONALDEHYDE $CH_3.CH_2.CHO$ C_3H_6O Beil. I-629

B.P. 48.8° **M.P. −81°** D_4^{20} = **0.8066** n_D^{19} = **1.36460**

Pungent odor — Sol. in 5 pts. aq. at 20° — Volat. with steam. [For prepn. (45–49% yield) by oxidn. of *n*-propyl alc. with $K_2Cr_2O_7$ + H_2SO_4 see ⟨1⟩.]

Reduces Tollens' reagt. (T 1.11) — With satd. aq. $NaHSO_3$ (cf. T 1.12) yields cryst. bisulfite compd. [Use in quant. detn. of $\bar{C}$ ⟨2⟩.]

$\bar{C}$ treated with HCl gas below 0° yields mainly the trimeric parapropionaldehyde [Beil. XIX-389], b.p. 169–170°, m.p. −20°, accompanied by a little solid metapropionaldehyde ⟨3⟩ — Pure $\bar{C}$ is unstable and liable to spontaneous polymerization which occurs the more readily the lower the temp. ⟨4⟩.

$\bar{C}$ with NH_2OH yields a low-melting propionaldoxime [Beil. I-631]; with phenylhydrazine a liq. propionaldehyde phenylhydrazone [Beil. XV-128]; with semicarbazide propionaldehyde semicarbazone; known in two stereoisomeric forms: tbls. from aq. m.p. 154° ⟨5⟩; ndls. from C_6H_6 + lgr., m.p. 88–90° [cf. Beil. II-101].

Ⓟ **Skatole formation:** C̄, warmed with 2 pts. phenylhydrazine, resulting phenylhydrazone washed with dil. AcOH, filtd. through wet filter, and residual oil htd. with equal vol. $ZnCl_2$ at 180° gives disgusting skatole odor ⟨6⟩.

Ⓓ **Propionaldehyde dimethone** (cf. T 1.13): lfts. from alc., m.p. 154–156° ⟨12⟩, 155° ⟨13⟩ ⟨14⟩; corresp. anhydride, cryst. from alc., m.p. 142–143° cor. ⟨12⟩, 148° ⟨14⟩.

Ⓓ **Propionaldehyde-*p*-nitrophenylhydrazone:** yel. ndls. from 50% alc., m.p. 124° ⟨7⟩ ⟨8⟩; 125° ⟨9⟩.

Ⓓ **Propionaldehyde-2,4-dinitrophenylhydrazone** (see T 1.14): m.p. 155° ⟨11⟩; 156° ⟨10⟩.

1.0110 ⟨1⟩ Hurd, Meinert, *Organic Syntheses* **12,** 64–65 (1932). ⟨2⟩ Parkinson, Wagner, *Ind. Eng. Chem., Anal. Ed.* **6,** 433–436 (1934). ⟨3⟩ Orndorff, Balcom, *Am. Chem. J.* **16,** 646–647 (1894). ⟨4⟩ Buckler, *J. Chem. Soc.* **1937,** 1036. ⟨5⟩ Urion, *Ann. chim.* (11) **1,** 35 (1934). ⟨6⟩ Fischer, Laycock, *Ber.* **22,** 104 Note (1899). ⟨7⟩ Erdmann, Bedford, Rashe, *Ber.* **42,** 1342 (1909). ⟨8⟩ Ref. 5, page 40. ⟨9⟩ Bauer, Strauss, *Ber.* **65,** 311 (1932). ⟨10⟩ Brady, Elsmie, *Analyst* **51,** 77 (1926).

⟨11⟩ Allen, *J. Am. Chem. Soc.* **52,** 2957 (1930). ⟨12⟩ Vorländer, *Z. anal. Chem.* **77,** 251 (1929). ⟨13⟩ Kao, Yen, *Science Repts. Natl. Tsing Hua Univ.*, Ser. **A-1,** 187 (1932). ⟨14⟩ Klein, Linser, *Mikrochemie, Pregl Festschrift* **1929,** 226.

1:0115 ACROLEIN $CH_2{=}CH.CHO$ C_3H_4O Beil. I-725

B.P. 52.4° **M.P. −87.7°** D_4^{20} **= 0.8410** n_D^{20} **= 1.39975**

Powerful lachrymator. Sol. in 2–3 pts. aq. — [For prepn. (33–48% yield) from glycerol + $KHSO_4$ see ⟨1⟩.]

C̄ reduces Tollens' reagt. (T 1.11) and Fehling's soln. (T 1.22) — C̄ reduces alk. $KMnO_4$ (Baeyer test T 1.34); with NaOH + I_2 (T 1.81) gives CHI_3. [For use in micro-detn. see ⟨2⟩.] — C̄ with satd. aq. $NaHSO_3$ (cf. T 1.12) adds 2 moles $NaHSO_3$ with unusually vig. evol. of heat but ppt. appears slowly.

C̄ on stdg. very rapidly polymerizes to an amorphous white solid (disacryl), insol. aq., acids, or alk.; this occurs even in purest prepns. ⟨3⟩ but is favored by heat, light, and certain impurities — In presence of inhibitors (such as traces of polyhydric phenols) keeps almost indefinitely.

In presence of aq. NaOH at 25° C̄ polymerizes to a white fluffy powdr. (pentamer) which cannot be crystd.; sol. in alcs., ketones, and dioxane; insol. hydrocarbons ⟨4⟩.

With phenylhydrazine C̄ yields (22%) phenylpyrazoline [Beil. XXIII-29], yellowish tbls. from hot lgr., m.p. 50–51° ⟨5⟩.

Ⓟ **Special fuchsin-aldehyde test:** To 5 ml. fuchsin-ald. reagt. add 2 ml. aq. acrolein soln.; stopper tube and stand overnight. Soln. will then appear opaque by reflected light with deep violet-blue color. Add equal vol. of conc. HCl; within half a minute color changes to impure OY-S_2, and on diln. of sample with 15 vols. aq. passes through YG and BG to VB. [These color changes, collectively, disting. C̄ from all other common volat. ald., although initial coloration alone is not characteristic.] ⟨6.⟩

Ⓟ **Phloroglucinol color test:** Dil. soln. of C̄ (3–4 drops) is treated with equal vol. 3% H_2O_2, stood 1 min., then 5 ml. conc. HCl and 5 ml. 1% ethereal phloroglucinol soln. are added. After shaking 1 min. the acid layer is colored intensely red ⟨7⟩ ⟨8⟩. [For use of similar reaction for detect. of C̄ in presence of glycerol see ⟨9⟩.]

Ⓓ **Acrolein semicarbazone:** ndls. from aq., m.p. 171° ⟨10⟩.

Ⓓ **Acrolein *p*-nitrophenylhydrazone:** m.p. 150–151° ⟨11⟩. [For photomicrographs see ⟨12⟩.]

Ⓓ **Acrolein 2,4-dinitrophenylhydrazone:** m.p. 165° ⟨13⟩ [cf. T 1.14].

Ⓓ **Acrolein dimethone** [T 1.13]: cryst. from 50% alc., m.p. 192° (after sintering at 186°) ⟨14⟩, 135° ⟨15⟩; corresp. anhydride: pr. from alc., m.p. 162–163° ⟨14⟩, 170–188° ⟨15⟩.

1:0115 ⟨1⟩ Adkins, Hartung, *Organic Syntheses, Coll. Vol.* I, 14–17 (1932). ⟨2⟩ Korenman, *J. Applied Chem.* (*U.S.S.R.*) **8,** 1476–1477 (1935); *Cent.* **1936,** II, 3707. ⟨3⟩ Moureu, DuFraisse, *Ann. chim.* (9) **15,** 160–164 (1921). ⟨4⟩ Gilbert, Donleavy, *J. Am. Chem. Soc.* **60,** 1913 (1938). ⟨5⟩ von Auwers, Kreuder, *Ber.* **58,** 1977 (1925). ⟨6⟩ Mulliken, " Method " I, 23 (1904). ⟨7⟩ Powick, *Ind. Eng. Chem.* **15,** 66 (1923). ⟨8⟩ Pritzker, *Helv. Chim. Acta* **11,** 445–448 (1928). ⟨9⟩ Hovey, Hodgkins, *Ind. Eng. Chem., Anal. Ed.* **9,** 509–511 (1937). ⟨10⟩ von Auwers, Heimke, *Ann.* **458,** 202, 194 (1927).

⟨11⟩ Henrich, Herzog, *Ber.* **52,** 2130 (1919). ⟨12⟩ Griebel, Weiss, *Z. Untersuch. Lebensm.* **56,** 161 (1928). ⟨13⟩ Allen, *J. Am. Chem. Soc.* **52,** 2958 (1930). ⟨14⟩ Vorländer, *Z. anal. Chem.* **77,** 252 (1929). ⟨15⟩ Klein, Linser, *Mikrochemie, Pregl Festschrift* **1929,** 226.

1:0120 ISOBUTYRALDEHYDE $(CH_3)_2CH.CHO$ C_4H_8O Beil. I-671

B.P. 64° **F.P. −65.9°** **D_4^{20} = 0.7938** **n_D^{20} = 1.37302**

Sol. in 9 vols. aq. at 20° — With satd. aq. $NaHSO_3$ soln. yields spar. sol. bisulfite cpd. [Use in quant. detn. of C̄ ⟨1⟩.]

Oxidizes in air (especially in presence of Pt black) to isobutyric ac. (1:1030). [For study of oxidn. with various oxid. agts such as $K_3Fe(CN)_6$, $K_2Cr_2O_7 + H_2SO_4$, $Ce(SO_4)_2$, acid $KMnO_4$, etc., see ⟨2⟩.]

With drop of conc. H_2SO_4 polymerizes in cold to trimeric paraisobutyraldehyde (1:0035), m.p. 59°; also polymerized on long stdg. (especially in u.v. light) or by halogens, $ZnCl_2$, etc.

Isobutyraldoxime and isobutyraldehyde phenylhydrazone are both oils.

Ⓓ **Isobutyraldehyde semicarbazone:** m.p. 125–126° ⟨3⟩.

Ⓓ **Isobutyraldehyde *p*-nitrophenylhydrazone:** or.-yel. ndls. from alc., m.p. 130–131° ⟨4⟩.

Ⓓ **Isobutyraldehyde 2,4-dinitrophenylhydrazone:** or.-yel. ndls. from alc., m.p. 187° ⟨5⟩, 182° ⟨6⟩ ⟨7⟩ [cf. T 1.14].

Ⓓ **Isobutyraldehyde dimethone** [T 1.13]: m.p. 154° ⟨8⟩; corresp. anhydride, m.p. 144° ⟨8⟩.

1:0120 ⟨1⟩ Parkinson, Wagner, *Ind. Eng. Chem., Anal. Ed.* **6,** 433–436 (1934). ⟨2⟩ Conant, Aston, *J. Am. Chem. Soc.* **50,** 2783–2798 (1928). ⟨3⟩ Wöllmer, *Ber.* **49,** 786 (1916). ⟨4⟩ Harries, *Cent.* **1916,** II, 992. ⟨5⟩ Bryant, *J. Am. Chem. Soc.* **54,** 3760 (1932). ⟨6⟩ Allen, *J. Am. Chem. Soc.* **52,** 2957 (1930). ⟨7⟩ Brady, Elsmie, *Analyst* **51,** 77 (1926). ⟨8⟩ Klein, Linser, *Mikrochemie, Pregl Festschrift* **1929,** 226.

1:0125 ACETALDEHYDE DIMETHYLACETAL $C_4H_{10}O_2$ Beil. I-603

(Dimethylacetal; ethylidene dimethyl ether) $CH_3.CH(OCH_3)_2$

B.P. 64.3° ⟨1⟩ **D_4^{20} = 0.85015 ⟨1⟩** **n_D^{20} = 1.3668 ⟨1⟩**

Sl. sol. aq. — Forms with aq. heterogeneous binary const.-boilg. mixt. contg. 96.4% C̄ and boilg. at 61.3°; forms with MeOH a binary const.-boilg. mixt. (b.p. 57.5°) contg. 75.8% C̄ ⟨1⟩. C̄, MeOH + aq. do not form a ternary const.-boilg. mixt. ⟨1⟩.

When absolutely pure, C̄ does not give fuchsin-aldehyde test (Generic Test 1) but does so after boilg. for a few moments with dil. minl. acid — Hydrolyzes readily with acids, yielding acetaldehyde (1:0100) and MeOH (1:6120), but stable to aq. alk.

Ⓟ Distil C̄ with dil. H_2SO_4 and test distillate for acetaldehyde (1:0100).

1:0125 ⟨1⟩ Béduwé, *Bull. soc. chim. Belg.* **34,** 41–55 (1925).

1:0130 *n*-BUTYRALDEHYDE $CH_3.CH_2.CH_2.CHO$ C_4H_8O Beil. I-663

B.P. 74.7° ⟨1⟩ **F.P. −97.1° ⟨1⟩** **D_4^{20} = 0.8170** **n_D^{20} = 1.38433**

Sol. in 27 pts. aq. — Forms const.-boilg. mixt. with aq. — With satd. aq. $NaHSO_3$ soln. forms bisulfite cpd. but its use for purification of C̄ is not recommended ⟨2⟩. [Use in quant. detn. of C̄ ⟨3⟩.]

With aq. alk. yields α-ethyl-β-n-propylacrolein (1:0193).

With O_2 + Pt black or with alk. $KMnO_4$ ⟨4⟩ C̄ oxidizes to *n*-butyric acid (1:1035).

With HCl gas at −20° polymerizes to 80% liq. trimer, para-*n*-butyraldehyde [Beil. XIX_1-(807)], accompanied by 2% solid meta-*n*-butyraldehyde $(C_4H_8O)_x$, ndls. from ether, m.p. 173° ⟨5⟩.

Ⓓ ***n*-Butyraldehyde semicarbazone:** cryst. from lgr., m.p. 95.5° ⟨6⟩; 106° ⟨4⟩.

Ⓓ ***n*-Butyraldehyde *p*-nitrophenylhydrazone:** yel. ndls. from alc., m.p. 87° ⟨7⟩; m.p. 91° ⟨8⟩; red ndls. m.p. 93–95° ⟨9⟩.

Ⓓ ***n*-Butyraldehyde 2,4-dinitrophenylhydrazone:** cryst. from alc., m.p. 123° ⟨10⟩; m.p. 122° ⟨11⟩ ⟨12⟩ [T 1.14].

Ⓓ ***n*-Butyraldehyde dimethone:** m.p. 133.8° ⟨13⟩; 142° ⟨14⟩: corresp. anhydride, m.p. 141° ⟨14⟩.

1:0130 ⟨1⟩ Timmermans, *Bull. soc. chim. Belg.* **36,** 506 (1927). ⟨2⟩ Lieben, Rossi, *Ann.* **158,** 149 (1871). ⟨3⟩ Parkinson, Wagner, *Ind. Eng. Chem., Anal. Ed.* **6,** 433–436 (1934). ⟨4⟩ Fournier, *Bull. soc. chim.* (4) **7,** 25 (1910). ⟨5⟩ Franke, Wozelka, *Monatsh.* **33,** 350–355 (1912). ⟨6⟩ Blaise, *Bull. soc. chim.* (4) **15,** 666 (1914). ⟨7⟩ Harries, *Cent.* **1916,** II, 992. ⟨8⟩ Dakin, *J. Biol. Chem.* **4,** 235 (1908). ⟨9⟩ Shima, *Cent.* **1930,** II, 226. ⟨10⟩ Bryant, *J. Am. Chem. Soc.* **54,** 3760 (1932).

⟨11⟩ Allen, *J. Am. Chem. Soc.* **52,** 2957 (1930). ⟨12⟩ Brady, Elsmie, *Analyst* **51,** 77 (1926). ⟨13⟩ Kao, Yen, *Science Repts. Natl. Tsing Hua Univ.*, Ser. **A-1,** 187 (1932). ⟨14⟩ Klein, Linser, *Mikrochemie, Pregl Festschrift* **1929,** 226.

1:0133 TRIMETHYLACETALDEHYDE $(CH_3)_3.C.CHO$ $C_5H_{10}O$ **Beil. I-688**
(Pivalaldehyde)

B.P. 75° ⟨1⟩ **M.P. 3° ⟨2⟩ ⟨10⟩** D^{17} **= 0.7927 ⟨2⟩** n_D^{20} **= 1.379 ⟨3⟩**
6° ⟨1⟩

Mobile liq. of charact. odor — Reduces $NH_4OH + AgNO_3$ in cold — Yields $NaHSO_3$ cpd. (cf. T 1.12), best reconverted to C̄ with H_2SO_4 + steam distn. since Na_2CO_3 tends to cause polymerization ⟨4⟩.

With conc. H_2SO_4, 70% H_2SO_4, or even mixt. of AcOH + HCl polymerizes to a trimeric white solid (paratrimethylacetaldehyde), insol. aq. or acids, dif. sol. alc., eas. sol. ether; cryst. from alc. + ether, m.p. 82.5° ⟨5⟩ ⟨6⟩ — The trimer shows (when pure) no aldehyde reactns. but on htg. with dil. H_2SO_4 regenerates monomeric C̄ ⟨5⟩ ⟨6⟩.

C̄ oxidizes in air, oxygen, or with oxidg. agts. (e.g. CrO_3 ⟨10⟩) to trimethylacetic ac. (1:0410), m.p. 35°; in air 77.5% oxidized in 32 hrs., in oxygen 83% in 5 hrs.; oxidation retarded by trace of hydroquinone ⟨7⟩.

C̄ in alc. soln. stirred 1 day with conc. KOH gives neopentyl alcohol (1:5812) + trimethylacetic ac. (1:0410) (Cannizzaro reactn.) ⟨8⟩.

[For prepn. of C̄ (60–66% yield) from neopentyl alc. by dehydrogenation over Cu at 250–300° see ⟨7⟩.]

Ⓓ **Trimethylacetaldoxime:** m.p. 41° ⟨9⟩.

Ⓓ **Trimethylacetaldehyde semicarbazone:** forms readily in quant. yield, m.p. 190.5° ⟨5⟩; 189–190° ⟨12⟩.

Ⓓ **Trimethylacetaldehyde *p*-nitrophenylhydrazone:** prepd. in alc. + AcOH soln., red-yel. ndls., m.p. 119° ⟨10⟩.

Ⓓ **Trimethylacetaldehyde 2,4-dinitrophenylhydrazone:** yel. cryst., m.p. 210° ⟨11⟩; 208–209° ⟨12⟩.

1:0133 ⟨1⟩ Richard, *Ann. chim.* (8) **21,** 395 (1910). ⟨2⟩ Tissier, *Ann. chim.* (6) **29,** 354 (1893). ⟨3⟩ Campbell, *J. Am. Chem. Soc.* **59,** 1983 (1937). ⟨4⟩ Hibbert, Gillespie, Montonna, *J. Am. Chem. Soc.* **50,** 1953 (1928). ⟨5⟩ Daniloff, Venus-Danilova, *Ber.* **59,** 381 (1926). ⟨6⟩ Franke, Hinterberger, *Monatsh.* **42,** 659 (1922). ⟨7⟩ Conant, Webb, Meldrum, *J. Am. Chem. Soc.*

51, 1250–1251 (1929). ⟨8⟩ Ref. 7, page 1254. ⟨9⟩ Ref. 1, page 373. ⟨10⟩ Pringsheim, Leibowitz, *Ber.* **56,** 2039 (1923).
⟨11⟩ Allen, *J. Am. Chem. Soc.* **52,** 2957 (1930). ⟨12⟩ Magnani, McElvain, *J. Am. Chem. Soc.* **60,** 819 (1938).

1:0135 FORMALDEHYDE DIETHYLACETAL $C_5H_{12}O_2$ **Beil. I-574**
("Ethylal") $CH_2(O.C_2H_5)_2$

B.P. 87.5° ⟨1⟩ **M.P. −66.5° ⟨1⟩** D_0^{20} **= 0.8319** $n_D^{17.5}$ **= 1.3748**

Sol. in 11 pts. aq. at 18° — Forms with aq. a heterogeneous binary const.-boilg. mixt. (b.p. 75.2°) contg. 90% C̄; forms with EtOH a binary const.-boilg. mixt. (b.p. 74.2°) contg. 57% C̄ ⟨2⟩ — With EtOH + H_2O, C̄ forms a homogeneous ternary const.-boilg. mixt. contg. 69.5% C̄, 18.4% EtOH + 12.1% aq. ⟨2⟩.

When absolutely pure, C̄ does not give fuchsin-aldehyde test (Generic Test 1), but does so after boilg. for a few moments with dil. minl. acid. Hydrolyzes readily with dil. minl. acids yielding HCHO (1:0145) and EtOH (1:6130) but not with alk.

Ⓟ Distil C̄ with dil. H_2SO_4 and test distillate as for formaldehyde (1:0145).

1:0135 ⟨1⟩ Timmermans, *Bull. soc. chim. Belg.* **36,** 505 (1927). ⟨2⟩ Ghysels, *Bull. soc. chim. Belg.* **33,** 63–66 (1924).

1:0138 METHOXYACETALDEHYDE $C_3H_6O_2$ **Beil. S.N.-113**
$CH_3.O.CH_2.CHO$

B.P. 92.3° ⟨1⟩ D_4^{25} **= 1.005 ⟨1⟩** n_D^{20} **= 1.3950 ⟨1⟩**

Forms with aq. a const.-boilg. mixt., b.p. 88.8°, D_4^{25} = 1.116, n_D^{20} = 1.4270, contg. 12.8% aq. ⟨1⟩.

Odor reminis. of acetaldehyde — C̄ reduces Fehling's sol. (T 1.22) and Tollens' reagt. (T 1.11) ⟨1⟩.

Polymerizes readily to liq. water sol. trimer and solid tetramer which on distn. with a trace of *p*-toluenesulfonic ac. regenerate C̄ — Autoxidizes rapidly in air. ⟨1.⟩

Ⓓ **Methoxyacetaldehyde *p*-nitrophenylhydrazone:** m.p. 115–115.5 ⟨1⟩.
Ⓓ **Methoxyacetaldehyde 2,4-dinitrophenylhydrazone:** m.p. 124–125° ⟨1⟩. [Cf. T 1.14.]

1:0138 ⟨1⟩ Drake, Duvall, Jacobs, Thompson, Sonnichsen, *J. Am. Chem. Soc.* **60,** 73–76 (1938).

1:0140 ISOVALERALDEHYDE $(CH_3)_2.CH.CH_2.CHO$ $C_5H_{10}O$ **Beil. I-684**
(2-Methyl-*n*-butyraldehyde; 3-methylbutanal-1)

B.P. 92.5° D_{20}^{20} **= 0.7845** n_D^{20} **= 1.39225**

Odor (when free from isovaleric ac.) sweet and aromatic — Forms hydrate with 1 H_2O, b.p. 82°; on distn. aq. comes over in forerun. ⟨1⟩.

With satd. aq. $NaHSO_3$ soln. yields dif. sol. bisulfite cpd. (cf. T 1.12).

On oxidation yields isovaleric ac. (1:1050).

With HCl gas at −20° polymerizes to liq. trimeric paraisovaleraldehyde ⟨2⟩.

With NH_2OH yields isovaleraldoxime, m.p. 48.5° ⟨3⟩; with phenylhydrazine yields liq. isovaleraldehyde phenylhydrazone [Beil. XV-130]; with semicarbazide yields isovaleraldehyde semicarbazone, cryst. from lgr., m.p. 131–132° ⟨4⟩.

C̄ shaken with conc. aq. NH_4OH rapidly yields isovaleraldehyde ammonia, $C_5H_{10}O.NH_3 + 7\ H_2O$, m.p. 56–58° ⟨5⟩.

C̄ gives no color with sodium nitroprusside + alk. [dif. from *n*-valeraldehyde (1:0155)].

Ⓓ **Isovaleraldehyde *p*-nitrophenylhydrazone:** ndls. from alc.; m.p. 109–110° ⟨6⟩; 110–111° ⟨7⟩; 107–108° ⟨8⟩.

Ⓓ **Isovaleraldehyde 2,4-dinitrophenylhydrazone:** yel. or orange ndls., cryst. from alc., m.p. 123° ⟨9⟩ ⟨10⟩ [cf. T 1.14].

Ⓓ **Isovaleraldehyde dimethone:** tbls. from 50% alc., m.p. 154–155° ⟨11⟩; 137° ⟨12⟩; corresp. anhydride; 172–173° cor. ⟨11⟩; 168° ⟨12⟩.

1:0140 ⟨1⟩ Nef, *Ann.* **318,** 162 Note (1901). ⟨2⟩ Franke, Wozelka, *Monatsh.* **33,** 359 (1912). ⟨3⟩ Bourgeois, Dambmann, *Ber.* **26,** 2859 (1893). ⟨4⟩ Heilmann, *Bull. soc. chim.* (5) **4,** 1074 (1937). ⟨5⟩ Strecker, *Ann.* **130,** 218 (1864). ⟨6⟩ Dakin, *J. Biol. Chem.* **4,** 237 (1908). ⟨7⟩ Sato, *Biochem. Z.* **71,** 172 (1915). ⟨8⟩ Clarke, Patch, *J. Am. Chem. Soc.* **34,** 915 (1912). ⟨9⟩ Allen, *J. Am. Chem. Soc.* **52,** 2957 (1930). ⟨10⟩ Brady, Elsmie, *Analyst* **51,** 78 (1926).
⟨11⟩ Vorländer, *Z. anal. Chem.* **77,** 251–252 (1929). ⟨12⟩ Klein, Linser, *Mikrochemie, Pregl Festschrift* **1929,** 226.

1:0142 **α-METHYL-*n*-BUTYRALDEHYDE** $C_5H_{10}O$ **Beil. I-682**
(Ethyl-methyl-acetaldehyde; 2-methylbutanal-1)

$CH_3.CH_2.CH(CH_3).CHO$

B.P. 92-93° ⟨1⟩ D_4^{20} = **0.80294** ⟨2⟩ n_D^{20} = **1.38960** ⟨2⟩

Mobile liq. with charact. odor — Insol. aq. — Sol. in ether from which it cannot be sepd. by distn. [for quant. estn. of $\bar{C}$ in ether solns. via NH_3 addn. see ⟨3⟩].

Polymerized by dry HCl to trimer, para-ethyl-methyl-acetaldehyde [Beil. XIX-391], ndls., m.p. 20° ⟨4⟩.

Ⓓ **Ethyl-methyl-acetaldehyde semicarbazone:** cryst. from mixt. of C_6H_6 + pet. ether, m.p. 103–105° ⟨5⟩.

Ⓓ **Ethyl-methyl-acetaldehyde 2,4-dinitrophenylhydrazone:** m.p. 120.5° ⟨6⟩.

1:0142 ⟨1⟩ Linstead, Mann, *J. Chem. Soc.* **1930,** 2070. ⟨2⟩ Bruylants, *Bull. sci. acad. roy. Belg.* (5) **17,** 1008–1026 (1931); *Chem. Abs.* **26,** 1576 (1932). ⟨3⟩ Ingold, *J. Chem. Soc.* **125,** 437 (1924). ⟨4⟩ Neustadter, *Monatsh.* **27,** 898 (1906). ⟨5⟩ Sommelet, *Ann. chim.* (8) **9,** 555 (1906). ⟨6⟩ Morgan, Hardy, *Chemistry & Industry* **52,** 518–519 (1933).

1:0145 **FORMALDEHYDE** H_2CO CH_2O **Beil. I-558**
(" Formalin," comml. 40% soln. in water)

B.P. 98-99°

Pure H_2CO gas boils at −21°; the comml. aq. soln. usually conts. 34–40% dislvd. gas + 8–20% CH_3OH — Distn. leaves white residue of paraformaldehyde (1:0080) — For removal of CH_3OH see ⟨1⟩ — An aq. soln. contg. 30% HCHO forms minim. const.-boilg. mixt., b.p. 98.8°; distn. of weaker solns. concentrates HCHO in distillate; distn. of stronger solns. in residue ⟨2⟩. [For study of distn. of solns. of $\bar{C}$ see ⟨14⟩.] — Refractive indices of aq. — HCHO solns. proportional to concn.; graph 6–27% ⟨3⟩, extended to 35% ⟨4⟩.

$\bar{C}$ reduces Tollens' reagt. (T 1.11) and Fehling's soln. (T 1.22).

Ⓟ₁ **Resorcinol condensation:** Mix 1 drop 0.5% aqueous resorcinol with 1 ml. dil. aq. soln. HCHO of such concn. (abt. 0.2%) that odor is barely perceptible in cold, though unpleasantly strong at 100°. Allow mixt. to flow gently onto surface of 3–5 ml. pure conc. H_2SO_4. Impart a gentle rotary motion to the tt. such that the layers do not disappear. If HCHO is present a red ring, slightly tinged with violet, will soon appear. Above this ring a light floc. ppt., at first nearly white on its upper surface and red-violet beneath, but soon changing to flocks that are red throughout, will be seen suspended in the aqueous upper layer ⟨5⟩.

Ⓟ₂ **Gallic acid condensation:** Repeat Ⓟ₁ substituting for the resorcinol 6 drops of cold satd. alc. soln. gallic acid. If HCHO is present a pure blue ring will be formed. [In either Ⓟ$_1$ or Ⓟ$_2$ too conc. solns. of aldehyde should be avoided since the deep-colored ppts. then resulting obscure the purer and more characteristic hues desired.]

Ⓓ **Methylene-di-β-naphthol:** H_2 C OH HO To 3 drops formalin soln. add 3 ml. dil. (33%) alc., 0.05 g. β-naphthol, and 3–5 drops conc. HCl. Boil gently till ppt. of small white ndls. appears. Filter hot, wash with 1 ml. 33% alc. Boil the ppt. with 4 ml. 50% alc. (it is not necessary that all should dissolve), cool, filter, wash with 1 ml. 50% alc., dry. When htd. at rate of 1° in 15 sec., cryst. turn brown at 180°; melt with decn. to brown-red liq. 189–192° u.c. ⟨5⟩.

Ⓓ **Formaldehyde *p*-nitrophenylhydrazone:** Even dil. solns. of $\bar{C}$ react with *p*-nitrophenylhydrazine hydrochloride on stdg. or warming. Yel. ndls. from C_6H_6, m.p. 181–182° ⟨6⟩ — [An excess of HCHO must be avoided since a subst. m.p. 222–225° is then obtained ⟨7⟩.]

Ⓓ **Formaldehyde 2,4-dinitrophenylhydrazone:** yel. cryst. from alc., m.p. 167° ⟨8⟩; 166° ⟨9⟩ [cf. T 1.14].

Ⓓ **Formaldehyde dimethone:** ndls. from alc., m.p. 189° cor. ⟨10⟩; 191.4° ⟨11⟩; corresp. anhydride, lfts. from alc., m.p. 171° ⟨10⟩. [Use in quant. detn. of $\bar{C}$ in presence of acetaldehyde ⟨12⟩ ⟨13⟩.] [Cf. T 1.13.]

1:0145 ⟨1⟩ Blair, Ledbury, *J. Chem. Soc.* **127**, 26 (1925). ⟨2⟩ Blair, Taylor, *J. Soc. Chem. Ind.* **45**, 65–66 T (1926). ⟨3⟩ Reicher, Jansen, *Chem. Weekblad* **9**, 104–109 (1912). ⟨4⟩ Stutterheim, *Pharm. Weekblad* **54**, 716–717 (1917). ⟨5⟩ Mulliken, "Method" I, 24 (1904). ⟨6⟩ Bamberger, *Ber.* **32**, 1807 (1899). ⟨7⟩ Zerner, *Monatsh.* **34**, 957–961 (1913). ⟨8⟩ Bryant, *J. Am. Chem. Soc.* **54**, 3760 (1932). ⟨9⟩ Campbell, *Analyst* **61**, 392 (1936). ⟨10⟩ Vorländer, *Z. anal. Chem.* **77**, 247–248 (1929).

⟨11⟩ Kao, Yen, *Science Repts. Natl. Tsing Hua Univ.*, Ser. **A-1**, 187 (1932). ⟨12⟩ Vorländer, *Z. anal. Chem.* **77**, 321–327 (1929). ⟨13⟩ Ionescu, Sluschanchi, *Bull. soc. chim.* (4) **53**, 909–918 (1933). ⟨14⟩ Walker, *Ind. Eng. Chem.* **32**, 1016–1018 (1940).

1:0150 CROTONALDEHYDE $CH_3.CH:CH.CHO$ C_4H_6O **Beil. I-728**

B.P. 102.15° **F.P. −76.5°** $D_4^{20.5}$ = **0.8477** $n_D^{20.5}$ = **1.43620**

Odor fruity, then irritating — Lachrymator — Abt. 18% sol. aq.; forms const.-boilg. mixt. with aq. contg. 80% $\bar{C}$ and boiling 84° — Eas. volatile with steam.

With satd. aq. $NaHSO_3$ soln. yields bisulfite addn. cpd., crystn. but fairly sol.; does not regenerate $\bar{C}$.

Ordinary comml. $\bar{C}$ is *trans* isomer ⟨1⟩ — $\bar{C}$ absorbs O_2 even from air, and when shaken with O_2 below 30° or with an aq. susp. of AgOH at 15–20° for 6 hrs. ⟨2⟩ yields 90–95% *trans*-crotonic acid (1:0425) ⟨1⟩.

With dil. HCl at b.p. $\bar{C}$ polymerizes to a trimer, m.p. 63° ⟨3⟩; with dil. aq. acids is also reversibly hydrated to aldol (1:0270) ⟨4⟩.

Adds Br_2 (T 1.91) yielding liq. α,β-dibromo-*n*-butyraldehyde — $\bar{C}$ in isopropyl alc., reduced with Al isopropylate gives (60–70% yield) crotyl alc. [Beil. I-442] ⟨5⟩.

$\bar{C}$ with $NH_2OH.HCl$ in aq. Na_2CO_3 yields crotonaldoxime, cryst. from C_6H_6, m.p. 119–120° ⟨6⟩; with equal moles of phenylhydrazine yields crotonaldehyde phenylhydrazone, pr. from pet. ether, m.p. 56–57° ⟨7⟩; with semicarbazide HCl yields crotonaldehyde semicarbazone, cryst. from dil. alc., m.p. 191–192° ⟨8⟩; 198–199° slow htg. ⟨9⟩.

Ⓓ **Crotonaldehyde *p*-nitrophenylhydrazone:** m.p. 184–185° ⟨10⟩. [Must not be used where distinction from HCHO is involved.]

Ⓓ **Crotonaldehyde 2,4-dinitrophenylhydrazone:** rosettes of crimson ndls. from C_6H_6 + lt. pet., m.p. 190° ⟨11⟩ [T 1.14].

Ⓓ **Crotonaldehyde dimethone:** m.p. 183° ⟨12⟩; 185–186° ⟨13⟩; corresp. anhydride, m.p. 167° (sint. 163°) ⟨12⟩.

1:0150 ⟨1⟩ Young, *J. Am. Chem. Soc.* **54,** 2498–2503 (1932). ⟨2⟩ Delépine, Bonnet, *Bull. soc. chim.* (4) **5,** 882 (1909). ⟨3⟩ Bernhauer, Irrgang, *Ann.* **525,** 64 (1936). ⟨4⟩ Winstein, Lucas, *J. Am. Chem. Soc.* **59,** 1461 (1937). ⟨5⟩ Young, Hartung, Crossley, *J. Am. Chem. Soc.* **58,** 101 (1936). ⟨6⟩ Schindler, *Monatsh.* **12,** 410 (1891). ⟨7⟩ von Auwers, Kreuder, *Ber.* **58,** 1977 (1925). ⟨8⟩ Urion, *Ann. chim.* (11) **1,** 36 (1934). ⟨9⟩ von Auwers, Heimke, *Ann.* **458,** 203 (1927). ⟨10⟩ Wegscheider, Späth, *Monatsh.* **31,** 1027 (1910).

⟨11⟩ Brady, *J. Chem. Soc.* **1931,** 756–759. ⟨12⟩ Vorländer, *Z. anal. Chem.* **77,** 252 (1929). ⟨13⟩ Kasuya, *J. Am. Chem. Soc.* **59,** 2742 (1937).

1:0155 *n*-VALERALDEHYDE *n*-C_4H_9.CHO $C_5H_{10}O$ Beil. I-676

B.P. 103.7° ⟨1⟩ **M.P. −91.5°** ⟨1⟩ D_4^{20} = **0.80952** ⟨2⟩ n_D^{20} = **1.39436** ⟨2⟩

Mobile liq. with penetrating odor — Dif. sol. aq. — With aq. forms const.-boilg. mixt. (b.p. 80.6° at 747 mm.) contg. 86% vol. % C̄ ⟨2⟩.

With satd. aq. $NaHSO_3$ soln. yields dif. sol. bisulfite addn. cpd. [cf. T 1.12].

Ⓟ **Sodium nitroprusside color test:** Aq. susp. of C̄, treated with 0.5% sodium nitroprusside soln. + alkali gives violet-red color, grad. disappearing on addn. of AcOH [dif. from isovaleraldehyde (1:0140)].

Ⓓ ***n*-Valeraldoxime:** Aq. soln. of C̄, shaken with $NH_2OH.HCl$ + K_2CO_3, readily yields oxime; after recrystn. from pet. ether, m.p. 52° ⟨3⟩.

Ⓓ ***n*-Valeraldehyde 2,4-dinitrophenylhydrazone:** yel. cryst. from alc., m.p. 98° ⟨4⟩; 106.5–107°? ⟨5⟩ [cf. T 1.14].

Ⓓ ***n*-Valeraldehyde dimethone:** m.p. 104.5° ⟨6⟩.

1:0155 ⟨1⟩ Simon, *Bull. soc. chim. Belg.* **38,** 56 (1929). ⟨2⟩ Bruylants, Ernould, *Bull. sci. acad. roy. Belg.* (5) **17,** 1174–1179 (1931); *Chem. Abs.* **26,** 3232 (1932). ⟨3⟩ Blaise, *Bull. soc. chim.* (3) **31,** 491 (1904). ⟨4⟩ Allen, *J. Am. Chem. Soc.* **52,** 2957 (1930). ⟨5⟩ Backer, Haack, *Rec. trav. chim.* **57,** 232 (1938). ⟨6⟩ Kao, Yen, *Science Repts. Natl. Tsing Hua Univ.*, Ser. **A-1,** 187 (1932).

1:0156 ACETAL $CH_3.CH(OC_2H_5)_2$ $C_6H_{14}O_2$ Beil. I-603

(Acetaldehyde diethylacetal; ethylidene diethyl ether)

B.P. 103.6° ⟨1⟩ D_4^{20} = **0.8248** ⟨1⟩ n_D^{20} = **1.3811** ⟨1⟩

Agreeable odor — Sol. in 18 vols. cold aq.; misc. with alc. but salted out by $CaCl_2$ only on addn. of aq.

[For prepn. from acetaldehyde + EtOH (61–64% yield) see ⟨2⟩.]

With aq. forms heterogeneous binary const.-boilg. mixt. (b.p. 82.6°) contg. 85.5% C̄; with alc. forms homogeneous binary const.-boilg. mixt. (b.p. 78.2°) contg. 34.5% C̄ ⟨1⟩ — With EtOH + H_2O forms homogeneous ternary const.-boilg. mixt. (b.p. 77.8°) contg. 61% C̄, 27.6% EtOH, 11.4% aq. ⟨1⟩.

For data on soly. of C̄ in aq.-alc. mixt. see ⟨3⟩.

Absolutely pure C̄ does not give fuchsin-aldehyde test (Generic Test 1), does not reduce Tollens' reagt. (T 1.11), nor give CHI_3 with I_2 + NaOH (T 1.81). After shaking with a few drops HCl, however, the resultant acetaldehyde responds readily.

Ⓟ Shake C̄ with a few drops HCl and then treat as for acetaldehyde (1:0100).

1:0156 ⟨1⟩ Béduwé, *Bull. soc. chim. Belg.* **34,** 41–55 (1925). ⟨2⟩ Adkins, Nissen, *Organic Syntheses, Coll. Vol.* I, 1–2 (1932). ⟨3⟩ Adkins, Nissen, *J. Am. Chem. Soc.* **44,** 2752 (1922).

1:0158 FORMALDEHYDE TRIMETHYLENEACETAL $C_4H_8O_2$ **Beil. XIX-2**

(Trimethylene glycol methylene ether; trimethylene formal; 1,3-dioxane)

$$H_2C\langle{}^{O}_{O}\rangle(CH_2)_3$$

B.P. 105° ⟨1⟩ **F.P. −42° ⟨3⟩** D_4^{20} **= 1.03422 ⟨1⟩** n_α^{20} **= 1.41652 ⟨1⟩**
n_γ^{20} **= 1.42730 ⟨1⟩**

Colorless liq. with acetal-like odor — Misc. aq.

[For prepn. from trioxymethylene + trimethylene glycol see ⟨1⟩.]

Traces of aldehyde may be removed from C̄ by repeated shakg. with silver oxide ⟨2⟩.

From cold aq. soln. $HgCl_2$ ppts. a white mercurichloride; this is sol. in hot aq. from which it cryst. on cooling. Sinters and decomposes abt. 120° [dif. from corresp. deriv. of 1,4-dioxane (1:6400) which subl. unchanged] ⟨1⟩.

Hydrol. with acids yields formaldehyde (1:0145) and trimethylene glycol (1:6490). [For kinetics of hydrolysis see ⟨4⟩.] When pure does not give fuchsin-aldehyde test (Generic Test 1) until after boilg. with acid.

1:0158 ⟨1⟩ Clarke, *J. Chem. Soc.* **101,** 1803 (1912). ⟨2⟩ Hepworth, *J. Chem. Soc.* **119,** 1256 (1921). ⟨3⟩ Henry, Dewael, *Cent.* **1902,** II, 929. ⟨4⟩ Leutner, *Monatsh.* **60,** 333 (1932).

1:0159 ETHOXYACETALDEHYDE $C_2H_5.O.CH_2.CHO$ $C_4H_8O_2$ **Beil. I-818**

B.P. 105-106° ⟨1⟩ D_4^{20} **= 0.942 ⟨1⟩** n_D^{20} **= 1.3956 ⟨1⟩**

Clear mobile liq., sol. aq. and org. solv. — Forms with aq. a const.-boilg. mixt., b.p. 90–91° at 760 mm., contg. 21.8% aq.

Reduces $NH_4OH—AgNO_3$ (T 1.11) or warm Fehling's soln. (T 1.22) — [Can be determined by $I_2—NaHSO_3$ method ⟨2⟩ ⟨3⟩.]

On stdg. in cold polymerizes to a visc. water-insol. liq. which on slow distn. with *p*-toluenesulfonic acid can be reconverted to C̄.

Ⓓ **Ethoxyacetaldehyde *p*-nitrophenylhydrazone:** cryst. from MeOH or EtOH, m.p. 113–114° ⟨1⟩.

Ⓓ **Ethoxyacetaldehyde 2,4-dinitrophenylhydrazone:** cryst. from MeOH, m.p. 116–117° ⟨1⟩.

1:0159 ⟨1⟩ Drake, Duvall, Jacobs, Thompson, Sonnichsen, *J. Am. Chem. Soc.* **60,** 73–76 (1938). ⟨2⟩ Dunn, Redemann, Smith, *J. Biol. Chem.* **104,** 511–517 (1934). ⟨3⟩ Donnally, *Ind. Eng. Chem., Anal. Ed.* **5,** 91 (1933).

1:0162 ACETALDEHYDE TRIMETHYLENEACETAL $C_5H_{10}O_2$ **Beil. XIX-9**

(Trimethylene glycol acetal; trimethyleneacetal; 2-methyldioxane-1,3)

$$CH_3.CH\langle{}^{O}_{O}\rangle(CH_2)_3$$

B.P. 109° ⟨1⟩ D^{25} **= 0.96455 ⟨1⟩** n_D^{25} **= 1.41147 ⟨1⟩**
B.P. 108-111° ⟨4⟩ D^{23} **= 0.9675 ⟨4⟩** n_D^{23} **= 1.4160 ⟨4⟩**

Colorless liq. with peppermint odor ⟨2⟩ — Sol. in 1½ vols. aq.; misc. with alc. or ether — Salted out from aq. solns. by $CaCl_2$, K_2CO_3 or Na_2CO_3 ⟨3⟩.

[For prepn. from MeOH + trimethylene glycol + BF_3 see ⟨4⟩.]

Reacts readily with Tollens' reagent (T 1.11) but only slowly with $NH_4OH + AgNO_3$ ⟨3⟩.

Htg. with aq., dil. alk. or better dil. minl. acid hydrolyzes to acetaldehyde (1:0100) and trimethylene glycol (1:6490). [For kinetics of hydrolysis see ⟨2⟩.]

1:0162 ⟨1⟩ Otto, *J. Am. Chem. Soc.* **59,** 1591 (1937). ⟨2⟩ Leutner, *Monatsh.* **60,** 335 (1932). ⟨3⟩ Lochert, *Ann. chim.* (6) **16,** 49–50 (1889). ⟨4⟩ Nieuwland, Vogt, Foohey, *J. Am. Chem. Soc.* **52,** 1021–1022 (1930).

1:0163 ***α*-ETHYL-*n*-BUTYRALDEHYDE** $C_6H_{12}O$ **Beil. I-693**
(Diethylacetaldehyde;
2-ethylbutanal-1)

$$CH_3CH_2.\overset{H}{\underset{C_2H_5}{C}}.CHO$$

B.P. 117° D_4^{20} = **0.811** ⟨1⟩ n_D^{20} = **1.4025** ⟨1⟩

Reduces $NH_4OH + AgNO_3$ — Yields $NaHSO_3$ cpd.

Ⓓ ***α*-Ethyl-*n*-butyraldehyde 2,4-dinitrophenylhydrazone:** pale or. pl. from lt. pet., m.p. 94.5–95° ⟨2⟩; cryst. from EtOAc, m.p. 129–130° ⟨1⟩. [Cf. T 1.14.]

Ⓓ ***α*-Ethyl-*n*-butyraldehyde semicarbazone:** colorless pr. from C_6H_6 + lt. pet., m.p. 97.5–99.5° ⟨2⟩.

Ⓓ ***α*-Ethyl-*n*-butyraldehyde dimethone:** colorless pr. from MeOH, m.p. 102–102.5° ⟨2⟩. [See T 1.13.]

1:0163 ⟨1⟩ Drake, Marvel, *J. Org. Chem.* **2,** 396 (1937). ⟨2⟩ Brunner, Farmer, *J. Chem. Soc.* **1937,** 1044.

1:0166 **METHYL-*n*-PROPYL-ACETALDEHYDE** $C_6H_{12}O$ **Beil. I-690**
(2-Methylpentanal-1)

$$CH_3—\overset{H}{\underset{CH_3.CH_2.CH_2}{C}}—CHO$$

B.P. 116° cor. at 737 mm. ⟨1⟩ ⟨2⟩
119-121° ⟨3⟩

Gives with satd. aq. $NaHSO_3$ soln. (cf. T 1.12) a dif. sol. bisulfite addition cpd., decomposed by aq. Na_2CO_3 regenerating $\bar{C}$.

$\bar{C}$ on oxidn. with calcd. amt. $K_2Cr_2O_7 + H_2SO_4$ yields methyl-*n*-propyl-acetic acid (1:1117), whose *p*-phenylphenacyl ester (cf. T 1.391) has m.p. 46° ⟨5⟩; 64–65° ⟨6⟩.

Ⓓ **Methyl-*n*-propyl-acetaldehyde semicarbazone:** cryst. from C_6H_6, m.p. 100–102° ⟨3⟩.

Ⓓ **Methyl-*n*-propyl-acetaldehyde 2,4-dinitrophenylhydrazone:** m.p. 103° ⟨4⟩.

1:0166 ⟨1⟩ Skita, Stuckhart, *Ber.* **48,** 1491 (1915). ⟨2⟩ Lieben, Zeisel, *Monatsh.* **4,** 22 (1883). ⟨3⟩ Sommelet, *Bull. soc. chim.* (4) **1,** 406 (1907); *Ann. chim.* (8) **9,** 555–556 (1906). ⟨4⟩ Morgan, Hardy, *Chemistry & Industry* **52,** 519 (1933). ⟨5⟩ Wrede, Rothhaas, *Ber.* **67,** 740 (1934). ⟨6⟩ Magnani,McElvain, *J. Am. Chem. Soc.* **60,** 819 (1938).

1:0169 **ACROLEIN DIETHYLACETAL** $C_7H_{14}O_2$ **Beil. I-727**

$$CH_2{=}CH.CH(OC_2H_5)_2$$

B.P. 123.5° ⟨1⟩ D^{15} = **0.85425**
125° ⟨2⟩

Mobile liq. of characteristic not unpleasant odor — Spar. sol. aq., misc. alc., ether.

[For prepn. from *β*-chloropropionaldehyde diethylacetal by action of dry powd. KOH (75% yield) see ⟨3⟩ ⟨4⟩ ⟨5⟩; from acrolein + triethyl orthoformate (73% yield) see ⟨2⟩.]

Readily hydrolyzed by dil. HCl even in cold ⟨1⟩ yielding acrolein (1:0115) and EtOH (1:6130).

Oxidn. with aq. $KMnO_4$ at 0° gives 67% yield *d,l*-glyceraldehyde diethylacetal (1:0280) ⟨6⟩ ⟨2⟩ ⟨5⟩.

1:0169 ⟨1⟩ Wohl, *Ber.* **31,** 1798 (1898). ⟨2⟩ Fischer, Baer, *Helv. Chim. Acta* **18,** 516 (1935). ⟨3⟩ Witzemann, Evans, Hass, Schroeder, *Organic Syntheses* **11,** 1–2 (1931). ⟨4⟩ Reeves, *J. Chem. Soc.* **1927,** 2481. ⟨5⟩ Witzemann, *J. Am. Chem. Soc.* **36,** 1911–1912 (1914). ⟨6⟩ Witzemann, Evans, Hass, Schroeder, *Organic Syntheses* **11,** 52–53 (1931).

1:0170 PARALDEHYDE (cyclic trimer: three CH(CH₃) groups joined by O bridges, ring CH_3—CH—O—CH(CH_3)—O—CH(CH_3)—O—) $C_6H_{12}O_3$ **Beil. XIX-385**

B.P. 124° **M.P. 12.6°** $D_4^{20} = 0.9943$ $n_D^{20} = 1.4198$

Less sol. in warm water than cold; 100 vols. aq. at 13° dis. 12 vols. C̄, but on warming to 30° soln. clouds and at 100° half the dislvd. C̄ separates.

The polymerization of acetaldehyde (1:0100) to paraldehyde (in presence of traces of acid as catalyst) is an equilibrium which at 15° corresponds to 94.3% paraldehyde + 5.7% acetaldehyde ⟨1⟩ — On long stdg. even pure C̄ is partially reconverted to acetaldehyde and this can also occur on distn. ⟨2⟩.

Ord. C̄ is often contaminated with peroxides (probably peracetic acid) which with KI soln. give free iodine ⟨3⟩ — C̄ can be freed from peroxides or acetaldehyde by shaking with mixt. of dil. alk. + $AgNO_3$ (i.e., AgOH susp.) ⟨4⟩.

When absolutely pure, C̄ does not give the fuchsin-aldehyde react. (Generic Test 1) or any other aldehyde reaction; unchanged on distn. with Na or conc. KOH ⟨5⟩. On warming with a little dil. H_2SO_4 or even 0.2 *N* HCl ⟨6⟩ is rapidly and quant. depolymerized to acetaldehyde (1:0100), q.v.

Ⓟ Warm with dil. acid and test distillate for acetaldehyde (1:0100).

1:0170 ⟨1⟩ Hatcher, Brodie, *Can. J. Research* **4,** 574–581 (1931). ⟨2⟩ Troeger, *Ber.* **25,** 3316 (1892). ⟨3⟩ Hanssen, *Z. angew. Chem.* **39,** 1291–1292 (1926). ⟨4⟩ Schulek, *Pharm. Zentralhalle,* **71,** 177–179 (1930); *Chem. Abs.* **24,** 3320 (1930). ⟨5⟩ Franchimont, *Rec. trav. chim.* **1,** 240 (1882). ⟨6⟩ Orton, McKie, *J. Chem. Soc.* **109,** 185 (1916).

1:0172 PROPIONALDEHYDE DIETHYLACETAL $C_7H_{16}O_2$ **Beil. I-630**
(Diethylpropional; propylal; ethylpropylal) $CH_3.CH_2.CH(OC_2H_5)_2$

B.P. 124° ⟨1⟩ $D_4 = 0.8232$ ⟨2⟩

Readily hydrolyzed by minl. ac. to propionaldehyde (1:0110) and C_2H_5OH (1:6130).

When abs. pure may fail to give fuchsin-ald. test (Generic Test 1) but does so readily after boiling for a moment with minl. ac.

1:0172 ⟨1⟩ Adams, Adkins, *J. Am. Chem. Soc.* **47,** 1365 (1925). ⟨2⟩ Hartung, Adkins, *J. Am. Chem. Soc.* **49,** 2520 (1927).

1:0176 *n*-CAPROALDEHYDE $CH_3.(CH_2)_4.CHO$ $C_6H_{12}O$ **Beil. I-688**
(*n*-Hexylaldehyde; *n*-hexaldehyde; hexanal)

B.P. 131° ⟨1⟩ $D_4^{20} = 0.8176$ ⟨2⟩ $n_D^{20} = 1.0468$ ⟨2⟩
128.1° ⟨3⟩ $D_4^{20} = 0.8139$ ⟨3⟩ $n_D^{20} = 1.4039$ ⟨3⟩

Colorless mobile liq. of characteristic and penetrating odor — Forms with aq. an azeotropic mixt., b.p. 90.6° at 758 mm., contg. 25 ± 1% by vol. of water ⟨3⟩.

[For prepn. (45–50% yield) from *n*-AmMgBr + $H(OC_2H_5)_3$ see ⟨2⟩.]

With satd. aq. $NaHSO_3$ (cf. T 1.12) forms dif. sol. $NaHSO_3$ cpd. — With drop of conc.

H_2SO_4 polymerizes with evol. of ht.; on distn. under reduced press. the polymer is partly depolymerized to C̄ ⟨4⟩.

C̄ readily oxidizes, even in air, to *n*-caproic ac. (1:1130).

Ⓓ ***n*-Caproaldoxime:** cryst. from pet. ether or MeOH m.p. 51° ⟨4⟩. [Use in quant. detn. of C̄ ⟨5⟩.]

Ⓓ ***n*-Caproaldehyde semicarbazone:** cryst. from C_6H_6 + pet. ether, m.p. 106° ⟨4⟩ ⟨6⟩ [known to depress m.p. of *n*-heptaldehyde semicarbazone ⟨6⟩].

Ⓓ ***n*-Caproaldehyde 2,4-dinitrophenylhydrazone:** or. yel. ndls., m.p. 104° ⟨7⟩ ⟨8⟩ ⟨1⟩; m.p. 106–107° ⟨9⟩ (cf. T 1.14).

Ⓓ ***n*-Caproaldehyde dimethone:** cryst. from dil. alc., m.p. 108.5° ⟨1⟩ ⟨10⟩.

1:0176 ⟨1⟩ Brunner, Farmer, *J. Chem. Soc.* **1937,** 1044. ⟨2⟩ Bachmann, *Organic Syntheses* **16,** 41–43 (1936); *J. Am. Chem. Soc.* **55,** 428 (1933). ⟨3⟩ Bruylants, *Bull. soc. chim. Belg.* **41,** 334 (1932). ⟨4⟩ Bagard, *Bull. soc. chim.* (4) **1,** 319 (1907). ⟨5⟩ Schultes, *Angew. Chem.* **47,** 258 (1934). ⟨6⟩ McCrae, Manske, *J. Chem. Soc.* **1928,** 488. ⟨7⟩ Brady, Elsmie, *Analyst* **51,** 78 (1926). ⟨8⟩ Allen, *J. Am. Chem. Soc.* **52,** 2957 (1930). ⟨9⟩ Newman, *J. Am. Chem. Soc.* **57,** 734 (1935). ⟨10⟩ Kao, Yen, *Science Repts. Natl. Tsing Hua Univ.*, Ser. **A-1,** 187 (1932).

1:0179 β-ETHYL-α-METHYLACROLEIN $C_6H_{10}O$ Beil. I-735

(2-Methylpenten-2-al-1) $CH_3.CH_2.CH{=}C(CH_3).CHO$

B.P. 136.8° ⟨1⟩ D_4^{20} = **0.8581 ⟨1⟩** n_D^{20} = **1.4488 ⟨1⟩**

D_4^{15} = **0.8544 ⟨2⟩**

Liq. with penetrating odor — Alm. insol. aq. — Adds Br_2 (T 1.91).

With satd. aq. $NaHSO_3$ soln. (cf. T 1.12) yields solid bisulfite addn. cpd. but from it Na_2CO_3 does not regenerate C̄ ⟨3⟩.

Oxidn. with $AgNO_3$ + NaOH in dil. alc. at room temp. gives (60% yield) β-ethyl-α-methylacrylic acid [Beil. II-437], m.p. 22–23° ⟨4⟩.

Reductn. of C̄ in MeOH with H_2 + $PdCl_2$ gives (67% yield) methyl-*n*-propyl-acetaldehyde (1:0166) ⟨5⟩.

[For prepn. of C̄ by dehydration (65–70% yield) of the aldol from propionaldehyde see ⟨2⟩ ⟨6⟩; direct from propionaldehyde (64% yield) by action of 10% KOH at 0° see ⟨7⟩.]

Ⓓ **β-Ethyl-α-methylacrolein oxime:** m.p. 48–48.8° cor. ⟨1⟩.

Ⓓ **β-Ethyl-α-methylacrolein phenylhydrazone:** m.p. 58–60° ⟨8⟩.

Ⓓ **β-Ethyl-α-methylacrolein semicarbazone:** m.p. 207° ⟨9⟩.

Ⓓ **β-Ethyl-α-methylacrolein 2,4-dinitrophenylhydrazone:** carmine-red cryst. from alc., m.p. 159° ⟨10⟩, 160–161° ⟨11⟩ [cf. T 1.14].

1:0179 ⟨1⟩ Goethals, *Bull. soc. chim. Belg.* **46,** 415 (1937). ⟨2⟩ Grignard, Abelmann, *Bull. soc. chim.* (4) **7,** 642–643 (1910). ⟨3⟩ Lieben, Zeisel, *Monatsh.* **4,** 19 (1883). ⟨4⟩ Goldberg, Linstead, *J. Chem. Soc.* **1928,** 2355. ⟨5⟩ Skita, *Ber.* **48,** 1491 (1915). ⟨6⟩ Lichtenberger, Naftali, *Bull. soc. chim.* (5) **4,** 329 (1937). ⟨7⟩ Doebner, *Ber.* **35,** 1144 (1902). ⟨8⟩ von Auwers, Kreuder, *Ber.* **58,** 1979 (1925). ⟨9⟩ Backes, *Compt. rend.* **196,** 278 (1933). ⟨10⟩ Allen, *J. Am. Chem. Soc.* **52,** 2958 (1930).

⟨11⟩ Morgan, Hardy, *Chemistry & Industry* **52,** 519 (1938).

1:0182 TETRAHYDROFURFURAL $C_5H_8O_2$ Beil. S.N. 2459

(Tetrahydrofuran-2-aldehyde)

```
H2C———CH2
|      | H
|      |/
H2C      C—CHO
  \    /
    O
```

B.P. 144-145°$_{740}$ ⟨1⟩ D_4^{25} = **1.10947 ⟨1⟩** n_D^{25} = **1.4704 ⟨1⟩**

B.P. 142-143°$_{779}$ ⟨2⟩ D_4^{20} = **1.10727 ⟨3⟩** n_D^{20} = **1.43658 ⟨3⟩**

Colorless somewhat visc. liq. of acrid odor — On stdg. several weeks becomes yel., solid appears and formic ac. is present.

Sol. in equal vol. aq.; eas. sol. org. solv.

Reduces warm Fehling's soln. immed. (T 1.22) and cold Fehling's soln. on stdg. Reduces Tollens' reagt. (T 1.11).

Relatively stable to alk. but with conc. HCl gives intense red color. [Dif. from furfural (1:0185) which with alk. gives Cannizzaro react. and with conc. HCl gives first a violet color then resinifies.] ⟨2.⟩

C̄ does not respond to aniline acetate test (T 1.23) for furfural ⟨2⟩.

Tetrahydrofurfuraldoxime and tetrahydrofurfural phenylhydrazone are oils and not recommended as derivs.

Ⓓ **Tetrahydrofurfural α-phenyl-α-benzylhydrazone:** from C̄ + *unsym.* benzylphenylhydrazine in alc.; cryst. from MeOH, m.p. 67° ⟨2⟩.

Ⓓ **Tetrahydrofurfural semicarbazone:** m.p. 166° u.c. ⟨4⟩.

1:0182 ⟨1⟩ Minné, Adkins, *J. Am. Chem. Soc.* **55,** 305–306 (1933). ⟨2⟩ Scheibler, Sotscheck, Friese, *Ber.* **57,** 1448 (1924). ⟨3⟩ Scheibler, Sotscheck, Friese, *Ber.* **58,** 1961 (1925). ⟨4⟩ Dunbar, Adkins, *J. Am. Chem. Soc.* **56,** 444 (1934).

1:0183 ENANTHALDEHYDE n-C_6H_{13}.CHO $C_7H_{14}O$ Beil. I-695

(n-Heptaldehyde; heptanal)

B.P. 155° **F.P. −43.3°** ⟨1⟩ D_4^{20} = **0.81742** ⟨1⟩ n_D^{20} = **1.42571** ⟨3⟩
152.8°⟨1⟩ D_4^{15} = **0.8219** ⟨2⟩ $n_{He (yellow)}^{20}$ = **1.41216** ⟨2⟩

Liquid with arom. penetrating odor — Forms with aq. a monohydrate, m.p. + 11.4°, and a dehydrate, m.p. 50–70° acc. to rate of htg. ⟨4⟩.

With satd. aq. $NaHSO_3$ soln. (cf. T 1.12) forms a cryst. bisulfite addn. cpd. [Use in quant. detn. of C̄ ⟨5⟩ ⟨6⟩.]

C̄ treated with HCl gas at −20° yields 75% trimeric para-enanthaldehyde [Beil. XIX_1-(807)], m.p. +20°, together with 1% meta-enanthaldehyde, cryst. from ether, m.p. 140° ⟨7⟩.

C̄ on reductn. with Fe filings + AcOH gives (75–81% yield) n-heptyl alc. (1:6240) ⟨8⟩.

C̄ on oxidn. with CrO_3 (cf. T 1.72), alk. $KMnO_4$, or acid $KMnO_4$ (76–78% yield)⟨9⟩, gives n-heptylic acid (1:1140).

With NH_2OH.HCl + aq. Na_2CO_3 C̄ gives (81–93% yield) n-heptaldoxime, lfts. from 60% alc., m.p. 53–55° acc. to rate of htg. ⟨10⟩; with phenylhydrazine gives liq. n-heptaldehyde phenylhydrazone [Beil. XV-131].

Ⓓ **Enanthaldehyde semicarbazone:** pl. from alc., m.p. 108–109° ⟨2⟩.

Ⓓ **Enanthaldehyde p-nitrophenylhydrazone:** m.p. 73° ⟨4⟩.

Ⓓ **Enanthaldehyde 2,4-dinitrophenylhydrazone:** yel. cryst. from alc., m.p. 108° ⟨11⟩; 106° ⟨12⟩ ⟨13⟩ [cf. T 1.14].

Ⓓ **Enanthaldehyde dimethone:** cryst. from dil. alc., m.p. 101.7° ⟨14⟩; 103° ⟨15⟩; 135° ⟨16⟩; corresp. anhydride; m.p. 112° ⟨15⟩; 110° ⟨16⟩.

1:0183 ⟨1⟩ Duffet, *Bull. soc. chim. Belg.* **40,** 390 (1931). ⟨2⟩ Sherrill, *J. Am. Chem. Soc.* **52,** 1990–1991 (1930). ⟨3⟩ Brühl, *Ann.* **203,** 28 (1880). ⟨4⟩ Noorduyn, *Rec. trav. chim.* **38,** 347–348 (1919). ⟨5⟩ Lea, *Ind. Eng. Chem., Anal. Ed.* **6,** 242–244 (1934). ⟨6⟩ Parkinson, Wagner, *Ind. Eng. Chem., Anal. Ed.* **6,** 433–436 (1934). ⟨7⟩ Franke, Wozelka, *Monatsh.* **33,** 355–357 (1912). ⟨8⟩ Clarke, Dreger, *Organic Syntheses, Coll. Vol.* I, 298–299 (1932). ⟨9⟩ Ruhoff, *Organic Syntheses* **16,** 39–40 (1936). ⟨10⟩ Bousquet, *Organic Syntheses* **11,** 54–56 (1931).

⟨11⟩ Campbell, *Analyst* **61,** 392 (1936). ⟨12⟩ Brady, Elsmie, *Analyst* **51,** 78 (1926). ⟨13⟩ Allen, *J. Am. Chem. Soc.* **52,** 2957 (1930). ⟨14⟩ Kao, Yen, *Science Repts. Natl. Tsing Hua Univ.,* Ser. **A-1,** 187 (1932). ⟨15⟩ Vorländer, *Z. anal. Chem.* **77,** 252 (1929). ⟨16⟩ Klein, Linser, *Mikrochemie, Pregl Festschrift* **1929,** 226.

1:0184 ***n*-BUTYL-ETHYL-ACETALDEHYDE** $C_8H_{16}O$ **Beil. I-707**

(2-Ethylhexanal-1) $CH_3.CH_2.CH_2.CH_2.CH.CHO$ (with C_2H_5 attached to CH)

B.P. 160° ⟨1⟩ D_4^{20} = **0.8205 ⟨2⟩** n_D^{20} = **1.4150 ⟨2⟩**
162-165° ⟨2⟩ n_D^{30} = **1.4130 ⟨1⟩**

Commercially available under name " octylaldehyde."

Gives with satd. aq. $NaHSO_3$ (cf. T 1.12) a cryst. sodium bisulfite cpd. (used in purifn.) ⟨1⟩.

Oxidn. with susp. of Ag_2O or with calcd. amt. CrO_3 in AcOH yields 2-ethylhexanoic acid (1:1143), b.p. 220–222° at 754 mm.; *p*-phenylphenacyl ester, cryst. from 90% alc., then lt. pet., m.p. 49.5–50° ⟨1⟩, 53–54° ⟨4⟩.

Reduction with Fe + AcOH or with Na + moist ether (45% yield ⟨3⟩) gives 2-ethylhexanol-1 (1:6248), b.p. 180°.

Ⓓ ***n*-Butyl-ethyl-acetaldehyde 2,4-dinitrophenylhydrazone:** cryst. from dil. alc., m.p. 114–115° ⟨2⟩; or. yel. ndls. from alc., m.p. 120–121° ⟨1⟩.

1:0184 ⟨1⟩ Weizmann, Bergmann, Haskelberg, *Chemistry & Industry* **56,** 589 (1937). ⟨2⟩ Drake, Marvel, *J. Org. Chem.* **2,** 396 (1937). ⟨3⟩ Powell, Baldwin, *J. Am. Chem. Soc.* **58,** 1872 (1936). ⟨4⟩ Magnani, McElvain, *J. Am. Chem. Soc.* **60,** 818–819 (1938).

1:0185 **FURFURAL** (H—C═C—H / H—C═C—CHO, ring closed through O) $C_5H_4O_2$ **Beil. XVII-272**

B.P. 161.7° ⟨1⟩ **F.P. −36.5°** D_4^{20} = **1.1594 ⟨2⟩** n_D^{20} = **1.52608 ⟨1⟩ ⟨2⟩**

Odor suggests benzaldehyde — Liq. darkens rapidly on stdg., especially in lt. or air; this effect is retarded by presence of traces of pyrogallol. [For study of thermal stability of C̄ see ⟨22⟩.]

C̄ is 8.3% sol. in aq. at 20°; for complete temp. soly. data see ⟨1⟩ ⟨3⟩ — Eas. volatile with steam. [For prepn. from corn cobs + HCl see ⟨4⟩.]

With satd. aq. $NaHSO_3$ yields cryst. bisulfite addn. cpd. (cf. T 1.12). [Use in detn. of C̄ in furfuryl alc. soln. ⟨23⟩.] — Reduces Tollens' reagt. (T 1.11) and Fehling's soln. (T 1.22) — With aniline acetate gives intense red color (T 1.23). [Use in colorimetric detn. of C̄ ⟨24⟩.] — Adds Br_2 (T 1.91). [Use in quant. detn. of C̄ ⟨5⟩ and of mixtures of C̄ with 5-methylfurfural (1:0198) ⟨6⟩.]

Oxidn. with air, $KMnO_4$, AgOH, $K_2Cr_2O_7$ + H_2SO_4 (75% yield) ⟨7⟩ or alk. $K_3Fe(CN)_6$ ⟨8⟩ gives furoic acid (1:0475) — C̄ with conc. aqueous ⟨9⟩ ⟨7⟩ or alc. alk. undergoes Cannizzaro reaction giving (61–63% yield) 2-furancarbinol (1:6425) and (60–63% yield) furoic acid (1:0475) — C̄ in abs. alc. stood 5 days at 25° with $Al(OEt)_3$ gave (88% yield) 2-furancarbinol (1:6425) ⟨21⟩. [For study of system: C̄ + furancarbinol see ⟨25⟩.]

C̄ allowed to stand with 5 vols. conc. aq. NH_4OH yields after several days " furfuramide," ndls. from alc., m.p. 117° ⟨10⟩.

With $NH_2OH.HCl$ + alk., C̄ yields α-furfuraldoxime, cryst. from C_6H_6 + lt. pet., m.p. 75–76° ⟨11⟩; with $NH_2OH.HCl$ + AcONa in dil. alc. C̄ yields β-furfuraldoxime, cryst. from alc., m.p. 91–92° ⟨11⟩ — With phenylhydrazine C̄ yields furfural phenylhydrazone [Beil. XVII-282], m.p. 97–98° (see below) — With semicarbazide C̄ yields furfuraldehyde semicarbazone, brownish yel. ndls., m.p. 202–203° ⟨12⟩; 190° ⟨13⟩.

Ⓓ **Furfural phenylhydrazone:** In a dry tt. mix 1 drop C̄ with 2 drops phenylhydrazine. Dissolve pasty react. prod. in 3 ml. boiling 50% alc. Cool in running water, and shake until the ppt. (often amorphous at first) sep. in pearly cryst. scales. Collect on small filter and wash with 5 ml. cold 33% alc. Transfer to tt. and redissolve in 5 ml. boiling 33% alc. If dark droplets separate allow to settle and decant clear hot soln. Cool and shake until pearly cryst. again ppt. Filter, wash with 5 ml. cold 33% alc. M.p. 97° u.c. ⟨13⟩.

Ⓓ **Furfural *p*-nitrophenylhydrazone:** m.p. 154° ⟨15⟩. [Use in quant. detn. of C̄ ⟨15⟩.]

Ⓓ **Furfural 2,4-dinitrophenylhydrazone:** occurs in two stereoisomeric forms (cf. acetaldehyde 1:0100): red cryst. from alc. or pyridine, m.p. 230° cor. ⟨16⟩, 229° ⟨17⟩, 222° ⟨18⟩ ⟨19⟩; yel. cryst., m.p. 212–214° ⟨16⟩. Mixed m.p. of red and yellow forms abt. 185° ⟨16⟩. [Use in quant. detn. of C̄ ⟨19⟩.] [Cf. T 1.14.]

Ⓓ **Furfural dimethone:** ndls. from 80% alc., m.p. 160° after prelim. browning ⟨20⟩; corresp. anhydride, lfts. from alc., m.p. 162–165° ⟨20⟩.

1:0185 ⟨1⟩ Evans, Aylesworth, *Ind. Eng. Chem.* **18,** 24–27 (1925). ⟨2⟩ Brühl, *Ann.* **235,** 7 (1886). ⟨3⟩ Mains, *Chem. Met. Eng.* **26,** 779–784 (1922). ⟨4⟩ Adams, Vorhees, *Organic Syntheses, Coll. Vol.* I, 274–277 (1932). ⟨5⟩ Hughes, Acree, *Ind. Eng. Chem., Anal. Ed.* **6,** 123–124 (1934). ⟨6⟩ Hughes, Acree, *Ind. Eng. Chem., Anal. Ed.* **9,** 318–321 (1937). ⟨7⟩ Hurd, Garrett, Osborne, *J. Am. Chem. Soc.* **55,** 1083–1084 (1933). ⟨8⟩ Brown, *Iowa State Coll. J. Sci.* **11,** 227–229 (1937); *Chem. Abs.* **31,** 8528 (1937). ⟨9⟩ Wilson, *Organic Syntheses, Coll. Vol.* I, 270–274 (1932). ⟨10⟩ Schiff, *Ber.* **10,** 1188 (1877).

⟨11⟩ Brady, Goldstein, *J. Chem. Soc.* **1927,** 1960–1961. ⟨12⟩ Knöpfer, *Monatsh.* **31,** 95 (1910). ⟨13⟩ Wolff, *Ann.* **394,** 101 (1912). ⟨14⟩ Mulliken, "Method" I, 25 (1904). ⟨15⟩ Maaskant, *Rec. trav. chim.* **55,** 1068 (1936). ⟨16⟩ Bredereck, *Ber.* **65,** 1836–1837 (1932). ⟨17⟩ Campbell, *Analyst* **61,** 392 (1936). ⟨18⟩ Simon, *Ber.* **66,** 320 (1933). ⟨19⟩ Simon, *Biochem. Z.* **247,** 171 (1932). ⟨20⟩ Vorländer, *Z. anal. Chem.* **77,** 267 (1929).

⟨21⟩ Meerwein, Schmidt, *Ann.* **444,** 232 (1925). ⟨22⟩ Dunlop, Peters, *Ind. Eng. Chem.* **32,** 1639–1641 (1940). ⟨23⟩ Dunlop, Trimble, *Ind. Eng. Chem., Anal. Ed.* **11,** 602–603 (1939). ⟨24⟩ Stillings, Browning, *Ind. Eng. Chem., Anal. Ed.* **12,** 499–502 (1940). ⟨25⟩ Dunlop, Trimble, *Ind. Eng. Chem.* **32,** 1000–1002 (1940).

1:0186 HEXAHYDROBENZALDEHYDE $C_6H_{11}.CHO$ $C_7H_{12}O$ Beil. VII-19

(Cyclohexylaldehyde)

B.P. 162° ⟨1⟩ ⟨2⟩ D^{19} = **0.9263** ⟨1⟩ n_D^{19} = **1.4495** ⟨1⟩

D_4^{25} = **0.9235** ⟨3⟩ n_D^{25} = **1.4506** ⟨3⟩

Liq. with powerful odor reminis. of valeraldehyde + benzaldehyde — Readily forms $NaHSO_3$ cpd. (cf. T 1.12) — Polymerizes easily.

Rapidly oxid. by air ⟨4⟩ or with AgOH in dil. alc. at 115–120° yielding hexahydrobenzoic ac. (1:0575).

[For prepn. (61–73% yield) from $C_6H_{11}.MgBr$ + triethyl orthoformate see ⟨5⟩ ⟨6⟩.]

Ⓓ **Hexahydrobenzaldoxime:** ndls. from pet. ether, m.p. 90–91° ⟨7⟩.

Ⓓ **Hexahydrobenzaldehyde semicarbazone:** m.p. 172.5–173° ⟨8⟩; 173–174° ⟨7⟩; 174–175° ⟨9⟩. [Other m.p.'s are given from 164° to 176°.]

1:0186 ⟨1⟩ Wallach, *Ann.* **347,** 333 (1906). ⟨2⟩ Backer, Winter, *Rec. trav. chim.* **56,** 504 (1937). ⟨3⟩ Dunbar, Adkins, *J. Am. Chem. Soc.* **56,** 444 (1934). ⟨4⟩ Sabatier, Mailhe, *Ann. chim.* (8) **10,** 537 (1907). ⟨5⟩ Kön, *J. Chem. Soc.* **1926,** 1797. ⟨6⟩ Wood, Comley, *J. Soc. Chem. Ind.* **42,** 431 T (1923). ⟨7⟩ Zelinsky, Gutt, *Ber.* **40,** 3051 (1907). ⟨8⟩ Mosettig, Burger, *J. Am. Chem. Soc.* **52,** 3461 (1930). ⟨9⟩ Diels, Alder, *Ann.* **460,** 122 (1928).

1:0191 GLYCOLALDEHYDE DIETHYLACETAL $C_6H_{14}O_3$ Beil. I-818

$HO.CH_2.CH(OC_2H_5)_2$

B.P. 167° D_4^{24} = **0.888** ⟨1⟩ $n_D^{19.5}$ = **1.4073** ⟨2⟩

[Prepn. from chloroacetal (95% yield ⟨3⟩) or bromoacetal (40–60% yield ⟨1⟩) + alc. KOH.]

Readily hydrolyzed ⟨4⟩ by boilg. with aq. + few drops HCl to C_2H_5OH (1:6130) and glycolaldehyde [Beil. I-817], the latter identified by htg. with excess phenylhydrazine acetate soln. pptg. glyoxal phenylosazone [Beil. XV-154], yel. tbls. from alc. or ether, m.p. 171° ⟨5⟩.

Absolutely pure C̄ fails to give fuchsin-aldehyde test (Generic Test 1) but does so after boilg. with minl. acid.

1:0191 ⟨1⟩ Hartung, Adkins, *J. Am. Chem. Soc.* **49,** 2520 (1927). ⟨2⟩ Bergmann, Miekely, *Ber.* **54,** 2156 (1921). ⟨3⟩ Beyerstedt, McElvain, *J. Am. Chem. Soc.* **58,** 530 (1936). ⟨4⟩ Marckwald, Ellinger, *Ber.* **25,** 2984 (1892). ⟨5⟩ Fischer, Baer, *Helv. Chim. Acta* **18,** 520 (1935).

1:0192 ***n*-CAPRYLALDEHYDE** $CH_3.(CH_2)_6.CHO$ $C_8H_{16}O$ **Beil. I-704**
(*n*-Octylaldehyde; octanal)

B.P. 167-170° ⟨1⟩ D^{20}_{20} = **0.82583** ⟨2⟩ n^{20}_D = **1.42167** ⟨2⟩
171-173° ⟨2⟩ n^{26}_D = **1.41667** ⟨3⟩

Volatile with steam ⟨4⟩ — Yields $NaHSO_3$ cpd.

Oxidn. with $KMnO_4$ ⟨5⟩ yields *n*-caprylic acid (1:1145).

C̄ htd. with pyruvic acid + *β*-naphthylamine yields *α*-*n*-heptyl-*β*-naphthocinchoninic acid [Beil. XXII-103], yel. pl. from alc., m.p. 234° ⟨3⟩ ⟨6⟩.

Ⓓ ***n*-Caprylaldoxime:** ndls. from MeOH, m.p. 60° ⟨7⟩ ⟨4⟩.

Ⓓ ***n*-Caprylaldehyde semicarbazone:** forms in quant. yield; cryst. from dil. MeOH, m.p. 98° ⟨2⟩ ⟨4⟩; 101° ⟨7⟩ ⟨8⟩.

Ⓓ ***n*-Caprylaldehyde thiosemicarbazone:** m.p. 94–94.5° ⟨9⟩.

Ⓓ ***n*-Caprylaldehyde *p*-nitrophenylhydrazone:** bright yel. ndls., m.p. 80° ⟨4⟩.

Ⓓ ***n*-Caprylaldehyde 2,4-dinitrophenylhydrazone:** yel. cryst. from alc., m.p. 106° ⟨10⟩. [Cf. T 1.14.]

Ⓓ ***n*-Caprylaldehyde dimethone:** cryst. from dil. alc., m.p. 89.8° ⟨11⟩. [Cf. T 1.13.]

1:0192 ⟨1⟩ Sabatier, Mailhe, *Compt. rend.* **158,** 986 (1914). ⟨2⟩ Harries, Oppenheim, *Cent.* **1916,** II, 993. ⟨3⟩ Schimmel & Co., *Cent.* **1901,** II, 1375. ⟨4⟩ Stephen, *J. Chem. Soc.* **127,** 1875 (1925). ⟨5⟩ Nelson, Mottern, *Ind. Eng. Chem.* **26,** 635 (1934). ⟨6⟩ Schimmel & Co. *Cent.* **1899,** I, 1043. ⟨7⟩ Semmler, *Ber.* **42,** 1163 (1909). ⟨8⟩ Fischer, Düll, Ertel, *Ber.* **65,** 1432 (1932). ⟨9⟩ Uhl, *J. Am. Pharm. Assoc.* **24,** 381 (1935). ⟨10⟩ Allen, *J. Am. Chem. Soc.* **52,** 2957 (1930).
⟨11⟩ Kao, Yen, *Science Repts. Natl. Tsing Hua Univ.*, Ser. **A-1,** 187 (1932).

1:0193 ***α*-ETHYL-*β*-*n*-PROPYLACROLEIN** $C_8H_{14}O$ **Beil. I-774**
(2-Ethylhexen-2-al-1)

$$CH_3.CH_2.CH_2.CH{=}\overset{\overset{\displaystyle C_2H_5}{|}}{C}.CHO$$

B.P. 173° D^{22}_{4} = **0.859** ⟨1⟩ n^{22}_D = **1.4518** ⟨1⟩
D^{20}_{4} = **0.8528** ⟨2⟩

Colorless liq. with agreeable odor — Alm. insol. aq. — Does not form $NaHSO_3$ cpd.
Reduces Tollen's reagt. (T 1.11), Fehling's soln. (T 1.22), alk. $KMnO_4$ (T 1.34).
Adds Br_2 (T 1.91).
[For prepn. from *n*-butyraldehyde (1:0130) with aq. KOH see ⟨3⟩ ⟨2⟩.]

C̄ reduced with amalgamated Al ⟨3⟩ or by catalytic hydrog. under high press. ⟨4⟩ gives 2-ethylhexanol-1 (1:6248).

C̄ oxidized by shaking with moist AgOH ($AgNO_3$ + NaOH) gives (53% yield) 2-ethylhexen-2-oic acid-1 ⟨1⟩ which on reduction with Zn + H_2SO_4 gives ⟨3⟩ 2-ethylhexanoic acid (1:1143). Oxidn. with $KMnO_4$ + dil. H_2SO_4 yields *n*-butyric ac. (1:1035) + propionic ac. (1:1025) ⟨5⟩.

Ⓓ **α-Ethyl-β-n-propylacrolein semicarbazone:** m.p. 153.5° ⟨6⟩, 150–151° ⟨2⟩, 148–149° ⟨7⟩, 132° ⟨3⟩.

Ⓓ **α-Ethyl-β-n-propylacrolein 2,4-dinitrophenylhydrazone:** m.p. 124–125° ⟨4⟩, 122° ⟨6⟩. [Cf. T 1.14.]

1:0193 ⟨1⟩ Lichtenberger, Naftali, *Bull. soc. chim.* (5) **4,** 329, 332 (1937). ⟨2⟩ Batalin, Slawina, *J. Gen. Chem., U.S.S.R.* **7,** 202–206 (1937); *Chem. Abs.* **31,** 4267 (1937). ⟨3⟩ Weizmann, Garrard, *J. Chem. Soc.* **117,** 329–330 (1920). ⟨4⟩ Morgan, Hardy, *Chemistry & Industry* **52,** 519 (1933). ⟨5⟩ Kadiera, *Monatsh.* **25,** 338 (1904). ⟨6⟩ Backes, *Compt. rend.* **196,** 278 (1933). ⟨7⟩ Hoffer, *Chem. Abs.* **30,** 1396 (1936).

1:0195 BENZALDEHYDE

C_6H_5—CHO C_7H_6O **Beil. VII-178**

B.P. 178.9° **F.P. −55.6°** D_4^{15} = **1.0504** n_D^{20} = **1.5460** ⟨1⟩
D_4^{30} = **1.0365** ⟨1⟩

Bitter almond odor — Sol. in abt. 300 pts. cold aq.; misc. alc., ether — Volatile with steam.

With satd. aq. $NaHSO_3$ soln. (cf. T 1.12) readily yields bisulfite addn. cpd. Reduces Tollen's reagt. (T 1.11) but not Fehling's soln. (T 1.22) — Oxidized by air or oxid. agents to benzoic ac. (1:0715).

With conc. aq. alk. C̄ undergoes Cannizzaro reactn. ⟨2⟩ [catalyzed by pres. of peroxides ⟨3⟩] yielding benzyl alc. (1:6480) and benzoic ac. (1:0715) — C̄ in MeOH treated with CH_2O + solid KOH at 60° undergoes "crossed Cannizzaro reactn." giving (80% yield) benzyl alc. (1:6480) ⟨4⟩.

Pure C̄ in dil. alc. refluxed with NaCN gives (90–92% yield) benzoin (1:5210), cryst. from 95% alc., m.p. 129° ⟨5⟩. [For study of benzoin condens. see ⟨6⟩.]

C̄ on stdg. or shaking with conc. aq. or alc. ⟨7⟩ NH_4OH yields "hydrobenzamide" [Beil. VII-215], cryst. from alc. or ether, m.p. 110° — C̄ merely mixed with equivalent aniline at ord. temp. evolves heat and gives (84–87% yield) benzalaniline, cryst. from 85% alc., m.p. 52° ⟨8⟩.

C̄ with $NH_2OH.HCl$ + excess aq. alk. yields α-benzaldoxime, m.p. 35° [Beil. VII-218]. [This form can be converted with acids, etc., to β-benzaldoxime, m.p. 132° [Beil. VII-221].] — C̄ with phenylhydrazine yields benzaldehyde phenylhydrazone [Beil. XV-134], ndls. from 50% alc. or pet. ether, m.p. 156° (see below) — C̄ with semicarbazide HCl + NaOAc yields benzaldehyde semicarbazone [Beil. VII-229], m.p. 217° ⟨9⟩, but varies with rate of htg.

Ⓟ **Colored condensation product with phenol:** In a dry 3-in. tt. mix in order 1 drop melted phenol, 1 drop C̄, and 1 drop conc. H_2SO_4. Then treat with 2–3 ml. 10% NaOH soln. BzH gives intensely violet-red (V-R) soln. immediately ⟨10⟩. [For nature of reactn. see ⟨11⟩.]

Ⓟ **Colored condensation product with β-naphthol:** Prepare cold satd. aq. soln. by shaking together 1 drop C̄, a pinch of β-naphthol, and 10 ml. aq. Filter, and pour 2–3 ml. onto surface of 3 ml. conc. H_2SO_4 in small tt. A violet-red colored zone appears at the interfacial layer ⟨10⟩. [For nature of reactn. see ⟨12⟩.]

Ⓓ **Benzaldehyde phenylhydrazone:** Dis. 1 drop C̄ in 12 ml. 50% alc. Add 1 drop pure phenylhydrazine and boil ½ min. Cool, shake well and collect bulky ppt. on a small filter. Wash with 5 ml. cold 50% alc. Redissolve ppt. in 12 ml. boiling 50% alc., cool, filter and wash again with 5 ml. cold 50% alc. Dry 15 min. at 100°. M.p. 156° u.c. After exposure to daylight for 1 hr. changes from white to O-T_2. ⟨10.⟩

Ⓓ **Benzaldehyde p-nitrophenylhydrazone:** or. red ndls. from alc., m.p. 190° ⟨13⟩; 192° ⟨14⟩. [Use in quant. detn. of C̄ ⟨15⟩.]

Ⓓ **Benzaldehyde 2,4-dinitrophenylhydrazone:** or. cryst. from AcOH, m.p. 237° ⟨16⟩; 235° ⟨17⟩ [cf. T 1.14]. [Use in quant. detn. of C̄ ⟨15⟩ ⟨18⟩.]

Ⓓ **Benzaldehyde dimethone:** m.p. abt. 193° u.c. ⟨19⟩; corresp. anhydride, m.p. 200° ⟨19⟩ [cf. T 1.13].

1:0195 ⟨1⟩ Pound, *J. Phys. Chem.* **35,** 1496 (1931). ⟨2⟩ Blanksma, Zaaijer, *Rec. trav. chim.* **57,** 727–728 (1938). ⟨3⟩ Kharasch, Foy, *J. Am. Chem. Soc.* **57,** 1510 (1935). ⟨4⟩ Davidson, Weiss, *Organic Syntheses* **18,** 80 (1938). ⟨5⟩ Adams, Marvel, *Organic Syntheses, Coll. Vol.* I, 88–89 (1932). ⟨6⟩ Nadkarni, Mehta, Wheeler, *J. Phys. Chem.* **39,** 727–739 (1935). ⟨7⟩ Johnson, Livak, *J. Am. Chem. Soc.* **58,** 301 (1936). ⟨8⟩ Bigelow, Eatough, *Organic Syntheses, Coll. Vol.* I, 73–74 (1932). ⟨9⟩ Wilson, Keenan, *J. Assoc. Official Agr. Chem.* **13,** 390, 393 (1930). ⟨10⟩ Mulliken, " Method " I, 23–24 (1904).

⟨11⟩ Tanasescu, Simonescu, *J. prakt. Chem.* (2) **141,** 312 (1934). ⟨12⟩ Ipatieff, Dolgoff, *Bull. soc. chim.* (4) **45,** 951 (1929). ⟨13⟩ Shoppee, *J. Chem. Soc.* **1932,** 705. ⟨14⟩ Biltz, Sieden, *Ann.* **324,** 321 (1902). ⟨15⟩ Iddles, Jackson, *Ind. Eng. Chem., Anal. Ed.* **6,** 455–456 (1934). ⟨16⟩ Campbell, *Analyst* **61,** 392 (1936). ⟨17⟩ Curtius, Dedichen, *J. prakt. Chem.* **50,** 264 (1894). ⟨18⟩ Perkins, Edwards, *Am. J. Pharm.* **107,** 209–211 (1935). ⟨19⟩ Vorländer, Strauss, *Am.* **309,** 379 (1899).

1:0197 PELARGONALDEHYDE $CH_3.(CH_2)_7.CHO$ $C_9H_{18}O$ Beil. I-708

(*n*-Nonylaldehyde; nonanal)

B.P. 185° ⟨1⟩ D^{19}_{19} = **0.8268** ⟨2⟩ $n^{18.6}_{D}$ = **1.42417** ⟨2⟩
n^{20}_{D} = **1.4273** ⟨3⟩

Liq. with penetrating but not disagreeable odor — With satd. aq. $NaHSO_3$ soln. forms bisulfite cpd. ⟨4⟩.

Under influence of conc. H_2SO_4 readily polymerizes to a liq. ⟨5⟩.

$\bar{C}$ in air or warmed with moist AgOH 30 min. at 100° gives pelargonic ac. (1:0560) ⟨6⟩ ⟨7⟩.

Reduction with Fe filings + AcOH according to ⟨8⟩ gives (41–57% yield) nonanol-1 (1:6265) ⟨9⟩.

$\bar{C}$ htd. with pyruvic ac. + β-naphthylamine gives α-*n*-octyl-β-naphthocinchoninic acid [Beil. XXII-103], cryst. from H.COOH + MeOH, m.p. 238–240° ⟨5⟩.

Ⓓ **Pelargonaldoxime:** cryst. from pet. ether, m.p. 64° ⟨5⟩.

Ⓓ **Pelargonaldehyde semicarbazone:** lfts. from MeOH, m.p. 84° ⟨4⟩ ⟨10⟩; 100° ⟨5⟩ ⟨11⟩.

Ⓓ **Pelargonaldehyde thiosemicarbazone:** m.p. 77° ⟨3⟩.

Ⓓ **Pelargonaldehyde 2,4-dinitrophenylhydrazone:** yel. cryst. from alc., m.p. 100° cor. ⟨12⟩; m.p. 96° ⟨13⟩ ⟨14⟩ [cf. T 1.14].

Ⓓ **Pelargonaldehyde dimethone:** m.p. 86.3° ⟨15⟩ [cf. T 1.13].

1:0197 ⟨1⟩ Sabatier, Mailhe, *Compt. rend.* **158,** 987 (1914). ⟨2⟩ Harries, Oppenheim, *Cent.* **1916,** II, 993. ⟨3⟩ Uhl, *J. Am. Pharm. Assoc.* **24,** 381 (1935). ⟨4⟩ Harries, Turk, *Ber.* **39,** 3733 (1906). ⟨5⟩ Bagard, *Bull. soc. chim.* (4) **1,** 351–352 (1907). ⟨6⟩ Walbaum, Stephan, *Ber.* **33,** 2303 (1900). ⟨7⟩ Holde, Zadek, *Ber.* **56,** 2056 (1923). ⟨8⟩ Clarke, Dreger, *Organic Syntheses, Coll. Vol.* I, 298–299 (1932). ⟨9⟩ Tomecko, Adams, *J. Am. Chem. Soc.* **49,** 529 (1927). ⟨10⟩ Harries, *Ann.* **343,** 355 (1905).

⟨11⟩ Fischer, Düll, Ertel, *Ber.* **65,** 1471 (1932). ⟨12⟩ Strain, *J. Am. Chem. Soc.* **57,** 760 (1935). ⟨13⟩ Brady, Elsmie, *Analyst* **51,** 77 (1926). ⟨14⟩ Allen, *J. Am. Chem. Soc.* **52,** 2957 (1930). ⟨15⟩ Kao, Yen, *Science Repts. Natl. Tsing Hua Univ.*, Ser. **A-1,** 187 (1932).

1:0198 5-METHYLFURFURAL $C_6H_6O_2$ Beil. XVII-289

```
      HC——————CH
      ‖        ‖
CH₃—C          C—CHO
      \      /
         O
```

B.P. 187° D^{25}_{4} = **1.1219** n^{25}_{D} = **1.5147**
D^{18}_{4} = **1.1072**

Oil, sol. in 30 pts. aq. — Volatile with steam.

With α-naphthol + conc. H_2SO_4 (cf. Generic Test 2) gives intense violet color — With phloroglucinol + HCl (T 1.24) gives chlorine-contg. brown red condens. prod.

With satd. aq. $NaHSO_3$ soln. (cf. T 1.12) gives bisulfite addn. cpd. — Reduces Tollens' reagt. (T 1.11) and Fehling's soln. (T 1.22) — Adds Br_2 (T 1.91).

Oxidn. with AgOH in hot aq. (94% yield) ⟨1⟩ ⟨2⟩, or with AgOH + $Ba(OH)_2$ ⟨3⟩, or with $K_3Fe(CN)_6$ ⟨4⟩ gives 5-methylfuroic ac. [Beil. XVIII-294], tbls. or ndls. from aq. or C_6H_6, m.p. 108–109° — Oxidn. with CrO_3 gives acetic ac. (1:1010).

With 50% aq. NaOH undergoes Cannizzaro reaction yielding 5-methylfurancarbinol [Beil. XVII_1-(56)] and 5-methylfuroic ac. (see above) ⟨5⟩.

With conc. aq. NH_4OH gives 5-methylfurfural hydramide, ndls. from dil. alc., m.p. 86–87° ⟨6⟩ — With Ac_2O + few drops conc. H_2SO_4 yields 5-methylfurfural diacetate, cryst. from pet. ether, m.p. 95° ⟨7⟩.

[For prepn. from cane sugar see ⟨8⟩ — For comparative studies of methods for quant. detn. see ⟨9⟩ ⟨10⟩ ⟨11⟩.]

Ⓓ **5-Methylfurfuraldoxime:** C̄ + $NH_2OH.HCl$ + excess alk. gives *anti* isomer, m.p. 51–52° ⟨12⟩.

Ⓓ **5-Methylfurfural semicarbazone:** m.p. 210–211° ⟨13⟩.

Ⓓ **5-Methylfurfural phenylhydrazone:** m.p. 147–148° ⟨13⟩.

Ⓓ **5-Methylfurfural *p*-nitrophenylhydrazone:** scarlet ppt. from aq. alc., m.p. 130° ⟨14⟩.

Ⓓ **5-Methylfurfural 2,4-dinitrophenylhydrazone:** m.p. 212° cor. ⟨15⟩. [Use in quant. detn. ⟨15⟩.] [Cf. T 1.14.]

1:0198 ⟨1⟩ Hill, Sawyer, *Am. Chem. J.* **20,** 171 (1898). ⟨2⟩ Hill, Sylvester, *Am. Chem. J.* **32,** 187–188 (1904). ⟨3⟩ Runde, Scott, Johnson, *J. Am. Chem. Soc.* **52,** 1288 (1930). ⟨4⟩ Brown, *Iowa State Coll. J. Sci.* **11,** 227–229 (1937); *Cent.* **1938,** I, 1580. ⟨5⟩ Blanksma, *Chem. Weekblad* **9,** 186–187 (1912). ⟨6⟩ Bieler, Tollens, *Ann.* **258,** 123 (1890). ⟨7⟩ Blanksma, *Chem. Weekblad* **6,** 727 (1909). ⟨8⟩ Rinkes, *Organic Syntheses* **14,** 62–64 (1934). ⟨9⟩ Iddles, French, *Ind. Eng. Chem., Anal. Ed.* **8,** 283–285 (1936). ⟨10⟩ Hughes, Acree, *Ind. Eng. Chem., Anal. Ed.* **9,** 318–321 (1937).

⟨11⟩ Marshall, Norris, *Biochem. J.* **31,** 1053–1060, 1289–1298, 1939–1944 (1937). ⟨12⟩ Fromherz, Meigen, *Ber.* **40,** 3568 (1907). ⟨13⟩ Masson, *Compt. rend.* **149,** 796 (1909). ⟨14⟩ Feist, *Ber.* **33,** 2098 (1900). ⟨15⟩ Simon, *Biochem. Z.* **247,** 171–177 (1932); *Cent.* **1932,** I, 3472.

1:0200 PHENYLACETALDEHYDE C_8H_8O Beil. VII-292

(α-Tolualdehyde)

⟨phenyl⟩—$CH_2.CHO$

B.P. 193-194° D^{20} = **1.0252** n_D^{20} = **1.53191**

Oil of odor like hyacinths — Volatile with steam — With satd. aq. $NaHSO_3$ soln. (cf. T 1.12) forms bisulfite addn. cpd. from which it is best recovered by steam distn. with dil. H_2SO_4 ⟨1⟩ [alk. causes polymerization].

Polymerizes on stdg. ⟨2⟩ yielding viscous mixture of polymers — C̄ on stdg. at room temp. several days with 23% H_2SO_4 polymerizes to the trimer, triphenylparaldehyde [Beil. XIX_1-(810)], cryst. from alc., m.p. 155–156° ⟨3⟩; this polymer is inert to usual aldehyde reagents but on distn. at ord. press. is alm. quant. depolymerized to C̄ ⟨3⟩; similar polymerization also caused by conc. H_2SO_4, 23% HCl, dry HCl gas, etc. ⟨3⟩.

With cold 10% aq. KOH or with piperidine C̄ polymerizes alm. instantly to an amorphous dimer which at 90–100° under ord. press. depolymerizes to C̄ ⟨4⟩.

C̄ does *not* oxidize appreciably in air at ord. temp. ⟨1⟩ — Oxidn. with CrO_3 yields benzoic acid (1:0715) ⟨5⟩.

[For prepn. (55–58% yield) from benzyl chloride + triethyl orthoformate see ⟨1⟩.]

Ⓓ **Phenylacetaldoxime:** cryst. from ether or lgr., m.p. 97–98° ⟨6⟩; 98.5° ⟨1⟩; 99–100° ⟨7⟩.

Ⓓ **Phenylacetaldehyde phenylhydrazone:** cryst. from lgr., m.p. 58° ⟨8⟩ ⟨7⟩; 62–63° ⟨9⟩.

Ⓓ **Phenylacetaldehyde semicarbazone:** cryst. from dil. alc. or AcOEt, m.p. 153° ⟨10⟩; 156° ⟨9⟩.

Ⓓ **Phenylacetaldehyde 2,4-dinitrophenylhydrazone:** golden yel. lfts. from alc., m.p. 121° ⟨11⟩; 110° ⟨12⟩ [cf. T 1.14].

Ⓓ **Phenylacetaldehyde dimethone:** m.p. 165–165.5° ⟨13⟩. [Cf. T 1.13.]

1:0200 ⟨1⟩ Wood, Comley, *J. Soc. Chem. Ind.* **42,** 432 T (1923). ⟨2⟩ Pound, *J. Phys. Chem.* **35,** 1174–1179 (1931). ⟨3⟩ Stobbe, Lippold, *J. prakt. Chem.* (2) **90,** 280–284 (1914). ⟨4⟩ Stobbe, Lippold, *J. prakt. Chem.* (2) **90,** 284–285 (1914). ⟨5⟩ Etard, *Ann. chim.* (5) **22,** 249 (1881). ⟨6⟩ Dollfuss, *Ber.* **25,** 1917 (1892). ⟨7⟩ Weerman, *Ann.* **401,** 7–8 (1913). ⟨8⟩ Fischer, Schmitt, *Ber.* **21,** 1072 (1888). ⟨9⟩ Henle, *Ber.* **38,** 1365–1366 (1905). ⟨10⟩ von Auwers, Keil, *Ber.* **36,** 3911 (1903).

⟨11⟩ Campbell, *Analyst* **61,** 392 (1936). ⟨12⟩ Brady, *J. Chem. Soc.* **1931,** 758. ⟨13⟩ Hershberg, *Helv. Chim. Acta* **17,** 355 (1934).

1:0205 SALICYLALDEHYDE (*o*-Hydroxybenzaldehyde; *o*-aldehydophenol, *o*-formylphenol) —CHO, OH $C_7H_6O_2$ **Beil. VIII-31**

B.P. 197° cor. **196.4-196.5°** ⟨1⟩ **F.P. +1.6°** ⟨1⟩ D^{20}_{20} **= 1.1690** ⟨1⟩ n^{20}_{D} **= 1.574** n^{25}_{D} **= 1.57017**

For purifn. via Cu salt see ⟨2⟩ — Odor faintly aromatic — Volatile with steam; dif. sol. aq.; misc. alc., ether.

Gives satisfactory fuchsin-ald. react. only with sensitized reagt. [cf. " Manual "; Generic Test 1, Note 2]. [For detailed study see ⟨3⟩.] — With satd. aq. $NaHSO_3$ soln. (cf. T 1.12) yields $NaHSO_3$ addn. cpd., cryst. from 10% alc. ⟨1⟩, from which C̄ can be regenerated with dil. acid — C̄ reduces Tollens' reagt. (T 1.11) but not Fehling's soln. (T 1.22).

Satd. aq. soln. of C̄ gives intense violet color with $FeCl_3$ (T 1.41) — C̄ is sol. in alk. yielding yellow soln. but is repptd. by CO_2; is too weakly acidic, however, to give quant. titration equiv. ⟨4⟩ — Pure C̄ in 1 *N* NaOH treated with slightly more than 1 mole 3% H_2O_2 at room temp., stood 15–20 hrs., gives (69–73% yield) catechol (1:1520) ⟨5⟩.

Na salt of C̄ treated in dry ether with AcCl ⟨6⟩ or in dry C_6H_6 with Ac_2O ⟨7⟩ yields 2-acetoxybenzaldehyde, ndls. from ether, m.p. 38–39° — C̄ refluxed 4 hrs. with Ac_2O ⟨8⟩ or treated at 30° with Ac_2O + conc. H_2SO_4 ⟨9⟩ gives 2-acetoxybenzaldiacetate (salicylaldehyde triacetate), ndls. or tbls. from alc. or Ac_2O, m.p. 102° — Mg salt of C̄ boiled in $CHCl_3$ with *p*-nitrobenzoyl chloride yields salicylaldehyde *p*-nitrobenzoate, white ndls. from xylene, m.p. 123–124° ⟨29⟩.

C̄ in ether with phenylisocyanate yields *o*-formylphenyl *N*-phenylcarbamate, ndls. from C_6H_6, m.p. 133° ⟨10⟩ — C̄ htd. with chloroacetic ac. + 2 moles aq. alk. (cf. T 1.46) gives (45% yield) *o*-formylphenoxyacetic ac., yel. lfts. from aq., m.p. 132° ⟨11⟩ ⟨12⟩ — C̄ + *p*-toluenesulfonyl chloride in pyridine 20 hrs. at 20° yields *o*-formylphenyl *p*-toluenesulfonate, cryst. from MeOH, m.p. 63–64° ⟨13⟩.

C̄ + equal moles aniline warmed at 100° yields salicylaldehyde anil, which seps. as red oil, but after recrystn. from alc. forms yel. cryst., m.p. 50.5° ⟨14⟩ ⟨15⟩ — C̄ in alc. + 2 equiv. aq. NaOH + 1 equiv. $NH_2OH.HCl$ stood 24 hrs., acidified (with AcOH or CO_2), yields salicylaldoxime, cryst. from C_6H_6 + pet. ether, m.p. 57° ⟨16⟩. [Use for detect. and detn. of Cu^{++} ⟨17⟩ and other metallic ions ⟨30⟩] — C̄ in lgr. treated with 1 mole phenylhydrazine in ether, yields salicylaldehyde phenylhydrazone, m.p. 142–143° ⟨18⟩ — C̄ in hot alc. shaken with warm aq. soln. of semicarbazide HCl ⟨19⟩ yields salicylaldehyde semicarbazone, ndls. from alc., m.p. 230° dec. ⟨20⟩.

Ⓓ **Salicylaldehyde *p*-nitrophenylhydrazone:** red brown pr. from alc., m.p. 227° ⟨21⟩. [Use in quant. detn. of C̄ ⟨2⟩.]

Ⓓ **Salicylaldehyde 2,4-dinitrophenylhydrazone:** lt. red cryst. from AcOH, m.p. 252° dec. ⟨23⟩; red cryst. from abs. alc., m.p. 248° ⟨24⟩; 237° ⟨25⟩. [Use in quant. detn. of C̄ ⟨26⟩ ⟨27⟩] [cf. T 1.14].

Ⓓ **Salicylaldehyde dimethone** [cf. T 1.13]: The methone itself is unknown, the corresp. anhydride forming directly, cryst. from 70% alc., m.p. 208° cor. ⟨28⟩.

1:0205 ⟨1⟩ Carswell, Pfeifer, *J. Am. Chem. Soc.* **50,** 1765–1766 (1928). ⟨2⟩ Claisen, Eisleb, *Ann.* **401,** 95 (Note 1) (1913). ⟨3⟩ Shoesmith, Sosson, Hetherington, *J. Chem. Soc.* **1927,** 2221–2230. ⟨4⟩ Meyer, *Monatsh.* **24,** 833 (1903). ⟨5⟩ Dakin, *Organic Syntheses, Coll. Vol.* I, 143 (1932). ⟨6⟩ von Auwers, *Ann.* **408,** 239 (1915). ⟨7⟩ Pfeiffer, *Ann.* **383,** 134 (1911). ⟨8⟩ Wegscheider, Späth, *Monatsh.* **30,** 853 (1909). ⟨9⟩ Knoevenagel, *Ann.* **402,** 126 (1914). ⟨10⟩ Brady, Dunn, *J. Chem. Soc.* **109,** 675 (1916).

⟨11⟩ Cajar, *Ber.* **31,** 2809 (1898). ⟨12⟩ Rössing, *Ber.* **17,** 2990 (1884). ⟨13⟩ Freudenberg, *Hess.* **448,** 129 (1926). ⟨14⟩ Hantzsch, Schwab, *Ber.* **34,** 832 (1901). ⟨15⟩ Emmerich, *Ann.* **241,** 344 (1887). ⟨16⟩ Brady, Dunn, *J. Chem. Soc.* **105,** 825 (1914). ⟨17⟩ Ephraim, *Ber.* **63,** 1928 (1930). ⟨18⟩ Lockeman, Lucius, *Ber.* **46,** 1013–1021 (1913). ⟨19⟩ Rupe, Oestreicher, *Ber.* **45,** 36 (1912). ⟨20⟩ Widman, *Ber.* **52,** 1657 (1919).

⟨21⟩ Biltz, Sieden, *Ann.* **324**, 322 (1902). ⟨22⟩ Dakin, *Am. Chem. J.* **49,** 105–107 (1913). ⟨23⟩ Campbell, *Analyst* **61,** 392 (1936). ⟨24⟩ Curtius, Dedichen, *J. prakt. Chem.* (2) **50,** 265 (1894). ⟨25⟩ Purgiotti, *Gazz. chim. ital.* **24,** I, 566 (1894). ⟨26⟩ Iddles, Jackson, *Ind. Eng. Chem., Anal. Ed.* **6,** 455–456 (1934). ⟨27⟩ Parkinson, Wagner, *Ind. Eng. Chem., Anal. Ed.* **6,** 433–436 (1934). ⟨28⟩ Vorländer, *Z. anal. Chem.* **77,** 264–265 (1929). ⟨29⟩ Zetsche, Silbermann, Vieli, *Helv. Chim. Acta* **8,** 602 (1925). ⟨30⟩ Flagg, Furman, *Ind. Eng. Chem., Anal. Ed.* **12,** 529–531 (1940).

1:0208 *m*-TOLUALDEHYDE

(*m*-Methylbenzaldehyde)

CHO / CH₃ (ring structure) C_8H_8O **Beil. VII-296**

B.P. 198-199° D_4^{20} = **1.020** $n_D^{21.4}$ = **1.5413**

Volatile with steam — Forms $NaHSO_3$ cpd. ⟨1⟩.
Readily oxid. in air to *m*-toluic acid (1:0705). [For prepn. from *m*-toluanilide see ⟨1⟩.]

Ⓓ ***m*-Tolualdoxime:** pr. from lgr., m.p. 60° ⟨1⟩.
Ⓓ ***m*-Tolualdehyde phenylhydrazone:** pr. from lgr. or dil. alc., m.p. 91° ⟨2⟩; 87–88.5° ⟨3⟩.
Ⓓ ***m*-Tolualdehyde *p*-nitrophenylhydrazone:** m.p. 157° ⟨1⟩.

1:0208 ⟨1⟩ Shoppee, *J. Chem. Soc.* **1932,** 700–705. ⟨2⟩ Bornemann, *Ber.* **17,** 1468 (1884). ⟨3⟩ Rudolph, *Ann.* **248,** 100 (1888).

1:0210 *o*-TOLUALDEHYDE

(*o*-Methylbenzaldehyde)

—CHO / —CH₃ (ring structure) C_8H_8O **Beil. VII-295**

B.P. 199-200°
197° cor.

D_4^{20} = **1.038** ⟨1⟩ n_D^{20} = **1.5481** ⟨1⟩

Odor like BzH — Volatile with steam — [For prepn. (45% yield) from *o*-tolyl MgBr + triethyl orthoformate see ⟨2⟩.] — With satd. aq. $NaHSO_3$ yields bisulfite addn. cpd. (cf. T 1.12).

Reduces Tollens' reagt. (T 1.11) — Oxidizes even in air to *o*-toluic acid (1:0690). Reduction with NaHg yields *o*-tolylcarbinol (1:5922), ndls., m.p. 35° — C̄ in 66% alc. refluxed 1 hr. with 10–15% pure KCN yields *o*-toluoin, ndls. from dil. alc., m.p. 79° ⟨3⟩.

C̄ in alc. treated with $NH_2OH.HCl$ + excess alk. yields *o*-tolualdoxime, cryst. from ether, m.p. 48–49° ⟨4⟩ ⟨5⟩ — With semicarbazide yields *o*-tolualdehyde semicarbazone, ndls. from

AmOH, or alc., m.p. 209° ⟨6⟩; 212° ⟨7⟩ ⟨1⟩; 210–211° ⟨8⟩ — The formation of *o*-tolualdehyde phenylhydrazone (reported only by indirect means) gives m.p. 105–106° ⟨9⟩.

Ⓓ ***o*-Tolualdehyde *p*-nitrophenylhydrazone:** red ndls. from alc., m.p. 222° ⟨10⟩.

Ⓓ ***o*-Tolualdehyde 2,4-dinitrophenylhydrazone:** red ndls. from AcOH, m.p. 193–194° ⟨8⟩ [cf. T 1.14].

1:0210 ⟨1⟩ von Auwers, *Ann.* **408,** 236 (1915). ⟨2⟩ Gattermann, *Ann.* **393,** 218 (1912). ⟨3⟩ Ekecrantz, Ahlqvist, *Cent.* **1908,** II, 1689. ⟨4⟩ Dollfuss, *Ber.* **25,** 1921 (1892). ⟨5⟩ Scholl, Kacer, *Ber.* **36,** 325 (1903). ⟨6⟩ Rupe, Bernstein, *Helv. Chim. Acta* **13,** 460 (1930). ⟨7⟩ Blaise, Courtot, *Bull. soc. chim.* (3) **35,** 373 (1906). ⟨8⟩ King, L'Ecuyer, Openshaw, *J. Chem. Soc.* **1936,** 353. ⟨9⟩ Wuyts, *Bull. soc. chim. Belg.* **38,** 201 (1929). ⟨10⟩ Stephen, *J. Chem. Soc.* **127,** 1877 (1925).

1:0215 *p*-TOLUALDEHYDE (*p*-Methylbenzaldehyde) CH_3—⟨benzene ring⟩—CHO C_8H_8O Beil. VII-297

B.P. 204–205° D_4^{20} = **1.016** ⟨1⟩ n_D^{20} = **1.5454** ⟨1⟩

Peppermint-like odor — With satd. aq. $NaHSO_3$ soln. (cf. T 1.12) yields $NaHSO_3$ addn. cpd. [For prepn. (50–55% yield) from toluene, CO, HCl + $AlCl_3$ see ⟨2⟩; for use of toluene, HCN + $AlCl_3$ (100% yield) see ⟨3⟩.]

Readily oxid. even in air to *p*-toluic ac. (1:0795) — $\bar{C}$ shaken with 2 vols. H_3PO_4 (D = 1.7) evolves ht. and gives crystn. addn. prod., $\bar{C}.H_3PO_4$ [dif. from *o*-tolualdehyde (1:0210) or *m*-tolualdehyde (1:0208)].

$\bar{C}$ in MeOH treated at 60–70° with H.CHO + KOH gives (90% yield) *p*-tolylcarbinol (1:5954) ⟨4⟩ — $\bar{C}$ with alc. NaOH or KOH undergoes Cannizzaro reaction yielding *p*-tolylcarbinol (1:5954) and *p*-toluic ac. (1:0795). [For study of influence of various factors on speed of reaction see ⟨5⟩; react. catalyzed by peroxides ⟨6⟩.] — $\bar{C}$ in alc. refluxed 1 hr. with a little aq. KCN soln. yields *p,p'*-dimethylbenzoin, cryst. from alc., m.p. 88° ⟨7⟩ — $\bar{C}$ shaken with excess conc. aq. NH_4OH gives quant. yield of hydro-*p*-toluamide, ndls. from ether + alc., m.p. 92° ⟨17⟩.

Ⓓ ***p*-Tolualdoxime:** m.p. 79–80° ⟨8⟩.

Ⓓ ***p*-Tolualdehyde semicarbazone:** ndls. from alc., pl. from AmOH, m.p. 234° ⟨9⟩.

Ⓓ ***p*-Tolualdehyde phenylhydrazone:** lfts. from alc., m.p. 112–113° ⟨10⟩ ⟨11⟩; 114° ⟨12⟩.

Ⓓ ***p*-Tolualdehyde *p*-nitrophenylhydrazone:** dark red ndls. from AcOH, m.p. 200.5° cor. ⟨13⟩; 198° ⟨14⟩; 196° ⟨15⟩.

Ⓓ ***p*-Tolualdehyde 2,4-dinitrophenylhydrazone:** or. yel. cryst. from alc. + nitrobenzene, m.p. 232.5–234.5° cor. ⟨16⟩ [cf. T 1.14].

1:0215 ⟨1⟩ von Auwers, *Ann.* **408,** 238 (1915). ⟨2⟩ Coleman, Craig, *Organic Syntheses* **12,** 80–83 (1932). ⟨3⟩ Hinkel, Ayling, Morgan, *J. Chem. Soc.* **1932,** 2797. ⟨4⟩ Davidson, Weiss, *Organic Syntheses* **18,** 79–81 (1938). ⟨5⟩ Molt, *Rec. trav. chim.* **56,** 233–246 (1937). ⟨6⟩ Kharasch, Foy, *J. Am. Chem. Soc.* **57,** 1510 (1935). ⟨7⟩ Gattermann, *Ann.* **347,** 364–365 (1906). ⟨8⟩ Hantzsch, *Z. physik. Chem.* **13,** 510, 523 (1894). ⟨9⟩ Blaise, Courtot, *Bull. soc. chim.* (3) **35,** 373 (1906). ⟨10⟩ Korczynski, Mrozinski, *Bull. soc. chim.* (4) **29,** 460 (1921).
⟨11⟩ Ref. 7, page 353. ⟨12⟩ Hinkel, Ayling, Benyon, *J. Chem. Soc.* **1935,** 677. ⟨13⟩ Stephen, *J. Chem. Soc.* **127,** 1877 (1925). ⟨14⟩ van Ekenstein, Blanksma, *Rec. trav. chim.* **22,** 439 (1903). ⟨15⟩ Hanzlik, Bianchi, *Ber.* **32,** 1286 (1899). ⟨16⟩ Strain, *J. Am. Chem. Soc.* **57,** 760 (1935). ⟨17⟩ Fürth, *Monatsh.* **27,** 841 (1896).

1:0220 *d*-CITRONELLAL $C_{10}H_{18}O$ Beil. I-745

$$CH_2{=}\overset{CH_3}{\overset{|}{C}}.CH_2.CH_2.CH_2.\overset{CH_3}{\overset{|}{C}}H.CH_2.CHO$$

B.P. 206.9° D_4^{20} = **0.855** n_D^{20} = **1.4485** ⟨10⟩

Strong geranium odor — Opt. act. $[\alpha]_D^{15}$ = +13.09°.

Ord. C̄ is a mixture of 2,6-dimethylocten-1-al-8 (citronellal) and 2,6-dimethylocten-2-al-8 (rhodinal) ⟨1⟩, but the mobility of the unsatn. is so great that homogeneous derivatives usually result.

C̄ with satd. aq. $NaHSO_3$ soln. yields normal $NaHSO_3$ addn. prod. (cf. T 1.12) but on warm. with excess $NaHSO_3$, or in dil. acid soln. a sulfonate is formed which is not decomp. by Na_2CO_3 or NaOH ⟨2⟩ — C̄ adds Br_2 (T 1.91); reduces Tollens' reagt. (T 1.11).

C̄ on stdg. or on treatment with acids changes to isopulegol [Beil. VI-65].

Oxidn. with $KMnO_4$ ⟨3⟩ yields acetone (1:5400) — Oxidn. by air at room temp. yields citronellic acid, CO_2 and peroxides. [For quant. study see ⟨4⟩.]

Ⓓ ***d*-Citronellal semicarbazone:** C̄, dislvd. in dil. alc., treated with somewhat less than equiv. of semicarbazide hydrochloride in aq. AcONa soln., gives solid, recrystd. by pptn. from $CHCl_3$ with lgr., m.p. 83–84° ⟨5⟩ ⟨1⟩ ⟨3⟩. [The bisulfite addn. compd. may be substituted for alc. C̄ soln. in above process ⟨6⟩.]

Ⓓ ***d*-Citronellal 2,4-dinitrophenylhydrazone:** yel. cryst. from alc., m.p. 78° ⟨7⟩; 77° ⟨8⟩; yel. lfts. from dil. AcOH, m.p. 76.5° ⟨9⟩. [Cf. T 1.14.]

Ⓓ ***d*-Citronellal dimethone:** lfts. from dil. alc., m.p. 77–79° ⟨11⟩; corresp. anhydride, m.p. abt. 173° ⟨11⟩. [Cf. T 1.13.]

1:0220 ⟨1⟩ Harries, *Ann.* **410,** 12–13 (1915). ⟨2⟩ Dodge, *J. Am. Chem. Soc.* **37,** 2760 (1915). ⟨3⟩ Doeuvre, *Bull. soc. chim.* (4) **45,** 1099–1100 (1929). ⟨4⟩ Waterman, Elsbach, *Rec. trav. chim.* **53,** 730–736 (1934). ⟨5⟩ Tiemann, Schmitt, *Ber.* **30,** 34 (1897). ⟨6⟩ Tiemann, *Ber.* **31,** 3307 (1898). ⟨7⟩ Allen, *J. Am. Chem. Soc.* **52,** 2958 (1930). ⟨8⟩ Campbell, *Analyst* **61,** 392 (1936). ⟨9⟩ Grundmann, *Ann.* **524,** 42 (1936). ⟨10⟩ Waterman, Elsbach, *Bull. soc. chim.* (4) **45,** 137 (1929).
⟨11⟩ Vorländer, *Z. anal. Chem.* **77,** 252–253 (1929).

1:0222 ***n*-DECYLALDEHYDE** $CH_3.(CH_2)_8.CHO$ $C_{10}H_{20}O$ **Beil. I-711**
(*n*-Capraldehyde; decanal)

B.P. 207-209° ⟨1⟩ D^{20} = **0.8502 ⟨2⟩** n_D^{20} = **1.4287 ⟨2⟩**
D^{15} = **0.828 ⟨1⟩** n_D^{15} = **1.4298 ⟨1⟩**

With satd. aq. $NaHSO_3$ (cf. T 1.12) yields $NaHSO_3$ cpd. decomposed by aq. Na_2CO_3. [Use in sepn. from citronellal (1:0220) or citral (1:0230) ⟨3⟩.]

C̄, oxid. with air, or by shaking with alk. AgOH ⟨4⟩ or with $KMnO_4$ ⟨8⟩ yields *n*-capric ac. (1:0585).

With halogen or halogen acids C̄ polymerizes to a white solid, m.p. 43° ⟨5⟩.

C̄ htd. with pyruvic ac. + β-naphthylamine yields α-*n*-nonylnaphthocinchoninic acid [Beil. XXII-103], cryst. from alc., or H.COOH + MeOH, m.p. 237° ⟨1⟩; 239–242° ⟨5⟩.

Ⓓ ***n*-Decylaldoxime:** lfts. from dil. MeOH, m.p. 69° ⟨5⟩.

Ⓓ ***n*-Decylaldehyde semicarbazone:** m.p. 102° (Heilbron).

Ⓓ ***n*-Decylaldehyde thiosemicarbazone:** m.p. 99–100° ⟨2⟩.

Ⓓ ***n*-Decylaldehyde 2,4-dinitrophenylhydrazone:** yel. cryst., m.p. 104° ⟨6⟩ [see T 1.14].

Ⓓ ***n*-Decylaldehyde dimethone:** cryst. from dil. alc., m.p. 91.7° ⟨7⟩ [see T 1.13].

1:0222 ⟨1⟩ Stephan, *J. prakt. Chem.* (2) **62,** 525 (1900). ⟨2⟩ Uhl, *J. Am. Pharm. Assoc.* **24,** 381 (1935). ⟨3⟩ Dodge, *J. Am. Chem. Soc.* **37,** 2760 (1915). ⟨4⟩ Koolhaas, *Rec. trav. chim.* **51,** 465 (1932). ⟨5⟩ Bagard, *Bull. soc. chim.* (4) **1,** 358 (1907). ⟨6⟩ Allen, *J. Am. Chem. Soc.* **52,** 2958 (1930). ⟨7⟩ Kao, Yen, *Science Repts. Natl. Tsing Hua Univ.*, Ser. **A-1,** 187 (1932). ⟨8⟩ Nelson, Mottern, *Ind. Eng. Chem.* **26,** 635 (1934).

1:0224 **PHENOXYACETALDEHYDE** $C_8H_8O_2$ **Beil. VI-151**
(Glycolaldehyde phenyl ether) C_6H_5—O.CH_2.CHO

B.P. 215° dec. ⟨1⟩ D_4^{21} = **1.1310 ⟨2⟩** n_D^{21} = **1.5380 ⟨2⟩**

Anhydrous C̄ is colorless liq. of aromatic odor — With 1 mole aq. gives crystalline monohydrate, m.p. 38°, fairly eas. sol. excess aq.; on htg. latter under red. press., water is lost and C̄ distils at 118–119° at 30 mm. ⟨1⟩.

C̄ with satd. aq. $NaHSO_3$ yields cpd. from which C̄ can be regenerated with dil. H_2SO_4 ⟨3⟩.

Oxidn. yields phenoxyacetic ac. (1:0680), m.p. 98°.

[For prepn. from bromoacetal see ⟨4⟩.]

Ⓓ **Phenoxyacetaldoxime:** pr. from pet. ether, m.p. 95° ⟨1⟩.

Ⓓ **Phenoxyacetaldehyde phenylhydrazone:** pale yel. pr. from alc., m.p. 86° ⟨1⟩ ⟨3⟩.

Ⓓ **Phenoxyacetaldehyde semicarbazone:** cryst. from AcOEt, m.p. 145° (Maquenne block) ⟨2⟩.

1:0224 ⟨1⟩ Pomeranz, *Monatsh.* **15,** 741–745 (1894). ⟨2⟩ Rothbart, *Ann. chim.* (11) **1,** 480 (1934. ⟨3⟩ Rosenmund, Zetsche, *Ber.* **56,** 1483 (1923). ⟨4⟩ Dey, *J. Chem. Soc.* **1937,** 1059.

1:0225 HYDROCINNAMALDEHYDE $C_9H_{10}O$ Beil. VII-304

(β-Phenylpropionaldehyde; benzylacetaldehyde)

⬡—$CH_2.CH_2.CHO$

B.P. 224°

Mobile pale yel. liq. of hyacinth odor — With satd. aq. $NaHSO_3$ soln. yields $NaHSO_3$ addn. cpd.

C̄ oxidizes in air to hydrocinnamic ac. (1:0615).

[For prepn. (67% yield) from β-phenylethyl MgCl + triethylorthoformate see ⟨1⟩.]

Ⓓ **Hydrocinnamaldoxime:** long pr. from dil. alc., or alc. + ether; m.p. 93–94.5° ⟨2⟩ ⟨3⟩; 97° cor. ⟨4⟩.

Ⓓ **Hydrocinnamaldehyde semicarbazone:** lfts. from alc. or C_6H_6, m.p. 127° ⟨1⟩ ⟨5⟩.

Ⓓ **Hydrocinnamaldehyde *p*-nitrophenylhydrazone:** yel. ndls. from C_6H_6 + lgr. or from dil. alc., m.p. 122–123° ⟨6⟩.

Ⓓ **Hydrocinnamaldehyde 2,4-dinitrophenylhydrazone:** yel. cryst. from alc., m.p. 149° ⟨7⟩. [Cf. T 1.14.]

1:0225 ⟨1⟩ Cohen, *J. Chem. Soc.* **1935,** 432. ⟨2⟩ Dollfuss, *Ber.* **26,** 1971 (1893). ⟨3⟩ Straus, Grindel, *Ann.* **439,** 309 (1924). ⟨4⟩ Weston, Adkins, *J. Am. Chem. Soc.* **51,** 2589 (1929). ⟨5⟩ Bouveault, *Bull. soc. chim.* (3) **31,** 1327 (1904). ⟨6⟩ Róna, *Biochem. Z.* **67,** 141 (1914). ⟨7⟩ Allen, Richmond, *J. Org. Chem.* **2,** 224 (1936).

1:0230 CITRAL $C_{10}H_{16}O$ Beil. I-753

```
    CH3                CH3
    |                  |
CH3.C=CH.CH2.CH2.C=CH.CHO
```

B.P. 228-229° sl. dec. $D^{20} = 0.8868$ $n_D^{20} = 1.48752$

Ord. comml. citral is a mixture of two geom. stereoisomers, citral *a* (geranial) and citral *b* (neral) (see below) — Odor of lemon oil — Opt. inactive.

With satd. aq. $NaHSO_3$ soln. it can yield several dif. prod. according to conditions used. [For extensive discussion of possibilities see ⟨1⟩.] The addn. prod. from C̄ + 1 mole $NaHSO_3$ seps. as a cryst. solid from which NaOH or Na_2CO_3 regenerates most of the original citral. This prod. is obtd. on shaking 100 pts. C̄ with a soln. contg. 100 pts. $NaHSO_3$ + 25 pts. AcOH in 200 pts. aq. ⟨2⟩.

Under conditions which effect the addn. of 2 moles $NaHSO_3$, however, two other prods. may be formed acc. to conditions: one of these, the so-called "labile" dihydrodisulfonic acid salt regenerates C̄ on treatment with alk. but not Na_2CO_3 ⟨3⟩; the other, the so-called "stable" dihydrodisulfonic ac. deriv. does *not* regenerate C̄ either with NaOH or Na_2CO_3 ⟨4⟩ ⟨5⟩. To obt. the "labile" form C̄ is shaken with an aq. soln. of $Na_2SO_3.7H_2O$ +

$NaHCO_3$; the C̄ dis. and may be thrown out again by addn. of NaOH ⟨4⟩. [For examples of this use see ⟨6⟩ ⟨7⟩ ⟨8⟩ ⟨9⟩.]

Distn. of C̄ (1 mole) with I_2 (1 g.) yields 68% *p*-cymene (1:7505) ⟨10⟩ — Oxidn. with $KMnO_4$, or $CrO_3 + H_2SO_4$ (cf. T 1.72) gives good yield acetone (1:5400) + levulinic acid (1:0405) ⟨11⟩ — Oxidn. with Ag_2O ($AgNO_3$ + NaOH) in dil. alc. gives (70% yield) geranic ac. ⟨12⟩ — C̄ exposed to O_2 at room temp. polymerizes to a thick yel. liq. ⟨13⟩.

Ord. C̄ with semicarbazide HCl + AcONa yields a mixt. of geranial semicarbazone (m.p. 164°) and neral semicarbazone (m.p. 171°) which melts at 132° ⟨14⟩ ⟨15⟩. From this mixt. the latter can be extracted by ether, leaving the geranial semicarbazone ⟨8⟩. [In the absence of AcONa only the geranial semicarbazone ppts. ⟨16⟩.] — With 2,4-dinitrophenylhydrazine C̄ yields citral 2,4-dinitrophenylhydrazone: yel. cryst. from alc., m.p. 116° ⟨17⟩; 99–115° cor. ⟨18⟩.

Citral *a* (**Geranial**)

Geranial semicarbazone: from semicarbazide HCl + AcOH (60–70% yield), *ndls.* from MeOH, m.p. 164° ⟨16⟩.

Geranial 2,4-dinitrophenylhydrazone: red-or. cryst. from alc., m.p. 108–110° ⟨19⟩ [cf. T 1.14].

Citral *b* (**Neral**)

Neral semicarbazone: m.p. 171° ⟨16⟩.

Neral 2,4-dinitrophenylhydrazone: red- or. cryst. from alc., m.p. 96° ⟨19⟩ [cf. T 1.14].

1:0230 ⟨1⟩ Dodge, *Am. Perfumer* **32,** No. 3, 67–69 (1936); *Chem. Abs.* **30,** 3403 (1936). ⟨2⟩ Tiemann, *Ber.* **31,** 3311–3312 (1898). ⟨3⟩ Tiemann, *Ber* **31,** 3313–3315 (1898). ⟨4⟩ Tiemann, *Ber.* **31,** 3315–3320 (1898). ⟨5⟩ Dodge, *J. Am. Chem. Soc.* **37,** 2760 (1915). ⟨6⟩ Pope, Bogert, *J. Org. Chem.* **2,** 284 (1937). ⟨7⟩ Hibbert, Cannon, *J. Am. Chem. Soc.* **46,** 121–122 (1924). ⟨8⟩ Guenther, Grimm, *J. Am. Chem. Soc.* **60,** 934 (1938). ⟨9⟩ Nelson, Mottern, *J. Am. Chem. Soc.* **56,** 1238 (1934). ⟨10⟩ Bogert, Fourman, *Am. Perfumer* **28,** 345–347 (1933); *Chem. Abs.* **28,** 101 (1934).

⟨11⟩ Tiemann, *Ber.* **32,** 118 (1899). ⟨12⟩ Bernhauer, Forster, *J. prakt. Chem.* (2) **147,** 200 (1936). ⟨13⟩ Thompson, Burk, *J. Am. Chem. Soc.* **57,** 711 (1935). ⟨14⟩ Wilson, Keenan, *J. Assoc. Official Agr. Chem.* **13,** 390, 394 (1930). ⟨15⟩ Tiemann, *Ber.* **32,** 115 (1899). ⟨16⟩ Tiemann, *Ber.* **31,** 3331 (1898). ⟨17⟩ Campbell, *Analyst* **61,** 382 (1936). ⟨18⟩ Strain, *J. Am. Chem. Soc.* **57,** 760 (1935). ⟨19⟩ Allen, *J. Am. Chem. Soc.* **52,** 2958 (1930).

1:0232 *m*-METHOXYBENZALDEHYDE $C_8H_8O_2$ Beil. VIII-59

(*m*-Anisaldehyde)

—CHO

CH_3O

B.P. 230° ⟨1⟩ ⟨2⟩ D_4^{20} = **1.1187** ⟨3⟩ n_D^{20} = **1.5538** ⟨2⟩

Volatile with steam — Yields dif. sol. $NaHSO_3$ cpd. (cf. T 1.12).

For prepn. (70% yield) from *m*-hydroxybenzaldehyde (1:0055) by actn. of $(CH_3)_2SO_4$ + alk. see ⟨4⟩ ⟨5⟩ ⟨6⟩. [Note that in presence of alk. C̄ undergoes Cannizzaro react. yielding *m*-methoxybenzyl alc. which is inseparable from C̄ ⟨1⟩ ⟨5⟩.] C̄ on oxidn. with $KMnO_4$ gives 90% yield *m*-methoxybenzoic acid (1:0703) ⟨10⟩.

C̄ + malonic ac. + pyridine + piperidine gives (69% yield) *m*-methoxycinnamic ac. [Beil. X-295], m.p. 117° ⟨7⟩; alm. quant. yield ⟨6⟩.

Ⓓ ***m*-Methoxybenzaldoxime:** cryst. from pet. ether, m.p. 39–40° ⟨8⟩.

Ⓓ ***m*-Methoxybenzaldehyde *p*-nitrophenylhydrazone:** m.p. 171° ⟨9⟩.

1:0232 ⟨1⟩ Staudinger, Kön, *Ann.* **384,** 90 (1911). ⟨2⟩ von Auwers, *Ann.* **408,** 239–240 (1915). ⟨3⟩ Fritsch, *Ann.* **286,** 6 (1895). ⟨4⟩ Reimer, Kamerling, *J. Am. Chem. Soc.* **55,** 4644 (1933). ⟨5⟩ Easson, Stedman, *J. Chem. Soc.* **1933,** 1094. ⟨6⟩ Chakravarti, Haworth, Perkin, *J. Chem. Soc.* **1927,** 2269. ⟨7⟩ Slotta, Heller, *Ber.* **63,** 3038 (1930). ⟨8⟩ Brady, Dunn, *J. Chem. Soc.* **105,** 2412 (1914). ⟨9⟩ Shoppee, *J. Chem. Soc.* **1932,** 705. ⟨10⟩ Chakravarti, Perkin, *J. Chem. Soc.* **1929,** 198–199.

1:0234 CUMALDEHYDE $C_{10}H_{12}O$ **Beil. VII-318**

(p-Isopropylbenzaldehyde; cuminal) $(CH_3)_2CH—C_6H_4—CHO$

B.P. 236° D^{20} = **0.9775** n_D^{20} = **1.5301**

Oil, volatile with steam — With satd. aq. $NaHSO_3$ soln. yields $NaHSO_3$ add. cpd. (cf. T 1.12) from which alk. regenerates orig. C̄ — Does not reduce Fehling's soln. ⟨1⟩.

Oxidn. of C̄ with moist Ag_2O ⟨2⟩ or with alk. $KMnO_4$ (95% yield ⟨3⟩) gives cumic acid [Beil. IX-546], pl. from alc., m.p. 117° — Oxidn. of C̄ with $K_2Cr_2O_7$ + H_2SO_4 first yields cumic ac., then terephthalic ac. (1:0910).

C̄ with alc. KOH undergoes Cannizzaro reactn. yielding cumyl alc. [Beil. VI-543] and cumic acid (see above) — C̄ htd. 2.5 hrs. with KOH (0.5 N) in benzyl alc. yields cumyl alc. + BzOH ⟨4⟩.

C̄ with $NH_2OH.HCl$ + excess NaOH + alc. yields α-cumaldoxime, cryst. from alc. or lgr., m.p. 61°; C̄ with $NH_2OH.HCl$ + abs. alc. ⟨5⟩ gives hydrochloride from which subsequent treatment with alk. yields β-cumaldoxime, pr. from ether, m.p. 112° — C̄ with semicarbazide HCl + KOAc in MeOH ⟨6⟩ yields cumaldehyde semicarbazone, cryst. from MeOH, m.p. 211° ⟨6⟩, 212° ⟨7⟩, 222° (Maquenne block) ⟨2⟩.

Ⓓ **Cumaldehyde phenylhydrazone:** from C̄ in dil. alc. + phenylhydrazine, ndls. from alc. or lgr., m.p. 129° ⟨8⟩.

Ⓓ **Cumaldehyde *p*-nitrophenylhydrazone:** cryst. from alc., m.p. 190° ⟨9⟩.

Ⓓ **Cumaldehyde 2,4-dinitrophenylhydrazone:** red cryst. from AcOH, m.p. 243° ⟨10⟩; red ndls. from C_6H_6, m.p. 241° ⟨11⟩; cryst. from alc. + $CHCl_3$, m.p. 244–245° ⟨7⟩ [cf. T 1.14].

Ⓓ **Cumaldehyde dimethone:** lfts. from alc., m.p. 170–171° ⟨12⟩; corresp. anhydride, m.p. 172–173° ⟨12⟩ [cf. T 1.13].

1:0234 ⟨1⟩ Paolini, *Gazz. chim. ital.* **65,** 630–632 (1935). ⟨2⟩ Bert, *Bull. soc. chim.* (4) **37,** 1408 (1925). ⟨3⟩ Meyer, *Ann.* **219,** 243–248 (1883). ⟨4⟩ Sabetay, Palfray, *Ann. chim. anal. chim. appl.* **17,** 289 (1935); *Chem. Abs.* **30,** 240 (1936). ⟨5⟩ Beckmann, *Ann.* **365,** 202 (1909). ⟨6⟩ Warunis, Lekos, *Ber.* **43,** 660 (1910). ⟨7⟩ Macbeth, Smith, West, *J. Chem. Soc.* **1938,** 122. ⟨8⟩ Rudolph, *Ann.* **248,** 101 (1888). ⟨9⟩ Baker, Nathan, Shoppee, *J. Chem. Soc.* **1935,** 1848. ⟨10⟩ Campbell, *Analyst* **61,** 392 (1936).
⟨11⟩ Brady, *J. Chem. Soc.* **1931,** 758. ⟨12⟩ Vorländer, *Z. anal. Chem.* **77,** 263 (1929).

1:0235 *o*-METHOXYBENZALDEHYDE $C_8H_8O_2$ **Beil. VIII-43**

(Salicylaldehyde methyl ether; *o*-anisaldehyde) $C_6H_4(CHO)(OCH_3)$

B.P. 243-244° cor. ⟨1⟩ ⟨2⟩ $D_4^{20.2}$ = **1.1326** ⟨5⟩ n_D^{20} = **1.5598** ⟨5⟩
M.P. 38-39° ⟨3⟩ ⟨4⟩

Liq., insol. aq., very eas. sol. ether, $CHCl_3$; less sol. alc., C_6H_6 — After fusion and subsequent crystn. (induced by scratching) sometimes separates in another crystn. form, m.p. 2.7–3.0° ⟨2⟩.

[For prepn. from salicylaldehyde (1:0205) with $(CH_3)_2SO_4$ + aq. NaOH see ⟨4⟩ ⟨6⟩; from di-*o*-tolyl carbonate via chlorination, hydrolysis, and methylation see ⟨7⟩.]

With satd. aq. $NaHSO_3$ soln. yields $NaHSO_3$ addn. cpd. (cf. T 1.12).

Ⓓ ***o*-Methoxybenzaldoxime:** from C̄ by warm. with neut. NH_2OH soln., ndls. from dil. alc., m.p. 92° ⟨8⟩.

Ⓓ ***o*-Methoxybenzaldehyde semicarbazone:** from alc. soln. of C̄ + semicarbazide HCl + KOAc, ndls. from alc., m.p. 215° dec. ⟨9⟩.

Ⓓ **o-Methoxybenzaldehyde p-nitrophenylhydrazone:** brick red cryst., m.p. 204–205° (Heilbron).

Ⓓ **o-Methoxybenzaldehyde 2,4-dinitrophenylhydrazone:** red cryst. from xylene, m.p. 253.5 cor. ⟨10⟩ [cf. T 1.14].

1:0235 ⟨1⟩ Posner, *J. prakt. Chem.* (2) **82,** 430 (1910). ⟨2⟩ Perkin, *J. Chem. Soc.* **55,** 549–551 (1889). ⟨3⟩ Burawoy, Markowitsch-Burawoy, *J. Chem. Soc.* **1936,** 39. ⟨4⟩ Katschalowsky, von Kostanecki, *Ber.* **37,** 2347, Note 4 (1904). ⟨5⟩ von Auwers, *Ann.* **408,** 239 (1915). ⟨6⟩ Hiers, Hager, *Organic Syntheses, Coll. Vol.* I, 50–52 (1932). ⟨7⟩ Copisarow, *J. Chem. Soc.* **1929,** 589. ⟨8⟩ Goldschmidt, Ernst, *Ber.* **23,** 2740 (1890). ⟨9⟩ Henderson, Heilbron, *J. Chem. Soc.* **107,** 1746 (1915). ⟨10⟩ Anon., *Am. J. Pharm.* **105,** 381–384 (1933).

1:0238 m-ETHOXYBENZALDEHYDE $C_9H_{10}O_2$ Beil. VIII-60

(benzene ring with —CHO and C_2H_5O in meta position)

B.P. 245.5° D_4^{20} = **1.0768** ⟨3⟩ n_D^{20} = **1.5408** ⟨3⟩

Volat. with steam — Gives dif. sol. $NaHSO_3$ cpd. (cf. T 1.12) ⟨1⟩.

C̄ htd. with malonic ac. in pyridine + piperidine for 4 hrs. at 100° gives (89% yield) *m*-ethoxybenzalmalonic acid, ndls. from 90% alc., m.p. 129–130° ⟨2⟩.

1:0238 ⟨1⟩ Werner, *Ber.* **28,** 2001 (1895). ⟨2⟩ Peak, Robinson, Walker, *J. Chem. Soc.* **1936,** 756. ⟨3⟩ Fritsch, *Ann.* **286,** 6 (1895).

1:0240 p-ANISALDEHYDE CH_3O—⟨benzene⟩—CHO $C_8H_8O_2$ Beil. VIII-67

(*p*-Methoxybenzaldehyde; Aubépine)

B.P. 248° **M.P. +2.5°** ⟨1⟩ D_4^{20} = **1.123** ⟨2⟩ n_D^{20} = **1.5731** ⟨2⟩

Oil, alm. insol. aq.; misc. alc. or ether — Volatile with steam — Gives fuchsin-aldehyde react. (Generic Test 1) only with sensitized reagt. (cf. " Manual," Generic Test 1, Note 2).

Reduces Tollens' reagt. (T 1.11) but not Fehling's soln. (T 1.22) — Oxidizes in air or with dil. $KMnO_4$ or with sodium persulfate (100% yield) ⟨3⟩ to anisic acid (1:0805)

With finely powd. KOH or alc. KOH C̄ undergoes Cannizzaro reactn. yielding *p*-anisyl alc. (1:5915) and *p*-anisic acid (1:0805). [For influence of various factors see ⟨4⟩; reaction catalyzed by peroxides ⟨5⟩.] — C̄ with large excess CH_2O + KOH in aq. MeOH gives alm. quant. yield of *p*-anisyl alc. ⟨6⟩.

C̄ in alc., refluxed 2 hrs. with aq. KCN gives (50–60%) yield anisoin (1:5195) ⟨7⟩ — With 4–5 pts. conc. aq. NH_4OH C̄ yields hydroanisamide, cryst. from ether + alc., m.p. 130°.

C̄ with NH_2OH + excess 30% aq. NaOH yields α-anisaldoxime [Beil. VIII-76], m.p. 64° ⟨8⟩. [This stereoisomer also occurs in another cryst. form of m.p. 45° obtd. by fusion and rapid cooling of the former ⟨9⟩.] — With $NH_2OH.HCl$ + abs. alc. C̄ yields ⟨10⟩ β-anisaldoxime [Beil. VIII-77], ndls. from C_6H_6, m.p. 133°. [For study of m.p. of mixtures of α-and β-anisaldoximes see ⟨11⟩.]

Ⓓ **p-Anisaldehyde semicarbazone:** m.p. 210° ⟨12⟩.

Ⓓ **p-Anisaldehyde phenylhydrazone:** prepd. from C̄ by same procedure as used for BzH (1:0195), except that ½ quant. of dil. alc. there prescribed should be used in each operation. Pearly white ppt., m.p. 120–121° ⟨13⟩.

Ⓓ **p-Anisaldehyde p-nitrophenylhydrazone:** red violet ndls., m.p. 160° ⟨14⟩; 160–161° ⟨17⟩. [Use in quant. detn. of C̄ ⟨15⟩.]

Ⓓ ***p*-Anisaldehyde 2,4-dinitrophenylhydrazone:** or. red. ndls. from AcOH, m.p. 253–254° dec. ⟨16⟩; red lfts. from xylene, m.p. 250° ⟨18⟩. [See T 1.14.] [Use in quant. detn. of C̄ ⟨15⟩.]

Ⓓ ***p*-Anisaldehyde dimethone:** tbls. from alc., m.p. 144–145° cor. ⟨19⟩; corresp. anhydride, pr. from alc., m.p. 243° cor. ⟨19⟩ [cf. T 1.13].

1:0240 ⟨1⟩ Jaeger, *Z. anorg. allgem. Chem.* **101,** 142 (1917). ⟨2⟩ von Auwers, *Ann.* **408,** 240 (1915). ⟨3⟩ Elbs, Lerch, *J. prakt. Chem.* (2) **93,** 1–2 (1916). ⟨4⟩ Mott, *Rec. trav. chim.* **56,** 233–246 (1937). ⟨5⟩ Kharasch, Foy, *J. Am. Chem. Soc.* **57,** 1510 (1935). ⟨6⟩ Nenitzescu, Gavăt, *Bull. soc. chim. România,* **16A,** 42–46 (1934); *Chem. Abs.* **30,** 5572 (1936). ⟨7⟩ van Alphen, *Rec. trav. chim.* **48,** 1112–1113 (1929). ⟨8⟩ Bamberger, Scheutz, *Ber.* **34,** 2024, Note 1 (1901). ⟨9⟩ Beckmann, *Ber.* **37,** 3043 (1904). ⟨10⟩ Beckmann, *Ann.* **365,** 202 (1909).

⟨11⟩ Skau, Saxton, *J. Phys. Chem.* **37,** 196–207 (1933). ⟨12⟩ Wilson, Keenan, *J. Assoc. Official Agr. Chem.* **13,** 390, 393 (1930). ⟨13⟩ Rudolph, *Ann.* **248,** 103 (1888). ⟨14⟩ Ciusa, Vecchiotti, *Gazz. chim. ital.* **42,** I, 532 (1912). ⟨15⟩ Iddles, Jackson, *Ind. Eng. Chem., Anal. Ed.* **6,** 454–456 (1934). ⟨16⟩ Campbell, *Analyst* **61,** 392 (1936). ⟨17⟩ Hébert, *Bull. soc. chim.* (4) **27,** 52 (1920). ⟨18⟩ Brady, *J. Chem. Soc.* **1931,** 758. ⟨19⟩ Vorländer, *Z. anal. Chem.* **77,** 264 (1929).

1:0242 *o*-ETHOXYBENZALDEHYDE (Salicylaldehyde ethyl ether; *o*-phenetylaldehyde) — C_6H_4(—CHO)(—$O.C_2H_5$) $C_9H_{10}O_2$ **Beil. VIII-43**

B.P. 247–249° ⟨1⟩ M.P. 20–22° ⟨2⟩
6–7° ⟨1⟩

Misc. alc., ether — Volatile with steam.

Reduces Tollens' reagt. (T 1.11) — With satd. aq. $NaHSO_3$ gives cryst. addn. ⟨3⟩ cpd. (cf. T 1.12).

C̄ slowly added to fuming HNO_3 (D = 1.5) below 10° gives 5-nitro-2-ethoxybenzaldehyde, yel. ndls. from dil. alc., m.p. 71–72° ⟨4⟩ ⟨6⟩ — C̄ in ether shaken with aq. soln. of KCN + NH_4Cl gives (83% yield) *o*-ethoxymandelonitrile, cryst. from C_6H_6, m.p. 86–89° ⟨5⟩.

[For prepn. of C̄ (90% yield) by ethylation of salicylaldehyde with diethyl sulfate + aq. 2 *N* KOH or NaOH see ⟨5⟩.]

Ⓓ ***o*-Ethoxybenzylidene diacetate:** from C̄ + Ac_2O htd. 4–5 hrs. at 140–150°, pr. from alc., m.p. 88–89° ⟨3⟩.

Ⓓ ***o*-Ethoxybenzaldoxime:** cryst. from pet. ether, m.p. 57–59° ⟨2⟩.

Ⓓ ***o*-Ethoxybenzaldehyde semicarbazone:** ndls. from alc., m.p. 219° ⟨6⟩.

1:0242 ⟨1⟩ Perkin, *J. Chem. Soc.* **55,** 551 (1889). ⟨2⟩ Löw, *Monatsh.* **12,** 396 (1891). ⟨3⟩ Perkin, *Ann.* **146,** 372 (1868). ⟨4⟩ Dayton, *J. Chem. Soc.* **97,** 2109 (1910). ⟨5⟩ Weissberger, Dym, *Ann.* **502,** 78–79 (1933). ⟨6⟩ Gattermann, *Ann.* **393,** 224 (1912).

1:0245 CINNAMALDEHYDE (β-Phenylacrolein) — C_6H_5—CH=CH—CHO C_9H_8O **Beil. VII-348**

B.P. 252° dec. M.P. −7.5° D_4^{20} **= 1.0497** n_D^{20} **= 1.61949**

Oil with cinnamon odor, changed by shaking with excess 10% $KMnO_4$ soln. to that of benzaldehyde — Sl. sol. aq.; sol. alc., ether; insol. pet. ether. Volatile with steam.

C̄ shaken with cold conc. aq. $NaHSO_3$ soln. yields dif. sol. ppt. of normal aldehyde addn. cpd., C̄.$NaHSO_3$, from which orig. C̄ can be regenerated with Na_2CO_3. However, on boilg. the above addn. cpd. with aq. it disproportionates to C̄ + the sol. hydrosulfonic ac. salt mentioned below. On treating C̄ with excess *hot* aq. $NaHSO_3$ soln., or with a mixt. of Na_2SO_3 + $NaHCO_3$, C̄ dissolves because of addn. of a second mole of $NaHSO_3$, yielding a sol. prod. from which aq. NaOH at room temp. regenerates only part (75%) of the original C̄ ⟨1⟩.

C̄ readily oxid. in air to cinnamic ac. (1:0735). [For full study see ⟨2⟩.] — Oxidn. of C̄ with CrO_3 yields BzOH (1:0715) and acetic acid (1:1010) — Oxidn. of C̄ with hot HNO_3 yields BzOH (1:0715) and BzH (1:0195). [With conc. HNO_3 C̄ forms an addn. prod. C̄.HNO_3 which cryst. out, is dissocd. by aq. and from which the C̄ can then be steam distd.; used for purifn. of C̄ ⟨3⟩.] — Oxidn. with $Ca(OCl)_2$ soln. yields BzOH (1:0715).

C̄ in cold $CHCl_3$ or CS_2 adds Br_2 — C̄ refluxed with Al isopropylate in isopropyl alc. gives (68% yield) cinnamyl alc. (1:5920) ⟨4⟩ — C̄ in 1 mole of Ac_2O treated with a few drops of conc. H_2SO_4 or other acids evolves ht., crystallizes, and yields cinnamal diacetate, tbls. from alc., lfts. from pet. ether, m.p. 85° ⟨5⟩ — C̄ in abs. alc. treated with dry NH_3 gives hydrocinnamide [Beil. VII-356], ndls. with $\frac{1}{2}$ H_2O from alc., m.p. 106–108°.

C̄ with strong alk. + $NH_2OH.HCl$ yields *syn*-cinnamaldoxime (together with some *anti*-isomer (m.p. 64°) extractable by lgr. ⟨6⟩), ndls. from hot C_6H_6 or aq., m.p. 138.5° ⟨6⟩ ⟨7⟩ — C̄ in alc. treated with aq. semicarbazide HCl yields cinnamaldehyde semicarbazone, pptd. from boilg aq., m.p. 215–216° ⟨8⟩; 217° ⟨9⟩; 229–230° (Maquenne block) ⟨10⟩.

Ⓓ **Cinnamaldehyde phenylhydrazone:** Use procedure given for BzH (1:0195) except that prod. should be boiled up 3 times with 15 ml. 50% alc. (instead of twice with 12 ml.); yel. ndls. or pl., m.p. 168° u.c. ⟨11⟩ ⟨12⟩.

Ⓓ **Cinnamaldehyde *p*-nitrophenylhydrazone:** or. red cryst. from alc., m.p. 195° ⟨13⟩.

Ⓓ **Cinnamaldehyde 2,4-dinitrophenylhydrazone:** red cryst. from AcOH, m.p. 255° dec. ⟨14⟩, m.p. 248° ⟨15⟩ [cf. T 1.14].

Ⓓ **Cinnamaldehyde dimethone:** pr. from alc., m.p. 208–210° u.c., 212–214° cor. ⟨16⟩; [a metastable form, m.p. 161° sometimes seps. from alc. at 10° ⟨16⟩]; corresp. anhydride, lfts. from alc., m.p. 174–175° ⟨16⟩ [cf. T 1.13].

1:0245 ⟨1⟩ Tiemann, *Ber.* **31,** 3302–3305 (1898). ⟨2⟩ Pound, Pound, *J. Phys. Chem.* **38,** 1045–1049 (1934). ⟨3⟩ Pfeiffer, *Ann.* **376,** 298–299 (1910). ⟨4⟩ Young, Hartung, Crossley, *J. Am. Chem. Soc.* **58,** 101 (1936). ⟨5⟩ Barbier, Leser, *Bull. soc. chim.* (3) **33,** 858–859 (1905). ⟨6⟩ Bamberger, Goldschmidt, *Ber.* **27,** 3428–3429 (1894). ⟨7⟩ Dollfuss, *Ber.* **25,** 1919 (1892). ⟨8⟩ Young, Witham, *J. Chem. Soc.* **77,** 230 (1900). ⟨9⟩ Wilson, Heilbron, Sutherland, *J. Chem. Soc.* **105,** 2898 (1914). ⟨10⟩ Bert, Dorier, *Compt. rend.* **191,** 333 (1930).

⟨11⟩ Fischer, *Ber.* **17,** 575 (1884). ⟨12⟩ Mulliken, "Method" I, 21 (1904). ⟨13⟩ Hyde, *Ber.* **32,** 1814 (1899). ⟨14⟩ Campbell, *Analyst* **61,** 392 (1936). ⟨15⟩ Brady, *J. Chem. Soc.* **1931,** 758. ⟨16⟩ Vorländer, *Z. anal. Chem.* **77,** 260–261 (1929).

1:0251 *p*-ETHOXYBENZALDEHYDE $C_9H_{10}O_2$ Beil. VIII-73

(*p*-Phenetylaldehyde) C_2H_5O—⟨benzene ring⟩—CHO

B.P. 255° ⟨1⟩ **M.P. 13-14°** ⟨3⟩ D^{21}_{21} = **1.08** ⟨2⟩
249° ⟨2⟩

Readily oxid. by air ⟨4⟩ or by alk. $KMnO_4$ yielding *p*-ethoxybenzoic ac. (1:0817), m.p. 195°.

C̄ + anthranilic ac. in conc. alc. or C_6H_6 soln. at 0° gives *p*-ethoxybenzalanthranilic acid, yel. ndls., m.p. 117° ⟨5⟩ — C̄, in conc. H_2SO_4, treated with mixt. of conc. H_2SO_4 + conc. HNO_3 at 2–8° gives (58% yield) 3-nitro-4-ethoxybenzaldehyde, yel. ndls. from alc., m.p. 62° ⟨6⟩.

[For prepn. (74% yield) from *p*-hydroxybenzaldehyde by treat. with diethyl sulfate + 10% aq. NaOH at 100° see ⟨6⟩.]

Ⓓ ***p*-Ethoxybenzaldoxime:** ndls. from lgr., m.p. 83° ⟨2⟩.

Ⓓ ***p*-Ethoxybenzaldehyde semicarbazone:** cryst. from alc., m.p. 202° dec. ⟨7⟩; 208° ⟨1⟩.

1:0251 ⟨1⟩ Béhal, Tiffeneau, *Bull. soc. chim.* (4) **3,** 306 (1908). ⟨2⟩ Gattermann, *Ann.* **357,** 347–348 (1907). ⟨3⟩ Hildesheimer, *Monatsh.* **22,** 499, Note (1901). ⟨4⟩ St. Kostanecki, Schneider, *Ber.* **29,** 1892, Note (1896). ⟨5⟩ Ekely, Rogers, Swisher, *J. Am. Chem. Soc.* **44,** 1757 (1922). ⟨6⟩ Hodgson, Smith, *J. Soc. Chem. Ind.* **49T,** 409 (1930). ⟨7⟩ Stoermer, Wodarg, *Ber.* **61,** 2326 (1928).

—— **PIPERONAL** $CH_2\langle O, O\rangle C_6H_3.CHO$ (1,2,4) $C_8H_6O_3$ **Beil. XIX-115**

B.P. 263°

See 1:0010. Genus 1: Division A: Solid aldehydes. M.P. 37°.

1:0261 **3,4-DIETHOXYBENZALDEHYDE** (Protocatechualdehyde diethyl ether) CHO, OC_2H_5, OC_2H_5 $C_{11}H_{14}O_3$ **Beil. VIII-256**

B.P. 277-280° ⟨1⟩

[For prepn. in 85% yield by act. of C_2H_5Br + NaOH on 3-hydroxy-4-ethoxybenzaldehyde see ⟨3⟩.]

$\bar{C}$ in 75% MeOH + H_2 + Pd (at 2 atm.) yields 88% 3,4-diethoxybenzyl alc. ⟨2⟩.

$\bar{C}$ oxidized with alk. H_2O_2 (80% yield) ⟨4⟩ or with alk. NaOBr ⟨5⟩ according to ⟨6⟩ gives 3,4-diethoxybenzoic acid, m.p. 165° ⟨1⟩.

Ⓓ **3,4-Diethoxybenzaldoxime:** ndls., m.p. 98° ⟨7⟩.

Ⓓ **3,4-Diethoxybenzonitrile:** from above oxime by htg. 2 hrs. with Ac_2O; flat pr. from dil. alc., m.p. 68° ⟨7⟩.

1:0261 ⟨1⟩ Gattermann, *Ann.* **357,** 368 (1907). ⟨2⟩ Kindler, Gehlhaar, *Arch. pharm.* **374,** 387 (1936). ⟨3⟩ Kindler, Peschke, *Arch. pharm.* **272,** 65 (1934). ⟨4⟩ Slotta, Nold, *Ber.* **68,** 2227 (1935). ⟨5⟩ Slotta, Haberlund, *Angew. Chem.* **46,** 770 (1933). ⟨6⟩ St. Kostanecki, Tamber, *Ber.* **39,** 4022 (1906). ⟨7⟩ Buck, Ide, *J. Am. Chem. Soc.* **54,** 3309 (1932).

Important Aldehydes That Can Be Distilled Only under Reduced Pressure

1:0270 **ALDOL** $CH_3.CH(OH).CH_2.CHO$ $C_4H_8O_2$ **Beil. I-824**
(Acetaldol; butanol-3-al-1; β-hydroxy-*n*-butyraldehyde)

B.P. 83°_{20} ⟨1⟩ D^{16} = **1.1094**
77°_{16} ⟨2⟩
72°_{12} ⟨3⟩

Colorless visc. liq.; misc. aq. or alc.; sol. ether — [For prepn. from acetaldehyde see ⟨1⟩ ⟨3⟩ ⟨4⟩.] [The hydration of crotonaldehyde in pres. of H^+ at 25° yields equil. contg. 47% crotonaldehyde + 53% aldol ⟨5⟩.]

On stdg. slowly becomes more visc. and finally crystallizes out a dimer, paraldol $(C_4H_8O_2)_2$, m.p. 90° ⟨6⟩ — On htg. beginning at 85° ⟨7⟩ or on slow distn. with a trace of I_2 ⟨8⟩ (49% yield) $\bar{C}$ gives crotonaldehyde (1:0150) and acetaldehyde (1:0100) — $\bar{C}$ htd. at 135° for 30 min. yields " crotonaldehyde dimer " whose dimethone has m.p. 190°; corresp. anhydride, m.p. 176° ⟨9⟩.

C̄ reduces Tollens' reagt. (T 1.11) or warm Fehling's soln. (T 1.22) — C̄ oxid. with moist AgOH or with Br_2 aq. at room temp. ⟨10⟩ yields β-hydroxy-*n*-butyric acid [Beil. III-307] — C̄ with amalgamated Al yields butanediol-1,3 (1:6482) ⟨11⟩.

Ⓓ **Aldol *p*-nitrophenylhydrazone:** red. yel. ndls. from dil. alc., sinters **107°**, m.p. 109–111° ⟨12⟩.

Ⓓ **Aldol *p*-bromophenylhydrazone:** m.p. 127–128° ⟨4⟩.

Ⓓ **Aldol dimethone:** pr. from 30% MeOH, m.p. 146–148° ⟨13⟩; corresp. anhydride, m.p. 126° ⟨14⟩.

1:0270 ⟨1⟩ Claisen, *Ann.* **306,** 323 (1899). ⟨2⟩ Kohn, *Monatsh.* **21,** 90 (1900). ⟨3⟩ Kyriakides, *J. Am. Chem. Soc.* **36,** 532–533 (1914). ⟨4⟩ Neuberg, Kerb, *Biochem. Z.* **92,** 108–109 (1919). ⟨5⟩ Winstein, Lucas, *J. Am. Chem. Soc.* **59,** 1461–1465 (1937). ⟨6⟩ Nowak, *Monatsh.* **22,** 1140–1145 (1901). ⟨7⟩ Grignard, Reiff, *Bull. soc. chim.* (4) **1,** 116 (1907). ⟨8⟩ Hibbert, *J. Am. Chem. Soc.* **37,** 1758 (1915). ⟨9⟩ Ionescu, *Bull. soc. chim.* (4) **41,** 1317–1318 (1927). ⟨10⟩ Anderson, *Am. Chem. J.* **49,** 183 (1913).
⟨11⟩ Halpern, *Monatsh.* **22,** 63–64 (1901). ⟨12⟩ Wegscheider, Späth, *Monatsh.* **31,** 1027 (1910). ⟨13⟩ Kasuya, *J. Am. Chem. Soc.* **59,** 2742 (1937). ⟨14⟩ Klein, Linser, *Mikrochemie Pregl Festschrift* **1929,** 226.

1:0275 PARA-*n*-BUTYRALDEHYDE $C_{12}H_{24}O_3$ **Beil. XIX_1-(807)**
(2,4,6-Tri-*n*-propyl-1,3,5-trioxan)

B.P. 105-108°$_{12}$ ⟨1⟩
B.P. 103-110°$_{12}$ ⟨2⟩

Colorless oil with not unpleasant odor — Insol. aq. — [For prepn. via polymerization of *n*-butyraldehyde see ⟨1⟩ ⟨2⟩.]

When pure does not directly give fuchsin-aldehyde test (Generic Test 1) but does so after depolymerization with minl. ac. — On distn. at ord. press. or on warming with minl. acid depolymerizes to *n*-butyraldehyde, b.p. 75° (1:0130) + resinous products ⟨1⟩ — When conc. H_2SO_4 is used for depolymerization there is also obtd. a small amt. of α-ethyl-β-*n*-propylacrolein, b.p. 173° (1:0193) ⟨1⟩.

Ⓟ **Depolymerization:** Depolymerize to *n*-butyraldehyde as above and identify latter.

1:0275 ⟨1⟩ Franke, Wozelka, *Monatsh.* **33,** 350–353 (1912). ⟨2⟩ Dworzak, Pierri, *Monatsh.* **52,** 142 (1929).

1:0278 PHENYLGLYOXAL C_6H_5—CO.CHO $C_8H_6O_2$ **Beil. VII-670**
(Benzoylformaldehyde)

B.P. 108-110°$_{15}$ ⟨1⟩
96-97°$_{25}$ ⟨2⟩
120°$_{50}$ ⟨3⟩
142°$_{125}$ ⟨4⟩

Yel. oil — With aq. forms crystn. monohydrate (1:0053), m.p. 91°.

[For prepn. (69–72% yield) from acetophenone (or phenylacetaldehyde) by htg. with SeO_2 in dioxane see ⟨5⟩ or without solvent see ⟨2⟩ — For prepn. (82% yield) by distn. of bromophenacyl acetate see ⟨1⟩.]

On stdg. C̄ sets to a stiff gel (polymer or hydrate?) from which C̄ can be quant. recovered by distn. ⟨5⟩.

$\bar{C}$ reduces Tollens' reagt. (T 1.11) but not Fehling's soln. (T 1.22), latter due to following reactn. with alk. — $\bar{C}$ boiled a few moments with dil. aq. NaOH ⟨6⟩ or $Ca(OH)_2$ soln. ⟨7⟩ yields mandelic acid (1:0465) — Oxidn. of $\bar{C}$ in cold with CrO_3 or *neutral* cold aq. $KMnO_4$ yields benzoic acid (1:0715).

With 1 equiv. of phenylhydrazine in dil. AcOH, $\bar{C}$ yields phenylglyoxal β-monophenylhydrazone, yel. lfts. from alc., m.p. 142° ⟨6⟩ [for extensive study see ⟨8⟩]; with excess phenylhydrazine acetate in aq. soln. $\bar{C}$ yields phenylglyoxal bisphenylhydrazone, yel. ndls. from alc., m.p. 151–152° ⟨9⟩; 153° ⟨2⟩.

With 1 equiv. of semicarbazide $\bar{C}$ yields phenylglyoxal monosemicarbazone, yel. cryst. from alc., m.p. 208–209° dec. ⟨10⟩; with excess semicarbazide $\bar{C}$ yields phenylglyoxal bis-semicarbazone, dec. abt. 229° acc. to rate of htg. ⟨10⟩; m.p. 143° ⟨2⟩.

Ⓓ **Phenylglyoxal bis-*p*-nitrophenylhydrazone:** m.p. 309° ⟨11⟩; 310–311° ⟨12⟩.

1:0278 ⟨1⟩ Madelung, Oberwegner, *Ber.* **65,** 935 (1932). ⟨2⟩ Riley, Morley, Friend, *J. Chem. Soc.* **1932,** 1877. ⟨3⟩ Smedley, *J. Chem. Soc.* **95,** 218 (1909). ⟨4⟩ von Pechmann, *Ber.* **20,** 2905 (1887). ⟨5⟩ Riley, Gray, *Organic Syntheses* **15,** 67–69 (1935). ⟨6⟩ Müller, von Pechmann, *Ber.* **22,** 2556–2559 (1889). ⟨7⟩ Evans, *Am. Chem. J.* **35,** 122 (1906). ⟨8⟩ Sidgwick, Ewbank, *J. Chem. Soc.* **119,** 487–491 (1921). ⟨9⟩ Weygand, *Ann.* **459,** 122 (1927). ⟨10⟩ von Auwers, Ludewig, Müller, *Ann.* **526,** 171–172 (1936).

⟨11⟩ Isacescu, *Bull. soc. chim. România* **18A,** 63–65 (1936); *Chem. Abs.* **31,** 3036 (1937). ⟨12⟩ Straus, *Ann.* **393,** 282, Note 1 (1912).

1:0280 *d,l*-GLYCERALDEHYDE DIETHYLACETAL $C_7H_{16}O_4$ Beil. I-846

CH_2OH
|
CHOH
|
$CH(O_2H_5)_2$

B.P. 130° at 20 mm. ⟨1⟩

Colorless visc. liq. with burning and not sweet taste — Misc. aq., alc., ether.

[For prepn. via oxidn. of acrolein diethylacetal (1:0169) with aq. $KMnO_4$ at 0° (67% yield) see ⟨2⟩ ⟨3⟩ ⟨4⟩ ⟨5⟩.]

Readily hydrolyzed by minl. ac. to *d,l*-glyceraldehyde (1:0070) and EtOH (1:6130). [The resultant soln. therefore reduces Fehling's soln. (T 1.22) at ord. temp. and with excess phenylhydrazine acetate yields *d,l*-glyceraldehyde phenylosazone [Beil. XV-202], m.p. 131° ⟨1⟩.] $\bar{C}$ itself is claimed to reduce Fehling's soln. in cold ⟨4⟩.

1:0280 ⟨1⟩ Wohl, *Ber.* **31,** 1800 (1898). ⟨2⟩ Witzemann, Evans, Hass, Schroeder, *Organic Syntheses* **11,** 52–53 (1931). ⟨3⟩ Fischer, Baer, *Helv. Chim. Acta* **18,** 516 (1935). ⟨4⟩ Reeves, *J. Chem. Soc.* **1927,** 2482. ⟨5⟩ Witzemann, *J. Am. Chem. Soc.* **36,** 1912 (1914).

1:0285 α-*n*-AMYLCINNAMALDEHYDE $C_{14}H_{18}O$ Beil. S.N. 644

(Jasminaldehyde)

C_6H_5—CH=C(C_5H_{11}).CHO

B.P. 161-163° at 18 mm. D^{20}_{20} = **0.97108** n^{20}_D = **1.5381**

D^{15} = **0.9718** n^{20}_D = **1.5552**

[Prepn. (70% yield) from BzH + enanthaldehyde + $POCl_3$ at 30–35° ⟨1⟩.]

Ord. comml. $\bar{C}$ is *trans*-stereoisomer ⟨2⟩. $\bar{C}$ on oxidn. with Ag_2O ($AgNO_3$ + KOH) in boilg. dil. alc. gives (77% yield) *trans*-α-*n*-amylcinnamic ac., cryst. from 75% acetic ac., m.p. 80° ⟨2⟩ — $\bar{C}$ autoxidizes readily at room temp. in dark with formation of *n*-caproic ac., BzOH and *cis*-α-*n*-amylcinnamic ac., m.p. 40° ⟨2⟩. $\bar{C}$ shows no tendency to polymerize.

$\bar{C}$ htd. at 100° with 2 *N* NaOH in benzyl alc. gives H_2 + α-*n*-amylcinnamyl alcohol ⟨3⟩.

Ⓓ *α-n*-**Amylcinnamaldoxime:** from alc. soln. of C̄ by refluxing 1 hr. with $NH_2OH.HCl$ + AcONa; cryst. from alc. by pptn. with aq., m.p. 74° ⟨2⟩.

Ⓓ *α-n*-**Amylcinnamaldehyde semicarbazone:** m.p. 118° ⟨4⟩.

Ⓓ *α-n*-**Amylcinnamaldehyde 2,4-dinitrophenylhydrazone:** scarlet cryst. from alc., m.p. 164° [cf. T 1.14] ⟨5⟩.

1:0285 ⟨1⟩ Backes, *Compt. rend.* **196,** 1674 (1933). ⟨2⟩ Bogert, Davidson, *J. Am. Chem. Soc.* **53,** 3125–3128 (1931). ⟨3⟩ Mastagh, *Compt. rend.* **205,** 802–805 (1937). ⟨4⟩ Rutowski, Koroleu, *J. prakt. Chem.* (2) **119,** 273 (1928). ⟨5⟩ Allen, *J. Am. Chem. Soc.* **52,** 2958 (1930).

1:0298 5-HYDROXYMETHYL-2-FURYLALDEHYDE $C_6H_6O_3$ **Beil. XVIII-15**
(ω-Hydroxymethylfurfural)

```
        HC——————CH
        ‖        ‖
HO.CH2—C        C—CHO
         \      /
            O
```

B.P. 115-120° at 0.5 mm. ⟨1⟩

Ordinarily met as colorless syrup turning yellow in air — At very low temps. seps. as crystals which then melt at 35°; these are extremely hygroscopic and deliquesce rapidly in air. [For m.p.-comp. diagram of C̄ + aq. see ⟨2⟩] — C̄ can be distd. only in high vac.; on attempted distn. at ord. press. or on stdg. over conc. H_2SO_4 yields bis-(5-formylfuryl) ether, ndls. from alc., m.p. 112° ⟨3⟩ — C̄ is much less volatile with steam than furfural (1:0185) or 5-methylfurfural (1:0198) — C̄ is eas. sol. aq., MeOH, EtOH, ether, $CHCl_3$, C_6H_6; dif. sol. CCl_4; insol. pet. ether.

C̄ reduces Tollens' reagt. (T 1.11) and Fehling's soln. (T 1.22) — C̄ with aniline acetate (T 1.23) gives yel. color turning orange [dif. from furfural]. — C̄ with phloroglucinol + HCl (T 1.24) gives dark brown ppt. [For extensive study see ⟨13⟩.] — With α-naphthol + conc. H_2SO_4 (Generic Test 2) gives violet color.

C̄ oxidized with $AgNO_3$ + NaOH gives rapidly and smoothly (84% yield) 5-hydroxymethylfuroic acid, m.p. 166° dec. ⟨1⟩ — C̄ with NH_2OH gives two stereoisomeric 5-hydroxymethylfurfuraldoximes, m.p.'s 77° and 108° ⟨4⟩ ⟨5⟩ — C̄ shaken with aq. NaOH + BzCl yields 5-benzoxymethylfurfural, cryst. from alc., m.p. 57° ⟨6⟩ — C̄ with Ac_2O + few drops conc. H_2SO_4 yields 5-acetoxymethylfural diacetate, cryst. from pet. ether, m.p. 73° ⟨7⟩.

Ⓓ **5-Hydroxymethylfurfuraldehyde semicarbazone:** prepd. in alc.; recrystd. from toluene + lgr., m.p. 194–195° dec. ⟨1⟩; 192° dec. ⟨8⟩.

Ⓓ **5-Hydroxymethylfurfuraldehyde phenylhydrazone:** cryst. from toluene, m.p. 140–141° ⟨1⟩.

Ⓓ **5-Hydroxymethylfurfuraldehyde *p*-nitrophenylhydrazone:** dark red cryst. from alc., m.p. 185° dec. ⟨9⟩; 183° ⟨10⟩. [Use for quant. detn. of C̄ ⟨10⟩.]

Ⓓ **5-Hydroxymethylfurfuraldehyde 2,4-dinitrophenylhydrazone:** red cryst., m.p. 184° ⟨11⟩. [Use in quant. detn. of C̄ ⟨12⟩.] [Cf. T 1.14.]

1:0298 ⟨1⟩ Reichstein, *Helv. Chim. Acta* **9,** 1066–1068 (1926). ⟨2⟩ Middendorp, *Rec.* **38,** 15 (1919). ⟨3⟩ Ref. 2, pages 8–9. ⟨4⟩ Kiermayer, *Chem. Ztg.* **19,** 1003 (1895). ⟨5⟩ Gilman, Dickey, *J. Am. Chem. Soc.* **52,** 2011 (1930). ⟨6⟩ Ref. 2, page 33. ⟨7⟩ Blanksma, *Chem. Weekblad* **6,** 727 (1909). ⟨8⟩ Blanksma, *Rec. trav. chim.* **29,** 405 (1910). ⟨9⟩ van Ekenstein, Blanksma, *Chem. Weekblad* **6,** 217–226 (1909); *Cent.* **1909,** I, 1509; *Ber.* **43,** 2355–2361 (1910). ⟨10⟩ Maaskant, *Rec. trav. chim.* **55,** 1068–1070 (1936).
⟨11⟩ Blanksma, Wackers, *Rec. trav. chim.* **55,** 658 (1936). ⟨12⟩ Barta, *Biochem. Z.* **274,** 212–219 (1934); *Cent.* **1935,** I, 974 . ⟨13⟩ Klingstedt, *Z. anal. Chem.* **66,** 133–137 (1925).

CHAPTER IV

ORDER I: SUBORDER I: GENUS 2: CARBOHYDRATES

Section 1

Carbohydrates soluble in less than 10 parts of water at 20°, giving solutions which are not opalescent after filtration.

Subsection A

(Compounds giving nearly white precipitate within 1 minute in T 1.21)

1:0300 *d*-MANNOSE $C_6H_{12}O_6$ **Beil. I-905; XXXI-284**

Hard amorph. mass or pr. from 90% alc., m.p. 132° — Taste sweet — Solubility: 1 g. aq. at 17° dis. 2.48 g. mannose; 100 ml. satd. soln. in abs. alc. at 17° cont. 4.2 g. — $(\alpha)_D$ = +14.6° — Reduces Fehling's soln. (T 1.22).

Ⓟ Ⓓ ***d*-Mannose phenylhydrazone:** T 1.21 gives nearly white cryst. ppt. of *phenylhydrazone* after 0.5 min. htg. which after recrystn. from boiling aq. melts 195–200° (rap. htg.). (On prolonged htg. changes grad. to *yellow* *d*-glucosazone, m.p. 205° ⟨1⟩!)

Ⓓ ***d*-Mannose-*p*-nitrophenylhydrazone:** 0.25 g. $\bar{C}$ are htd. with 3 ml. alc., then 0.25 g. *p*-nitrophenylhydrazine added, and the susp. htd. till change is complete. A hydrazone soon separates, is filtered after 24 hrs., and washed with alc. After recrystn. from alc. forms pale yel. pr., m.p. 201–202° ⟨2⟩.

1:0300 ⟨1⟩ Mulliken, "Method" I, 29. ⟨2⟩ van der Haar, "Anleitung zum Nachweis, zur Trennung und Bestimmung der Monosaccharide und Aldehydsäuren," Berlin, 1920, p. 188.

Subsection B

(Compounds giving a yellow or orange-yellow precipitate from hot solution within 20 minutes in T 1.21, and also reducing Fehling's solution in T 1.22)

1:0305 *d*-GLUCOSE $C_6H_{12}O_6$ **Beil. I-879; XXXI-83**
(Dextrose, grape-sugar)

Anhyd. ndls. or crusts from alc., m.p. 146°, or in tbls. with 1 H_2O from cold aq., m.p. 85–90°. Anhydrous form sol. in 1.2 pts. aq. at 17.5°; dif. sol. cold 90% alc., but dis. in abt. 5 pts. hot; insol. ether — Taste abt. half as sweet as sucrose. $(\alpha)_D$ = +52.3°.

Distn. with HCl gives no color with aniline acetate (T 1.23) (dif. from *d*-fructose) — Reduces Fehling's soln. (T 1.22) — Oxidn. with HNO_3 (T 1.25) gives saccharic but no mucic acid.

Ⓟ Ⓓ ***d*-Glucose phenylosazone:** In T 1.21 heavy yellow ppt. of osazone, m.p. 204–205° rap. htg., sep. suddenly from hot soln. after 4–5 min. ⟨1⟩.

Ⓓ ***d*-Glucose *p*-nitrophenylhydrazone:** from 0.25 g. $\bar{C}$ by same proc. given for *d*-mannose (1:0300). After recrystn. from alc. gives or.-yel. lfts., m.p. 189° ⟨2⟩.

1:0305 ⟨1⟩ Mulliken, "Method" I, 30. ⟨2⟩ van der Haar, "Anleitung, etc.," p. 186.

1:0310 *d*-GALACTOSE $C_6H_{12}O_6$ **Beil. I-909; XXXI-295**

Small anhyd. hexag. tbls. from abs. alc., m.p. 165–166° rap. htg.; pr. with 1 H_2O from aq., m.p. abt. 118–120° — Soly. in aq., 68%; in 80% alc. 0.27 g. per 100 ml. soln. — $(\alpha)_D$ = +81°.

Distn. with HCl gives no red color with aniline acetate (T 1.23) — Reduces Fehling's soln. (T 1.22) — Oxidn. with HNO_3 (T 1.25) gives good yield mucic ac. (1:0845).

Ⓟ Ⓓ ***d*-Galactosephenylosazone:** T 1.21 gives heavy yel. or or.-yel. ppt. of osazone, m.p. 201° rap. htg., sepg. from hot soln. after abt. 15–19 min. ⟨1⟩.

Ⓓ ***d*-Galactose *o*-tolylhydrazone:** 1 pt. $\bar{C}$ in 1 pt. aq. is htd. 30 min. with a soln. of 1 pt. *o*-tolylhydrazine in 20 pts. alc. On cooling colorless ndls. sep., recrystd. from alc., m.p. 176°. (This test gives no ppt. with *d*-arabinose, xylose, rhamnose, *d*-glucose, *d*-mannose, or *d*-glucuronic ac.) ⟨2.⟩ ⟨3.⟩

1:0310 ⟨1⟩ Mulliken, " Method " I, 30. ⟨2⟩ van der Haar, *Rec. trav. chim.* **37,** 108–110, 251–253 (1917). ⟨3⟩ van der Haar, " Anleitung," pp. 206–207.

1:0315 *l*-ARABINOSE $C_5H_{10}O_5$ **Beil. I-860; XXXI-34**

Pr. from alc., m.p. abt. 160° — Sol. in 2.18 pts. aq. at 0°; in 238 pts. 90% alc. at 9°; insol. ether — Sweeter than galactose but less so than sucrose. Distn. with HCl gives red color to aniline acetate (T 1.23) — Phloroglucinol test (T 1.24) gives purplish-black ppt. — Reduces Fehling's soln. (T 1.22).

Ⓟ Ⓓ ***l*-Arabinose phenylosazone:** In T 1.21 or.-yel. osazone, m.p. 166°, sep. after 10 min. htg., but unless sugar is very pure often appears in part as brownish-yel. oily drops ⟨1⟩.

Ⓓ ***l*-Arabinose-β-naphthylhydrazone:** To 1 g. $\bar{C}$ dislvd. in 1 ml. aq. is added warm soln. of 1 g. β-naphthylhydrazine in 40 ml. alc. and mixt. filtered. On short standing arabinose β-naphthylhydrazone sep. in warts. After recrystn. from hot alc. forms white cryst., m.p. 176–177° cor. ⟨2⟩. Since the corresp. β-naphthylhydrazone of xylose is very sol. and melts 124° this method may be used for distinction or sepn. ⟨3⟩.

Ⓓ ***l*-Arabinose-*p*-bromophenylhydrazone:** 0.5 g. $\bar{C}$ dislvd. in 6 ml. aq. treated with a filtered soln. from 1 g. *p*-bromophenylhydrazine in 12 ml. aq. + 3.5 ml. 50% AcOH. After stdg. a few hrs., filtered off, washed with abs. alc. and ether, recrystd. from 50% alc., pr., m.p. 167–168° ⟨4⟩.

1:0315 ⟨1⟩ Mulliken, " Method " I, 30. ⟨2⟩ Hilger, Rothenfusser, *Ber.* **35,** 1843 (1902). ⟨3⟩ *ibid.* 4445. ⟨4⟩ van der Haar, " Anleitung," pp. 154–156.

1:0320 *l*-XYLOSE $C_5H_{10}O_5$ **Beil. I-865; XXXI-55**

Ndls. or pr., m.p. 144° — 100 pts. aq. at 20° dis. 117 pts. xylose; alm. insol. cold alc., but readily sol. hot; insol. ether — Very sweet — $(\alpha)_D$ = +18.7°.

Distn. with HCl gives red color on aniline acetate paper (T 1.23) — Phloroglucinol test (T 1.24) gives purplish-black precipitate — Reduces Fehling's solution (T 1.22).

Ⓟ Ⓓ ***l*-Xylosephenylosazone:** In T 1.21 or.-yel. osazone, m.p. 164°, sep. from hot soln. after abt. 7 min. ⟨1⟩.

Ⓓ **Cadmium xylonate-cadmium bromide double salt.** $Cd(C_5H_9O_6)_2.CdBr_2.2H_2O$ — To mixt. of 0.2 g. $\bar{C}$ with 1 ml. aq. and 0.5 g. $CdCO_3$ in tt. is added 7–8 drops Br_2, warmed, loosely stoppered, and allowed to stand 8–12 hrs. The mixt. then poured into a watch-glass, evapd. alm. to dryness, dislvd. in 4–5 ml. aq., filtered, again evapd. alm. to dryness, and 1 ml. alc. added. The crystd. salt soon begins to sep. and after 3–4 hrs. is compared under the microscope with prod. obtd. from authentic sample (dif. from *l*-arabinose) ⟨2⟩.

Ⓓ ***l*-Xylose-*m*-nitrophenylhydrazone:** from 0.25 g. C̄ by proc. given for *d*-mannose (1:0300). After recrystn. from alc. forms yel. cryst., m.p. 163° ⟨3⟩.

1:0320 ⟨1⟩ Mulliken, " Method " I, 30. ⟨2⟩ Widtsoe, Tollens, *Ber.* **33,** 136, Note (1900). ⟨3⟩ van der Haar, " Anleitung," p. 184.

1:0325 ***d*-FRUCTOSE** $C_6H_{12}O_6$ **Beil. I-918; XXXI-321**
(Levulose, fruit-sugar)

Cryst. or crusts from abs. alc.; ndls. with $\frac{1}{2}H_2O$ from aq., m.p. 102–104°—Very sol. aq.; 1 pt. anhyd. fructose dis. in 11.8 pts. abs. alc. at 17°; sol. in alc.-ether mixt., insol. cold acetone — Sweeter than sucrose — $(\alpha)_D^{20} = -92°$.

Reduces Fehling's soln. (T 1.22) in *cold.* — Distn. with HCl (T 1.23) gives red color with aniline acetate (dif. from *d*-glucose) — Phloroglucinol test (T 1.24) gives dark rusty brown ppt. (dif. from arabinose and xylose).

Ⓟ Ⓓ ***d*-Glucosephenylosazone:** In T 1.21 heavy yel. ppt., m.p. 204° (rap. htg.), sep. after abt. 2 min. ⟨1⟩.

Ⓟ **Color reaction with alkali:** In a small porcelain dish is sprinkled 0.01–0.03 g. fructose, followed by 3–5 drops 2 *N* KOH or NaOH, and then 0.5–1.0 g. solid caustic alkali. If fructose is present a red to blood-red border is acquired by the alkali in course of 0.5 min., the color extending finally throughout the liquid. (Under these conditions following give shades of yellow: arabinose, xylose, rhamnose, mannose, glucose, lactose, maltose, dextrin. The following give no color: sucrose, glycogen.) ⟨2.⟩

Ⓓ ***d*-Fructose-*p*-nitrophenylhydrazone:** 0.25 g. C̄ treated by proc. given for *d*-mannose, recrystd. from alc., gives woolly yellow cryst., m.p. 180–181° ⟨3⟩.

1:0325 ⟨1⟩ Mulliken, " Method " I, 30. ⟨2⟩ Ekkert, *Pharm. Zentralhalle* **69,** 805–806 (1928); *C.A.* **23,** 932 (1929). ⟨3⟩ van der Haar, " Anleitung," p. 191.

1:0330 **RHAMNOSE (hydrate)** $C_6H_{12}O_5 + H_2O$ **Beil. I-870; XXXI-65**
(Isodulcitol)

Cryst. with 1 H_2O — m.p. 87–88° — 100 pts. aq. at 20° dis. 58 pts. rhamnose; 100 pts. MeOH dis. 54 pts. rhamnose — Sweet — $(\alpha)_D = +8.3°$.

Reduces Fehling's soln. (T 1.22) — In phloroglucinol test (T 1.24) gives brown ppt. (dif. from arabinose, xylose).

Ⓟ Ⓓ **Rhamnosephenylosazone:** In T 1.21 osazone sep. from hot soln. after abt. 9 min. as heavy yel. ppt., m.p. abt. 185° dec. cor., rap. htg. ⟨1⟩.

Ⓓ ***p*-Nitrophenylhydrazone:** 0.25 g. C̄ and 0.25 g. *p*-nitrophenylhydrazine susp. in 3 ml. alc. and htd. on aq. bath gives ppt. in 10 min. After stdg. 24 hrs. product is filtered with suction, washed with alc., recrystd. from hot alc., m.p. 190°.

1:0330 ⟨1⟩ Mulliken, " Method " I, 30. ⟨2⟩ van der Haar, " Anleitung," p. 185.

Subsection C

(Compounds giving no precipitate from hot solution within 20 minutes in T 1.21)

1:0350 **MALTOSE (hydrate)** $C_{12}H_{22}O_{11}$ **Beil. XXXI-386**

Fine white ndls. losing aq. at 100–110° — Very sol. cold aq.; very dif. sol. cold alc. —

Tastes half as sweet as sucrose — $(\alpha)_D$ = +137.7°. For further data see Abderhalden. ⟨1.⟩

Reduces Fehling's soln. readily (T 1.22) — In T 1.21 no osazone sep. from soln. while hot even after 2 hrs. — Oxidn. with HNO_3 (T 1.25) gives saccharic acid but no mucic acid. (Dif. from lactose.)

Ⓟ Ⓓ Warm with a few drops HCl, neutralize, and proceed as for *d*-glucose (1:0305).

1:0350 ⟨1⟩ Abderhalden, "Biochemisches Handlexikon," Vol. XIII, pp. 566, 570.

1:0355 LACTOSE (hydrate) $C_{12}H_{22}O_{11} + H_2O$ **Beil. XXXI-407**
(Milk-sugar)

Large, hard, white cryst., losing water at 130°; turns yellow abt. 160° and melts abt. 200° dec. — Taste very faintly sweet — Sol. in 6 pts. cold aq. or in 2.5 pts. hot; insol. alc. or ether. $(\alpha)_D$ = +52.5° (hydrate) — For further data see Abderhalden. ⟨1.⟩

Reduces Fehling's soln. (T 1.22) (dif. from sucrose) — Oxidn. with HNO_3 (T 1.25) gives both mucic and saccharic acids (dif. from maltose) — In T 1.21 no osazone sep. from hot soln. even after 2 hrs.

1:0355 ⟨1⟩ Abderhalden, "Biochemisches Handlexikon," Vol. XIII, pp. 587–589.

1:0360 SUCROSE $C_{12}H_{22}O_{11}$ **Beil. XXXI-424**
(Cane-sugar; beet-sugar; saccharose)

Colorless monoclinic cryst., sol. in 0.5 pt. cold aq., dif. sol. cold alc., 100 ml. abs. MeOH dis. 0.4 g. — M.p. abt. 160–170° dec. — $(\alpha)_D$ = +66.5° — Sweet — For further data see Abderhalden. ⟨1.⟩

Fresh soln. reduces Fehling's soln. slightly or not at all (dif. from maltose, lactose). After boiling with drop of min. acid, however, reduces Fehling's soln. readily (T 1.22) and rotates to left, $(\alpha)_D$ = −37.4° (dif. from maltose, lactose) — Oxidn. with HNO_3 (T 1.25) gives saccharic acid, but no mucic (dif. from lactose). In T 1.21 yel. osazone begins to sep. from hot soln. if heating is continued for abt. 30 min.

1:0360 ⟨1⟩ Abderhalden, "Biochemisches Handlexikon," Vol. XIII, pp. 528, 531, et seq.

1:0365 RAFFINOSE (hydrate) $C_{18}H_{32}O_{16} + 5H_2O$ **Beil. XXXI-462**

Ndls. losing all aq. at 110°; when anhyd. melts 118–119° — Sol. in 6 pts. aq. at 16°; 100 ml. abs. MeOH dis. 9.5 g. anhyd. raffinose (dif. from sucrose); alm. insol. alc. — Taste not noticeably sweet — $(\alpha)_D$ = +104.5°. For further data see Abderhalden ⟨1⟩.

Does not reduce Fehling's soln. (T 1.22) (dif. from maltose and lactose) — Oxidn. with HNO_3 (T 1.25) gives both saccharic and mucic acids (dif. from sucrose) — In T 1.21 yel. osazone does not sep. from hot soln. unless htg. cont. for abt. 60 min.

1:0365 ⟨1⟩ Abderhalden "Biochemisches Handlexikon," Vol. XIII, p. 617, et seq.

1:0368 α-METHYLGLUCOSIDE $C_6H_{11}O_5.OCH_3$ $C_7H_{14}O_6$ **Beil. I-898; XXXI-179**

M.P. 166°. (For detailed description and behavior see Abderhalden ⟨1⟩.) [For prepn. (49% yield) see ⟨3⟩.]

Ⓓ **Benzal-α-methylglucoside:** $C_6H_9O_5(OCH_3):CH.C_6H_5$. C̄, shaken 3 hrs. with powd. anhyd. $ZnCl_2$ and BzH; prod. washed with cold aq., then with pet. ether, and residue recrystd. from hot aq. M.p. 161–162° ⟨2⟩. (Corresp. deriv. of β-methylglucoside melts 205°.)

Ⓓ **α-Methylglucoside tetraacetate:** m.p. 100.5–101.5° ⟨4⟩.

1:0368 ⟨1⟩ Abderhalden, " Biochemisches Handlexikon," Vol. XIII, p. 866. ⟨2⟩ Freudenberg, Toepffer, Anderson, *Ber.* **61,** 1758 (1928). ⟨3⟩ Helferich, Schäfer, *Organic Syntheses, Coll. Vol.* I, 356–357 (1932). ⟨4⟩ Clarke, Gillespie, *J. Am. Chem. Soc.* **54,** 2086 (1932).

1:0370 " DEXTRIN " **Beil. S.N. 4768**

Although comml. dextrin is not a true chem. species, but a mixt. of several hydrolytic decompn. prod. of starch, its practical importance necessitates brief mention here. It is usually a white, yellow, or slightly brownish powder with insipid mucilaginous taste; very sol. in hot aq. and for the most part also in cold aq., although in latter case soln. apt to be milky.

T 1.21 usually gives no ppt. of osazone in hot soln. after 20 min. — Unless unusually free from reducing sugars reduces Fehling's soln. (T 1.22) — Unless so much starch is present as to give a blue color, a very dilute soln. of I_2 in KI produces strong brown coloration. (Generally serves to identify the material.) ⟨1.⟩

1:0370 ⟨1⟩ Dehn, Jackson, Ballard, *Ind. Eng. Chem., Anal. Ed.* **4,** 413–414 (1932).

ORDER I: SUBORDER I: GENUS 2: CARBOHYDRATES

Section 2

Carbohydrates which either are not soluble in 10 parts of cold water, or which dissolve giving solutions that remain strongly opalescent after filtration.

1:0375 α[*d*-**GLUCOSE PENTAACETATE**] **Beil. II-159; XXXI-120**
(Dextose pentaacetate)

M.P. 111-112°. (For detailed description and behavior see Abderhalden ⟨1⟩.)

1:0375 ⟨1⟩ Abderhalden " Biochemisches Handlexikon," Vol. XIII, p. 398.

1:0380 STARCH $(C_6H_{10}O_5)_x$ **Beil. S.N. 4766**

Ord. air-dried starch is a white tasteless powd., contg. abt. 18% aq. Under microscope seen to consist of granules showing concentrically stratified structure whose size and shape are often characteristic of the plant by which they were produced.

Starch is undislvd. and unacted upon by cold aq., alc., or ether. A few cg. rubbed to thin cream with cold aq. and then gradually stirred into 100 ml. boiling aq. quickly dis. to nearly clear soln. This soln. after cooling, gives a white ppt. with tannin or with much alc. — A drop of very dil. soln. of I_2 in KI gives intense, deep-blue coloration (!) temporarily decolorized by heat, or by traces of free alkali, but restored on cooling or acidifying. (This characteristic color reaction will be masked by the presence of much erythrodextrin unless care is taken to use a very weak iodine soln. and to add it gradually.) ⟨1.⟩ ⟨2.⟩

1:0380 ⟨1⟩ Mulliken, " Method " I, 31. ⟨2⟩ Dehn, Jackson, Ballard, *Ind. Eng. Chem., Anal. Ed.* **4,** 413–414 (1932).

1:0385 CELLULOSE $(C_6H_{10}O_5)_n$ **Beil. S.N. 4770**

White, tasteless, amorphous solid, insol. in aq. and all ord. org. solvents, either hot or cold, but dissolving in Schweitzer's reagent (strong NH_4OH saturated with $Cu(OH)_2$ washed free from salts) giving a viscous soln., from which it may be repptd. in floc. state by addn. of acid. Cf. ⟨1⟩.

After few seconds immersion in cold mixt. of 2 vol. conc. H_2SO_4 with 1 vol. aq. cellulose assumes deep blue color if wet (either immediately or after hasty rinsing with cold aq.) with a few drops of 2% iodine soln. contg. KI. For further data, see Abderhalden ⟨2⟩.

1:0385 ⟨1⟩ Dehn, Jackson, Ballard, *Ind. Eng. Chem., Anal. Ed.* **4,** 413–414 (1932). ⟨2⟩ Abderhalden, " Biochemisches Handlexikon," Vol. XIII, pp. 108, 114.

1:0390 INULIN **Beil. S.N. 4773**

Tasteless white powd.; after drying at 130° melts abt. 178° dec. — Under microscope seen to consist of spheroidal cryst. aggregates — Alm. insol. cold aq.; very sol. hot aq. giving clear soln. which tends to remain supersatd. for a long time; alm. insol. alc. — $(\alpha)_D = -39.5°$ — Easily hydrolyzed by hot dil. HCl, chief prod. being levulose — Does not reduce

Fehling's soln. (T 1.22) — T 1.21 gives a yellow osazone which begins to sep. from hot soln. after abt. 25 min. — Gives no coloration with dil. iodine soln. For further details see Abderhalden ⟨1⟩.

1:0390 ⟨1⟩ Abderhalden," Biochemisches Handlexikon," Vol. XIII, p. 99, et seq.

1:0395 GLYCOGEN $(C_6H_{10}O_5)_y$ **Beil. S.N. 4773**

White amorph. powd. — Eas. sol. aq. giving intensely opalescent soln.! This opalescence is not destroyed by repeated filtration, but is removed by addn. of AcOH — Insol. alc. — $(\alpha)_D = +198°$.

Does not reduce Fehling's soln. (T 1.22) — T 1.21 gives no ppt. of osazone after htg. 1 hr. — With I_2-KI soln. gives wine coloration ⟨1⟩. For further information see Abderhalden. ⟨2.⟩

1:0395 ⟨1⟩ Dehn, Jackson, Ballard, *Ind. Eng. Chem., Anal. Ed.* **4,** 413–414 (1932). ⟨2⟩ Abderhalden, " Biochemisches Handlexikon," Vol. XIII, pp. 230, 235.

CHAPTER V

GENUS 3. ACIDS

1. Alphabetical Name Index*

*For complete alphabetical name index covering all listed names of all numbered compounds in this book see the main alphabetical index.

2. Chemical Type Index

(Names used here are not necessarily same as subject index names)

I. Purely Aliphatic Acids

A. *Monobasic, saturated*

Formic acid.............. **1:1005**
Acetic acid.............. **1:1010**
Propionic acid........... **1:1025**
n-Butyric acid........... **1:1035**
Isobutyric acid........... **1:1030**

n-Valeric acid............ **1:1060**
Ethyl-methyl-acetic acid.. **1:1105**
Isovaleric acid........... **1:1050**
Trimethylacetic acid...... **1:0410**

n-Caproic acid........... **1:1130**
2-Methylpentanoic acid-1.. **1:1117**
3-Methylpentanoic acid-1.. **1:1125**
4-Methylpentanoic acid-1.. **1:1127**
2,2-Dimethylbutanoic acid-1 **1:1113**
2,3-Dimethylbutanoic acid-1 **1:1114**
3,3-Dimethylbutanoic acid-1 **1:1112**
2-Ethylbutanoic acid-1.... **1:1115**

n-Heptanoic acid......... **1:1140**
2-Methylhexanoic acid-1... **1:1134**
4-Methylhexanoic acid-1... **1:1136**
2-Ethylpentanoic acid-1... **1:1133**

n-Caprylic acid.......... **1:1145**
2-Ethylhexanoic acid-1.... **1:1143**

n-Nonylic (pelargonic) acid. **1:0560**
n-Decanoic acid.......... **1:0585**
n-Undecylic acid......... **1:0573**
Lauric acid.............. **1:0605**
Tridecylic acid........... **1:0600**
Myristic acid............ **1:0630**

Pentadecylic acid......... **1:0620**
Palmitic acid............ **1:0650**
Margaric acid............ **1:0635**
Stearic acid............. **1:0660**

B. *Monobasic, unsaturated*

Acrylic acid............. **1:1020**
α-Crotonic acid (*trans*).... **1:0425**
Isocrotonic acid (*cis*)...... **1:1045**
Vinylacetic acid.......... **1:1042**
α-Methylcrotonic acid (*cis*) **1:0420**
α-Methylcrotonic acid (*trans*) **1:0612**
n-Undecylenic acid....... **1:0570**

Oleic acid (*cis*)........... **1:0565**
Elaidic acid (*trans*)....... **1:0610**

Erucic acid (*cis*).......... **1:0590**
Brassidic acid (*trans*)..... **1:0633**

C. *Dibasic, saturated*

Oxalic acid, anhydrous.... **1:0535**
Oxalic acid, dihydrate..... **1:0445**
Malonic acid............. **1:0480**
n-Heptylmalonic acid..... **1:0675**
Succinic acid............ **1:0530**
Glutaric acid............ **1:0440**
Adipic acid.............. **1:0775**
Pimelic acid............. **1:0456**
Suberic acid............. **1:0755**
Azelaic acid............. **1:0695**
Sebacic acid............. **1:0730**

d-Camphoric............. **1:0810**

D. *Dibasic, unsaturated*

Maleic acid (*cis*)......... **1:0470**
Fumaric acid (*trans*)...... **1:0895**

Methylmaleic acid (*cis*) (citraconic)............ **1:0435**
Methylfumaric acid (*trans*) (mesaconic) **1:0548**

Itaconic acid............. **1:0515**

E. *Tribasic, saturated*

Tricarballylic acid........ **1:0520**

F. *Tribasic, unsaturated*

Aconitic acid............. **1:0540**

G. *Hydroxy acids*

Glycolic acid............. **1:0430**

d,l-Lactic acid........... **1:0400**
α-Hydroxyisobutyric acid. **1:0431**

Tartronic acid........... **1:0510**
l-Malic acid............. **1:0450**
d-Tartaric acid........... **1:0525**
Racemic (d,l-tartaric) acid. **1:0550**
meso-Tartaric acid........ **1:0490**
Mucic acid............. **1:0845**
Citric acid, anhydrous..... **1:0505**
Citric acid, monohydrate .. **1:0455**

H. *Alkoxy or ether acids*

Methoxyacetic acid....... **1:1065**
Ethoxyacetic acid........ **1:1070**

Diglycolic acid........... **1:0495**

I. *Keto acids*

Pyruvic acid............. **1:1040**

Levulinic acid............ **1:0405**
Acetonedicarboxylic acid.. **1:0485**

J. *Ester acids*

Methyl hydrogen adipate.. **1:0399**
Ethyl hydrogen adipate... **1:0403**

Benzyl hydrogen succinate. **1:0640**

II. Aryl Substituted Aliphatic Acids

A. *Monobasic, saturated*

Phenylacetic acid........ **1:0665**
α-Ethylphenylacetic acid.. **1:0594**
Diphenylacetic acid....... **1:0765**
Dibenzylacetic acid....... **1:0668**

β-Phenylpropionic acid.... **1:0615**
β-Phenyl-α-methylpropionic acid.............. **1:0593**

α-Naphthylacetic acid.... **1:0728**
β-Naphthylacetic acid..... **1:0761**

Pyromucic acid.......... **1:0475**

B. *Monobasic, unsaturated*

Cinnamic acid........... **1:0735**
Phenylpropiolic acid...... **1:0745**
d-Hydnocarpic acid....... **1:0634**
d-Chaulmoogric acid...... **1:0655**
Furanacrylic acid......... **1:0760**

C. *Dibasic, saturated*

d,l-Phenylsuccinic acid..... **1:0790**

III. Aromatic Acids

A. *Monobasic*

Benzoic acid............. **1:0715**
Hexahydrobenzoic acid.... **1:0575**
o-Toluic acid............ **1:0690**
m-Toluic acid............ **1:0705**
p-Toluic acid............ **1:0795**

α-Naphthoic acid......... **1:0785**
β-Naphthoic acid......... **1:0800**

B. *Dibasic*

Phthalic acid............ **1:0820**
Isophthalic acid.......... **1:0900**
Terephthalic acid **1:0910**

Diphenic acid............ **1:0870**
Naphthalic acid.......... **1:0890**

C. *Tribasic*

Hemimellitic acid (1,2,3).. **1:0538**
Trimellitic acid (1,2,4).... **1:0551**
Trimesic acid (1,3,5)...... **1:0559**

D. *Tetrabasic*

Prehnitic acid (1,2,3,4).... **1:0553**
Mellophanic acid (1,2,3,5).. **1:0555**
Pyromellitic acid (1,2,4,5).. **1:0557**

E. *Phenolic acids*

o-Hydroxybenzoic acid.... **1:0780**
m-Hydroxybenzoic acid ... **1:0825**
p-Hydroxybenzoic acid.... **1:0840**

o-Hydroxycinnamic acid... **1:0835**
p-Hydroxyphenylacetic acid.................. **1:0500**
2-Hydroxy-3-naphthoic acid **1:0850**

2,4-Dihydroxybenzoic acid (β-resorcylic acid)...... **1:0843**
3,4-Dihydroxybenzoic acid (protocatechuic acid).... **1:0545**
3,5-Dimethoxy-4-hydroxybenzoic acid (syringic acid)................. **1:0830**
Phenolphthalin........... **1:0873**

3,4,5-Trihydroxybenzoic acid (gallic)............ **1:0875**

F. *Alkoxy acids*

o-Methoxybenzoic acid.... **1:0685**
m-Methoxybenzoic acid... **1:0703**
p-Methoxybenzoic acid (anisic) **1:0805**
o-Ethoxybenzoic acid..... **1:0571**
m-Ethoxybenzoic acid..... **1:0746**
p-Ethoxybenzoic acid..... **1:0817**

3,4-Methylenedioxybenzoic acid (piperonylic acid).. **1:0865**
3,5-Dimethoxy-4-hydroxybenzoic acid (syringic).. **1:0830**

Phenoxyacetic acid....... **1:0680**
o-Carboxyphenoxyacetic acid.................. **1:0815**

G. *Alcohol acids*

d,l-α-Hydroxyphenylacetic acid (mandelic acid)..... **1:0465**
α-Hydroxydiphenylacetic acid (benzilic acid)..... **1:0770**
β-Hydroxy-α-phenylpropionic acid (tropic)....... **1:0460**

H. *Keto acids*

o-Benzoylbenzoic acid..... **1:0720**
o-Benzoylbenzoic acid, monohydrate.......... **1:0670**
o-(*p*-Toluyl)benzoic acid .. **1:0750**

I. *Ester acids*

Acetylsalicylic acid....... **1:0740**

IV. ANHYDRIDES

A. *of aliphatic acids*

Acetic anhydride	**1:1015**
Propionic anhydride	**1:1100**
n-Butyric anhydride	**1:1126**
Isobutyric anhydride	**1:1110**
n-Valeric anhydride	**1:1137**
n-Caproic anhydride	**1:1150**
n-Heptylic anhydride	**1:1165**
n-Caprylic anhydride	**1:1175**
n-Capric anhydride	**1:0569**
Lauric anhydride	**1:0601**
Myristic anhydride	**1:0629**
Palmitic anhydride	**1:0651**
[Stearic anhydride	**1:4915**]
Succinic anhydride	**1:0710**
d-Camphoric anhydride	**1:0860**
Crotonic anhydride	**1:1155**
Maleic anhydride	**1:0625**
Methylmaleic (citraconic) anhydride	**1:1135**
Itaconic (methylene succinic) anhydride	**1:0654**

B. *of aromatic acids*

Benzoic anhydride	**1:0595**
Phthalic anhydride	**1:0725**
Diphenic anhydride	**1:0851**
Naphthalic anhydride	**1:0891**

V. MISCELLANEOUS

Methyl formate	**1:1000**
Dimethyl oxalate	**1:0415**
Diethyl oxalate	**1:1055**
Glycolid	**1:0667**
d,l-Lactid	**1:0722**
δ-Valerolactone	**1:1139**
Dehydroacetic acid	**1:0700**
Dimethyldihydroresorcinol	**1:0768**

ORDER I: SUBORDER I: GENUS 3: ACIDS

Division A. Solid acids

Section 1: " Soluble " in 50 parts of cold water

—— **FORMIC ACID,** anhydrous H.CO.OH CH_2O_2 **Beil. II-8**

M.P. +8.4° **Neut. Eq. 46** D_4^{20} = **1.22026** n_D^{20} = **1.37137**

See 1:1005. Genus 3: Division B: Section 1. B.P. 100.7°.

1:0399 METHYL HYDROGEN ADIPATE $C_7H_{12}O_4$ **Beil. II-652**

$CH_3OOC.(CH_2)_4.COOH$

M.P. +9° ⟨1⟩ **Neut. Eq. 160**

C̄ can be distd. only at reduced pressure; e.g., b.p. 178° at 30 mm. **⟨1⟩**.

C̄ with $SOCl_2$ for 6 hrs. below 40° gives (81% yield) δ-carbomethoxy-*n*-valeryl chloride, b.p. 141° at 36 mm. **⟨1⟩**.

Ⓓ **Saponification:** hydrolysis with alk. (T 1.51) gives Sap. Equiv. 80, and yields methyl alc. (1:6120) and adipic ac. (1:0775), q.v.

1:0399 **⟨1⟩** Morgan, Walton, *J. Chem. Soc.* **1933,** 91–92.

—— **ACRYLIC ACID,** anhydrous $CH_2=CH.COOH$ $C_3H_4O_2$ **Beil. II-397**

M.P. +13.0° **Neut. Eq. 72** D_4^{16} = **1.0621** n_D^{20} = **1.4224**

See 1:1020. Genus 3: Division B: Section 1. B.P. 140°.

—— **PYRUVIC ACID,** anhydrous $CH_3.CO.COOH$ $C_3H_4O_3$ **Beil. III-608**

M.P. +13.6° **Neut. Eq. 88** D_4^{15} = **1.2668** $n_D^{15.3}$ = **1.43025**

See 1:1040. Genus 3: Division B: Section 1. B.P. 165° sl. dec.

—— **ISOCROTONIC ACID** $CH_3.CH=CH.COOH$ $C_4H_6O_2$ **Beil. II-412**

M.P. 15° **Neut. Eq. 86** D_4^{20} = **1.0265** n_D^{20} = **1.4456**

See 1:1045. Genus 3: Division B: Section 1. B.P. 169°.

—— **ACETIC ACID,** anhydrous $CH_3.COOH$ $C_2H_4O_2$ **Beil. II-96**

M.P. +16.635° **Neut. Eq. 60** D_4^{20} = **1.04926** n_D^{20} = **1.36976**

See 1:1010. Genus 3: Division B: Section 1. B.P. 118.2°.

1:0400 *d,l*-LACTIC ACID $C_3H_6O_3$ **Beil. III-268**
(α-Hydroxypropionic acid)

$$CH_3-\overset{\displaystyle H}{\underset{\displaystyle OH}{C}}-COOH$$

M.P. +16.8° ⟨1⟩ **Neut. Eq. 90** (See text.)

Comml. C̄ is viscous hygroscopic sirup consisting of a mixt. of around 50% C̄, 30% lactic anhydride [Beil. III-282], lactyl-lactic acid [Beil. III-282], and lactid (1:0722), together with water ⟨2⟩ ⟨3⟩ ⟨4⟩ ⟨5⟩ ⟨32⟩; hence on direct titration gives too high Neut. Eq. [Comml. C̄ usually shows a low opt. activity corresponding to a slight excess of which of the two optical isomers it happens to contain in excess ⟨6⟩.] [For survey of mfg. of comml. C̄ see ⟨7⟩ ⟨8⟩ ⟨9⟩.]

[Much confusion exists regarding the optically active forms of lactic acid. That which shows dextrorotation (sarcolactic acid) should be designated as *l*-(+) lactic ac.; when pure it has m.p. +52.8° ⟨1⟩ ⟨10⟩ and is metabolized completely by the animal body ⟨11⟩; its salts, however, are laevorotatory. The laevorotatory lactic acid, properly designated as *d*-(−) lactic acid, has m.p. +52.8° ⟨1⟩, is not metabolized by the body but largely excreted as such ⟨11⟩; its salts are dextrorotatory.]

C̄ may be purified by fract. distn. at 0.1 mm. followed by fractional crystn. from mixt. of equal vols. of diethyl ether + diisopropyl ether ⟨12⟩ — C̄ is only very slightly volatile with steam at 100° ⟨13⟩, but is said to distil with superheated steam. C̄ is misc. with aq. or alc. but is only sparingly sol. in dry ether or $CHCl_3$ and cannot effectively be extracted by them from aq. solns.

C̄ gives with $FeCl_3$ (T 1.32) the usual charact. yel. color of α-hydroxy acids — C̄ on warming with I_2.KI soln. + aq. KOH (T 1.81) yields iodoform. [For study of sensitivity with respect to temp. and KOH concn. see ⟨14⟩.] — *Warm* aq. soln. of C̄ quickly decolorizes dil. neutral $KMnO_4$ soln. with effervescence, but when C̄ is dislvd. in excess Na_2CO_3 soln. and treated with 1% $KMnO_4$ (T 1.34) no reduction occurs until heated.

Ⓟ **Acetaldehyde formation on heating:** Arrange a large tt. with rubber stopper bearing 25 cm. long gas delivery tube so that latter dips into 2 ml. aq. in a 6-in. tt. resting in a beaker of cold aq. Place 1 ml. C̄ in reaction tube, insert ebullator tube, and heat nearly to dryness over low flame. Test the aq. soln. thus obtd. for acetaldehyde (1:0100) ⟨15⟩.

Ⓟ **Resorcinol-sulfuric acid color test:** Several drops of C̄ are treated with 5 ml. 1% aq. resorcinol soln. and allowed to flow slowly onto 5 ml. conc. H_2SO_4 in a 6-in. tt. On stdg. for 2 min. with gentle rotation red color develops at interface ⟨16⟩ ⟨17⟩. [This test distinguishes C̄ from *d*-tartaric ac. (1:0525) (pale yel.), oxalic ac. (1:0445) (green), and citric ac. (1:0455) (colorless) ⟨16⟩.]

Ⓓ **Phenacyl *d,l*-lactate:** m.p. 96.0° ⟨18⟩ [cf. T 1.391].

Ⓓ ***p*-Bromophenacyl *d,l*-lactate:** m.p. 112.8° ⟨19⟩ [cf. T 1.391].

Ⓓ ***p*-Iodophenacyl *d,l*-lactate:** m.p. 139.8° ⟨19⟩ [cf. T 1.391].

Ⓓ ***p*-Phenylphenacyl *d,l*-lactate:** m.p. 145° ⟨20⟩ [cf. T 1.391].

—— ***d,l*-Lactamide:** cryst. from C_6H_6 + alc. (3:1); m.p. 78.5–79.0° cor. ⟨21⟩ [from ethyl *d,l*-lactate (1:3303) + NH_3 gas].

Ⓓ ***d,l*-Lactanilide:** cryst. from hot aq., m.p. 58.5–59° [from C̄ htd. with aniline 6–7 hrs. at 180° ⟨22⟩; also from ethyl *d,l*-lactate (1:3303) htd. with 1 mole aniline in s.t. at 150–160° ⟨22⟩, or from lactid (1:0722) ⟨23⟩].

Ⓓ ***d,l*-Lacto-*p*-toluidide:** m.p. 107° ⟨24⟩.

Ⓓ **Quinine *d,l*-lactate:** To a soln. of C̄ is added the equiv. quant. of an alc. soln. of quinine (prepd. from sulfate by pptn. with NaOH and extn. with $CHCl_3$) and the mixt. evapd. to dryness under dimin. press. The residue is washed once with CCl_4 (to remove quinine acetate, propionate, or butyrate), the residual quinine lactate dislvd. in alc. free $CHCl_3$ (leaving any quinine sulfate) and the $CHCl_3$ soln. evapd. The crude salt is then recrystd. from abs. EtOAc or C_6H_6; m.p. 165.5° dec. ⟨25⟩ ⟨26⟩. [For use in detn. of C̄ in presence of acetic, benzoic, citric, malic, or tartaric acids see ⟨26⟩.]

Ⓓ **2-(α-Hydroxyethyl)benzimidazole:** from C̄ + $\frac{2}{3}$ mole *o*-phenylenediamine in 4 *N* HCl, boiled 30–40 min. and neutralized with NH_4OH (70% yield ⟨27⟩); pl. from 50% alc., m.p. 178–179° ⟨27⟩; 179–180° ⟨28⟩. [The picrate of this deriv. has m.p. 131° ⟨29⟩.]

Ⓓ *S*-**Benzylthiuronium *d,l*-lactate:** m.p. 153° cor. ⟨30⟩.

Ⓓ **Piperazonium 1,4-di-*d,l*-lactate:** cryst. from cellosolve (60% yield); m.p. 96–96.5° cor. ⟨31⟩.

1:0400 ⟨1⟩ Borsook, Huffman, Liu, *J. Biol. Chem.* **102,** 456–457 (1933). ⟨2⟩ Ref. 1, page 450. ⟨3⟩ Eder, Kutter, *Helv. Chim. Acta* **9,** 355–364 (1926). ⟨4⟩ Eder, Kutter, *Helv. Chim. Acta* **9,** 557–578 (1926). ⟨5⟩ Thurmond, Edgar, *Ind. Eng. Chem.* **16,** 823–826 (1924). ⟨6⟩ Ref. 1, page 449. ⟨7⟩ Smith, Claborn, *Ind. Eng. Chem.* **32,** 692–694 (1940). ⟨8⟩ Smith, Claborn, *Ind. Eng. Chem., News Ed.* **17,** 641 (1939). ⟨9⟩ Garrett, *Ind. Eng. Chem.* **22,** 1153–1154 (1930). ⟨10⟩ Ward, Lockwood, Tabenkin, Wells, *Ind. Eng. Chem.* **30,** 1235 (1938).

⟨11⟩ C. F. Cori, G. T. Cori, *J. Biol. Chem.* **81,** 389 (1929). ⟨12⟩ Ref. 1, pages 450–452. ⟨13⟩ Hart, Willaman, *J. Am. Chem. Soc.* **35,** 923 (1913). ⟨14⟩ Korenman, *Z. anal. Chem.* **93,** 341–342 (1933). ⟨15⟩ Mulliken, "Method" I, 39 (1904). ⟨16⟩ Brauer, *Chem. Ztg.* **44,** 494 (1920). ⟨17⟩ Arny, Dimler, *J. Am. Pharm. Assoc.* **18,** 459–462 (1929). ⟨18⟩ Rather, Reid, *J. Am. Chem. Soc.* **41,** 79 (1919). ⟨19⟩ Judefind, Reid, *J. Am. Chem. Soc.* **42,** 1055 (1920). ⟨20⟩ Drake, Bronitsky, *J. Am. Chem. Soc.* **52,** 3719 (1930).

⟨21⟩ Ôeda, *Bull. Chem. Soc. Japan* **11,** 388 (1936). ⟨22⟩ Leipen, *Monatsh.* **9,** 48–49 (1888). ⟨23⟩ Bischoff, Walden, *Ann.* **279,** 73 (1894). ⟨24⟩ Ref. 23, page 89. ⟨25⟩ Phelps, Palmer, *J. Am. Chem. Soc.* **39,** 136–149 (1917). ⟨26⟩ Nelson, *J. Assoc. Official Agr. Chem.* **9,** 331–333 (1926). ⟨27⟩ Phillips, *J. Chem. Soc.* **1928,** 2395. ⟨28⟩ Bistrzycki, Przeworski, *Ber.* **45,** 3487–3488 (1912). ⟨29⟩ Brown, Campbell, *J. Chem. Soc.* **1937,** 1701. ⟨30⟩ Donleavy, *J. Am. Chem. Soc.* **58,** 1005 (1936).

⟨31⟩ Pollard, Adelson, Bain, *J. Am. Chem. Soc.* **56,** 1759 (1934). ⟨32⟩ Watson, *Ind. Eng. Chem.* **32,** 399–401 (1940).

1:0403 ETHYL HYDROGEN ADIPATE $C_8H_{14}O_4$ Beil. II₁-(277)

$C_2H_5OOC.(CH_2)_4.COOH$

M.P. 28-29° ⟨1⟩ ⟨2⟩ **Neut. Eq. 174**

Very hygroscopic cryst. from mixt. of dry ether and hexane — C̄ can be distilled without decompn. only at reduced pressure, e.g., b.p. 185° at 35 mm. ⟨3⟩. [On distn. at ord. press. b.p. is 285–287° with sl. decompn. such that f.p. of distillate is lowered to 23.2° ⟨4⟩.]

C̄ with $SOCl_2$ for 6 hrs. below 40° gives δ-carbethoxy-*n*-valeryl chloride, b.p. 145° at 35 mm. ⟨3⟩.

Ⓓ **Saponification:** hydrolysis with alk. (T 1.51) gives Sap. Equiv. 83 and yields ethyl alcohol (1:6130) and adipic acid (1:0775), q.v.

1:0403 ⟨1⟩ Nielsen, *J. Am. Chem. Soc.* **58,** 207 (1936). ⟨2⟩ Fourneau, Sabetay, *Bull. soc. chim.* (4) **43,** 861 (1928). ⟨3⟩ Morgan, Walton, *J. Chem. Soc.* **1933,** 92. ⟨4⟩ Contzen-Crowet, *Bull. soc. chim. Belg.* **35,** 180 (1926).

1:0405 LEVULINIC ACID $C_5H_8O_3$ Beil. III-672

(γ-Oxo-*n*-valeric acid; β-acetylpropionic acid) $CH_3.CO.CH_2.CH_2.COOH$

M.P. 33° **Neut. Eq. 116**

B.P. 245-246° undec.

Eas. sol. aq., alc., ether — Not volatile with steam ⟨1⟩ — Deliquescent and often met as liquid.

[For prepn. (21–22% yield) from cane sugar + HCl see ⟨2⟩; for prepn. from *d*-glucose + conc. HCl see ⟨3⟩; for study of prepn. from these and also levulose and starch see ⟨4⟩.]

C̄ in Na_2CO_3 soln. is unaffected by $KMnO_4$ (T 1.34) — C̄ with $I_2.KI$ soln. + NaOH (T 1.81) gives CHI_3 immediately in cold.

C̄ on subjecting to very slow distn. at ord. press. loses aq. and ring closes to yield ⟨5⟩ ⟨6⟩ α-angelicalactone [Beil. XVII-252], accompanied by some β-angelicalactone [Beil. XVII-253]. [After 3–4 hrs. slow distn. the lower layer of dist. is separated, dried with K_2CO_3

and fract. distd.; α-angelicalactone, b.p. 167°, freezes at abt. 0° to a solid, m.p. +18–18.5° ⟨5⟩ ⟨6⟩; the β-angelicalactone has b.p. $208–209°_{751}$ and does not solidify even at −17°.]

C̄ with equal amt. Ac_2O ⟨7⟩ (+ a few drops AcCl ⟨8⟩) stood overnight at ord. temp. gives quant. yield of γ-acetoxy-γ-valerolactone ("acetyllevulinic acid") [Beil. XVIII-2]; pr. from alc., m.p. 78–79° — C̄ on treatment with $SOCl_2$ ⟨8⟩ ⟨9⟩ or with 2 moles AcCl ⟨10⟩ gives γ-chloro-γ-valerolactone ("levulyl chloride"); this product cannot be distd. even under reduced press. because of its easy loss of HCl to give β-angelicalactone (above); in its reactions, however, it behaves exactly as an acid chloride ⟨8⟩.

C̄ on reduction with Na + EtOH (60% yield ⟨11⟩) or in ether soln. with H_2 (at 2–3 atm.) + PtO_2 cat. (87% yield ⟨12⟩) gives γ-valerolactone (1:5080).

AgĀ, sol. in 150 pts. aq. at 17°; $Ca\bar{A}_2$ and $Ba\bar{A}_2$ eas. sol. aq.; for other salts see ⟨13⟩.

—— **Levulinic acid oxime:** m.p. 95–96° ⟨18⟩.

Ⓓ **Levulinic acid phenylhydrazone** [Beil. XV-346]: To soln. of 1 drop phenylhydrazine + 1 drop AcOH in 3 ml. distd. aq. add 2 drops C̄ and reflux 15 min. over low flame. Cool, sep. yel. white flocks on point of small filter, wash with 5 ml. cold aq., dry and recryst. from 1 ml. hot C_6H_6. Fine colorless pr., m.p. 108° ⟨14⟩. [This product, on htg. above 160°, loses 1 mole H_2O and is converted to 1-phenyl-3-methylpyridazinone-6 [Beil. XXIV-62], m.p. 107° ⟨14⟩.]

Ⓓ **Levulinic acid *p*-nitrophenylhydrazone** [Beil. XV-481]: m.p. 174–175° ⟨15⟩.

Ⓓ **Levulinic acid 2,4-dinitrophenylhydrazone:** or.-yel. cryst. from AcOH ⟨16⟩ or $CHCl_3$ ⟨17⟩; m.p. 206° cor. ⟨16⟩; 206.5° ⟨17⟩ [cf. T 1.14]. [This deriv. must be prepd. in aq. soln. (not alc.) ⟨17⟩.]

Ⓓ ***p*-Nitrobenzyl levulinate:** m.p. 61° ⟨19⟩ [cf. T 1.39].

Ⓓ ***p*-Bromophenacyl levulinate:** m.p. 84° ⟨20⟩ [cf. T 1.391].

—— **Levulinamide:** m.p. 107–108° dec. [from α-angelicalactone (above) + aq. or from ethyl levulinate (1:3616) + conc. alc. NH_3 at 100° ⟨21⟩].

—— **Levulinanilide:** cryst. from C_6H_6 or aq.; m.p. 102° ⟨22⟩ [from aniline + α-angelicalactone (above) or "acetyllevulinic ac." (above) ⟨22⟩]. [This anilide on further htg. with aniline yields levulinanilide-anil, m.p. 145° ⟨22⟩.]

—— **Levulin-*p*-toluidide:** cryst. from C_6H_6 or aq.; m.p. 108–109° ⟨22⟩ [prepd. like corresponding anilide (above)].

1:0405 ⟨1⟩ Virtanen, Pulkki, *J. Am. Chem. Soc.* **50,** 3145 (1928). ⟨2⟩ McKenzie, *Organic Syntheses, Coll. Vol.* I, 328–329 (1932). ⟨3⟩ Sah, Ma, *J. Am. Chem. Soc.* **52,** 4880–4881 (1930). ⟨4⟩ Thomas, Schuette, *J. Am. Chem. Soc.* **53,** 2324–2328 (1931). ⟨5⟩ von Auwers, *Ber.* **56,** 1672 (1923). ⟨6⟩ Wolff, *Ann.* **229,** 250–258 (1885). ⟨7⟩ Bredt, *Ann.* **256,** 321 (1890). ⟨8⟩ Helberger, *Ann.* **522,** 274–275 (1936). ⟨9⟩ Clemo, Ramage, *J. Chem. Soc.* **1931,** 54. ⟨10⟩ Ref. 7, page 334.

⟨11⟩ Schuette, Sah, *J. Am. Chem. Soc.* **48,** 3163–3165 (1926). ⟨12⟩ Schuette, Thomas, *J. Am. Chem. Soc.* **52,** 3010–3012 (1930). ⟨13⟩ Proskouriakoff, *J. Am. Chem. Soc.* **55,** 2132–2134 (1933). ⟨14⟩ Fischer, *Ann.* **236,** 146–147 (1886). ⟨15⟩ Feist, *Ber.* **33,** 2099 (1900). ⟨16⟩ Strain, *J. Am. Chem. Soc.* **57,** 760 (1935). ⟨17⟩ Cowley, Schuette, *J. Am. Chem. Soc.* **55,** 3465 (1933). ⟨18⟩ Müller, *Ber.* **16,** 1617–1618 (1883). ⟨19⟩ Lyons, Reid, *J. Am. Chem. Soc.* **39,** 1731–1732 (1917). ⟨20⟩ Judefind, Reid, *J. Am. Chem. Soc.* **42,** 1055 (1920).

⟨21⟩ Ref. 6, page 260. ⟨22⟩ Lukes, Prelog, *Collection Czechoslov. Chem. Commun.* **1,** 284–286 (1929); *Chem. Abs.* **23,** 4193 (1929).

1:0410 TRIMETHYLACETIC ACID $C_5H_{10}O_2$ Beil. II-319

(Pivalic acid) $(CH_3)_3.C.COOH$

M.P. 35.5° **Neut. Eq. 102**

B.P. 163-164°

Ndls., sol. at 20° in 45.5 pts. aq. — Appreciably volatile even at 80°; also volatile with steam.

[For prepn. (69–70% yield ⟨1⟩) from *ter*-butyl MgCl + CO_2 see ⟨1⟩ ⟨2⟩; from pinacolone (1:5425) by oxidn. with NaOBr (71–74% yield) see ⟨3⟩.]

$\bar{C}$ with PCl_5 ⟨4⟩ or PCl_3 ⟨5⟩ or with $SOCl_2$ (80% yield ⟨6⟩) gives trimethylacetyl chloride, b.p. 107° ⟨7⟩, 70.5–71°$_{250}$ ⟨6⟩, n_D^{20} = 1.4118 ⟨6⟩.

Ag$\bar{A}$ seps. from conc. aq. soln. in anhydrous form; % Ag = 51.63 (T 1.36); Hg$\bar{A}_2$, from soln. of Na$\bar{A}$ + calcd. amt. Hg $(NO_3)_2$; white ndls. from $CHCl_3$, m.p. 235° ⟨8⟩.

Ⓓ ***p*-Bromophenacyl trimethylacetate:** m.p. 76.5° ⟨9⟩; 75–76° ⟨10⟩ [cf. T 1.391].

Ⓓ **Trimethylacetamide:** ndls. from aq., tbls. from alc.; cryst. from AcOEt by addn. of pet. ether; m.p. 153–154° ⟨11⟩ ⟨12⟩; 155–157° ⟨5⟩ [from $NH_4\bar{A}$ on htg. in s.t. at 220–230° ⟨12⟩, or from trimethylacetyl chloride (above) + conc. aq. NH_4OH at 0° ⟨5⟩].

Ⓓ **Trimethylacetanilide** [Beil. XII_1-(196)]: m.p. 132–133° ⟨13⟩; 128° cor. ⟨14⟩ (indirectly).

Ⓓ **Trimethylaceto-*p*-toluidide:** m.p. 119–120° ⟨13⟩ (indirectly).

1:0410 ⟨1⟩ Puntambeker, Zoellner, *Organic Syntheses, Coll. Vol.* I, 510–512 (1932). ⟨2⟩ Gilman, Zoellner, *Rec. trav. chim.* **47,** 1061–1062 (1928). ⟨3⟩ Sandborn, Bousquet, *Organic Syntheses, Coll. Vol.* I, 512–514 (1932). ⟨4⟩ Butlerow, *Ann.* **173,** 373 (1874). ⟨5⟩ Whitmore, Langlois, *J. Am. Chem. Soc.* **54,** 3439 (1932). ⟨6⟩ Whitmore, *Rec. trav. chim.* **57,** 565 (1938). ⟨7⟩ Boeseken, *Rec. trav. chim.* **29,** 99 (1910). ⟨8⟩ Kharasch, Stavely, *J. Am. Chem. Soc.* **45,** 2970 (1923). ⟨9⟩ Powell, *J. Am. Chem. Soc.* **53,** 1172 (1931). ⟨10⟩ Ford, Thompson, Marvel, *J. Am. Chem. Soc.* **57,** 2621 (1935).

⟨11⟩ Magnani, McElvain, *J. Am. Chem. Soc.* **60,** 819 (1938). ⟨12⟩ Franchimont, Klobbie, *Rec. trav. chim.* **6,** 238 (1887). ⟨13⟩ Underwood, Gale, *J. Am. Chem. Soc.* **56,** 2119 (1934). ⟨14⟩ Schwartz, Johnson, *J. Am. Chem. Soc.* **53,** 1065 (1931).

1:0415 DIMETHYL OXALATE

$COOCH_3$ | $COOCH_3$ $C_4H_6O_4$ **Beil. II-534**

M.P. 54° **Neut. Eq. 118** (see text)
B.P. 163.5°$_{262}$ **Sap. Eq. 59**

Monoclinic tbls. — With aq. alk. first ester group hydrolyzes abt. 10,000 times as fast as second; hence $\bar{C}$ titrates (T 1.31) like a monobasic ac. but on total alk. hydrol. (T 1.51) gives Sap. Eq. 59.

100 g. aq. at 20–25° dis. abt. 6.2 g. $\bar{C}$; 100 g. pyridine at 20–25° dis. 4.8 g. $\bar{C}$; but 100 g. 50% aq. pyridine at 20–25° dis. 93.1 g. $\bar{C}$ ⟨1⟩ — [For m.p.-compn. diagram of system $\bar{C}$ + H_2O see ⟨2⟩.] [For use of alc. solns. of $\bar{C}$ as demonstration of supersatn. see ⟨3⟩.]

[For prepn. of $\bar{C}$ (68–76% yield) from anhydrous oxalic ac. (1:0535) see ⟨4⟩ ⟨5⟩; from cryst. oxalic acid (1:0445) see ⟨6⟩.]

Ⓟ **Oxamide formation:** $\bar{C}$ in conc. aq. soln. shaken with several vols. conc. aq. NH_4OH gives immediate ppt. of oxamide. [The m.p. of this product is so high (417° s.t.) that it is valueless as a deriv.; other dialkyl oxalates of course give same reaction but less rapidly.]

Ⓓ **Methyl oxamate:** from $\bar{C}$ in ice cold abs. alc. treated with 1 mole conc. aq. NH_4OH at 0°, and stood overnight at 0°; after htg. to boiling and filtering hot (to remove oxamide) soln. is cooled and prod. recrystd. from MeOH; m.p. 122–123° ⟨5⟩.

Ⓓ **Oxanilide:** from $\bar{C}$ by htg. with 2 moles aniline, extg. with dil. HCl, recrystg. residue from C_6H_6; m.p. 246°. [The mono-anilide (methyl oxanilate) [Beil. XII-282] forms tbls. from alc., ndls. from pet. ether, m.p. 114° ⟨7⟩.]

Ⓓ **Oxal-di-*p*-toluidide:** from $\bar{C}$ on htg. with *p*-toluidine, as above; cryst. from boilg. AcOH or much hot alc.; m.p. 268°. [The mono-*p*-toluidide (methyl *N*-*p*-tolyloxamate) [Beil. XII-930], forms cryst. from alc., m.p. 145°.]

1:0415 ⟨1⟩ Dehn, *J. Am. Chem. Soc.* **39,** 1401 (1917). ⟨2⟩ Skrabal, *Monatsh.* **38,** 25–28 (1917). ⟨3⟩ Bowden, *J. Chem. Education* **7,** 827 (1930). ⟨4⟩ Bowden, *Organic Syntheses,* **10,** 70–72 (1930). ⟨5⟩ Sah, Chien, *J. Am. Chem. Soc.* **53,** 3902 (1931). ⟨6⟩ Kenyon, *Organic Syntheses, Coll. Vol.* I, 258–260 (1932). ⟨7⟩ Anschütz, *Ann.* **254,** 10 (1889).

1:0420 TIGLIC ACID (*cis*-α-Methylcrotonic acid; (*cis*-α,β-dimethylacrylic acid) $C_5H_8O_2$ **Beil. II-430**

$CH_3.C.H$
‖
$CH_3.C.COOH$

M.P. 64.5-65° **Neut. Eq. 100**
B.P. 198.5° cor.

Pr. or tbls. with peculiar spicy odor, rather spar. sol. cold aq., more eas. hot aq. — [C̄ is *cis*-stereoisomer of angelic ac. (1:0612).] [For prepn. of C̄ in 70% yield from methylmalonic acid, paraldehyde, Ac_2O + AcOH see ⟨1⟩.]

C̄ in alk. soln. reduces $KMnO_4$ instantly (T 1.34) — C̄ adds Br_2 (T 1.91) but rather slowly. [C̄ in CS_2 treated with 1 mole Br_2 in CS_2, stood 3 days, evapd. yields tiglic acid dibromide (α,β-dibromo-α-methyl-*n*-butyric acid), m.p. 86–87° ⟨2⟩ ⟨3⟩.]

C̄ adds HI yielding tiglic acid hydriodide, m.p. 86.2–86.3° cor. ⟨4⟩.

C̄ with PCl_3 htd. at 70–80° for 2 hrs. gives (90% yield ⟨5⟩) tiglyl chloride, b.p. $64°_{35}$.

$Ca\bar{A}_2.3H_2O$; lfts. from aq.; much more sol. hot aq. than in cold (dif. from corresp. salt of angelic ac. (1:0612)); much less sol. in cold aq. than Ca angelate; fairly eas. sol. in alc. (dif. from corresponding salt of angelic ac.).

Ⓓ ***p*-Nitrobenzyl tiglate:** m.p. 63.9° u.c. ⟨6⟩ [cf. T 1.39].
Ⓓ ***p*-Bromophenacyl tiglate:** m.p. 67.9° cor. ⟨7⟩ [cf. T 1.391].
—— **Tiglamide:** ndls. from C_6H_6, m.p. 75–76° ⟨8⟩; 76.5–77° ⟨9⟩.
Ⓓ **Tiglanilide** [Beil. XII-259]: cryst. from pet. eth., m.p. 77° ⟨9⟩ [from tiglyl chloride + aniline in ether ⟨10⟩].
Ⓓ **Tiglic-*p*-toluidide:** m.p. 70–71.5° ⟨11⟩.

1:0420 ⟨1⟩ Michael, Ross, *J. Am. Chem. Soc.* **55,** 3692 (1933). ⟨2⟩ Wislicenus, *Ann.* **250,** 244 (1888). ⟨3⟩ Pagenstecher, *Ann.* **195,** 122–124 (1879). ⟨4⟩ Young, Dillon, Lucas, *J. Am. Chem. Soc.* **51,** 2530–2533 (1929). ⟨5⟩ Barger, Martin, Mitchell, *J. Chem. Soc.* **1937,** 1822. ⟨6⟩ Cowles, *M.I.T. Thesis.* ⟨7⟩ Lund, Langvad, *J. Am. Chem. Soc.* **54,** 4107 (1932). ⟨8⟩ Naster, Gavriloff, *Bull. soc. chim. Belg.* **42,** 524 (1933). ⟨9⟩ Seib, *Ber.* **60,** 1396 (1927). ⟨10⟩ Blaise, Bagard, *Ann. chim.* (8) **11,** 120 (1907).
⟨11⟩ Drake, Spies, *J. Am. Chem. Soc.* **57,** 186 (1935).

1:0425 α-CROTONIC ACID (*trans*-Buten-2-oic acid-1) $C_4H_6O_2$ **Beil. II-408**

$CH_3—C—H$
‖
$H—C—COOH$

M.P. 72° **Neut. Eq. 86**
B.P. 189° cor.

Ndls. or pr. from aq., or better from lgr. — Sol. in 12 pts. aq. at 15°; fairly eas. sol. hot lgr. but spar. sol. cold lgr. — Volatile with steam.

[For prepn. from crotonaldehyde (1:0150) by oxidn. with gaseous O_2 or with aq. susp. of AgOH (90–95% yield) see ⟨1⟩; from acetaldehyde + malonic acid + pyridine (86% yield ⟨2⟩; 55% yield ⟨3⟩) see ⟨2⟩ ⟨3⟩.] [For anal. of mixts. of C̄ with isocrotonic ac. (1:1045) see latter.]

For actn. of heat on C̄ see ⟨4⟩ ⟨5⟩.

C̄ reduces alk. $KMnO_4$ (T 1.34) or Tollens' reagt. (T 1.11) — C̄ adds Br_2 (T 1.91) [C̄, dislvd. in CS_2, treated with 1 mole Br_2 in equal vol. CS_2, mixt. stood in large beaker in sunlight (the reaction being controlled by cooling as required) and CS_2 evapd. after 24 hrs.

yields α-crotonic acid dibromide (α,β-dibromo-n-butyric acid) [Beil. II-284], cryst. from ether, m.p. 87° ⟨6⟩].

C̄, fused at 80° and treated with dry HBr gas for 2 hrs., then cooled and resaturated with HBr gives only β-bromo-n-butyric ac. [Beil. II-283], m.p. 17–17.5° ⟨7⟩, 18–19° ⟨8⟩; Neut. Eq. 167. [Even under most favorable peroxidic conditions, such as presence of dibenzoyl peroxide or perbenzoic ac., only β-bromo-n-butyric ac. is formed ⟨8⟩ ⟨9⟩.]

C̄ with 3.5 pts. PCl_5 ⟨10⟩, or C̄ with PCl_3 (84% yield ⟨11⟩), or C̄ with $SOCl_2$ (86% yield ⟨12⟩, 80% yield ⟨13⟩) gives α-crotonyl chloride, b.p. 125°.

C̄, htd. with 2 moles aniline 4 hrs. at 180–190°, cooled mass treated with excess HCl and poured onto ice gradually yields crystn. HCl salt of β-anilino-n-butyranilide [Beil. XII-558], cryst. from acetone, m.p. 212–213° ⟨14⟩ ⟨15⟩, which with aq. Na_2CO_3 gives free base, cryst. from alc., m.p. 93° ⟨15⟩. [Does not distinguish C̄ from vinylacetic ac. (1:1042), isocrotonic ac. (1:1045), since they also give same product on similar treatment; nor from acrylic ac. (1:1020) which gives β-anilinopropionanilide also with m.p. 93°.]

AgĀ, curdy ppt. rap. darkening in light; $Ca\bar{A}_2$ and $Ba\bar{A}_2$, eas. sol. aq.; $Pb\bar{A}_2$ insol. aq.

Ⓓ **p-Nitrobenzyl α-crotonate:** m.p. 67.4° ⟨16⟩ [cf. T 1.39]. [Requires mixed m.p. with C̄.]

Ⓓ **p-Bromophenacyl α-crotonate:** m.p. 95–96° ⟨17⟩ [cf. T 1.391].

—— **α-Crotonamide:** ndls. from acetone or C_6H_6, m.p. 159–160° ⟨18⟩ [from crotonyl chloride (above) in ether + liquid NH_3 at temp. of solid CO_2 ⟨18⟩ cf. ⟨2⟩; best separated from NH_4Cl by fract. crystn. from aq. ⟨2⟩; on exposure of acetone soln. for 3 weeks to u.v. light is partly isomerized to isocrotonamide, m.p. 101–102° ⟨18⟩].

Ⓓ **α-Crotonanilide** [Beil. XII-257]: ndls. from aq., pr. from dil. alc., m.p. 118° ⟨18⟩; 120° ⟨15⟩; 115° ⟨2⟩ ⟨10⟩ [from crotonyl chloride (above) shaken with aniline + excess aq. 10% NaOH ⟨18⟩ ⟨15⟩]. [This anilide in $CHCl_3$ treated with 1 Br_2 gives 100% yield α,β-dibromo-n-butyranilide, lfts. from alc., m.p. 159–160° ⟨19⟩ ⟨10⟩.]

Ⓓ **α-Crotono-p-toluidide** [Beil. XII-925]: cryst. from C_6H_6, m.p. 132° ⟨20⟩ [from C̄ htd. with 1 mole p-toluidine, then vac. distd. ⟨20⟩; if excess p-toluidine is used there also results β-(p-toluidino)-n-butyro-p-toluidide, cryst. from C_6H_6 + pet. ether, m.p. 101°, but this is easily separated from the above by its higher b.p. ⟨20⟩.]

Ⓓ **S-Benzylthiuronium α-crotonate:** m.p. 162° cor. ⟨21⟩.

1:0425 ⟨1⟩ Young, *J. Am. Chem. Soc.* **54,** 2498–2503 (1932). ⟨2⟩ Letch, Linstead, *J. Chem. Soc.* **1932,** 454–455. ⟨3⟩ Scheibler, Magasanik, *Ber.* **48,** 1814–1815 (1915). ⟨4⟩ Skau, Saxton, *J. Am. Chem. Soc.* **52,** 335–341 (1930). ⟨5⟩ Linstead, Noble, *J. Chem. Soc.* **1934,** 622. ⟨6⟩ Michael, Norton, *Am. Chem. J.* **2,** 12 (1880–1881). ⟨7⟩ Boorman, Linstead, Rydon, *J. Chem. Soc.* **1933,** 572. ⟨8⟩ Grimshaw, Guy, Smith, *J. Chem. Soc.* **1940,** 69. ⟨9⟩ Walling, Kharasch, Mayo, *J. Am. Chem. Soc.* **61,** 2696 (1939). ⟨10⟩ Autenrieth, Spiess, *Ber.* **34,** 193 (1901).
⟨11⟩ Luniak, *Ber.* **42,** 915 (1909). ⟨12⟩ Fuson, Christ, Whitman, *J. Am. Chem. Soc.* **58,** 2450 (1936). ⟨13⟩ Staudinger, Becker, Herzel, *Ber.* **49,** 1991 (1916). ⟨14⟩ Stoermer, Robert, *Ber.* **55,** 1035 (1922). ⟨15⟩ Autenrieth, Pretzell, *Ber.* **36,** 1266–1267 (1903). ⟨16⟩ Cowles, *M.I.T. Thesis.* ⟨17⟩ von Auwers, *Ann.* **432,** 59 (1923). ⟨18⟩ Stoermer, Stockmann, *Ber.* **47,** 1789–1790 (1914). ⟨19⟩ Autenrieth, *Ber.* **38,** 2546 (1905). ⟨20⟩ Fichter, *J. prakt. Chem.* (2) **74,** 318 (1906).
⟨21⟩ Donleavy, *J. Am. Chem. Soc.* **58,** 1005 (1936).

1:0430 GLYCOLIC ACID (Hydroxyacetic acid) $CH_2.OH$ | COOH $C_2H_4O_3$ Beil. III-228

M.P. 78-79° (80°) **Neut. Eq. 76**

Cryst. from ether or acetone ⟨1⟩; deliquescent and dif. to crystallize if not pure — Eas. sol. aq., alc., ether; not easily extracted from aq. solns. by ether [for distribution coeff. and use in sepn. from lactic ac. (1:0400), malic ac. (1:0450), and citric ac. (1:0505) see ⟨2⟩].

C̄ on protracted htg. at 100° yields glycolic anhydride (α,α′-dihydroxyacetic anhydride), powder insol. ether, alc. or cold aq., m.p. 128–130° — C̄ on htg. at 200–240° gives polyglycolid (1:4970), m.p. 220° together with a little diglycolic acid (1:0495), m.p. 148°, and polyoxymethylene — C̄ on distn. in vac. gives glycolid (1:0667).

C̄ htd. at 120° with 2 moles PCl_5 gives chloroacetyl chloride.

C̄, warmed with 2 pts. AcCl, excess reagt. distd. off and residue recrystd. from C_6H_6 or $CHCl_3$ gives acetoxyacetic acid, ndls., m.p. 66° ⟨3⟩ ⟨4⟩ — [Note, however, that benzoyloxyacetic acid (glycolic acid benzoate), m.p. 112° cannot be prepd. by direct benzoylation ⟨5⟩.]

Ⓓ ***p*-Nitrobenzyl glycolate:** m.p. 106.8° ⟨6⟩ [cf. T 1.39].

Ⓓ ***p*-Bromophenacyl glycolate:** m.p. 138° ⟨7⟩ [cf. T 1.391].

—— **Glycolamide:** cryst. from alc. + EtOAc, m.p. 120° ⟨8⟩ [from ethyl glycolate (1:3338) + NH_3 ⟨8⟩].

Ⓓ **Glycolic anilide** [Beil. XII-481]: from C̄ htd. with aniline at 130° ⟨9⟩; cryst. from aq. or C_6H_6; m.p. 97° ⟨9⟩.

Ⓓ **Glycolic *p*-toluidide:** [Beil. XII-960]: from C̄ + equiv. amt. *p*-toluidine, htd. 2–3 hrs. at 100°, cooled, recrystd. from aq. (70% yield ⟨10⟩); m.p. 143°.

Ⓓ **2-(Hydroxymethyl)benzimidazole:** from C̄ + ⅔ mole *o*-phenylenediamine on boilg. 30–40 min. with 4 *N* HCl, then neutralized with NH_4OH (65% yield); pl. from 50% alc., m.p. 171–172° ⟨11⟩ ⟨12⟩. [The picrate of this deriv. forms yel. ndls., m.p. 214° ⟨13⟩.]

Ⓓ ***S*-Benzylthiuronium glycolate:** m.p. 141° cor. ⟨14⟩; 146–147° ⟨15⟩.

1:0430 ⟨1⟩ Polstorff, Meyer, *Ber.* **45,** 1909 (1912). ⟨2⟩ Pinnow, *Z. Untersuch. Lebensm.* **37,** 49–52 (1919). ⟨3⟩ Senter, Ward, *J. Chem. Soc.* **101,** 2538 (1912). ⟨4⟩ Anschütz, Bertram, *Ber.* **36,** 467 (1903). ⟨5⟩ Brigl, Grüner, *Ber.* **65,** 645 (1932). ⟨6⟩ Cowles, *M.I.T. Thesis.* ⟨7⟩ Judefind, Reid, *J. Am. Chem. Soc.* **42,** 1055 (1920). ⟨8⟩ Schmuck, *Biochem. Z.* **147,** 193–202 (1924). ⟨9⟩ Bischoff, Walden, *Ann.* **279,** 49 (1894). ⟨10⟩ Ref. 9, page 63.

⟨11⟩ Phillips, *J. Chem. Soc.* **1928,** 2395. ⟨12⟩ Bistrzycki, Przeworski, *Ber.* **45,** 3488 (1912). ⟨13⟩ Brown, Campbell, *J. Chem. Soc.* **1937,** 1701. ⟨14⟩ Donleavy, *J. Am. Chem. Soc.* **58,** 1005 (1936). ⟨15⟩ Veibel, Lillelund, *Bull. soc. chim.* (5) **5,** 1157 (1938).

1:0431 α-HYDROXYISOBUTYRIC ACID $C_4H_8O_3$ Beil. III-313

(Acetonic acid, dimethylglycolic acid) $(CH_3)_2.C(OH).COOH$

M.P. 79° **Neut. Eq. 104**

Hygros. pr. — m.p. often lowered by traces of moisture — sl. volat. with st. — very sol. aq., alc., ether, hot C_6H_6 — cryst. from pet. eth.

C̄ with $FeCl_3$ gives intense yel. color (T 1.32) — C̄ grad. reduces $NH_4OH/AgNO_3$ or $KMnO_4$ — C̄ on oxidn. with CrO_3 (T 1.72) or fusion with KOH yields acetone (1:5400).

C̄ on htg. ⟨1⟩ yields 48% acetone (1:5400), 13% methacrylic ac. [Beil. II-421], and 30% tetramethylglycolid [Beil. XIX-155].

$Ca\bar{A}_2$, $Ba\bar{A}_2$, both very sol. aq.; $Ag\bar{A}$, sol. in 14 pts. cold aq.; $Zn\bar{A}_2.2H_2O$ sol. in 160 pts. aq. at 15°, alm. insol. abs. alc.

Ⓓ **α-Acetoxyisobutyric acid:** from C̄ by htg. with excess Ac_2O at 100°; on cooling prod. seps. in long ndls., recrystd. from CS_2, m.p. 61°; Neut. Eq. 146 ⟨2⟩.

Ⓓ ***p*-Nitrobenzyl α-hydroxyisobutyrate:** m.p. 80.5° ⟨3⟩ ⟨4⟩ [cf. T 1.39]. [Note that this ester depresses m.p. of original C̄ ⟨3⟩.]

—— **α-Hydroxyisobutyramide:** pl. from acetone, m.p. 98° (indirectly) [very sol. aq.].

—— **α-Hydroxyisobutyranilide:** tbls. from aq., cryst. from C_6H_6 + ether, m.p. 136° ⟨5⟩.

Ⓓ **α-Hydroxyisobutyro-*p*-toluidide:** from C̄ on htg. at 140° with *p*-toluidine; lfts. from hot aq., m.p. 132–133° ⟨6⟩.

1:0431 ⟨1⟩ Blaise, Bagard, *Ann. chim.* (8) **11,** 115–116 (1907). ⟨2⟩ Anschütz, Motschmann, *Ann.* **392,** 108 (1912). ⟨3⟩ Lyons, Reid, *J. Am. Chem. Soc.* **39,** 1732 (1917). ⟨4⟩ Campbell, *J. Am. Chem. Soc.* **59,** 1983 (1937). ⟨5⟩ Bischoff, Walden, *Ann.* **279,** 112 (1894). ⟨6⟩ Tigerstedt, *Ber.* **25,** 2929 (1892).

1:0435 CITRACONIC ACID (Methylmaleic acid)

$CH_3—C—COOH$ ‖ $H—C—COOH$ $C_5H_6O_4$ **Beil. II-768**

M.P. 92-93° ⟨1⟩ **Neut. Eq. 65**

Thin flat very hygroscopic ndls. from ether + lgr.; tbls. from ether + C_6H_6 — Sol. in 0.42 pts. aq. at 15°; sol. ether, spar. sol. cold $CHCl_3$; insol. CS_2, C_6H_6, lgr. — C̄ on distn. with steam is converted to citraconic anhydride (1:1135), q.v., which is somewhat volatile with steam (dif. and sepn. from itaconic ac. (1:0515) and mesaconic ac. (1:0548) ⟨2⟩).

[For prepn. of C̄ (94% yield) by actn. of aq. on citraconic anhydride (1:1135) see ⟨1⟩.]

C̄ in $CHCl_3$ + ether soln. + trace Br_2 exposed to light gives (85% yield ⟨3⟩, 67% yield ⟨2⟩) mesaconic ac. (1:0548) — C̄ on evapn. with HCl or HBr or dil. HNO_3 yields mesaconic acid (1:0548) — C̄ on long (e.g., 120 hrs.) boilg. with 25% aq. KOH yields an equilibrium mixt. contg. 15% C̄, 69% mesaconic ac. (1:0548), and 16% itaconic acid (1:0515) ⟨4⟩ — C̄ in aq. soln. boiled 1 min. with a trace of HgCl + a little $K_2S_2O_8$ gives itaconic ac. (1:0515) ⟨5⟩.

C̄ on htg. or on treatment with $SOCl_2$ ⟨6⟩ gives citraconic anhydride (**1:1135**). C̄ htd. with PCl_5 gives citraconyl (di)chloride, b.p. $95^{\circ}_{17.5}$ ⟨7⟩, $96–97^{\circ}_{15}$ ⟨3⟩ which with aq. is quant. hydrolyzed to C̄ ⟨3⟩.

Ⓓ **Di-*p*-nitrobenzyl citraconate:** m.p. 70.6° ⟨8⟩ [cf. T 1.39].

Ⓓ **Diphenacyl citraconate:** m.p. 108.5° ⟨9⟩ [cf. T 1.391].

—— **Citraconic diamide:** cryst. from alc., aq., or boilg. C_6H_6; browning at 185°, then dec. 185–191° to NH_3 and citraconimide [Beil. XXI-406], m.p. 109–110° [from dimethyl citraconate (1:3686) with conc. aq. NH_4OH in cold ⟨7⟩ for a week ⟨10⟩]. [The monoamide (citraconamidic acid) has m.p. 125° (see citraconic anhydride 1:1135).]

—— **Citraconic dianilide** [Beil. XII-308]: ndls. from alc., m.p. 175.5° ⟨7⟩ [from citraconyl (di)chloride + aniline both in ether soln. ⟨7⟩]. [The monoanilide (citraconanilic acid) has m.p. 153° ⟨11⟩.] [*N*-Phenylcitraconimide (citraconanil) [Beil. XXI-407] from equal moles C̄ + aniline htd. at 170° ⟨12⟩ forms ndls. from aq., m.p. 98–99°.]

—— **Citraconic di-*p*-toluidide:** not recorded. [The mono-*p*-toluidide (from citraconic anhydride (1:1135) + 1 mole *p*-toluidine, both in ether ⟨11⟩, is a citron-yel. pdr., m.p. 170–171°. On boiling with aq. it yields *N*-(*p*-tolyl)citraconimide (citracon-*p*-tolil) [Beil. XXI-407] white ndls. from aq., m.p. 114–115° ⟨11⟩.]

1:0435 ⟨1⟩ Shriner, Ford, Roll, *Organic Syntheses* **11,** 28–29 (1931). ⟨2⟩ Linstead, Mann, *J. Chem. Soc.* **1931,** 734. ⟨3⟩ Lutz, Taylor, *J. Am. Chem. Soc.* **55,** 1173 (1933). ⟨4⟩ Ref. 2, pages 728, 735. ⟨5⟩ Wieland, Zilg, *Ann.* **530,** 273 (1937). ⟨6⟩ Meyer, *Monatsh.* **22,** 422 (1901). ⟨7⟩ Strecker, *Ber.* **15,** 1640–1641 (1882). ⟨8⟩ Cowles, *M.I.T. Thesis.* ⟨9⟩ Rather, Reid, *J. Am. Chem. Soc.* **41,** 80 (1919). ⟨10⟩ van de Straete, *Bull. soc. chim. Belg.* **44,** 317 (1935).

⟨11⟩ Anschütz, *Ann.* **461,** 167–168 (1928). ⟨12⟩ Reissert, *Ber.* **21,** 1368 (1888); *Ber.* **22,** 2287 (1889).

1:0440 GLUTARIC ACID (Propane-1,3-dicarboxylic acid)

$HOOC.(CH_2)_3.COOH$ $C_5H_8O_4$ **Beil. II-631**

M.P. 98° **Neut. Eq. 66**
B.P. 302-304°

Pr. from aq. or C_6H_6 — 100 ml. aq. soln. at 0° cont. 42.9 g. C̄; at 50°, 63.9 g. C̄ — C̄ is very sol. alc., ether.

[For prepn. from trimethylene (di)cyanide (83–85% yield) ⟨1⟩; 56% yield ⟨2⟩ see ⟨1⟩; from diethyl malonate + formaldehyde (46–50%) see ⟨3⟩; from cyclopentanone (1:5446) (80–85% yield) by oxidn. with HNO_3 + V_2O_5 see ⟨4⟩.]

C̄ refluxed several hrs. at 10 mm. press., then distd. at same press. ⟨5⟩; or C̄ + 2 moles AcCl at 40°, followed by distn. at 15 mm. ⟨6⟩; or C̄, htd. with 1 mole PCl_5 at 110°, the $POCl_3$ distd. off, and residual prod. htd. with a second mole C̄ and finally distd. in vac. ⟨7⟩; or C̄ distd. with Ac_2O ⟨8⟩, or C̄ + 2–3 moles $SOCl_2$ (78% yield ⟨9⟩) gives monomeric glutaric anhydride [Beil. XVII-411], hygroscopic ndls. from ether, or from $CHCl_3$ + pet. ether, m.p. 56–57°, b.p. 286–288° cor., b.p. 150°_{10}. [This glutaric anhydride may be used in Friedel-Crafts' reactions, e.g., with C_6H_6 to prepare γ-benzoyl-*n*-butyric ac. (80–85% yield ⟨10⟩).] [For detn. of the anyhdride via reaction with aniline see ⟨11⟩, via titration with NaOMe see ⟨12⟩.]

C̄ treated with 4.5–5 pts. PCl_5 at 40–50° ⟨13⟩ ⟨14⟩ gives (80–88% yield ⟨13⟩) glutaryl (di)chloride, b.p. 216–218° cor., b.p. $107\text{–}108^\circ_{16}$, $D_4^{20} = 1.324$, $n_D^{20} = 1.4728$ ⟨14⟩. [This glutaryl (di)chloride may react either in sym. or unsym. form ⟨15⟩.]

[For sepn. from succinic ac. (1:0530), adipic ac. (1:0775) and pimelic ac. (1:0456) see ⟨27⟩.]

Ⓓ **Di-(*p*-nitrobenzyl) glutarate:** m.p. 69° ⟨16⟩ [cf. T 1.39].
Ⓓ **Di-(phenacyl) glutarate:** m.p. 104.5° ⟨17⟩ [cf. T 1.391].
Ⓓ **Di-(*p*-bromophenacyl) glutarate:** m.p. 136.8° ⟨18⟩ [cf. T 1.391].
Ⓓ **Di(*p*-phenylphenacyl) glutarate:** m.p. 152° ⟨19⟩ [cf. T 1.391].
—— **Glutaric diamide:** m.p. 175–176° [very sol. aq.; from diethyl glutarate (1:3967) + alc. NH_3 at 100°]. [The mono-amide (glutaramic acid), from glutaric anhydride (above) via treat. with conc. aq. NH_4OH, pptn. as silver salt, and isolation via H_2S, forms cryst. from acetone + ether, m.p. 93–94° ⟨8⟩]. [C̄ on neutralization with NH_4OH and evapn. gives $(NH_4)_2\bar{A}$, which on fusion at 170–180° ⟨20⟩ ⟨21⟩ or on dry distn. ⟨22⟩ gives good yield of the monomeric cyclic glutarimide [Beil. XXI-382], pl. from alc., m.p. 152°.]
Ⓓ **Glutaric dianilide** [Beil. XII-298]: In dry tt. fitted with cork carrying a 25 cm. long glass tubing as air condenser, heat 0.1 g. C̄ with 0.4–0.6 ml. aniline at 175–190° for 1 hr. Boil with 10 ml. 50% alc., cool, filter off ppt. Wash with 2 ml. cold 50% alc., and recryst. from 5 ml. boiling strong alc., cooling and shaking if no ppt. appears at once. Filter, wash with 1 ml. cold alc., dry at 100° ⟨23⟩; white ndls., m.p. 223–224° ⟨24⟩. [The mono-anilide (glutaranilic acid) [Beil. XII-297], from glutaric anhydride (above) + 1 mole aniline at 15° ⟨25⟩, cryst. from aq. in pearly lfts., m.p. 128° ⟨25⟩.] [*N*-phenylglutarimide (glutaranil) [Beil. XXI-383], sometimes obtd. in prepn. of dianilide, or by dry distn. of dianilide, can be sublimed; cryst. from alc., m.p. 144–145°.]
Ⓓ **Glutaric di-*p*-toluidide:** m.p. 218° ⟨24⟩.
Ⓓ **Piperazonium 1,4-diacid glutarate:** from C̄ + ½ mole piperazine hexahydrate (77% yield), cryst. from 95% alc., m.p. 152° cor., Neut. Eq. 116.7 ⟨26⟩.

1:0440 ⟨1⟩ Marvel, Tuley, *Organic Syntheses, Coll. Vol.* I, 283–284 (1932). ⟨2⟩ Serwy, *Bull. soc. chim. Belg.* **42,** 485 (1933). ⟨3⟩ Otterbacher, *Organic Syntheses, Coll. Vol.* I, 284–286 (1932); **10,** 58–59 (1930). ⟨4⟩ Allen, Ball, *Organic Syntheses,* **14,** 90–91 (1934). ⟨5⟩ Krafft, Noerdlinger, *Ber.* **22,** 817 (1889). ⟨6⟩ Mol, *Rec. trav. chim.* **26,** 381 (1907). ⟨7⟩ Voerman, *Rec. trav. chim.* **23,** 267 (1904). ⟨8⟩ Jeffery, Vogel, *J. Chem. Soc.* **1934,** 1103. ⟨9⟩ McMaster, Ahmann, *J. Am. Chem. Soc.* **50,** 146 (1928). ⟨10⟩ Somerville, Allen, *Organic Syntheses* **13,** 13 (1933). ⟨11⟩ Vles, *Rec. trav. chim.* **52,** 822–823 (1933). ⟨12⟩ Smith, Bryant, *J. Am. Chem. Soc.* **58,** 2453 (1936). ⟨13⟩ Skraup, Guggenheimer, *Ber.* **58,** 2498 (1925). ⟨14⟩ von Auwers, Schmidt, *Ber.* **46,** 479 (1913). ⟨15⟩ Plant, Tomlinson, *J. Chem. Soc.* **1935,** 856. ⟨16⟩ Kelly, Segura, *J. Am. Chem. Soc.* **56,** 2497 (1934). ⟨17⟩ Rather, Reid, *J. Am. Chem. Soc.* **41,** 79 (1919). ⟨18⟩ Kelly, Kleff, *J. Am. Chem. Soc.* **54,** 4444 (1932). ⟨19⟩ Drake, Sweeney, *J. Am. Chem. Soc.* **54,** 2060 (1932). ⟨20⟩ Sakurai, *Bull. Chem. Soc. Japan* **13,** 483 (1938).

⟨21⟩ Bernheimer, *Gazz. chim. ital.* **12,** 281–282 (1882). ⟨22⟩ Sircar, *J. Chem. Soc.* **1927,** 602 ⟨23⟩ Mulliken, " Method " I, 84 (1904). ⟨24⟩ Barnicoat, *J. Chem. Soc.* **1927,** 2927–2928. ⟨25⟩ Morgan, Walton, *J. Chem. Soc.* **1932,** 279. ⟨26⟩ Pollard, Adelson, Bain, *J. Am. Chem. Soc.* **56,** 1759 (1934). ⟨27⟩ Bouveault, *Bull. soc. chim.* (3) **19,** 562–565 (1898).

1:0445 OXALIC ACID, dihydrate $\begin{matrix} COOH \\ | \\ COOH \end{matrix} .2H_2O$ $C_2H_2O_4.2H_2O$ **Beil. II-502**

M.P. 100±1° **Neut. Eq. 63**

Monoclinic prisms, stable in (moist) air but readily losing aq. on htg., or on distn. with CCl_4, toluene, etc., yielding anhydrous oxalic ac. (1:0535).

Sol. in 10.5 pts. aq. at 15°; moderately sol. alc.; 100 pts. abs. ether dis. 1.5 g. $\bar{C}$ at 25°.

$\bar{C}$ (or its salts) htd. with conc. H_2SO_4 give both $CO + CO_2$, latter detected by leading into $Ba(OH)_2$ soln. (dif. from formic ac. (or its salts) which yield only CO) — $\bar{C}$ decolorizes acid $KMnO_4$ soln. on warming (use in detn. of $\bar{C}$ or salts and in standardization of $KMnO_4$ solns.), but alk. $KMnO_4$ (T 1.34) is *not* reduced.

$\bar{C}$ treated with Ac_2O rapidly decomposes with $CO_2 + CO$ ⟨1⟩. [Formic ac. (1:1005) yields only CO, while no gas at all is obtd. with citric, lactic, malic, malonic, succinic, or *d*-tartaric acids ⟨1⟩.] [For use of method with aq. sol. salts first evap. with 15% HCl and use moist residue of $\bar{C}$ + metallic chloride ⟨1⟩. The reaction is markedly catalyzed by pyridine (cf. anhydrous oxalic ac.) (1:0535).]

$\bar{C}$ in acetone soln. treated with pyridine gives bulky ppt. of pyridine acid oxalate (useful for purification of pyridine ⟨2⟩); addn. of Ac_2O to suspension or to ppt. causes evolution of $CO + CO_2$ ⟨2⟩.

Salts: Dif. sol. except those of alkalies and Mg, but many dis. in excess of alkali oxalate soln. — $Ca\bar{A}$ most insol. salt, viz., 0.09 m.e. per liter at 20° (insol. in oxalic ac., $(NH_4)_2$ oxalate, or AcOH, but readily sol. in dil. HCl or HNO_3) — $Ag_2\bar{A}$ explosive when dry. [For study of thermal decomp. see ⟨9⟩.] Impt. salts freq. met: $(NH_4)_2\bar{A}.2H_2O$, $Na_2\bar{A}$, $K_2\bar{A}$, $KH\bar{A}$ (K binoxalate), $KH\bar{A}.H_2\bar{A}.2H_2O$ (K quadroxalate).]

Neither $\bar{C}$ nor its salts char on ignition; oxalates of Au, Ag, Pt, Fe, Co, Ni, Cu, give free metal; salts of alk. earths and alkalies give carbonate + CO; other salts give metal oxide.

Ⓟ **Aniline blue formation:** $\bar{C}$ melted with diphenylamine over free flame, cooled, and dislvd. in alc., gives blue color ⟨3⟩ [not given by formic, acetic, propionic, succinic, glycolic, citric, tartaric, benzoic, phthalic, or tricarballylic acids ⟨3⟩].

Ⓓ **Di-(*p*-nitrobenzyl) oxalate:** m.p. 204° ⟨4⟩ (but in poor yield) [cf. T 1.39].

Ⓓ **Di-(*p*-phenylphenacyl) oxalate:** m.p. 165.5° dec. ⟨5⟩ [cf. T 1.391].

Ⓓ **Oxanilide:** from $\bar{C}$ on htg. with excess aniline; cryst. from C_6H_6, m.p. 246°. [The monoanilide (oxanilic acid) [Beil. XII-281] has m.p. 149°.]

Ⓓ **Oxalic di-*p*-toluidide:** Clamp a 6-in. tt. in an upright position so that it rests in a 1-cm. hole in an asbestos board laid across an iron ring. Add 0.1 g. $\bar{C}$ and 0.5–0.7 g. *p*-toluidine and reflux over a small flame for 15 min. so that *p*-toluidine condenses on lower third of tube. Add 10 ml. 50% alc., boil, cool, filter. Wash residue on filter with 5 ml. water, transfer to tt., and boil with 10 ml. strong alc. Cool, filter, wash with 2 ml. alc., dry at 110°, m.p. 268° ⟨6⟩. [The mono-*p*-toluidide (*N*-*p*-tolyloxamic acid) [Beil. XII-930], has m.p. 169°.]

Ⓓ **Di-(*S*-benzylthiuronium) oxalate:** m.p. 193° cor. ⟨7⟩; 195–196° ⟨8⟩.

1:0445 ⟨1⟩ Krause, *Ber.* **52,** 426–432 (1919). ⟨2⟩ Whitford, *J. Am. Chem. Soc.* **47,** 2934–2938 (1925). ⟨3⟩ Feigl, Frehden, *Mikrochemie* **18,** 272–276 (1935). ⟨4⟩ Lyman, Reid, *J. Am. Chem. Soc.* **39,** 705 (1917). ⟨5⟩ Drake, Bronitsky, *J. Am. Chem. Soc.* **52,** 3719 (1930). ⟨6⟩ Mulliken, " Method " I, 84 (1904). ⟨7⟩ Donleavy, *J. Am. Chem. Soc.* **58,** 1005 (1936). ⟨8⟩ Veibel, Lillelund, *Bull. soc. chim.* (5) **5,** 1157 (1938). ⟨9⟩ Macdonald, *J. Chem. Soc.* **1936,** 832–847.

1:0450 ***l*-MALIC ACID** (Hydroxysuccinic acid) HO—CH.COOH / H_2C—COOH $C_4H_6O_5$ **Beil. III-419**

M.P. 100°-101° ⟨1⟩ Neut. Eq. 67

Deliquescent ndls. crystg. with difficulty — Soly. in aq. at 26° is 144.8 g. per 100 g. aq., very sol. alc. — 100 pts. ether at 15° dis. 8.4 pts. C̄ — [Distribution coeff. of C̄ between aq. and ether at 15° is abt. 62.4, at 25.5° abt. 70.9 ⟨2⟩.] — C̄ in dil. aq. soln. is slightly laevorotatory but optical rotation diminishes with increasing concn. passing through 0° around 30–35%, then becoming dextrorotatory cf. ⟨3⟩. [*d,l*-Malic acid cryst. more readily than C̄ and is not deliquescent; its m.p. is variously reported from 125–126° to 133°.] [For m.p.'s of mixts. of *l*-malic + *d*-malic acids see ⟨1⟩.]

C̄ (20–50 mg.) on htg. in a dry tt. at abt. 200° yields ⟨4⟩ a fine crystn. sublimate of fumaric ac. (1:0895) — C̄ on boilg. 24 hrs. with large excess 20% NaOH yields fumaric acid (1:0895). [*d,l*-Malic ac. on evapn. with 2 moles excess NaOH and htg. residue 3 hrs. at 130° gives fumaric ac. in alm. quant. yield ⟨5⟩.] [*d,l*-Malic ac. on drying at even 75–95° is partly transformed to an anhydride ⟨6⟩.]

C̄ gives with $FeCl_3$ (T 1.32) the yel. color characteristic of α-hydroxy acids — Comml. C̄ with I_2.KI + aq. alk. (T 1.81) gives CHI_3 reaction ⟨7⟩ — C̄ on treatment with 100% H_2SO_4 evolves CO even at room temp. ⟨8⟩; on htg. C̄ with ord. conc. H_2SO_4 CO is evolved but much charring and side reaction occurs.

C̄ is unaffected by $SOCl_2$ at room temp. but C̄, on htg. with 4 pts. $SOCl_2$ at 100° for 1 hr. dissolves; after removal of excess reagt. under reduced press. and pouring resultant oil into aq. yields *d*-chlorosuccinic acid, extd. with ether; cryst. from C_6H_6 + a little acetone, m.p. 174° in 30% yield ⟨9⟩. [If htg. with $SOCl_2$ is prolonged, e.g., to $3\frac{1}{2}$ hrs. much racemization occurs and m.p. of prod. is low.]

C̄ treated at 40° with 50% excess of theoretical AcCl ⟨10⟩ ⟨11⟩ yields acetyl malic anhydride [Beil. XVIII-81] b.p. $160–162°_{14}$, m.p. 53–54°, which on treatment with ice cold aq. gives acetyl-*l*-malic acid, pptd. from AcOEt by C_6H_6, m.p. on rapid htg. 139–140°, slow htg. 135–136° ⟨12⟩. [The corresp. acetyl *d,l*-malic ac. has m.p. 129–130° ⟨12⟩] — C̄ + $2\frac{1}{2}$ pts. BzCl htd. 6 hrs. at 100° gives 32% yield benzoyl-*l*-malic ac., cryst. from aq., m.p. 162° ⟨13⟩.

C̄, in neutral soln. contg. NH_4Cl, not pptd. by $CaCl_2$ even on boilg., but on addn. of 1–2 vols. alc. CaĀ is pptd. (dif. from oxalic ac. (1:0445), *d*-tartaric ac. (1:0525), or citric ac. (1:0455) — C̄ with $Pb(OAc)_2$ soln. gives voluminous white ppt., fusing to resinous mass on boilg. with aq. — C̄ ppts. Ag_2Ā (T 1.36); %Ag = 65.04.

Ⓟ **Color reaction with β-naphthol + H_2SO_4:** To 0.05 g. of finely powdered C̄ in small porcelain evapg. dish add 10–15 drops of freshly prepared soln. of 0.1 g. β-naphthol in pure conc. H_2SO_4. Place the dish on a boiling-water bath and remove it at 0.5–1.0 minute intervals for observation of the rapidly successive color changes. Malic acid gives first a greenish-yellow (GY-Y) that rapidly changes to an intense yellow (Y) which is quite permanent. Dilution with 4–5 volumes of water gives a yellow-orange ⟨14⟩ ⟨15⟩.

Ⓓ **Di-(*p*-nitrobenzyl) *l*-malate:** m.p. 124.5° ⟨16⟩ [cf. T 1.39]. [The mono *p*-nitrobenzyl ester has m.p. 87.2° ⟨16⟩.]

Ⓓ **Di-(phenacyl) *l*-malate:** m.p. 106° ⟨17⟩ [cf. T 1.391]. [For use in presence of acetic ac. (1:1010), citric ac. (1:0455), oxalic ac. (1:0445), succinic ac. (1:0530), or *d*-tartaric ac. (1:0525) see ⟨26⟩.]

Ⓓ **Di-(*p*-bromophenacyl) *l*-malate:** m.p. 179° ⟨18⟩ [cf. T 1.391].

—— ***l*-Malamide:** pr. from aq., m.p. 156–157° ⟨19⟩, 157° ⟨20⟩, 156.5–158° dec. ⟨21⟩ [from dimethyl *l*-malate (1:3992) + NH_3 in MeOH, 95% yield ⟨22⟩; similarly from diethyl *l*-malate (1:4116) ⟨20⟩]. [The corresp. *d,l*-malamide has m.p. 162–163° ⟨1⟩ ⟨19⟩.] [For m.p. of mixts. of *d*-malamide + *l*-malamide see ⟨1⟩.]

—— ***l*-Malanilide** [Beil. XII-509]: m.p. 197° [from $1\frac{1}{2}$ moles $\bar{C}$ htd. with 2 moles aniline at 175° (95% yield) ⟨23⟩].

—— ***l*-Malic di-*p*-toluidide** [Beil. XII-967]: ndls. from alc., m.p. 206–207° [from $\bar{C}$ htd. at 150–160° with *p*-toluidine ⟨24⟩].

—— **Di-(*S*-benzylthiuronium) *d,l*-malate:** m.p. 159–160° ⟨25⟩.

1:0450 ⟨1⟩ Timmermans, Vesselovsky, *Bull. soc. chim. Belg.* **41,** 54, 56 (1932). ⟨2⟩ Pinnow, *Z. anal. Chem.* **54,** 327–328 (1915). ⟨3⟩ Bancroft, Davis, *J. Phys. Chem.* **34,** 897–928 (1930). ⟨4⟩ Sanchez, *Cent.* **1927,** II, 302. ⟨5⟩ Nelson, *J. Assoc. Official Agr. Chem.* **9,** 379 (1926). ⟨6⟩ Morse, *J. Am. Chem. Soc.* **51,** 1276–1279 (1929). ⟨7⟩ Broeksmit, *Pharm. Weekblad* **56,** 1047–1052 (1919); *Chem. Abs.* **13,** 3113 (1919). ⟨8⟩ Whitford, *J. Am. Chem. Soc.* **47,** 953–968 (1925). ⟨9⟩ McKenzie, Barrow, *J. Chem. Soc.* **99,** 1919 (1911). ⟨10⟩ Anschütz, *Ber.* **14,** 2791 (1881).

⟨11⟩ Anschütz, Bennert, *Ann.* **254,** 166–167 (1889). ⟨12⟩ Holmberg, *Ber.* **60,** 2193 (1927). ⟨13⟩ Freudenberg, Noë, *Ber.* **58,** 2406 (1925). ⟨14⟩ Mulliken, "Method" I, 83 (1904). ⟨15⟩ Eegriwe, *Z. anal. Chem.* **89,** 122–123 (1932). ⟨16⟩ Lyman, Reid, *J. Am. Chem. Soc.* **39,** 708 (1917). ⟨17⟩ Rather, Reid, *J. Am. Chem. Soc.* **41,** 79 (1919). ⟨18⟩ Kelly, Kleff, *J. Am. Chem. Soc.* **54,** 4444 (1932). ⟨19⟩ Freudenberg, Brauns, *Ber.* **55,** 1352 (1922). ⟨20⟩ McCrae, *J. Chem. Soc.* **83,** 1325 (1903).

⟨21⟩ McKenzie, Smith, *J. Chem. Soc.* **121,** 1360 (1922). ⟨22⟩ Freudenberg, *Ber.* **47,** 2031 (1914). ⟨23⟩ Bischoff, Nastvogel, *Ber.* **23,** 2040 (1890). ⟨24⟩ Ref. 23, page 2045. ⟨25⟩ Veibel, Ottung, *Bull. soc. chim.* (5) **6,** 1435 (1939). ⟨26⟩ Rather, Reid, *J. Am. Chem. Soc.* **43,** 635 (1921).

1:0455 CITRIC ACID (monohydrate) $C_6H_8O_7.H_2O$ Beil. III-556

```
        CH2—COOH
         |
    HO—C—COOH
         |
        CH2—COOH
```

M.P. 100° rap. htg. **Neut. Eq. 70**

Rhomb. pr. with 1 H_2O; on stdg. over conc. H_2SO_4 or on htg. to 130° loses aq. yielding anhydrous citric acid (1:0505). Evapn. of boilg. aq. solns. yields anhydrous form which, once obtd., seps. as such even on recrystallization from cold aq. ⟨1⟩ ⟨2⟩.

Solubility of $\bar{C}$ in aq. at 25° is 62.07% ⟨3⟩; 100 g. 90% alc. soln. at 15° conts. 34.6 g. $\bar{C}$; 100 g. abs. ether dis. 9.1 g. $\bar{C}$ — Distribution-coefficient between aq. and ether at 15° is 128; at 25.5° is 155 ⟨4⟩ — Solid $\bar{C}$ (D = 1.542) floats on CCl_4 ⟨5⟩ [dif. from *d*-tartaric ac. (1:0525) (D = 1.594) which sinks ⟨5⟩].

$\bar{C}$ with $FeCl_3$ (T 1.32) gives yel. color characteristic of aliphatic hydroxy acids — $\bar{C}$ does not reduce $NH_4OH/AgNO_3$ [dif. from *d*-tartaric ac. (1:0525)] — $\bar{C}$ with I_2 + KI + NaOH (T 1.81) yields CHI_3 ⟨6⟩ — $\bar{C}$ in aq. soln. at 80° treated with trace of powd. $KMnO_4$ decolorizes latter (owing to formn. of acetonedicarboxylic ac. (1:0485)) and after addn. of NH_4OH readily gives CHI_3 test (T 1.81) — $\bar{C}$, warmed with 5–6 pts. conc. H_2SO_4 at 80–90°, does not char, but evolves CO and gives yel. soln. contg. acetonedicarboxylic ac. (1:0485); on diluting, making alk. and adding sodium nitroprusside soln. gives blood-red color, changing to violet on addn. of AcOH, and finally fading [dif. from oxalic ac. (1:0445), *d*-tartaric ac. (1:0525), or *l*-malic ac. (1:0450)].

[For conversion of $\bar{C}$ to 37–47% yield of itaconic anhydride (1:0654) by rapid distn. see ⟨7⟩; to aconitic ac. (1:0540) in 41–44% yield with conc. H_2SO_4 see ⟨8⟩; to acetonedicarboxylic ac. (1:0485) in 85–90% yield with fumg. H_2SO_4 see ⟨9⟩ ⟨10⟩.]

Aq. soln. neutd. with $Ca(OH)_2$ soln. remains clear in cold, but ppts. $Ca_3\bar{A}_2.4H_2O$ on boilg.; on cooling in absence of CO_2 ppt. redis. — $CaCl_2$ gives same ppt. with neut. solns. of alk. citrates only on boiling; ppt. sol. in excess alk. citrate, citric ac., or AcOH [alk. tartrate or oxalate give *immed.* ppt. with $CaCl_2$ while malic ac. and neut. malates do so only on addn. of alc.] — Conc. aq. soln. of C̄ or salts, acidified with AcOH, gives no ppt. with 5% KOAc soln. [dif. from tartrate].

C̄ on treatment with excess Br_2-aq. in sunlight ⟨27⟩ or with KBr-$KBrO_3$ soln. + dil. H_2SO_4 gives pentabromoacetone, m.p. 79–80° u.c. but falling to 72–74° on old material ⟨28⟩. [Use in quant. detn. of C̄ ⟨29⟩ ⟨30⟩ ⟨31⟩.]

Ⓟ **Color reaction with β-naphthol + conc. H_2SO_4:** For procedure see under *l*-malic ac. (1:0450). C̄ gives first a pale greenish blue soon turning to blue-green (BG), and finally, rather slowly on continued htg., to an impure green of very slight intensity and permanence. After dilution with aq. the color is yel.-or. (YO) but much paler than that from either *d*-tartaric ac. or *l*-malic ac. ⟨11⟩.

Ⓟ **Color reaction with Ac_2O + pyridine:** C̄ on warming with Ac_2O + pyridine gives carmine-red color ⟨12⟩ [cf. also remarks under corresp. test for aconitic ac. (1:0540)]. [Not given by the esters of C̄ ⟨13⟩.]

Ⓓ **Acetanhydrocitric acid** [Beil. XVIII-539]: C̄ (1 g.), after dehydration by cautious htg. at 140–150°, is cooled, treated with 4–5 ml. AcCl, and refluxed 2 hrs. ($CaCl_2$ tube in condenser exit). After allowing to stand overnight, ppt. is filtered, washed with AcCl, then C_6H_6; m.p. 115–116° ⟨14⟩; 121° ⟨15⟩.

Ⓓ **Tri-(*p*-nitrobenzyl) citrate:** m.p. 102° ⟨16⟩ [cf. T 1.39].

Ⓓ **Tri-(phenacyl) citrate:** m.p. 104° ⟨17⟩ ⟨18⟩ [cf. T 1.391]. [Use in sepn. from acetic ac. (1:1010) benzoic ac. (1:0715), *l*-malic ac. (1:0450), oxalic ac. (1:0445), and *d*-tartaric ac. (1:0525) ⟨19⟩.]

Ⓓ **Tri-(*p*-bromophenacyl) citrate:** m.p. 148.0° ⟨20⟩ [cf. T 1.391].

Ⓓ **Tri-(*p*-phenylphenacyl) citrate:** m.p. 146° ⟨21⟩ [cf. T 1.391].

—— **Citric acid triamide** (**citramide**) [Beil. III-569]; cryst. from aq., browning above 200° and melting 210–215° to a black liq. [from trimethyl citrate (1:2315) in 50–60% yield on stdg. with 4–5 pts. *conc.* aq. NH_4OH ⟨22⟩].

—— **Citric acid trianilide** (**citranilide**) [Beil. XII-514]: pr. from alc., m.p. 199° ⟨23⟩, 192° ⟨24⟩ [from C̄ in 41% yield on htg. with 5/3 pt. aniline at 60–70° for 1 hr., then at 100° for 1 hr. and finally at 120–130° for 3–4 hrs. ⟨23⟩]. [The monoanilide has m.p. 164°; the dianilide, m.p. 179° ⟨23⟩.] [Citric acid α,β-anil (citranilic acid) [Beil. XXII-374], has m.p. 189° ⟨25⟩; citric acid α,β-anil-α′-anilide (citranilic anilide) [Beil. XXII-375], has m.p. 182°.]

—— **Citric acid tri-*p*-toluidide** [Beil. XII-968]: ndls. from alc., m.p. 189° [from C̄ htd. with 3 moles *p*-toluidine at 140–145° for 10 hrs. ⟨26⟩]. [Citric acid α,β-(*N*-*p*-tolyl) imide-α′-*p*-toluidide [Beil. XXII-375] forms yel. cryst. from alc. or AcOH, m.p. 205° ⟨26⟩.]

1:0455 ⟨1⟩ Meyer, *Ber.* **36**, 3601 (1903). ⟨2⟩ Bennett, Yuill, *J. Chem. Soc.* **1935**, 130. ⟨3⟩ Dalman, *J. Am. Chem. Soc.* **59**, 2548 (1937). ⟨4⟩ Pinnow, *Z. anal. Chem.* **54**, 323 (1915). ⟨5⟩ Evrard, *Chem. Abs.* **32**, 1863 (1938). ⟨6⟩ Broeksmit, *Chem. Abs.* **11**, 130 (1917). ⟨7⟩ Shriner, Ford, Roll, *Organic Syntheses* **11**, 70–72 (1931). ⟨8⟩ Bruce, *Organic Syntheses* **17**, 1–3 (1937). ⟨9⟩ Adams, Chiles, Rassweiler, *Organic Syntheses, Coll. Vol.* I, 9–11 (1932). ⟨10⟩ Wiig, *J. Am. Chem. Soc.* **52**, 4729–4737 (1930).

⟨11⟩ Mulliken, "Method" I, 83 (1904). ⟨12⟩ Casares-Lopez, *Biochem. Z.* **284**, 365–366 (1930); *Cent.* **1937**, I, 392. ⟨13⟩ Casares, *Cent.* **1936**, II, 1981. ⟨14⟩ Easterfeld, Sell, *J. Chem. Soc.* **61**, 1003–1004 (1892). ⟨15⟩ Klingemann, *J. Chem. Soc.* **63**, 699 (1893). ⟨16⟩ Reid, *J. Am. Chem. Soc.* **39**, 131–132 (1917). ⟨17⟩ Rather, Reid, *J. Am. Chem. Soc.* **41**, 80 (1919). ⟨18⟩ Kremers, Hall, *J. Biol. Chem.* **41**, 15 (1920). ⟨19⟩ Rather, Reid, *J. Am. Chem. Soc.* **43**, 635 (1921). ⟨20⟩ Judefind, Reid, *J. Am. Chem. Soc.* **42**, 1055 (1920).

⟨21⟩ Drake, Bronitsky, *J. Am. Chem. Soc.* **52**, 3719 (1930). ⟨22⟩ Behrmann, Hofmann, *Ber.* **17**, 2684 (1884). ⟨23⟩ DiMento, *Chem. Abs.* **29**, 740 (1935); *Cent.* **1935**, I, 693. ⟨24⟩ Curtius, *J. prakt. Chem.* (2) **95**, 249 (1917). ⟨25⟩ Nau, Brown, Baily, *J. Am. Chem. Soc.* **47**, 2600–2601

(1925). ⟨26⟩ Gill, *Ber.* **19,** 2352 (1886). ⟨27⟩ Ciusa, Piergallini, *Gazz. chim. ital.* **45,** I, 63 (1915). ⟨28⟩ Moore, Thomas, *J. Am. Chem. Soc.* **39,** 1007 (1917). ⟨29⟩ Kometiani, *Z. anal. Chem.* **86,** 359–366 (1931). ⟨30⟩ Hartmann, Hillig, *J. Assoc. Official Agr. Chem.* **10,** 264–272 (1927); **11,** 257–266 (1928). ⟨31⟩ Reichard, *Z. Untersuch. Lebensm.* **68,** 138–172 (1934).

1:0456 PIMELIC ACID HOOC.$(CH_2)_5$.COOH $C_7H_{12}O_4$ **Beil. II-670**
(Pentane-1,5-dicarboxylic acid)

M.P. 105° **Neut. Eq. 80**

Monoclin. prismat. tbls. from aq. — Sol. in 24 pts. aq. at 20°; eas. sol. ether; sol. alc. or hot C_6H_6 — Subl. without decn. but *not* volat. with steam.

[For prepn. (50% yield) by reduction of salicylic ac. (1:0780) with Na + AmOH see ⟨1⟩; in 64% yield from trimethylene dibromide via malonic ester synthesis see ⟨2⟩.] [For sepn. from succinic (1:0530), glutaric (1:0440); and adipic acids (1:0775) see ⟨3⟩.]

Dry distn. of CaĀ yields cyclohexanone (1:5465) ⟨4⟩ ⟨5⟩.

C̄ with 15% more than 2 moles $SOCl_2$ at 30° yields pimelyl (di)chloride, b.p. 137°_{15} without decn. ⟨6⟩ ⟨7⟩.

C̄ refluxed 4–6 hrs. with 3 pts. Ac_2O, excess reagt. and resultant AcOH distd. off under reduced pressure, yields a linear polymeric pimelic α-anhydride, CH_3.CO.[O.CO.$(CH_2)_5$.-CO$]_x$.O.CO.CH_3, sol. in hot C_6H_6 from which it is pptd. by addn. of pet. ether as a white micro-crystn. pdr., m.p. 53–55° ⟨8⟩. It reacts with aq. to yield C̄ + acetic ac. [When this α-anhydride is htd. in a molecular still it yields an extremely unstable monomeric pimelic β-anhydride which rapidly changes to another linear polymeric pimelic γ-anhydride ⟨8⟩.]

Ⓓ **Diphenacyl pimelate:** m.p. 72.4° ⟨9⟩ [cf. T 1.391].
Ⓓ **Di-*p*-bromophenacyl pimelate:** m.p. 136.6° ⟨9⟩ [cf. T 1.391].
Ⓓ **Di (*p*-phenylphenacyl) pimelate:** m.p. 145–148° dec. ⟨10⟩ [T 1.391].
—— **Pimelic diamide:** (apparently unknown).
Ⓓ **Pimelic dianilide** [Beil. XII-299]: cryst. from MeOH + aq.; m.p. 155–156° ⟨6⟩ ⟨8⟩; 152° ⟨11⟩ [from C̄ on htg. with 4 pts. aniline for 20 hrs. at 180° ⟨12⟩; or from pimelyl (di)chloride (above) + aniline ⟨6⟩]. [The monoanilide (pimelanilic acid), cryst. from aq., has m.p. 108–109° ⟨8⟩.]
Ⓓ **Pimelic di-*p*-toluidide** [Beil. XII_1-(424)]: lfts. from alc., m.p. 206° ⟨11⟩.

1:0456 ⟨1⟩ Müller, *Monatsh.* **65,** 18–20 (1935). ⟨2⟩ Altman, *Rec. trav. chim.* **57,** 949–950 (1938). ⟨3⟩ Bouveault, *Bull. soc. chim.* (3) **19,** 562–565 (1898). ⟨4⟩ Wislicenus, *Ann.* **275,** 361 (1893). ⟨5⟩ Baeyer, *Ann.* **278,** 100 (1893). ⟨6⟩ Blaise, Koehler, *Bull. soc. chim.* (4) **5,** 687 (1909). ⟨7⟩ Skraup, Guggenheimer, *Ber.* **58,** 2498 (1925). ⟨8⟩ Hill, Carothers, *J. Am. Chem. Soc.* **55,** 5027–5029 (1933). ⟨9⟩ Kelly, Kleff, *J. Am. Chem. Soc.* **54,** 4444 (1932). ⟨10⟩ Drake, Sweeney, *J. Am. Chem. Soc.* **54,** 2060 (1932).
⟨11⟩ Barnicoat, *J. Chem. Soc.* **1927,** 2927–2928. ⟨12⟩ Einhorn, Ehret, *Ann.* **295,** 179 (1897).

1:0460 *d,l*-TROPIC ACID C_6H_5–CH(CH_2OH)–COOH $C_9H_{10}O_3$ **Beil. X-261**
(β-Hydroxy-α-phenyl-propionic acid)

M.P. 117-118° **Neut. Eq. 166**

Ndls. from hot conc. aq. soln.; on evapn. seps. in tbls. — Very sol. hot aq.; 100 pts. aq. at 20° dis. 1.98 g. C̄ — Sol. alc., ether; spar. sol. cold C_6H_6, insol. CS_2 or pet. — Not volatile with steam.

C̄ refluxed 40 min. with 6 pts. 50% aq. KOH, soln. extd. with ether, acidified with HCl, and again ether extracted yields on evapn. of ether 50% yield ⟨1⟩ of atropic acid C_6H_5.C(: CH_2)(COOH) [Beil. IX-610], lfts. from alc., sol. in 790 pts. cold aq., m.p. 107°.

C̄, refluxed with 7 pts. $SOCl_2$, excess reagt. distilled off, residual oil dislvd. in C_6H_6 and shaken first with ice water and then very dil. aq. K_2CO_3 (to split intermediate sulfite ester), dried with $CaCl_2$, and C_6H_6 distd. gives 78% yield of a yellow oily *d,l*-tropoyl chloride. On distn. (even under reduced pressure) this splits out aq. and yields atropoyl chloride [Beil. IX-610] in distillate and atropic acid, m.p. 107°, in residue ⟨2⟩.

C̄ warmed with 3 pts. PCl_5 and poured into ice aq. yields β-chloro-α-phenylpropionic acid; pr. from hot aq., m.p. 88.5° ⟨3⟩. [On boilg. with aq. Na_2CO_3 this product can be converted back to tropic ac. in 70% yield ⟨4⟩.]

C̄ allowed to stand with equal wt. AcCl ⟨5⟩ or warmed at 80° for 2 hrs. with Ac_2O, poured into aq. ⟨6⟩ gives β-acetoxy-α-phenylpropionic acid (acetyl *d,l*-tropic ac.), m.p. 88–90° ⟨5⟩, 80° ⟨6⟩.

[For resolution of C̄ via quinine salts see ⟨7⟩.]

1:0460 ⟨1⟩ Baker, Eccles, *J. Chem. Soc.* **1927,** 2128–2129. ⟨2⟩ Wolffenstein, Mamlock, *Ber.* **41,** 727 (1908). ⟨3⟩ Ladenburg, *Ann.* **217,** 77 (1883). ⟨4⟩ McKenzie, Wood, *J. Chem. Soc.* **115,** 836–837 (1919). ⟨5⟩ Ref. 2, page 730. ⟨6⟩ Hesse, *J. prakt. Chem.* (2) **64,** 287–288 (1901). ⟨7⟩ McKenzie, Wood, *J. Chem. Soc.* **115,** 838–840 (1919).

1:0465 ***d,l*-MANDELIC ACID** $C_8H_8O_3$ **Beil. X-197**
(Phenylglycolic acid;
α-hydroxyphenylacetic acid)

C_6H_5—C(H)(OH)—COOH

M.P. 118° **Neut. Eq. 152**

Cryst. from aq., ether or C_6H_6 + acetone (90:10) — 100 pts. aq. at 20° dis. 15.97 g. C̄ — C̄ is very sol. in alc. or ether — [For prepn. (50–52% yield) from benzaldehyde (1:0195) via $NaHSO_3$ cpd. + NaCN, followed by hydrolysis see ⟨1⟩.] [For resolution of C̄ with (−) natural ephedrine see ⟨2⟩ ⟨3⟩ ⟨4⟩; with (+) ephedrine see ⟨3⟩ ⟨4⟩; m.p. of either *d*- or *l*-mandelic acid is 133°.]

C̄ with $FeCl_3$ (T 1.32) gives yel. color of α-hydroxy acids — C̄, on distn. at ord. press. or on distn. with MnO_2 + aq. gives odor of benzaldehyde; on oxidn. with aq. $KMnO_4$ gives benzoic ac. (1:0715) — C̄ on warming with conc. H_2SO_4 yields CO.

C̄ + 2.5 pts. PCl_5 htd. 4 hrs. at 100°, resultant $POCl_3$ distd. off at reduced press., residual oil htd. 1 hr. at 140°, then distd. gives (50% yield ⟨5⟩) phenylchloroacetyl chloride [Beil. IX-450], b.p. $110°_{14}$ ⟨6⟩, which on stdg. with cold aq. gives (100% yield ⟨5⟩) *d,l*-phenylchloroacetic acid, m.p. 78° — C̄ htd. with 2 pts. $SOCl_2$ for 7 hrs. yields mainly benzal (di)chloride + some phenylchloroacetyl chloride ⟨7⟩. [For study of mechanism see ⟨8⟩.]

C̄ + 3 moles AcCl reacts spontaneously with evol. of ht.; after soln. has occurred excess AcCl is distd. off and on stdg. 1 or 2 days the residual oil cryst. to 97–99% yield ⟨9⟩ of acetylmandelic acid [Beil. X-202], anhydrous cryst. from C_6H_6 (or from $CHCl_3$ by pptn. with pet. ether ⟨10⟩), m.p. 79–80° ⟨9⟩ [from aq. *d,l*-acetylmandelic ac. cryst. with 1 H_2O, m.p. 38–39°, lost in vac. or on htg.].

C̄ gives AgĀ in T 1.36 — $MgĀ_2$, $CaĀ_2$ both spar. sol. aq. — $BaĀ_2$, sol. in 12 pts. aq. at 24°. [For extensive study of cpds. of C̄ with its own metallic salts see ⟨11⟩ ⟨12⟩.]

C̄ + MeOH + conc. H_2SO_4 yields methyl *d,l*-mandelate (1:2166), cryst. from mixt. of lgr. + C_6H_6, m.p. 54°, changing on stdg. to 57° ⟨13⟩ — C̄ + EtOH + conc. H_2SO_4 gives ethyl *d,l*-mandelate (1:2049), m.p. 29° ⟨13⟩.

Ⓓ ***p*-Nitrobenzyl *d,l*-mandelate:** m.p. 123–124° ⟨14⟩ [cf. T 1.39].

Ⓓ **Phenacyl *d,l*-mandelate:** m.p. 85° ⟨15⟩ [cf. T 1.391].

Ⓓ ***d,l*-Mandelamide:** tbls. from abs. alc. or C_6H_6; m.p. 132° ⟨16⟩ 133–134° cor. ⟨17⟩ [from C̄ via condensation with acetone + H_2SO_4 and reaction of this intermediate (m.p. 47.5–48.0° ⟨19⟩) with liq. NH_3; 62% yield ⟨16⟩; or from methyl *d,l*-mandelate

(1:2166) in EtOH, satd. with NH_3 first at ord. temp., then at 0°; on stdg. 3 days prod. seps. in 80% yield ⟨18⟩] [*l*-mandelamide (from methyl ⟨20⟩ or ethyl ⟨21⟩ *l*-mandelate as above); cryst. from C_6H_6, m.p. 122–122.5° ⟨18⟩ ⟨22⟩].

Ⓓ ***d,l*-Mandelanilide** [Beil. XII-503]: from C̄ + 1 mole aniline htd. at 180–190°; 75% yield ⟨23⟩; lfts. from alc., m.p. 151–152°.

Ⓓ ***d,l*-Mandelo-*p*-toluidide** [Beil. XII-966]: from C̄ + 1 mole *p*-toluidine at 180–190° ⟨24⟩; lfts. from alc., m.p. 172°.

Ⓓ **2-(α-Hydroxybenzyl)benzimidazole:** from C̄ + ⅔ mole *o*-phenylenediamine in 4 *N* HCl boiled 30–40 min. and neutralized with NH_4OH (50% yield ⟨25⟩); pl. from 50% alc., m.p. 202–203° ⟨25⟩, 200.5–201.5° ⟨26⟩. [The picrate of this base has m.p. 209° ⟨27⟩.]

Ⓓ ***S*-Benzylthiuronium *d,l*-mandelate:** m.p. 166° cor. ⟨28⟩; 164–165° ⟨29⟩.

1:0465 ⟨1⟩ Corson, Dodge, Harris, Yeaw, *Organic Syntheses, Coll. Vol.* I, 329–333 (1932). ⟨2⟩ Roger, *J. Chem. Soc.* **1935,** 1544. ⟨3⟩ Skita, Keil, Meiner, *Ber.* **66,** 979 (1933). ⟨4⟩ Manske, Johnson, *J. Am. Chem. Soc.* **51,** 1908 (1929). ⟨5⟩ Bischoff, Walden, *Ann.* **279,** 122 (1894). ⟨6⟩ Staudinger, *Ber.* **44,** 536 (1911). ⟨7⟩ McKenzie, Barrow, *J. Chem. Soc.* **99,** 1916 (1911). ⟨8⟩ Carré, Libermann, *Compt. rend.* **200,** 1215–1217 (1935). ⟨9⟩ Thayer, *Organic Syntheses, Coll. Vol.* I, 12 (1932). ⟨10⟩ Anschütz, Böcker, *Ann.* **368,** 57 (1909).

⟨11⟩ Ross, Morrison, *J. Chem. Soc.* **1933,** 1016–1022. ⟨12⟩ Ross, Morrison, *J. Chem. Soc.* **1936,** 867–872. ⟨13⟩ Findlay, Turner, *J. Chem. Soc.* **87,** 752–753 (1905). ⟨14⟩ Cowles, *M.I.T. Thesis.* ⟨15⟩ Rather, Reid, *J. Am. Chem. Soc.* **41,** 80 (1919). ⟨16⟩ Audrieth, Sveda, *Organic Syntheses,* **20,** 62–64 (1940). ⟨17⟩ Ôeda, *Bull. Chem. Soc. Japan* **11,** 388 (1936). ⟨18⟩ McKenzie, Wren, *J. Chem. Soc.* **93,** 311–313 (1908). ⟨19⟩ Willstätter, Königsberger, *Ber.* **56,** 2108–2109 (1923). ⟨20⟩ Freudenberg, Markert, *Ber.* **58,** 1759 (1925).

⟨21⟩ McKenzie, Smith, *J. Chem. Soc.* **121,** 1353 (1922). ⟨22⟩ Freudenberg, Todd, Seidler, *Ann.* **501,** 210–211 (1933). ⟨23⟩ Ref. 5, page 123. ⟨24⟩ Ref. 5, page 126. ⟨25⟩ Phillips, *J. Chem. Soc.* **1928,** 2395. ⟨26⟩ Bistrzycki, Przeworski, *Ber.* **42,** 3487 (1912). ⟨27⟩ Brown, Campbell, *J. Chem. Soc.* **1937,** 1701. ⟨28⟩ Donleavy, *J. Am. Chem. Soc.* **58,** 1005 (1936). ⟨29⟩ Veibel, Lillelund, *Bull. soc. chim.* (5) **5,** 1157 (1938).

1:0470 MALEIC ACID (Toxilic Acid)

H—C—COOH
‖
H—C—COOH

$C_4H_4O_4$ **Beil. II-748**

M.P. 137° **Neut. Eq. 58**
(**130°**) see text

Monoclin. pr. — *Pure* C̄ melts at 137–138°; such material can be obtd. by soln. of maleic anhydride (1:0625) in aq. and evapn. in vacuo. On fusion, however, some isomerization occurs and the ordinary form melts at 130° due to abt. 3% content of fumaric ac. (1:0895) ⟨1⟩. [For anal. of mixts. of C̄ + fumaric ac. (1:0895) see ⟨1⟩.]

Soly. of C̄ at 25°: 78.8 g. per 100 g. aq.; 8.2 g. per 100 g. ether ⟨2⟩ — Soly. of C̄ at 30°: 69.9 g. per 100 g. 95% alc. ⟨2⟩. [For study of soly., spec. grav. and refractive index of system C̄ + aq. see ⟨3⟩.]

C̄ on htg. in vac. above 100° ⟨2⟩, or C̄ distilled with xylene or tetrachloroethane, followed by distn. of residue ⟨4⟩ or C̄ refluxed 1 hr. with Ac_2O and reagt. + AcOH distd. in stream of dry air at reduced press. ⟨1⟩ gives maleic anhydride (1:0625).

C̄ decolorizes Br_2-aq. only slowly and on warming and does not add Br_2 in CCl_4. C̄ in satd. aq. soln. + trace of Br_2 exposed to direct sunlight or brilliant electric light rapidly isomerizes to fumaric ac. (1:0895) which is much less sol. and ppts. — C̄ in aq. + trace HgCl + trace $K_2S_2O_8$ gives quant. yield fumaric ac. ⟨25⟩.

C̄ dissolved in aq. Na_2CO_3 reduces $KMnO_4$ (T 1.34) [dif. from malonic ac. (1:0480)].

C̄ dissolves readily in $SOCl_2$ and on cooling yields maleic anhydride (1:0625) ⟨5⟩ ⟨6⟩; with PCl_5, however, C̄ gives maleyl (di)chloride, b.p. 72–73°$_{15}$ ⟨7⟩, 65°$_2$ ⟨8⟩ in small yield, accompanied by fumaryl (di)chloride and other products. [Maleyl (di)chloride appears to react in unsymmetrical form [Beil. XVII_1-(138)].]

$Ag_2\bar{A}$; $Ba\bar{A}.H_2O$; $Pb\bar{A}$; all insol. cold aq.; $Ca\bar{A}.5H_2O$, eas. sol. aq.; insol. alc.

Ⓓ **Di-(*p*-nitrobenzyl) maleate:** m.p. 89.3° ⟨9⟩; 91° cor. ⟨10⟩ [cf. T 1.39].

Ⓓ **Di-(phenacyl) maleate:** m.p. 128–129° cor. ⟨10⟩; 126° ⟨11⟩; 119° ⟨12⟩ [cf. T **1.391**]. [for purification details see ⟨10⟩].

Ⓓ **Di-(*p*-phenylphenacyl) maleate:** m.p. 168° ⟨13⟩ [cf. T 1.391].

—— **Maleic diamide:** cryst. from MeOH, m.p. 181° ⟨14⟩; 180° ⟨15⟩ [from dimethyl maleate (1:3606) + 3.1 pts. aq. NH_4OH (satd. at 10°) in cold and dark for $\frac{1}{2}$ hr., finally cooled to −5°; yield 24% together with 4–5% fumaric diamide ⟨14⟩]. [This maleic diamide htd. in vac. with $ZnCl_2$ gives sublimate of maleimide [Beil. XXI-399], cryst. from C_6H_6, m.p. 93° ⟨16⟩.] [Maleic acid monoamide (maleamic acid), from maleic anhydride (1:0625) + NH_3 in C_6H_6 ⟨17⟩ ⟨18⟩ forms cryst. from aq., m.p. 172–173° ⟨17⟩ ⟨18⟩.]

—— **Maleic dianilide** [Beil. XII-306]: lfts. or pr. from MeOH or EtOH, m.p. 187° ⟨19⟩. [Maleic acid monoanilide (maleanilic acid), from maleic anhydride + 1 mole aniline in dry ether ⟨21⟩, also forms yel. pr. from alc., m.p. 187°.] [Maleanil (*N*-phenylmaleimide) [Beil. XXI-400] forms yel. ndls. from C_6H_6 + lgr., m.p. 90–91°.]

Ⓓ **Phenylaspartanil** [Beil. XXII-529]: Place 0.1 g. $\bar{C}$ + 0.2 ml. aniline in a 6-in. tt. bearing 10 cm. air condenser and reflux 1 hr. at 190–200°. Recryst. from 15 ml. boilg. alc.; cool, filter, and wash with 2 ml. cold alc. Recryst. from 10 ml. boilg. alc. and dry at 110°; white cryst., m.p. 210–211° ⟨20⟩ ⟨21⟩.

—— **Maleic di-*p*-toluidide** [Beil. XII-937]: cryst. from ether, m.p. 142° (indirectly). [The mono-*p*-toluidide (*N*-*p*-tolylmaleamic acid), prepd. from maleic anhydride + 1 mole *p*-toluidine in $CHCl_3$ ⟨1⟩, forms cryst. from $CHCl_3$, m.p. 195° dec. ⟨1⟩, 201° ⟨22⟩.]

Ⓓ ***S*-benzylthiuronium hydrogen maleate:** m.p. 163° cor. ⟨23⟩; 173–174° dec. ⟨24⟩.

1:0470 ⟨1⟩ Hurd, Roe, Williams, *J. Org. Chem.* **2,** 314–318 (1937). ⟨2⟩ Weiss, Downs, *J. Am. Chem. Soc.* **45,** 1003–1008 (1923). ⟨3⟩ Lange, Sinks, *J. Am. Chem. Soc.* **52,** 2602–2604 (1930). ⟨4⟩ Mason, *J. Chem. Soc.* **1930,** 700–701. ⟨5⟩ Meyer, *Monatsh.* **22,** 421 (1901). ⟨6⟩ McMaster, Ahmann, *J. Am. Chem. Soc.* **50,** 147 (1928). ⟨7⟩ Ott, *Ann.* **392,** 246, 272 (1912). ⟨8⟩ Lutz, *J. Am. Chem. Soc.* **52,** 3436 (1930). ⟨9⟩ Lyman, Reid, *J. Am. Chem. Soc.* **39,** 708 (1917). ⟨10⟩ van Duin, *Rec. trav. chim.* **47,** 734 (1928).

⟨11⟩ Rather, Reid, *J. Am. Chem. Soc.* **43,** 633 (1921). ⟨12⟩ Rather, Reid, *J. Am. Chem. Soc.* **41,** 80 (1919). ⟨13⟩ Drake, Bronitsky, *J. Am. Chem. Soc.* **52,** 3719 (1930). ⟨14⟩ DeWolf, Van de Straete, *Bull. soc. chim. Belg.* **44,** 293–294 (1935). ⟨15⟩ Rinkes, *Rec. trav. chim.* **46,** 272 (1927). ⟨16⟩ Rinkes, *Rec. trav. chim.* **48,** 961 (1929). ⟨17⟩ Rinkes, *Rec. trav. chim.* **45,** 821 (1926). ⟨18⟩ Jennen, *Cent.* **1937,** I, 2956. ⟨19⟩ Anschütz, *Ann.* **259,** 141 (1890). ⟨20⟩ Mulliken, " Method " I, 45 (1904).

⟨21⟩ Tingle, Bates, *J. Am. Chem. Soc.* **31,** 1239 (1909). ⟨22⟩ Dunlap, Phelps, *Am. Chem. J.* **19,** 494 (1897). ⟨23⟩ Donleavy, *J. Am. Chem. Soc.* **58,** 1005 (1936). ⟨24⟩ Veibel, Lillelund, *Bull. soc. chim.* (5) **5,** 1157 (1938). ⟨25⟩ Wieland, Zilg, *Ann.* **530,** 272–273 (1937).

1:0475 PYROMUCIC ACID (Furoic acid; furan-2-carboxylic acid)

```
HC———CH
‖     ‖
HC    C—COOH
  \  /
   O
```

$C_5H_4O_3$ **Beil. XVIII-272**

M.P. 133-134° **Neut. Eq. 112**

B.P. 230-232°

Lfts. from hot aq.; ndls. by sublimation — Sublimes even at 100° and very readily at reduced pressure — $\bar{C}$ is sol. in 28 pts. aq. at 15° and in 4 pts. at 100°; eas. sol. alc., ether. [For use as acidimetric standard see ⟨1⟩.]

[For prepn. from furfural (1:0185) by oxidn. with alk. $KMnO_4$ (80% yield) see ⟨2⟩, by oxidn. with $K_2Cr_2O_7 + H_2SO_4$ (75% yield) see ⟨3⟩; via Cannizzaro reaction + aq. NaOH see ⟨4⟩; via Cannizzaro react. using MeOH + NaOH see ⟨5⟩.]

$\bar{C}$ dislvd. in Na_2CO_3 reduces $KMnO_4$ (T 1.34) — $\bar{C}$ with aq. $FeCl_3$ (T 1.41) gives a red.-yel ppt. — $\bar{C}$ in $CHCl_3$ or $CCl_4 + Br_2$ yields 40–45% 5-bromofuroic acid, cryst. from hot aq., m.p. 186° ⟨6⟩.

$\bar{C}$ on htg. at 200–205° loses CO_2 and gives (72–78% yield ⟨7⟩) furan (1:8015), b.p. 31°. [This decarboxylation is much facilitated by use of catalysts, such as $CuSO_4$, CuO, or quinoline: see ⟨8⟩ ⟨2⟩.] [For influence of substitution on ease of decarboxylation see ⟨9⟩.]

$\bar{C}$ with excess PCl_5 in dry $CHCl_3$ under specified conditions (alm. quant. yield ⟨10⟩), or $\bar{C}$ refluxed 2 hrs. with PCl_3 (77% yield ⟨13⟩), or $\bar{C}$ refluxed $1\frac{1}{2}$ hrs. with 5 pts. $SOCl_2$ (60% yield ⟨11⟩), or $\bar{C}$ refluxed with $1\frac{1}{2}$ moles $SOCl_2$ in C_6H_6 (89.5% yield ⟨12⟩) gives furoyl chloride, b.p. 173°.

$\bar{C}$ boiled for 8 hrs. with 2 pts. Ac_2O in 2–3 pts. toluene ⟨14⟩, or furoyl chloride (above) dissolved in ether and treated with pyridine, then with aq. ⟨15⟩ gives furoic anhydride, cryst. from alc. or pet. ether, m.p. 73°. [For quant. detn. of this anhydride via NaOMe titration see ⟨16⟩.]

Ⓟ **Pyrrole formation:** Pine splinter, soaked in conc. HCl and held in vapor evolved on htg. dry NH_4 salt of $\bar{C}$, becomes deep red (from pyrrole formn.).

Ⓟ **Isatin color reaction:** $\bar{C}$, dislvd. in conc. H_2SO_4, warmed with trace of isatin, turns violet-blue ⟨16A⟩. [Also shown by ethyl furoate (1:2082) and by dehydromucic ac. and its ester ⟨16A⟩.]

Ⓓ ***p*-Nitrobenzyl furoate:** m.p. 133.5° ⟨17⟩ [cf. T 1.39].

Ⓓ ***p*-Bromophenacyl furoate:** m.p. 138.5° ⟨18⟩ [cf. T 1.391].

—— **Furoamide** [Beil. XVIII-276]: m.p. 142–143° [from furoyl chloride + dry NH_3 in ether ⟨19⟩ or from methyl furoate (1:3452) ⟨20⟩ or ethyl furoate (1:2082) ⟨21⟩ on htg. with conc. aq. NH_4OH in s.t.].

—— **Furoanilide** [Beil. XVIII-277]: cryst. from ether, alc. or C_6H_6, m.p. 123.5° [from $\bar{C}$ on htg. with excess aniline ⟨22⟩, or from furoyl chloride + aniline + aq. KOH (100% yield) ⟨23⟩].

—— **Furo-*p*-toluidide** [Beil. XVIII-277]: pr. from alc., m.p. 107.5° [from furoyl chloride in ether + *p*-toluidine in pyridine ⟨23⟩].

Ⓓ ***S*-Benzylthiuronium furoate:** m.p. 211–212° ⟨24⟩.

1:0475 ⟨1⟩ H. B. Kellog, A. M. Kellog, *Ind. Eng. Chem., Anal. Ed.* **6,** 251–252 (1934). ⟨2⟩ Wagner, Simons, *J. Chem. Education* **13,** 270 (1936). ⟨3⟩ Hurd, Garrett, Osborne, *J. Am. Chem. Soc.* **55,** 1084 (1933). ⟨4⟩ Wilson, *Organic Syntheses, Coll. Vol.* I, 270–274 (1932). ⟨5⟩ Gilman, Selby, *Iowa State Coll. J. Sci.* **5,** 15–18 (1930); *Chem. Abs.* **25,** 4263 (1931). ⟨6⟩ Whittaker, *Rec. trav. chim.* **52,** 352–356 (1933). ⟨7⟩ Wilson, *Organic Syntheses, Coll. Vol.* I, 269–270 (1932). ⟨8⟩ Gilman, Louisinian, *Rec. trav. chim.* **52,** 156–159 (1933). ⟨9⟩ Gilman, Janner, Bradley, *Iowa State Coll. J. Sci.* **7,** 429–431 (1933); *Chem. Abs.* **28,** 763 (1934). ⟨10⟩ Frankland, Aston, *J. Chem. Soc.* **79,** 516–517 (1901).

⟨11⟩ Gelissen, van Roon, *Rec. trav. chim.* **43,** 361 (1924). ⟨12⟩ Hartmann, Dickey, *Ind. Eng. Chem.* **24,** 151–152 (1932). ⟨13⟩ Reichstein, Morsman, *Helv. Chim. Acta* **17,** 1122 (1934). ⟨14⟩ Katsnel'son, Gol'dfarb, *Chem. Abs.* **31,** 3491 (1937); *Cent.* **1937,** I, 3806. ⟨15⟩ Baum, *Ber.* **34,** 2505 (1901). ⟨16⟩ Smith, Bryant, *J. Am. Chem. Soc.* **58,** 2453 (1936). ⟨16A⟩ Yoder, Tollens, *Ber.* **34,** 3460–3461 (1901). ⟨17⟩ Lyons, Reid, *J. Am. Chem. Soc.* **39,** 1732 (1917). ⟨18⟩ Judefind, Reid, *J. Am. Chem. Soc.* **42,** 1055 (1920). ⟨19⟩ Ciamician, Dennstedt, *Gazz. chim. ital.* **11,** 293–294 (1881). ⟨20⟩ Freundler, *Bull. soc. chim.* (3) **17,** 422 (1897).

⟨21⟩ Schwanert, *Ann.* **116,** 282 (1860). ⟨22⟩ Schiff, *Ann.* **239,** 367 (1887). ⟨23⟩ Baum, *Ber.* **37,** 2954 (1904). ⟨24⟩ Veibel, Ottung, *Bull. soc. chim.* (5) **6,** 1435 (1939).

1:0480 MALONIC ACID HOOC.CH_2.COOH $C_3H_4O_4$ **Beil. II-566**
(Methanedicarboxylic acid)

M.P. 133° **Neut. Eq. 52**
(134.8-134.9° cor. ⟨1⟩)

Colorless cryst. — 100 g. aq. at 15° dis. 139 g. C̄; 100 g. satd. alc. soln. at 19° conts. 40 g. C̄; 100 g. abs. ether soln. at 15° conts. 8 g. C̄.

[For prepn. in 77–82% yield from chloroacetic ac. + NaCN via intermediate sepn. of CaĀ, see ⟨2⟩.]

C̄ on htg. above m.p. (T 1.33) decomposes into CO_2 and acetic ac. (1:1010). [For study of relation of m.p.'s and decn. temps. for C̄ and substituted malonic acids see ⟨3⟩ ⟨4⟩.]

C̄ with PCl_5 (68% yield ⟨5⟩), or C̄ with 3 pts. $SOCl_2$ for 2 days at 40°, then 6 hrs. at 60° followed by vac. distn. (70% yield ⟨7⟩; 60% yield ⟨6⟩) gives malonyl (di)chloride, b.p. 58°_{26}, $D^{20}_{4} = 1.454$; $n^{23.4}_{D} = 1.45973$ ⟨8⟩.

Ag_2Ā, stable cryst. ppt.; CaĀ.$2H_2O$; BaĀ.$2H_2O$; PbĀ; all insol. aq.

Ⓟ **Color reaction with acetic anhydride:** In a 6-in. tt. boil 1–2 cg. C̄ with 3 ml. Ac_2O for 3 min.; then dilute with 3 ml. AcOH. C̄ gives a yel.-red soln. with greenish-yel. fluorescence [dif. from furoic ac. (1:0475)] ⟨9⟩.

Ⓓ **Di-*p*-nitrobenzyl malonate:** m.p. 85.5° ⟨10⟩ [cf. T 1.39].

Ⓓ **Di-(*p*-phenylphenacyl) malonate:** m.p. 175° ⟨11⟩ [cf. T 1.391].

—— **Malonic(di)amide:** ndls. from aq. alc., m.p. 170° ⟨13⟩ [from dimethyl malonate (1:3457) or diethyl malonate (1:3581) with aq. NH_4OH, followed by evapn.]. [The monoamide (malonamic acid), has m.p. 106–110° ⟨12⟩.]

—— **Malonic dianilide** [Beil. XII-293]: ndls. from alc., m.p. 227–228° ⟨14⟩; 224° ⟨15⟩; 225° ⟨16⟩ [from diethyl malonate (1:3581) + aniline htd. 5 hrs. at 120° ⟨17⟩, or at b.p. (81% yield ⟨16⟩)]. [The mono-anilide (malonanilic acid) [Beil. XII-293] has m.p. 132°, smoothly decomposing into CO_2 and acetanilide ⟨18⟩.] [Malonanil has m.p. 249° u.c. ⟨19⟩.]

—— **Malonic di-*p*-toluidide** [Beil. XII-933]: ndls. from alc., m.p. 252–253° ⟨20⟩; 247° ⟨15⟩ [from diethyl malonate htd. with *p*-toluidine for 7 hrs. at 140° ⟨17⟩ (53% yield ⟨21⟩)]. [The mono-*p*-toluidide (*N*-*p*-tolylmalonamic acid) [Beil. XII-933] has m.p. 156° dec. rap. htg. ⟨22⟩ ⟨18⟩.]

Ⓓ ***S*-Benzylthiuronium hydrogen malonate:** m.p. 145–146° dec. ⟨23⟩.

1:0480 ⟨1⟩ Serwy, *Bull. soc. chim. Belg.* **42,** 484 (1933). ⟨2⟩ Weiner, *Organic Syntheses* **18,** 50–53 (1938). ⟨3⟩ Norris, Young, *J. Am. Chem. Soc.* **52,** 5069 (1930). ⟨4⟩ Verkade, Coops, *Rec. trav. chim.* **49,** 568–577 (1930). ⟨5⟩ Clark, Bell, *Trans. Roy. Soc. Canada* (3) **27,** III, 97–103 (1933). ⟨6⟩ McMaster, Ahmann, *J. Am. Chem. Soc.* **50,** 146 (1928). ⟨7⟩ Staudinger, St. Bereza, *Ber.* **41,** 4463 (1908). ⟨8⟩ von Auwers, Schmidt, *Ber.* **46,** 477 (1913). ⟨9⟩ Kleeman, *Ber.* **19,** 2030 (1886). ⟨10⟩ Reid, *J. Am. Chem. Soc.* **39,** 131 (1917).

⟨11⟩ Drake, Sweeney, *J. Am. Chem. Soc.* **54,** 2060 (1932). ⟨12⟩ Jeffery, Vogel, *J. Chem. Soc.* **1934,** 1102. ⟨13⟩ Pauw, *Rec. trav. chim.* **55,** 218 (1936). ⟨14⟩ Ref. 13, page 221. ⟨15⟩ Barnicoat, *J. Chem. Soc.* **1927,** 2927. ⟨16⟩ Whitely, *J. Chem. Soc.* **83,** 34 (1903). ⟨17⟩ Ramart, Naik, Trivedi, *Bull. soc. chim.* (5) **1,** 537 (1934). ⟨18⟩ Chattaway, Olmsted, *J. Chem. Soc.* **97,** 939–940 (1910). ⟨19⟩ Warren, Briggs, *Ber.* **64,** 28 (1931). ⟨20⟩ Ref. 13, page 222.

⟨21⟩ Ref. 16, page 36. ⟨22⟩ Rügheimer, Hoffmann, *Ber.* **18,** 2971 (1885). ⟨23⟩ Veibel, Lillelund, *Bull. soc. chim.* (5) **5,** 1157 (1938).

1:0485 ACETONE α,α′-DICARBOXYLIC ACID $C_5H_6O_5$ **Beil. III-789**
(β-Oxoglutaric acid;
β-ketoglutaric acid)

CH_2.COOH
|
C=O
|
CH_2.COOH

M.P. 135° dec. **Neut. Eq. 73**

Ndls. from AcOEt; when so crystallized and thoroughly dried may be kept unchanged at room temp. in a desic. for at least 7 months ⟨1⟩ — $\bar{C}$ is very sol. aq. or alc.; spar. sol. dry ether, insol. in C_6H_6, $CHCl_3$ or lgr. [For prepn. in 85–90% yield from citric ac. (1:0455) + fumg. H_2SO_4 see ⟨2⟩ ⟨3⟩.]

$\bar{C}$, on htg. above m.p. (T 1.33), or on long standing or on boiling with aq., acids, or alk., decomposes to acetone (1:5400) and CO_2 ⟨1⟩ — $\bar{C}$, on treatment with aq. NaOH + I_2 (T 1.81) therefore gives iodoform — $\bar{C}$ in aq. soln. gives violet color with $FeCl_3$ (T 1.41) — [For conv. to $\bar{C}$ of diethyl acetonedicarboxylate (1:1772), b.p. 240° see ⟨4⟩.]

[For detn. of $\bar{C}$ (in absence of citric acid) by conversion via KBr-$KBrO_3$ titration to pentabromoacetone, m.p. 76° see ⟨5⟩ ⟨6⟩ ⟨7⟩. The method is specific for $\bar{C}$ and for citric ac. ⟨6⟩.]

Ⓟ **Denigès mercuric oxide test:** To 5 ml. of aq. soln. of $\bar{C}$ add 0.5 ml. of reagt. (contg. 5 g. HgO, 20 ml. H_2SO_4, and 100 ml. aq.) and ht. to boilg. A white turbidity ($2Hg\bar{A}_2 + HgSO_4 + 2HgO$) is obtd. with $\bar{C}$ in concn. as low as 1 mg. per liter ⟨8⟩.

Ⓓ **Conversion to acetone derivatives:** Distil $\bar{C}$ and test distillate for acetone (1:5400), q.v.

—— **Acetonedicarboxylic acid dianilide:** cryst. from C_6H_6, m.p. 155° [from diethyl acetonedicarboxylate (1:1772) on htg. with aniline in s.t. for 24 hrs. at 100° ⟨9⟩].

1:0485 ⟨1⟩ Wiig, *J. Phys. Chem.* **32**, 961 (1928). ⟨2⟩ Adams, Chiles, Rassweiler, *Organic Syntheses, Coll. Vol.* I, 9–11 (1932). ⟨3⟩ Wiig, *J. Am. Chem. Soc.* **52**, 4729–4737 (1930). ⟨4⟩ Adams, Chiles, *Organic Syntheses, Coll. Vol.* I, 232–233 (1932). ⟨5⟩ Langecker, *Biochem. Z.* **273**, 43–51 (1934); *Cent.* **1935**, I, 2841. ⟨6⟩ Breusch, *Z. physiol. Chem.* **250**, 265–266 (1937); *Cent.* **1938**, I, 2749. ⟨7⟩ Kometiani, *Z. anal. Chem.* **86**, 359–366 (1931). ⟨8⟩ Denigès, *Ann. chim.* (8) **12**, 396 (1907). ⟨9⟩ Besthorn, Garben, *Ber.* **33**, 3443 (1900).

1:0490 *meso*-TARTARIC ACID

$$\begin{array}{c} COOH \\ | \\ H\text{—}C\text{—}OH \\ | \\ H\text{—}C\text{—}OH \\ | \\ COOH \end{array}$$

$C_4H_6O_6$ **Beil. III-528**

M.P. 140° [cf. ⟨1⟩] **Neut. Eq. 75**

Rect. tbls. with 1 H_2O, readily lost at 100° or at room temp. — $\bar{C}$ is very sol. aq.; sol. in 0.8 pt. aq. at 15°; satd. aq. soln. at 0° conts. 50.7 g. $\bar{C}$ per 100 ml. soln. [For prepn. of $\bar{C}$ in 13–17% yield as by-product of racemization of *d*-tartaric ac. (1:0525) see ⟨2⟩; 20–30% yield ⟨3⟩ ⟨4⟩.]

$\bar{C}$, htd. with 4 moles BzCl at 100° until evolution of HCl stops, product washed with ether (to remove discoloration) yields dibenzoyl-*meso*-tartaric anhydride, lfts. from aq., m.p. 207–208° ⟨5⟩.

Salts: $KH\bar{A}$ is much more sol. than corresp. deriv. of *d*-tartaric ac. (1:0525); 100 g. of satd. aq. soln. at 15° contains 9.547 g. $KH\bar{A}$; at 20° 11.656 g. [use in sepn. of *d*- and *d,l*-tartaric acids from $\bar{C}$ ⟨4⟩] — $Ca\bar{A}.3H_2O$; 100 g. satd. soln. in aq. at 20° conts. 0.034 g. Ca salt; at 110° loses 2 moles of cryst. aq., at 170° loses the 3rd mole; pract. insol. in AcOH — $Ba\bar{A}.H_2O$ loses cryst. aq. at 120–150°; 100 g. satd. aq. soln. at 18° contains 0.0593 g. Ba salt [use in pptn. of $\bar{C}$ and subsequent regeneration of free acid ⟨3⟩] — [For data on other salts see ⟨6⟩.]

$\bar{C}$ yields no ppt. with satd. aq. $CaSO_4$ soln. [dif. from racemic acid (1:0550)].

$\bar{C}$ converted at room temp. to $Ag_2\bar{A}$, suspended in abs. MeOH and treated with CH_3I, refluxing 7 hrs. after initial spontaneous reaction, yields dimethyl *meso*-tartrate (1:2460), m.p. 114° cor. ⟨10⟩.

Ⓟ **Color reaction with Ac_2O + pyridine:** C̄ warmed with Ac_2O + pyridine gives an emerald-green color. This reaction is also shown by *d*-, *l*-, and *d,l*-tartaric acids ⟨7⟩; citric ac. (1:0455) gives carmine-red, and aconitic ac. (1:0540) a violet-red; other dicarboxylic acids give a brown color or none at all.

—— ***meso*-Tartramide:** cryst. from dil. MeOH, m.p. 189–190° ⟨11⟩ [from dimethyl *meso*-tartrate (1:2460) + NH_3 in MeOH ⟨11⟩].

Ⓓ ***meso*-Tartaric acid mono-*p*-nitranilide** (*p*-nitro-*meso*tartranilic acid): from C̄ in good yield on htg. with 1 mole *p*-nitroaniline 5 min. at 170°, then 40 mm. at 155–160°; pale yel. ndls. from aq., m.p. 193–194°; Neut. Eq. 242 ⟨8⟩.

—— ***meso*-Tartaric bis-(phenylhydrazide)** [Beil. XV-331]: m.p. 245° [prepd. indirectly ⟨9⟩].

1:0490 ⟨1⟩ Timmermans, Heuse, *Bull. soc. chim. Belg.* **40,** 111 (1931). ⟨2⟩ Holleman, *Organic Syntheses, Coll. Vol.* I, 484–485 (1932). ⟨3⟩ Coops, Verkade, *Rec. trav. chim.* **44,** 988 (1925). ⟨4⟩ Winther, *Z. physik. Chem.* **56,** 507–508 (1906). ⟨5⟩ Brigl, Grüner, *Ber.* **65,** 644 (1932). ⟨6⟩ Heckele, *Oesterr. Chem. Ztg.* **31,** 28–32 (1928); *Chem. Abs.* **22,** 1553 (1928). ⟨7⟩ Casares-Lopez, *Biochem. Z.* **284,** 365–366 (1936); *Cent.* **1937,** I, 392. ⟨8⟩ Landsteiner, van der Scheer, *J. Exptl. Med.* **50,** 408–409 (1929). ⟨9⟩ Lobry de Bruyn, van Ekenstein, *Rec. trav. chim.* **21,** 312 (1902). ⟨10⟩ van Duin, *Rec. trav. chim.* **47,** 727–728 (1928).
⟨11⟩ Williams, *J. Chem. Soc.* **1937,** 1518.

1:0495 DIGLYCOLIC ACID

$O(CH_2.COOH)_2$ — $C_4H_6O_5$ — **Beil. III-234**

M.P. 148° **Neut. Eq. 67**

Monoclin. pr. with 1 H_2O from aq. (Neut. Eq. 76) — Eas. sol. aq. or alc., spar. sol. ether or $CHCl_3$. [For prepn. from chloroacetic ac. in 82% yield see ⟨1⟩.]

C̄ on distn. at 12 mm. at 200° ⟨2⟩, or C̄ susp. in $CHCl_3$ and treated with 1 mole PCl_5 ⟨3⟩ or (best) powdered C̄ refluxed with AcCl until dislvd., excess reagent evapd. ⟨4⟩ gives diglycolic anhydride [Beil. XIX-153]; cryst. from warm $CHCl_3$, m.p. 97°; b.p. $120°_{12}$. [This anhydride with aq. readily hydrolyzes to orig. C̄; for other reactions see below.]

C̄ susp. in $CHCl_3$ and treated with 2 moles PCl_5, resultant $POCl_3$ distd. off, and residual oil fractionated under reduced press. yields diglycolic acid (di)chloride, b.p. $116°_{12}$ ⟨3⟩.

C̄ dislvd. in 4 pts. in MeOH contg. 5% HCl gas, refluxed several hrs. and distd. in vac. yields dimethyl diglycolate, b.p. $120°_{13}$ and solidifying in side tube to cryst., m.p. 35° ⟨5⟩ ⟨6⟩ [also obtd. from di-acid chloride (above) + MeOH, tbls. from ether, m.p. 36° ⟨7⟩]. [The mono-methyl ester is an oil, b.p. abt. 40° higher than the neutral ester ⟨6⟩.]

Ⓓ **Diglycolic acid dianilide:** from diglycolic ac. dichloride (above) + 2 moles aniline in dry ether; ndls. from mixt. of 2 pts. ether + 1 pt. alc., m.p. 152° ⟨8⟩. [The mono-anilide (diglycolanilic acid) results from actn. of 1 mole of diglycolic anhydride (above) with 1 mole aniline in $CHCl_3$ soln.; after evapn. of solvent prod. is recrystd. from aq., m.p. 118° ⟨9⟩; on boiling this monoanilide with AcCl it loses H_2O ring closing to diglycolic acid anil [Beil. XXVII-249], pr. from $CHCl_3$, m.p. 195° ⟨10⟩].

Ⓓ **Diglycolic acid mono-*p*-toluide:** from 1 mole diglycolic anhydride (above) + 1 mole *p*-toluidine in $CHCl_3$ soln.; lfts. from $CHCl_3$, ndls. from aq., m.p. 148° ⟨9⟩. [On boiling this mono-*p*-toluidide with AcCl it yields diglycolic acid *p*-tolil, ndls. from alc., m.p. 180° ⟨11⟩.]

Ⓓ **Di-(*S*-benzylthiuronium) diglycolate:** m.p. 154° cor. ⟨12⟩.

1:0495 ⟨1⟩ Lossen, Eichloff, *Ann.* **342,** 121–122 (1905). ⟨2⟩ Anschütz, *Ann.* **259,** 191 (1890). ⟨3⟩ Anschütz, Biernaux, *Ann.* **273,** 64 (1893). ⟨4⟩ Ref. 2, page 190. ⟨5⟩ Darapsky, Stauber,

J. prakt. Chem. (2) **146,** 212 (1936). ⟨6⟩ Anschütz, Jaeger, *Ber.* **55,** 676 (1922). ⟨7⟩ Ref. 3, page 65. ⟨8⟩ Ref. 3, page 67. ⟨9⟩ Ref. 6, page 673. ⟨10⟩ Ref. 6, page 674.
⟨11⟩ Ref. 6, page 675. ⟨12⟩ Donleavy, *J. Am. Chem. Soc.* **58,** 1005 (1936).

1:0500 *p*-HYDROXYPHENYLACETIC ACID $C_8H_8O_3$ Beil. X-190

HO—C_6H_4—CH_2.COOH

M.P. 148° Neut. Eq. 142

Flat ndls. from aq. — Fairly eas. sol. cold aq., very eas. sol. hot aq.; sol. alc., ether.

$\bar{C}$ in aq. soln. gives with $FeCl_3$ (T 1.41) a pale violet color changing quickly to a dirty grayish green.

$\bar{C}$ distills undecomposed but on htg. with soda lime yields *p*-cresol (1:1410).

$\bar{C}$ + dimethyl sulfate in boilg. aq. 10% NaOH ⟨1⟩ yields *p*-methoxyphenylacetic ac., lfts. from aq., m.p. 86°.

$Ca\bar{A}_2.4H_2O$; $Ba\bar{A}_2$ both spar. sol. cold aq.

1:0500 ⟨1⟩ Dakin, *J. Biol. Chem.* **8,** 22 (1910).

1:0505 CITRIC ACID, anhydrous $C_6H_8O_7$ Beil. III-556

HO—C(—COOH)(CH_2.COOH)$_2$

M.P. 153° Neut. Eq. 54

$\bar{C}$, once anhydrous, cryst. as such from cold aq. ⟨1⟩ ⟨2⟩. [For crystallographic data see ⟨2⟩.] [For reactions see citric ac. monohydrate (1:0455).]

100 pts. abs. alc. soln. at 15° conts. 43.2 g. anhydrous $\bar{C}$; 100 pts. ether soln. at 15° conts. 2.2 g.

1:0505 ⟨1⟩ Meyer, *Ber.* **36,** 3601 (1903). ⟨2⟩ Bennett, Yuill, *J. Chem. Soc.* **1935,** 130.

1:0510 TARTRONIC ACID $C_3H_4O_5$ Beil. III-415
(Hydroxymalonic acid)

H—C(—OH)(COOH)$_2$

M.P. 156-158° dec. ⟨1⟩ **Neut. Eq. 60**

Colorless pr. with $\frac{1}{2}$ H_2O from aq., losing aq. at 60° or in desiccator — Eas. sol. aq., alc., ether, but spar. sol. in ether when hydrated. [For prepn. by htg. aq. soln. of dihydroxytartaric acid [Beil. III-830] see ⟨2⟩.]

$\bar{C}$ on htg. at 180–190° loses CO_2 (T 1.32) and aq. and leaves polyglycolid (1:4970), m.p. 220°.

$Ag_2\bar{A}$, (explosive); $Ca\bar{A}.H_2O$; $Ba\bar{A}.xH_2O$, $Pb\bar{A}$; all insol. aq.

Ⓟ **Resorcinol color test:** $\bar{C}$ (0.1–0.2 ml. of conc. soln.) added to 2 ml. of a hot mixt. of 10 ml. AcOH (free from furfural), 10 ml. conc. H_2SO_4 and 1 ml. fresh 2% aq. resorcinol gives dark green color (also given by glyoxylic acid) ⟨3⟩.

Tartrondiamide: ndls. from dil. alc., m.p. 198° ⟨4⟩; 195–196° dec. ⟨5⟩ [from diethyl tartronate (1:3796) on shaking with conc. aq. NH_4OH ⟨4⟩ ⟨5⟩].

1:0510 ⟨1⟩ Behrend, Prüase, *Ann.* **416,** 233–239 (1918). ⟨2⟩ Pryde, Williams, *J. Chem. Soc.* **1933,** 643. ⟨3⟩ Denigès, *Ann. chim.* (8) **18,** 184 (1909). ⟨4⟩ Freund, *Ber.* **17,** 786 (1884). ⟨5⟩ Pinner, *Ber.* **18,** 2854 (1885).

1:0515 ITACONIC ACID (Methylenesuccinic acid)

$$\begin{array}{l} CH_2 \\ \| \\ C\text{—}COOH \\ | \\ H_2C\text{—}COOH \end{array}$$

$C_5H_6O_4$ **Beil. II-760**

M.P. 165° ⟨1⟩ **Neut. Eq. 65**

Rhomb. bipyramids, sol. in 17 pts. aq. at 10°, in 12 pts. at 20°; sol. alc., ether, very spar. sol. $CHCl_3$, CS_2, C_6H_6, lgr. — C̄ is not volatile with steam ⟨2⟩ [dif. and sepn. from citraconic ac. (1:0435)].

[For prepn. (26–27% yield) by rapid distn. of cryst. citric acid (1:0455) see ⟨1⟩ ⟨3⟩.]

C̄ on distn. at ord. press. rearranges yielding citraconic anhydride (1:1135) ⟨4⟩ ⟨5⟩. C̄, on warming with AcCl ⟨6⟩, or Ac_2O ⟨7⟩, or $SOCl_2$ ⟨8⟩ yields itaconic anhydride (1:0654).

C̄ on boiling with aq. KOH yields an equilibrium mixt. contg. 16% C̄, 15% citraconic ac. (1:0435), and 69% mesaconic ac. (1:0548) ⟨9⟩; C̄ boiled 6 hrs. with excess 10% KOH, acidified, recrystd. from hot aq. gave 76% yield mesaconic ac. (1:0548) ⟨10⟩.

C̄ reduces alk. $KMnO_4$ (T 1.34), and decolorizes from Br_2-aq. ⟨11⟩.

Ⓓ **Di-*p*-nitrobenzyl itaconate:** m.p. 90.6° ⟨12⟩ [cf. T 1.39].

Ⓓ **Diphenacyl itaconate:** m.p. 79.5° ⟨13⟩ [cf. T 1.391].

Ⓓ **Di-(*p*-bromophenacyl) itaconate:** m.p. 117.4° (70% yield) ⟨14⟩ [cf. T 1.391].

Ⓓ **Itaconic diamide:** cryst. from alc., m.p. 191.2–191.8° ⟨15⟩ [from dimethyl itaconate (1:3641) in 45% yield ⟨15⟩ with conc. aq. NH_4OH]. [The diamide on htg. loses NH_3 and yields itaconic imide which sublimes; m.p. 103.2–103.6° ⟨15⟩.]

Ⓓ **Itaconic dianilide:** not reported. [C̄ (5 g.) dislvd. in 50 g. aq., 3 g. aniline added and mixt. boiled for ½ hr. gives on cooling ⟨16⟩ ppt. of 1-phenylpyrrolidone-5-carboxylic acid (" pseudo-itaconanilic acid ") [Beil. XXII-285]; ndls. from aq., tbls. from dil. alc., m.p. 189–190°]. [C̄ on htg. with 1 mole aniline at 100–150° for 20 min. also ⟨17⟩ gives above product; but C̄ on htg. with excess aniline at b.p. gives the anilide of the above; lfts. from alc., m.p. 185° ⟨18⟩.] [Itaconic mono-anilide (itaconanilic acid) [Beil. XII-306], from itaconic anhydride (1:0654) + aniline in ether, has m.p. 151.5° ⟨19⟩.]

1:0515 ⟨1⟩ Wilson, Allen, *Organic Syntheses* **13,** 111 (1933). ⟨2⟩ Linstead, Mann, *J. Chem. Soc.* **1931,** 734. ⟨3⟩ Shriner, Ford, Roll, *Organic Syntheses* **11,** 70–71 (1931). ⟨4⟩ Shriner, Ford, Roll, *Organic Syntheses* **11,** 28–29 (1931). ⟨5⟩ van de Straete, *Bull. soc. chim. Belg.* **44,** 315 (1935). ⟨6⟩ Anschütz, Petri, *Ber.* **13,** 1539–1540 (1880). ⟨7⟩ Fittig, Bock, *Ann.* **331,** 174 (1904). ⟨8⟩ Meyer, *Monatsh.* **22,** 422 (1901). ⟨9⟩ Ref. 2, page 728. ⟨10⟩ Kinoshita, *Acta Phytochimica* **5,** 271–287 (1931).

⟨11⟩ Read, Reid, *J. Chem. Soc.* **1928,** 748. ⟨12⟩ Kelly, Segura, *J. Am. Chem. Soc.* **56,** 2497 (1934). ⟨13⟩ Rather, Reid, *J. Am. Chem. Soc.* **41,** 80 (1919). ⟨14⟩ Kelly, Kleff, *J. Am. Chem. Soc.* **54,** 4444 (1932). ⟨15⟩ DeWolf, *Bull. soc. chim. Belg.* **46,** 256–257 (1937). ⟨16⟩ Michael, Palmer, *Am. Chem. J.* **9,** 189 (1887). ⟨17⟩ Tingle, Bates, *J. Am. Chem. Soc.* **31,** 1239 (1909). ⟨18⟩ Gottlieb, *Ann.* **77,** 282–283 (1851). ⟨19⟩ Anschütz, Reuter, *Ann.* **254,** 140 (1889).

1:0520 TRICARBALLYLIC ACID (Propane-1,2,3-tricarboxylic acid)

$$\begin{array}{l} \quad\;\; CH_2.COOH \\ \quad\;\; | \\ H\text{—}C\text{—}COOH \\ \quad\;\; | \\ \quad\;\; CH_2.COOH \end{array}$$

$C_6H_8O_6$ **Beil. II-815**

M.P. 166° **Neut. Eq. 58.7**

Large pr. from aq. or dry ether; cryst. from MeOH + $CHCl_3$ or AcOH + $CHCl_3$ — Eas. sol. aq. or alc.; less so in ether. — 100 pts. aq. at 14° dis. 40.5 pts. C̄. [For prepn. in 95–96% yield from tetraethyl 1,1,2,3-tetracarboxylate (in turn from NaOEt condensation of diethyl malonate + diethyl fumarate) see ⟨1⟩.]

C̄ mixed with 3 moles PCl_5 evolves ht. + HCl, and after removal of resultant $POCl_3$ yields on distn. tricarballyl (tri)-chloride, b.p. 140°_{14} ⟨2⟩.

C̄ on refluxing 2–3 hrs. with AcCl, distg. off excess reagt. and then distg. under reduced press. ⟨3⟩ ⟨4⟩ gives *α,β*-anhydro-tricarballylic acid [Beil. XVIII-451]; ndls. from $CHCl_3$ + AcOH, m.p. 131°, b.p. $215–225^{\circ}_{45}$ (m.p. 133–134° ⟨5⟩). [This anhydro-acid, htd. short time with 1 mole aniline, then the mixt. repeatedly extracted with boilg. aq., gives on cooling aq. filtrate, tricarballylanilic acid [Beil. XXII-325], lfts. from aq., m.p. 137° ⟨6⟩; however, on htg. the anhydro-acid with 3 moles aniline at 185° the predominant product is tricarballylanilic anilide [Beil. XXII-325], ndls. from dil. alc.; m.p. 168° ⟨7⟩.] [The anhydro-acid boiled 2 hrs. with an ether soln. of 2 moles aniline yields the aniline salt of tricarballylic mono-anilide, ndls. from alc., m.p. 127–128° ⟨7⟩.]

$Ca_3\bar{A}_2$ is readily sol. in cold aq. but alm. entirely pptd. on boiling soln.; redissolves again on cooling. ⟨4.⟩

Ⓓ **Tri-(*p*-chlorophenacyl) tricarballylate:** m.p. 125.6° ⟨8⟩ [cf. T 1.391].

Ⓓ **Tri-(*p*-bromophenacyl) tricarballylate:** m.p. 138.2° ⟨8⟩ [cf. T 1.391].

—— **Tricarballylic triamide:** pr. eas. sol. aq. but insol. alc., ether, or $CHCl_3$; m.p. 205–207° dec. ⟨2⟩ [from trimethyl tricarballylate + 2 vols. conc. aq. NH_4OH at 0° ⟨2⟩].

Ⓓ **Tricarballylic trianilide:** ndls. from nitrobenzene, m.p. 252° ⟨2⟩; 262–264° ⟨9⟩ [from tricarballyl trichloride (above) + 6 moles aniline in C_6H_6 ⟨2⟩].

1:0520 ⟨1⟩ Clarke, Murray, *Organic Syntheses, Coll. Vol.* I, 508–510 (1932). ⟨2⟩ Emery, *Ber.* **22,** 2921–2923 (1889). ⟨3⟩ Emery, *Ber.* **24,** 596–598 (1891). ⟨4⟩ Bone, Sprankling, *J. Chem. Soc.* **81,** 35 (1902). ⟨5⟩ Malachowski, *Cent.* **1929,** II, 2176. ⟨6⟩ Ref. 3, page 599. ⟨7⟩ Bertram, *Ber.* **38,** 1620, 1622 (1905). ⟨8⟩ Judefind, Reid, *J. Am. Chem. Soc.* **42,** 1054–1055 (1920). ⟨9⟩ Meldrum, Kotwal, *J. Indian Chem. Soc.* **13,** 216 (1936).

1:0525 ***d*-TARTARIC ACID** $C_4H_6O_6$ **Beil. III-481**

```
     COOH
      |
  H—C—OH
      |
HO—C—H
      |
     COOH
```

M.P. 170° **Neut. Eq. 75**

Monoclinic cryst. — 100 pts. aq. at 20° dis. 139 g. C̄; at 100°, 343 g. — 100 pts. soln. in 90% alc. at 15° conts. 29.1 pts. C̄ — 100 pts. abs. alc. conts. 20.4 pts. C̄ at 15° — 100 pts. ether soln. at 15° conts. 0.39 pt. C̄ — C̄ in aq. soln. is dextrorotatory; $[\alpha]^{20}_{D} = +11.98°$ (20% aq. soln.). [For study of aq. soly. see ⟨1⟩.] [Cryst. of C̄ (D = 1.760) sink in CCl_4 (D = 1.594): (dif. from cryst. of citric ac. monohydrate (1:0455) (D = 1.542) which float ⟨2⟩.]

C̄ can be dried at 105° without loss of acidity or decompn. ⟨3⟩ — C̄, when ignited on a spatula draws into a dry ball, burning with a blue flame and shrinking till consumed. (dif. from citric acid (1:0455) which liquefies and burns ⟨4⟩). C̄ on dry htg. chars yielding burnt sugar odor and many decompn. products.

C̄ is stable to cold conc. H_2SO_4 but on htg. chars and decomposes. — C̄ on htg. with $KHSO_4$ yields pyruvic ac. (1:1040) [use in prepn. of latter in 50–55% yield ⟨5⟩] — C̄ reduces $NH_3/AgNO_3$ or Tollens' reagt. (T 1.11) — C̄ with $FeCl_3$ gives yel. color characteristic of aliphatic hydroxy-acids (T 1.32).

C̄ on boilg. with aq. alk. racemizes to *d,l*-tartaric ac. (1:0550), q.v. — From aq. solns. contg. more than 1% C̄, addn. of 5% aq. KOAc soln. ppts. KHA (solns. of alk. tartrates require also addn. of AcOH, and the pptn. is always facilitated by addn. of alc.) [Caution: to avoid possible confusion with KH oxalate, the ppt. should always be tested for tartrate by Fenton's test (below).] [For use of KHĀ in detn. of C̄ see ⟨6⟩ ⟨7⟩.] — Solns. of alk.

tartrates + aq. alk. give with $CuSO_4$ soln. the deep blue copper-containing complex ion (Fehling's solution: see T 1.22) — Salts of C̄ char on htg. (dif. from oxalates).

CaĀ.$4H_2O$, spar. sol. cold aq.; pptd. from neutral tartrates by addn. of $CaCl_2$ soln. but not from soln. of C̄; ppt. is sol. in acids, alk. or excess alk. tartrates.

Ag_2A; spar. sol. aq.; CuĀ, dif. sol. aq. (dif. from citrate), and undislvd. by dil. HCl (dif. from oxalate) or 30% NaOH ⟨8⟩.

C̄ treated with 2.2 pts. Ac_2O + trace conc. H_2SO_4 evolves ht. and dissolves; after short boiling and cooling diacetyl-*d*-tartaric anhydride [Beil. XVIII-162], cryst. from C_6H_6, m.p. 135° seps. in quant. yield ⟨9⟩ — C̄ htd. with 3.2 moles BzCl at 150° for 3 hrs. gives quant. yield ⟨10⟩ of dibenzoyl-*d*-tartaric anhydride [Beil. XVIII-162]; ndls. from xylene, m.p. 173° ⟨10⟩ ⟨11⟩. [This anhydride on stdg. in moist air, or on boiling with aq. yields an oil which solidifies on stdg. to dibenzoyl-*d*-tartaric ac. [Beil. IX-170], ndls. from C_6H_6, m.p. 88–89° ⟨10⟩; 88–90° ⟨11⟩.] [This product is a monohydrate; anhydrous form has m.p. 138–140° ⟨11⟩.]

Ⓟ **Ferrous sulfate-hydrogen peroxide color test** (Fenton's test): To aq. soln. of C̄ (or its salts) add 1 drop $FeSO_4$ soln., a few drops of H_2O_2, and excess aq. NaOH; a deep violet to black color is immediately produced (due to formation of dihydroxymaleic acid). [For study of this test see ⟨12⟩.] [Not given by citric ac. (1:0455), *l*-malic ac. (1:0450), succinic ac. (1:0530), or oxalic acid (1:0445).]

Ⓟ **Color reaction with acetic anhydride + pyridine:** C̄ on warming with Ac_2O + pyridine gives an emerald green coloration ⟨13⟩. [This test is also given by *meso*-tartaric ac. (1:0490) or by diacetyl-*d*-tartaric anhydride (above), but not by tartrate esters. Citric ac. (1:0455) gives a carmine-red, aconitic ac. (1:0540) a violet-red; other dicarboxylic acids give a brown color or none at all ⟨14⟩.]

Ⓓ **Di-(*p*-nitrobenzyl)*d*-tartrate:** m.p. 163° ⟨15⟩ [cf. T 1.39].

Ⓓ **Di-(phenacyl)*d*-tartrate:** m.p. 130° ⟨16⟩ [can be used for C̄ in presence of acetic ac. (1:1010), benzoic ac. (1:0715), citric ac. (1:0455), oxalic ac. (1:0445), *l*-malic ac. (1:0450), or succinic ac. (1:0530) ⟨17⟩].

Ⓓ **Di-(*p*-phenylphenacyl)*d*-tartrate:** m.p. 203–204° dec. ⟨18⟩.

—— ***d*-Tartaric acid diamide (*d*-tartramide):** ndls. from dil. alc. ⟨19⟩, or from alc. ⟨20⟩; m.p. 196° dec. ⟨20⟩; 208.5–209° dec. ⟨19⟩. [From dimethyl *d*-tartrate (1:2227) in MeOH treated with dry NH_3 gas ⟨19⟩, or from diethyl *d*-tartrate (1:4256) in abs. alc. satd. with NH_3 at 0° ⟨20⟩ (100% yield).] [The monoamide (*d*-tartramidic acid) has m.p. 171–172° ⟨21⟩.]

—— ***d*-Tartaric acid dianilide (*d*-tartranilide)** [Beil. XII-512]: pr. from MeOH, ndls. from alc., lfts. from AcOH, m.p. 263–264° ⟨22⟩ ⟨23⟩; 275° cor. ⟨24⟩ [from C̄ on soln. in 5 pts. boilg. aniline, followed by distn. of excess reagt. ⟨25⟩]. [The mono-anilide (tartranilic acid) [Beil. XII-512] forms ndls. from AcOH, m.p. 194° cor. ⟨26⟩.]

1:0525 ⟨1⟩ Dalman, *J. Am. Chem. Soc.* **59,** 2548 (1937). ⟨2⟩ Evrard, *Cent.* **1938**, I, 134. ⟨3⟩ Engler, *Chem. Ztg.* **51,** 158–159 (1927). ⟨4⟩ Stevens, *Ind. Eng. Chem.* **16,** 155 (1924). ⟨5⟩ Howard, Fraser, *Organic Syntheses, Coll. Vol.* I, 462–463 (1932). ⟨6⟩ Hartmann, Hillig, *J. Assoc. Official Agr. Chem.* **13,** 103–106 (1930). ⟨7⟩ Täufel, Marloth, *Z. anal. Chem.* **80,** 161–185 (1930). ⟨8⟩ Perietzeanu, *Chem. Abs.* **22,** 4409 (1928). ⟨9⟩ Wohl, Cresterlin, *Ber.* **34,** 1144 (1901). ⟨10⟩ Butler, Cretcher, *J. Am. Chem. Soc.* **55,** 2605–2606 (1933).

⟨11⟩ Zetsche, Hubacher, *Helv. Chim. Acta* **9,** 293–294 (1926). ⟨12⟩ Fenton, *J. Chem. Soc.* **65,** 899–910 (1894); **69,** 546–562 (1896). ⟨13⟩ Casares-Lopez, *Biochem. Z.* **284,** 365–366 (1936); *Cent.* **1937**, I, 392. ⟨14⟩ Fürth, Herrmann, *Biochem. Z.* **280,** 448–457 (1935), *Chem. Abs.* **30,** 54 (1936). ⟨15⟩ Reid, *J. Am. Chem. Soc.* **39,** 131 (1917). ⟨16⟩ Rather, Reid, *J. Am. Chem. Soc.* **41,** 79 (1919). ⟨17⟩ Rather, Reid, *J. Am. Chem. Soc.* **43,** 635 (1921). ⟨18⟩ Drake, Sweeney, *J. Am. Chem. Soc.* **54,** 2060 (1932). ⟨19⟩ Coops, Verkade, *Rec. trav. chim.* **44,** 998–999 (1925). ⟨20⟩ Timmermans, Vesselovsky, *Bull. soc. chim. Belg.* **41,** 55 (1932).

⟨21⟩ Weerman, *Rec. trav. chim.* **37,** 48 (1918). ⟨22⟩ Chattaway, Parkes, *J. Chem. Soc.* **123,** 666 (1923). ⟨23⟩ Bischoff, Walden, *Ann.* **279,** 138 (1894). ⟨24⟩ Casale, *Gazz. chim. ital.* **47,** I, 284 (1917). ⟨25⟩ Polikier, *Ber.* **24,** 2959 (1891). ⟨26⟩ Ref. 24, page 277.

1:0530 SUCCINIC ACID (Ethane-1,2-dicarboxylic acid) CH_2—COOH | CH_2—COOH $C_4H_6O_4$ **Beil. II-601**

M.P. 185° **Neut. Eq. 59**

Monoclinic pr. — 100 g. aq. dis.; at 0° 2.75 g. C̄; at 12.5° 4.9 g. C̄; at 25° 8.35 g. C̄; at 50° 23.83 g. C̄; at 75° 60.37 g. C̄ — 100 pts. 96% alc. at 15° conts. 10.0 g. C̄; 100 pts. MeOH at 15° conts. 15.7 g. C̄; 100 pts. acetone at 15° conts. 5.54 g. C̄ — 100 pts. satd. soln. in dry ether at 15° conts. 1.25 g. C̄ — C̄ is insol. in $CHCl_3$ or CS_2 — Distribution coefficient aq./ether is abt. 6.2 at 15°, 6.8 at 20°, and 7.6 at 25.5° ⟨1⟩.

C̄ distils at 235° being largely converted to succinic anhydride (1:0710) — Although not an α-hydroxyacid gives yellow color with $FeCl_3$ (T 1.32).

C̄ htd. with PCl_5 at 110° ⟨2⟩ gives (85% yield ⟨3⟩ ⟨4⟩) succinyl (di)chloride, b.p. 193°, m.p. 20° ⟨5⟩, 17° ⟨6⟩; sol. in C_6H_6 but insol. in pet. ether. [This compd. can react in either the sym. or unsym. forms according to circumstances.]

C̄ refluxed with excess $SOCl_2$ ⟨7⟩ (78% yield ⟨8⟩), or htd. with $POCl_3$ (82–96% yield ⟨9⟩) gives succinic anhydride (1:0710).

C̄ neutralized with NH_4OH, evapd. and dry $(NH_4)_2$Ā distd. gives (82–83% yield ⟨10⟩) succinimide [Beil. XXI-369], cryst. from alc. or acetone, m.p. 126° [also obtd. from C̄ by distn. with $(NH_4)_2CO_3$ + AcOH ⟨11⟩].

Ag_2Ā, insol. cold aq.; CaĀ.$3H_2O$ ppts. at room temp., CaĀ.H_2O at b.p. (but with $CaCl_2$ only from concd. solns. of alk. succinates); ppt. sol. in dil. acetic ac., HCl or hot NH_4Cl soln., insol. alc.

Ⓟ **Pyrrole formation and color reaction:** $(NH_4)_2$Ā on distn. with Zn dust gives pyrrole ⟨12⟩, easily detected by the red color which it gives to a pine splinter soaked in HCl. [Although as little as 0.6 mg. C̄ can thus be detected, the reaction is not specific and is also shown by lactic ac. (1:0400), pyruvic ac. (1:1040), or dihydroxyacetone ⟨13⟩.]

Ⓓ **Di-(*p*-nitrobenzyl) succinate:** m.p. 88° [cf. T 1.39].

Ⓓ **Di-(phenacyl) succinate:** m.p. 148° ⟨15⟩ [cf. T 1.39]. [For use in presence of acetic ac. (1:1010), citric ac. (1:0455), *l*-malic ac. (1:0450), oxalic ac. (1:0445), or *d*-tartaric ac. (1:0525) see ⟨16⟩.]

Ⓓ **Di-(*p*-chlorophenacyl) succinate:** m.p. 197.5° ⟨17⟩ [cf. T 1.391].

Ⓓ **Di-(*p*-bromophenacyl) succinate:** m.p. 211.0° ⟨17⟩ [cf. T 1.391].

Ⓓ **Di-(*p*-phenylphenacyl) succinate:** m.p. 208° ⟨18⟩ [cf. T 1.391].

—— **Succinic acid diamide (succinamide)** [Beil. II-614]: ndls. from aq., m.p. 260° rap. htg. ⟨19⟩ [from dimethyl succinate (1:3556) in alc. stood with excess conc. aq. NH_4OH for 3 days (80% yield ⟨19⟩), or from diethyl succinate (1:3756) similarly for 12 days. (80% yield ⟨19⟩, 70% yield ⟨20⟩]. [On slow htg. the m.p. observed is much lower ⟨19⟩.] [Note also that succinyl (di)chloride + conc. aq. NH_4OH gives only about 5% of succinamide ⟨21⟩.] [The monoamide (succinamic acid) has m.p. 157° ⟨22⟩.] [Succinimide (see above text) has m.p. 126°.]

—— **Succinic acid dianilide (succinanilide)** [Beil. XII-296]: ndls. from alc., m.p. 230° ⟨21⟩ ⟨23⟩; 227° ⟨24⟩ ⟨25⟩ [from C̄ + 2 pts. aniline htd. at 200° for 3–4 hrs. so that aq. (but not aniline) escapes, the monoanilide (see below) also being formed ⟨23⟩; or from succinyl (di)chloride + aniline in C_6H_6 ⟨21⟩ ⟨25⟩ (90% yield)]. [The monoanilide (succinanilic acid) [Beil. XII-295], has m.p. 148.5° (see under succinic anhydride (1:0710)); with $SOCl_2$ ⟨26⟩ it yields *N*-phenylsuccinimide (succinanil) [Beil. XXI-374], ndls. from aq., m.p. 156°.]

Ⓓ **Succinic acid di-*p*-toluidide** [Beil. XII-934]: m.p. 254.5–255.5° u.c. ⟨27⟩; 260° ⟨24⟩. Place in dry 6-in. tt. 0.1 g. C̄ and 0.5 g. *p*-toluidine. Arrange a 25-cm. glass tube as a condenser and heat the lower part of the tt. in a small beaker of sulfuric acid or paraffin for half an hour at 200–220°. Remove tt., cool, add 10 ml. 50% alc. and boil. Cool well and filter off the cryst. ppt., washing with 2 ml. cold dil. 50% alc. Recryst. from 5 ml. boilg. strong alc., filter, wash cryst. with 1 ml. cold strong alc., and dry at 100° ⟨27⟩. [The mono-*p*-toluidide (*N*-*p*-tolylsuccinamic ac.) has m.p. 179–180° sl. htg.] [*N*-*p*-tolylsuccinimide [Beil. XXI-375], ndls. from aq., has m.p. 151°.]

Ⓓ **Di-(*S*-benzylthiuronium) succinate** (dihydrate): m.p. 149° cor. ⟨28⟩.

Ⓓ **Piperazonium 1-acid succinate:** cryst. from 95% alc., m.p. 205–206° dec.; Neut. Eq. 204 ⟨29⟩ [from $\bar{C}$ + ½ mole piperazine hexahydrate (90% yield) ⟨29⟩].

1:0530 ⟨1⟩ Pinnow, *Z. anal. Chem.* **54,** 325–327 (1916); *Z. Untersuch. Nahr. Genussm.* **37,** 52–54 (1919). ⟨2⟩ Fröschl, Maier, *Monatsh.* **59,** 264 (1932). ⟨3⟩ Curtius, Hechtenberg, *J. prakt. Chem.* (2) **105,** 302, Note 2 (1923). ⟨4⟩ Clark, Bell, *Trans. Roy. Soc. Canada,* III (3), **27,** 97–103 (1933). ⟨5⟩ Morrell, *J. Chem. Soc.* **105,** 1736 (1914). ⟨6⟩ Purvis, Jones, Tasker, *J. Chem. Soc.* **99,** 2289 (1910). ⟨7⟩ Meyer, *Monatsh.* **22,** 420 (1901). ⟨8⟩ McMaster, Ahmann, *J. Am. Chem. Soc.* **50,** 146 (1928). ⟨9⟩ Shriner, Struck, *Organic Syntheses* **12,** 66–67 (1932). ⟨10⟩ Clarke, Behr, *Organic Syntheses,* **16,** 75–76 (1936).

⟨11⟩ Kao, Ma, *J. Chem. Soc.* **1931,** 444; **1930,** 2788. ⟨12⟩ Neuberg, *Z. physiol. Chem.* **31,** 574–578 (1901). ⟨13⟩ Virtanen, Fontell, *Chem. Abs.* **21,** 2859 (1927). ⟨14⟩ Lyman, Reid, *J. Am. Chem. Soc.* **39,** 707 (1917). ⟨15⟩ Rather, Reid, *J. Am. Chem. Soc.* **41,** 79 (1919). ⟨16⟩ Rather, Reid, *J. Am. Chem. Soc.* **43,** 635 (1921). ⟨17⟩ Judefind, Reid, *J. Am. Chem. Soc.* **42,** 1055 (1920). ⟨18⟩ Drake, Bronitsky, *J. Am. Chem. Soc.* **52,** 3719 (1930). ⟨19⟩ Morrell, *J. Chem. Soc.* **105,** 2701, 2705–2706 (1914). ⟨20⟩ Wojcik, Adkins, *J. Am. Chem. Soc.* **56,** 2421 (1934).

⟨21⟩ Morrell, *J. Chem. Soc.* **105,** 1736–1737 (1914). ⟨22⟩ Jeffery, Vogel, *J. Chem. Soc.* **1934,** 1103. ⟨23⟩ Ref. 19, pages 2702–2703. ⟨24⟩ Barnicoat, *J. Chem. Soc.* **1927,** 2927. ⟨25⟩ Dunlap, Cummer, *J. Am. Chem. Soc.* **25,** 621 (1903). ⟨26⟩ Warren, Briggs, *Ber.* **64,** 29 (1931). ⟨27⟩ Mulliken, " Method " I, 86 (1904). ⟨28⟩ Donleavy, *J. Am. Chem. Soc.* **58,** 1005 (1936). ⟨29⟩ Pollard, Adelson, Bain, *J. Am. Chem. Soc.* **56,** 1759 (1934).

1:0535 OXALIC ACID, anhydrous

COOH
|
COOH

$C_2H_2O_4$ **Beil. II-502**

M.P. 189.5° **Neut. Eq. 45**

Rhombic octahedra — beginning to sublime even below 100° — On stdg. exposed to (moist) air readily hydrates yielding $\bar{C}.2H_2O$ (1:0445).

[For prepn. (96–98% yield) via distn. of hydrated oxalic ac. (1:0445) with CCl_4 see ⟨1⟩, or by distn. with toluene ⟨2⟩, or by htg. alone ⟨3⟩.]

100 pts. aq. at 0° dis. 3.5 g. $\bar{C}$; at 20° 9.5 g. $\bar{C}$; at 60° 44.3 g. $\bar{C}$; at 90° 120 g. $\bar{C}$ ⟨4⟩ — 100 pts. abs. alc. at 15° dis. 23.7 pts. $\bar{C}$ — 100 pts. abs. ether at 25° dis. 23.6 g. $\bar{C}$.

$\bar{C}$, in pyridine, decomposes quant. according to equation: $\bar{C} + Ac_2O = CO_2 + CO + 2CH_3.COOH$. [Use in quant. detn. of Ac_2O ⟨5⟩ ⟨6⟩ ⟨7⟩.] — $\bar{C}$ treated with 4 moles PCl_5 gives 50–60% yield oxalyl (di)chloride, b.p. 64° ⟨8⟩ ⟨9⟩ ⟨10⟩.

For other reactions of $\bar{C}$ see hydrated oxalic ac. (1:0445).

1:0535 ⟨1⟩ Clarke, Davis, *Organic Syntheses, Coll. Vol.* I, 412–416 (1932). ⟨2⟩ Johnson, Partington, *J. Chem. Soc.* **1930,** 1510–1511. ⟨3⟩ Bowden, *Organic Syntheses* **10,** 78–79 (1930). ⟨4⟩ Cahn, *Z. anorg. allgem. Chem.* **60,** 110 (1908). ⟨5⟩ Rosenbaum, Walton, *J. Am. Chem. Soc.* **52,** 3366–3368 (1930). ⟨6⟩ Whitford, *J. Am. Chem. Soc.* **47,** 2934–2938 (1925). ⟨7⟩ Krause, *Ber.* **52,** 426–432 (1919). ⟨8⟩ Staudinger, *Ber.* **41,** 3559–3560 (1908). ⟨9⟩ Biltz, Topp, *Ber.* **46,** 1392, Note 2 (1913). ⟨10⟩ Staudinger, Anthes, *Ber.* **46,** 1431; Note 1 (1913).

1:0538 HEMIMELLITIC ACID

(Benzene-1,2,3-tricarboxylic acid)

COOH, —COOH, —COOH

$C_9H_6O_6$ **Beil. IX-976**

M.P. 190° dec. **Neut. Eq. 70**

Tbls. with 2 H_2O from aq., ether or conc. HCl; loses aq. at 100° — 100 pts. aq. at 19° dis. 3.15 g. C̄; very eas. sol. hot aq.; fairly eas. sol. ether — C̄ is pptd. from aq. soln. as such by addn. of conc. HCl; as charact. glistening flakes of *mono* potassium salt dihydrate by addn. of conc. aq. KCl soln. ⟨1⟩ ⟨2⟩ [dif. from phthalic ac. (1:0820)].

[For prepn. (in 44% yield ⟨3⟩; 79% yield ⟨4⟩; 82% yield ⟨5⟩) via alk. $KMnO_4$ oxidn. of naphthalic anhydride (1:0891) see ⟨3⟩ ⟨5⟩.]

C̄ on htg. at m.p. loses aq. and yields hemimellitic anhydride (anhydromellitic acid) [Beil. XVIII-468], m.p. 196°.

C̄ on htg. at 250–300° yields CO_2 and sublimate of phthalic anhydride (1:0725); hence on htg. with resorcinol + drop of conc. H_2SO_4 yields fluorescein, detectable by charact. fluorescence of alk. soln.

Ⓓ **Trimethyl hemimellitate:** m.p. 100° ⟨6⟩ 101–102° ⟨4⟩ [from $Ag_3\bar{A}$ htd. with excess CH_3I in s.t. at 120–125° for several hrs. ⟨6⟩]. [Unlike the several mono- and di-esters it is insol. in aq. Na_2CO_3.]

1:0538 ⟨1⟩ Adelson, Bogert, *J. Am. Chem. Soc.* **58,** 2238 (1936). ⟨2⟩ Graebe, Leonhardt, *Ann.* **290,** 223 (1896). ⟨3⟩ Whitmore, Perkin, *J. Am. Chem. Soc.* **51,** 3352 (1929). ⟨4⟩ Meyer, Wesche, *Ber.* **50,** 453 (1917). ⟨5⟩ Ref. 2, pages 218–219. ⟨6⟩ Ref. 2, page 227.

1:0540 ACONITIC ACID HOOC.CH₂—C—COOH $C_6H_6O_6$ Beil. II-849

$$\begin{array}{c} HOOC.CH_2{-}C{-}COOH \\ \| \\ HOOC{-}C{-}H \end{array}$$

M.P. 191° dec.
194–195° cor. ⟨1⟩ **Neut. Eq. 58**

Owing to fact that C̄ on htg. dec. to itaconic ac. (1:0515) and CO_2, the observed values of m.p. may vary widely [cf. ⟨2⟩ ⟨1⟩ ⟨3⟩].

Lfts. or ndls. from conc. HCl or from aq. — C̄ is sol. in 5.5 pts. aq. at 13°; in 2 pts. 88% alc. at 12°; spar. sol. ether ⟨4⟩. [For prepn. (41–44% yield) from cryst. citric ac. (1:0455) + conc. H_2SO_4 see ⟨5⟩.]

C̄ in alk. soln. reduces $KMnO_4$ (T 1.34) but in CCl_4 or aq. adds Br_2 (T 1.91) only very slowly on warming.

C̄ on treatment with AcCl may yield either or both α,γ-anhydroaconitic acid [Beil. XVIII₁-(511)], or β,γ-anhydroaconitic ac. [Beil. XVIII₁-(511)], the former giving a greenish yel. aq. soln. colored reddish brown by $FeCl_3$ — C̄, finely powd. and stood 2–3 days at room temp. or a few hrs. at 40–45° with equal wt. Ac_2O gives (35–45% yield ⟨6⟩) of the former or α,γ-anhydroaconitic ac., ndls. from AcOEt, m.p. 135° — C̄ boiled with 2 wts. AcCl + 5 wts. $CHCl_3$ ⟨7⟩ yields β,γ-anhydroaconitic ac., ndls. from C_6H_6, $C_6H_4O_5.\frac{1}{2}C_6H_6$ (Neut. Eq. 65); in dry air C_6H_6 is lost and product has m.p. 78–78.5° cor.; Neut. Eq. 52 ⟨1⟩. [This benzene-free product on soln. in 2 pts. cold aq. and evapn. at ord. temp. in vac. desic. gives quant. yield of *cis*-aconitic ac., m.p. 125° ⟨8⟩.] [The β,γ-anhydroaconitic acid (m.p. 78°) on htg. at 175–190° and 15–20 mm. press. loses CO_2 and gives 62% yield of itaconic anhydride (1:0654) ⟨9⟩.]

C̄ does not yield an acid chloride either with PCl_5 or $SOCl_2$ ⟨10⟩.

C̄ on boiling aq. soln. with excess $Ca(OH)_2$ gives no ppt. [dif. from citric ac. (1:0455) or tricarballylic ac. (1:0520)].

Ⓟ **Color reaction with Ac_2O + pyridine:** C̄ on warm. with Ac_2O + pyridine gives a beautiful violet-red coloration. The reaction is very sensitive and in filtered ultra-violet light even 1 γ of C̄ can be detected by the yellow fluorescence of the reaction product ⟨11⟩, cf. also ⟨12⟩. [Tartaric ac. (1:0525) and even *meso*tartaric ac. (1:0490) ⟨13⟩ gives an emerald-green color; citric ac. (1:0455) a carmine-red; other dicarboxylic acids give a brown color or none at all ⟨12⟩.]

Ⓓ **Tri-(phenacyl) aconitate:** m.p. 90° ⟨14⟩ [cf. T 1.391].
Ⓓ **Tri-(*p*-chlorophenacyl) aconitate:** m.p. 169.0° ⟨15⟩ [cf. T 1.391].
Ⓓ **Tri-(*p*-bromophenacyl) aconitate:** m.p. 186.0° ⟨15⟩ [cf. T 1.391].

1:0540 ⟨1⟩ Malachowski, Maslowski, *Ber.* **61,** 2522–2523 (1928). ⟨2⟩ Bruce, *Organic Syntheses* **17,** 2, Note 6 (1937). ⟨3⟩ Beath, *J. Am. Chem. Soc.* **48,** 2155–2158 (1926). ⟨4⟩ Michael, *J. prakt. Chem.* (2) **52,** 342, Note (1895). ⟨5⟩ Bruce, *Organic Syntheses* **17,** 1–3 (1937). ⟨6⟩ Malachowski, Giedroyc, Jerzmanowska, *Ber.* **61,** 2532 (1928). ⟨7⟩ Anschütz, Bertram, *Ber.* **37,** 3967 (1904). ⟨8⟩ Ref. 1, page 2524. ⟨9⟩ Ref. 7, page 3969. ⟨10⟩ Fröschl, Maier, *Monatsh.* **59,** 274 (1932).

⟨11⟩ Taylor, *J. Chem. Soc.* **115,** 887–889 (1919). ⟨12⟩ Fürth, Herrmann, *Biochem. Z.* **280,** 448–457 (1935); *Chem. Abs.* **30,** 54 (1936). ⟨13⟩ Casares-Lopez, *Biochem. Z.* **284,** 365–366 (1936); *Cent.* **1937,** I, 392. ⟨14⟩ Rather, Reid, *J. Am. Chem. Soc.* **41,** 80 (1919). ⟨15⟩ Judefind, Reid, *J. Am. Chem. Soc.* **42,** 1055 (1920).

1:0545 PROTOCATECHUIC ACID $C_7H_6O_4$ Beil. X-389

(3,4-Dihydroxybenzoic acid) HO—⟨ring⟩—COOH, HO (3,4-positions)

M.P. 199-200° dec. **Neut. Eq. 154**

Ndls. or tbls. with 1 H_2O from aq.; cryst. aq. lost above 100° — Sol. in 53–55 pts. aq. at 14°; very eas. sol. alc.; mod. sol. ether, alm. insol. hot C_6H_6. [For prepn. of C̄ from piperonylic ac. see latter (1:0865); from 3-bromo-4-hydroxybenzoic ac. by KOH fusion (70% yield) see ⟨1⟩.]

C̄ reduces $NH_4OH + AgNO_3$ and Tollens' reagt. (T 1.11) but not Fehling's soln. (T 1.22) — C̄ in aq. soln. gives with $FeCl_3$ (T 1.41) an intense green color changing to dark red on addn. of NH_4OH, Na_2CO_3 or $NaHCO_3$.

C̄ on dry distn., or on htg. with aniline at 130° loses CO_2 yielding pyrocatechol (1:1520).

C̄ dislvd. in $3\frac{1}{2}$ moles 10% aq. NaOH, shaken with 4 moles dimethyl sulfate in cold, then warmed 2 hrs. at 100° and finally boiled until all ester is saponified, gives on acidification (90% yield ⟨2⟩ ⟨3⟩) 3,4-dimethoxybenzoic ac. (veratric acid) [Beil. X-394], m.p. anhydrous, 181°. [From conc. aq. solns. above 50° this product crystallizes in anhydrous form; from dil. aq. solns. below 50° it seps. as a monohydrate, losing aq. above 100°.] [The monomethyl ethers, viz. 4-hydroxy-3-methoxybenzoic acid (vanillic acid) [Beil. X-392], m.p. 207°, and 3-hydroxy-4-methoxybenzoic acid (isovanillic acid) [Beil. X-393], m.p. 250°, do not show characteristic $FeCl_3$ colors and this means cannot be used to detect them if mixed with veratric ac.]

C̄ in 10 pts. Ac_2O treated with 1 pt. solid anhydrous K_2CO_3 (87% yield ⟨4⟩), or C̄ in 2 *N* aq. NaOH at 60° treated with 2 moles Ac_2O ⟨5⟩, or C̄ htd. at 100° for 2 hrs. with a little $ZnCl_2$ ⟨6⟩ yields 3,4-diacetoxybenzoic acid, m.p. 157–158° cor. ⟨5⟩ ⟨6⟩, 162° ⟨4⟩. [3-Acetoxy-4-hydroxybenzoic acid has m.p. 202–203° cor. ⟨6⟩.]

C̄ (1 g.) + NaOH (4 g.) in 36 ml. aq. shaken at 0° with BzCl (9.1 g.) yields benzoyl (3,4-dibenzoyloxy)benzoate, cryst. from aq., m.p. 198° ⟨7⟩.

Ⓓ **Methyl protocatechuate:** from C̄ in CH_3OH satd. with HCl gas, or contg. 1% conc. H_2SO_4; white ndls. from hot aq., m.p. 134.5°.

1:0545 ⟨1⟩ Couturier, *Ann. chim.* (11) **10,** 572–573 (1938). ⟨2⟩ Graebe, Martz, *Ann.* **340,** 216–217 (1905). ⟨3⟩ Wieland, Konz, Sonderhoff, *Ann.* **527,** 168 (1936). ⟨4⟩ Malkin, Nierenstein, *Ber.* **61,** 797 (1928). ⟨5⟩ Lesser, Gad, *Ber.* **59,** 234 (1926). ⟨6⟩ Fischer, Bergmann, Lipschitz, *Ber.* **51,** 74 (1918). ⟨7⟩ Ono, Imoto, *Bull. Chem. Soc. Japan* **10,** 330 (1935). ⟨8⟩ Matsmoto, *Ber.* **11,** 129 (1878).

1:0548 MESACONIC ACID (Methylfumaric acid) $CH_3—C—COOH$ (β) / (α) HOOC—C—H $C_5H_6O_4$ **Beil. II-763**

M.P. 204.5° cor. ⟨1⟩ **Neut. Eq. 65**

Rhombic ndls. from alc. or dil. HNO_3; tbls. from ether or AcOEt; cryst. pdr. from hot aq. or ether + lgr. — Sublimes undecomposed but is not volatile with steam. Sol. in 38 pts. aq. at 14°; eas. sol. alc., ether; spar. sol. $CHCl_3$, CS_2, lgr.

[For prepn. of C̄ from citraconic acid (1:0435) via action of light on $CHCl_3$ or $CHCl_3$ + ether soln. contg. trace of Br_2 (67%–85% yield) see ⟨2⟩ ⟨3⟩ ⟨4⟩; from citraconic anhydride (1:1135) or acid via evapn. of dil. HNO_3 soln. (43–52% yield) see ⟨5⟩.]

C̄ on htg. at 250°, or htg. with AcCl in s.t., yields citraconic anhydride (1:1135) — C̄ with 2 moles PCl_5 ⟨4⟩ ⟨6⟩ ⟨7⟩, or $SOCl_2$ ⟨8⟩ yields mesaconyl (di)chloride, b.p. 64–65°$_{14}$ ⟨7⟩. [This acid chloride is completely hydrolyzed to C̄ by stdg. with aq. for 24 hrs., but if it is first refluxed for 3 hrs., or htd. with 20% of $AlCl_3$ at 100°, some conversion to citraconyl chloride occurs ⟨4⟩.]

[For detn. of C̄ in mixts. with itaconic ac. (1:0515) see ⟨9⟩.]

Ⓓ **Di-*p*-nitrobenzyl mesaconate:** m.p. 134° cor. ⟨1⟩ [cf. T 1.39].

Ⓓ **Mesaconic dihydrazide:** cryst. from dil. alc., m.p. 217–218° cor. ⟨1⟩ [from diethyl mesaconate (1:3892) in alc. on stdg. overnight with 42% aq. hydrazine hydrate ⟨1⟩].

Ⓓ **Mesaconic diamide:** pl. from aq. or alc., m.p. 176.5° ⟨10⟩; 177–177.5° ⟨11⟩ 179.6° ⟨3⟩ [from dimethyl mesaconate (1:3591) + conc. aq. NH_4OH]. [Of the two monoamides the α (mesacon-α-amidic ac.) has m.p. 22°; the β (mesacon-β-amidic acid) has m.p. 174°.]

Ⓓ **Mesaconic dianilide** [Beil. XII-307]: from mesaconyl (di)chloride (above) + excess aniline both in ether soln. (100% yield); ndls. from aq., m.p. 185.7° ⟨10⟩. [Note that aniline mesaconate htd. at 240° does not give the corresp. dianilide but instead citraconanil [Beil. XXI-407], m.p. 98–99°.] [Of the two monoanilides, the α- (mesacon-α-anilic acid) has m.p. 202°; the β- (mesacon-β-anilic acid) has m.p. 163°.]

Ⓓ **Mesaconic di-*p*-toluidide** [Beil. XII-938]: from mesaconyl (di)chloride (above) + excess aniline, both in ether soln.; ndls. from alc., m.p. 212° ⟨12⟩ (but accompanied by much β-chloride-α-*p*-toluidide, yel. ndls. from C_6H_6, m.p. 115° ⟨13⟩). [The α-mono-*p*-toluidide (*N*-*p*-tolyl-mesacon-α-amidic acid) has m.p. 196.]

1:0548 ⟨1⟩ Mottern, Keenan, *J. Am. Chem. Soc.* **53,** 2347–2349 (1931). ⟨2⟩ Linstead, Mann, *J. Chem. Soc.* **1931,** 734. ⟨3⟩ van de Straete, *Bull. soc. chim. Belg.* **44,** 318–319 (1935). ⟨4⟩ Lutz, Taylor, *J. Am. Chem. Soc.* **55,** 1173 (1933). ⟨5⟩ Shriner, Ford, Roll, *Organic Syntheses* **11,** 74–75 (1931). ⟨6⟩ Petri, *Ber.* **14,** 1635 (1881). ⟨7⟩ Anschütz, *Ann.* **353,** 190 (1907). ⟨8⟩ Meyer, *Monatsh.* **22,** 423 (1901). ⟨9⟩ Ref. 2, pages 735–736. ⟨10⟩ Strecker, *Ber.* **15,** 1641 (1882).

⟨11⟩ Demarcay, *Ann. chim.* (5) **20,** 479 (1880). ⟨12⟩ Ref. 7, page 196. ⟨13⟩ Ref. 7, page 192.

1:0550 RACEMIC ACID (*d,l*-Tartaric acid) COOH / H—C—OH / HO—C—H / COOH and COOH / HO—C—H / H—C—OH / COOH $C_4H_6O_6$ **Beil. III-522**

M.P. 205-206° (anhydrous) **Neut. Eq. 75** (anhydrous)
M.P. 203-204° (monohydrate) **84** (monohydrate)

C̄ cryst. from aq. solns. above 73°, from strong H_2SO_4 solns. at 25°, or from abs. alc., in anhydrous form — Otherwise cryst. with 1 H_2O, efflorescing in air and losing aq. completely at 100° — The monohydrate is sol. in 5 pts. aq. at 20° (less than either *d*- or *l*-acids) or in 48 pts. cold alc. — At 15° C̄ is spar. sol. ether, viz., 1.08%. [In colorimetric detns. mol. wt. must be considered as 2 $C_4H_6O_6$ ⟨1⟩.]

[For prepn. of C̄ from *d*-tartaric ac. (1:0525) by racemization with alk. see ⟨2⟩ ⟨3⟩ ⟨4⟩ ⟨5⟩.] [For detn. of C̄ in presence of *d*-tartaric and *meso*-tartaric (1:0490) see ⟨6⟩ ⟨7⟩.]

C̄ htd. with 4 moles BzCl at 100° until evol. of HCl stops (abt. 10 hrs.), product washed with ether gives dibenzoyl-*d,l*-tartaric anhydride, m.p. 182° ⟨8⟩ which on boilg. with aq. hydrolyzes to dibenzoyl-*d,l*-tartaric ac., pr., m.p. after air drying, 112–113° ⟨8⟩.

Salts: KHĀ; sol. in 180 pts. aq. at 19°, in 139 pts. at 25°, in 14.3 pts. at 100°.

CaĀ.$4H_2O$ pptd. by satd. $CaSO_4$ soln. (dif. from *d*-tartaric ac. (1:0525) or *meso*-tartaric ac. (1:0490); ppt. sol. in dil. HCl and repptd. immed. by NH_4OH (dif. from salt of *d*-tartaric ac.) — [For comparison of aq. soly. of Mg, Ca, Sr, Ba, and Pb salts of C̄ with corresponding derivs. of *d*-tartaric ac. see ⟨9⟩.]

C̄ in equal wt. MeOH, satd. with dry HCl, and stood 24 hrs. ⟨10⟩ yields dimethyl *d,l*-tartrate (1:2385). [This is known in two forms: stable form, m.p. 90°; metastable form, m.p. 84°.]

Ⓟ **Color reaction with Ac_2O + pyridine:** C̄ warmed with Ac_2O + pyridine gives an emerald-green color ⟨11⟩. [For further comment see also *meso*-tartaric ac. (1:0490).]

Ⓓ **Di-(*p*-nitrobenzyl) *d,l*-tartrate:** m.p. 147.6° ⟨12⟩ [cf. T 1.39].

—— ***d,l*-Tartramide:** rect. pr. from aq. MeOH, m.p. 226° ⟨13⟩.

—— ***d,l*-Tartranil** [Beil. XXI-625]: from aniline acid racemate, htd. at 190°; lfts. m.p. 235–236° ⟨14⟩.

1:0550 ⟨1⟩ Blank, *J. Chem. Education* **14,** 393 (1937). ⟨2⟩ Holleman, *Organic Syntheses, Coll. Vol.* I, 462–463 (1932). ⟨3⟩ Campbell, Slotin, Johnson, *J. Am. Chem. Soc.* **55,** 2604 (1933). ⟨4⟩ Newman, Riley, *J. Chem. Soc.* **1933,** 46. ⟨5⟩ Coops, Verkade, *Rec. trav. chim.* **44,** 986–987 (1925). ⟨6⟩ Holleman, *Rec. trav. chim.* **17,** 69 (1898). ⟨7⟩ Winther, *Z. physik. Chem.* **56,** 488–492 (1906). ⟨8⟩ Brigl, Grüner, *Ber.* **65,** 641–644 (1932). ⟨9⟩ Duboux, Cuttat, *Helv. Chim. Acta* **4,** 740–748 (1921). ⟨10⟩ Anschütz, Pictet, *Ber.* **13,** 1176 (1880).

⟨11⟩ Casares-Lopez, *Biochem. Z.* **284,** 365–366 (1936). ⟨12⟩ Lyman, Reid, *J. Am. Chem. Soc.* **39,** 709 (1917). ⟨13⟩ Williams, *J. Chem. Soc.* **1937,** 1518. ⟨14⟩ Wende, *Ber.* **29,** 2720 (1896).

1:0551 TRIMELLITIC ACID $C_9H_6O_6$ Beil. IX-977

(Benzene-1,2,4-tricarboxylic acid)

HOOC—C_6H_3(—COOH)(—COOH)

M.P. 228° ⟨1⟩ ⟨2⟩ ⟨6⟩ **Neut. Eq. 70**
238° ⟨3⟩ ⟨4⟩ ⟨9⟩

Ndls. from aq.; cryst. from AcOH, dil. alc., or C_6H_6 + acetone — Eas. sol. aq., alc., ether; spar. sol. acetone; alm. insol. $CHCl_3$, CCl_4, C_6H_6,CS_2.

C̄ on distn. ⟨5⟩ or on htg. at 210–220° at 2 mm. ⟨6⟩ ⟨7⟩ loses aq. yielding the corresponding anhydride (anhydromellitic acid) [Beil. XVIII-468] which sublimes; m.p. 162° ⟨6⟩, 162.5–163.5° ⟨8⟩, 163° ⟨7⟩, 165–167° ⟨5⟩.

C̄ (as 2% soln. of neutral ammonium salt) is pptd. by Hg, Cd, Pb, and Ag salts, but not by Mg, Ca, Sr, Ba, Cu, Ni or Co salts ⟨10⟩. [The Ba salt is nevertheless much less sol. than Ba isophthalate and can be used to sep. C̄ from isophthalic ac. (1:0900) ⟨6⟩.] [The Ca salt forms charact. feather ndls., insol. cold aq. ⟨11⟩.]

[The m.p. of mixtures of C̄ with either benzene-1,2,3,4-tetracarboxylic ac. (1:0553) or benzene-1,2,3,5-tetracarboxylic ac. (1:0555) is depressed ⟨12⟩.]

1:0551 ⟨1⟩ Ekstrand, *J. prakt. Chem.* (2) **43,** 428 (1891). ⟨2⟩ Ruzicka, de Graaff, Hosking, *Helv. Chim. Acta* **14,** 237 (1931). ⟨3⟩ Maxwell, Partington, *Trans. Faraday Soc.* **32,** 775 (1932). ⟨4⟩ Morgan, Coulson, *J. Chem. Soc.* **1929,** 2554. ⟨5⟩ Späth, Kuffner, *Ber.* **64,** 375–376 (1931). ⟨6⟩ Mills, Nodder, *J. Chem. Soc.* **119,** 2104 (1921). ⟨7⟩ Fichter, Stenzl, Beglinger, *Helv. Chim. Acta* **21,** 379 (1938). ⟨8⟩ Schultze, *Ann.* **359,** 142 (1908). ⟨9⟩ *Feist, Ann.* **496,** 104 (1932). ⟨10⟩ Wegscheider, Perndanner, Auspitzer, *Monatsh.* **31,** 1265 (1910).
⟨11⟩ Perkin, Stone, *J. Chem. Soc.* **127,** 2297 (1925). ⟨12⟩ Ruzicka, Schinz, Meyer, *Helv. Chim. Acta* **6,** 1091 (1923).

1:0553 BENZENE-1,2,3,4-TETRACARBOXYLIC ACID $C_{10}H_6O_8$ Beil. IX-997

(Mellophanic acid: prehnitic acid) (see text)

COOH
—COOH
—COOH
COOH

M.P. 236-238° ⟨1⟩ **Neut. Eq. 63.5**
238° dec. **⟨3⟩**

[The trivial name to be applied to this acid is badly confused in the literature: in view of its relationship to prehnitene (1,2,3,4-tetramethylbenzene) the name prehnitic acid is now preferred ⟨1⟩ ⟨2⟩; however, the name mellophanic acid is used by *Chem. Abs.*, 1939–1936 and also in 3rd *Decennial Index* (1936–1927); also by the *Centralblatt*, 1938–1925. In Beilstein the name prehnitic is used in IX-997, the name mellophanic in IX_1-(435). Other reference books vary and care must be exercised in all researches.]

Prisms from aq. with 2 H_2O, lost above 100° — $\bar{C}$ can be recrystd. from conc. HCl, dil. HCl (1:1) ⟨1⟩ or conc. HNO_3 — $\bar{C}$ is readily sol. aq. or acetone, but spar. sol. in other org. solvents. ⟨3.⟩

[For prepn. in 33–40% yield by alk. $KMnO_4$ oxidn. of naphthalene-1,4-dicarboxylic acid (in turn from carbonation of 1,4-disodiumnaphthalene ⟨4⟩) see ⟨1⟩.]

$\bar{C}$ on sublimation in vac. ⟨5⟩ or on htg. at 250° for 15 min. at ord. press. ⟨6⟩ yields a dianhydride [Beil. XIX_1-(706)], cryst. from lgr. + C_6H_6 (1:1), m.p. 193–196° after sintering at 185° ⟨6⟩; cf. ⟨5⟩. [This anhydride is insol. in aq. but sol. in NH_4OH ⟨6⟩.]

$Ag_4\bar{A}$; $Ba_2\bar{A}.6H_2O$ (sepg. on pptn. with aq. $Ba(OAc)_2$ and losing $4H_2O$ readily, last two with difficulty ⟨5⟩); $Ca_2\bar{A}$, $Pb_2\bar{A}$ ⟨7⟩, all dif. sol. aq.

Ⓓ **Tetramethyl benzene-1,2,3,4-tetracarboxylate:** cryst. from MeOH; m.p. 129–130° ⟨8⟩, 132° ⟨9⟩; 133–135° ⟨3⟩ [from $\bar{C}$ + excess diazomethane in ether ⟨10⟩ ⟨11⟩ or from $Ag_4\bar{A}$ + CH_3I ⟨3⟩]. [This ester depresses the m.p. of the corresp. deriv. of benzene-1,-2,4,5-tetracarboxylic acid (1:0557) ⟨11⟩. It also has peculiar prop. of acquiring a beautiful purple color on exposure to light without visible change in cryst. form; on fusion or on solution the purple cryst. give colorless liquids from which a colorless solid deposits and this again turns purple on reexposure to light ⟨1⟩.]

1:0553 ⟨1⟩ Smith, Carlson, *J. Am. Chem. Soc.* **61,** 288–291 (1939). ⟨2⟩ Smith, Byrkit, *J. Am. Chem. Soc.* **55,** 4306 (1933). ⟨3⟩ Bamford, Simonsen, *J. Chem. Soc.* **97,** 1909 (1910). ⟨4⟩ Walker, Scott, *J. Am. Chem. Soc.* **60,** 953 (1938). ⟨5⟩ Schroeter, *Ber.* **57,** 2032 (1924). ⟨6⟩ Freund, Fleischer, *Ann.* **411,** 26 (1916). ⟨7⟩ Smith, Kiess, *J. Am. Chem. Soc.* **61,** 288 (1939). ⟨8⟩ Fieser, Peters, *J. Am. Chem. Soc.* **54,** 4352 (1932). ⟨9⟩ Ruzicka, et al., *Helv. Chim. Acta* **15,** 1502 (1932). ⟨10⟩ Warnat, *Ber.* **58,** 2773 (1925).
⟨11⟩ Hillemann, *Ber.* **68,** 105 (1935).

1:0555 BENZENE-1,2,3,5-TETRACARBOXYLIC ACID $C_{10}H_6O_8$ **Beil. IX-997**
(Prehnitic acid: mellophanic acid)
(see text)

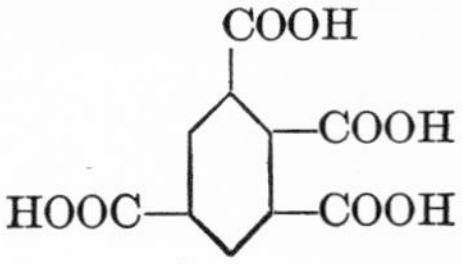

M.P. abt. 253° (see text) **Neut. Eq. 63.5**

[The trivial name to be applied to this acid is badly confused in the literature; the designation mellophanic acid is now preferred ⟨1⟩; however, the name prehnitic acid is used by *Chem. Abs.* and by *Centralblatt.* Care must be exercised in all searches. See also comment under benzene-1,2,3,4-tetracarboxylic acid (1:0553).]

Pr. from HCl — M.p.'s reported vary widely, viz., m.p. 238–253° ⟨1⟩, 253–262° ⟨2⟩, 252° after softening at 240° ⟨3⟩, 263–266° ⟨4⟩ — Eas. sol. aq.

$\bar{C}$ on htg. above m.p. loses aq. and on cooling yields the anhydride, 1,2-anhydroprehnitic ac. or 3,5-dicarboxyphthalic anhydride [Beil. XVIII-508], m.p. 239° ⟨5⟩.

Ⓓ **Tetramethyl benzene-1,2,3,5-tetracarboxylate:** ndls. from MeOH, m.p. 108–109° ⟨3⟩, 107–109° ⟨1⟩ [from $\bar{C}$ in ether treated with diazomethane ⟨1⟩ or from $Ag_4\bar{A}$ + CH_3I ⟨3⟩].

1:0555 ⟨1⟩ Smith, Byrkit, *J. Am. Chem. Soc.* **55,** 4306, 4308 (1933). ⟨2⟩ Freund, Fleischer, *Ann.* **411,** 35 (1916). ⟨3⟩ Bamford, Simonsen, *J. Chem. Soc.* **97,** 1907 (1910). ⟨4⟩ Maxwell, Partington, *Trans. Faraday Soc.* **32,** 778–779 (1936). ⟨5⟩ Baeyer, *Ann.* **166,** 328 (1873).

1:0557 PYROMELLITIC ACID $C_{10}H_6O_8$ **Beil. IX-997**
(Benzene-1,2,4,5-tetracarboxylic acid)

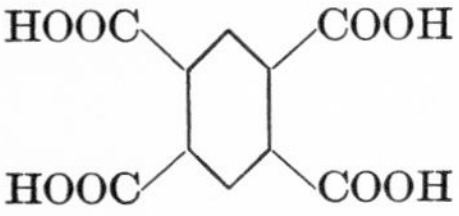

M.P. 275° ⟨1⟩ **Neut. Eq. 63.5 ⟨1⟩**
273-275° ⟨2⟩
270-272° ⟨3⟩

Tbls. or pr. with 2 H_2O from aq., m.p. 242° ⟨1⟩ — Owing to the formation of this hydrate and also to conv. of $\bar{C}$ to pyromellitic dianhydride on htg., m.p. of $\bar{C}$ is variously reported from 264° to 275° — 100 pts. aq. at 16° dis. 1.42 pts. anhydrous $\bar{C}$; eas. sol. alc., sol. ether. [For prepn. from pine or spruce charcoal by oxidn. with 82–88% H_2SO_4 + drop of Hg at 290–315° see ⟨4⟩; for prepn. starting with xylene see ⟨5⟩; for prepn. by $KMnO_4$ oxidn. of techn. octahydroanthracene see ⟨14⟩.]

$\bar{C}$ htd. at 290° at 13 mm. ⟨6⟩, or htd. at 250° and then sublimed in vac. ⟨7⟩, or vac. dried finely powdered $\bar{C}$ refluxed 15 min. with 2 pts. Ac_2O and soln. allowed to cool in vac. dessicator over KOH ⟨8⟩ gives pyromellitic dianhydride [Beil. XIX-196], m.p. 286° ⟨6⟩; 277–279° ⟨7⟩. [This anhydride is insol. in cold aq. Na_2CO_3 (dif. from $\bar{C}$).]

$\bar{C}$ + slightly more than 4 moles PCl_5 htd. over free flame until mixt. is completely liquid and no more HCl is evolved, then $POCl_3$ distd. off, gives (60% yield ⟨9⟩) pyromellitic acid (tetra)chloride, b.p. about 320°, m.p. 64° ⟨10⟩.

Ⓓ **Tetramethyl pyromellitate:** from $\bar{C}$ + MeOH + dry HCl (90% yield) ⟨11⟩), or from Ag pyromellitate + excess CH_3I in s.t. htd. 6 hrs. at 100° ⟨1⟩; lfts. from MeOH, m.p. 141.5° ⟨1⟩; 141° ⟨12⟩; 142° ⟨13⟩ [also from pyromellityl tetrachloride (above) + NaOH in 88% yield ⟨9⟩].

Ⓓ **Tetraethyl pyromellitate:** from C̄ + EtOH htd. in stream of HCl gas ⟨14⟩, or from Ag pyromellitate + excess EtI in s.t. htd. at 100°; m.p. 54° ⟨14⟩; 53° ⟨12⟩.

1:0557 ⟨1⟩ Feist, *Ber.* **44,** 137–138 (1911). ⟨2⟩ Meyer, Steiner, *Monatsh.* **35,** 393 (1914). ⟨3⟩ Smith, Byrkit, *J. Am. Chem. Soc.* **55,** 4306 (1933). ⟨4⟩ Philippi, Thelen, *Organic Syntheses* **10,** 90–92 (1930). ⟨5⟩ de Diesbach, Schmidt, Decker, *Helv. Chim. Acta* **6,** 548–549 (1923). ⟨6⟩ Schroeter, *Ber.* **57,** 2023 (1924). ⟨7⟩ Fieser, Hershberg, *J. Am. Chem. Soc.* **57,** 2196 (1935). ⟨8⟩ Philippi, Seka, *Monatsh.* **43,** 617 (1922). ⟨9⟩ Seka, Sedlatschek, Preissecker, *Monatsh.* **57,** 95 (1931). ⟨10⟩ Ott, Langenohl, Zerweck, *Ber.* **70,** 2362 (1937).

⟨11⟩ Meyer, Sudborough, *Ber.* **27,** 1589 (1894). ⟨12⟩ Farmer, Ingold, *J. Chem. Soc.* **119,** 2014 (1921). ⟨14⟩ Ruzicka, Schinz, Meyer, *Helv. Chim. Acta* **6,** 1095 (1923). ⟨14⟩ von Braun, Lemke, *Ber.* **57,** 681–682 (1924).

1:0559 TRIMESIC ACID (Benzene-1,3,5-tricarboxylic acid) $C_9H_6O_6$ **Beil. IX-978**

COOH

HOOC— —COOH

M.P. 380° cor. ⟨1⟩ ⟨2⟩ **Neut. Eq. 70**

This ac. melts at such a high temp. that much disagreement is recorded. Ndls. or salt-like pr. from hot water; very sol. alc.; insol. in ether, C_6H_6 or $CHCl_3$ — Soly. in aq. 2.6% at 22.5°; 0.38% at 16°.

[For prepn. by $KMnO_4$ oxidn. of mesitylene (1:7455) in 78% yield see ⟨1⟩ ⟨3⟩.]

C̄, htd. with PCl_5 (3.5 moles) yields trimesityl (tri)chloride (b.p. 213° at 13 mm.), colorless ndls. from lt. pet., m.p. 35–37° ⟨3⟩.

$Ba_3\bar{A}_2$ + aq.; alm. insol. cold aq.; very dif. sol. hot [dif. from isophthalic ac. (1:0900)]. $NaH_2C_9H_3O_6$, $KH_2C_9H_3O_6$ both dif. sol. aq.; sol. in excess alk. carbonate ⟨4⟩.

Ⓓ **Trimethyl trimesate:** ndls. from MeOH, m.p. 143–144° ⟨5⟩, 142° ⟨6⟩ [from C̄ in abs. MeOH + dry HCl ⟨5⟩].

Ⓓ **Triethyl trimesate:** pr. from alc., m.p. 132–133°, 133° after sintering at 127° ⟨6⟩ [from C̄ in abs. EtOH + dry HCl ⟨7⟩ or from $Ag_3\bar{A}$ + C_2H_5I ⟨8⟩].

—— **Trimesic triamide:** m.p. 365° cor. dec. ⟨3⟩.

—— **Trimesic trianilide:** cryst. from AcOH, m.p. 118–120° dec. ⟨9⟩ [prepd. indirectly].

1:0559 ⟨1⟩ Ullmann, Uzbachian, *Ber.* **36,** 1799 (1903). ⟨2⟩ Graebe, Krafft, *Ber.* **39,** 2509 (1906). ⟨3⟩ Bennett, Wain, *J. Chem. Soc.* **1936,** 1111. ⟨4⟩ Fittig, Furtenbach, *Ann.* **147,** 305 (1868). ⟨5⟩ Pechmann, *Ann.* **264,** 296 (1891). ⟨6⟩ Schorger, *J. Am. Chem. Soc.* **39,** 2677 (1917). ⟨7⟩ Ref. 5, page 309. ⟨8⟩ Baeyer, *Ber.* **19,** 2186 (1886). ⟨9⟩ Curtius, *J. prakt. Chem.* (2) **91,** 89 (1915).

ORDER I: SUBORDER I: GENUS 3: ACIDS

Division A. Solid Acids

Section 2: " Not soluble " in 50 parts of cold water

1:0560 **PELARGONIC ACID** $CH_3.(CH_2)_7.COOH$ $C_9H_{18}O_2$ **Beil. II-352**
(Nonanoic acid; *n*-nonylic acid)

M.P. + 12.3°⟨1⟩ **Neut. Eq. 158** D_4^{20} = **0.90552 ⟨1⟩** $n_{He\,(yel.)}^{15}$ = **1.43446 ⟨1⟩**
B.P. 254.4°⟨1⟩

Oily liq. which on cooling freezes to lfts. — Dif. sol. aq.; slowly volatile with steam.

[For prepn. in 66–75% yield *n*-heptyl bromide via malonic ester synthesis see ⟨2⟩.]

$\bar{C}$ with PCl_5 (65% yield ⟨3⟩), or PCl_3 (72% yield ⟨1⟩), or $PCl_3 + ZnCl_2$ (93% yield ⟨3⟩) or 1.5 moles $SOCl_2$ (85% yield ⟨3⟩) gives *n*-nonanoyl chloride, b.p. 215.35°; m.p. −60.5°: D_4^{20} = 0.94206 ⟨1⟩.

$Pb\bar{A}_2$, cryst. from alc., m.p. 94–95° ⟨4⟩; $Ca\bar{A}_2$, cryst. from dil. MeOH, m.p. 216° ⟨5⟩; $Zn\bar{A}_2$, cryst. from alc., m.p. 131–132° ⟨6⟩; $Cd\bar{A}_2$, cryst. from hot alc., m.p. 96° ⟨6⟩; $Cu\bar{A}_2$, cryst. from hot alc., m.p. 260° ⟨6⟩.

The *p*-nitrobenzyl and phenacyl esters of $\bar{C}$ are oils ⟨11⟩ and not recommended as derivs. for identification.

Ⓓ ***p*-Chlorophenacyl pelargonate:** m.p. 59.0° ⟨7⟩ [cf. T 1.391].
Ⓓ ***p*-Bromophenacyl pelargonate:** m.p. 68.5° ⟨7⟩ [cf. T 1.391].
Ⓓ ***p*-Iodophenacyl pelargonate:** m.p. 77.0° ⟨7⟩ [cf. T 1.391].
Ⓓ ***p*-Phenylphenacyl pelargonate:** m.p. 71° ⟨8⟩; 70.8–71.3° cor. ⟨11⟩ [cf. T 1.391].
Ⓓ **Pelargonamide:** m.p. 99° ⟨9⟩.
Ⓓ **Pelargonanilide:** m.p. 57° ⟨9⟩.
Ⓓ **Pelargon-*p*-toluidide:** m.p. 84° ⟨9⟩.
Ⓓ **2-(*n*-Octyl)benzimidazole:** from $\bar{C}$ + 1 mole *o*-phenylenediamine on htg. at b.p. for ½ hr.; m.p. 139.5–140.5° cor. ⟨10⟩.

1:0560 ⟨1⟩ Deffet, *Bull. soc. chim. Belg.* **40,** 388–393 (1931). ⟨2⟩ Reid, Ruhoff, *Organic Syntheses* **16,** 60–62 (1936). ⟨3⟩ Clark, Bell, *Trans. Roy. Soc. Canada* (3) **27,** III, 97–103 (1933). ⟨4⟩ Neaves, *Analyst* **37,** 399 (1912). ⟨5⟩ Harries, *Ann.* **343,** 358 (1905). ⟨6⟩ Zincke, Franchimont, *Ann.* **164,** 337 (1872). ⟨7⟩ Moses, Reid, *J. Am. Chem. Soc.* **54,** 2101 (1932). ⟨8⟩ St. Pfau, *Helv. Chim. Acta* **15,** 1270 (1932). ⟨9⟩ Robertson, *J. Chem. Soc.* **115,** 1220–1221 (1919). ⟨10⟩ Pool, Harwood, Ralston, *J. Am. Chem. Soc.* **59,** 178 (1937).
⟨11⟩ Price, Griffith, *J. Am. Chem. Soc.* **62,** 2884 (1940).

1:0565 **OLEIC ACID** $CH_3.(CH_2)_7.CH{=}CH.(CH_2)_7.COOH$ ($CH_3.(CH_2)_7.CH$ ‖ $HOOC.(CH_2)_7.CH$) $C_{18}H_{34}O_2$ **Beil. II-463**

M.P. +13.36° α-form **⟨1⟩** **Neut. Eq. 282** n_D^{15} = **1.4614 ⟨1⟩**
+16.25° β-form **⟨1⟩** n_D^{20} = **1.4597 ⟨1⟩**

$\bar{C}$ cryst. first in α-form; on keeping this may change slowly into the slowly crystg. stable β-form ⟨1⟩ — Pure samples of $\bar{C}$ oxidize on stdg. in corked vessels and m.p. falls about 0.1° per month; if pure $\bar{C}$ is kept in solid form in refrigerator there is little change in m.p. ⟨1⟩ — $\bar{C}$ is insol. aq.; misc. with alc. or ether — $\bar{C}$ dec. on distn. at ord. press. but distils with superheated steam at 250°.

[For prepn. of pure C̄ from methyl oleate via fractional distn. in vac., hydrolysis, and purification of C̄ by low temp. recrystn. from acetone at −75° see ⟨1⟩.] [For further study of purification see ⟨2⟩ ⟨3⟩.] [For study of methods of sepn. of C̄ from satd. acids and from linoleic acid see ⟨14⟩.]

C̄ adds Br_2; reduces alk. $KMnO_4$ (T 1.34) — C̄ on fusion in tt. with excess moist KOH at 300–320° is alm. quant. converted to K palmitate, KOAc + H_2.

C̄ treated with PCl_5 (27% yield ⟨4⟩; 75% yield ⟨5⟩), PCl_3 (46% yield ⟨6⟩), PCl_3 + $ZnCl_2$ (50% yield ⟨4⟩), or $SOCl_2$ (75% yield ⟨5⟩; 80% yield ⟨4⟩) gives oleyl chloride, b.p. abt. 213° at 13 mm.

C̄, on treatment with nitrous fumes (oxides of nitrogen) ⟨7⟩, or with conc. cold HNO_3, or dil. HNO_3 + $NaNO_2$ ⟨7⟩ ⟨1⟩ gives the isomeric *trans* acid, elaidic acid (1:0610), m.p. 44° [resultant equilibrium mixt. conts. 34% C̄ + 66% elaidic ac. ⟨7⟩ ⟨1⟩]. [For m.p. + compn. curve for the system see ⟨7⟩.]

[For m.p. compn. curves for systems: C̄ + palmitic ac. (1:0650) and C̄ + stearic ac. (1:0660) see ⟨1⟩.]

PbĀ$_2$ is sol. in ether or pet. ether [dif. from satd. acids]; CaĀ$_2$, m.p. 83–84° ⟨13⟩.

Ⓓ **9,10-Dihydroxystearic acid:** 3 pts. C̄, dislvd. in 900 pts. aq. + 1 pt. KOH, and oxid. at 0° with 0.5 *N* $KMnO_4$ gives quant. yield 9,10-dihydroxystearic ac., m.p. 132° ⟨8⟩ — [The temp. must be kept between 0–10°, the conc. of K oleate must not exceed 1%, the $KMnO_4$ soln. must not exceed 0.1%, a slight excess of alkali must be present, and the time must not exceed 5 min. ⟨9⟩. After decolorizing soln. with SO_2 the product is filtered off and washed with pet. ether in which it is insoluble.] [Cf. also ⟨1⟩.]

Ⓓ ***p*-Chlorophenacyl oleate:** m.p. 40° ⟨10⟩ [cf. T 1.391].

Ⓓ ***p*-Bromophenacyl oleate:** m.p. 46° ⟨10⟩ [cf. T 1.391].

Ⓓ ***p*-Phenylphenacyl oleate:** m.p. 61° ⟨10⟩; 60.5° ⟨11⟩; 58–59.5° ⟨12⟩ [cf. T 1.391].

—— [**Oleamide:** m.p. 75–76°.]

—— [**Oleanilide:** m.p. 41°.]

—— [**Oleic-*p*-toluidide:** m.p. 42.5°.]

1:0565 ⟨1⟩ Smith, *J. Chem. Soc.* **1939,** 974–980. ⟨2⟩ Lapworth, Pearson, Mottram, *Biochem. J.* **19,** 7–18 (1925). ⟨3⟩ Brown, Shinowara, *J. Am. Chem. Soc.* **59,** 6–8 (1937). ⟨4⟩ Clark, Bell, *Trans. Roy. Soc. Canada* (3) **27,** III, 97–103 (1933). ⟨5⟩ Sulzberger, *Z. angew. Chem.* **27,** 40 (1914). ⟨6⟩ Täufel, Künkele, *Chem. Umschau* **42,** 27–29 (1935). ⟨7⟩ Griffiths, Hilditch, *J. Chem. Soc.* **1932,** 2315–2324. ⟨8⟩ Robinson, Robinson, *J. Chem. Soc.* **127,** 177 (1925). ⟨9⟩ Lapworth, Mottram, *J. Chem. Soc.* **127,** 1629 (1925). ⟨10⟩ Kimura, *Chem. Abs.* **26,** 4583 (1932).

⟨11⟩ Drake, Bronitsky, *J. Am. Chem. Soc.* **52,** 3719 (1930). ⟨12⟩ Noller, Bannerot, *J. Am. Chem. Soc.* **56,** 1565 (1934). ⟨13⟩ Klimont, *J. prakt. Chem.* (2) **109,** 271 (1925). ⟨14⟩ Hartsuch, *J. Am. Chem. Soc.* **61,** 1142–1144 (1939).

—— ***n*-CAPRYLIC ACID** $CH_3(CH_2)_6.COOH$ $C_8H_{16}O_2$ **Beil. II-349**

M.P. +16.3° **Neut. Eq. 144** D_4^{20} = **0.90884** n_D^{20} = **1.4268**

See 1:1145. Genus 3: Division B: Section 2. B.P. 239.3°.

—— ***n*-ENANTHIC ANHYDRIDE** $[CH_3.(CH_2)_5.CO]_2O$ $C_{14}H_{26}O_3$ **Beil. II-340**
(*n*-Heptylic anhydride)

M.P. +17° D_4^{20} = **0.91745** n_D^{15} = **1.43346**

See 1:1165. Genus 3: Division B: Section 2. B.P. 258°.

1:0569 ***n*-CAPRIC ANHYDRIDE** $[CH_3.(CH_2)_8.CO]_2O$ $C_{20}H_{38}O_3$ **Beil. S.N.-162**

M.P. 23.9° ⟨1⟩ D_4^{70} = **0.8596** ⟨1⟩ n_D^{70} = **1.4234** ⟨1⟩

Prob. responds to Generic Test 3-B (titration in alc.) — Hydrolysis with aq. alk. (T 1.51) gives Sap. Eq. 163 and yields soln. contg. salt of *n*-capric acid (1:0585), q.v.

1:0569 ⟨1⟩ Holde, Gentner, *Ber.* **58,** 1418–1424 (1925).

1:0570 UNDECYLENIC ACID $CH_2{=}CH.(CH_2)_8.COOH$ $C_{11}H_{20}O_2$ **Beil. II-458**
(Undecen-10-oic acid-1)

M.P. 24.5° **Neut. Eq. 184** D_4^{24} = **0.9072**
B.P. 275°

C̄ reduces alk. $KMnO_4$ [T 1.34] — C̄ adds Br_2 (T 1.91) [yielding ⟨1⟩ ⟨2⟩ 10,11-dibromo-undecanoic ac. [Beil. II-358], m.p. 38°] [dif. from *n*-undecylic ac. (1:0573)].

C̄ adds HBr in any solvent *in absence of air* to give mainly 10-bromoundecanoic ac., m.p. 27°; in presence of air " abnormal " addition occurs yielding mainly 11-bromoundecanoic ac., m.p. 51°. [For m.p. + compn. data on system: 10-bromo- and 11-bromoundecanoic acids see ⟨3⟩.] [For further study of this reaction see ⟨4⟩ ⟨5⟩ ⟨6⟩.]

[C̄ in C_6H_6 treated with HI gas yields only 10-iodoundecanoic ac., m.p. 22° ⟨7⟩; C̄ in C_6H_6 adds dry HCl only very slowly but yields only 10-chloroundecanoic ac., m.p. 32° ⟨7⟩.]

C̄ with PCl_5 (100% yield ⟨8⟩) or PCl_3 ⟨9⟩ or $SOCl_2$ ⟨12⟩ [cf. T 1.37] gives undecylenyl chloride, b.p. 128.5°$_{14}$.

C̄, dislvd. in 3–4 pts. fumg. HNO_3 and warmed to 60° evolves CO_2 and on cooling gives crystn. cream of sebacic ac. (1:0730), cryst. from aq., m.p. 133° ⟨10⟩ — C̄, oxidized with CrO_3 in AcOH gives (80% yield ⟨11⟩) sebacic ac.

CuĀ$_2$, m.p. 232–234°; ZnĀ$_2$, m.p. 115–116°; PbĀ$_2$, m.p. 80°; BaĀ$_2$, sol. in 1073 pts. aq. at 15.5°.

Ⓓ **Undecylenamide:** m.p. 87°.

1:0570 ⟨1⟩ Myddleton, Barrett, *J. Am. Chem. Soc.* **49,** 2260 (1927). ⟨2⟩ Myddleton, Berchem, *J. Chem. Soc.* **1927,** 1928–1929. ⟨3⟩ Harris, Smith, *J. Chem. Soc.* **1935,** 1109. ⟨4⟩ Ashton, Smith, *J. Chem. Soc.* **1934,** 435–440; 1308–1310. ⟨5⟩ Harris, Smith, *J. Chem. Soc.* **1935,** 1572–1576. ⟨6⟩ Smith, *Chemistry and Industry* **56,** 833–839 (1937); **57,** 461–466 (1938). ⟨7⟩ Abraham, Smith, *J. Chem. Soc.* **1936,** 1605–1607. ⟨8⟩ Krafft, Tritschler, *Ber.* **33,** 3580 (1900). ⟨9⟩ Aschan, *Ber.* **31,** 2349 (1898). ⟨10⟩ Becker, *Ber.* **11,** 1414 (1878). ⟨11⟩ Krafft, Seldis, *Ber.* **33,** 3573 (1900). ⟨12⟩ Grundmann, *Ann.* **524,** 39 (1936).

1:0571 *o*-ETHOXYBENZOIC ACID [benzene ring]—COOH, —OC_2H_5 $C_9H_{10}O_3$ **Beil. X-64**
(Salicylic acid ethyl ether)

M.P. 24.5-25.5° ⟨1⟩ **(19.5°)** **Neut. Eq. 166**

Spar. sol. cold aq.; eas. sol. hot aq. — Slightly volatile with steam.

C̄ on distn. at ord. press. decomposes about 300° into CO_2 and phenetole (1:7485) — C̄ dislvd. in 4 pts. conc. H_2SO_4 and treated with 5 pts. conc. HNO_3 at not above 60–70° gives (67% yield ⟨2⟩) 5-nitrosalicylic acid ethyl ether [Beil. X-118], m.p. 163°.

Ⓓ ***o*-Ethoxybenzamide** [Beil. X-93]: m.p. 132° [prepd. indirectly].

1:0571 ⟨1⟩ Weissberger, Dym, *Ann.* **502,** 84 (1933). ⟨2⟩ Herrmann, *Ann.* **429,** 170 (1922).

1:0573 *n*-UNDECYLIC ACID $CH_3.(CH_2)_9.COOH$ $C_{11}H_{22}O_2$ **Beil. II-358**
(Undecanoic acid)

M.P. 28.5° ⟨1⟩ **Neut. Eq. 186**
29.30° ⟨2⟩
B.P. 280°

Cryst. from acetone (at −10°) ⟨2⟩ — [For m.p. + compn. diagram with lauric ac. (1:0605) see ⟨6⟩.] — Insol. aq., very eas. sol. alc., ether.

[For prepn. from undecylenic ac. (1:0570) with H_2 + Pd ⟨2⟩.]

C̄ does *not* add Br_2 ⟨1⟩ [dif. from undecylenic ac. (1:0570)].

The *p*-nitrobenzyl and phenacyl esters of C̄ are oils ⟨7⟩ and not recommended as derivs. for identification of C̄.

Ⓓ ***p*-Chlorophenacyl *n*-undecylate:** m.p. 60.2° ⟨3⟩ [cf. T 1.391].
Ⓓ ***p*-Bromophenacyl *n*-undecylate:** m.p. 68.2° ⟨3⟩ [cf. T 1.391].
Ⓓ ***p*-Iodophenacyl *n*-undecylate:** m.p. 81.8° ⟨3⟩ [cf. T 1.391].
Ⓓ ***p*-Phenylphenacyl *n*-undecylate:** m.p. 79.5–80° ⟨7⟩ [cf. T 1.391].
Ⓓ ***n*-Undecylamide:** m.p. 103° ⟨2⟩; 99° ⟨4⟩.
Ⓓ ***n*-Undecylanilide:** m.p. 71° ⟨4⟩.
Ⓓ ***n*-Undecyl-*p*-toluidide:** m.p. 80° ⟨4⟩.
Ⓓ **2-(*n*-Decyl)benzimidazole:** from C̄ by htg. with *o*-phenylenediamine; m.p. 114.0–114.5° cor. ⟨5⟩.

1:0573 ⟨1⟩ Krafft, *Ber.* **11**, 2219 (1878). ⟨2⟩ Levene, West, *J. Biol. Chem.*, **18**, 464–465 (1914). ⟨3⟩ Moses, Reid, *J. Am. Chem. Soc.* **54**, 2101 (1932). ⟨4⟩ Robertson, *J. Chem. Soc.* **115**, 1220–1221 (1919). ⟨5⟩ Pool, Harwood, Ralston, *J. Am. Chem. Soc.* **59**, 178 (1937). ⟨6⟩ Kulka, Sandin, *J. Am. Chem. Soc.* **59**, 1348 (1937). ⟨7⟩ Price, Griffith, *J. Am. Chem. Soc.* **62**, 2884 (1940).

1:0575 HEXAHYDROBENZOIC ACID $C_6H_{11}.COOH$ $C_7H_{12}O_2$ Beil. IX-7

(Cyclohexanecarboxylic acid)

M.P. 30-31° **Neut. Eq. 128**
B.P. 233°

C̄ is very sparingly sol. aq.; very sol. alc., ether, $CHCl_3$, C_6H_6 — C̄ is sl. volatile with steam but more so than BzOH — C̄ has remarkable penetrating and persistent fecal odor see ⟨1⟩.

[For prepn. (in 85% yield) from cyclohexyl MgCl + CO_2 see ⟨2⟩ ⟨3⟩; similarly from cyclohexyl MgBr (69–70% yield) see ⟨4⟩.]

C̄ with PCl_5 ⟨5⟩ ⟨6⟩ ⟨7⟩ or $SOCl_2$ (92% yield ⟨8⟩) [cf. T 1.37] gives hexahydrobenzoyl chloride, b.p. 179–180°.

Ⓓ **Hexahydrobenzamide:** m.p. 185–186°.
Ⓓ **Hexahydrobenzanilide** [Beil. XII-260]: m.p. 146° cor. ⟨9⟩; 143–144° u.c. ⟨10⟩.

1:0575 ⟨1⟩ Neunhoeffer, *Ann.* **509**, 125, Note 1 (1934). ⟨2⟩ Gilman, Kirby, *Organic Syntheses, Coll. Vol.* I, 355 (1932). ⟨3⟩ Gilman, Zoellner, *J. Am. Chem. Soc.* **53**, 1945–1948 (1931). ⟨4⟩ Hiers, Adams, *J. Am. Chem. Soc.* **48**, 2390 (1926). ⟨5⟩ Meyer, Scharwin, *Ber.* **30**, 1941 (1897). ⟨6⟩ Godchot, *Bull. soc. chim.* (4) **9**, 262 (1911). ⟨7⟩ Lumsden, *J. Chem. Soc.* **87**, 92 (1905). ⟨8⟩ Wieland, Schapiro, Metzger, *Ann.* **513**, 103 (1934). ⟨9⟩ Schwartz, Johnson, *J. Am. Chem. Soc.* **53**, 1065 (1931). ⟨10⟩ Underwood, Gale, *J. Am. Chem. Soc.* **56**, 2119 (1934).

1:0585 *n*-CAPRIC ACID $CH_3.(CH_2)_8.COOH$ $C_{10}H_{20}O_2$ Beil. II-355

(*n*-Decylic acid; decanoic acid)

M.P. +31.3° ⟨1⟩ **Neut. Eq. 172**
B.P. 268.7° ⟨1⟩

C̄ is alm. insol. in cold aq.; very dif. sol. hot aq. — C̄ can be crystd. from 50% alc.

[For sepn. from near homologues via fract. dist. of methyl ester (1:3827) or free acid see ⟨2⟩.]

[For m.p. + compn. diagram of C̄ + lauric acid (1:0605) see ⟨3⟩.]

C̄ with PCl_5 ⟨4⟩ or PCl_3 (70% yield ⟨1⟩) gives *n*-decanoyl chloride, b.p. 232.3°, m.p. −34.5° ⟨1⟩.

$Pb\bar{A}_2$, m.p. 100° ⟨5⟩.

Ⓓ ***p*-Chlorophenacyl *n*-caprate:** m.p. 61.6° ⟨6⟩ [cf. T 1.391].
Ⓓ ***p*-Bromophenacyl *n*-caprate:** m.p. 67.0° ⟨6⟩; 66.0° ⟨7⟩ [cf. T 1.391].
Ⓓ ***p*-Iodophenacyl *n*-caprate:** m.p. 82.0° ⟨6⟩; 80.0° ⟨7⟩ [cf. T 1.391].
Ⓓ ***n*-Capramide (*n*-decanoamide):** m.p. 100.1° ⟨1⟩; 99° ⟨8⟩.
Ⓓ ***n*-Capranilide (*n*-decanoanilide):** m.p. 70° ⟨8⟩.
Ⓓ ***n*-Capri-*p*-toluidide (*n*-decano-*p*-toluidide):** m.p. 78° ⟨8⟩; 80° ⟨9⟩.
Ⓓ **2-(*n*-Nonyl)benzimidazole:** from C̄ + 1 mole *o*-phenylenediamine htd. ½ hr. at b.p.; m.p. 127.0–127.5° cor. ⟨10⟩; m.p. 114–115° ⟨11⟩.

1:0585 ⟨1⟩ Deffet, *Bull. soc. chim. Belg.* **40,** 389–391 (1931). ⟨2⟩ Lepkovsky, Feskov, Evans, *J. Am. Chem. Soc.* **58,** 978–981 (1936). ⟨3⟩ Kulka, Sandin, *J. Am. Chem. Soc.* **59,** 1348 (1937). ⟨4⟩ Krafft, Koenig, *Ber.* **23,** 2385 (1890). ⟨5⟩ Neave, *Analyst,* **37,** 399 (1912). ⟨6⟩ Moses, Reid, *J. Am. Chem. Soc.* **54,** 2101 (1932). ⟨7⟩ Judefind, Reid, *J. Am. Chem. Soc.* **42,** 1055 (1920). ⟨8⟩ Robertson, *J. Chem. Soc.* **115,** 1220–1221 (1919). ⟨9⟩ Robertson, *J. Chem. Soc.* **93,** 1037 (1908). ⟨10⟩ Pool, Harwood, Ralston, *J. Am. Chem. Soc.* **59,** 178 (1937). ⟨11⟩ Seka, Müller, *Monatsh.* **57,** 103 (1931).

1:0590 ERUCIC ACID

$$\begin{array}{l} CH_3.(CH_2)_7\text{—}CH \\ \qquad\qquad\quad \| \\ HOOC.(CH_2)_{11}\text{—}CH \end{array}$$

$C_{22}H_{42}O_2$ **Beil. II-472**

M.P. 33-34° **Neut. Eq. 338**
B.P. 264°_{15}

Long ndls. from alc., tbls. from pet. ether — Insol. aq.; very eas. sol. alc. or ether — Sol. in 96% alc. even at −20° [dif. from satd. acids].

[For prepn. via hydrolysis of rape-seed oil see ⟨1⟩ ⟨2⟩ ⟨3⟩ ⟨4⟩.]

C̄, on treatment with oxides of nitrogen, HNO_2 or S isomerizes to the *trans* form, brassidic acid (1:0633). E.g., C̄ treated with Poutet's reagt. (Hg dislvd. in conc. HNO_3) gives about 60% brassidic ac. + 20% addn. prod. + 20% unchanged C̄ ⟨5⟩; C̄ + 25 pts. 30% HNO_3 at 56° + *not more* than 0.1 pt. $NaNO_2$ immediately solidifies giving 91% yield ⟨6⟩ ⟨11⟩ brassidic ac., m.p. 61.5° cor. [For isomerization with S see ⟨7⟩.] [For m.p. + compn. curves for system: erucic ac. + brassidic ac. see ⟨5⟩ ⟨8⟩; their eutectic conts. 90.5% erucic ac. and melts 31.8° ⟨8⟩.]

C̄ in alk. soln. reduces $KMnO_4$ (T 1.34) — C̄ adds Br_2 (T 1.91) [yielding 12,13-dibromobehenic acid (erucodibromobehenic acid) [Beil. II-392], m.p. 42–43° ⟨9⟩].

C̄ with PCl_3 htd. 3 hrs. at 90° ⟨10⟩ yields corresp. acid chloride — C̄, refluxed 7 hrs. with 0.6 pt. Ac_2O gives 97% yield ⟨11⟩ erucic anhydride, cryst. from pet. ether, m.p. 46–46.5°. [This prod. with HNO_2 isomerizes (80% yield ⟨11⟩) to brassidic anhydride, cryst. from ether, m.p. 63.5–64.5°.]

$Pb\bar{A}_2$, very spar. sol. alc.; $Ca\bar{A}_2$, m.p. 102–103° ⟨12⟩. [For isolation of C̄ as $KH\bar{A}$ see ⟨13⟩.] [For use metal salts of C̄ as soaps see ⟨14⟩.]

Ⓓ ***p*-Chlorophenacyl erucate:** m.p. 56° ⟨15⟩ [cf. T 1.391].
Ⓓ ***p*-Bromophenacyl erucate:** m.p. 62.5° ⟨15⟩; 61.0° ⟨16⟩ [cf. T 1.391].
Ⓓ ***p*-Iodophenacyl erucate:** m.p. 73.8° ⟨16⟩ [cf. T 1.391].
Ⓓ ***p*-Phenylphenacyl erucate:** m.p. 76° ⟨15⟩.
Ⓓ **Erucamide:** m.p. 84° ⟨17⟩.
Ⓓ **Erucanilide:** m.p. 55° ⟨17⟩ ⟨18⟩.
Ⓓ **Erucic-*p*-toluidide:** m.p. 57–58° [indirectly] ⟨19⟩.

1:0590 ⟨1⟩ Noller, Talbot, *Organic Syntheses* **10,** 44–46 (1930). ⟨2⟩ Caldwell, Dye, *Ind. Eng. Chem.* **25,** 341–342 (1933). ⟨3⟩ Täufel, Bauschinger, *Z. angew. Chem.* **41,** 157–159 (1928).

⟨4⟩ Lepkovsky, Feskov, Evans, *J. Am. Chem. Soc.* **58,** 981 (1936). ⟨5⟩ Griffiths, Hilditch, *J. Chem. Soc.* **1932,** 2317–2322. ⟨6⟩ Rankoff, *J. prakt. Chem.* (2) **131,**, 293–300 (1930). ⟨7⟩ Rankoff, *Ber.* **63,** 2139–2142 (1930). ⟨8⟩ Keffler, Maiden, *J. Phys. Chem.* **40,** 909–911 (1936). ⟨9⟩ Maruyama, *Cent.* **1935,** II, 2358. ⟨10⟩ Loevenich, Losen, Dierichs, *Ber.* **60,** 950 (1927).

⟨11⟩ Holde, Zadek, *Ber.* **56,** 2053 (1923). ⟨12⟩ Klimont, *J. prakt. Chem.* (2) **109,** 271 (1925). ⟨13⟩ Kimura, *Cent.* **1930,** I, 35. ⟨14⟩ Whitmore, Lauro, *Ind. Eng. Chem.* **22,** 646–649 (1930). ⟨15⟩ Kimura, *Chem. Abs.* **26,** 4583 (1932). ⟨16⟩ Judefind, Reid, *J. Am. Chem. Soc.* **42,** 1055 (1920). ⟨17⟩ Reimer, Will, *Ber.* **19,** 3326 (1886). ⟨18⟩ De'Conno, *Gazz. chim. ital.* **47,** I, 104 (1917). ⟨19⟩ Zetsche, Liescher, Meyer, *Ber.* **71,** 1093 (1938).

1:0593 *d,l*-α-**METHYLHYDROCINNAMIC ACID** $C_{10}H_{12}O_2$ **Beil. IX-542**

(Benzyl-methyl-acetic acid, α-benzylpropionic acid)

C_6H_5—$CH_2.C(H)(CH_3).COOH$

M.P. 36.5° ⟨1⟩ **Neut. Eq. 164**
B.P. 272°

Dif. to crystallize ⟨1⟩ — Eas. sol. alc., ether, hot aq.; at 15° 100 pts. aq. dis. 0.30 g. C̄.

C̄ on nitration ⟨2⟩ yields β-(4-nitrophenyl)isobutyric ac. [Beil. IX-543]; pr. from alc., m.p. 123°.

C̄ with PCl_5 ⟨3⟩, or PCl_3 in C_6H_6 ⟨4⟩ or $SOCl_2$ by itself ⟨5⟩ or in $CHCl_3$ soln. ⟨6⟩ yields α-methylhydrocinnamoyl chloride.

Ⓓ ***p*-Phenylphenacyl α-methylhydrocinnamate:** m.p. 73° ⟨7⟩; 71–72° ⟨10⟩ [cf. T 1.391].

Ⓓ **α-Methylhydrocinnamide:** m.p. 109° ⟨5⟩; 107–108° ⟨6⟩. [The corresp. deriv. of the *d*-acid has m.p. 113–114° ⟨9⟩.]

Ⓓ **α-Methylhydrocinnamo-*p*-toluidide:** m.p. 130° ⟨8⟩. [The corresp. deriv. of the *d*-acid has m.p. 115–116° ⟨8⟩.]

1:0593 ⟨1⟩ Jones, Wallis, *J. Am. Chem. Soc.* **48,** 175 (1926). ⟨2⟩ Holden, Lapworth, *J. Chem. Soc.* **1931,** 2375. ⟨3⟩ Kipping, Clarke, *J. Chem. Soc.* **83,** 915 (1903). ⟨4⟩ Rupe, *Ann.* **369,** 321 (1909). ⟨5⟩ Meyer, *Monatsh.* **27,** 1091 (1906). ⟨6⟩ Woodruff, Conger, *J. Am. Chem. Soc.* **60,** 466 (1938). ⟨7⟩ Weizmann, Bergmann, Haskelberg, *Chemistry and Industry* **56,** 589 (1937). ⟨8⟩ Kipping, Salway, *J. Chem. Soc.* **85,** 445–446 (1904). ⟨9⟩ Kenyon, Phillips, Pittman, *J. Chem. Soc.* **1935,** 1084. ⟨10⟩ Carter, *J. Am. Chem. Soc.* **62,** 2244 (1940).

1:0594 *d,l*-α-**ETHYLPHENYLACETIC ACID** $C_{10}H_{12}O_2$ **Beil. IX-541**

(α-Phenyl-*n*-butyric acid)

C_6H_5—$C(H)(C_2H_5).COOH$

M.P. 42° **Neut. Eq. 164**
B.P. 271°

Tbls. from ether — At 30° 100 g. dis. 0.0423 g. C̄ ⟨1⟩.

[For prepn. in 80–85% yield from benzyl cyanide + C_2H_5I see ⟨2⟩; via actn. of CO_2 on α-phenyl-*n*-propyl MgBr see ⟨3⟩.]

C̄ refluxed with 7–8 pts. $SOCl_2$ for 8 hrs. ⟨4⟩, or in cold ⟨5⟩ gives (90% yield ⟨4⟩) α-phenyl-*n*-butyryl chloride, b.p. $104°_{12}$.

Ⓓ **α-Phenyl-*n*-butyramide:** m.p. 86°; 83° u.c. ⟨4⟩; 85–87° ⟨6⟩.

1:0594 ⟨1⟩ Baldinger, Nieuwland, *J. Am. Pharm. Assoc.* **22,** 711–716 (1933). ⟨2⟩ Wegler, *Ann* **510,** 80–81 (1934). ⟨3⟩ Gilman, Harris, *J. Am. Chem. Soc.* **53,** 3545 (1931). ⟨4⟩ Rising, Swartz, *J. Am. Chem. Soc.* **54,** 2024 (1932). ⟨5⟩ Bergs, *Ber.* **67,** 1622 (1934). ⟨6⟩ Volwiler, Tabern, *J. Am. Chem. Soc.* **58,** 1352–1353 (1936).

1:0595 BENZOIC ANHYDRIDE $(C_6H_5CO)_2O$ $C_{14}H_{10}O_3$ **Beil. IX-164**

M.P. 42° **Neut. Eq. 113** (in water)
B.P. 360° **Neut. Eq. 226** (in alcohol)

[For prepn. in 72–74% yield from BzOH (1:0715) see ⟨1⟩.]
C̄ is insol. in aq. and only slowly hydrolyzed by it; C̄ is fairly sol. alc. or ether.
For behavior on titration see Generic Test, Note 7 of "Manual."
[For quant. detn. of C̄ via titration with $NaOCH_3$ see ⟨2⟩.]

Ⓓ **Saponification:** Hydrolysis with aq. alk. (T 1.51) gives Sap. Eq. 113 and yields soln. from which mineral ac. ppts. benzoic acid (1:0715), cryst. from hot aq., m.p. 121°.

1:0595 ⟨1⟩ Clarke, Rahrs, *Organic Syntheses, Coll. Vol.* I, 85–87 (1932). ⟨2⟩ Smith, Bryant, *J. Am. Chem. Soc.* **58,** 2452–2454 (1936).

1:0600 TRIDECYLIC ACID $CH_3.(CH_2)_{11}.COOH$ $C_{13}H_{26}O_2$ **Beil. II-364**
(*n*-Tridecanoic acid)

M.P. 41.55° ⟨1⟩ **Neut. Eq. 214**
43° ⟨2⟩

Lfts. from acetone; insol. aq.; eas. sol. org. solvents — [For prepn. from lauryl bromide + KCN see ⟨3⟩].
C̄ with $SOCl_2$ [T 1.37] gives tridecanoyl chloride, b.p. $145–146^{\circ}_{11}$.
$Zn\bar{A}_2$; ndls. from isoamyl alc., m.p. 128° ⟨2⟩.
The *p*-nitrobenzyl ester of C̄ is an oil ⟨7⟩ and not recommended as a deriv.

Ⓓ **Phenacyl tridecylate:** m.p. 45.0–45.5° cor. ⟨7⟩ [cf. T 1.391].
Ⓓ ***p*-Chlorophenacyl tridecylate:** m.p. 67.0° ⟨4⟩ [cf. T 1.391].
Ⓓ ***p*-Bromophenacyl tridecylate:** m.p. 75.0° ⟨4⟩ [cf. T 1.391].
Ⓓ ***p*-Iodophenacyl tridecylate:** m.p. 88.5° ⟨4⟩ [cf. T 1.391].
Ⓓ ***p*-Phenylphenacyl tridecylate:** m.p. 86.5–87° cor. ⟨7⟩ [cf. T 1.391].
Ⓓ ***n*-Tridecanoamide:** m.p. 100° ⟨5⟩.
Ⓓ ***n*-Tridecanoanilide:** m.p. 80° ⟨5⟩.
Ⓓ ***n*-Tridecano-*p*-toluidide:** m.p. 88° ⟨5⟩.
Ⓓ **2-(*n*-Dodecyl)benzimidazole:** m.p. 109–109.5° cor. ⟨6⟩.

1:0600 ⟨1⟩ Meyer, Reid, *J. Am. Chem. Soc.* **55,** 1577 (1933). ⟨2⟩ Robinson, *J. Chem. Soc.* **125,** 230 (1924). ⟨3⟩ Ruhoff, *Organic Syntheses* **16,** 35–36 (1936). ⟨4⟩ Moses, Reid, *J. Am. Chem. Soc.* **54,** 2101 (1932). ⟨5⟩ Robertson, *J. Chem. Soc.* **115,** 1220–1221 (1919). ⟨6⟩ Pool, Harwood, Ralston, *J. Am. Chem. Soc.* **59,** 178 (1937). ⟨7⟩ Price, Griffith, *J. Am. Chem. Soc.* **62,** 2884 (1940).

1:0601 LAURIC ANHYDRIDE $[CH_3.(CH_2)_{10}.CO]_2O$ $C_{24}H_{46}O_3$ **Beil. II-362**

M.P. 41.8° ⟨1⟩

Responds to Generic Test 3-B (titration in alc.) but does not react quant. as monobasic ac. (T 1.31: Neut. Eq. found: 254; theoret. 382).

Ⓓ **Saponification:** Hydrolysis with aq. alk. (T 1.51) gives Sap. Eq. 191 and yields soln. contg. salt of lauric ac. (1:0605), q.v.

1:0601 ⟨1⟩ Holde, Gentner, *Ber.* **58,** 1418–1424 (1925).

1:0605 LAURIC ACID $CH_3.(CH_2)_{10}.COOH$ $C_{12}H_{24}O_2$ **Beil. II-359**
(*n*-Dodecanoic acid)

M.P. 43.2° ⟨1⟩; 44° ⟨2⟩ ⟨3⟩ Neut. Eq. 200

Ndls. from alc. — Insol. aq., eas. sol. alc., ether — Volatile with superheated steam.

[For m.p.-compn. curves for system: C̄ + *n*-capric ac. (1:0585) and C̄ + *n*-undecylic ac. (1:0573) see ⟨3⟩.]

C̄ + PCl_5 (66% yield ⟨4⟩), or PCl_3 + $ZnCl_2$ (79% yield ⟨4⟩) or $SOCl_2$ (79% yield ⟨4⟩) [cf. T 1.37] gives lauroyl chloride, b.p. $145°_{18}$.

Non-alk. salts all very dif. sol. aq.: AgĀ, m.p. 212–213° ⟨5⟩; $CaĀ_2.H_2O$, m.p. 182–183° ⟨6⟩; C̄.$MgĀ_2$, m.p. 75° ⟨6⟩; $ZnĀ_2$, m.p. 127° ⟨6⟩; $PbĀ_2$, m.p. 103–104° ⟨7⟩, 104–105° ⟨8⟩. [For sepn. of C̄ from myristic, palmitic, and stearic acids via Li and Mg salts see ⟨8⟩.]

Ⓓ **Phenacyl laurate:** m.p. 48–49° ⟨9⟩ [cf. T 1.391].
Ⓓ ***p*-Chlorophenacyl laurate:** m.p. 70° ⟨9⟩ ⟨10⟩ [cf. T 1.391].
Ⓓ ***p*-Bromophenacyl laurate:** m.p. 76° ⟨9⟩ ⟨10⟩ [cf. T 1.391].
Ⓓ ***p*-Iodophenacyl laurate:** m.p. 85.8° ⟨10⟩ [cf. T 1.391].
Ⓓ ***p*-Phenylphenacyl laurate:** m.p. 86° ⟨11⟩; 84.0 ⟨12⟩ [cf. T 1.391].
Ⓓ **Lauramide:** m.p. 100° ⟨13⟩; 99° ⟨6⟩.
Ⓓ **Lauranilide:** m.p. 78° ⟨13⟩; 76.5° ⟨6⟩.
Ⓓ **Lauro-*p*-toluidide:** m.p. 87° ⟨13⟩.
Ⓓ **2-(*n*-Undecyl)benzimidazole:** from C̄ on htg. with 1 mole *o*-phenylenediamine for ½ hr.; m.p. 107.5° cor. ⟨4⟩; 101–103° ⟨15⟩.
Ⓓ ***S*-Benzylthiuronium laurate:** m.p. 141° ⟨16⟩.

1:0605 ⟨1⟩ Meyer, Reid, *J. Am. Chem. Soc.* **55**, 1577 (1933). ⟨2⟩ Holde, Gentner, *Ber.* **58**, 1423, Note 17 (1925). ⟨3⟩ Kulka, Sandin, *J. Am. Chem. Soc.* **59**, 1347–1349 (1937). ⟨4⟩ Clark, Bell, *Trans. Roy. Soc. Canada* (3) **27**, III, 97–103 (1933). ⟨5⟩ Jacobson, Holmes, *J. Biol. Chem.* **25**, 55-62 (1916). ⟨6⟩ Caspari, *Am. Chem. J.* **27**, 305–309 (1902). ⟨7⟩ Neave, *Analyst* **37**, 399 (1912). ⟨8⟩ Jacobson, Holmes, *J. Biol. Chem.* **25**, 29 (1916). ⟨9⟩ Hann, Reid, Jamieson, *J. Am. Chem. Soc.* **52**, 819 (1930). ⟨10⟩ Moses, Reid, *J. Am. Chem. Soc.* **54**, 2101 (1932). ⟨11⟩ Ford, *Iowa State J. Sci.* **12**, 121–122 (1937); **13**, 135–147 (1939); *Chem. Abs.* **32**, 4943 (1938). ⟨12⟩ Drake, Bronitsky, *J. Am. Chem. Soc.* **52**, 3719 (1930). ⟨13⟩ Robertson, *J. Chem. Soc.* **115**, 1220–1221 (1919). ⟨14⟩ Pool, Harwood, Ralston, *J. Am. Chem. Soc.* **59**, 178 (1937). ⟨15⟩ Seka, Müller, *Monatsh.* **57**, 103 (1931). ⟨16⟩ Donleavy, *J. Am. Chem. Soc.* **58**, 1005 (1936).

1:0610 ELAIDIC ACID $CH_3.(CH_2)_7.CH{=}HC.(CH_2)_7.COOH$ $C_{18}H_{34}O_2$ **Beil. II-469**
(*trans*-isomer of oleic acid (1:0565), q.v.)

M.P. 44-45° Neut. Eq. 282

Lfts. from alc. — C̄ is insol. aq., very eas. sol. alc., ether.

[For prepn. via isomerization with nitrous fumes, cold conc. HNO_3 or dil. HNO_3 + $NaNO_2$ see comments under oleic ac. (1:0565).]

C̄ adds Br_2 (T 1.91); reduces alk. $KMnO_4$ (T 1.34).

C̄ with PCl_5 at 45° ⟨1⟩ or with $SOCl_2$ ⟨5⟩ [cf. T 1.37] yields elaidyl chloride.

[For m.p. + compn. curves of system: C̄ + palmitic ac. (1:0650) and C̄ + stearic ac. (1:0660) see ⟨2⟩.]

$PbĀ_2$; insol. in aq. or in ether [dif. from oleic ac.]; $HgĀ_2$, m.p. 115° ⟨3⟩ $CaĀ_2$, m.p. 137° ⟨3⟩.

Ⓓ ***p*-Chlorophenacyl elaidate:** m.p. 56° ⟨4⟩ [cf. T 1.391].
Ⓓ ***p*-Bromophenacyl elaidate:** m.p. 65° ⟨4⟩ [cf. T 1.391].
Ⓓ ***p*-Iodophenacyl elaidate:** m.p. 74° ⟨4⟩ [cf. T 1.391].

Ⓓ *p*-**Phenylphenacyl elaidate:** m.p. 73.5° ⟨4⟩ [cf. T 1.391].
Ⓓ **Elaidamide:** m.p. 89–90° ⟨1⟩.

1:0610 ⟨1⟩ Krafft, Tritschler, *Ber.* **33,** 3582 (1900). ⟨2⟩ Smith, *J. Chem. Soc.* **1939,** 974–980. ⟨3⟩ Klimont, *J. prakt. Chem.* (2) **109,** 271 (1925). ⟨4⟩ Kimura, *Cent.* **1934,** II, 2207. ⟨5⟩ Grundmann, *Ann.* **524,** 43 (1936).

1:0612 ANGELIC ACID $C_5H_8O_2$ **Beil. II-428**
(*trans*-α-Methylcrotonic acid; *trans*-α,β-dimethylacrylic acid)

$CH_3—C—H$
$\quad\quad\|$
$HOOC—C—CH_3$

M.P. 45° **Neut. Eq. 100**
B.P. 185° cor.

Pr. with spicy odor — Spar. sol. cold aq.; eas. sol. hot aq. — Volatile with steam. C̄ is *trans* stereoisomer of tiglic acid (1:0420), q.v. [For prepn. of C̄ from tiglic acid see ⟨1⟩.]

C̄, htd. in s.t. 2 hrs. at 300° is quant. isomerized to tiglic acid (1:0420) ⟨2⟩ — C̄ on boiling 40 hrs. ⟨3⟩, or htg. with conc. H_2SO_4 at 100° ⟨4⟩, or on boiling 20 hrs. with 10–20% aq. NaOH ⟨5⟩ is alm. completely isomerized to tiglic ac. (1:0420). [See also next paragraph.]

C̄ in alk. soln. reduces $KMnO_4$ (T 1.34) — C̄ adds Br_2 (T 1.91) slowly. [C̄ in dry CS_2 treated with slight excess 1% Br_2 soln. in CS_2 loses color after 4 hrs. and on evapn. of CS_2 leaves an oil which cryst. on rubbing; after 3 recrystns. from pet. ether (b.p. 38–40°) gives colorless cryst. of angelic ac. dibromide (α,β-dibromo-α-methyl-*n*-butyric acid), m.p. 86° ⟨2⟩.] [C̄ in aq. or CS_2 + trace Br_2 in direct sunlight gives alm. quant. yield tiglic ac. (1:0420) in a few minutes ⟨6⟩.]

C̄ in $CHCl_3$ adds HI but prepn. of pure angelic acid hydriodide, m.p. 57.9–58.5° cor. ⟨7⟩ is difficult owing to isomerization to tiglic acid hydriodide, m.p. 86.2–86.3° cor. ⟨7⟩.

$Ca\bar{A}_2.2H_2O$; lfts. from aq. or long ndls. from aq. on addn. of alc.; much less sol. in aq. at 60–70° than at ord. temp. so that htg. of cold aq. soln. satd. at room temp. gives ppt. on htg. which redissolves on cooling (dif. from tiglic ac. (1:0420); insol. alc. (dif. and sepn. from corresp. salt of tiglic ac. (1:0420).

—— **Angelamide:** m.p. 127–128° ⟨8⟩.
—— **Angelanilide:** cryst. from C_6H_6, m.p. 126° ⟨9⟩ (indirectly).

1:0612 ⟨1⟩ Kaufmann, Küchler, *Ber.* **70,** 915–916 (1937). ⟨2⟩ Brand, Lohmann, *Ber.* **68,** 1493 (1935). ⟨3⟩ Kopp, *Ann.* **195,** 90–91 (1879). ⟨4⟩ Demarcay, *Ber.* **9,** 1933 (1876). ⟨5⟩ Fittig, *Ann.* **283,** 108 (1894). ⟨6⟩ Wislicenus, *Cent.* **1897,** II, 259. ⟨7⟩ Young, Dillon, Lucas, *J. Am. Chem. Soc.* **51,** 2530–2533 (1929). ⟨8⟩ Naster, Gavriloff, *Bull. soc. chim. Belg.* **42,** 528 (1933). ⟨9⟩ Blaise, Bagard, *Ann. chim.* (8) **11,** 119–120 (1907).

1:0615 HYDROCINNAMIC ACID $C_9H_{10}O_2$ **Beil. IX-508**
(β-Phenylpropionic acid)

$C_6H_5—CH_2.CH_2.COOH$

M.P. 48.7° **Neut. Eq. 150**
B.P. 279–280° cor.

Ndls. from aq., alc., or lgr. — Sol. in 168 pts. aq. at 20°; 6–7 pts. lgr. — Volatile with steam. [For prepn. (80–90% yield) by electrolytic reduct. of cinnamic ac. see ⟨1⟩.]

C̄ boiled with CrO_3 mixt. [cf. T 1.72] gives benzoic ac. (1:0715) — C̄ treated with fumg. H_2SO_4 at 140° for 5 min. gives (27% yield ⟨13⟩) indanone-1 (1:5144).

C̄ with PCl_5 ⟨2⟩, or PCl_3 in C_6H_6 ⟨3⟩ or with $SOCl_2$ (85% yield ⟨4⟩) [cf. T 1.37] gives β-phenylpropionyl chloride, b.p. 225° dec., b.p. 115–118° at 16–17 mm. ⟨4⟩. [This acid chloride treated with $AlCl_3$ ring closes yielding indanone-1 (1:5144), m.p. 42° ⟨5⟩.]

$Ag\bar{A}_2$; $Cu\bar{A}_2$, insol. cold aq.; $Ca\bar{A}_2.xH_2O$, sol. 25 pts. aq.; $Ba\bar{A}_2.2H_2O$, sol. 33 pts. aq.; $Pb\bar{A}_2$, insol. but resinous in hot aq.

Ⓓ ***p*-Nitrobenzyl hydrocinnamate:** m.p. 36.3° ⟨6⟩ [cf. T 1.39].
Ⓓ **Phenacyl hydrocinnamate:** m.p. 42° ⟨7⟩ [cf. T 1.391].
Ⓓ ***p*-Bromophenacyl hydrocinnamate:** m.p. 104.0° ⟨8⟩ [cf. T 1.391].
Ⓓ ***p*-Phenylphenacyl hydrocinnamate:** m.p. 95° ⟨9⟩ [cf. T 1.391].
Ⓓ **Hydrocinnamide (β-phenylpropionamide):** m.p. 105° ⟨10⟩.
Ⓓ **Hydrocinnamanilide (β-phenylpropionanilide)** [Beil. XII-277]: m.p. 96° ⟨11⟩.
Ⓓ **Hydrocinnamo-*p*-toluidide (β-phenylpropion-*p*-toluidide):** m.p. 135°.
Ⓓ **2-(β-Phenylethyl)benzimidazole:** from $\bar{C}$ + 1 mole *o*-phenylenediamine boiled 2 hrs. with 4 *N* HCl (50–60% yield); colorless pr., m.p. 186° ⟨12⟩.

1:0615 ⟨1⟩ Ingersoll, *Organic Syntheses, Coll. Vol.* I, 304–307 (1932). ⟨2⟩ Wedekind, *Ann.* **323,** 255, Note 14 (1902). ⟨3⟩ Rupe, *Ann.* **369,** 319–320 (1909). ⟨4⟩ Shriner, Damschroder, *J. Am. Chem. Soc.* **60,** 895 (1938). ⟨5⟩ Amagat, *Bull. soc. chim.* (4) **41,** 942 (1927). ⟨6⟩ Lyman, Reid, *J. Am. Chem. Soc.* **39,** 711 (1917). ⟨7⟩ Chen, *Trans. Science Soc. China* **7,** 73–80 (1931). ⟨8⟩ Judefind, Reid, *J. Am. Chem. Soc.* **42,** 1055 (1920). ⟨9⟩ Drake, Sweeney, *J. Am. Chem. Soc.* **54,** 2060 (1932). ⟨10⟩ Haworth, Perkin, Pink, *J. Chem. Soc.* **127,** 1714 (1925).
⟨11⟩ Dieckmann, Hoppe, Stein, *Ber.* **37,** 4633, Note 2 (1904). ⟨12⟩ Hughes, Lions, *Chem. Abs.* **32,** 5831 (1938). ⟨13⟩ Price, Lewis, *J. Am. Chem. Soc.* **61,** 2553–2554 (1939).

1:0620 ***n*-PENTADECYLIC ACID** $C_{15}H_{30}O_2$ **Beil. II-369**
(*n*-Pentadecanoic acid) $CH_3.(CH_2)_{13}.COOH$

M.P. 52.3° ⟨1⟩; 52.5-53.5° ⟨2⟩ Neut. Eq. 242

Lfts. from acetone; insol. aq., eas. sol. org. solvents. [For prepn. from myristyl bromide + KCN see ⟨3⟩.]

Ⓓ ***p*-Nitrobenzyl pentadecylate:** m.p. 39.5–40° cor. ⟨7⟩ [cf. T 1.39].
Ⓓ **Phenacyl pentadecylate:** m.p. 53.6° cor. (rap. htg.) ⟨7⟩ [cf. T 1.391].
Ⓓ ***p*-Chlorophenacyl pentadecylate:** m.p. 74.0° ⟨4⟩ [cf. T 1.391].
Ⓓ ***p*-Bromophenacyl pentadecylate:** m.p. 77.2° ⟨4⟩ [cf. T 1.391].
Ⓓ ***p*-Phenylphenacyl pentadecylate:** m.p. 91.3–91.8° cor. ⟨7⟩ [cf. T 1.391].
Ⓓ ***p*-Iodophenacyl pentadecylate:** m.p. 93.0° ⟨4⟩ [cf. T 1.391].
Ⓓ ***n*-Pentadecano-amide:** m.p. 102.5° ⟨5⟩.
Ⓓ ***n*-Pentadecano-anilide:** m.p. 78° ⟨6⟩.
Ⓓ **2-(*n*-Tetradecyl)benzimidazole:** m.p. 98.5–99.5° cor. ⟨2⟩.

1:0620 ⟨1⟩ Meyer, Reid, *J. Am. Chem. Soc.* **55,** 1577 (1933). ⟨2⟩ Pool, Harwood, Ralston, *J. Am. Chem. Soc.* **59,** 178 (1937). ⟨3⟩ Ruhoff, *Organic Syntheses* **16,** 37, Note 10 (1936). ⟨4⟩ Moses, Reid, *J. Am. Chem. Soc.* **54,** 2101 (1932). ⟨5⟩ Le Sueur, *J. Chem. Soc.* **87,** 1899 (1905). ⟨6⟩ Asahina, Akasu, *Cent.* **1926,** I, 915. ⟨7⟩ Price, Griffith, *J. Am. Chem. Soc.* **62,** 2884 (1940).

1:0625 **MALEIC ANHYDRIDE** (Toxilic anhydride) $C_4H_2O_3$ **Beil. XVII-432**

```
HC—C=O
‖    \
‖     O
‖    /
HC—C=O
```

M.P. 52° ⟨1⟩; 56° Neut. Eq. 49
B.P. 197–199° ⟨1⟩

Ndls. from $CHCl_3$ or ether — Sol. acetone, $CHCl_3$; spar. sol. lgr. Although odorless at ord. temp. vapor grad. attacks mucous membrane producing heavy catarrh of nasal passages

⟨1⟩. [For prepn. in 89.5% yield by distn. of maleic ac. (1:0470) with tetrachloroethane see ⟨1⟩.]

C̄ on warming with aq. melts and dissolves yielding maleic ac. (1:0470), q.v. [For quant. detn. or C̄ via titration with $NaOCH_3$ see ⟨2⟩.]

C̄ in even very dil. $CHCl_3$ soln. treated at room temp. with a few drops of a 20% soln. of triphenylphosphine in $CHCl_3$ gives immed. perm. or.-red color ⟨4⟩. [For study of interferences and theory see ⟨4⟩.]

C̄, refluxed with 1 mole aniline yields *N*-phenylaspartanil [Beil. XXII-529], ndls. from alc., m.p. 211° ⟨3⟩.

Ⓓ **Saponification:** Hydrolysis with aq. alk. (T 1.51) gives Sap. Eq. 49 and yields soln. contg. salts of maleic ac. (1:0470), q.v.

1:0625 ⟨1⟩ Mason, *J. Chem. Soc.* **1930,** 700–701. ⟨2⟩ Smith, Bryant, *J. Am. Chem. Soc.* **58,** 2452–2454 (1936). ⟨3⟩ Anschütz, Wirtz, *Ann.* **239,** 154 (1887). ⟨4⟩ Schönberg, Ismail, *J. Chem. Soc.* **1940,** 1374–1378.

1:0629 MYRISTIC ANHYDRIDE $C_{28}H_{54}O_3$ Beil. II-367

$[CH_3.(CH_2)_{12}.CO]_2O$

M.P. 53.4° ⟨1⟩ **D_4^{70} = 0.8502 ⟨1⟩** **n_D^{70} = 1.4335 ⟨1⟩**

White lfts. (from pet. ether) ⟨1⟩ — Prob. responds to Generic Test 3-B (titration in alc.).

Ⓓ **Saponification:** Hydrolysis with aq. alk. (T 1.51) gives Sap. Eq. 219 and yields soln. contg. salt of myristic ac. (1:0630), q.v.

1:0629 ⟨1⟩ Holde, Gentner, *Ber.* **58,** 1418–1424 (1925).

1:0630 MYRISTIC ACID $CH_3.(CH_2)_{12}.COOH$ $C_{14}H_{28}O_2$ Beil. II-365

(*n*-Tetradecanoic acid)

M.P. 53.86° ⟨1⟩ **Neut. Eq. 228**
54.1° ⟨2⟩

Insol. aq.; eas. sol. abs. alc., ether, C_6H_6, $CHCl_3$. [For prepn. (89–95% yield) by hydrolysis of glyceryl trimyristate see ⟨3⟩; for sepn. from other fatty acids via distn. see ⟨4⟩.]

[For f.p.-compn. diagram for mixts. of C̄ with palmitic ac. (1:0650) see ⟨2⟩.]

C̄ with PCl_5 (89% yield ⟨5⟩), or $PCl_3 + ZnCl_2$ (79% yield ⟨5⟩) or $SOCl_2$ (79% yield ⟨5⟩) [cf. T 1.37] gives *n*-tetradecanoyl chloride, b.p. $168°_{15}$.

AgĀ, m.p. 211° ⟨6⟩; $Mg\bar{A}_2$, m.p. 131.6° ⟨6⟩; [use in sepn. of C̄ from palmitic (1:0650) and stearic ac. (1:0660) ⟨8⟩]; $Pb\bar{A}_2$, m.p. 108.6–108.8° ⟨6⟩, 107° ⟨7⟩.

Ⓓ **Phenacyl myristate:** m.p. 56° ⟨9⟩ [cf. T 1.391].
Ⓓ ***p*-Chlorophenacyl myristate:** m.p. 76° ⟨9⟩ ⟨10⟩ [cf. T 1.391].
Ⓓ ***p*-Bromophenacyl myristate:** m.p. 81° ⟨9⟩ ⟨10⟩ [cf. T 1.391].
Ⓓ ***p*-Iodophenacyl myristate:** m.p. 89.8° ⟨10⟩ [cf. T 1.391].
Ⓓ ***p*-Phenylphenacyl myristate:** m.p. 90° ⟨11⟩.
Ⓓ ***n*-Myristamide:** m.p. 103° ⟨12⟩.
Ⓓ ***n*-Myristanilide:** m.p. 84° ⟨13⟩; 80–82° ⟨14⟩.
Ⓓ ***n*-Myristo-*p*-toluidide:** m.p. 93° ⟨12⟩.
Ⓓ **2-(*n*-Tridecyl)benzimidazole:** from C̄ + 1 mole *o*-phenylenediamine on reflux. for ½ hr.; m.p. 105.0–105.5° cor. ⟨15⟩.

1:0630 ⟨1⟩ Meyer, Reid, *J. Am. Chem. Soc.* **55,** 1577 (1933). ⟨2⟩ Kulka, Sandin, *J. Am. Chem. Soc.* **59,** 1348–1349 (1937). ⟨3⟩ Beal, *Organic Syntheses, Coll. Vol.* I, 371–372 (1932). ⟨4⟩ Lepkovsky, Feskov, Evans, *J. Am. Chem. Soc.* **58,** 978–981 (1936). ⟨5⟩ Clark, Bell, *Trans. Roy. Soc. Canada* (3) **27,** III, 97–103 (1933). ⟨6⟩ Jacobson, Holmes, *J. Biol. Chem.* **25, 29–54**

(1916). ⟨7⟩ Neave, *Analyst* **37,** 399 (1912). ⟨8⟩ Jacobson, Holmes, *J. Biol. Chem.* **25,** 55–62 (1916). ⟨9⟩ Hann, Reid, Jamieson, *J. Am. Chem. Soc.* **52,** 819 (1930). ⟨10⟩ Moses, Reid, *J. Am. Chem. Soc.* **54,** 2101 (1932).

⟨11⟩ Ford, *Iowa State Coll. J. Sci.* **12,** 121–122 (1937); Gilman, Ford, *Iowa State Coll. J. Sci.* **13,** 135–147 (1939); *Chem. Abs.* **32,** 4943 (1938). ⟨12⟩ Robertson, *J. Chem. Soc.* **115,** 1220–1221 (1919). ⟨13⟩ Masino, *Ann.* **202,** 174 (1880). ⟨14⟩ Kharasch, Potts, *J. Org. Chem.* **2,** 197 (1938). ⟨15⟩ Pool, Harwood, Ralston, *J. Am. Chem. Soc.* **59,** 178 (1937).

1:0633 BRASSIDIC ACID $CH_3.(CH_2)_7.C.H$ $C_{22}H_{42}O_2$ Beil. II-474

$$\begin{array}{c} CH_3.(CH_2)_7.C.H \\ \| \\ H—C—(CH_2)_{11}.COOH \end{array}$$

M.P. 59.75° ⟨1⟩ **Neut. Eq. 338**

Pl. from alc. [For prepn. from erucic ac. by isomerization see (1:0590).] [For m.p.-compn. curves for systems: C̄ + erucic ac. see ⟨2⟩ ⟨1⟩; their eutectic conts. 9.5% C̄ and melts 31.8° ⟨1⟩.] [For prepn. of pure C̄ see ⟨3⟩ ⟨4⟩.]

C̄ in alk. soln. reduces $KMnO_4$ (T 1.34) — C̄ adds Br_2 (T 1.91) [yielding 12,13-dibromobehenic acid (brassido-dibromobehenic ac.) [Beil. II-392], m.p. 53–54° ⟨5⟩].

C̄ htd. with PCl_3 3 hrs. at 90° ⟨6⟩, or with $SOCl_2$ ⟨7⟩ yields brassidyl chloride, m.p. 14° — C̄ refluxed 6 hrs. with 2 pts. Ac_2O yields brassidic anhydride; m.p. 63.5–64.5° ⟨8⟩.

Ⓓ ***p*-Chlorophenacyl brassidate:** m.p. 69.5° ⟨9⟩ [cf. T 1.391].

Ⓓ ***p*-Bromophenacyl brassidate:** m.p. 74.2° ⟨9⟩ [cf. T 1.391].

Ⓓ ***p*-Iodophenacyl brassidate:** m.p. 84.0° ⟨9⟩ [cf. T 1.391].

Ⓓ ***p*-Phenylphenacyl brassidate:** m.p. 85.6° ⟨9⟩ [cf. T 1.391].

Ⓓ **Brassidamide:** m.p. 94° ⟨10⟩.

Ⓓ **Brassidanilide:** m.p. 78° ⟨11⟩.

1:0633 ⟨1⟩ Keffler, Maiden, *J. Phys. Chem.* **40,** 909–911 (1936). ⟨2⟩ Griffiths, Hilditch, *J. Chem. Soc.* **1932,** 2317–2322. ⟨3⟩ Keffler, *J. Soc. Chem. Ind.* **55T,** 331–333 (1936). ⟨4⟩ Keffler, Maiden, *Bull. soc. chim. Belg.* **44,** 467–472 (1935). ⟨5⟩ Maruyama, *Cent.* **1935,** II, 2358. ⟨6⟩ Loevenich, Losen, Dierichs, *Ber.* **60,** 950 (1927). ⟨7⟩ Meyer, *Monatsh.* **22,** 419 (1901). ⟨8⟩ Holde, Zadek, *Ber.* **56,** 2053–2054 (1923). ⟨9⟩ Kimura, *Cent.* **1934,** II, 2207. ⟨10⟩ Krafft, Tritschler, *Ber.* **33,** 3584 (1900).

⟨11⟩ Reimer, Will, *Ber.* **19,** 3326 (1886).

1:0634 *d*-HYDNOCARPIC ACID $C_{16}H_{28}O_2$ Beil. IX-79

(ω-Cyclopentylundecylic acid)

$$\begin{array}{l} CH{=}CH \quad\quad H \\ | \quad\quad\quad \diagdown \; \diagup \\ | \quad\quad\quad\quad C—(CH_2)_{10}.COOH \\ | \quad\quad\quad \diagup \\ CH_2—CH_2 \end{array}$$

M.P. 60.5° ⟨1⟩ **Neut. Eq. 252**

Colorless pl. from lgr. (b.p. 70–90°) or from 80% alc. ⟨1⟩; eas. sol. $CHCl_3$ but spar. sol. in other org. solv. in cold — Loose cryst. soon attacked by air, but if fused and allowed to solidify, C̄ keeps well ⟨2⟩ — On solidification of fused C̄, cryst. grow upward in branching forms from melted acid, but this very characteristic growth is inhibited by even small amt. of impurity and a flat upper surface then results ⟨1⟩ [also shown by chaulmoogric ac. (1:0655)].

For purif. of C̄ by fract. distn. of ethyl ester at 10–20 mm. see ⟨1⟩ ⟨2⟩. [For m.p. + compn. curves for system: C̄ + palmitic ac. see ⟨1⟩; for C̄ + chaulmoogric ac. see ⟨1⟩.]

C̄ is opt. active: $[\alpha]_D^{25}$ in $CHCl_3$ = +69.3° ⟨1⟩. [Lower values indicate presence of palmitic or chaulmoogric acids ⟨1⟩.]

C̄ in alk. soln. reduces $KMnO_4$ (T 1.34); C̄ adds Br_2 (T 1.91).

$Pb\bar{A}_2$, m.p. 77–78° ⟨3⟩; $Ba\bar{A}_2$, m.p. 120° ⟨3⟩.

Ⓓ ***d*-Hydnocarpamide:** from C̄ by warm. with excess PCl_3, soln. dislvd. in ether, and slowly added to 10 vols. conc. NH_4OH at 0°; ppt. filtered, washed with aq. then dil. alk., recrystd. from alc.; m.p. 112–113° ⟨4⟩; 111–112° ⟨5⟩. [$[\alpha]_D^{25} = +69.4°$ ⟨5⟩.]

1:0634 ⟨1⟩ Cole, Cardoso, *J. Am. Chem. Soc.* **59,** 963–965 (1937). ⟨2⟩ Perkins, Cruz, Reyes, *Ind. Eng. Chem.* **19,** 939–942 (1927). ⟨3⟩ Cole, *Philippine J. Sci.* **47,** 351–355 (1932). ⟨4⟩ Power, Barrowcliff, *J. Chem. Soc.* **87,** 889–890 (1905). ⟨5⟩ Hinegardner, *J. Am. Chem. Soc.* **55,** 2833 (1933).

1:0635 MARGARIC ACID $CH_3.(CH_2)_{15}.COOH$ $C_{17}H_{34}O_2$ Beil. II-376

(*n*-Heptadecanoic acid)

M.P. 61.19° ⟨1⟩; in cap. tube **61.5-62°** ⟨1⟩ **Neut. Eq. 270**

Cryst. from 80% alc. ⟨2⟩. [For m.p. + compn. data on binary systems: C̄ + palmitic ac. (1:0650) see ⟨1⟩; C̄ + stearic ac. (1:0660) see ⟨1⟩; ternary system; C̄ + palmitic + stearic ac. see ⟨3⟩.]

C̄ with $SOCl_2$ ⟨4⟩ yields *n*-heptadecanoyl chloride, b.p. 157° at 5 mm. ⟨5⟩.

Ⓓ ***p*-Nitrobenzyl margarate:** m.p. 48.5–49.0° cor. ⟨10⟩ [cf. T 1.39].
Ⓓ **Phenacyl margarate:** m.p. 60.0–60.5° cor. ⟨10⟩ [cf. T 1.391].
Ⓓ ***p*-Chlorophenacyl margarate:** m.p. 78.8° ⟨6⟩ [cf. T 1.391].
Ⓓ ***p*-Bromophenacyl margarate:** m.p. 82.6° ⟨6⟩; 78.2° ⟨7⟩ [cf. T 1.391].
Ⓓ ***p*-Iodophenacyl margarate:** m.p. 92.0° ⟨6⟩; 88.8° ⟨7⟩ [cf. T 1.391].
Ⓓ ***p*-Phenylphenacyl margarate:** m.p. 95.3–95.8° cor. ⟨10⟩ [cf. T 1.391].
Ⓓ **Margaramide:** m.p. 106° ⟨8⟩.
Ⓓ **2-(*n*-Hexadecyl)benzimidazole:** m.p. 93.5–94.0° cor. ⟨9⟩.

1:0635 ⟨1⟩ Smith, *J. Chem. Soc.* **1936,** 626–627. ⟨2⟩ Heiduschka, Ripper, *Ber.* **56,** 1739 (1923). ⟨3⟩ Shriner, Fulton, Burks, *J. Am. Chem. Soc.* **55,** 1494–1499 (1933). ⟨4⟩ Skraup, Schwamberger, *Ann.* **462,** 153 (1928). ⟨5⟩ Ford-Moore, Phillips, *Rec. trav. chim.* **53,** 857 (1934). ⟨6⟩ Moses, Reid, *J. Am. Chem. Soc.* **54,** 2101 (1932). ⟨7⟩ Judefind, Reid, *J. Am. Chem. Soc.*, **42,** 1055 (1920). ⟨8⟩ Le Sueur, *J. Chem. Soc.* **85,** 837 (1904). ⟨9⟩ Pool, Harwood, Ralston *J. Am. Chem. Soc.* **59,** 178 (1937). ⟨10⟩ Price, Griffith, *J. Am. Chem Soc.* **62,** 2884 (1940).

1:0640 BENZYL HYDROGEN SUCCINATE $C_{11}H_{12}O_4$ Beil. VI-436

⬡—$CH_2.OOC.CH_2.CH_2.COOH$

M.P. 62° **Neut. Eq. 208**

Ⓓ **Saponification:** Hydrolysis with aq. alk. (T 1.51) gives Sap. Eq. 104 and yields benzyl alc. (1:6480) and succinic ac. (1:0530).

1:0650 PALMITIC ACID $CH_3.(CH_2)_{14}.COOH$ $C_{16}H_{32}O_2$ Beil. II-370

(*n*-Hexadecanoic acid)

M.P. 62.76° ⟨1⟩ **Neut. Eq. 256**

Ndls. or greasy scales insol. aq. — Can be crystd. from alc., C_6H_6, or acetone ⟨1⟩. At 19.5° 100 g. abs. alc. dis. 9.32 g. C̄ — C̄ can be titrated (T 1.31) in alc. but not in aq.

[For m.p. + compn. data on systems: C̄ + myristic ac. (1:0630) see ⟨2⟩; C̄ + margaric ac. (1:0635) see ⟨3⟩; C̄ + stearic ac. (1:0660) see ⟨2⟩; C̄ + oleic ac. (1:0565) see ⟨16⟩; C̄ + elaidic ac. (1:0610) see ⟨16⟩.]

C̄ treated with PCl_5 (49% yield ⟨4⟩), $PCl_3 + ZnCl_2$ (72% yield ⟨4⟩), or $SOCl_2$ (80% yield ⟨4⟩) [cf. T 1.37] gives palmityl chloride (*n*-hexadecanoyl chloride), m.p. +12°.

AgĀ, m.p. 209° ⟨5⟩; $PbĀ_2$, m.p. 112° ⟨5⟩ ⟨6⟩ (insol. ether); $MgĀ_2$, m.p. 121–122° ⟨5⟩.

Ⓓ *p*-**Nitrobenzyl palmitate:** m.p. 42.5° ⟨7⟩ [cf. T 1.39].
Ⓓ **Phenacyl palmitate:** m.p. 63° ⟨8⟩ [cf. T 1.391].
Ⓓ *p*-**Chlorophenacyl palmitate:** m.p. 82.0° ⟨8⟩ ⟨9⟩ [cf. T 1.391].
Ⓓ *p*-**Bromophenacyl palmitate:** m.p. 86.0° ⟨8⟩ ⟨9⟩; 81.5° ⟨10⟩ [cf. T 1.391].
Ⓓ *p*-**Iodophenacyl palmitate:** m.p. 94.2° ⟨9⟩; 90.0° ⟨10⟩ [cf. T 1.391].
Ⓓ *p*-**Phenylphenacyl palmitate:** m.p. 94° ⟨11⟩ [cf. T 1.391].
Ⓓ **Palmitamide:** from C̄ via acid chloride with NH_3; cryst. from alc. or C_6H_6, m.p. 105.3° ⟨1⟩; 106° ⟨12⟩. [For m.p. + compn. diagram of mixtures of palmitamide and stearamide see ⟨1⟩.]
Ⓓ **Palmitanilide:** from C̄ via acid chloride with ice cold aniline; cryst. from C_6H_6 or alc., m.p. 90.6° ⟨1⟩; 90.5° ⟨13⟩. [For m.p.-compn. diagram of mixts. of palmitanilide and stearanilide see ⟨1⟩.]
Ⓓ **Palmito-*p*-toluidide:** m.p. 98° ⟨12⟩.
Ⓓ **2-(*n*-Pentadecyl)benzimidazole:** from C̄ on htg. with 1 mole *o*-phenylenediamine for ½ hr.; m.p. 96.5–97.5° cor. ⟨14⟩; 91–92° ⟨15⟩.

1:0650 ⟨1⟩ Guy, Smith, *J. Chem. Soc.* **1939,** 615–618. ⟨2⟩ Kulka, Sandin, *J. Am. Chem. Soc.* **59,** 1347–1349 (1937). ⟨3⟩ Smith, *J. Chem. Soc.* **1936,** 627. ⟨4⟩ Clark, Bell, *Trans. Roy. Soc. Canada* (3) **27,** III, 97–103 (1933). ⟨5⟩ Jacobson, Holmes, *J. Biol. Chem.* **25,** 29–54 (1916). ⟨6⟩ Neave, *Analyst* **37,** 399 (1912). ⟨7⟩ Lyons, Reid, *J. Am. Chem. Soc.* **39,** 1733 (1917). ⟨8⟩ Hann, Reid, Jamieson, *J. Am. Chem. Soc* **52,** 819 (1930). ⟨9⟩ Moses, Reid, *J. Am. Chem. Soc.* **54,** 2101 (1932). ⟨10⟩ Judefind, Reid, *J. Am. Chem. Soc.* **42,** 1055 (1920).
⟨11⟩ Ford, *Iowa State Coll. J. Sci.* **12,** 121–122 (1937); Gilman, Ford, *Iowa State Coll. J. Sci.* **13,** 135–147 (1939); *Chem. Abs.* **32,** 4943 (1938). ⟨12⟩ Robertson, *J. Chem. Soc.* **115,** 1220–1221 (1919). ⟨13⟩ Hell, Jordanoff, *Ber.* **24,** 943 (1891). ⟨14⟩ Pool, Harwood, Ralston, *J. Am. Chem. Soc.* **59,** 178 (1937). ⟨15⟩ Seka, Müller, *Monatsh.* **57,** 103 (1931). ⟨16⟩ Smith, *J. Chem. Soc.* **1939,** 980.

1:0651 PALMITIC ANHYDRIDE $C_{36}H_{62}O_3$ Beil. II-374

$[CH_3.(CH_2)_{14}.CO]_2O$

M.P. 63-64° ⟨1⟩ D_4^{70} = **0.847 ⟨1⟩** n_D^{70} = **1.4357 ⟨1⟩**

White lfts. (from pet. ether) ⟨1⟩ — C̄ barely responds to Generic Test 3-B (titration in alc.) reacting as a monobasic acid. Neut. Eq. *in alcohol* (T 1.31) nearly quant.; found 488.6; theoret. 494.5.

C̄ can be freed from palmitic acid by repeated recrystn. from boilg. alc. (100 g. alc. at 15° dis. 0.165 g. C̄; corresp. value for palmitic acid is 6.5 g.) ⟨2⟩ — [C̄ does not react with NH_4OH, aniline or phenylhydrazine ⟨2⟩.]

Ⓓ **Saponification:** Hydrolysis with alk. (T 1.51) gives Sap. Eq. of 247 and yields soln. contg. salt of palmitic ac. (1:0650), q.v.

1:0651 ⟨1⟩ Holde, Gentner, *Ber.* **58,** 1418–1424 (1925). ⟨2⟩ Autenrieth, Thomae, *Ber.* **57,** 430 (1924).

1:0654 ITACONIC ANHYDRIDE $C_5H_4O_3$ Beil. XVII-442

$CH_2{=}C{-}C({=}O){-}O{-}C({=}O){-}CH_2$ (ring: $CH_2{=}C$—C(=O)—O—C(=O)—H_2C, closed)

M.P. 67-68°

Scales from AcOH; pr. from dry ether or $CHCl_3$ — Very eas. sol. $CHCl_3$; spar. sol. cold ether. [For prepn. in 37–47% yield by rapid distn. of citric ac. (1:0455) see ⟨1⟩.]

C̄ on rapid distn. at ord. press. gives 62–66% yield citraconic anhydride (1:1135) q.v. ⟨2⟩ — C̄ boiled with $2\frac{1}{2}$ pts. aq. for 1 hr. gives 24–39% yield itaconic ac. (1:0515) ⟨1⟩.

1:0654 ⟨1⟩ Shriner, Ford, Roll, *Organic Syntheses* **11,** 70–72 (1931). ⟨2⟩ Shriner, Ford, Roll, *Organic Syntheses* **11,** 28–29 (1931).

1:0655 ***d*-CHAULMOOGRIC ACID** $C_{18}H_{32}O_2$ **Beil. IX-80**
(ω-Cyclopentyltridecanoic acid)

```
CH =CH         H
|      \      /
|       C.(CH2)12.COOH
|      /
CH2—CH2
```

M.P. 68.5° ⟨1⟩ **Neut. Eq. 280**

Colorless pl. from 80% alc. ⟨1⟩ or AcOEt; eas. sol. ether or $CHCl_3$; spar. sol. in other org. solv. — On solidification of fused C̄, cryst. grow upward in branching forms from melted acid, but this very characteristic growth is inhibited by even small amts. of impurity and a flat upper surface then results ⟨1⟩ [also shown by *d*-hydnocarpic ac. (1:0634)].

For purif. of C̄ by fract. distn. of ethyl ester at 10–20 mm. see ⟨1⟩. [For m.p. + compn. curves for system: C̄ + hydnocarpic ac. see ⟨1⟩.]

C̄ is opt. act.: $[\alpha]_D^{25}$ in $CHCl_3$ = +60.3° ⟨1⟩ [higher values often indicate presence of hydnocarpic ac.].

C̄ in alk. soln. reduces $KMnO_4$ (T 1.34); C̄ adds Br_2 (T 1.91).

C̄ with 2 pts. PCl_3 at 70–80° for 1 hr. gives 80% yield ⟨2⟩ *d*-chaulmoogryl chloride. After removal of excess PCl_3 this may be used directly, although it can be distilled at low pressures ⟨3⟩. [PCl_5 or $SOCl_2$ on C̄ cause partial decompn. ⟨7⟩.]

$Pb\bar{A}_2$, m.p. 62–63° ⟨4⟩; $Ba\bar{A}_2$, m.p. 123° ⟨5⟩.

Ⓓ ***d*-Chaulmoogramide:** from C̄ by warm. with PCl_3, pouring prod. into cold conc. aq. NH_4OH; cryst. from hot alc., m.p. 106° ⟨6⟩; 104° ⟨8⟩.

—— ***d*-Chaulmoogranilide:** m.p. 89°. [Prepd. from amide by htg. with aniline 5 hrs. at 200° ⟨9⟩.]

—— ***d*-Chaulmoogro-*p*-toluidide:** m.p. 100° [similarly: ⟨9⟩].

1:0655 ⟨1⟩ Cole, Cardoso, *J. Am. Chem. Soc.* **59,** 963–965 (1937). ⟨2⟩ Naegeli, Vogt-Markus, *Helv. Chim. Acta* **15,** 65–66 (1932). ⟨3⟩ Wagner-Jauregg, Reinemund, *J. prakt. Chem.* (2) **150,** 252 (1938). ⟨4⟩ Wagner-Jauregg, Arnold, *Ber.* **70,** 1461 (1937). ⟨5⟩ Cole, *Philippine J. Sci.* **47,** 351–355 (1932). ⟨6⟩ Power, Gornall, *J. Chem. Soc.* **85,** 855 (1904). ⟨7⟩ Hinegardner, Johnson, *J. Am. Chem. Soc.* **51,** 1506 (1929). ⟨8⟩ Stanley, Adams, *J. Am. Chem. Soc.* **51,** 1518 (1929). ⟨9⟩ Herrera, Batteke, *Philippine J. Sci.* **32,** 35–40 (1927); *Chem. Abs.* **21,** 1449 (1927).

1:0660 **STEARIC ACID** $CH_3.(CH_2)_{16}.COOH$ $C_{18}H_{36}O_2$ **Beil. II-377**
(*n*-Octadecanoic acid)

M.P. 69.62° ⟨1⟩ **Neut. Eq. 284**

Odorless, tasteless lfts.; insol. aq.; sol. in 40 pts. cold alc., eas. sol. cold ether, C_6H_6, CS_2, or $CHCl_3$ — C̄ does not dis. on shaking with cold Na_2CO_3 soln. or even 0.1 *N* aq. KOH, but titrates (T 1.31) in alc.

[For m.p.-compn. data on systems: C̄ + margaric ac. (1:0635) see ⟨2⟩; C̄ + palmitic ac. (1:0650) see ⟨3⟩; C̄ + oleic ac. (1:0565) see ⟨4⟩; C̄ + elaidic acid (1:0610) see ⟨4⟩.]

C̄ with PCl_5 or $SOCl_2$ (cf. T 1.37) yields stearyl chloride (*n*-octadecanoyl chloride), m.p. 23°.

$Ag\bar{A}$, m.p. 205° ⟨5⟩; $Pb\bar{A}_2$, m.p. 125° ⟨6⟩; 115–116° ⟨5⟩; $Ca\bar{A}_2$, m.p. 179–180°.

Ⓓ **Phenacyl stearate:** m.p. 69° ⟨7⟩ [cf. T 1.391].
Ⓓ ***p*-Chlorophenacyl stearate:** m.p. 86.0° ⟨7⟩ ⟨8⟩ [cf. T 1.391].
Ⓓ ***p*-Bromophenacyl stearate:** m.p. 90.0° ⟨7⟩ ⟨8⟩; 78.5° ⟨9⟩ [cf. T 1.391].
Ⓓ ***p*-Iodophenacyl stearate:** m.p. 97.2° ⟨8⟩; 90° ⟨9⟩ [cf. T 1.391].
Ⓓ ***p*-Phenylphenacyl stearate:** m.p. 97° ⟨10⟩; 91° ⟨11⟩ [cf. T 1.391].
Ⓓ **Stearamide:** from C̄ via the acid chloride; cryst. from C_6H_6 or alc., m.p. 108.4° ⟨1⟩; 109° ⟨12⟩. [For m.p. + compn. diagram of mixts. of stearamide and palmitamide, see ⟨1⟩.]
Ⓓ **Stearanilide:** from C̄ via the acid chloride + cold aniline; cryst. from C_6H_6 or alc., m.p. 95.5° ⟨1⟩; 94° ⟨12⟩. [For m.p. + compn. diagram of mixts. of stearanilide and palmitanilide see ⟨1⟩.]
Ⓓ **Stearo-*p*-toluidide:** m.p. 102° ⟨12⟩.
Ⓓ **2-(*n*-Heptadecyl)benzimidazole:** from C̄ + 1 mole *o*-phenylenediamine on htg. at b.p. ½ hr.; m.p. 93.5–94.5° cor. ⟨13⟩; 90–91° ⟨14⟩.

1:0660 ⟨1⟩ Guy, Smith, *J. Chem. Soc.* **1939,** 615–618. ⟨2⟩ Smith, *J. Chem. Soc.* **1936,** 627. ⟨3⟩ Kulka, Sandin, *J. Am. Chem. Soc.* **59,** 1347–1349. ⟨4⟩ Smith, *J. Chem. Soc.* **1939,** 980. ⟨5⟩ Jacobson, Holmes, *J. Biol. Chem.* **25,** 29–54 (1916). ⟨6⟩ Neave, *Analyst* **37,** 339 (1912). ⟨7⟩ Hann, Reid, Jamieson, *J. Am. Chem. Soc.* **52,** 819 (1930). ⟨8⟩ Moses, Reid, *J. Am. Chem. Soc.* **54,** 2101 (1932). ⟨9⟩ Judefind, Reid, *J. Am. Chem. Soc.* **42,** 1055 (1920). ⟨10⟩ Ford, *Iowa, State Coll. J. Sci.* **12,** 121–122 (1937); Gilman, Ford, *Iowa State Coll. J. Sci.* **13,** 135–147 (1939); *Chem. Abs.* **32,** 4943 (1938).

⟨11⟩ Drake, Bronitsky, *J. Am. Chem. Soc.* **52,** 3719 (1930). ⟨12⟩ Robertson, *J. Chem. Soc.* **115,** 1220–1221 (1919). ⟨13⟩ Pool, Harwood, Ralston, *J. Am. Chem. Soc.* **59,** 178 (1937). ⟨14⟩ Seka, Müller, *Monatsh.* **57,** 104 (1931).

— STEARIC ANHYDRIDE $[CH_3(CH_2)_{16}.CO]_2O$ $C_{36}H_{70}O_3$ Beil. II-384

M.P. 71-71.5° D_4^{70} **= 0.8443** n_D^{70} **= 1.4379**

See 1:4915. Genus 6: Division A.

1:0665 PHENYLACETIC ACID ⬡—$CH_2.COOH$ $C_8H_8O_2$ Beil. IX-431

M.P. 76.5° **Neut. Eq. 136**
B.P. 265.5° cor.

Lfts. dif. sol. cold aq.; eas. sol. hot aq.; very sol. alc. or ether — Sublimes readily. [For prepn. in 77.5% yield by hydrolysis of benzyl cyanide see ⟨1⟩.]

C̄ warmed with dil. H_2SO_4 + MnO_2 gives odor of benzaldehyde; with alk. $KMnO_4$ is oxid. to BzOH (1:0715).

C̄ with PCl_5 (63% yield ⟨2⟩) or PCl_3 + $ZnCl_2$ (73% yield ⟨2⟩), or $SOCl_2$ ⟨3⟩ (54% yield ⟨2⟩) (cf. T 1.37) gives phenylacetyl chloride, b.p. 183° sl. dec. ⟨3⟩ — C̄ refluxed with 3 pts. Ac_2O for 4 hrs. gives (75% yield ⟨4⟩ ⟨5⟩) phenylacetic anhydride, ndls. from lt. pet., m.p. 72°. [For data on soly. of salts see ⟨11⟩.]

Ⓓ ***p*-Nitrobenzyl phenylacetate:** m.p. 65° ⟨6⟩ [cf. T 1.39].
Ⓓ **Phenacyl phenylacetate:** m.p. 50.5° ⟨7⟩ [cf. T 1.391].
Ⓓ ***p*-Bromophenacyl phenylacetate:** m.p. 89° ⟨8⟩ [cf. T 1.391].
Ⓓ ***p*-Phenylphenacyl phenylacetate:** m.p. 63° dec. ⟨9⟩ [cf. T 1.391].
Ⓓ **Phenylacetamide:** m.p. 156°.
Ⓓ **Phenylacetanilide** [Beil. XII-275]: m.p. 117–118°.
Ⓓ **Phenylaceto-*p*-toluidide** [Beil. XII-929]: m.p. 135–136°.
Ⓓ **2-Benzylbenzimidazole:** from C̄ + 1 mole *o*-phenylenediamine boiled for 2 hrs. with 4 *N* HCl; 50–60% yield ⟨10⟩; ndls. from alc., m.p. 187°.

1:0665 ⟨1⟩ Adams, Thal, *Organic Syntheses, Coll. Vol.* I, 427–428 (1932). ⟨2⟩ Clark, Bell, *Trans. Roy. Soc. Canada* (3) **27,** III, 97–103 (1933). ⟨3⟩ Meyer, *Monatsh.* **22,** 427 (1901). ⟨4⟩ Autenrieth, Thomae, *Ber.* **57,** 431 (1924). ⟨5⟩ Heilbron, Hey, Lythgoe, *J. Chem. Soc.* **1936,** 297. ⟨6⟩ Lyman, Reid, *J. Am. Chem. Soc.* **39,** 703 (1917). ⟨7⟩ Chen, *Trans. Science Soc. China* **7,** 73–80 (1931). ⟨8⟩ Judefind, Reid, *J. Am. Chem. Soc.* **42,** 1055 (1920). ⟨9⟩ Drake, Sweeney, *J. Am. Chem. Soc.* **54,** 2060 (1932). ⟨10⟩ Hughes, Lions, *J. Proc. Roy. Soc. N. S. Wales* **71,** 209–222 (1938); *Chem. Abs.* **32,** 5831 (1938).
⟨11⟩ Ephraim, *Ber.* **55,** 3482 (1922).

1:0667 GLYCOLID

O
H_2C CO
OC CH_2
O

$C_4H_4O_4$ **Beil. XIX-153**

M.P. 86°

Lfts. (from alc. and $CHCl_3$), very eas. sol. acetone; eas. sol. hot alc., $CHCl_3$; dif. sol. ether.

C̄ in Generic Test 3-A (titration in aq.) gives Neut. Eq. of abt. 128 (theoret. is 116); in Generic Test 3-B (titration in alc.) gives Neut. Eq. of 240.

C̄ on protracted boilg. with aq. gives glycolic ac., m.p. 78° (1:0430).

C̄ htd. alone or with trace $ZnCl_2$ in s.t. at 120–150° yields polyglycolid, m.p. 220° (1:4970).

Ⓓ **Glycolicanilide:** from C̄ (5.8 g.) in aniline (9.3 g.) htd. 4 hrs. at 100°, cooled, separating solid recrystd. (from aq.), m.p. 97° ⟨1⟩.

Ⓓ **Glycolic-*p*-toluidide:** from C̄ + equiv. amt. *p*-toluidine, htd. 2–3 hrs. at 100°, cooled, recrystd. from aq. (70% yield), m.p. 143° ⟨1⟩.

1:0667 ⟨1⟩ Bischoff, Walden, *Ann.* **279,** 49, 63 (1894).

1:0668 DIBENZYLACETIC ACID

$C_{16}H_{16}O_2$ **Beil. IX-682**

$(C_6H_5-CH_2)_2.CH.COOH$

M.P. 89° **Neut. Eq. 240**

Tbls. from pet. eth. or dil. AcOH; ndls. from aq. — Dif. sol. boilg. aq.; eas. sol. alc., ether, $CHCl_3$, AcOH, or C_6H_6.

C̄, treated with slightly more than 1 mole PCl_5 in cold $CHCl_3$ ⟨1⟩ ⟨2⟩ or with PCl_3 in hot C_6H_6 ⟨3⟩ or C̄ refluxed with $SOCl_2$ ⟨2⟩ ⟨4⟩ ⟨5⟩ gives (95% yield ⟨6⟩) dibenzylacetyl chloride, b.p. $203–204^{\circ}_{15}$. [By-products of $SOCl_2$ process are dibenzylacetic anhydride (see below) and 2-benzylhydrindone (from ring closure of the acid chloride) ⟨2⟩ ⟨4⟩.]

C̄ refluxed with excess of AcCl for 2–3 hrs. yields dibenzylacetic anhydride, cryst. pptd. from C_6H_6 by addn. of pet. ether, m.p. 76–77° ⟨7⟩.

Ⓓ **Dibenzylacetamide:** from the acid chloride (above) + excess conc. aq. NH_4OH, at 0° in 90% yield ⟨6⟩; cryst. from C_6H_6, m.p. 128–129° ⟨4⟩ ⟨6⟩.

Ⓓ **Dibenzylacetanilide:** from acid chloride + aniline in C_6H_6 (95% yield); cryst. from abs. alc., m.p. 155° ⟨6⟩.

Ⓓ **Dibenzylacet-*p*-toluidide:** similarly; m.p. 175° ⟨6⟩.

1:0668 ⟨1⟩ Schneidewind, *Ber.* **21,** 1328 (1888). ⟨2⟩ Leuchs, Wutke, Giessler, *Ber.* **46,** 2208–2211 (1913). ⟨3⟩ Rupe, *Ann.* **395,** 110 (1913). ⟨4⟩ Mills, Akers, *J. Chem. Soc.* **127,** 2477 (1925). ⟨5⟩ Jones, Scott, *J. Am. Chem. Soc.* **44,** 416–417 (1922). ⟨6⟩ Maxim, *Bull. soc. chim.* (4) **39,** 1025–1028 (1926). ⟨7⟩ Verkade, *Rec. trav. chim.* **37,** 336 (1918).

1:0670 ***o*-BENZOYLBENZOIC ACID** (monohydrate) $C_{14}H_{10}O_3.H_2O$ **Beil. X-747**

M.P. 93-94° **Neut. Eq. 244**

Pr. with 1 H_2O from aq., dil. alc., or on shaking C_6H_6 soln. of anhydrous *o*-benzoylbenzoic ac. (1:0720) with aq. — Readily loses aq. above 100° or on distn. with xylene giving anhydrous form, m.p. 127–128° (1:0720), q.v.

1:0675 ***n*-HEPTYLMALONIC ACID** $C_{10}H_{18}O_4$ **Beil. II-721**

$C_7H_{15}.CH(COOH)_2$

M.P. 96.5-98° ⟨1⟩ **Neut. Eq. 202**

C̄, on htg. (T 1.33) evolves CO_2 and leaves pelargonic ac. (1:0560), q.v.

1:0675 **⟨1⟩** Verkade, Coops, *Rec. trav. chim.* **49,** 568 (1930).

1:0680 **PHENOXYACETIC ACID** (Glycolic acid phenyl ether) $C_8H_8O_3$ **Beil. VI-161**

—$O.CH_2.COOH$

M.P. 98-99° **Neut. Eq. 152**
B.P. 285° sl. dec.

Ndls. from aq. — Not volatile with steam. [For prepn. from phenol + chloroacetic ac. see ⟨1⟩ (T 1.46).] [Use for making mixed m.p. detn.]

C̄ with PCl_5 (80% yield ⟨2⟩ ⟨3⟩) or with $SOCl_2$ at 35–45° for 1 hr. (100% yield ⟨4⟩) gives phenoxyacetyl chloride, b.p. 225–226° ⟨2⟩.

Ⓓ ***p*-Bromophenacyl phenoxyacetate:** m.p. 148.5° ⟨5⟩ [cf. T 1.391].

Ⓓ **Phenoxyacetamide:** m.p. 101.5° ⟨6⟩.

Ⓓ **Phenoxyacetanilide:** from C̄ htd. with 1 mole aniline at 150° ⟨7⟩, or from C̄ htd. with 1 mole phenylisocyanate at 55–110° ⟨8⟩; cryst. from alc., m.p. 99° ⟨7⟩ ⟨8⟩.

Ⓓ **2-Phenoxymethylbenzimidazole:** from C̄ + 1 mole *o*-phenylenediamine boiled 2 hrs. with 4 *N* HCl (50–60% yield); colorless ndls. from aq. alc., m.p. 162° ⟨9⟩.

1:0680 **⟨1⟩** Koelsch, *J. Am. Chem. Soc.* **53,** 304–305 (1931). **⟨2⟩** Vandevelde, *Cent.* **1898,** I, 988. **⟨3⟩** Stoermer, Atenstädt, *Ber.* **35,** 3562, Note 3 (1902). **⟨4⟩** Blaise, Picard, *Ann. chim.* (8) **26,** 274 (1912). **⟨5⟩** Chen, Shih, *Trans. Science Soc. China* **7,** 81–87 (1932). **⟨6⟩** Fritzsche, *J. prakt. Chem.* (2) **20,** 277 (1879). **⟨7⟩** Ref. 6, page 280. **⟨8⟩** Lambling, *Bull. soc. chim.* (3) **17,** 359 (1897). **⟨9⟩** Hughes, Lions, *Chem. Abs.* **32,** 5831 (1938); *Cent.* **1938,** II, 1598.

1:0685 ***o*-METHOXYBENZOIC ACID** (*o*-Anisic acid; salicylic acid methyl ether) $C_8H_8O_3$ **Beil. X-64**

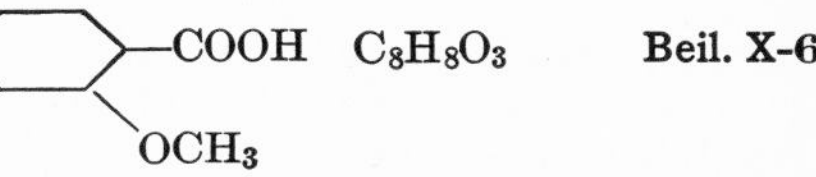

M.P. 100-101° **Neut. Eq. 152**

Tbls. from aq.; scales from alc. — Sol. in 200 pts. aq. at 30°; more eas. in hot aq.; very eas. sol. alc., ether — At 25° distrib. ratio between toluene and water is 2.8; between $CHCl_3$ and aq. is 48 ⟨1⟩. [For sepn. from salicylic ac. by means of AcOH + NaOAc soln. (which liberates C̄ but not salicylic acid) see ⟨2⟩.]

[For prepn. in 75% yield from salicylic ac. (1:0780) by shak. alk. soln. with dimethyl sulfate see ⟨3⟩.]

C̄ on htg. (T 1.33) begins to lose CO_2 at 213–215° ⟨4⟩ and yields CO_2 + anisole (1:7445) — C̄ htd. in s.t. at 130° with HI yields salicylic ac. (1:0780) and CH_3I ⟨5⟩.

C̄ htd. with PCl_5 ⟨6⟩ (every trace of salicylic ac. must first be removed), or warmed ½ hr. with 1½ moles $SOCl_2$ ⟨7⟩ ⟨8⟩ (prolonged htg. tends to demethylate prod.) yields *o*-methoxybenzoyl chloride, b.p. 254°; b.p. $119.6^{\circ}_{1\ mm.}$ ⟨8⟩. [This acid chloride shaken with ignited Na_2CO_3 + pyridine for ½ hr. poured onto ice, recrystd. from $CHCl_3$ yields *o*-methoxybenzoic anhydride, ndls. from lt. pet., m.p. 72.4° ⟨9⟩; this anhydride forms in small amt. during $SOCl_2$ method of preparing acid chloride ⟨10⟩.]

[For identification of C̄ as salt of benzylamine, m.p. 119.8–120.6° u.c., or as salt of α-phenylethylamine, m.p. 155.6–156.0 u.c. see ⟨14⟩.]

Ⓓ ***p*-Bromophenacyl *o*-methoxybenzoate:** m.p. 113° ⟨11⟩ [cf. T 1.391].

Ⓓ ***p*-Phenylphenacyl *o*-methoxybenzoate:** m.p. 131° ⟨12⟩ [cf. T 1.391].

Ⓓ ***o*-Methoxybenzamide:** m.p. 129° [from *o*-methoxybenzoyl chloride + $(NH_4)_2CO_3$ ⟨13⟩].

Ⓓ ***o*-Methoxybenzanilide:** [Beil. XII-501]: m.p. 62° [prepd. indirectly].

1:0685 ⟨1⟩ Smith, White, *J. Phys. Chem.* **33,** 1960, 1972 (1929). ⟨2⟩ Cattelain, *Bull. soc. chim.* (4) **41,** 114–115 (1927). ⟨3⟩ Graebe, *Ann.* **340,** 210 (1905). ⟨4⟩ Gilman, Janney, Bradley, *Iowa State Coll. J. Sci.* **7,** 429–431 (1933); *Chem. Abs.* **28,** 763 (1934). ⟨5⟩ Graebe, *Ann.* **139,** 139 (1866). ⟨6⟩ Ullman, Goldberg, *Ber.* **35,** 2811 (1902). ⟨7⟩ Marsh, Stephen, *J. Chem. Soc.* **127,** 1635 (1925). ⟨8⟩ Thompson, Norris, *J. Am. Chem. Soc.* **58,** 1956 (1936). ⟨9⟩ Rule, Patterson, *J. Chem. Soc.* **125,** 2161 (1924). ⟨10⟩ Billon, *Ann. chim.* (10) **7,** 338–339 (1927).
⟨11⟩ Chen, Shih, *Trans. Science Soc. China* **7,** 81–87 (1932). ⟨12⟩ Drake, Sweeney, *J. Am. Chem. Soc.* **54,** 2060 (1932). ⟨13⟩ Pinnow, Müller, *Ber.* **28,** 158 (1895). ⟨14⟩ Buehler, Carson, Edds, *J. Am. Chem. Soc.* **57,** 2181–2182 (1935).

1:0690 *o*-TOLUIC ACID (*o*-Methylbenzoic acid) —COOH, CH_3 $C_8H_8O_2$ **Beil. IX-462**

M.P. 104° **Neut. Eq. 136**
B.P. 259°_{751}

Ndls.; dif. sol. cold aq.; fairly eas. sol. hot aq.; very eas. sol. cold alc. [For prepn. in 80–89% yield via hydrolysis of *o*-tolunitrile see ⟨1⟩; in 50% yield via CO_2 on *o*-tolyl Mg-iodide see ⟨2⟩.]

C̄ with CrO_3 + H_2SO_4 is completely oxidized to CO_2 + H_2O; C̄ with 5% $KMnO_4$ at 60° yields phthalic ac. ⟨3⟩; C̄ boiled (not too long!) with HNO_3 (1 pt. conc. HNO_3 + 2 pts. H_2O) also yields ⟨4⟩ phthalic ac. (1:0820).

C̄ with PCl_5 ⟨5⟩ or PCl_5 in $CHCl_3$ ⟨6⟩, or with PCl_3 at 110° ⟨7⟩, or with $SOCl_2$ ⟨8⟩ gives *o*-toluyl chloride, b.p. 212°; 75.6° at 5.5 mm. ⟨8⟩.

C̄ refluxed 2–3 hrs. with 5 pts. Ac_2O gives (60% yield ⟨17⟩) *o*-toluic anhydride, ndls. from cold alc. soln. on addn. of aq., m.p. 38–39°.

C̄ dislvd. in 3 pts. conc. H_2SO_4 by warming, then treated dropwise with 2 pts. fumg. HNO_3 at 100–110°, stood 24 hrs. poured onto ice, yields 3,5-dinitro-2-methylbenzoic acid [Beil. IX-474], cryst. from aq., m.p. 205–206° ⟨16⟩. [For use in ident. of amines see ⟨16⟩.]

Ⓓ ***p*-Nitrobenzyl *o*-toluate:** m.p. 90.7° ⟨9⟩ [cf. T 1.39].

Ⓓ **Phenacyl *o*-toluate:** m.p. 74.5° ⟨10⟩ [cf. T 1.391].

Ⓓ ***p*-Bromophenacyl *o*-toluate:** m.p. 56.9° ⟨11⟩ [cf. T 1.391].

Ⓓ ***p*-Phenylphenacyl *o*-toluate:** m.p. 94.5° ⟨12⟩ [cf. T 1.391].

Ⓓ ***o*-Toluamide:** m.p. 142.8° cor. ⟨13⟩; 141–141.5° ⟨14⟩. [For prepn. from *o*-tolunitrile with NaOH + H_2O_2 see ⟨14⟩.]

Ⓓ ***o*-Toluanilide** [Beil. XII-276]: m.p. 125° [prepd. indirectly].

Ⓓ ***o*-Tolu-*p*-toluidide** [Beil. XII-929]: m.p. 144° [prepd. indirectly].

Ⓓ ***S*-Benzylthiuronium *o*-toluate:** m.p. 140° cor. ⟨15⟩; 145–146° ⟨18⟩.

1:0690 ⟨1⟩ Clarke, Taylor, *Organic Syntheses* **11,** 96–97 (1931). ⟨2⟩ Lucas, Kennedy, Wilmot, *J. Am. Chem. Soc.* **58,** 159 (1936). ⟨3⟩ Claus, Pieszcek, *Ber.* **19,** 3085 (1886). ⟨4⟩ Piccard, *Ber.* **12,** 579 (1879). ⟨5⟩ Tanner, Lasselle, *J. Am. Chem. Soc.* **48,** 2164 (1926). ⟨6⟩ Klages, Lickroth, *Ber.* **32,** 1561 (1899). ⟨7⟩ Frankland, Wharton, *J. Chem. Soc.* **69,** 1311 (1896). ⟨8⟩ Thompson, Norris, *J. Am. Chem. Soc.* **58,** 1955 (1936). ⟨9⟩ Reid, *J. Am. Chem. Soc.* **39,** 132 (1917). ⟨10⟩ Chen, *Trans. Science Soc. China* **7,** 73–80 (1931).

⟨11⟩ Judefind, Reid, *J. Am. Chem. Soc.* **42,** 1055 (1920). ⟨12⟩ Drake, Bronitsky, *J. Am. Chem. Soc.* **52,** 3719 (1930). ⟨13⟩ Reid, *Am. Chem. J.* **21,** 290 (1899). ⟨14⟩ Noller, *Organic Syntheses* **13,** 94–95 (1933). ⟨15⟩ Donleavy, *J. Am. Chem. Soc.* **58,** 1005 (1936). ⟨16⟩ Sah, Tien, *J. Chinese Chem. Soc.* **4,** 491 (1936); *Chem. Abs.* **31,** 3823 (1937). ⟨17⟩ Autenrieth, Thomae, *Ber.* **57,** 431 (1934). ⟨18⟩ Veibel, Ottung, *Bull. soc. chim.* (5) **6,** 1435 (1939).

1:0695 AZELAIC ACID HOOC.$(CH_2)_7$.COOH $C_9H_{16}O_4$ Beil. II-707

(Heptane-1,7-dicarboxylic acid)

M.P. 106° **Neut. Eq. 94**

B.P. above 360° sl. dec.

Lfts. or flattened ndls. — Not volatile with steam — 100 pts. aq. at 15° dis. 0.2 g. C̄; at 55° 1.65 pts. C̄ — 100 pts. ether at 15° dis. 2.7 pts. C̄ — Very eas. sol. alc. [for sepn. of C̄ from suberic ac. (1:0755) via spar. soly. of latter in mixt. of C_6H_6 + abs. alc. see ⟨1⟩].

[For prepn. in 32–36% yield by alk. $KMnO_4$ oxidn. of crude ricinoleic ac. (from saponif. of castor oil) see ⟨2⟩; in 35% yield by oxidn. of oleic ac. with H_2O_2 in AcOH, followed by $Na_2Cr_2O_7$ + H_2SO_4 see ⟨3⟩.]

C̄ with PCl_5 ⟨4⟩ or 2 moles $SOCl_2$ ⟨5⟩ yields azelayl chloride, b.p. 166°_{18} ⟨5⟩, 165°_{13} ⟨4⟩.

C̄, refluxed with 3 pts. Ac_2O for 4–6 hrs., excess reagt. removed under reduced press. (aq. pump), residue dislvd. in hot dry C_6H_6, filtered, and pptd. by addn. of pet. ether, yields linear polymeric azelaic α-anhydride, white microcrystn. pdr., m.p. 53–53.5° ⟨6⟩.

Ⓓ **Di-(*p*-nitrobenzyl) azelate:** m.p. 43.8° ⟨7⟩ [cf. T 1.39].

Ⓓ **Di-(phenacyl) azelate:** m.p. 69.7° ⟨8⟩ [cf. T 1.391].

Ⓓ **Di-(*p*-bromophenacyl) azelate:** m.p. 130.6° ⟨8⟩ [cf. T 1.391].

Ⓓ **Di-(*p*-phenylphenacyl) azelate:** m.p. 141° ⟨9⟩ [cf. T 1.391].

Ⓓ **Azelaic diamide:** m.p. 172° ⟨10⟩. [The half amide (azelamic acid) has m.p. 93–95° ⟨10⟩.]

Ⓓ **Azelaic dianilide** [Beil. XII-303]: cryst. from xylene, m.p. 186–187° ⟨6⟩; 184° ⟨11⟩ [from linear polymeric azelaic α-anhydride (above) on triturating with $2\frac{1}{2}$–5 pts. aniline, together with monoanilide (azelanilic acid). After removal of excess aniline with 10% HCl, the monoanilide + any C̄ is dislvd. in dil. aq. alk. leaving the dianilide. Acidification of the alk. soln. ppts. monoanilide + C̄ which are sepd. via boiling aq. ⟨6⟩.] [Azelaic monoanilide: cryst. from dil. alc.; m.p. 107–108° ⟨6⟩.]

Ⓓ **Azelaic di-*p*-toluidide:** m.p. 201–202° ⟨12⟩; 198° ⟨11⟩.

Ⓓ **Di-(*S*-benzylthiuronium) azelate:** m.p. 163–164° ⟨13⟩.

1:0695 ⟨1⟩ Day, Kön, Stevenson, *J. Chem. Soc.* **117,** 642 (1920). ⟨2⟩ Hill, McEwen, *Organic Syntheses* **13,** 4–6 (1933). ⟨3⟩ Bennett, Gudgeon, *J. Chem. Soc.* **1938,** 1679. ⟨4⟩ Etaix, *Ann. chim.* (7) **9,** 397–398 (1896). ⟨5⟩ Blaise, Koehler, *Bull. soc. chim.* (4) **5,** 692 (1909). ⟨6⟩ Hill, Carothers, *J. Am. Chem. Soc.* **55,** 5027–5028 (1933). ⟨7⟩ Kelly, Segura, *J. Am. Chem. Soc.* **56,** 2497 (1934). ⟨8⟩ Kelly, Kleff, *J. Am. Chem. Soc.* **54,** 4444 (1932). ⟨9⟩ Drake, Sweeney, *J. Am. Chem. Soc.* **54,** 2060 (1932). ⟨10⟩ Ref. 4, pages 402–403.

⟨11⟩ Barnicoat, *J. Chem. Soc.* **1927,** 2927–2928. ⟨12⟩ Spies, *J. Org. Chem.* **2,** 66 (1937). ⟨13⟩ Veibel, Ottung, *Bull. soc. chim.* (5) **6,** 1434–1435 (1939).

1:0700 DEHYDROACETIC ACID $C_8H_8O_4$ **Beil. XVII-559**

```
              O
              ‖
              C     H
            /   \  /
         HC       C—CO.CH3
         ‖        |
   CH3—C          C=O
           \    /
              O
```

M.P. 109° **Neut. Eq. 168**
B.P. 270°

White cryst. by distn. or by recrystn. from aq., alc. or C_6H_6 — Sol. in 100 pts. aq. at 6°; eas. sol. hot aq.; spar. sol. cold alc., eas. sol. hot alc.; sol. ether. C̄ is somewhat volat. with steam and by water is sl. decd. to CO_2 and 2,6-dimethylpyrone (loss in evapn. of aq. soln.).

[For prepn. in 60–65% yield by refluxing ethyl acetoacetate (1:1710) with a trace of $NaHCO_3$ see ⟨1⟩; 53% yield ⟨9⟩.]

Alk. solns. of C̄ are pale yel. — C̄ in aq. soln. gives with 1 drop $FeCl_3$ soln. yel. or yel.-or. ppt.

C̄, boiled with 3 pts. conc. HCl in a spacious flask until foaming ceases and alm. complete soln. has occurred, then poured out in evapg. dish and evapd. to dryness yields hydrochloride of 2,6-dimethylpyrone, recrystn. of which from pyridine gives (60% yield ⟨1⟩) 2,6-dimethyl-

```
              O
              ‖
              C
            /   \
pyrone   HC       CH
         ‖        ‖
   CH3—C          C—CH3
           \    /
              O
```

[Beil. XVII-291]; m.p. 132°, b.p. 249°; exceedingly sol. aq., alc.; sol. ether but not volatile with st. [cf. ⟨2⟩].

C̄ htd. for a short time with 3 pts. 90% H_2SO_4 to 135°, poured into 4 pts. aq. soon yields

```
                               O
                               ‖
                               C
                             /   \
cryst. of 6-methylpyronone  H—C       C=H2
                              ‖        |
                        CH3—C          C=O
                               \    /
                                  O
```

[Beil. XVII-442]; ndls. from aq., m.p. 188–189° cor. ⟨1⟩ ⟨3⟩.

C̄ warmed with excess aniline, and latter cautiously removed with dil. HCl yields dehydracetic acid monanil [Beil. XVII-564]; ndls. m.p. 115° ⟨5⟩. C̄ in warm alc. soln., treated with excess phenylhydrazine, yields dehydracetic acid monophenylhydrazone [Beil. XVII-564], yel. tbls. from alc. or C_6H_6; m.p. 207° rap. htg. ⟨6⟩, 202° ⟨7⟩ — C̄ in AcOH treated with conc. aq. soln. of semicarbazide.HCl + NaOAc yields dehydracetic ac. monosemicarbazone [Beil. XVII-565], ndls. from aq. m.p. 197–198° ⟨8⟩.

1:0700 ⟨1⟩ Arndt, Eistert, Scholz, Aron, *Ber.* **69,** 2379 (1936). ⟨2⟩ Collie, *J. Chem. Soc.* **59,** 619 (1891). ⟨3⟩ Ref. 2, page 609. ⟨4⟩ Collie, Hilditch, *J. Chem. Soc.* **91,** 787 (1907). ⟨5⟩ Oppenheim, Precht, *Ber.* **9,** 1100 (1876). ⟨6⟩ Perkin, *J. Chem. Soc.* **51,** 494–495 (1887). ⟨7⟩ Bülow, Filchner, *Ber.* **41,** 4166 (1908). ⟨8⟩ Ref. 7, page 4168. ⟨9⟩ Arndt, *Organic Syntheses* **20,** 26–29 (1940).

1:0703 ***m*-METHOXYBENZOIC ACID** (*m*-Anisic acid) —COOH, OCH$_3$ $C_8H_8O_3$ **Beil. X-137**

M.P. 109-110° ⟨1⟩

Ndls. from aq.; dist. undecomposed at ord. press. [For prepn. in 90% yield by oxidn. of *m*-methoxybenzaldehyde (1:0232) with aq. $KMnO_4$ see ⟨1⟩.] [For m.p. + compn. data for mixts. of C̄ with *p*-methoxybenzoic acid (1:0805) see ⟨5⟩.]

C̄ with PCl_5 ⟨2⟩ or $SOCl_2$ ⟨3⟩ yields *m*-methoxybenzoyl chloride, b.p. $242–243^{\circ}_{733}$ ⟨2⟩, b.p. $110.9^{\circ}_{8.5}$ ⟨3⟩.

[For identification of C̄ as salt with benzylamine, m.p. 111.8–112.8° u.c., or with α-phenylethylamine, m.p. 128.6–129.0° u.c. see ⟨4⟩.]

1:0703 ⟨1⟩ Chakravarti, Perkin, *J. Chem. Soc.* **1929,** 198–199. ⟨2⟩ Ullman, Goldberg, *Ber.* **35,** 2813 (1902). ⟨3⟩ Thompson, Norris, *J. Am. Chem. Soc.* **58,** 1956 (1936). ⟨4⟩ Buehler, Carson, Edds, *J. Am. Chem. Soc.* **57,** 2181–2182 (1935). ⟨5⟩ Lea, Robinson, *J. Chem. Soc.* **1926,** 2355.

1:0705 ***m*-TOLUIC ACID** (*m*-Methylbenzoic acid) —COOH, CH$_3$ $C_8H_8O_2$ **Beil. IX-475**

M.P. 110-111° **Neut. Eq. 136**
B.P. 263°

Cryst. from aq.; sol. at 15° in 1170 pts., and at 100° in 60 pts. aq.; eas. sol. alc. or ether — Eas. volatile with steam — Sublimes.

C̄ on oxidn. with CrO_3 (cf. T 1.72) yields isophthalic ac. (1:0900).

C̄ with PCl_5 ⟨1⟩, or PCl_5 in $CHCl_3$ ⟨2⟩, or with PCl_3 ⟨3⟩ or with $SOCl_2$ ⟨4⟩ ⟨5⟩ (cf. T 1.37) yields *m*-toluyl chloride, b.p. 219°_{770}; b.p. 71.2° at 4 mm. ⟨5⟩.

C̄ refluxed 2–3 hrs. with 5 pts. Ac_2O gives (60% yield ⟨6⟩) *o*-toluic anhydride, ndls. from pet. ether, m.p. 70–71° ⟨6⟩.

- Ⓓ ***p*-Nitrobenzyl *m*-toluate:** m.p. 86.6° ⟨7⟩ [cf. T 1.39].
- Ⓓ ***p*-Bromophenacyl *m*-toluate:** m.p. 108.0° ⟨8⟩ [cf. T 1.391].
- Ⓓ ***p*-Phenylphenacyl *m*-toluate:** m.p. 136.5° ⟨9⟩ [cf. T 1.391].
- Ⓓ ***m*-Toluamide:** m.p. 94° [from *m*-toluyl chloride ⟨10⟩ or from anhydride ⟨11⟩].
- Ⓓ ***m*-Toluanilide:** m.p. 126° [from *m*-toluyl chloride ⟨4⟩].
- Ⓓ ***m*-Tolu-*p*-toluidide:** m.p. 118°.
- Ⓓ ***S*-Benzylthiuronium *m*-toluate:** m.p. 164° ⟨12⟩.

1:0705 ⟨1⟩ Ador, Rilliet, *Ber.* **12,** 2301 (1879). ⟨2⟩ Klages, Lickroth, *Ber.* **32,** 1560 (1899). ⟨3⟩ Frankland, Wharton, *J. Chem. Soc.* **69,** 1311 (1896). ⟨4⟩ Shoppee, *J. Chem. Soc.* **1932,** 700. ⟨5⟩ Thompson, Norris, *J. Am. Chem. Soc.* **58,** 1955 (1936). ⟨6⟩ Autenrieth, Thomae, *Ber.* **57,** 431 (1924). ⟨7⟩ Lyman, Reid, *J. Am. Chem. Soc.* **39,** 703–704 (1917). ⟨8⟩ Judefind, Reid, *J. Am. Chem. Soc.* **42,** 1055 (1920). ⟨9⟩ Drake, Bronitsky, *J. Am. Chem. Soc.* **52,** 3719 (1930). ⟨10⟩ Remsen, Reid, *Am. Chem. J.* **21,** 289–290 (1899). ⟨11⟩ Ref. 6, page 436. ⟨12⟩ Donleavy, *J. Am. Chem. Soc.* **58,** 1005 (1936).

1:0710 **SUCCINIC ANHYDRIDE** $C_4H_4O_3$ **Beil. XVII-407**

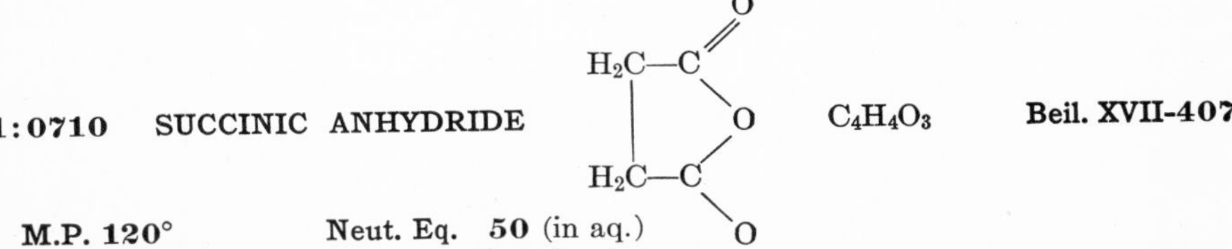

M.P. 120° **Neut. Eq. 50** (in aq.)
B.P. 261° **100** (in alc.)

White cryst. from $CHCl_3$; dif. sol. ether. [For prepn. in 82–96% yield from succinic ac. (1:0530) + $POCl_3$ see ⟨1⟩.]

[For behavior on titration in Generic Test 3, see Generic Test 3, Note 7 of " Manual."] [For quant. detn. via titration with $NaOCH_3$ see ⟨2⟩.]

C̄ on warming with aq. readily hydrolyzes yielding succinic acid (1:0530), q.v. — C̄ on warming with excess MeOH and distg. off excess yields quant. ⟨3⟩ methyl hydrogen succinate, white pl. from MeOH, m.p. 58°, Neut. Eq. 132 — C̄, on soln. in excess conc. aq. NH_4OH, gives soln. of NH_4 succinamate from which (after boiling off excess NH_4OH) $AgNO_3$ ppts. Ag succinamate ⟨4⟩. [For isolation of succinamic ac. via H_2S treatment see ⟨6⟩.]

Ⓓ **Saponification:** Hydrolysis with aq. alk. (T 1.51) gives Sap. Eq. 50 and yields soln. from which addn. of mineral acid ppts. succinic acid (1:0530), q.v.

Ⓓ **Succinanilic acid:** from C̄ + equiv. aniline mixed in hot $CHCl_3$; the pptg. acid is separated and recrystd. from dil. alc.; m.p. 148.5° ⟨5⟩.

1:0710 ⟨1⟩ Shriner, Struck, *Organic Syntheses* **12,** 66–67 (1932). ⟨2⟩ Smith, Bryant, *J. Am. Chem. Soc.* **58,** 2543 (1936). ⟨3⟩ Bone, Sudborough, Sprankling, *J. Chem. Soc.* **85,** 539 (1904). ⟨4⟩ Hoogewerff, van Dorp, *Rec. trav. chim.* **18,** 361 (Note 1) (1899). ⟨5⟩ von Auwers, Mayer, *Ann.* **309,** 326–327 (1899). ⟨6⟩ Jeffery, Vogel, *J. Chem. Soc.* **1934,** 1103.

1:0715 BENZOIC ACID 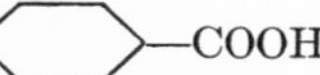—COOH $C_7H_6O_2$ Beil. IX-92

M.P. 121.4° **Neut. Eq. 122**
B.P. 249.2°

Cryst. from hot aq.; sol. in 345 pts. of aq. at 20°, or in 17 pts. at 100° — Sublimes even at 100°; easily volatile with steam — C̄ is sol. in 2.14 pts. abs. alc. at 15°; in 3.19 pts. ether at 15°; very sol. in $CHCl_3$ [dif. and sepn. from phthalic ac. (1:0820), isophthalic ac. (1:0900), and terephthalic ac. (1:0910)]. [For discussion of sepn. of C̄ from these see ⟨1⟩.] — [For table of soly. of metal salts of C̄ see ⟨2⟩.]

C̄ with PCl_5 (70% yield ⟨3⟩), or $PCl_3 + ZnCl_2$ (77% yield ⟨3⟩) or $SOCl_2$ (90% yield ⟨3⟩) gives benzoyl chloride, b.p. 197° — C̄ on reflux. with Ac_2O and subsequent vac. distn. gives (72–74% yield ⟨4⟩) benzoic anhydride (1:0595), m.p. 42° [cf. ⟨5⟩].

Ⓓ ***p*-Nitrobenzyl benzoate:** m.p. 89° ⟨6⟩ [cf. T 1.39].
Ⓓ **Phenacyl benzoate:** m.p. 118.5° ⟨7⟩ [cf. T 1.391].
Ⓓ ***p*-Chlorophenacyl benzoate:** m.p. 118.6° ⟨8⟩ [cf. T 1.391].
Ⓓ ***p*-Bromophenacyl benzoate:** m.p. 119.0° ⟨8⟩ [cf. T 1.391].
Ⓓ ***p*-Iodophenacyl benzoate:** m.p. 126.5° ⟨8⟩ [cf. T 1.391].
Ⓓ ***p*-Phenylphenacyl benzoate:** m.p. 167° ⟨9⟩ [cf. T 1.391].
Ⓓ **Benzamide:** m.p. 130°.
Ⓓ **Benzanilide:** To 0.1 g. C̄ in a dry 6-in. tt. add 0.17–0.20 g. PCl_5 and warm, stirring with glass rod until clear soln. is obtd. Cool, add dropwise with cooling, 1 ml. ice water. Then add slowly 0.4–0.5 ml. pure aniline and shake. Dissolve the reaction prod. in 2–5 ml. boiling 50% alc., cool, filter crystals, and dry at 100°. Pearly white scales, m.p. 160° u.c. ⟨10⟩.
Ⓓ **Benz-*p*-toluidide:** m.p. 158°.
Ⓓ ***S*-Benzylthiuronium benzoate:** m.p. 166° cor. ⟨11⟩; 166.5–167.5° ⟨12⟩.

1:0715 ⟨1⟩ Gilman, Kirby, *J. Am. Chem. Soc.* **54,** 351 (1932). ⟨2⟩ Ephraim, Pfister, *Helv. Chim. Acta* **8,** 369 (1925). ⟨3⟩ Clark, Bell, *Trans. Roy. Soc. Canada* (3) **27,** III, 97–103 (1933). ⟨4⟩ Clarke, Rahrs, *Organic Syntheses, Coll. Vol.* I, 85–87 (1932). ⟨5⟩ Autenrieth, Thomae, *Ber.* **57,** 430–431 (1924). ⟨6⟩ Reid, *J. Am. Chem. Soc.* **39,** 132 (1917). ⟨7⟩ Rather, Reid, *J. Am. Chem. Soc.* **41,** 80 (1919). ⟨8⟩ Judefind, Reid, *J. Am. Chem. Soc.* **42,** 1055 (1920). ⟨9⟩ Drake, Bronitsky, *J. Am. Chem. Soc.* **52,** 3719 (1930). ⟨10⟩ Mulliken, " Method " I,82 (1904).

⟨11⟩ Donleavy, *J. Am. Chem. Soc.* **58,** 1005 (1936). ⟨12⟩ Veibel, Lillelund, *Bull. soc. chim.* (5) **5,** 1157 (1938).

1:0720 ***o*-BENZOYLBENZOIC ACID** (Benzophenone-*o*-carboxylic acid) $C_{14}H_{10}O_3$ **Beil. X-747**

M.P. 127-128° ⟨1⟩ Neut. Eq. 226

Colorless cryst. $\bar{C}$ on recrystn. from aq., dil. alc., or on shaking C_6H_6 soln. with aq. yields monohydrate, $\bar{C}.H_2O$; pr., m.p. 93–94° (1:0670); on htg. above 100° or on distn. with xylene readily loses cryst. aq. yielding $\bar{C}$.

$\bar{C}$ with PCl_5 ⟨2⟩ ⟨3⟩, or PCl_3 ⟨2⟩ ⟨3⟩, or $SOCl_2$ ⟨2⟩ ⟨3⟩ yields a normal *o*-benzoylbenzoyl chloride, m.p. 59–60°. [With MeOH and EtOH this prod. yields normal esters (see below); with phenols there is formed in addition to normal derivatives more or less arylphthalide corresponding to a *pseudo* chloride ⟨4⟩.]

$\bar{C}$ + MeOH esterified by HCl method ⟨5⟩, or $\bar{C}$ in conc. H_2SO_4 treated with MeOH ⟨6⟩, or above *o*-benzoylbenzoyl chloride treated with MeOH ⟨3⟩ yields normal methyl *o*-benzoylbenzoate, m.p. 51–52°. [The *pseudo* methyl ester (3-methoxy-3-phenylphthalide [Beil. XVIII-48] has m.p. 80–81°.]

$\bar{C}$ + EtOH with conc. H_2SO_4 ⟨7⟩, or Ag salt of $\bar{C}$ + C_2H_5I ⟨7⟩, or K salt of $\bar{C}$ + dimethyl sulfate ⟨7⟩ yields normal ethyl *o*-benzoylbenzoate, m.p. 58° ⟨8⟩. [The *pseudo* ethyl ester (3-ethoxy-3-phenylphthalide) [Beil. XVIII_1-(316)] has m.p. 51–53° ⟨7⟩, 56° ⟨8⟩.]

$\bar{C}$, htd. at 100° for 2 hrs. with 10 pts. conc. H_2SO_4, poured into aq. gives quant. yield ⟨9⟩ anthraquinone (1:9095). [For study of this ring closure see ⟨1⟩ ⟨9⟩ ⟨10⟩.]

Salts of $\bar{C}$: alk. salts all sol. aq.; $Hg\bar{A}_2$, $Mg\bar{A}_2$, $Sr\bar{A}_2$, $Ca\bar{A}_2$ also sol. aq.; other heavy metal salts are insol. ⟨11⟩.

Ⓓ ***p*-Nitrobenzyl *o*-benzoylbenzoate:** m.p. 100.4° ⟨12⟩.

Ⓓ ***o*-Benzoylbenzamide:** m.p. 165° cor. (162°). [From normal *o*-benzoylbenzoyl chloride + conc. aq. NH_4OH.]

Ⓓ ***o*-Benzoylbenzanilide:** m.p. 195° ⟨13⟩. [From normal *o*-benzoylbenzoyl chloride + aniline.]

1:0720 ⟨1⟩ Deane, *J. Am. Chem. Soc.* **59**, 850 (1937). ⟨2⟩ Martin, *J. Am. Chem. Soc.* **38**, 1142–1144 (1916). ⟨3⟩ McMullen, *J. Am. Chem. Soc.* **38**, 1228–1230 (1916). ⟨4⟩ Blicke, Swisher, *J. Am. Chem. Soc.* **56**, 902–904 (1934). ⟨5⟩ Haller, Guyot, *Bull. soc. chim.* (3) **25**, 54–55 (1901). ⟨6⟩ Meyer, *Monatsh.* **25**, 477 (1904). ⟨7⟩ Egerer, Meyer, *Monatsh.* **34**, 78 (1913). ⟨8⟩ von Auwers, Heinze, *Ber.* **52**, 599 (1919). ⟨9⟩ Gleason, Dougherty, *J. Am. Chem. Soc.* **51**, 311 (1929). ⟨10⟩ Dougherty, Gleason, *J. Am. Chem. Soc.* **52**, 1024–1027 (1930).
⟨11⟩ Ephraim, *Ber.* **55**, 3482 (1922). ⟨12⟩ Kelly, Segura, *J. Am. Chem. Soc.* **56**, 2497 (1934). ⟨13⟩ Meyer, *Monatsh.* **25**, 1226–1227 (1907).

1:0722 ***d,l*-LACTID** $C_6H_8O_4$ **Beil. XIX-154**

M.P. 128° **Neut. Eq. 144**
B.P. 255°

Cryst. (from alc. or ether) — **For prepn. by htg. lactic acid in vac. see ⟨1⟩ ⟨3⟩ — Reacts with first mole alk. much more rapidly than second: thus Generic Test 3-A gives Neut. Eq. 144, but** Generic Test 5 (with alc. NaOH) gives Sap. Eq. = 73.5.

Very dif. sol. aq. or alc.; eas. sol. in acetone, C_6H_6, lgr. — On long boilg. with aq. or rapidly with alk. hydrolyzes to *d,l*-lactic acid (1:0400) — C̄ htd. at 250–275° rapidly polymerizes, and does so at 140–150° if K_2CO_3 is present ⟨2⟩.

Ⓓ ***d,l*-Lactanilide:** From C̄ on htg. with aniline, cryst. (from aq.), m.p. 58° ⟨4⟩ — Dif. sol. cold aq., very eas. sol. alc., ether, $CHCl_3$.

1:0722 ⟨1⟩ Carothers, Dorough, Van Natta, *J. Am. Chem. Soc.* **54,** 772 (1932). ⟨2⟩ Ref. 1, page 764. ⟨3⟩ Dietzel, Krug, *Ber.* **58,** 1313 (1925). ⟨4⟩ Bischoff, Walden, *Ann.* **279,** 73 (1894).

1:0725 PHTHALIC ANHYDRIDE $C_8H_4O_3$ **Beil. XVII-469**

F.P. 131.6° ⟨1⟩
B.P. 295.1° ⟨1⟩

The m.p. of C̄ taken in cap. tubes may be as much as 0.5° higher than the freezing point of large samples (above) ⟨2⟩ — The eutectic of C̄ with phthalic acid (1:0820) conts. 2% of latter and melts 129.74° ⟨3⟩.

C̄ sublimes readily in beautiful long white ndls. or may be purified (from the acid) by recrystn. from CCl_4 in which its soly. at b.p. of CCl_4 is 2.5% ⟨4⟩ — C̄ is alm. insol. in cold aq. ⟨5⟩ but on warming with aq. hydrolyzes to phthalic ac. (1:0820).

[For detn. of C̄ in phthalic ac. see ⟨6⟩; for detn. of C̄ via titration with $NaOCH_3$ see ⟨7⟩.]

Ⓟ **Fluorescein formation:** Mix a few mg. C̄ with eq. wt. of resorcinol, barely moisten with conc. H_2SO_4 and heat at 160° for 3 min. Cool, add 2 ml. cold aq., then 1–2 ml. 10% NaOH. Stir to dissolve solid, dil. with eq. vol. aq. and filter ⟨8⟩. Phthalic anhydride gives characteristic powerful green fluorescence of fluorescein — [If distinction from other anhydrides, e.g., succinic anhydride, is required, addn. of H_2SO_4 is omitted and temp. raised to 205–210°, under which conditions interference is avoided ⟨9⟩.]

Ⓓ **Methyl hydrogen phthalate:** from C̄ with dry MeOH for 30 min.; ndls. from C_6H_6 m.p. 82–82.5° ⟨10⟩, 82.4–82.7° cor. ⟨11⟩; Neut. Eq. 180. [The *p*-nitrobenzyl ester (cf. T 1.39) of this methyl hydrogen phthalate has m.p. 105.7° ⟨12⟩.] [For m.p.'s of alkyl hydrogen phthalates of *n*-primary alcs. see ⟨11⟩.]

Ⓓ **Phthalamic acid (phthalic acid monamide):** from C̄ on soln. in 1½ pts. warm conc. NH_4OH; the NH_4 phthalamate seps. in fine white ndls. (94% yield after cooling); on treating their conc. aq. soln. with conc. HCl, free acid separates (81% yield) and may be washed free of NH_4Cl with cold aq., m.p. 148–149° ⟨13⟩. [On fusion the phthalamic acid loses aq., resolidifies at 155° owing to conversion to phthalimide, and this on further htg. melts 231° ⟨13⟩.]

Ⓓ **Phthalanilic acid (phthalic acid mono-anilide)** [Beil. XII-311]: from C̄ + 0.5 mole aniline in $CHCl_3$ at room temp. ⟨14⟩; ndls. from alc., m.p. 169–170°. [On melting this prod. it loses aq. and is converted to phthalanil, m.p. 207° ⟨14⟩.] [Phthalanilic ac. is insol. in $CHCl_3$, while phthalanil is extremely soluble (use in sepn. ⟨14⟩).]

Ⓓ **Phthalanil** [Beil. XXI-464]: from C̄ on fusion with aniline at 250°; after washing with alc., soln. in $CHCl_3$ and pptn. by addn. of alc. forms white ndls., m.p. 207° ⟨14⟩ [cf. also phthalic ac. (1:0820)].

Ⓓ **Phthalic acid mono-*p*-toluidide** [Beil. XII-939]: white flakes from 40% alc., m.p. 160° ⟨15⟩.

Ⓓ ***N*-*p*-tolylphthalimide** [Beil. XXI-466]: m.p. 204°.

1:0725 ⟨1⟩ Marti, *Bull. soc. chim. Belg.* **39,** 621 (1930). ⟨2⟩ Bebie, *Ind. Eng. Chem.* **13,** 91–92 (1921). ⟨3⟩ Monroe, *Ind. Eng. Chem.* **11,** 1118 (1919). ⟨4⟩ Lombaers, *Bull. soc. chim. Belg.* **33,** 232 (1924). ⟨5⟩ van de Stadt, *Z. physik. Chem.* **41,** 361–364 (1902). ⟨6⟩ Downs, Stupp, *Ind. Eng. Chem.* **10,** 596–598 (1918). ⟨7⟩ Bryant, Smith, *J. Am. Chem. Soc.* **58,** 2453 (1936). ⟨8⟩ Mulliken, "Method" I, 61 (1904). ⟨9⟩ Holde, Bleyburg, Aziz, *Z. angew. Chem.* **42,** 283–284 (1929). ⟨10⟩ Underwood, Barker, *J. Am. Chem. Soc.* **52,** 4085 (1930).

⟨11⟩ Goggans, Copenhaver, *J. Am. Chem. Soc.* **61,** 2909 (1939). ⟨12⟩ Reid, *J. Am. Chem. Soc.* **39,** 1250–1251 (1917). ⟨13⟩ Chapman, Stephen, *J. Chem. Soc.* **127,** 1793 (1925). ⟨14⟩ Sherrill, Schaeffer, Shoyer, *J. Am. Chem. Soc.* **50,** 477 (1928). ⟨15⟩ Tingle, Rolker, *J. Am. Chem. Soc.* **30,** 1888 (1908).

1:0728 α-NAPHTHYLACETIC ACID $C_{12}H_{10}O_2$ Beil. IX-666

(1-Naphthaleneacetic acid) [naphthalene ring]—$CH_2.COOH$

M.P. 131° **Neut. Eq. 186**
(135.0-135.5° ⟨1⟩)

Ndls. from aq. — Spar. sol. cold aq., eas. sol. hot aq., alc., ether, AcOH, C_6H_6. [For review of methods of prepn. see ⟨2⟩.]

C̄ treated with PCl_5 ⟨3⟩ or with $SOCl_2$ alone ⟨7⟩ or in C_6H_6 ⟨4⟩ gives α-naphthylacetyl chloride, b.p. 174°_{15} ⟨7⟩.

C̄ htd. with CaO yields CO_2 as $CaCO_3$ + 1-methylnaphthalene (1:7600), b.p. 241° in good yield ⟨5⟩.

Ⓓ **α-Naphthylacetamide:** from α-naphthylacetyl chloride + $(NH_4)_2CO_3$; cryst. from boilg. alc.; m.p. 180–181° ⟨3⟩ ⟨6⟩ ⟨4⟩.

Ⓓ **α-Naphthylacetanilide:** from α-naphthylacetyl chloride + aniline; cryst. from alc., m.p. 155° ⟨4⟩, 156° ⟨6⟩, 159.5° ⟨1⟩.

1:0728 ⟨1⟩ Olivier, Wit, *Rec. trav. chim.* **56,** 857 (1937). ⟨2⟩ Cambron, *Can. J. Research* **17-B,** 10–13 (1939). ⟨3⟩ Boessneck, *Ber.* **16,** 641 (1883). ⟨4⟩ Gilman, Kirby, *J. Am. Chem. Soc.* **51,** 3477, especially Note 18 (1929). ⟨5⟩ Boessneck, *Ber.* **16,** 1547 (1883). ⟨6⟩ Higginbottom, Short, *Rec. trav. chim.* **53,** 1141 (1934). ⟨7⟩ Cook, Hewett, *J. Chem. Soc.* **1933,** 1106.

1:0730 SEBACIC ACID $HOOC.(CH_2)_8.COOH$ $C_{10}H_{18}O_4$ Beil. II-718

(Octane-1,8-dicarboxylic acid)

M.P. 133°

Thin lfts.; sol. in 1000 pts. aq. at 17°, or in 50 pts. at 100°; eas. sol. alc. or ether.

C̄ is stable to CrO_3 oxidn. but $KMnO_4$ or dil. HNO_3 yields succinic ac. (1:0530), adipic ac. (1:0775) and glutaric ac. (1:0440).

C̄ with PCl_5 ⟨1⟩ ⟨2⟩, or PCl_3 ⟨3⟩, or $SOCl_2$ (84–86% yield) ⟨4⟩ ⟨5⟩ (cf. T 1.37) gives sebacyl (di)chloride, b.p. $155–156^{\circ}_{8}$ ⟨4⟩.

C̄, refluxed 5 hrs. with 3 pts. Ac_2O, excess reagt. and resultant AcOH distd. off under reduced press. ⟨6⟩ yields a linear polymeric sebacic α-anhydride, $CH_3.CO[O.CO.(CH_2)_8.CO]_xO.COCH_3$, sol. in C_6H_6 from which it is pptd. by addn. of pet. ether; m.p. varies, but a typical specimen showed m.p. 79–80° ⟨7⟩. It reacts with aq. to yield C̄ + acetic ac. [When this α-anhydride is htd. under ord. conditions no smooth depolymerization occurs, but in molecular still at least three other polymeric anhydrides are formed; viz. β-anhydride, m.p. 68°, γ-anhydride and an ω-anyhdride ⟨8⟩.]

Ⓓ **Di-(*p*-nitrobenzyl) sebacate:** m.p. 72.6° ⟨9⟩ [cf. T 1.39].
Ⓓ **Di-(phenacyl) sebacate:** m.p. 80.4° ⟨10⟩ [cf. T 1.391].
Ⓓ **Di-(*p*-bromophenacyl) sebacate:** m.p. 147.0° ⟨11⟩ [cf. T 1.391].
Ⓓ **Di- *p*-phenylphenacyl) sebacate:** m.p. 140° ⟨12⟩ [cf. T 1.391].
Ⓓ **Sebacic diamide:** m.p. 210° ⟨13⟩; 208° ⟨14⟩ [from sebacyl chloride + conc. NH_4OH ⟨14⟩]. [The monoamide (sebacamic ac.) has m.p. 126.5° ⟨15⟩.]
Ⓓ **Sebacic dianilide:** m.p. 201–202° ⟨16⟩; 200° ⟨17⟩. [The monoanilide (sebacanilic ac.) has m.p. 122–123° ⟨16⟩, 121–122° ⟨18⟩.]
Ⓓ **Sebacic di-*p*-toluidide:** m.p. 201° ⟨17⟩.
Ⓓ **Piperazonium hydrogen sebacate:** from C̄ + ½ mole piperazine hexahydrate (82% yield); cryst. from aq., m.p. 166–168° dec.; Neut. Eq. 284 ⟨19⟩.

1:0730 ⟨1⟩ von Auwers, Schmidt, *Ber.* **46**, 480 (1913). ⟨2⟩ Auger, *Ann. chim.* (6) **22**, 361–362 (1891). ⟨3⟩ Borsche, Wolleman, *Ber.* **44**, 3185 (1911). ⟨4⟩ Fordyce, Johnson, *J. Am. Chem. Soc.* **55**, 3369 (1933). ⟨5⟩ Waser, *Helv. Chim. Acta* **8**, 124 (1925). ⟨6⟩ Hill, *J. Am. Chem. Soc.* **54**, 4105–4106 (1932). ⟨7⟩ Hill, Carothers, *J. Am. Chem. Soc.* **54**, 1570 (1932). ⟨8⟩ Ref. 7, pages 1574–1576. ⟨9⟩ Lyman, Reid, *J. Am. Chem. Soc.* **39**, 708 (1917). ⟨10⟩ Kelly, Kleff, *J. Am. Chem. Soc.* **54**, 4444 (1932).

⟨11⟩ Judefind, Reid, *J. Am. Chem. Soc.* **42**, 1055 (1920). ⟨12⟩ Drake, Sweeney, *J. Am. Chem. Soc.* **54**, 2060 (1932). ⟨13⟩ Meyer, *Monatsh.* **22**, 421 (1901). ⟨14⟩ Phookan, Krafft, *Ber.* **25**, 2252 (1892). ⟨15⟩ Flaschenträger, *Z. physiol. Chem.* **159**, 301, 305–307 (1926). ⟨16⟩ Ref. 7, pages 1575–1576. ⟨17⟩ Barnicoat, *J. Chem. Soc.* **1927**, 2927–2928. ⟨18⟩ Morgan, Walton, *J. Chem. Soc.* **1936**, 905. ⟨19⟩ Pollard, Adelson, Bain, *J. Am. Chem. Soc.* **56**, 1759 (1934).

1:0735 CINNAMIC ACID

C_6H_5—CH=HC.COOH $C_9H_8O_2$ **Beil. IX-572**

M.P. 133° **Neut. Eq. 148**
B.P. 300°

Lfts. from alc. — Sol. at 17° in 3500 pts. aq.; much more sol. in hot aq. — Sol. at 20° in 4.3 pts. alc.; eas. sol. ether; sol. at 15° in 16.8 pts. $CHCl_3$; spar. sol. CS_2; insol. pet. ether.

C̄ on long exposure to sunlight (e.g. 23 days) is largely dimerized to α-truxillic ac., m.p. 274° [Beil. IX-518] cf. ⟨1⟩ — C̄ on rapid htg. at b.p. decomposes into CO_2 and styrene (1:7435). [Use in prepn. of latter ⟨2⟩.]

C̄ in alk. soln. reduces $KMnO_4$ (T 1.34) — C̄ (0.05 g.) stirred into 3 ml. cold 10% $KMnO_4$ on watch glass gives odor of benzaldehyde — C̄ in dil. aq. soln. boiled with 1 drop $FeCl_3$, and 1 drop H_2O_2 soln. added also gives BzH odor on shaking.

C̄ in CS_2 ⟨3⟩ or in ether ⟨4⟩ adds Br_2 (cf. T 1.91) yielding cinnamic acid dibromide (α,β-dibromo-β-phenylpropionic acid) [Beil. IX-518], m.p. 203–204° ⟨5⟩; 197° rap. htg. ⟨6⟩ ⟨7⟩. [The reaction is very incomplete in the dark but pract. quant. in light ⟨5⟩.] [For studies in other solvents see, e.g., AcOH ⟨8⟩, $CHCl_3$ ⟨9⟩.]

C̄ with PCl_5 ⟨10⟩ (86% yield ⟨11⟩), or PCl_3 ⟨12⟩, or PCl_3 + $ZnCl_2$ (86% yield ⟨11⟩), or $SOCl_2$ ⟨13⟩ (98% yield ⟨11⟩) gives cinnamoyl chloride, b.p. 251–253° sl. dec., m.p. 35–36°.

Ⓓ ***p*-Nitrocinnamic acid:** Stir 0.1 g. C̄ into 3 ml. fumg. HNO_3 (D = 1.48–1.60) contd. in small glass evap. dish. Subst. first dis., then sep.; allowed to stand 10 min. After addn. of 30 ml. cold water filter off bulky ppt. of nitro acids with suction and wash with 10 ml. cold aq. Transfer to tt., dis. in 5 ml. strong alc., cool and shake to start crystn. After standing, filter, wash with 5 ml. cold alc. Transfer to tt. and boil with 5 ml.

ether, cool, shake, filter off scanty ppt. and wash with cold ether. Dry at 100°. Almost white cryst. darkening and softening at 265–270°, then meltg. 286–287° dec. ⟨14⟩. [As a result of oxidn. by the reagt. *p*-nitrobenzoic ac., m.p. 240°, may also be formed.]

Ⓓ ***p*-Nitrobenzyl cinnamate:** m.p. 116.8° ⟨15⟩ [cf. T 1.39].
Ⓓ **Phenacyl cinnamate:** m.p. 140.5° ⟨16⟩ [cf. T 1.391].
Ⓓ ***p*-Bromophenacyl cinnamate:** m.p. 145.6° ⟨17⟩ [cf. T 1.391].
Ⓓ ***p*-Phenylphenacyl cinnamate:** m.p. 182.5° ⟨18⟩ [cf. T 1.391].
Ⓓ **Cinnamamide:** m.p. 147–148° [from cinnamoyl chloride + conc. aq. NH_4OH].
Ⓓ **Cinnamanilide** [Beil. XII-279]: m.p. 151°.
Ⓓ **Cinnamo-*p*-toluidide** [Beil. XII-929]: m.p. 168°.
Ⓓ ***S*-Benzylthiuronium cinnamate:** m.p. 175° cor. ⟨19⟩; 178–179° ⟨20⟩.

1:0735 ⟨1⟩ Stobbe, Steinberger, *Ber.* **55,** 2230, 2244 (1922). ⟨2⟩ Abbott, Johnson, *Organic Syntheses, Coll Vol.* I, 430–432 (1932). ⟨3⟩ Michael, *Ber.* **34,** 3664 (1901). ⟨4⟩ Michael, *J. prakt. Chem.* (2) **52,** 292 (1895). ⟨5⟩ Duquesnois, *Bull. soc. chim.* (5) **4,** 197–198 (1937). ⟨6⟩ Hunter, Sorenson, *J. Am. Chem. Soc.* **54,** 3367 (1932). ⟨7⟩ Sudborough, Thompson, *J. Chem. Soc.* **83,** 670 (1903). ⟨8⟩ Williams, *J. Chem. Soc.* **1932,** 979–984. ⟨9⟩ Meyer, Pickall, *Z. physik. Chem.* **A-145,** 360–392 (1929). ⟨10⟩ Claisen, Antweiler, *Ber.* **13,** 2124 (1880). ⟨11⟩ Clark, Bell, *Trans. Roy. Soc. Canada* (3) **27,** III, 97–103 (1933). ⟨12⟩ Liebermann, *Ber.* **21,** 3372 (1888). ⟨13⟩ Meyer, *Monatsh.* **22,** 428 (1901). ⟨14⟩ Mulliken, "Method" I, 82 (1904). ⟨15⟩ Lyman, Reid, *J. Am. Chem. Soc.* **39,** 703 (1917). ⟨16⟩ Rather, Reid, *J. Am. Chem. Soc.* **41,** 81 (1919). ⟨17⟩ Judefind, Reid, *J. Am. Chem. Soc.* **42,** 1055 (1920). ⟨18⟩ Drake, Bronitsky, *J. Am. Chem. Soc.* **52,** 3719 (1930). ⟨19⟩ Donleavy, *J. Am. Chem. Soc.* **58,** 1005 (1936). ⟨20⟩ Veibel, Lillelund, *Bull. soc. chim.* (5) **5,** 1157 (1938).

1:0740 ACETYLSALICYLIC ACID — $C_9H_8O_4$ — Beil. X-67

"Aspirin"

—O.CO.CH_3
—COOH

M.P. 135° **Neut. Eq. 180**

White cryst. from aq. or abs. alc. Sol. in 300 pts. aq. at room temp., eas. in hot aq.; sol. in 20 pts. ether, sol. $CHCl_3$; spar. sol. C_6H_6. [For extensive studies on m.p. of $\bar{C}$ see ⟨1⟩ ⟨2⟩ ⟨3⟩ ⟨4⟩.]

On long stdg. $\bar{C}$ grad. absorbs aq., undergoes hydrolysis, m.p. is depressed and material then gives characteristic $FeCl_3$ color of salicylic ac. (1:0780). [Pure $\bar{C}$ gives no color with $FeCl_3$ (T 1.41).] — Rapid titration with $N/10$ aq. alk. in cold readily gives Neut. Eq. 180.

Ⓓ **Saponification:** Hydrolysis with excess aq. alk. (T 1.51) gives Sap. Eq. 90 and yields soln. contg. salts of salicylic ac. (1:0780) and acetic ac. (1:1010).
Ⓓ ***p*-Nitrobenzyl acetylsalicylate:** m.p. 90.5° ⟨5⟩ [cf. T 1.39].
Ⓓ **Phenacyl acetylsalicylate:** m.p. 105° ⟨6⟩ [cf. T 1.391].
Ⓓ **Piperazonium 1,4-bis(acetylsalicylate):** m.p. 112–113° cor. ⟨7⟩ ⟨8⟩.

1:0740 ⟨1⟩ Beal, Szalkowski, *J. Am. Pharm. Assoc.* **22,** 36–40 (1933). ⟨2⟩ Carswell, *J. Am. Pharm. Assoc.* **16,** 306–309 (1927). ⟨3⟩ Hayman, Wagener, Holden, *J. Am. Pharm. Assoc.* **14,** 388–392 (1925). ⟨4⟩ Putnam, *Ind. Eng. Chem.* **16,** 778 (1924). ⟨5⟩ Lyons, Reid, *J. Am. Chem. Soc.* **39,** 1738 (1917). ⟨6⟩ Lundquist, *J. Am. Chem. Soc.* **60,** 2000 (1938). ⟨7⟩ Adelson, Pollard, *J. Am. Chem. Soc.* **58,** 532 (1936). ⟨8⟩ Pollard, Adelson, Bain, *J. Am. Chem. Soc.* **56,** 1759 (1934).

1:0745 PHENYLPROPIOLIC ACID — $C_9H_6O_2$ — Beil. IX-633

—C≡C.COOH

M.P. 136-137° **Neut. Eq. 146**

Pr. or very long hair-like ndls. from hot aq. or CS_2 — Cryst. from CCl_4 ⟨1⟩ — Very eas. sol. alc., ether — Sublimes; melts under aq. at 80°. [For prepn. in 76–80% yield from ethyl cinnamate dibromide by actn. of alc. KOH see ⟨1⟩; cf. also ⟨2⟩.]

C̄ on oxidn. with CrO_3 (cf. T 1.72) gives BzOH (1:0715) — C̄ in alk. soln. reduces $KMnO_4$ (T 1.34).

C̄ on reduction with Zn dust + 50% AcOH + trace $PtCl_4$ (20% yield ⟨3⟩) or with Zn dust + 1 *N* NaOH for 16 hrs. at room temp. (75% yield ⟨4⟩), or with Zn dust + NH_4OH ⟨4⟩ yields cinnamic ac. (1:0735), m.p. 133° — C̄, reduced with Na/Hg yields hydrocinnamic ac. (1:0615), m.p. 48°.

C̄ on htg. (T 1.33) evolves CO_2 yielding phenylacetylene (1:7425). [The reaction may also be effected by htg. in phenol (35% yield ⟨5⟩), or in aniline (83% yield ⟨6⟩) or by dry distn. with finely powd. BaO; all water must be absent since otherwise acetophenone (1:5515) may be formed.]

C̄ adds Br_2 (T 1.91). [C̄ in $CHCl_3$ at 0–25° in diffuse daylight gives 2 pts. *cis*-α,β-dibromocinnamic ac. [Beil. IX-602], m.p. 100° + 1 pt. *trans*-α,β-dibromocinnamic ac. [Beil. IX-601], m.p. 137–138°; in dark gives 3 pts. *cis* + 2 pts. *trans* isomers ⟨7⟩.]

C̄ with PCl_5 ⟨8⟩ ⟨9⟩ or with $SOCl_2$ ⟨10⟩ (cf. T 1.37) but not with PCl_3 ⟨9⟩ yields phenylpropiolyl chloride, b.p. 115–116°$_{17}$. [C̄ dislvd. in 2 pts. $POCl_3$ at 100° and htd. 3 min. beyond first sepn. of cryst. ⟨11⟩, or C̄ refluxed with Ac_2O ⟨12⟩, gives good yield 1-phenylnaphthalene-2,3-dicarboxylic acid anhydride [Beil. XVII-541] ndls. from C_6H_6 + lgr., m.p. 255°.]

Ⓓ **p-Nitrobenzyl phenylpropiolate:** m.p. 83° ⟨13⟩ [cf. T 1.39].

Ⓓ **Phenylpropiolamide:** m.p. 99–100° ⟨8⟩.

Ⓓ **Phenylpropiolanilide** [Beil. XII-280]: m.p. 128° ⟨14⟩, 125° ⟨8⟩ ⟨15⟩ [from the acid chloride + aniline in ether at 0° ⟨14⟩].

Ⓓ **Phenylpropiol-p-toluidide:** m.p. 142° ⟨15⟩.

1:0745 ⟨1⟩ Abbott, *Organic Syntheses* **12,** 60–61 (1932). ⟨2⟩ Bogert, Marcus, *J. Am. Chem. Soc.* **41,** 88, Note 1 (1919). ⟨3⟩ Fischer, *Ann.* **386,** 385–386 (1912). ⟨4⟩ Fischer, *Ann.* **394,** 361 (1912). ⟨5⟩ Hollemann, *Ber.* **20,** 3081 (1887). ⟨6⟩ Hollemann, *Rec. trav. chim.* **15,** 157–158 (1896). ⟨7⟩ Ayyar, *Cent.* **1936,** I, 3669. ⟨8⟩ Stockhausen, Gattermann, *Ber.* **25,** 3537 (1892). ⟨9⟩ Rupe, *Ann.* **369,** 329 (1909). ⟨10⟩ Ruhemann, Merriman, *J. Chem. Soc.* **87,** 1389 (1905). ⟨11⟩ Michael, *Ber.* **39,** 1912 (1906). ⟨12⟩ Michael, Bucher, *Am. Chem. J.* **20,** 91–92 (1898). ⟨13⟩ Reid, *J. Am. Chem. Soc.* **39,** 133 (1917). ⟨14⟩ von Braun, Ostermayer, *Ber.* **70,** 1002 (1937). ⟨15⟩ Curtius, Kenngott, *J. prakt. Chem.* (2) **112,** 317 (1926).

1:0746 *m*-ETHOXYBENZOIC ACID $C_9H_{10}O_3$ Beil. X-138

(structure: benzene ring with —COOH and C_2H_5O in meta position)

M.P. 137° **Neut. Eq. 166**

Ndls. from aq. — Subl. — Dif. sol. cold aq.; sol. in alc. or ether.

Ⓓ ***m*-Ethoxybenzamide:** m.p. 139–139.5° ⟨1⟩.

1:0746 ⟨1⟩ Fritzsch, *Ann.* **329,** 69 (1903).

1:0750 *o*-(*p*-TOLUYL)BENZOIC ACID $C_{15}H_{12}O_3$ Beil. X-759

(4′-Methylbenzophenone-carboxylic acid-2)

(structure: two benzene rings joined by C=O; one ring bearing CH_3 (para), the other bearing HOOC (ortho))

M.P. 139-140° **Neut. Eq. 240**

Very spar. sol. even in boiling aq.; very eas. sol. in alc., ether, C_6H_6, acetone, or boilg. toluene. [Cryst. from aq. alc. as hydrate, but aq. is lost above 100°.] [For prepn. (96% yield ⟨1⟩) from phthalic anhydride + toluene + $AlCl_3$ see ⟨1⟩ ⟨2⟩.]

C̄, warmed with PCl_5 in CS_2 ⟨3⟩ or C_6H_6 ⟨4⟩, yields *o*-(*p*-toluyl)benzoyl chloride as a yellow oil; with dry NH_3 this yields ⟨4⟩ *o*-(*p*-toluyl)benzamide, ndls. from hot aq., m.p. 175–176°.
C̄, htd. with 10 pts. by wt. of fumg. H_2SO_4 (20% SO_3) for 2 hrs. at 100°, or 1 hr. at 125–130° gives (81–90% yield ⟨5⟩) 2-methylanthraquinone (1:9075) [cf. ⟨6⟩]. [For soly. of metallic salts of C̄ see ⟨7⟩.]

1:0750 ⟨1⟩ Fieser, *Organic Syntheses, Coll. Vol.* I, 503–505 (1932). ⟨2⟩ Groggins, Nagel, *Ind. Eng. Chem.* **26,** 1315–1316 (1934). ⟨3⟩ Limpricht, Wiegand, *Ann.* **311,** 188 (1900). ⟨4⟩ Kippenberg, *Ber.* **30,** 1133 (1897). ⟨5⟩ Fieser, *Organic Syntheses, Coll. Vol.* I, 345–347 (1932). ⟨6⟩ Dougherty, Gleason, *J. Am. Chem. Soc.* **52,** 1025 (1930). ⟨7⟩ Ephraim, *Ber.* **55,** 3482 (1922).

1:0755 SUBERIC ACID HOOC.$(CH_2)_6$.COOH $C_8H_{14}O_4$ **Beil. II-691**
(Hexane-1,6-dicarboxylic acid)

M.P. 141° ⟨1⟩ **Neut. Eq. 87**

Ndls. or irreg. tbls. — 100 pts. aq. at 15° dis. 0.142 g. C̄; 100 pts. ether at 15° dis. 0.81 g. C̄. [Use in sepn. from azelaic ac. (1:0695) which is more sol.]; alm. insol. in $CHCl_3$ or C_6H_6. [For study of prepn. of C̄ see ⟨1⟩.]
C̄ with PCl_5 ⟨2⟩, or PCl_3 ⟨3⟩ or $SOCl_2$ ⟨4⟩ ⟨5⟩ ⟨6⟩ (cf. T 1.37) yields suberyl (di)chloride, b.p. $159–160°_{12}$ ⟨4⟩.
C̄, refluxed 4–6 hrs. with 3 pts. Ac_2O, excess reagt. and resultant AcOH distd. off under reduced press., yields a linear polymeric suberic α-anhydride, CH_3.CO.[O.CO$(CH_2)_6$.CO$]_x$.-O.$COCH_3$, sol. in C_6H_6 from which it is pptd. by addn. of pet. ether as white micro-cryst. pdr., m.p. 65–66° ⟨7⟩. It reacts with aq. to yield C̄ + acetic ac. [When this α-anhyd. is htd. in mol. still it yields a cyclic dimeric suberic β-anhydride, m.p. 55–57°, which in turn htd. above its m.p. rapidly polymerizes to another linear polymer, suberic γ-anhydride, waxy solid, m.p. 65–68° ⟨7⟩.]

Ⓓ **Di-(*p*-nitrobenzyl) suberate:** m.p. 85° ⟨8⟩ [cf. T 1.39].
Ⓓ **Di-(phenacyl) suberate:** m.p. 102.4° ⟨7⟩ [cf. T 1.391].
Ⓓ **Di-(*p*-bromophenacyl) suberate:** m.p. 144.2° ⟨9⟩ [cf. T 1.391].
Ⓓ **Di-(*p*-phenylphenacyl) suberate:** m.p. 151° ⟨10⟩ [cf. T 1.391].
Ⓓ **Suberic diamide:** m.p. 216–217° ⟨11⟩ [from suberyl(di)chloride + conc. aq. NH_4OH ⟨11⟩]. [The monamide (suberamic ac.) has m.p. 125–127° ⟨12⟩.]
Ⓓ **Suberic dianilide** [Beil. XII-302]: m.p. 186–187° ⟨7⟩ ⟨13⟩; 182° ⟨14⟩. [The monoanilide (suberanilic ac.) has m.p. 128–129° ⟨7⟩.]
Ⓓ **Suberic di-*p*-toluidide:** m.p. 218° ⟨13⟩; 219° ⟨14⟩.

1:0755 ⟨1⟩ Verkade, Hartman, Coops, *Rec. trav. chim.* **45,** 383–384 (1926). ⟨2⟩ Etaix, *Ann. chim.* (7) **9,** 386–388 (1896). ⟨3⟩ Borsche, Wolleman, *Ber.* **45,** 3717 (1912). ⟨4⟩ Fröschl, Maier, *Monatsh.* **59,** 273 (1932). ⟨5⟩ von Auwers, Schmidt, *Ber.* **46,** 479 (1913). ⟨6⟩ Meyer, *Monatsh.* **22,** 421 (1901). ⟨7⟩ Hill, Carothers, *J. Am. Chem. Soc.* **55,** 5027–5029 (1933). ⟨8⟩ Kelly, Segura, *J. Am. Chem. Soc.* **56,** 2497 (1934). ⟨9⟩ Kelly, Kleff, *J. Am. Chem. Soc.* **54,** 4444 (1932). ⟨10⟩ Drake, Sweeney, *J. Am. Chem. Soc.* **54,** 2060 (1932).
⟨11⟩ Aschan, *Ber.* **31,** 2350 (1898). ⟨12⟩ Ref. 2, page 393. ⟨13⟩ Blaise, Koehler, *Bull. soc. chim.* (4) **5,** 690 (1909). ⟨14⟩ Barnicoat, *J. Chem. Soc.* **1927,** 2927.

1:0760 FURANACRYLIC ACID $C_7H_6O_3$ **Beil. XVIII-300**
β-(α-Furyl)acrylic acid

```
HC———CH
||    ||
HC    C—CH=CH.COOH
  \  /
   O
```

M.P. 141° **Neut. Eq. 138**
B.P. 286°

Ndls. from aq. — Subl.; eas. volatile with steam — Sol. in abt. 500 pts. cold aq.; more eas. in hot aq.; fairly eas. sol. alc.; eas. sol. ether, AcOH, C_6H_6. [Used in Orient as food preservative (" Shoyu ") ⟨1⟩.] [A labile stereoisomeric form, m.p. 103–104°, convertible to C̄ by exposure of its C_6H_6 soln. + I_2 to sunlight is also known ⟨2⟩.]

[For prepn. in 65–70% yield from furfural (1:0185) + KOAc + Ac_2O see ⟨5⟩.]

C̄ in alk. soln. reduces $KMnO_4$ (T 1.34) — C̄ adds Br_2 (T 1.91). [In $CHCl_3$ at −15° C̄ adds 2 Br_2 pptg. a very unstable tetrabromo deriv., m.p. 110–111° block ⟨3⟩.] C̄, htd. at 280–300°, evolves CO_2 and yields ⟨3⟩ α-furylethylene [Beil. XVII-47] oil, insol. aq., b.p. 99–101° ⟨3⟩ — C̄, fused with KOH smoothly decomposes into acetic acid and furoic ac. (1:0475).

C̄ with $SOCl_2$ in C_6H_6 ⟨4⟩ yields β-(α-furyl)acryloyl chloride; m.p. abt. 34°, b.p. 145°_{30} ⟨4⟩.

Ⓓ β-(α-**Furyl**)**acrylamide:** m.p. 168–169° ⟨4⟩.

1:0760 ⟨1⟩ Gilman, Wright, Hewlett, *Iowa State Coll. J. Sci.* **4,** 355–358 (1930). ⟨2⟩ Liebermann, *Ber.* **28,** 1444 (1895). ⟨3⟩ Moureu, Dufraisse, Johnson, *Ann. chim.* (10) **7,** 20–24 (1927). ⟨4⟩ Gilman, Hewlett, *Iowa State Coll. J. Sci.* **4,** 27–33 (1929); *Cent.* **1931,** II, 1428. ⟨5⟩ Johnson, *Organic Syntheses* **20,** 55–56 (1940).

1:0761 β-NAPHTHYLACETIC ACID $C_{12}H_{10}O_2$ **Beil. IX-667**

(2-Naphthaleneacetic acid)

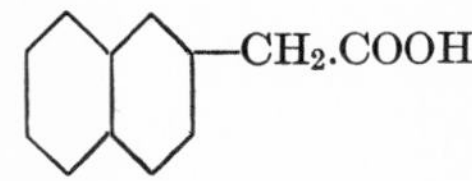

M.P. 141-142° ⟨1⟩ Neut. Eq. 186

Lfts. from aq.; cryst. from C_6H_6 — Sol. in ether, AcOEt, $CHCl_3$, lgr., warm alc.

C̄ on attempted distn. decomposes into CO_2 and β-methylnaphthalene (**1:7605**), **b.p.** 241°.

C̄, htd. with equal wt. phthalic anhydride + trace anhydrous NaOAc for 1 hr. at 225°, evolves CO_2 + H_2O and yields crude prod. from which repeated recrystn. from abs. alc. yields 3-(β-naphthylmethylene)phthalide [Beil. XVII-391], golden-yel. ndls., m.p. 170–171° ⟨2⟩.

—— β-**Naphthylacetamide:** m.p. 200° (indirectly).

1:0761 ⟨1⟩ Fulton, Robinson, *J. Chem. Soc.* **1939,** 201. ⟨2⟩ Blank, *Ber.* **29,** 2375 (1896).

1:0765 DIPHENYLACETIC ACID $C_{14}H_{12}O_2$ **Beil. IX-673**

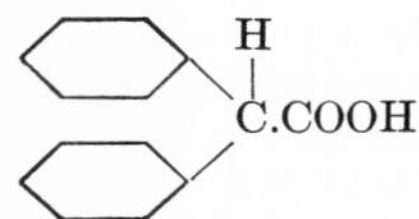

M.P. 148° Neut. Eq. 212

Ndls. from aq.; lfts. from alc.; dif. sol. cold aq.; eas. sol. hot aq.; eas. sol. alc., ether, $CHCl_3$. [For prepn. in 94–97% yield by reductn. of benzilic ac. (1:0770) with red P + HI see ⟨1⟩.]

C̄, on oxidn. with $K_2Cr_2O_7$ + H_2SO_4 (cf. T 1.72) gives benzophenone (1:5150).

C̄, with PCl_5 ⟨2⟩, or PCl_5 + $POCl_3$ ⟨3⟩, or with $SOCl_2$ ⟨4⟩ ⟨5⟩ (cf. T 1.37) yields diphenylacetyl chloride, tbls. from lgr., m.p. 56–57°.

C̄, refluxed 2 hrs. with equal wt. Ac_2O, latter + AcOH removed by distn.; residue treated with dry ether gives (90–92% yield ⟨6⟩) diphenylacetic anhydride, m.p. 98°.

C̄ + CH_3OH + HCl gives 100% yield ⟨7⟩ methyl diphenylacetate (1:2213), m.p. 60°; similarly, ethyl diphenylacetate ⟨8⟩ (1:2201), m.p. 58°.

Ⓓ **p-Phenylphenacyl diphenylacetate:** m.p. 111° ⟨9⟩ [cf. T 1.391].

Ⓓ **Diphenylacetamide:** m.p. 167.5–168.0° ⟨4⟩ [from diphenylacetyl chloride + conc. aq. NH_4OH ⟨4⟩].

Ⓓ **Diphenylacetanilide:** m.p. 180° ⟨2⟩.

Ⓓ **Diphenylaceto-p-toluidide:** m.p. 172–173° (prepd. indirectly).

Ⓓ ***S*-Benzylthiuronium diphenylacetate:** m.p. 145° cor. ⟨10⟩.

1:0765 ⟨1⟩ Marvel, Hager, Caudle, *Organic Syntheses, Coll. Vol.* I, 219–220 (1932). ⟨2⟩ Klingemann, *Ann.* **275,** 84–85 (1893). ⟨3⟩ Bistrzycki, Landtwing, *Ber.* **41,** 690 (1908). ⟨4⟩ Hellerman, Cohn, Hoen, *J. Am. Chem. Soc.* **50,** 1725 (1928). ⟨5⟩ Staudinger, *Ber.* **44,** 1620, Note 1 (1911). ⟨6⟩ Hurd, *J. Am. Chem. Soc.* **55,** 2591 (1933). ⟨7⟩ Heyl, Meyer, *Ber.* **28,** 2782 (1895). ⟨8⟩ Auschütz, Romig, *Ann.* **233,** 348 (1886). ⟨9⟩ Kelly, Morisani, *J. Am. Chem. Soc.* **58,** 1502 (1936). ⟨10⟩ Donleavy, *J. Am. Chem. Soc.* **58,** 1005 (1936).

1:0768 DIMETHYLDIHYDRORESORCINOL $C_8H_{12}O_2$ Beil. VII-559

(" Methone "; " Dimedon ")
(1,1-Dimethylcyclohexanedione-3,5)

```
             O                               O
             ‖                               ‖
             C                               C
           /   \                           /   \
       H2C       CH2                   H2C       CH
         |        |        ⇌             |        ‖
   (CH3)2C        C=O            (CH3)2C          C—OH
           \     /                         \     /
             C                               C
             H2                              H2
```

M.P. 148-150° dec. **Neut. Eq. 140**

Important reagt. for aldehydes [cf. " Manual " T 1.13]. [For prepn. (67–85% yield) from mesityl oxide (1:5445) and diethyl malonate (1:3581) see ⟨1⟩.]

White or sl. yel. cryst. from dil. acetone; ndls. from aq., pr. from alc. + ether. 100 ml. satd. aq. soln. at 19° conts. 0.4 g. C̄; at 90° 3.8 g. C̄ — Slightly volatile with steam (50 ml. dist. conts. 0.016 g. C̄) — Solid C̄ keeps indefinitely at room temp. but aq. solns. oxidize on stdg. in air and light, and decompose slowly even in dark.

C̄ titrates as monobasic ac. (T 1.31) and gives red color with $FeCl_3$ (T 1.41) — C̄ couples with solns. of diazonium salts.

C̄ in satd. aq. soln. or in dil. alc. gives insol. condensation products with all aldehydes but not with ketones (cf. T 1.13). These products are also enolic, sol. in alk., and their alc. solns. often give colors with $FeCl_3$ (T 1.41). Many can be titrated as monobasic acids.

Ⓓ **Formaldimethone:** On mixing alc. soln. of " methone " with formalin sol., and stdg., then pptg. with aq. and recrystg. from alc. gives white ndls., m.p. 189° cor. — [Titration with $N/10$ NaOH in dil. alc., using phenolphthalein, gives Neut. Eq. 292 — Boiling with Ac_2O converts to anhydride, lfts. from alc., m.p. 171° ⟨2⟩.]

1:0768 ⟨1⟩ Shriner, Todd, *Organic Syntheses* **15,** 14–16 (1935). ⟨2⟩ Vorländer, *Z. anal. Chem.* **77,** 241–268 (1929).

1:0770 BENZILIC ACID $C_{14}H_{12}O_3$ Beil. X-342

(α-Hydroxydiphenylacetic acid)

```
  C6H5 \
        C.COOH
  C6H5 / |
         OH
```

M.P. 150° **Neut. Eq. 228**

Ndls. from aq. or cryst. from C_6H_6 — Spar. sol. cold aq.; eas. sol. hot aq.; sol. alc., ether. [For prepn. in 84–90% yield from benzoin (1:5210) + NaOH + $NaBrO_3$ see ⟨1⟩; from benzoin in 93% yield by use of NaOH + $CuSO_4$ see ⟨2⟩.]

C̄ oxidized with CrO_3 in AcOH (cf. T 1.72) yields benzophenone (1:5150).

C̄ htd. with 2 moles PCl_5 at 120–130°, $POCl_3$ distd. off, and mixt. poured into cold aq. ⟨3⟩ gives diphenylchloroacetyl chloride, cryst. from lgr., m.p. 50°. [If reaction is incomplete mixt. of benzilic ac. chloride + diphenylchloracetyl chloride results which on distn. decomposes to benzophenone and benzophenone dichloride ⟨4⟩.]

C̄ dislvd. by gentle warming (not boiling) with equal pts. $POCl_3$ until red color appears, mixt. cooled and poured into aq. ⟨5⟩, gives diphenylchloroacetic ac. [Beil. IX-674], tbls. from C_6H_6 + lgr., m.p. 118–119° dec. [The amide and anilide corresp. to this prod. have m.p.'s 115° and 88° respectively.]

C̄ dislvd. in undiluted $SOCl_2$ yields benzophenone (1:5150) ⟨6⟩; however, C̄ treated with 3 moles $SOCl_2$ in CCl_4 for several days at room temp. ppts. diphenylchloroacetic acid (see above) in good yield ⟨7⟩. C̄ in CCl_4 + 6 moles $SOCl_2$ refluxed for several days, gives on conc. of soln. diphenylchloroacetic anhydride [Beil. IX_1-(228)], m.p. 129° ⟨7⟩.

C̄ with $FeCl_3$ gives the yellow color of α-OH aliphatic acids (T 1.32).

C̄ refluxed 3 hrs. with MeOH + H_2SO_4 yields quant. methyl benzilate (1:2310), cryst. from MeOH, m.p. 74–75° ⟨8⟩. C̄ in EtOH treated with HCl gas, refluxed 9 hrs., alc. distd., etc., gives (89% yield) ethyl benzilate (1:2086), m.p. 34° ⟨8⟩.

Ⓟ **Sulfuric acid color reaction:** 1 mg. C̄ dislvd. in 3 drops conc. H_2SO_4 on crucible cover immed. gives intense or.-red (OR) color which soon becomes red-violet ($RV\text{-}T_1$) at edges.

Ⓓ **Acetylbenzilic acid:** from C̄ refluxed with Ac_2O ⟨4⟩ ⟨9⟩; ndls. from AcOH, m.p. 98°. [This prod. is monohydrate: long drying over H_2SO_4 gives anhydrous material, m.p. 104.5°, Neut. Eq. 270 ⟨9⟩.]

Ⓓ ***p*-Nitrobenzyl benzilate:** m.p. 99.5° ⟨10⟩ [cf. T 1.39].

Ⓓ **Phenacyl benzilate:** m.p. 125.5° ⟨11⟩ [cf. T 1.391].

Ⓓ ***p*-Bromophenacyl benzilate:** m.p. 152° ⟨12⟩ [cf. T 1.391].

Ⓓ ***p*-Phenylphenacyl benzilate:** m.p. 122° ⟨13⟩ [cf. T 1.391].

Ⓓ **Benzilamide:** from C̄ on distn. with $(NH_4)_2CO_3$ + AcOH ⟨14⟩ ⟨15⟩, tbls. or pr. from $CHCl_3$, m.p. 153° ⟨14⟩, 155° ⟨16⟩.

Ⓓ **Benzilic anilide** [Beil. XII-506]: m.p. 174–175° (indirectly).

Ⓓ **Benzilic *p*-toluidide** [Beil. XII_1-(429)]: m.p. 189–190° (indirectly).

1:0770 ⟨1⟩ Ballard, Dehn, *Organic Syntheses, Coll. Vol.* I, 82–83 (1932). ⟨2⟩ Pearl, Dehn, *J. Am. Chem. Soc.* **60,** 57–58 (1938). ⟨3⟩ Bickel, *Ber.* **22,** 1538–1539 (1899). ⟨4⟩ Klinger, Stadke, *Ber.* **22,** 1212 (1889). ⟨5⟩ Bistrzycki, Herbst, *Ber.* **36,** 145–146 (1903). ⟨6⟩ Meyer, *Monatsh.* **22,** 793 (1901). ⟨7⟩ Stollé, *Ber.* **43,** 2471 (1910). ⟨8⟩ Acree, *Ber.* **37,** 2765–2766 (1904). ⟨9⟩ La Mer, Greenspan, *J. Am. Chem. Soc.* **56,** 956 (1934). ⟨10⟩ Lyons, Reid, *J. Am. Chem. Soc.* **39,** 1730–1731 (1927).

⟨11⟩ Chen, *Trans. Science Soc. China* **7,** 73–80 (1931). ⟨12⟩ Chen, Shih, *Trans. Science Soc. China* **7,** 81–87 (1931). ⟨13⟩ Drake, Sweeney, *J. Am. Chem. Soc.* **54,** 2060 (1932). ⟨14⟩ Kao, Ma, *J. Chem. Soc.* **1931,** 443. ⟨15⟩ Kao, Ma, *J. Chem. Soc.* **1930,** 2788. ⟨16⟩ Burton, *J. Chem. Soc.* **1930,** 2400.

1:0775 ADIPIC ACID (Butane-1,4-dicarboxylic acid) HOOC.$(CH_2)_4$.COOH $C_6H_{10}O_4$ Beil. II-649

M.P. 153-154° cor. **Neut. Eq. 73**

Pr. from AcOEt or better from conc. HNO_3 ⟨1⟩ — 100 pts. aq. at 15° dis. 1.44 g. C̄; 100 pts. ether at 15° dis. 0.61 g. C̄ — Eas. sol. alc.

[For prepn. in 58–60% yield from cyclohexanol (1:6415) by oxidn. with conc. HNO_3 see ⟨1⟩; for improvements raising yield to 72% see ⟨2⟩.]

C̄ treated with PCl_5 ⟨3⟩ (79% yield ⟨4⟩), or PCl_3 ⟨5⟩, or $PCl_3 + ZnCl_2$ (76% yield ⟨4⟩), or $SOCl_2$ ⟨6⟩ ⟨7⟩ ⟨8⟩ ⟨9⟩ (81% yield ⟨4⟩, 100% yield ⟨8⟩) (cf. T 1.37) gives adipyl (di)chloride, b.p. 125°_{11} ⟨8⟩.

C̄, refluxed 4–6 hrs. with 3 pts. Ac_2O, volatile material removed by distn. under reduced press. at 100°, residue repeatedly crystd. from C_6H_6, yields a linear polymeric adipic α-anhydride ⟨10⟩. On melting under aq. this α-anhyd. dissolves and on cooling adipic ac. cryst. out. The α-anhydride cannot be distd. as such but on htg. in vac. (or even by ord. distn. ⟨12⟩) is partly depolymerized to monomeric adipic anhydride, a colorless liq. freezing at about 20° and spontaneously reverting to polymeric form; especially in presence of a trace of aq. ⟨11⟩.

The monomeric and polymeric anhydrides are sharply differentiated by their behavior with aniline; both react instantly at room temp. but former yields *only* adipic acid monoanilide, while latter gives mixture of adipic ac., adipic acid monoanilide, and adipic dianilide ⟨10⟩. [See below.]

C̄ when distilled slowly at about 290–300° in stream of N_2 gives almost quant. yield of cyclopentanone (1:5446); 88% yield from Jena glass flask; 98.8% yield from quartz flask ⟨13⟩.

Ⓓ **Di-(*p*-nitrobenzyl) adipate:** m.p. 105.6° ⟨14⟩ [cf. T 1.39].

Ⓓ **Di-(phenacyl) adipate:** m.p. 87.6° ⟨15⟩ [cf. T 1.391].

Ⓓ **Di-(*p*-bromophenacyl) adipate:** m.p. 154.5° ⟨15⟩; 152.6° ⟨16⟩ [cf. T 1.391].

Ⓓ **Di-(*p*-phenylphenacyl) adipate:** m.p. 148° ⟨17⟩ [cf. T 1.391].

Ⓓ **Adipic (di)amide:** m.p. 220° [from adipyl chloride + conc. aq. NH_4OH ⟨18⟩ ⟨19⟩]. [The monoamide (adipamic acid) has m.p. 161° ⟨22⟩.]

Ⓓ **Adipic (di)anilide:** m.p. 240–241° ⟨10⟩; 235° ⟨20⟩. [The monoanilide (adipanilic acid) from monomeric adipic anhydride with aniline has m.p. 152–153° ⟨10⟩.]

Ⓓ **Adipic (di)*p*-toluidide:** m.p. 241° ⟨20⟩.

Ⓓ **Piperazonium hydrogen adipate:** from C̄ + 0.5 mole piperazine hexahydrate in 83% yield; cryst. from 50% alc., m.p. 244–245° dec. cor.; Neut. Eq. 232 ⟨21⟩.

1:0775 ⟨1⟩ Ellis, *Organic Syntheses, Coll. Vol.* I, 18–19 (1932). ⟨2⟩ Foster, *Organic Syntheses*, **13**, 110 (1933). ⟨3⟩ Etaix, *Ann. chim.* (7) **9** 369–370 (1896). ⟨4⟩ Clark, Bell, *Trans. Roy. Soc. Canada* (3) **27**, III, 97–103 (1933). ⟨5⟩ Borsche, Wollemann, *Ber.* **45,** 3715 (1912). ⟨6⟩ Meyer, *Ann.* **347,** 49-50 (1906). ⟨7⟩ Blaise, Koehler, *Bull. soc. chim.* (4) **5,** 683 (1909). ⟨8⟩ Fröschl, Maier, *Monatsh.* **59,** 271-272 (1932). ⟨9⟩ Fuson, Walker, *Organic Syntheses* **13,** 32–33 (1933). ⟨10⟩ Hill, *J. Am. Chem. Soc.* **52,** 4110–4114 (1930).

⟨11⟩ Carothers, *J. Am. Chem. Soc.* **52,** 3471 (1930). ⟨12⟩ Hill, Carothers, *J. Am. Chem. Soc.* **55,** 5024 (1933). ⟨13⟩ Neunhoeffer, Paschke, *Ber.* **72,** 927–928 (1939). ⟨14⟩ Kelly, Segura, *J. Am. Chem. Soc.* **56,** 2497 (1934). ⟨15⟩ Kelly, Kleff, *J. Am. Chem. Soc.* **54,** 4444 (1932). ⟨16⟩ Lund, Langvad, *J. Am. Chem. Soc.* **54,** 4107 (1932). ⟨17⟩ Drake, Sweeney, *J. Am. Chem. Soc.* **54,** 2060 (1932). ⟨18⟩ Blicke, Blake, *J. Am. Chem. Soc.* **53,** 1024 (1931). ⟨19⟩ Slotta, Tschesche, *Ber.* **62,** 1404 (1929). ⟨20⟩ Barnicoat, *J. Chem. Soc.* **1927,** 2927–2928.

⟨21⟩ Pollard, Adelson, Bain, *J. Am. Chem. Soc.* **56,** 1759 (1934). ⟨22⟩ Jeffery, Vogel, *J. Chem. Soc.* **1934,** 1103.

1:0780 SALICYLIC ACID (*o*-Hydroxybenzoic acid)

[benzene ring] —OH, —COOH $C_7H_6O_3$ **Beil. X-43**

M.P. 158° **Neut. Eq. 138**

Fine ndls. from aq.; scales from alc. — Below m.p. subl. undecomposed, above m.p. subl. with decompn. — Volatile with steam.

100 g. aq. at 20° dis. 0.22 g. C̄ — 100 pts. abs. alc. at 15° dis. 49.6 g. C̄ — 100 pts. satd. ether soln. at 17° conts. 23.4 g. C̄ — 100 pts. satd. acetone soln. at 23° conts. 31.3 g. C̄ — 100 g. C_6H_6 at 18° dis. 0.579 g. C̄ — 100 g. satd. $CHCl_3$ soln. at 30° contains 1.55 g. C̄ ⟨1⟩ [dif. and sepn. from *m*-hydroxybenzoic ac. (1:0825) and *p*-hydroxybenzoic ac. (1:0840)] — 1 pt. C̄ dis. at room temp. in 137 pts. dichloroethylene [dif. and sepn. from *p*-hydroxybenzoic ac. (1:0840) which requires 30,000 pts. ⟨2⟩].

C̄ in dil. aq. soln. (1:10,000) gives with 1 drop 10% $FeCl_3$ (cf. T 1.41) a purple color — C̄, treated with Br_2 aq. quant. eliminates CO_2 yielding tribromophenol bromide ⟨3⟩, which on treatment with $NaHSO_3$ soln. and recrystn. from 40% alc. gives 2,4,6-tribromophenol, m.p. 92.5–93.5° u.c. — For actn. of ht. on C̄ see ⟨4⟩.

C̄ treated with PCl_3 or PCl_5 does not give acid chloride but instead complex phosphorous derivs. or various salicylids — C̄ dis. in boilg. $SOCl_2$ but on removal of excess reagent gives only a mixt. of anhydrides ⟨5⟩; in presence of a little $AlCl_3$, however, finely powdered C̄ reacts with $SOCl_2$ at 45–50° yielding mobile liq. which, after distn. of excess reagt. in vacuo, freezes to *o*-hydroxybenzoyl chloride, m.p. 18° ⟨6⟩.

Salts: BaĀ₂, CdĀ₂, CuĀ₂, PbĀ₂, HgĀ₂ all dif. sol.; see ⟨7⟩.

Ⓟ **Odor of methyl salicylate:** C̄ or its salts treated with conc. H_2SO_4 + MeOH and warmed (T 1.35) gives characteristic odor of oil of wintergreen.

Ⓓ **5-Nitrosalicylic acid** (5-nitro-2-hydroxybenzoic acid) [Beil. X-116]: Dis. 0.1 g. C̄ in 5 ml. boilg. aq., add 1 ml. HNO_3 (D = 1.2) and boil gently 5 min. Pour into 20 ml. cold aq., filter off ppt., and wash with 2 ml. cold aq. Recryst. twice from 5 ml. and 3 ml. of boilg. aq. The product cryst. in white ndls., sintering at 220–222°, then melting sharply to a brown liq. at 226–227° u.c. ⟨8⟩.

Ⓓ **Acetylsalicylic acid** (2-acetoxybenzoic acid) [Beil. X-67]: from C̄ suspended in C_6H_6 and refluxed with Ac_2O ⟨9⟩; cryst. from abs. alc., m.p. 135° (1:0740) [cannot be prepd. from C̄ + aq. NaOH + Ac_2O ⟨10⟩].

Ⓓ **Benzoylsalicylic acid** (2-benzoxybenzoic acid) [Beil. X-68]: from C̄ + BzCl in ether + pyridine (82% yield) or from NaĀ + BzCl at room temp. (50% yield) ⟨11⟩; ndls. from dil. alc., m.p. 132°.

Ⓓ ***p*-Nitrobenzoylsalicylic acid** (2-(*p*-nitrobenzoxy)benzoic acid): from C̄ + *p*-nitrobenzoyl chloride in C_6H_6 + dimethylaniline; pale yel. cryst. from MeOH, m.p. 205° ⟨12⟩.

Ⓓ ***p*-Nitrobenzyl salicylate:** m.p. 97–98° ⟨13⟩ ⟨14⟩ (cf. T 1.39). [The corresponding ether-ester, viz., *p*-nitrobenzyl salicylate *p*-nitrobenzyl ether, can readily be obtd. under specified conditions ⟨13⟩; m.p. 137–139° ⟨13⟩; the corresponding ether-acid, viz., (*p*-nitrobenzyloxy)benzoic acid, has m.p. 166–168° ⟨13⟩.]

Ⓓ **Phenacyl salicylate:** m.p. 110° ⟨15⟩ [cf. T 1.391].

Ⓓ ***p*-Bromophenacyl salicylate:** m.p. 140° ⟨16⟩ [cf. T 1.391].

Ⓓ ***p*-Phenylphenacyl salicylate:** m.p. 148° ⟨17⟩ [cf. T 1.391].

—— **Salicylamide:** m.p. 139° [from methyl salicylate on 24 hrs. shaking with 4 pts. conc. aq. NH_4OH ⟨18⟩].

—— **Salicylanilide:** m.p. 135° [from C̄ htd. with aniline in presence of PCl_3 ⟨19⟩ ⟨20⟩].

Ⓓ ***S*-Benzylthiuronium salicylate:** m.p. 146° cor. ⟨21⟩; 147–148° ⟨22⟩.

1:0780 ⟨1⟩ Cohen, Miyake, *Z. physik. Chem.* **115A,** 440–443 (1926). ⟨2⟩ Mann, *Chem. Ztg.* **56,** 452 (1932). ⟨3⟩ Kolthoff, *Chem. Abs.* **27,** 280 (1933). ⟨4⟩ Kunz-Krause, Manicke, *Ber.* **53,** 191 (1920). ⟨5⟩ Meyer, *Monatsh.* **22,** 430 (1901). ⟨6⟩ Kirpal, *Ber.* **63,** 3190 (1930). ⟨7⟩ Ephraim, *Ber.* **55,** 3482 (1922). ⟨8⟩ Mulliken, " Method " I, 85 (1904). ⟨9⟩ Kaufmann, *Ber.* **42,** 3482 (1909). ⟨10⟩ Chattaway, *J. Chem. Soc.* **1931,** 2496.

⟨11⟩ Einhorn, Rothlauf, Seuffert, *Ber.* **44,** 3310–3311 (1911). ⟨12⟩ Einhorn, von Bagh, *Ber.* **43,** 328 (1910). ⟨13⟩ Blicke, Smith, *J. Am. Chem. Soc.* **51,** 1947–1949 (1929). ⟨14⟩ Lyman, Reid, *J. Am. Chem. Soc.* **39,** 704 (1917). ⟨15⟩ Rather, Reid, *J. Am. Chem. Soc.*

41, 80 (1919). ⟨16⟩ Judefind, Reid, *J. Am. Chem. Soc.* **42,** 1049 (1920). ⟨17⟩ Drake, Sweeney, *J. Am. Chem. Soc.* **54,** 2060 (1932). ⟨18⟩ Anschütz, *Ber.* **52,** 1886 (1919). ⟨19⟩ Kupferberg, *J. prakt. Chem.* (2) **16,** 442–443 (1877). ⟨20⟩ Hübner, *Ann.* **210,** 342 (1881).
⟨21⟩ Donleavy, *J. Am. Chem. Soc.* **58,** 1005 (1936). ⟨22⟩ Veibel, Lillelund, *Bull. soc. chim.* (5) **5,** 1157 (1938).

1:0785 α-NAPHTHOIC ACID $C_{11}H_8O_2$ Beil. IX-647

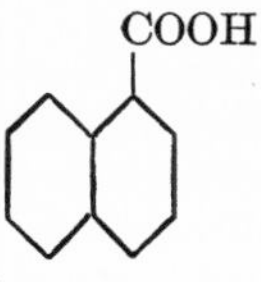

M.P. 161-162° cor. ⟨1⟩ **Neut. Eq. 172**

Ndls. from dil. alc. or dil. AcOH — Very dif. sol. hot aq.; eas. sol. hot alc.

[For prepn. in 90% yield from methyl α-naphthyl ketone (1:5600) by haloform reaction using $Ca(OCl)_2$ see ⟨1⟩; in 85% yield by carbonation of α-naphthyl MgBr see ⟨1⟩ ⟨2⟩]. [For purification via distn. under reduced press., b.p. 229–231° at 50 mm. and recrystn. from toluene, see ⟨3⟩.]

C̄ on htg. with CrO_3 in AcOH (cf. T 1.72) yields phthalic ac. (1:0820) — C̄ on htg. with BaO splits out CO_2 (as $BaCO_3$) and yields naphthalene (1:7200).

C̄ with PCl_5 at 100° ⟨4⟩ ⟨5⟩ ⟨6⟩ or with $SOCl_2$ ⟨7⟩ ⟨8⟩ (cf. T 1.37) yields α-naphthoyl chloride, b.p. 163°_{10}, m.p. 20° ⟨9⟩; 26° ⟨8⟩. [This α-naphthoyl chloride + pyridine + anhydrous Na_2CO_3 on addn. of a few drops of aq. gives vigorous reaction and from the residue C_6H_6 extracts 80% yield ⟨10⟩ of α-naphthoic anhydride, m.p. 145–146° ⟨10⟩.]

Ⓓ ***p*-Bromophenacyl α-naphthoate:** m.p. 135.5° ⟨11⟩ [cf. T 1.391].

Ⓓ **α-Naphthoamide:** m.p. 202° [from 2-naphthoyl chloride + conc. NH_4OH or by partial hydrolysis of α-naphthonitrile ⟨12⟩].

Ⓓ **α-Naphthoanilide:** m.p. 162–163° ⟨13⟩ [from α-naphthoyl chloride + aniline].

1:0785 ⟨1⟩ Fieser, Holmes, Newman, *J. Am. Chem. Soc.* **58,** 1055 (1936). ⟨2⟩ Gilman, St. John, Schutze, *Organic Syntheses* **11,** 80–83 (1931). ⟨3⟩ McRae, *J. Am. Chem. Soc.* **52,** 4551 (1930). ⟨4⟩ von Braun, *Ber.* **38,** 180 (1905). ⟨5⟩ Schmidlin, Garcia-Banus, *Ber.* **45,** 3183 (1912). ⟨6⟩ Reddelien, *Ber.* **46,** 2722, Note 2 (1913). ⟨7⟩ Blicke, *J. Am. Chem. Soc.* **49,** 2847, Note 16 (1927). ⟨8⟩ Bell, *J. Chem. Soc.* **1930,** 1984–1985. ⟨9⟩ Pope, Winmill, *J. Chem. Soc.* **101,** 2316 (1912). ⟨10⟩ Ref. 7, page 2848.
⟨11⟩ Chen, Shih, *Trans. Science Soc. China* **7,** 81–87 (1931). ⟨12⟩ McMaster, Langreck, *J. Am. Chem. Soc.* **39,** 106–107 (1917). ⟨13⟩ Gibson, Hariharan, Menon, Simonsen, *J. Chem. Soc.* **1926,** 2259, Note.

1:0790 *d,l*-PHENYLSUCCINIC ACID $C_{10}H_{10}O_4$ Beil. IX-865

H
—C.COOH (α)
H_2C.COOH (β)

M.P. 167-168° **Neut. Eq. 97**

Ndls. from aq. or hot $CHCl_3$ — Dif. sol. cold aq., eas. sol. hot aq.; very eas. sol. alc., ether, AcOH, acetone; alm. insol. C_6H_6, lgr., pet. ether. [For prepn. in 73–86% yield from α-cyano-β-phenylacrylic ac. (in turn from sodium chloroacetate, NaCN + BzH) see ⟨1⟩ ⟨2⟩ ⟨3⟩.]

C̄, htd. above its m.p., or distd. in vac. ⟨4⟩, or refluxed with AcCl (80–100% yield ⟨5⟩ ⟨3⟩), or treated with $SOCl_2$ ⟨6⟩ gives phenylsuccinic anhydride [Beil. XVII-493], ndls. from dry ether, m.p. 54°. [The corresp. anhydride of either *d*- or *l*- C̄ has m.p. 83.5–84.5° ⟨7⟩.]

C̄, or its anhydride, with PCl_5 yields phenylsuccinyl (di)chloride, b.p. $150\text{–}151^\circ_{12}$ ⟨8⟩.

C̄ is unaffected by conc. H_2SO_4 in cold, but C̄ htd. for 16–20 hrs. at 100° with 5–10 pts. conc. H_2SO_4 gives small yield of indanone-1-carboxylic acid-3 ⟨9⟩.

C̄ with MeOH + conc. H_2SO_4 ⟨10⟩ or with 5% MeOH + HCl ⟨8⟩ yields dimethyl phenylsuccinate, pr. from pet. ether, m.p. 57.5–58.5° [of the two half methyl esters, the α has m.p. 102–103°; the β, m.p. 92°].

Ⓓ **Phenylsuccin(di)amide:** m.p. 211° ⟨11⟩ [from dimethyl ester + conc. aq. NH_4OH together with β-monoamide; the acid chloride + conc. aq. NH_4OH at −10° gives only 4% diamide, main products being NH_4 salt of C̄ + monoamide ⟨11⟩]. [Of the two monoamides (phenylsuccinamic acids) the α- has m.p. 158–159°; the β- has m.p. 145°.] [Phenylsuccinimide (Beil. XXI-514) has m.p. 90°.]

Ⓓ **Phenylsuccin(di)anilide** [Beil. XII-314]: m.p. 222° [from phenylsuccinyl dichloride in ether + 2 moles aniline ⟨12⟩]. [Of the two half anilides (phenylsuccinanilic acids) the α-anilide has m.p. 175°; the β-anilide has m.p. 170°.] [Phenylsuccin-*N*-phenylimide (phenylsuccinanil) (Beil. XXI-514) has m.p. 138°.]

Ⓓ **Phenylsuccin(di)*p*-toluidide:** apparently not recorded. [Of the two half *p*-toluidides [Beil. XII-939] the α-*p*-toluidide has m p. 175°; the β-*p*-toluidide has m.p. 168–169°.] [Phenylsuccinic *N*-*p*-tolylimide (Beil. XXI-515) has m.p. 139°.]

1:0790 ⟨1⟩ Lapworth, Baker, *Organic Syntheses, Coll. Vol.* I, 440–442 (1932). ⟨2⟩ Manske, *J. Am. Chem. Soc.* **53,** 1106 (1931). ⟨3⟩ Robinson, Young, *J. Chem. Soc.* **1935,** 1415. ⟨4⟩ Ramart-Lucas, Papadakis, *Ann. chim.* (10) **18,** 48 (1932). ⟨5⟩ Weizmann, Blum-Bergmann, *J. Chem. Soc.* **1935,** 1371. ⟨6⟩ Ref. 4, page 52. ⟨7⟩ Wren, Williams, *J. Chem. Soc.* **109,** 580 (1916). ⟨8⟩ Anschütz, *Ann.* **354,** 128 (1907). ⟨9⟩ Splight, Stevenson, Thorpe, *J. Chem. Soc.* **125,** 2185 (1924). ⟨10⟩ Ref. 7, page 578.

⟨11⟩ McRae, Weston, Hubbs, *Can. J. Research* **15B,** 434–437 (1937); *Cent.* **1938,** I, 2169. ⟨12⟩ Ref. 8, pages 139–140.

1:0795 *p*-TOLUIC ACID (*p*-Methylbenzoic acid) CH_3—⟨⟩—COOH $C_8H_8O_2$ Beil. IX-483

M.P. 178° **Neut. Eq. 136**
B.P. 275° cor.

Cryst. from hot aq.; 100 g. aq. at 88° dis. less than 1 g. C̄ — Sublimes — Volatile with steam; 100 g. steam at 100° carries over abt. 2 g. C̄ — C̄ is eas. sol. alc., MeOH, ether.

C̄ on oxidn. with CrO_3 (cf. T 1.72) or alk. $KMnO_4$ yields terephthalic ac. (1:0910).

C̄ with PCl_5 ⟨1⟩, or PCl_3 ⟨2⟩ or $SOCl_2$ ⟨3⟩ ⟨4⟩ (cf. T 1.37) yields *p*-toluyl chloride, b.p. 227°; 72.9° at 4.5 mm. ⟨4⟩.

C̄ refluxed for 6 hrs. with 12 pts. Ac_2O, latter distd. off, and process repeated gives (91% yield ⟨5⟩) *p*-toluic anhydride; lfts. from pet. ether, m.p. 95° ⟨5⟩.

C̄ dislvd. in 3 pts. conc. H_2SO_4 by warming, then treated dropwise with 2 pts. fumg. HNO_3 at 100–110°, stood 24 hrs., poured into aq. yields ⟨6⟩ 3,5-dinitro-4-methylbenzoic ac., lt. yel. pl. from boilg. aq.; m.p. 158–159° ⟨6⟩. [For use of latter for identfn. of amines as salts see ⟨6⟩.]

Ⓓ ***p*-Nitrobenzyl *p*-toluate:** m.p. 104.5° ⟨7⟩ [cf. T 1.39].
Ⓓ **Phenacyl *p*-toluate:** m.p. 103° ⟨8⟩ [cf. T 1.391].
Ⓓ ***p*-Bromophenacyl *p*-toluate:** m.p. 153.0° ⟨9⟩ [cf. T 1.391].
Ⓓ ***p*-Phenylphenacyl *p*-toluate:** m.p. 165° ⟨10⟩ [cf. T 1.391].
Ⓓ ***p*-Toluamide:** m.p. 160° [from *p*-toluyl chloride + NH_4OH ⟨11⟩].
Ⓓ ***p*-Toluanilide:** m.p. 144–145°.
Ⓓ ***p*-Tolu-*p*-toluidide:** m.p. 160°.
Ⓓ ***S*-Benzylthiuronium *p*-toluate:** m.p. 190° cor. ⟨12⟩.

1:0795 ⟨1⟩ Cahours, *Ann.* **108**, 316 (1858). ⟨2⟩ Frankland, Wharton, *J. Chem. Soc.* **69**, 1311 (1896). ⟨3⟩ Meyer, *Monatsh.* **22**, 425 (1901). ⟨4⟩ Thompson, Norris, *J. Am. Chem. Soc.* **58**, 1955 (1936). ⟨5⟩ Autenrieth, Thomae, *Ber.* **57**, 432 (1924). ⟨6⟩ Sah, Yuin, *J. Chinese Chem. Soc.* **5**, 130 (1937); *Chem. Abs.* **31**, 6140 (1937). ⟨7⟩ Lyons, Reid, *J. Am. Chem. Soc.* **39**, 1736 (1917). ⟨8⟩ Chen, *Trans. Science Soc. China* **7**, 73–80 (1931). ⟨9⟩ Judefind, Reid, *J. Am. Chem. Soc.* **42**, 1055 (1920). ⟨10⟩ Drake, Bronitsky, *J. Am. Chem. Soc.* **52**, 3720 (1930).

⟨11⟩ Fischli, *Ber.* **12**, 615 (1879). ⟨12⟩ Donleavy, *J. Am. Chem. Soc.* **58**, 1005 (1936).

1:0800 β-NAPHTHOIC ACID —COOH $C_{11}H_8O_2$ Beil. IX-656

M.P. 184° **Neut. Eq. 172**

Ndls. from lgr. or tbls. from acetone — Spar. sol. hot aq. or lgr.; eas. sol. alc., ether, $CHCl_3$. [For prepn. in 97–98% yield from methyl β-naphthyl ketone (1:5153) via haloform reaction using $Ca(OCl)_2$ see ⟨1⟩ ⟨2⟩.]

C̄ on oxidn. with CrO_3 + AcOH (cf. T 1.72) yields phthalic ac. (1:0820); with alk. $KMnO_4$ trimellitic ac. (1:0551).

C̄ with PCl_5 ⟨3⟩ or with $SOCl_2$ ⟨4⟩ (cf. T 1.37) yields β-naphthoyl chloride, b.p. 304–306°; m.p. 43° ⟨3⟩; 51° ⟨4⟩. [This acid chloride + tertiary bases + $K_2S_2O_5$ in C_6H_6 yields β-naphthoic anhydride, m.p. 135° ⟨5⟩ [cf. analogous process for α-naphthoic ac. (1:0785)].

For soly. of heavy metal salts see ⟨6⟩.

Ⓓ **Methyl β-naphthoate:** from C̄ in MeOH treated with HCl gas ⟨7⟩ ⟨11⟩ or from β-naphthoyl chloride + MeOH ⟨3⟩; lfts. from MeOH; m.p. 77°.

Ⓓ **β-Naphthoamide:** from β-naphthoyl chloride + $(NH_4)_2CO_3$ at 100° ⟨8⟩; tbls. from alc., m.p. 192–193°.

Ⓓ **β-Naphthoanilide:** from β-naphthoyl chloride + aniline in C_6H_6 soln. ⟨9⟩; lfts. from C_6H_6, m.p. 171° ⟨10⟩.

Ⓓ **β-Naphtho-p-toluidide:** similarly from p-toluidine ⟨9⟩; cryst. from alc., m.p. 192°.

1:0800 ⟨1⟩ Newman, Holmes, *Organic Syntheses* **17**, 65–67 (1937). ⟨2⟩ Fieser, Holmes, Newman, *J. Am. Chem. Soc.* **58**, 1055 (1936). ⟨3⟩ Vieth, *Ann.* **180**, 317–319 (1875). ⟨4⟩ Bell, *J. Chem. Soc.* **1930**, 1985. ⟨5⟩ Gasopoulos, *Cent.* **1932**, I, 3172. ⟨6⟩ Ephraim, *Ber.* **55**, 3482 (1922). ⟨7⟩ Stokmann, Kleber, Langbein, *J. prakt. Chem.* (2) **40**, 346–347 (1889). ⟨8⟩ Ref. 3, pages 320–321. ⟨9⟩ Ref. 3, pages 323–324. ⟨10⟩ Gibson, Hariharan, Menon, Simonsen, *J. Chem. Soc.* **1926**, 2257.

⟨11⟩ Bergmann, Hirshberg, *J. Chem. Soc.* **1936**, 334.

1:0805 p-ANISIC ACID CH_3O—⟨ ⟩—COOH $C_8H_8O_3$ Beil. X-155

(p-Methoxybenzoic acid)

M.P. 184.2° cor. **Neut. Eq. 152**

B.P. 275-280°

Pr. or ndls. from hot aq. — 100 ml. aq. at 19° dis. 0.027 g. C̄; eas. sol. hot aq.; eas. sol. alc., ether. [For m.p. + compn. data on mixts. of C̄ with m-methoxybenzoic acid (1:0703) see ⟨16⟩.]

C̄ intimately mixed with 3–4 pts. aniline hydrochloride and htd. ½–1 hr. at 180–200° gives clear melt, evolution of CH_3Cl, and leaves (80% yield ⟨1⟩) p-hydroxybenzanilide, lfts. from aq., m.p. 201–202° ⟨1⟩ (196–197°).

C̄, finely powd. and dried in vac., on treatment with PCl_5 ⟨2⟩ ⟨3⟩, or with $SOCl_2$ ⟨4⟩⟨5⟩ (cf. T 1.37) gives anisoyl chloride, m.p. 24°, b.p. 262–263° sl. dec.

AgĀ; $PbĀ_2.H_2O$; $BaĀ_2.H_2O$ all dif. sol. aq. — $CaĀ_2.3H_2O$: soly. in aq. at 20° is 2.5 g. per 100 ml. soln. ⟨6⟩ ⟨7⟩. Dry distn. of anhydrous $CaĀ_2$ yields anisole (1:7445) ⟨8⟩ (dif. from *o*-, *m*-, or *p*-hydroxybenzoic acids).

[For identification of C̄ as salt with benzylamine, m.p. 142.6–143.4° u.c., or with α-phenylethylamine, m.p. 130.8–131.4° u.c. see ⟨9⟩.]

Ⓓ ***p*-Nitrobenzyl anisate:** m.p. 132° ⟨10⟩ [cf. T 1.39].
Ⓓ **Phenacyl anisate:** m.p. 134° ⟨11⟩ [cf. T 1.391].
Ⓓ ***p*-Bromophenacyl anisate:** m.p. 152° ⟨12⟩ [cf. T 1.391].
Ⓓ ***p*-Phenylphenacyl anisate:** m.p. 160° ⟨13⟩ [cf. T 1.391].
Ⓓ **Anisamide (*p*-methoxybenzamide):** ndls. or tbls. from aq., m.p. 162–163° [from anisoyl chloride (above) with conc. aq. NH_4OH or with $(NH_4)_2CO_3$].
Ⓓ **Anisanilide (*p*-methoxybenzanilide)** [Beil. XII-502]: m.p. 169°.
Ⓓ **Anis-*p*-toluidide (*p*-methoxybenzo-*p*-toluidide):** m.p. 186°.
Ⓓ ***S*-Benzylthiuronium anisate:** m.p. 177° cor. ⟨14⟩; 184–185° ⟨15⟩.

1:0805 ⟨1⟩ Klemenc, *Ber.* **49**, 1373 (1916). ⟨2⟩ Schoonjans, *Cent.* **1897**, II, 616. ⟨3⟩ Lossen, *Ann.* **175**, 284, Note (1875). ⟨4⟩ Meyer, *Monatsh.* **22**, 428 (1901). ⟨5⟩ Thompson, Norris, *J. Am. Chem. Soc.* **58**, 1956 (1936). ⟨6⟩ Ephraim, Pfister, *Helv. Chim. Acta* **8**, 370, 381–383 (1925). ⟨7⟩ Ephraim, *Ber.* **55**, 3482 (1922). ⟨8⟩ Goldschmiedt, Herzig, *Monatsh.* **3**, 127–132 (1882). ⟨9⟩ Buehler, Carson, Edds, *J. Am. Chem. Soc.* **57**, 2181–2182 (1935). ⟨10⟩ Lyons, Reid, *J. Am. Chem. Soc.* **39**, 1738 (1917).

⟨11⟩ Chen, *Trans. Science Soc. China* **7**, 73–80 (1931). ⟨12⟩ Judefind, Reid, *J. Am. Chem. Soc.* **42**, 1055 (1920). ⟨13⟩ Drake, Sweeney, *J. Am. Chem. Soc.* **54**, 2060 (1932). ⟨14⟩ Donleavy, *J. Am. Chem. Soc.* **58**, 1005 (1936). ⟨15⟩ Veibel, Lillelund, *Bull. soc. chim.* (5) **5**, 1157 (1938). ⟨16⟩ Lea, Robinson, *J. Chem. Soc.* **1926**, 2355.

1:0810 *d*-CAMPHORIC ACID $C_{10}H_{16}O_4$ Beil. IX-745

```
              CH3
              |
H2C-----------C-----------COOH (β)
 |            |
 |    CH3-----C-----CH3
 |            |
H2C-----------C-----------COOH (α)
              |
              H
```

M.P. 187.5–188° ⟨1⟩ Neut. Eq. 100

Lfts. from hot aq.; hexag. pr. from alc. — 100 pts. satd. aq. soln. at 20° conts. 0.7 pt. C̄, at 80° 3.1 pt. C̄ [cf. ⟨1⟩] — Very sol. alc., acetone; insol. $CHCl_3$, CS_2.

The ordinary C̄ is the *cis*-*d*-isomer; $[\alpha]^{20}_{D} = +47.4°$ in alc. — [The *d,l*-compd. has m.p. 202°.] [For m.p.+ compn. curve for mixts. of the *d*- and *l*- forms see ⟨2⟩.]

On distn. C̄ loses aq. and is transformed to *d*-camphoric anhydride (1:0860) — C̄, on warm. with conc. H_2SO_4, loses 1 mole CO and is converted to sulfocamphylic ac.

C̄, on warming with PCl_5 is first dehydrated to *d*-camphoric anhydride (1:0860), but on further actn. *d*-camphoryl (di)chloride has been obtd. [Beil. IX-754]. [Protracted treatment with PCl_5 at 140° yields 3-chloro-*d*-camphoryl dichloride, m.p. 26° ⟨3⟩.]

C̄, boiled for 10 min. with 1 mole Ac_2O + a little $ZnCl_2$ ⟨4⟩, or C̄ htd. in stream of CO_2 ⟨5⟩ or C̄ boiled with $SOCl_2$ ⟨6⟩ yields *d*-camphoric anhydride (1:0860). [The latter may be freed from any unchanged C̄ by washing with cold Na_2CO_3 soln. or by soln. in $CHCl_3$, in which anhydride (but not the acid) dissolves.]

Ⓓ **Di-(*p*-nitrobenzyl) *d*-camphorate:** m.p. 66.5° ⟨7⟩ [cf. T 1.39].
Ⓓ ***d*-Camphoric diamide:** m.p. 192–193°. [Reported only by indirect prepn.] [The monoamide (*d*-camphoramic acid) exists in two isomeric forms: the α-amide-β-acid has m.p. 176°; the β-amide-α-acid isomer has m.p. 182–183°.] [*d*-Camphoric imide [Beil. XXI-416] has m.p. 245°.]

Ⓓ ***d*-Camphoric dianilide** [Beil. XII-310]: m.p. 226° [from *d*-camphoryl dichloride + excess aniline in ether ⟨8⟩]. [The α-monoanilide (*d*-camphor-α-anilic acid) has m.p. 209–210° ⟨9⟩, 202–203° ⟨10⟩; the β-monoanilide (*d*-camphor-β-anilic acid) has m.p. 196°.] [*d*-Camphoric acid anil (*N*-phenyl-*d*-camphoric imide) [Beil. XXI-418] has m.p. 117°.]

1:0810 ⟨1⟩ Campbell, *J. Am. Chem. Soc.* **53,** 1662–1664 (1931). ⟨2⟩ Ross, Somerville, *J. Chem. Soc.* **1926,** 2776–2777. ⟨3⟩ Bredt, Aman, *Ber.* **45,** 1425–1426 (1912). ⟨4⟩ Koenigs, Hoerlin, *Ber.* **26,** 817 (1893). ⟨5⟩ Brühl, *Ber.* **26,** 285 (1893). ⟨6⟩ Meyer, *Monatsh.* **22,** 420–421 (1901). ⟨7⟩ Lyons, Reid, *J. Am. Chem. Soc.* **39,** 1734 (1917). ⟨8⟩ Aschan, *Ber.* **28,** 531 (1895). ⟨9⟩ Singh, Puri, *J. Chem. Soc.* **1926,** 506. ⟨10⟩ von Auwers, Schleicher, *Ann.* **309,** 341–342 (1899).

1:0815 SALICYL-*O*-ACETIC ACID (*o*-Carboxyphenoxyacetic acid) —COOH —O.CH₂.COOH $C_9H_8O_5$ **Beil. X-69**

M.P. 191° Neut. Eq. 98

Ndls. from aq.; lfts. from C_6H_6 — Spar. sol. cold but eas. sol. hot in aq. or C_6H_6; sol. hot alc., ether, AcOH.

[For prepn. (e.g., for mixed m.p. detn.) from salicylic ac. (1:0780) + chloroacetic acid in alk. soln. see ⟨1⟩.] [For reactn. of esters with hydrazine hydrate see ⟨2⟩.]

1:0815 ⟨1⟩ Meyer, Duczmal, *Ber.* **46,** 3370–3371 (1913). ⟨2⟩ Curtius, Moll, *J. prakt. Chem.* (2) **125,** 113–115 (1930).

1:0817 *p*-ETHOXYBENZOIC ACID $C_9O_{10}O_3$ **Beil. X-156**

C_2H_5O—⟨ ⟩—COOH

M.P. 195-196° Neut. Eq. 166

Ndls. almost insol. hot aq. — [For prepn. from *p*-hydroxybenzoic ac. (1:0840) see ⟨1⟩; from *p*-bromophenetole via actn. of CO_2 on corresp. $C_2H_5O.C_6H_4.MgBr$ see ⟨2⟩.]

C̄, htd. at 100° with 10 pts. conc. HNO_3, poured into aq., etc., gives (80% yield ⟨3⟩) 3-nitro-4-ethoxybenzoic ac., pl. or rods from alc., m.p. 200–201° ⟨3⟩.

C̄, htd. in s.t. with conc. HCl at 130° yields *p*-hydroxybenzoic ac. (1:0840), m.p. 210° ⟨4⟩.

C̄, refluxed 2 hrs. with excess Ac_2O, gives (80% yield ⟨5⟩) *p*-ethoxybenzoic anhydride, cryst. from hot pet. ether, m.p. 108°.

C̄, with PCl_5 ⟨6⟩ or $SOCl_2$ ⟨7⟩ gives *p*-ethoxybenzoyl chloride, b.p. 160°_{20} ⟨6⟩, b.p. 140°_{13} ⟨7⟩.

Ⓓ ***p*-Ethoxybenzamide** [Beil. X-167]: m.p. 202° ⟨8⟩ (prepd. indirectly).

Ⓓ ***p*-Ethoxybenzanilide:** m.p. 169° ⟨5⟩, 172° ⟨8⟩.

1:0817 ⟨1⟩ Stephen, Bleloch, *J. Chem. Soc.* **1931,** 893. ⟨2⟩ Bodroux, *Bull. soc. chim.* (3) **31,** 31 (1904). ⟨3⟩ King, Murch, *J. Chem. Soc.* **127,** 2645. ⟨4⟩ Gattermann, *Ann.* **244,** 64 (1888). ⟨5⟩ Autenrieth, Thomae, *Ber.* **57,** 433 (1924). ⟨6⟩ Cohen, Dudley, *J. Chem. Soc.* **97,** 1741 (1910). ⟨7⟩ Rohmann, Scheurle, *Arch. Pharm.* **274,** 122 (1936). ⟨8⟩ Curtius, Ulmer, *J. prakt. Chem.* **125,** 59 (1930).

1:0820 *o*-PHTHALIC ACID (Benzene-1,2-dicarboxylic acid) —COOH —COOH $C_8H_6O_4$ **Beil. IX-791**

M.P. abt. 200° Neut. Eq. 83

The abs. m.p. of phthalic ac. varies considerably owing to loss of aq. and conversion to phthalic anhydride (1:0725) — The most careful work ⟨1⟩ indicates 208° ± 2°, but the cap.

m.p. is always lower — Suspected samples should always be subl. to phthalic anhyd., m.p. 130° (cf. 1:0725).

100 pts. aq. at 14° dis. 0.54 g. C̄ and at 99° 18 g. — 100 pts. abs. alc. at 18° dis. 11.7 g. C̄ — 100 pts. ether at 15° dis. 0.684 g. C̄ — C̄ is insol. in $CHCl_3$. [Use in sepn. from BzOH (1:0715) which is sol. ⟨2⟩.]

Evapn. of ether soln. of C̄ on aq. bath does not cause formn. of anhydride ⟨3⟩, nor is C̄ extracted by ether from alk. soln. ⟨3⟩.

KHĀ is much less sol. in aq. than the neutral K_2Ā, cryst. from hot aq. in anhydrous form, and is widely used as alkalimetric standard. [For extensive data on other salts see ⟨4⟩ ⟨5⟩.]

C̄ with $SOCl_2$ loses aq. yielding phthalic anhydride (1:0725). [Two phthalyl chlorides are known, however. The symmetrical phthalyl chloride [Beil. IX-805] can be obtd. in 92% yield by actn. of PCl_5 on phthalic anhydride and has m.p. 11–12°. On treatment of this isomer with $AlCl_3$ at 100° for 8–10 hrs. it rearranges (72% yield) to the unsymmetrical phthalyl chloride [Beil. XVII₁-(162)], cryst. from pet. ether, m.p. 87–89° ⟨6⟩ ⟨7⟩. For m.p. compn. data on mixts. of the two phthalyl chlorides see ⟨8⟩.]

Ⓟ **Fluorescein test:** see phthalic anhydride (1:0725).

Ⓓ **Phthalanil** [Beil. XXI-464]: Support a 6-in. tt. in a clamp so that its lower end rests in a 1-in. circular hole in a piece of asbestos board supported on an iron ring. Place in the tube 0.1 g. C̄ and 0.4–0.6 ml. of aniline. Heat for 15 min. with a very small flame so that the aniline refluxes 2–3 cm. above bottom of tube. Boil reaction prod. with 10 ml. 50% alc., cool, and filter ppt. Wash with 5 ml. cold water and recrystallize from 10 ml. strong alc. Dry at 100°; *o*-phthalanil cryst. in white plates, m.p. 207° ⟨9⟩.

Ⓓ **Di-(*p*-nitrobenzyl) phthalate:** m.p. 155.5° ⟨10⟩ [cf. T 1.39].

Ⓓ **Di-(phenacyl) phthalate:** m.p. 154.4° ⟨11⟩ [cf. T 1.391].

Ⓓ **Di-(*p*-bromophenacyl) phthalate:** m.p. 152.8° ⟨11⟩ [cf. T 1.391].

Ⓓ **Di-(*p*-phenylphenacyl) phthalate:** m.p. 167.5° ⟨12⟩ [cf. T 1.391].

Ⓓ **Phthalic dianilide:** m.p. 253–255° ⟨13⟩ [from ord. liq. phthalyl chloride + aniline in ether or C_6H_6; as so prepd. and washed with C_6H_6, etc. it melts abt. 231°. When recrystd. from alc., however, m.p. becomes 253–255° varying several degrees acc. to rate of htg. For reason for this effect see ⟨13⟩].

Ⓓ **Di-(*S*-benzylthiuronium) phthalate:** m.p. 151° cor. ⟨14⟩; 157–158° ⟨15⟩.

1:0820 ⟨1⟩ Monroe, *J. Ind. Eng. Chem.* **11**, 1116–1119 (1919). ⟨2⟩ Gilman, Kirby, *J. Am. Chem. Soc.* **54**, 351 (1932). ⟨3⟩ Dieckmann, Hardt, *Ber.* **52**, 1141–1142 (1919). ⟨4⟩ Ekely, Banta, *J. Am. Chem. Soc.* **39**, 759–768 (1917). ⟨5⟩ Ephraim, *Ber.* **55**, 3482 (1922). ⟨6⟩ Ott, *Organic Syntheses* **11**, 88–89 (1931). ⟨7⟩ Ott, *Ann.* **392**, 273–276 (1912). ⟨8⟩ Csányi, *Monatsh.* **40**, 87 (1919). ⟨9⟩ Mulliken, " Method " I, 85 (1904). ⟨10⟩ Lyman, Reid, *J. Am. Chem. Soc.* **39**, 709 (1917).

⟨11⟩ Kelly, Kleff, *J. Am. Chem. Soc.* **54**, 4444 (1932). ⟨12⟩ Drake, Sweeney, *J. Am. Chem. Soc.* **54**, 2060 (1932). ⟨13⟩ Dann, Davies, Hambly, Paul, Semmens, *J. Chem. Soc.* **1933**, 17, Note. ⟨14⟩ Donleavy, *J. Am. Chem. Soc.* **58**, 1005 (1936). ⟨15⟩ Veibel, Ottung, *Bull. soc. chim.* (5) **6**, 1435 (1939).

1:0825 *m*-HYDROXYBENZOIC ACID (—COOH, OH) $C_7H_6O_3$ Beil. X-134

M.P. 200° **Neut. Eq. 138**

Ndls. from aq.; tbls. or pr. from alc. — 100 g. aq. at 18.8° dis. 0.84 g. C̄; 100 ml. ether soln. at 17° conts. 9.7 g. C̄; 100 ml. acetone soln. at 23° conts. 26.0 g. C̄ — Eas. sol. alc., dif. sol. C_6H_6 — Sublimes; volatile with steam.

C̄ tastes faintly sweet — C̄ gives no color with $FeCl_3$ (T 1.41) — C̄ (0.02 g.) boiled with

5 ml. conc. H_2SO_4 gives or.-red (OR) soln. probably due to anthraquinone derivs. ⟨1⟩ [dif. from salicylic ac. (1:0780) which gives only pale yel. and from *p*-hydroxybenzoic ac. (1:0840) which gives or. yel. (OY-T_1)].

C̄ with PCl_5 does not yield the acid chloride but instead cpds. contg. P — C̄ with $SOCl_2$ ⟨2⟩ or better NaĀ + $SOCl_2$ ⟨3⟩ gives *m*-hydroxybenzoyl chloride, b.p. 110–113° at 0.5 mm. ⟨3⟩.

C̄ in 10% aq. NaOH shaken ½ hr. with dimethyl sulfate ⟨4⟩ or C̄ in dil. MeOH + NaOH + dimethyl sulfate (85% yield ⟨5⟩) gives *m*-methoxybenzoic ac. (1:0703), m.p. 109–110°. C̄ in MeOH htd. with conc. H_2SO_4 ⟨6⟩ gives methyl *m*-hydroxybenzoate, m.p. 70°.

Ⓓ ***m*-Acetoxybenzoic acid:** from C̄ in dil. aq. NaOH at 40° on treatment with Ac_2O (73% yield ⟨7⟩); on acidification prod. ppts.; cryst. from alc. or C_6H_6 + lgr.; m.p. 131.5° ⟨8⟩, 128° ⟨7⟩; Neut. Eq. 180. [The *p*-nitrobenzyl ester of this deriv. (cf. T 1.39) has m.p. 139–140° ⟨9⟩.]

Ⓓ ***m*-Carboxy-phenoxyacetic acid:** from C̄ + chloroacetic ac. in boilg. conc. NaOH (68% yield), ndls. from boilg. aq., m.p. 206–207° ⟨10⟩; Neut. Eq. 98 [cf. T 1.46].

Ⓓ ***p*-Nitrobenzyl *m*-hydroxybenzoate:** m.p. 106–108° ⟨11⟩, 106° ⟨12⟩ [cf. T 1.39]. [The corresponding ether-ester, viz., *p*-nitrobenzyl *m*-(*p*-nitrobenzyloxy)benzoate can readily be obtd. under specified conditions ⟨11⟩; m.p. 142–144°; the corresponding ether-acid, viz., 3-(*p*-nitrobenzyloxy)benzoic acid, has m.p. 193–196° ⟨11⟩.]

Ⓓ **Phenacyl *m*-hydroxybenzoate:** m.p. 146.5° (79% yield) ⟨13⟩ [cf. T 1.391].

Ⓓ ***p*-Bromophenacyl *m*-hydroxybenzoate:** m.p. 176.1–176.4° cor. ⟨14⟩; 168° (79% yield ⟨13⟩ [cf. T 1.391].

Ⓓ ***m*-Hydroxybenzamide:** from *m*-hydroxybenzoyl chloride (above) in $CHCl_3$ + dry NH_3 ⟨3⟩ or from ethyl *m*-hydroxybenzoate (1:1471) + conc. aq. NH_4OH; lfts. from hot aq., m.p. 167° ⟨3⟩.

Ⓓ ***m*-Hydroxybenzanilide** [Beil. XII-502]: from *m*-hydroxybenzoyl chloride (above) in $CHCl_3$ + aniline ⟨3⟩; ndls. from hot aq. or dil. alc., m.p. 156–157°.

Ⓓ ***m*-Hydroxybenzo-*p*-toluidide:** similarly; ndls. from dil. alc., m.p. 163° ⟨3⟩.

1:0825 ⟨1⟩ Offerman, *Ann.* **280,** 7 (1894). ⟨2⟩ Meyer, *Monatsh.* **22,** 430 (1901). ⟨3⟩ Anschütz, Krone, *Ann.* **442,** 41–42 (1925). ⟨4⟩ Graebe, *Ann.* **340,** 211 (1905). ⟨5⟩ Ewins, *J. Chem. Soc.* **101,** 548 (1912). ⟨6⟩ Tingle, *Am. Chem. J.* **25,** 155 (1901). ⟨7⟩ Lesser, Gad, *Ber.* **59,** 234 (1926). ⟨8⟩ Anschütz, Motschmann, *Ann.* **392,** 114 (1912). ⟨9⟩ Lyons, Reid, *J. Am. Chem. Soc.* **39,** 1736 (1917). ⟨10⟩ Meyer, Duczmal, *Ber.* **46,** 3372 (1913).

⟨11⟩ Blicke, Smith, *J. Am. Chem. Soc.* **51,** 1948–1949 (1928). ⟨12⟩ Lyman, Reid, *J. Am. Chem. Soc.* **39,** 704 (1917). ⟨13⟩ Kelly, Howard, *J. Am. Chem. Soc.* **54,** 4384 (1932). ⟨14⟩ Lund, Langvad, *J. Am. Chem. Soc.* **54,** 4107 (1932).

1:0830 SYRINGIC ACID $C_9H_{10}O_5$ Beil. X-480

(3,5-Dimethoxy-4-hydroxybenzoic acid)

CH_3O / HO— / —COOH / CH_3O

M.P. 207-208° cor. ⟨1⟩ **Neut. Eq. 198**
after sintering
at 198° cor.

Ndls. from aq. or ether — Very spar. sol. cold aq.; fairly sol. alc., ether, $CHCl_3$.

[For prepn. (83% yield ⟨2⟩) by actn. of conc. H_2SO_4 at 40–50° on gallic acid trimethyl ether see ⟨3⟩ ⟨4⟩ ⟨5⟩ ⟨6⟩.]

C̄ htd. in a distg. flask to 240° evolves CO_2 and gives (70–72% yield ⟨7⟩ ⟨2⟩) 2,6-dimethoxyphenol (pyrogallol-1,3-dimethyl ether) [Beil. VI-1081], b.p. 262–263°, m.p. 55–56°.

C̄ in 15 vols. $CHCl_3$, refluxed 2 hrs. with 0.84 pt. by wt. of Br_2, solv. evapd. and prod. recrystd. from very dil. AcOH gives 95% yield 2-bromosyringic acid, m.p. 155° ⟨8⟩.

C̄ in MeOH, satd. with HCl gas, refluxed, gives (78% yield ⟨6⟩; 85% yield ⟨2⟩) methyl syringate, which after drying at 110° becomes anhydrous, m.p. 107–108° ⟨6⟩ ⟨5⟩.

Ⓓ **Acetylsyringic acid (4-acetoxy-3,5-dimethoxybenzoic acid):** from C̄ in cold alk. soln. shaken with ether soln. of Ac_2O, and acidif. of aq. layer (83% yield ⟨9⟩); or from C̄ + Ac_2O at 100° if $ZnCl_2$ or pyridine is added (98% yield ⟨4⟩); or from C̄ dislvd. in 3 pts. Ac_2O and stood overnight at room temp. with trace of NaOAc (78% yield ⟨5⟩). M.p. 187°. [Note that acetylation with boiling Ac_2O alone gives a mixt. ⟨9⟩ ⟨10⟩ (m.p. 190–191°) of acetylsyringic ac. (m.p. 187°) and its anhydride, m.p. 195–197°.]

Ⓓ **Benzoylsyringic acid (4-benzoxy-3,5-dimethoxybenzoic acid):** from C̄ in dil. aq. NaOH shaken with BzCl at room temp.; on acidif. + purif. by extraction with hot aq. gives residue (49% yield ⟨11⟩); ndls. from AcOH, m.p. 229–232° after softening at 215°.

1:0830 ⟨1⟩ Fischer, Freudenberg, *Ber.* **45**, 2718 (1912). ⟨2⟩ Hahn, Wassmuth, *Ber.* **67**, 701–702 (1934). ⟨3⟩ Mauthner, *J. prakt. Chem.* (2) **142**, 29 (1935). ⟨4⟩ Bradley, Robinson, *J. Chem. Soc.* **1928**, 1553. ⟨5⟩ Bogert, Coyne, *J. Am. Chem. Soc.* **51**, 571–572 (1929). ⟨6⟩ Bogert, Ehrlich, *J. Am. Chem. Soc.* **41**, 799–800 (1919). ⟨7⟩ Hunter, Levine, *J. Am. Chem. Soc.* **48**, 1611 (1926). ⟨8⟩ Levine, *J. Am. Chem. Soc.* **48**, 799 (1926). ⟨9⟩ Levy, Posternack, Robinson, *J. Chem. Soc.* **1931**, 2704–2705. ⟨10⟩ Anderson, Nabenhauer, *J. Am. Chem. Soc.* **48**, 3001–3002 (1926).
⟨11⟩ Heap, Robinson, *J. Chem. Soc.* **1929**, 70–71.

1:0835 *o*-COUMARIC ACID (*trans-o*-Hydroxycinnamic acid)

CH ‖ HC—COOH; OH $C_9H_8O_3$ **Beil. X-288**

M.P. 208° **Neut. Eq. 164**

Ndls. from aq. — Spar. sol. cold aq. or ether; insol. $CHCl_3$, CS_2 — Eas. sol. alc. — Sublimes but is not volatile with steam — C̄ cryst. from aq. with 1 H_2O which is lost only after 8 days at 120° ⟨1⟩.

C̄ on exposure to light for 2 weeks gives a dimer ⟨2⟩, α-dicoumaric acid [Beil. X-570], cryst. from boilg. aq., m.p. 318° ⟨3⟩.

C̄ htd. above its m.p. [cf. T 1.33] loses CO_2 and yields *o*-vinylphenol [Beil. VI-560] ⟨1⟩. C̄ on fusion with KOH yields salicylic acid (1:0780) and acetic ac. (1:1010) — C̄ with $FeCl_3$ (T 1.41) yields yel.-red ppt.

C̄ on boiling with small amt. $HgCl_2$ gives alm. quant. yield ⟨4⟩ of coumarin (1:4910), m.p. 67°.

Ⓟ **Fluorescence of alk. solns.:** solns. of C̄ in dil. alk. or NH_4OH show charact. green fluores. by reflected light.

Ⓓ **Acetylcoumaric acid (*o*-acetoxycinnamic acid):** from C̄ on htg. with Ac_2O, pouring into aq. ⟨5⟩ and repeated crystn. from C_6H_6, m.p. 154–155° ⟨6⟩.

Ⓓ ***p*-Nitrobenzyl *o*-coumarate:** m.p. 152.5° ⟨7⟩ [cf. T 1.39].

1:0835 ⟨1⟩ Kunze-Krause, Manicke, *Arch. Pharm.* **267**, 566–567 (1929). ⟨2⟩ Ström, *Ber.* **37**, 1384 (1904). ⟨3⟩ DeJong, *Rec. trav. chim.* **43**, 319 (1924). ⟨4⟩ Seshadri, Rao, *Cent.* **1937**, I, 4621. ⟨5⟩ Stoermer, *Ber.* **44**, 650–651 (1911). ⟨6⟩ Roth, Stoermer, *Ber.* **46**, 268 (1913). ⟨7⟩ Lyons, Reid, *J. Am. Chem. Soc.* **39**, 1739–1740 (1917).

1:0840 *p*-HYDROXYBENZOIC ACID HO—$\langle\ \ \rangle$—COOH $C_7H_6O_3$ Beil. X-149

M.P. 210° (213°) **Neut. Eq. 138**

Anhydrous pr. from xylene + abs. alc., acetone, EtOAc or CCl_4; tbls. with 1 H_2O from aq., ether, dil. alc., the hydrate water being lost over conc. H_2SO_4 or at 100°. Very eas. sol. alc.; 100 ml. ether soln. at 17° conts. 9.43 g. $\bar{C}$; 100 ml. acetone soln. at 23° conts. 22.7 g. $\bar{C}$ — Spar. sol. aq., C_6H_6; insol. $CHCl_3$ [dif. and sepn. from salicylic acid (1:0780)] or CS_2 [dif. and sepn. from benzoic acid (1:0715)]. [For prepn. (70–80% yield) by htg. K salicylate + K_2CO_3 at 230° see ⟨1⟩.]

$\bar{C}$ is best titrated (T 1.31) using bromthymol blue as indicator ⟨2⟩ — $\bar{C}$ with $FeCl_3$ (T 1.41) gives yel. amorph. ppt., sol. in excess reagt. — $\bar{C}$ htd. at 200-220° decomposes alm. quant. into CO_2 + phenol (1:1420) — $\bar{C}$ fused with phthalic anhyd. + H_2SO_4 (T 1.42) yields phenolphthalein ⟨3⟩ [dif. from *m*-hydroxybenzoic acid (1:0825)].

$\bar{C}$ with PCl_5 gives complex cpds. contg. P and with $SOCl_2$ ⟨4⟩ is unattacked; Na$\bar{A}$, however, with $SOCl_2$ ⟨5⟩ yields *p*-hydroxybenzoyl chloride as an oil.

$\bar{C}$ in dil. aq. NaOH shaken with dimethylsulfate yields methyl *p*-methoxybenzoate, which on boiling with addnl. alk. and subsequent acidification gives 80–84% yield *p*-methoxybenzoic ac. (1:0805), m.p. 184° ⟨6⟩ — $\bar{C}$ in MeOH with conc. H_2SO_4 ⟨7⟩ ⟨8⟩ or with HCl gas ⟨8⟩ yields methyl *p*-hydroxybenzoate (1:1549), m.p. 131°. [For study of detect. + detn. of $\bar{C}$ see ⟨9⟩ ⟨10⟩.]

Ⓓ ***p*-Acetoxybenzoic acid:** from $\bar{C}$ in dil. aq. NaOH at 40° on treatment with Ac_2O (73% yield) ⟨11⟩; on acidification prod. ppts.; lfts. from $CHCl_3$, m.p. 191–192° cor. ⟨11⟩; 185° ⟨12⟩, Neut. Eq. 180; in 100% yield from $\bar{C}$ + Ac_2O + 1 drop H_2SO_4 ⟨13⟩.

Ⓓ ***p*-Carboxyphenoxyacetic acid:** from $\bar{C}$ + chloroacetic ac. in boilg. conc. NaOH (70% yield) ⟨14⟩; ndls. from hot aq., m.p. 278°; Neut Eq.. 98 [cf. T 1.46].

Ⓓ ***p*-Nitrobenzyl *p*-hydroxybenzoate:** m.p. 180–182° ⟨15⟩ [cf. T 1.39]. [The corresponding ether-ester, viz., *p*-nitrobenzyl 4-(*p*-nitrobenzyloxy)benzoate can readily be obtd. under specified cond. ⟨15⟩, m.p. 196–197°; the corresponding ether-acid, viz., 4-(*p*-nitrobenzyloxy)benzoic acid has m.p. 259–261° ⟨15⟩.]

Ⓓ **Phenacyl *p*-hydroxybenzoate:** m.p. 178° (91% yield) ⟨16⟩ [cf. T 1.391].

Ⓓ ***p*-Bromophenacyl *p*-hydroxybenzoate:** m.p. 191.5° cor. ⟨17⟩; 184° (79% yield) ⟨16⟩ [cf. T 1.391].

Ⓓ ***p*-Phenylphenacyl *p*-hydroxybenzoate:** m.p. 240° ⟨18⟩ [cf. T 1.391].

Ⓓ ***p*-Hydroxybenzamide:** from *p*-hydroxybenzoyl chloride (above) in $CHCl_3$ + dry NH_3 ⟨5⟩; ndls. with 1 H_2O from aq., m.p. 162°.

Ⓓ ***p*-Hydroxybenzanilide** [Beil. XII-502]: similarly using aniline ⟨5⟩; yellowish lfts. from hot aq., m.p. 196–197° ⟨5⟩.

Ⓓ ***p*-Hydroxybenzo-*p*-toluidide:** similarly using *p*-toluidine ⟨5⟩; ndls. from alc., m.p. 203–204°.

Ⓓ ***S*-Benzylthiuronium *p*-hydroxybenzoate:** m.p. 143–145° ⟨19⟩.

1:0840 ⟨1⟩ Buehler, Cate, *Organic Syntheses* **14,** 48–50 (1934). ⟨2⟩ Kolthoff, *J. Am. Chem. Soc.* **57,** 973–974 (1935). ⟨3⟩ Formanek, Knop, *Z. anal. Chem.* **56,** 296 (1917). ⟨4⟩ Meyer, *Monatsh.* **22,** 431 (1901). ⟨5⟩ Anschütz, Zerbe, *Ann.* **442,** 38 (1925). ⟨6⟩ Graebe, *Ann.* **340,** 210–211 (1905). ⟨7⟩ Reverdin, *Bull soc. chim.* (4) **3,** 592 (1908). ⟨8⟩ von Hoessle, *J. prakt. Chem.* (2) **49,** 501 (1894). ⟨9⟩ Edwards, Nanji, Hassan, *Analyst* **62,** 178–185 (1937). ⟨10⟩ Stevenson, Resuggan, *Analyst* **63,** 152–155 (1938).

⟨11⟩ Lesser, Gad, *Ber.* **59,** 233–234 (1926). ⟨12⟩ Anschütz, Motschmann, *Ann.* **392,** 116 (1912). ⟨13⟩ Robertson, Robinson, *J. Chem. Soc.* **1926,** 1714. ⟨14⟩ Meyer, Duczmal, *Ber.* **46,** 3373–3374 (1913). ⟨15⟩ Blicke, Smith, *J. Am. Chem. Soc.* **51,** 1948–1949 (1929). ⟨16⟩ Kelly, Howard, *J. Am. Chem. Soc.* **54,** 4384 (1932). ⟨17⟩ Lund, Langvad, *J. Am. Chem. Soc.* **54,** 4107 (1932). ⟨18⟩ Drake, Sweeney, *J. Am. Chem. Soc.* **54,** 2060 (1932). ⟨19⟩ Veibel, Ottung, *Bull. soc. chim.* (5) **6,** 1435 (1939).

1:0843 **β-RESORCYLIC ACID** HO—⟨ring⟩—COOH (OH) $C_7H_6O_4$ **Beil. X-377**
(2,4-Dihydroxybenzoic acid)

M.P. 213° rap. htg., dec. **Neut. Eq. 154**
(see text)

Ndls. from ether with 3 moles H_2O; cryst. from aq. with various hydrations acc. to conditions; loses cryst. aq. at 100° — Owing to easy loss of CO_2 on htg. (even before fusion) C̄ is reported as melting at temps. varying from 194–236°. [For prepn. in 57–60% yield from resorcinol (1:1530) + $KHCO_3$ soln. + CO_2 see ⟨1⟩.]

C̄ with $FeCl_3$ (T 1.41) gives pure red color changing to brown with excess reagt. — C̄ with NaOCl or $Ca(OCl)_2$ soln. gives first a violet color, then red. C̄ htd. with phthalic anhyd. + trace conc. H_2SO_4 (T 1.42) loses CO_2 and therefore yields fluorescein ⟨2⟩, eas. detected by charact. fluorescence of its alk. soln.

C̄ refluxed 3 hrs. with $SOCl_2$ gives nearly quant. yield ⟨13⟩ 2,4-dihydroxybenzoyl chloride, m.p. 142° ⟨13⟩.

C̄ in AcOH treated at 30–35° with 1 mole Br_2 in AcOH and mixt. poured into aq. gives (57–63% yield) 2,4-dihydroxy-5-bromobenzoic ac., cryst. from aq., m.p. 206.5–208.5° cor. ⟨4⟩. [This prod. on 24-hr. refluxing with aq., followed by extn. with ether, gives (90–92% yield) 4-bromoresorcinol, m.p. after evapn. of $CHCl_3$ soln. 100–102° ⟨4⟩.]

C̄, refluxed 10 hrs. with 3.5 pts. MeOH + $\frac{1}{5}$ pt. conc. H_2SO_4, excess MeOH distd. and aq. added gives (55% yield ⟨5⟩) methyl 2,4-dihydroxybenzoate, cryst. from MeOH or $CHCl_3$ dried in vac. at 60–70°, m.p. 118–119° ⟨5⟩; 121–122° ⟨6⟩. [Note, however, that C̄ in abs. MeOH treated with dry HCl gas gives 65% yield of a methyl 2,4-dihydroxybenzoate, ndls. from hot aq.; m.p. 76° ⟨13⟩.]

- Ⓓ ***p*-Nitrobenzyl 2,4-dihydroxybenzoate:** m.p. 188–189° ⟨11⟩ [cf. T 1.39].
- Ⓓ **2,4-Dimethoxybenzoic acid:** from C̄ + dimethyl sulfate in 10% NaOH, followed by saponification of intermediate ester in hot excess alk.; 92% yield; cryst. from dil. AcOH, m.p. 108° ⟨7⟩.
- Ⓓ **2,4-Diacetoxybenzoic acid:** from C̄ treated with 2 pts. Ac_2O + 2 pts. dry pyridine with ice cooling; stood 18 hrs. at room temp., poured into dil. H_2SO_4, oil separated and extd. with $KHCO_3$ soln. gives on acidification of latter 91% yield ⟨8⟩; pr. from hot MeOH on addn. of aq., m.p. 136–138° ⟨9⟩, 142° ⟨12⟩ [also obt. from C̄ (74% yield) by warming with Ac_2O + $ZnCl_2$ ⟨9⟩]. [C̄ dislvd. 10 pts. 2 *N* NaOH, rap. treated at 50–60° with 1 pt. Ac_2O gives on stirring and cooling, the dif. sol. Na salt of the mono-acetyl deriv. After filtn. and decompn. with HCl, and recrystn. from C_6H_6 there is obtd. 4-acetoxy-2-hydroxybenzoic ac., m.p. 152–153° ⟨10⟩.]

1:0843 ⟨1⟩ Nierenstein, Clibbens, *Organic Syntheses* **10**, 94–95 (1930). ⟨2⟩ Sah, Yen, *Science Repts. Natl. Tsing Hua Univ.*, Ser. **A-1**, 269–276 (1932); *Cent.* **1933**, I, 3560. ⟨4⟩ Sandin, McKee, *Organic Syntheses* **17**, 22–23 (1937). ⟨5⟩ Robinson, Shah, *J. Chem. Soc.* **1934**, 1496. ⟨6⟩ Pacsu, *Ber.* **56**, 418 (1923). ⟨7⟩ Robinson, Venkataraman, *J. Chem. Soc.* **1929**, 62–63. ⟨8⟩ Ref. 6, page 413. ⟨9⟩ Bergmann, Dangschat, *Ber.* **52**, 379 (1919). ⟨10⟩ Lesser, Gad, *Ber.* **59**, 234 (1926).

⟨11⟩ Lyons, Reid, *J. Am. Chem. Soc.* **39**, 1735 (1917). ⟨12⟩ Couturier, *Ann. chim.* (11) **10**, 570 (1938). ⟨13⟩ Scott, Kearse, *J. Org. Chem.* **5**, 600–603 (1940).

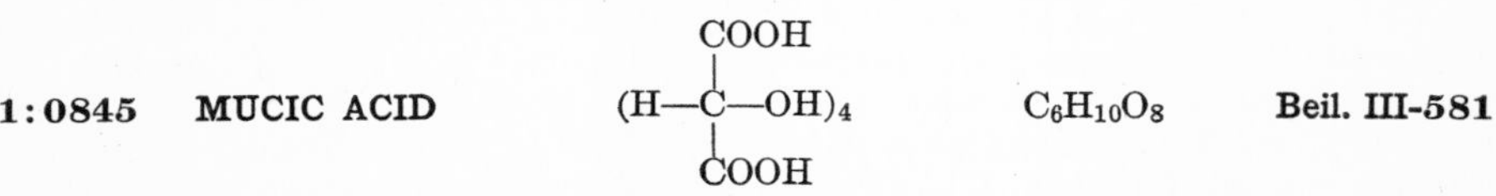

1:0845 **MUCIC ACID** COOH—(H—C—OH)$_4$—COOH $C_6H_{10}O_8$ **Beil. III-581**

M.P. 214° dec. (slow htg.)
223–224° dec. (rap. htg.) ⟨1⟩ **Neut. Eq.** (see text)

Sandy cryst. powd., sol. in 300 pts. aq. at 14° [dif. from saccharic acid which is eas. sol. aq.] — C̄ is more sol. in boric ac. soln. than in aq. — C̄ is insol. alc.

Boiling aq. soln. of C̄ or evapn. over free flame causes formation of lactone, very sol. in and unrecrystallizable from aq. — Titration of C̄ in ice water neutralizes only the mucic ac.; any lactone present is saponified only on htg. ⟨2⟩ ⟨3⟩ ⟨4⟩.

C̄ on dry htg. gives pyromucic (furoic) acid (1:0475) — C̄ evaporated with excess conc. aq. NH_4OH on steam bath, and resultant ammonium mucate mixed with glycerol and distilled gives (37–40% yield) pyrrole ⟨5⟩. [For further information see also ⟨6⟩ ⟨7⟩.]

Ⓟ **Pyrrole reaction:** In a 6-in. tt. mix 0.01 g. C̄ with 5 drops conc. NH_4OH and evap. to dryness. Hold in the upper part of the tt. a soft pine splinter that has been soaked in conc. HCl, and ignite the NH_4 mucate residue strongly. The evolved pyrrole vapors develop bright red color in the splinter! ⟨8.⟩

Ⓓ **Diethyl mucate:** from C̄ with EtOH + conc. H_2SO_4; (80% yield ⟨1⟩); cryst. from alc. or hot aq., m.p. 163–164° ⟨1⟩.

Ⓓ **Di-(*p*-phenylphenacyl) mucate:** m.p. 149.5° dec. ⟨9⟩ [cf. T 1.391].

Ⓓ **Tetra-acetylmucic acid (tetraacetoxyadipic acid):** from C̄ boiled with Ac_2O + $ZnCl_2$ ⟨10⟩ ⟨11⟩, or from C̄ + Ac_2O + conc. H_2SO_4 ⟨12⟩ ⟨11⟩; pr. with 2 EtOH from alc. or with 2 H_2O from aq., easily lost before fusion at 242–243° ⟨11⟩ ⟨12⟩. [This prod. is a strong ac. and readily titrated (Neut. Eq. 189) or saponified (Neut. Eq. 63).] [Dry tetra-acetylmucic ac. with PCl_5 + AcCl ⟨13⟩ or with $SOCl_2$ at 100° ⟨14⟩, or in AcCl + trace H_2SO_4 ⟨15⟩, or in C_6H_6 ⟨16⟩ gives tetra-acetylmucoyl chloride, m.p. 185°.]

Ⓓ **Di-(*S*-benzylthiuronium) mucate:** m.p. 194–195° ⟨17⟩.

1:0845 ⟨1⟩ Behrend, Heyer, *Ann.* **418,** 312 (1919). ⟨2⟩ Fischer, *Ber.* **24,** 2141 (1891). ⟨3⟩ Khotinsky, Epifanowa, *Bull. soc. chim.* (4) **37,** 552 (1925). ⟨4⟩ Taylor, Acree, *J. Phys. Chem.* **20,** 118–120 (1916). ⟨5⟩ McElvain, Bolliger, *Organic Syntheses, Coll. Vol.* I, 461–463 (1932). ⟨6⟩ Blicke, Blake, *J. Am. Chem. Soc.* **52,** 237 (1930). ⟨7⟩ Blicke, Powers, *Ind. Eng. Chem.* **19,** 1334–1335 (1927). ⟨8⟩ Mulliken, "Method" I, 69 (1904). ⟨9⟩ Drake, Bronitsky, *J. Am. Chem. Soc.* **52,** 3720 (1930). ⟨10⟩ Maquenne, *Bull. soc. chim.* (2) **48,** 720 (1887).

⟨11⟩ Kremann, *Monatsh.* **26,** 796 (1905). ⟨12⟩ Skraup, *Monatsh.* **14,** 488 (1893). ⟨13⟩ Diels, Löflund, *Ber.* **47,** 2352 (1914). ⟨14⟩ Müller, *Ber.* **47,** 2655 (1914). ⟨15⟩ Simon, Guillaumin, *Compt. rend.* **179,** 1324–1326 (1924). ⟨16⟩ Kariyone, Morotomi, *Cent.* **1929,** I, 2524. ⟨17⟩ Veibel, Ottung, *Bull. soc. chim.* (5) **6,** 1435 (1939).

1:0850 2-HYDROXY-3-NAPHTHOIC ACID $C_{11}H_8O_3$ Beil. X-333

—OH
—COOH

M.P. 216° u.c. **Neut. Eq. 188**
222-223° cor.

Impt. common component of Naphthol AS dyes [for survey of the AS-Naphthols derived from C̄ see ⟨1⟩].

Pale yel. lfts. from aq. [cf. ⟨2⟩] alc., acetone, or AcOH — Alm. insol. cold aq.; spar. sol. hot aq.; eas. sol. alc., ether; sol. $CHCl_3$, C_6H_6 — Volatile with steam.

C̄ in aq. soln. with $FeCl_3$ (T 1.41) gives blue color. [For study of nature of the complex see ⟨3⟩.] [C̄ on oxidn. in very dil. aq. soln. with excess $FeCl_3$ gives (75% yield ⟨4⟩; 60–90% yield ⟨5⟩) 2,2′-dihydroxy-3,3′-dicarboxy-1,1′-dinaphthyl, m.p. 331–333° cor. ⟨4⟩.]

C̄, suspended in 4 pts. pet. ether (b.p. 70–80°) + 1 pt. $SOCl_2$ and refluxed until clear brown soln. results (4–5 hrs.), gives on cooling 82% yield ⟨6⟩ of 2-hydroxy-3-naphthoyl chloride, m.p. 96° ⟨6⟩; 94.5° ⟨7⟩. [Under many other conditions C̄ with $SOCl_2$ yields a yellow amorphous cpd., m.p. indefinitely 290–295° and probably a depside from autocondensation of the chloride with itself ⟨6⟩ ⟨7⟩.]

C̄, htd. at 100° with slightly more than 1 mole PCl_5 gives P-contg. cpd. $C_{10}H_6$(O.PO.Cl_2)-(CO.Cl), m.p. 63°, which on stdg. over aq. KOH yields the corresp. ac. $C_{10}H_6$(O.PO(OH)$_2$)-(COOH), m.p. 174°, eas. sol. hot aq. ⟨8⟩.

C̄ dislvd. in 20% NaOH, treated at 15° with dimethyl sulfate, and subsequently acidified gives (96% yield ⟨9⟩) 2-methoxy-3-naphthoic ac., slightly yel. cryst. from AcOH or alc., m.p. 133–135° ⟨9⟩; 133–134° ⟨10⟩; Neut. Eq. 202. [Use of too much alk. decreases yield and too much dimethyl sulfate leads to contamination with methyl 2-methoxy-3-naphthoate, m.p. 49°; 63–65° ⟨11⟩.]

C̄ boiled with 1½–2 pts. Ac_2O and then treated with 1 drop conc. H_2SO_4 gives on cooling (alm. 100% yield ⟨12⟩) 2-acetoxynaphthoic acid-3; colorless ndls. from alc., m.p. 184–186° cor. ⟨12⟩; 178° ⟨13⟩.

C̄ in 20% aq. NaOH shaken with BzCl at 0° gives 2-benzoxynaphthoic acid-3, ndls. from alc., m.p. 208–209° cor. ⟨12⟩.

Ⓓ **Methyl 2-hydroxy-3-naphthoate:** pale yel. ndls. from alc., m.p. 73–74° [from C̄ in MeOH + dry HCl gas at 70° ⟨14⟩ or with conc. H_2SO_4 ⟨15⟩].

Ⓓ **Ethyl 2-hydroxy-3-naphthoate:** m.p. 85°.

Ⓓ **2-Hydroxy-3-naphthoamide:** yel. ndls. from AcOH or alc., m.p. 217–218° cor. [from acid chloride + dry NH_3 gas in C_6H_6 ⟨12⟩ ⟨16⟩].

Ⓓ **2-Hydroxy-3-naphthoic anilide** (Naphthol-AS) [Beil. XII-505]: lfts. from AcOH or chlorobenzene, m.p. 243–244° u.c.; 249° cor. [from C̄ htd. with 1 mole aniline in presence of a little PCl_3 ⟨17⟩]. [For hydrolysis of Naphthol AS and its homologues in their identification see ⟨18⟩ ⟨19⟩; for estimation see ⟨20⟩.]

Ⓓ **2-Hydroxy-3-naphthoic *p*-toluidide** [Beil. XII_1-(429)]: m.p. 221–222°.

Ⓓ **2-Hydroxy-3-naphthoic α-naphthalide** (Naphthol AS-BO) [Beil. XII_1-(528)]: cryst. from AcOH, m.p. 222–223° ⟨18⟩ ⟨20⟩.

Ⓓ **2-Hydroxy-3-naphthoic β-naphthalide** (Naphthol AS-SM): ndls. from chlorobenzene, m.p. 243–244° ⟨18⟩.

1:0850 ⟨1⟩ Dorman, *Am. Dyestuff Reptr.* **28,** 79, 101 (1939). ⟨2⟩ Lesser, Kranepuhl, Gad, *Ber.* **58,** 2115 (1925). ⟨3⟩ Ioffe, Krylova, *Chem. Abs.* **31,** 676 (1937); *Cent.* **1937,** I, 2590. ⟨4⟩ Stanley, Adams, *Rec. trav. chim.* **48,** 1037 (1929). ⟨5⟩ Ioffe, Smolyanitzkaya, *Chem. Abs.* **30,** 1048 (1936). ⟨6⟩ Bhat, Forster, Venkataraman, *J. Soc. Dyers Colourists* **56,** 170 (1940). ⟨7⟩ Abrahart, *J. Chem. Soc.* **1938,** 426. ⟨8⟩ Hosaeus, *Ber.* **26,** 667–668 (1893). ⟨9⟩ Jambuserwala, Holt, Mason, *J. Chem. Soc.* **1931,** 374. ⟨10⟩ von Auwers, Frühling, *Ann.* **422,** 197 (1921).

⟨11⟩ Ref. 2, page 2119. ⟨12⟩ Ref. 2, page 2116. ⟨13⟩ Brass, Sommer, *Ber.* **61,** 1002 (1928). ⟨14⟩ Friedl, *Monatsh.* **31,** 923 (1910). ⟨15⟩ Cohen, Dudley, *J. Chem. Soc.* **97,** 1748 (1910). ⟨16⟩ Fries, *Ber.* **58,** 2848 (1925). ⟨17⟩ Schöpff, *Ber.* **25,** 2744 (1892). ⟨18⟩ Rowe, Levin, *J. Soc. Dyers Colourists* **40,** 227–228 (1924). ⟨19⟩ Rowe, Giles, *J. Soc. Dyers Colourists* **51,** 287 (1935). ⟨20⟩ Mehta, Thosar, *J. Soc. Dyers Colourists* **56,** 160–165 (1940).

1:0851 DIPHENIC ANHYDRIDE $C_{14}H_8O_3$ **Beil. XVII-526**

O
C
O
C
O

M.P. 217° ⟨1⟩ ⟨2⟩

White cryst. insol. aq., very sl. sol. ether — Insol. cold aq. Na_2CO_3 [dif. and sepn. from diphenic ac.]; sol. in warm aq. alk. from which soln. minl. ac. ppts. diphenic acid (1:0870). [C̄ is readily prepd. (97% yield ⟨1⟩) by refluxing diphenic acid (1:0870) with equal wt. Ac_2O for 1 hr; the anhydride cryst. on cooling ⟨1⟩ ⟨2⟩.]

$\bar{C}$ responds to Generic Test 3-B (titration in alc.); Neut. Eq. in alcohol (T 1.31) is 224; Sap. Eq. in aq. alk. (T 1.51) is 112.

$\bar{C}$ on cautious htg. can be sublimed but htg. 2 hrs. at 360° gives quant. yield fluorenone (1:9014) + CO_2 ⟨3⟩ — $\bar{C}$, htd. with PCl_5, gives (91% yield ⟨1⟩) diphenic acid (di)chloride.

$\bar{C}$ boiled with MeOH gives methyl hydrogen diphenate, tbls. from MeOH, m.p. 110°; Neut. Eq. 256 — $\bar{C}$ boiled with EtOH gives ethyl hydrogen diphenate, m.p. 88°; Neut. Eq. 270.

Ⓓ **Fluorenone-4-carboxylic acid:** $\bar{C}$ dissolves in *cold* conc. H_2SO_4 without color; on warm. to 100–120° soln. turns red and on pouring into water gives quant. yield of fluorenone-4-carboxylic acid (1:9087), yel. cryst. from alc. or AcOH, m.p. 227° ⟨4⟩.

Ⓓ **Diphenamic acid:** from $\bar{C}$, digested with conc. NH_4OH at room temp. ⟨5⟩ or boiled for one hour ⟨6⟩, followed by pptn. with minl. ac. from hot soln., in quant. yield; lfts. from hot water, m.p. 190–191°. [On htg. above its m.p. this product loses aq. and yields diphenimide, m.p. 217–218° ⟨5⟩.]

Ⓓ **Diphenanilic acid (diphenic monoanilide):** from $\bar{C}$ + 1 mole aniline in C_6H_6 (best by mixing C_6H_6 solns. of equal moles); cryst. from alc., m.p. 176° ⟨7⟩; Neut. Eq. 317. [This monoanilide dis. in $SOCl_2$ and on evapn. + recrystn. from alc. yields diphenanil (*N*-phenyldiphenimide), colorless ndls., m.p. 199° ⟨7⟩.]

1:0851 ⟨1⟩ Roberts, Johnson, *J. Am. Chem. Soc.* **47,** 1399 (1925). ⟨2⟩ Graebe, Aubin, *Ann.* **247,** 264 (1888). ⟨3⟩ Huntress, Hershberg, Cliff, *J. Am. Chem. Soc.* **53,** 2724 (1931). ⟨4⟩ Ref. 2, pages 266, 275. ⟨5⟩ Wegerhoff, *Ann.* **252,** 24 (1889). ⟨6⟩ Oyster, Adkins, *J. Am. Chem. Soc.* **43,** 209 (1921). ⟨7⟩ Warren, Briggs, *Ber.* **64,** 30 (1931).

1:0860 *d*-CAMPHORIC ANHYDRIDE $C_{10}H_{14}O_3$ Beil. XVII-455

```
             CH3   O
              |   //
H2C-----------C---C
 |            |     \
 |    CH3-----C--CH3  O
 |            |     /
H2C-----------C---C
              H    \\
                    O
```

M.P. 220-221° **Neut. Eq. 91** (in aq.)
182 (in alc.)

Pr. from C_6H_6 or acetone; tbls. from ether, or alc. + acetone — Sl. sol. aq.; sol. at 14° in 123 pts. 95% alc., 68 pts. ether, or 17 pts. C_6H_6; very eas. sol. $CHCl_3$. [Use in sepn. from *d*-camphoric acid (1:0810) which is insol. $CHCl_3$.] — Slightly laevorotatory.

[For prepn. from *d*-camphoric acid see latter (1:0810).] [For quant. detn. by titration with $NaOCH_3$ see ⟨1⟩.]

Ⓓ **Saponification:** Hydrolysis with aq. alk. (T 1.51) gives Sap. Eq. 91 and yields soln. contg. salt of *d*-camphoric ac. (1:0810), q.v.

Ⓓ ***d*-Camphor-α-amic acid** (*d*-camphoric acid α-monamide) [Beil. IX-755]: [from $\bar{C}$ on shaking with conc. aq. NH_4OH; yield 45–55%; m.p. 174° ⟨2⟩ accompanied by 20–25% corresp. β-acid, m.p. 182–183° ⟨2⟩].

Ⓓ ***d*-Camphor-α-anilic acid** (*d*-camphoric acid α-monoanilide) [Beil. XII-309]: from $\bar{C}$ + 1 mole aniline in $CHCl_3$ htd. on water bath 4–5 hrs.; after cooling the separated prod. is recrystd. from alc.; ndls. m.p. 209–210° ⟨3⟩, 203–204° ⟨4⟩. [The corresponding β-monoanilide has m.p. 196°.] [See also text of *d*-camphoric ac. (1:0810).] [On htg. with $SOCl_2$ ⟨5⟩ the α-monoanilide yields *d*-camphoric acid anil [Beil. XXI-418], m.p. 116–117°.]

Ⓓ ***N*-(*p*-Tolyl)*d*-camphor-α-amic acid** (*d*-camphoric acid α-mono-*p*-toluidide) [Beil. XII-939]: from C̄ + 1 mole *p*-toluidine in $CHCl_3$ htd. on aq. bath 4–5 hrs.; m.p. 214–215° ⟨3⟩.

1:0860 ⟨1⟩ Smith, Bryant, *J. Am. Chem. Soc.* **58,** 2453 (1936). ⟨2⟩ Noyes, Taveau, *Am. Chem. J.* **32,** 287 (1904). ⟨3⟩ Singh, Puri, *J. Chem. Soc.* **1926,** 506. ⟨4⟩ Auwers, Schleicher, *Ann.* **309,** 341–342 (1899). ⟨5⟩ Warren, Briggs, *Ber.* **64,** 29 (1931).

1:0865 PIPERONYLIC ACID (3,4-Methylenedioxybenzoic acid) $C_8H_6O_4$ **Beil. XIX-269**

M.P. 228° **Neut. Eq. 166**

Ndls. from alc.; from hot aq. on very slow cooling in charact. slender cryst. Insol. cold aq. or $CHCl_3$; spar. sol. cold alc. or ether — Subl. on slow htg. at 210°. [For prepn. in 78–84% yield by $KMnO_4$ oxidn. of piperonal (1:0010) see ⟨1⟩; for other methods see piperonal.]

C̄, refluxed 4½ hrs. with $AlBr_3$ in C_6H_6 (94% yield ⟨3⟩) or C̄ stood 4 hrs. at room temp. with $AlBr_3$ in nitrobenzene (92% yield ⟨9⟩) or C̄ (0.25 g.) + conc. H_2SO_4 (3 ml.) + phenol (0.28 g.) stood 1¾ hrs. at room temp., poured into aq. and extd. with ether (84% yield ⟨10⟩), or C̄ dislvd. in 16 pts. chlorobenzene and htd. 1 hr. with 3 pts. $AlCl_3$ (64% yield ⟨2⟩) gives 3,4-dihydroxybenzoic ac. (1:0545).

C̄, on distn. with 12% HCl, gives 37% formaldehyde (1:0145) ⟨4⟩.

C̄ with PCl_5 ⟨5⟩ or htd. with excess $SOCl_2$ on aq. bath ⟨6⟩ gives piperonoyl chloride; m.p. 80°. [At higher temps., e.g., 8 hrs. at 180–200° in s.t. the dioxymethylene group is also attacked ⟨6⟩.]

C̄ with MeOH + dry HCl ⟨7⟩ ⟨8⟩ or C̄ + MeOH + conc. H_2SO_4 ⟨9⟩ yields methyl piperonylate, ndls. and lfts. from pet. ether, m.p. 53° ⟨8⟩, 51.5° ⟨7⟩.

Ⓓ **Piperonylamide:** anhydrous tbls. from alc., m.p. 169°.

1:0865 ⟨1⟩ Shriner, Kleiderer, *Organic Syntheses* **10,** 82–83 (1930). ⟨2⟩ Mauthner, *J. prakt. Chem.* (2) **119,** 76 (1928). ⟨3⟩ Pfeiffer, Loewe, *J. prakt. Chem.* (2) **147,** 305 (1937). ⟨4⟩ Freudenberg, Harder, *Ber.* **60,** 585 (1927). ⟨5⟩ Perkin, Robinson, *Chem. News* **92,** 293 (1905). ⟨6⟩ Barger, *J. Chem. Soc.* **93,** 567 (1908). ⟨7⟩ van Linge, *Rec. trav. chim.* **16,** 47 (1897). ⟨8⟩ Oertly, Pictet, *Ber.* **43,** 1336 (1910). ⟨9⟩ Mosettig, Burger, *J. Am. Chem. Soc.* **52,** 2991 (1930). ⟨10⟩ Späth, Quietensky, *Ber.* **60,** 1887 (1927).

1:0870 DIPHENIC ACID (Biphenyl-2,2′-dicarboxylic acid) $C_{14}H_{10}O_4$ **Beil. IX-922**

M.P. 229° **Neut. Eq. 121**

Lfts. from aq.; spar. sol. cold aq.; sol. hot aq., or in alc., ether — Sublimes on cautious htg. [For prepn. by coupling of diazotized anthranilic ac. in pres. of Cu (46–57% yield) see ⟨1⟩.]

$\bar{C}$ on distn. at 360° quant. yields fluorenone (1:9014) ⟨2⟩ — $\bar{C}$ htd. at 140° with conc. H_2SO_4 gives quant. yield of fluorenone-4-carboxylic acid (1:9087) ⟨3⟩. $\bar{C}$, refluxed with Ac_2O gives (97% yield ⟨4⟩) diphenic anhydride (1:0851), insol. in cold aq. Na_2CO_3 soln. (dif. and sepn. from $\bar{C}$).

$\bar{C}$, dislvd. in excess $SOCl_2$, excess reagt. evapd., residue boiled with C_6H_6 and soln. filtered from a little diphenic anhydride, gives on evapn. of C_6H_6 (80% yield ⟨5⟩) of diphenic acid (di)chloride, m.p. 97° ⟨5⟩ — $\bar{C}$ htd. at 190° with 2 moles PCl_5 gives (81% yield ⟨6⟩) diphenic acid (di)chloride.

$\bar{C}$ in MeOH treated with dry HCl gives dimethyl diphenate, tbls. or pr. from MeOH, m.p. 73–74° ⟨6⟩. [Methyl hydrogen diphenate has m.p. 110°.] — $\bar{C}$ in EtOH treated with HCl gives diethyl diphenate, m.p. 42° ⟨6⟩. [Ethyl hydrogen diphenate has m.p. 88°.]

Ⓓ **Di-(*p*-nitrobenzyl) diphenate:** m.p. 182.6° ⟨7⟩ [cf. T 1.39].

—— **Diphenic diamide:** tbls. from hot aq., m.p. 212° [on htg. above its m.p. this subst. loses NH_3 yielding diphenimide [Beil. XXI-533], m.p. 218–219°; eas. sol. aq. alk.]. [The monoamide (diphenamic acid) has m.p. 190–191° and on htg. above its m.p. loses H_2O also yielding diphenimide.]

Ⓓ **Diphenanilide:** octahedra from AcOH or alc., m.p. 229–230° ⟨4⟩ [from diphenic acid (di)chloride + aniline in ether or C_6H_6 (97% yield) ⟨4⟩]. The monoanilide (diphenanilic acid) has m.p. 176°.]

1:0870 ⟨1⟩ Huntress, *Organic Syntheses, Coll. Vol.* I, 216–219 (1932). ⟨2⟩ Huntress, Hershberg, Cliff, *J. Am. Chem. Soc.* **53,** 2723 (1931). ⟨3⟩ Moore, Huntress, *J. Am. Chem. Soc.* **49,** 1330 (1927). ⟨4⟩ Roberts, Johnson, *J. Am. Chem. Soc.* **47,** 1399–1400 (1925). ⟨5⟩ Bell, *J. Chem. Soc.* **1927,** 1698. ⟨6⟩ Underwood, Kochmann, *J. Am. Chem. Soc.* **46,** 2072–2073 (1924). ⟨7⟩ Kelly, Segura, *J. Am. Chem. Soc.* **56,** 2497 (1934).

1:0873 PHENOLPHTHALIN

(4′,4″-Dihydrcxytriphenylmethanecarboxylic acid-2)

$C_{20}H_{16}O_4$ **Beil. X-455**

M.P. 232° ⟨1⟩ **Neut. Eq.** indef.

Ndls. from aq. or dil. alc. — Very spar. sol. aq. — [For prepn. in 96% yield ⟨1⟩ from phenolphthalein (1:1635) by reduction with Zn dust + alk. see ⟨1⟩ ⟨2⟩.]

$\bar{C}$ is stable on stdg. in air but on htg. in air, or on treatment with alk. $K_3Fe(CN)_6$ or $KMnO_4$ or with H_2O_2 is reoxidized to phenolphthalein. [Use of this behavior as sensitive test for H_2O_2 detecting as little as 1:100,000,000 see ⟨3⟩.]

$\bar{C}$ is sol. in aq. alk. but does not give def. Neut. Eq. (cf. ⟨4⟩). The alk. solns. are colorless but grad. turn red in air (see above).

$\bar{C}$ in CH_3OH + HCl gives methyl ester, pr. from alc., m.p. 153–154° ⟨5⟩ — $\bar{C}$ in EtOH satd. with HCl and htd. gives ethyl ester, lfts. or ndls. from dil. alc., m.p. 156–158° ⟨6⟩.

Ⓓ **Diacetylphenolphthalin:** from $\bar{C}$ htd. with Ac_2O for 6 hrs. at 170–175°; ndls. from alc., m.p. 146° ⟨2⟩.

1:0873 ⟨1⟩ Blicke, Weinkauff, *J. Am. Chem. Soc.* **54,** 1458 (1932). ⟨2⟩ Baeyer, *Ann.* **202,** 80–83 (1880). ⟨3⟩ Schales, *Ber.* **71,** 448–450 (1938). ⟨4⟩ Acree, Slagle, *Am. Chem. J.* **42,** 135–136 (1909). ⟨5⟩ Finzi, Accarini, *Cent.* **1927,** I, 733. ⟨6⟩ Nietzki, Burckhardt, *Ber.* **30,** 175–176 (1897).

1:0875 GALLIC ACID (3,4,5-Trihydroxybenzoic acid) $C_7H_6O_5$ **Beil. X-470**

HO / HO—⟨ ⟩—COOH / HO

M.P. 253-254° dec. ⟨1⟩ **Neut. Eq.** (see text)

Since C̄ is very sensitive to heat and to oxidn. the observed m.p. may vary over wide range according to previous treatment and to method of taking m.p. itself. It is often merely recorded as 222–240° dec.

Ndls. with 1 H_2O from aq.; becoming anhydrous above 120° — Sol. in 130 pts. aq. at 12.5°; 100 pts. alc. at 15° dis. 28 g. C̄; ether 2.5 g.; acetone 29.4 g.; AcOEt 8.4 g. — C̄ is insol. in $CHCl_3$, C_6H_6.

C̄ on htg. at 250° (preferably in absence of air) gives CO_2 and a sublimate of pyrogallol (1:1555) ⟨2⟩ — C̄ in aq. soln. grad. absorbs oxygen from air and turns brown; C̄ in alk. soln. absorbs oxygen from air very rapidly becoming dark red, brown or even black. [This behavior interferes with detn. of Neut. Eq.]

C̄ in aq. soln. treated with $FeCl_3$ (cf. T 1.41) gives blue-black ppt. sol. in excess $FeCl_3$; *pure* ferrous salts (best to use pure ferrous ammonium sulfate) give no ppt. — C̄ reduces $NH_4OH/AgNO_3$ or Tollens' reagt. (T 1.11) or Fehling's soln. (T 1.22) — C̄ is pptd. by gelatin soln. in pres. of NaCl, but not by gelatin soln. alone ⟨3⟩ [dif. from tannic acid].

C̄ may be separated from pyrogallol (1:1555) by much greater soly. of latter in cold aq. or ether; from salicylic acid (1:0780) by greater soly. of latter in cold aq.

C̄ in cold aq. NaOH treated with successive portions of dimethyl sulfate (preferably in an atmosphere of N_2 ⟨4⟩) gives (89–92% yield ⟨5⟩ ⟨4⟩) 3,4,5-trimethoxybenzoic ac. [Beil. X-481], ndls. from 40% alc., m.p. 169°.

Ⓟ **KCN color reaction:** C̄ in aq. soln. treated with few drops KCN soln. gives red color which disappears on stdg. except at surface of soln. On shaking the color reappears and gradually fades; this process can be repeated many times ⟨6⟩ [*pure* tannin does not show this reaction].

Ⓓ **Tri-(*p*-phenylphenacyl) gallate:** m.p. 195–198° dec. ⟨7⟩ [cf. T 1.391].

Ⓓ **3,4,5-Triacetoxybenzoic acid:** from C̄ on htg. with Ac_2O + a little $ZnCl_2$ (76% yield ⟨8⟩), or with Ac_2O + pyridine at room temp. (86% yield ⟨8⟩), or in less pure form from C̄ in ice cold aq. NaOH shaken with Ac_2O (57% yield ⟨9⟩); cryst. from acidif. of $NaHCO_3$ soln. or from alc., m.p. 171–172° cor. ⟨8⟩. [3,5-Diacetoxy-4-hydroxybenzoic ac. (by cold alk. hydrolysis of the triacetoxy deriv. ⟨8⟩) has m.p. 174–175° cor. ⟨8⟩.]

Ⓓ **3,4,5-Tribenzoxybenzoic acid** [**tribenzoylgallic acid**]**:** from C̄ dislvd. in 4–5 pts. pyridine and shaken with BzCl in cold until excess latter is evident from odor; prod. pptd. with dil. acid; ndls. from alc., m.p. 191–192° ⟨10⟩. [Mono- and di-benzoyl derivs. are not produced by this method ⟨10⟩.]

1:0875 ⟨1⟩ Tutin, Clewer, *J. Chem. Soc.* **99**, 956–957 (1911). ⟨2⟩ Kunz-Krause, Manicke, *Ber.* **53**, 199–201 (1920). ⟨3⟩ Gorter, *Ann.* **358**, 342 (1907). ⟨4⟩ Slotta, Szyszka, *J. prakt. Chem.* (2) **137**, 343–344 (1933). ⟨5⟩ Mauthner, *Organic Syntheses, Coll. Vol.* I, 522–524 (1932). ⟨6⟩ Young, *Chem. News*, **48**, 31 (1883); *Z. anal. Chem.* **23**, 227 (1883). ⟨7⟩ Drake, Sweeney. *J. Am. Chem. Soc.* **54**, 2060 (1932). ⟨8⟩ Fischer, Bergmann, Lipschitz, *Ber.* **51**, 53–55 (1918), ⟨9⟩ Chattaway, *J. Chem. Soc.* **1931**, 2496. ⟨10⟩ Einhorn, Hollandt, *Ann.* **301**, 110 (1898).

1:0890 NAPHTHALIC ACID (Naphthalene-1,8-dicarboxylic acid) $C_{12}H_8O_4$ **Beil. IX-918**

—COOH / —COOH

M.P. 274° (see text)

Silky ndls. from alc. — Alm. insol. aq., spar. sol. ether — On htg. is conv. to naphthalic anhydride (1:0891) so that m.p. is really that of latter. [C̄ is fairly sol. in warm alc. but if soln. is boiled ndls. of the anhydride ppt. ⟨1⟩ ⟨2⟩.]

Salts: of heavy metal salts HgĀ, NiĀ, MgĀ are sol. aq.; others insol. ⟨3⟩.

C̄ cannot be directly esterified owing to conv. to anhydride, but C̄ dislvd. in 3 moles aq. NaOH, shaken with 3 moles dimethyl sulfate gives 25% yield ⟨4⟩ of dimethyl naphthalate (1:2425), pr. from dil. MeOH, m.p. 102–103° ⟨4⟩; 104° ⟨5⟩.

[See also naphthalic anhydride (1:0891).]

1:0890 ⟨1⟩ Behr, Dorp, *Ann.* **172,** 267 (1874). ⟨2⟩ Bistrzycki, Risi, *Helv. Chim. Acta* **8,** 811, Note 4 (1925). ⟨3⟩ Ephraim, *Ber.* **55,** 3482 (1922). ⟨4⟩ Graebe, *Ann.* **340,** 247–248 (1905). ⟨5⟩ Bradbrook, Linstead, *J. Chem. Soc.* **1936,** 1743.

1:0891 NAPHTHALIC ANHYDRIDE

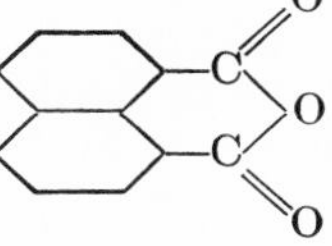

$C_{12}H_6O_3$ **Beil. XVII-521**

M.P. 274°

Ndls. (from alc.) — Very sl. sol. ether, dif. sol. alc., C_6H_6; easier in AcOH. Best purified by soln. in NaOH, repptn. from hot soln. by HCl, followed by recrystn. from AcOH ⟨1⟩. [Recrystn. from conc. HNO_3 is not recommended ⟨1⟩.]

Responds to Generic Test 3-B (titration in alc.); Neut. Eq. (*in alcohol*) (T 1.31) gives 188 (Theoret. 198) — Sap. Eq. in aq. alk. (T 1.51) gives 99.

Soln. in cold conc. H_2SO_4 yellow with blue fluores.

C̄ refluxed *continuously* for 40–60 hrs. with 1½ pts. $POCl_3$ + 1½pts. PCl_5 (1½ moles), resultant amber liq. filtered (to remove unchanged anhyd.), and $POCl_3$ largely removed (preferably under reduced press.), CS_2 added and mixt. stood, deposits 70–75% yield of naphthalyl chloride, large colorless transparent rhombic cryst., m.p. abt. 84–86° ⟨2⟩. [In this prepn. if refluxing be interrupted at any time the orig. anhyd. separates in lumps whose resolution requires very prolonged boiling.] [The naphthalyl chloride is extraordinarily reactive to moisture, cf. ⟨2⟩.]

C̄ does not react with MeOH or EtOH, but naphthalyl chloride (above) in 5 pts. dry $CHCl_3$ treated with 5 pts. dry MeOH seps. first some of original C̄, and filtrate on evapn. gives 31% yield dimethyl naphthalate (1:2425), pr. from dil. MeOH, m.p. 102–103° ⟨2⟩ — By similar process using abs. EtOH, diethyl naphthalate (1:2209) can be obtd. in 48% yield ⟨2⟩, cryst. from dil. alc., m.p. 58–60°.

Ⓓ **Naphthalimide** [Beil. XXI-527]: from C̄ in nearly quant. yield ⟨3⟩ by htg. with excess conc. aq. NH_4OH for 2–3 hrs.; the prod. is purified by boiling with Na_2CO_3 soln. (to remove traces of unchanged C̄) and residue recrystd. from hot conc. HNO_3; long white ndls., m.p. 300°. [Naphthalimide is sol. in aq. alk. and repptd. by CO_2, or it can also be sublimed.] [Naphthalyl chloride (above) treated in C_6H_6 with dry NH_3 gives poor yield of 1-cyano-8-naphthoic ac., m.p. 210–250° with conversion to naphthalimide, m.p. 300° ⟨4⟩.]

Ⓓ **Naphthalanil** (***N*-phenylnaphthalimide**) [Beil. XXI-527]: from C̄ refluxed 5 hrs. with 5 pts. aniline; after cooling excess aniline removed with dil. HCl, any unchanged C̄ with dil. Na_2CO_3, and residue recrystd. from alc.; white ndls., m.p. 202° cor. ⟨3⟩. [The half anilide of naphthalic ac. (*N*-phenylnaphthalamic acid) can be formed from the anil by 12 hrs. boiling with aq. NaOH and has m.p. 296° ⟨5⟩ but on treatment with HCl instantly is reconverted to naphthalanil.]

Ⓓ **1′,8′-Naphthoylenebenzimidazole-1,2:** from C̄ + *o*-phenylenediamine by condensation in boilg. AcOH soln.; pale yel. cryst., m.p. 206° ⟨6⟩. [The intermediate *o*-aminophenylnaphthalamic acid, m.p. 236–238° dec. ⟨7⟩ further condenses in AcOH to yield the indicated imidazole which is stable even after 2 hrs. at 215° ⟨6⟩.]

1:0891 ⟨1⟩ Mihailescu, Steopoe, *Bull. soc. sci. acad. Roumaine* **8,** 102–110 (1923), *Chem. Abs.* **18,** 831 (1924). ⟨2⟩ Mason, *J. Chem. Soc.* **125,** 2117–2118 (1924). ⟨3⟩ Jaubert, *Ber.* **28,** 360–362 (1895). ⟨4⟩ Davies, Leeper, *J. Chem. Soc.* **1927,** 1126. ⟨5⟩ Poraĭ-Koshits, *Chem. Abs.* **31,** 5787 (1937), *Cent.* **1938,** I, 303. ⟨6⟩ Rule, Thompson, *J. Chem. Soc.* **1937,** 1765. ⟨7⟩ Bistrzycki, Risi, *Helv. Chim. Acta* **8,** 816 (1925).

1:0895 FUMARIC ACID (*trans* stereoisomer of maleic acid (1:0470))

H—C—COOH
‖
HOOC—C—H

$C_4H_4O_4$ **Beil. II-737**

M.P. abt. **293–295°** subl. **Neut. Eq. 58**
286–287° in s.t.

Pr. ndls. or lfts. sol. in 148.7 pts. aq. at 16.5°; in 10 pts. aq. at 100°. [This is much less than soly. of maleic ac. (1:0470).] — Sol. in 17 pts. 95% alc. at 30°. Spar. sol. ether, acetone; insol. C_6H_6.

[For prepn. in 50–58% yield via oxidn. of furfural (1:0185) with $NaClO_3$ + V_2O_5 see ⟨1⟩.] [Small samples of C̄ can readly be prepd. by exposing satd. sol. of maleic ac. (1:0470) + trace of Br_2-aq. to sunlight or brilliant electric lt., the isomerized fumaric ac. pptg. out.]

C̄ in alk. soln. reduces $KMnO_4$ (T 1.34), but decolorizes Br_2-aq. only slowly even on warming. [For detn. of C̄ via $KBr/KBrO_3$ method see ⟨2⟩; via $KBr.Br_2$ titration see ⟨3⟩.]

C̄ warmed with 2 moles PCl_5 at 100° ⟨4⟩ ⟨5⟩ yields fumaryl (di)chloride, b.p. 158–160°. [C̄ does not react smoothly with $SOCl_2$ ⟨6⟩ ⟨5⟩.] [For prepn. of fumaryl (di)chloride in 82–95% yield from maleic anhydride (1:0625) + phthalyl (di)chloride + $ZnCl_2$ see ⟨19⟩.]

Ⓓ **Dimethyl fumarate** (1:2415): from C̄ on refluxing with 8 moles MeOH contg. 3% HCl gas; after distg. off excess MeOH yield is 95% ⟨7⟩; m.p. 101.5–101.6°; b.p. 192°. [Methyl hydrogen fumarate cryst. from C_6H_6 in white cryst., m.p. 144.5° cor. ⟨8⟩.]

Ⓓ **Di-(*p*-nitrobenzyl) fumarate:** m.p. 150.8° ⟨10⟩ [cf. T 1.39].

Ⓓ **Di-(phenacyl) fumarate:** m.p. 197.5° ⟨11⟩; by recrystn. from AcOH; m.p. 204–205° cor. ⟨18⟩ [cf. T 1.391].

Ⓓ **Fumaric diamide:** m.p. 266° dec. ⟨9⟩ ⟨7⟩ [readily obtd. in 80% yield from dimethyl fumarate on 24 hrs. stdg. with conc. aq. NH_4OH ⟨7⟩]. [The monoamide has m.p. 217° dec.] [For m.p. + compn. diagram of system: fumaric diamide + maleic diamide see ⟨9⟩.]

Ⓓ **Phenaspartanil** [Beil. XXII-529]: from C̄ htd. with aniline acc. to method given under maleic ac. (1:0470); cryst. from boilg. alc., m.p. 210–211° ⟨12⟩ ⟨13⟩.

Ⓓ **Fumaric dianilide** [Beil. XII-305]: from fumaryl dichloride + aniline in ether ⟨14⟩ ⟨15⟩ soln.; ndls. from AcOH, m.p. 313–314° after browning at 275°. [The monoanilide (fumaranilic ac.) has m.p. 233–234.5°.]

Ⓓ **Di-(*S*-benzylthiuronium) fumarate:** m.p. 178° cor. ⟨16⟩; 182–183° ⟨17⟩.

1:0895 ⟨1⟩ Milas, *Organic Syntheses* **11,** 46–48 (1931). ⟨2⟩ Lucas, Pressman, *Ind. Eng. Chem., Anal. Ed.* **10,** 140–142 (1938). ⟨3⟩ Szegedy, *Z. anal. Chem.* **109,** 95–107 (1937). ⟨4⟩ von Auwers, Schmidt, *Ber.* **46,** 480 (1913). ⟨5⟩ W. A. van Dorp, G. C. A. van Dorp, *Rec. trav. chim.* **25,** 96 (1906). ⟨6⟩ McMaster, Ahmann, *J. Am. Chem. Soc.* **50,** 147 (1928). ⟨7⟩ DeWolf, Van de Straete, *Bull. soc. chim. Belg.* **44,** 289–290 (1935). ⟨8⟩ Lutz, *J. Am. Chem. Soc.*

52, 3430 (1930). ⟨9⟩ Viseur, *Bull. soc. chim. Belg.* **35,** 427, 437 (1926). ⟨10⟩ Lyman, Reid, *J. Am. Chem. Soc.* **39,** 708 (1917).
⟨11⟩ Rather, Reid, *J. Am. Chem. Soc.* **41,** 80 (1919). ⟨12⟩ Warren, Grose, *J. Am. Chem. Soc.* **34,** 1603 (1912). ⟨13⟩ Tingle, Bates, *J. Am. Chem. Soc.* **31,** 1238 (1909). ⟨14⟩ Anschütz, Wirtz, *Ann.* **239,** 138 (1887). ⟨15⟩ Anschütz, *Ann.* **259,** 140 (1890). ⟨16⟩ Donleavy, *J. Am. Chem. Soc.* **58,** 1005 (1936). ⟨17⟩ Veibel, Lillelund, *Bull. soc. chim.* (5) **5,** 1157 (1938). ⟨18⟩ van Duin, *Rec. trav. chim.* **47,** 734 (1928). ⟨19⟩ Kyrides, *Organic Syntheses* **20,** 51–54 (1940).

1:0900 ISOPHTHALIC ACID (Benzene-1,3-dicarboxylic acid) —COOH, COOH $C_8H_6O_4$ **Beil. IX-832**

M.P. 348° (cf. ⟨11⟩) **Neut. Eq. 83**

Sublimes below m.p. without forming anhydride — Hair-like ndls. from hot aq. or alc. — Sol. in 7800 pts. aq. at 25° or in 460 pts. hot aq.; fairly eas. sol. alc., AcOH; insol. C_6H_6, lgr.

C̄, like terephthalic ac. (1:0910), yields no aniline salt either in aq. or alc. soln. ⟨1⟩ [dif. from phthalic ac. (1:0820)] — C̄ dislvd. in 6 pts. boilg. Ac_2O and latter distd. off at ord. press. leaves residue of polymeric anhydride, insol. in Na_2CO_3 soln., but readily sol. in hot NaOH regenerating C̄ ⟨2⟩.

C̄ with PCl_5 ⟨3⟩ in s.t. at 200° ⟨4⟩, or boiled with 5 pts. PCl_5 in 3.2 pts. $POCl_3$ for 6 hrs. ⟨5⟩, or htd. in a s.t. at 130° for 8 hrs. with 35 pts. AcCl ⟨6⟩, or refluxed for 12 hrs. with 2–3 pts. $SOCl_2$ (62% yield ⟨7⟩; 100% yield ⟨8⟩) gives isophthalyl (di)chloride, m.p. 41°, 43–44° ⟨6⟩.

$Ag_2\bar{A}$; amorph. ppt., insol. cold or hot aq., swelling like a zeolite on htg.; $Ba\bar{A}.6H_2O$, very sol. aq. [dif. and sepn. ⟨9⟩ from terephthalic ac. (1:0910)].

Ⓓ **Dimethyl isophthalate** (1:2244): Mix in a dry tt. 0.1 g. C̄ and 0.3 g. PCl_5. Heat cautiously over a small flame until fused, cool, and dis. in 2 ml. MeOH. Add 5 ml. cold aq. to ppt. ester, filter, and wash ppt. with 2 ml. cold aq. Recryst. from 4 ml. boilg. 50% MeOH,cooling well with shaking. Wash ppt. with 2 ml. cold aq. and dry cryst. below 50° ⟨10⟩; m.p. 64–65° ⟨11⟩; [this ester may also be obtd. from C̄ + MeOH + conc. H_2SO_4 ⟨12⟩]. [Methyl hydrogen isophthalate exists in two forms, m.p. 193° and 167–169°, the latter slowly changing at room temp. into former.]

Ⓓ **Di-(*p*-nitrobenzyl) isophthalate:** m.p. 202.5° ⟨13⟩ [cf. T 1.39].

Ⓓ **Di-(phenacyl) isophthalate:** m.p. 191° (57% yield) ⟨14⟩ [cf. T 1.391].

Ⓓ **Di-(*p*-bromophenacyl) isophthalate:** m.p. 179.1° (53% yield) ⟨14⟩; 179° ⟨15⟩ [cf. T 1.391].

Ⓓ **Isophthalic diamide:** m.p. 280° ⟨11⟩. [The monoamide (isophthalamidic acid) is also reported to have m.p. 280°.]

Ⓓ ***S*-Benzylthiuronium hydrogen isophthalate:** m.p. 215–216° ⟨16⟩.

1:0900 ⟨1⟩ Graebe, Buenzod, *Ber.* **32,** 1991–1992 (1899). ⟨2⟩ Bucher, Slade, *J. Am. Chem. Soc.* **31,** 1320–1321 (1909). ⟨3⟩ Schreder, *Ber.* **7,** 708 (1874). ⟨4⟩ Münchmeyer, *Ber.* **19,** 1849 (1886). ⟨5⟩ Ruggli, Gassenmeier, *Helv. Chim. Acta* **22,** 499 (1939). ⟨6⟩ Liebermann, Kardos, *Ber.* **46,** 211 (1913). ⟨7⟩ McMaster, Ahmann, *J. Am. Chem. Soc.* **50,** 148 (1928). ⟨8⟩ Meyer, *Monatsh.* **22,** 436 (1901). ⟨9⟩ Smith, *J. Am. Chem. Soc.* **43,** 1920–1921 (1921). ⟨10⟩ Mulliken, "Method" I, 85 (1904).
⟨11⟩ Aschan, *Ann.* **387,** 36, Note (1911). ⟨12⟩ Meyer, *Monatsh.* **25,** 1204 (1904). ⟨13⟩ Lyons, Reid, *J. Am. Chem. Soc.* **39,** 1740 (1917). ⟨14⟩ Kelly, Kleff, *J. Am. Chem. Soc.* **54,** 4444 (1932). ⟨15⟩ Morton, Fallwell, *J. Am. Chem. Soc.* **60,** 1926 1938). ⟨16⟩ Veibel, Ottung, *Bull. soc. chim.* (5) **6,** 1435 (1939).

1:0910 TEREPHTHALIC ACID $C_8H_6O_4$ **Beil. IX-841**
(Benzene-1,4-dicarboxylic acid) HOOC—C_6H_4—COOH

M.P. See text. **Neut. Eq. 83**

Sublimes without melting abt. 300° — $\bar{C}$, pptd. from *hot* alk. soln. by addn. of acids, cryst. in ndls.; from cold soln. ppts. as amorphous pdr. — $\bar{C}$ is exceedingly insol. aq. (1 pt. sol. in 67,000 pts. cold aq.); alm. insol. hot aq.; alm. insol. cold alc. but spar. sol. hot alc.; insol. AcOH or $CHCl_3$.

$\bar{C}$, like isophthalic ac. (1:0900), yields no aniline salt either in aq. or alc. soln. ⟨1⟩ [dif. from phthalic ac. (1:0820)] — $\bar{C}$ dislvd. in 90 pts. boilg. Ac_2O and latter distd. off at ord. press. leaves residue of polymeric anhydride, insol. in Na_2CO_3 soln. but readily sol. in hot NaOH, regenerating $\bar{C}$ ⟨2⟩.

$\bar{C}$ with PCl_5 at 40° ⟨3⟩, or with 3.5 moles PCl_5 + 3 moles $POCl_3$ ⟨4⟩ ⟨5⟩ (poor yield) or htd. in s.t. at 130° for 8 hrs. with 35 pts. AcCl ⟨6⟩, or with 2 moles $SOCl_2$ + 4 moles pyridine in ether (alm. quant. yield ⟨7⟩) gives terephthalyl (di)chloride, ndls. or pl. from lgr., m.p. 83–84° ⟨6⟩, 79–80° ⟨4⟩; b.p. 263° ⟨4⟩. [The mono acid chloride cryst. from C_6H_6 in ndls. m.p. above 300° ⟨6⟩.] [$\bar{C}$ is insol. in $SOCl_2$ ⟨8⟩ and unattacked in absence of pyridine.]

$Ba\bar{A}.4H_2O$ is very dif. sol. [dif. from corresp. deriv. of isophthalic ac. (1:0900); and use in sepn. from it ⟨16⟩].

Ⓓ **Dimethyl terephthalate** (1:2550): Mix in a dry tt. 0.1 g. $\bar{C}$ and 0.3 g. PCl_5. Heat cautiously over small flame until fused, cool, and dis. in 2 ml. MeOH. Add 10 ml. cold water to ppt. ester, filter, wash with 5 ml. aq. Recryst. from hot 80% MeOH, washing ppt. with 3 ml. 50% MeOH, and dry cryst. at 100°, m.p. 140–141° ⟨9⟩. [Methyl hydrogen terephthalate has m.p. abt. 230°.] [The dimethyl ester may also be obtd. directly from $\bar{C}$ by 8½ hr. reflux with 10 pts. MeOH ⟨10⟩.]

Ⓓ **Diethyl terephthalate** (1:2106): from terephthalyl chloride + alc. ⟨11⟩, pr. from pet. ether or alc., m.p. 44°; b.p. 302°. [Ethyl hydrogen terephthalate has m.p. 171°.]

Ⓓ **Di-(*p*-nitrobenzyl) terephthalate:** m.p. 263.5° ⟨12⟩ [cf. T 1.39].

Ⓓ **Di-(phenacyl) terephthalate:** m.p. 192.2° (38% yield) ⟨13⟩ [cf. T 1.391].

Ⓓ **Di-(*p*-bromophenacyl) terephthalate:** m.p. 225° (71% yield) ⟨13⟩ [cf. T 1.391].

—— **Terephthalic diamide:** does not melt below 250° and is unsuitable as a deriv. for identif. of $\bar{C}$.

—— **Terephthalic dianilide:** from terephthalyl (di)chloride in xylene + aniline; ndls. from nitrobenzene or ethyl acetoacetate, m.p. 334–337° u.c. ⟨14⟩ [unsuitable as deriv. for identif. of $\bar{C}$].

Ⓓ **Di-(*S*-benzylthiuronium) terephthalate:** m.p. 202–206° ⟨15⟩.

1:0910 ⟨1⟩ Graebe, Buenzod, *Ber.* **32,** 1991–1992 (1899). ⟨2⟩ Bucher, Slade, *J. Am. Chem. Soc.* **31,** 1321 (1909). ⟨3⟩ de la Rue, Müller, *Ann.* **121,** 90 (1862). ⟨4⟩ Berend, Herms, *J. prakt. Chem.* (2) **74,** 123 (1906). ⟨5⟩ Fröschl, Maier, *Monatsh.* **59,** 274 (1932). ⟨6⟩ Liebermann, Kardos, *Ber.* **46,** 211–212 (1913). ⟨7⟩ Carré, Libermann, *Compt. rend.* **199,** 1423 (1934). ⟨8⟩ Meyer, *Monatsh.* **22,** 436 (1901). ⟨9⟩ Mulliken, " Method " I, 85 (1904). ⟨10⟩ Feist, *Ber.* **67,** 939 (1934).

⟨11⟩ Perkin, *J. Chem. Soc.* **69,** 1178 (1896). ⟨12⟩ Lyons, Reid, *J. Am. Chem. Soc.* **39,** 1740–1741 (1917). ⟨13⟩ Kelly, Kleff, *J. Am. Chem. Soc.* **54,** 4444 (1932). ⟨14⟩ Rosenmund, Zetsche, *Ber.* **54,** 2892 (1921). ⟨15⟩ Veibel, Ottung, *Bull. soc. chim.* (5) **6,** 1435 (1939). ⟨16⟩ Smith, *J. Am. Chem. Soc.* **43,** 1920–1921 (1921).

ORDER I: SUBORDER I: GENUS 3: ACIDS

Division B, Liquids

Section 1: Liquid acids soluble in 50 parts water

1:1000 METHYL FORMATE H.COOCH$_3$ $C_2H_4O_2$ **Beil. II-18**

B.P. 31.5° ⟨1⟩ **Neut. Eq. 60** D_4^{20} = **0.97421** ⟨1⟩ n_D^{20} = **1.344**
M.P. −99.0° ⟨1⟩ D_4^{25} = **0.96697** ⟨1⟩ n_D^{25} = **1.3415** ⟨2⟩

Misc. with aq. — $\bar{C}$ saponifies so readily that it may be titrated slowly as a monobasic acid.

Ⓓ **Saponification:** hydrolyze with aq. alk. either by titration for Neut. Eq. (T 1.31) or as for Sapon. Equiv. (T 1.51). Distil the neutralized soln. and test distillate for MeOH (1:6120), e.g., by T 1.84 A + B of Manual.

Boil residual neut. soln. with $AgNO_3$; ppt. of Ag indicating presence of formate. For further evidence for formate see formic acid (1:1005).

1:1000 ⟨1⟩ Timmermans, Hennaut-Roland, *J. chim. phys.* **27,** 427–428 (1930). ⟨2⟩ Munch, *J. Am. Chem. Soc.* **48,** 997 (1926).

1:1005 FORMIC ACID H.COOH CH_2O_2 **Beil. II-8**

B.P. 100.7° ⟨1⟩ **Neut. Eq. 46** D_4^{20} = **1.22026** ⟨1⟩ n_D^{20} = **1.37137**
M.P. +8.4 ⟨1⟩ D_4^{25} = **1.21045** ⟨1⟩

$\bar{C}$ has very sharp odor — $\bar{C}$ is misc. with aq. and with it forms const. boilg. mixt. (b.p. 107.1°_{760}) contg. 77.5% $\bar{C}$ + 22.5% aq. [For table of D_4^{20} for system: $\bar{C}$ + aq. see ⟨2⟩.]

[For prepn. of anyhdrous $\bar{C}$ by distn. from B_2O_3 see ⟨3⟩.] [For use of C.S.T. of $\bar{C}$ in C_6H_6 (74.15° ⟨1⟩) as criterion of purity see ⟨4⟩.] — $\bar{C}$ is volatile with steam (see Duclaux Value below).

Neutral salts of $\bar{C}$ are all sol. aq.

$\bar{C}$ reduces cold $KMnO_4$ soln. (T 1.34) [dif. from acetic ac. (1:1010)] — $\bar{C}$, or its salts, warmed with conc. H_2SO_4 yields CO, which burns with a blue flame [dif. from acetic ac. (1:1010)].

[For detn. of $\bar{C}$ via oxidn. to CO_2 with $Hg(OAc)_2$ see ⟨5⟩; via oxidn. with HgO and use in presence of acetic or propionic acids see ⟨6⟩.]

Ⓟ **Test for reducing properties:** Warm 5 ml. of a 1–3% aq. soln. of the acid with excess powdered HgO, with shaking. Filter from undislvd. oxide and boil clear filtrate a half minute. A dark grey ppt. of finely divided mercury appears suddenly.

Ⓓ **Duclaux Value:** 3.95, 4.40; 4.55 [T 1.38]. [For application in detn. of $\bar{C}$ in presence of acetic, propionic, and *n*-butyric acids see ⟨7⟩.]

Ⓓ ***p*-Nitrobenzyl formate:** m.p. 31° ⟨8⟩ [cf. T 1.39].

Ⓓ ***p*-Chlorophenacyl formate:** m.p. 128.0° ⟨9⟩ [cf. T 1.391].

Ⓓ ***p*-Bromophenacyl formate:** m.p. 140° ⟨10⟩ ⟨11⟩; 135.2° ⟨9⟩ [cf. T 1.391].

Ⓓ ***p*-Iodophenacyl formate:** m.p. 163.0° ⟨9⟩ [cf. T 1.391].

Ⓓ ***p*-Phenylphenacyl formate:** m.p. 74° ⟨12⟩ [cf. T 1.391].

Ⓓ **Formamide:** [This deriv. is a liq. (m.p. +2.55° ⟨13⟩) and not suitable as a deriv. for identification].

Ⓓ **Formanilide:** m.p. 50°. [Use in prepn. of high conc. C̄ ⟨19⟩.]

Ⓓ **Formo-*p*-toluidide:** m.p. 53°.

Ⓓ **Benzimidazole:** from C̄ + 1 mole *o*-phenylenediamine on htg. at b.p. for ½ hr., m.p. 172.0–173.0° cor. ⟨14⟩; or from C̄ + ⅔ mole *o*-phenylenediamine + 4 *N* HCl boiled for 30–40 min. (60% yield), pl. from aq., m.p. 170° ⟨15⟩. [This deriv. depresses the m.p. of the corresp. deriv. from acetic ac. ⟨14⟩.] [The picrate of this deriv. has m.p. 230° ⟨16⟩.]

Ⓓ ***S*-Benzylthiuronium formate:** m.p. 146° cor. ⟨17⟩; 150–151° ⟨18⟩.

1:1005 ⟨1⟩ Timmermans, Hennaut-Roland, *J. chim. phys.* **27**, 420–421 (1930). ⟨2⟩ Richardson, Allaire, *Am. Chem. J.* **19**, 149–151 (1897). ⟨3⟩ Schlesinger, Martin, *J. Am. Chem. Soc.* **36**, 1589–1591 (1914). ⟨4⟩ Ewins, *J. Chem. Soc.* **105**, 350–364 (1914). ⟨5⟩ Reid, Weihe, *Ind. Eng. Chem., Anal. Ed.* **10**, 271–272 (1938). ⟨6⟩ Osburn, Wood, Werkman, *Ind. Eng. Chem., Anal. Ed.* **5**, 247–248 (1933). ⟨7⟩ McNair, *J. Am. Chem. Soc.* **55**, 1470–1474 (1933). ⟨8⟩ Reid, *J. Am. Chem. Soc.* **39**, 136 (1917). ⟨9⟩ Moses, Reid, *J. Am. Chem. Soc.* **54**, 2101 (1932). ⟨10⟩ Hurd, Christ, *J. Am. Chem. Soc.* **57**, 2007 (1935).

⟨11⟩ Summerbell, Bauer, *J. Am. Chem. Soc.* **57**, 2366 (1935). ⟨12⟩ Drake, Bronitsky, *J. Am. Chem. Soc.* **52**, 3719 (1930). ⟨13⟩ Timmermans, Hennaut-Roland, *J. chim. phys.* **32**, 513 (1935). ⟨14⟩ Pool, Harwood, Ralston, *J. Am. Chem. Soc.* **59**, 178 (1937). ⟨15⟩ Phillips, *J. Chem. Soc.* **1928**, 2395. ⟨16⟩ Brown, Campbell, *J. Chem. Soc.* **1937**, 1701. ⟨17⟩ Donleavy, *J. Am. Chem. Soc.* **58**, 1005 (1936). ⟨18⟩ Veibel, Lillelund, *Bull. soc. chim.* (5) **5**, 1157 (1938). ⟨19⟩ Ritter, *Ind. Eng. Chem.* **27**, 1224–1225 (1935).

1:1010 ACETIC ACID $CH_3.COOH$ $C_2H_4O_2$ Beil. II-96

B.P. 118.2° ⟨1⟩ **Neut. Eq. 60** D_4^{20} = **1.04926** ⟨1⟩ n_D^{20} = **1.36976**
M.P. +16.635° ⟨2⟩ D_4^{25} = **1.04351** ⟨1⟩

C̄ has characteristic sharp odor — Misc. with aq.; volatile with steam (see Duclaux Value below) — Neutral salts all sol. aq.

[For impt. study of prepn. of purest possible anhydrous C̄ see ⟨2⟩.] [For detn. of C̄ in aq. solns. by means of f.p. and density detn. see ⟨3⟩.] [For distribn. of C̄ between aq. and org. solvents see ⟨4⟩.]

C̄, treated with PCl_5 (80% yield ⟨5⟩), or $PCl_3 + ZnCl_2$ (90% yield ⟨5⟩), or $SOCl_2$ (46% yield ⟨5⟩) gives acetyl chloride, b.p. 51°, D_4^{20} = 1.1051; n_D^{20} = 1.3898.

C̄ does not reduce $KMnO_4$ (T 1.34) [dif. from formic ac. (1:1005), acrylic ac. (1:1020)].

[For detn. of C̄ in presence of propionic or *n*-butyric acids via distribution between aq. and diisopropyl ether see ⟨6⟩ ⟨7⟩.]

Ⓓ **Duclaux Value:** 6.8; 7.1; 7.4 [T 1.38] [dif. from formic ac. (1:1005) or propionic ac. (1:1025)].

Ⓓ **Analysis of silver salt:** %Ag = 64.67 [T 1.36].

Ⓓ ***p*-Nitrobenzyl acetate:** m.p. 78° ⟨8⟩ [cf. T 1.39].

Ⓓ **Phenacyl acetate:** m.p. 40° ⟨9⟩ [cf. T 1.391].

Ⓓ ***p*-Chlorophenacyl acetate:** m.p. 72.4° ⟨10⟩; 67.2° ⟨11⟩ [cf. T 1.391].

Ⓓ ***p*-Bromophenacyl acetate:** m.p. 86.0° ⟨10⟩; 85.0° ⟨11⟩ [cf. T 1.391].

Ⓓ ***p*-Iodophenacyl acetate:** m.p. 117.0° ⟨10⟩; 114.0° ⟨11⟩; [cf. T 1.391].

Ⓓ ***p*-Phenylphenacyl acetate:** m.p. 111° ⟨12⟩ [cf. T 1.391].

Ⓓ **Acetamide:** m.p. 81.5° ⟨13⟩ [very sol. aq.; insol. ether; best recrystd. from AcOEt by addn. of ether].

Ⓓ **Acetanilide:** m.p. 114.1° ⟨14⟩. [For f.p. + compn. diagram of system: acetanilide + propionanilide see ⟨14⟩.]

Ⓓ **Acet-*p*-toluidide:** m.p. 153° ⟨15⟩.

Ⓓ **2-Methylbenzimidazole:** from C̄ on htg. with 1 mole *o*-phenylenediamine at b.p. for ½ hr., m.p. 177.0–177.5° cor. ⟨16⟩; or from C̄ + ⅔ mole *o*-phenylenediamine + 4 *N* HCl boiled 30–40 min. (60% yield); pr. from aq.; m.p. 176° ⟨17⟩. [This deriv. depresses m.p. of corresponding deriv. of propionic ac. (1:1025) ⟨16⟩.] [The picrate of this deriv. has m.p. 214° ⟨18⟩.]

Ⓓ **Piperazonium 1,4-diacetate:** from C̄ + 0.5 mole piperazine hexahydrate (71% yield); cryst. from *n*-butyl alc., m.p. 208.5–209° cor.; Neut. Eq. 206.1 ⟨19⟩.

Ⓓ ***S*-Benzylthiuronium acetate:** m.p. 134° ⟨20⟩; 135–136° ⟨21⟩.

1:1010 ⟨1⟩ Timmermans, Hennaut-Roland, *J. chim. phys.* **27,** 422–424 (1930). ⟨2⟩ Hess, Haber, *Ber.* **70,** 2205–2209 (1937). ⟨3⟩ Richmond, England, *Analyst* **51,** 283–287 (1926). ⟨4⟩ Archibald, *J. Am. Chem. Soc.* **54,** 3180–3181 (1932). ⟨5⟩ Clark, Bell, *Trans. Roy. Soc. Canada* (3) **27,** III, 97–104 (1933). ⟨6⟩ Osburn, Werkman, *Ind. Eng. Chem., Anal. Ed.* **3,** 264–265 (1931). ⟨7⟩ Osburn, Wood, Werkman, *Ind. Eng. Chem., Anal. Ed.* **8,** 270–275 (1936). ⟨8⟩ Reid, *J. Am. Chem. Soc.* **39,** 136 (1917). ⟨9⟩ Rather, Reid, *J. Am. Chem. Soc.* **41,** 83 (1919). ⟨10⟩ Moses, Reid, *J. Am. Chem. Soc.* **54,** 2101 (1932).

⟨11⟩ Judefind, Reid, *J. Am. Chem. Soc.* **42,** 1055 (1920). ⟨12⟩ Drake, Bronitsky, *J. Am. Chem. Soc.* **52,** 3719 (1930). ⟨13⟩ Mitchell, Reid, *J. Am. Chem. Soc.* **53,** 1881 (1931). ⟨14⟩ Skau, Rowe, *J. Am. Chem. Soc.* **57,** 2437 (1935). ⟨15⟩ Robertson, *J. Chem. Soc.* **93,** 1033 (1908). ⟨16⟩ Pool, Harwood, Ralston, *J. Am. Chem. Soc.* **59,** 178 (1937). ⟨17⟩ Phillips, *J. Chem. Soc.* **1928,** 2395. ⟨18⟩ Brown, Campbell, *J. Chem. Soc.* **1937,** 1701. ⟨19⟩ Pollard, Adelson, Bain, *J. Am. Chem. Soc.* **56,** 1759 (1934). ⟨20⟩ Donleavy, *J. Am. Chem. Soc.* **58,** 1005 (1936).

⟨21⟩ Veibel, Lillelund, *Bull. soc. chim.* (5) **5,** 1157 (1938).

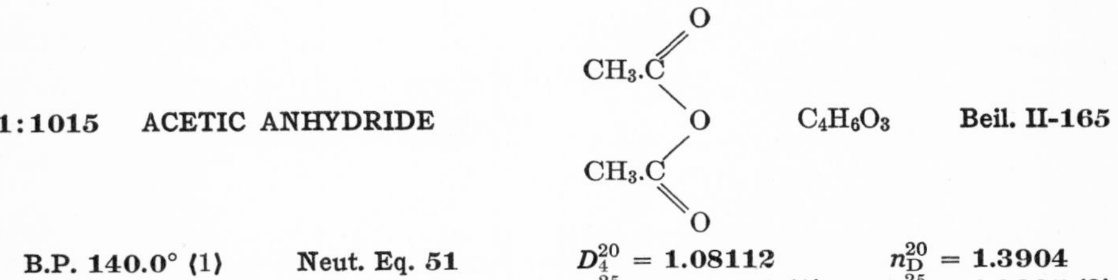

1:1015 ACETIC ANHYDRIDE $C_4H_6O_3$ Beil. II-165

B.P. 140.0° ⟨1⟩ **Neut. Eq. 51** D_4^{20} = **1.08112** n_D^{20} = **1.3904**
M.P. −73.1° ⟨1⟩ D_4^{25} = **1.07512 ⟨1⟩** n_D^{25} = **1.3885 ⟨2⟩**

C̄ has sharp irritating odor — C̄ is 12% sol. in cold aq. and slowly hydrolyzed to acetic ac. (1:1010) — C.S.T. in CS_2 is 29.8° ⟨1⟩.

For behavior on titration see Generic Test 3, Note 7 (" Manual ").

C̄, added to a soln. of anyhdrous oxalic ac. in dry pyridine, causes decompn. of the oxalic ac. to CO + CO_2 in amt. directly proportional to quant. of C̄ ⟨3⟩. [Use in quant. detn. of C̄ ⟨3⟩ ⟨4⟩.] [For decompn. of formic ac. into H_2O + CO by C̄ in presence of pyridine and use in detn. of C̄ see ⟨2⟩.]

[For analysis of C̄ by reactn. with 2,4-dichloroaniline and detn. of excess of latter see ⟨5⟩ ⟨6⟩ ⟨7⟩.]

[For quant. detn. of C̄ by titration with $NaOCH_3$ see ⟨8⟩.] [For detn. of C̄ via observation of rise in temperature when treated with aniline in toluene see ⟨9⟩.]

Ⓓ **Acetanilide:** from C̄ (3 drops), mixed with aniline (3 drops), boiled gently for 1 min., treated with 15 ml. aq., shaken and scratched, recrystd. from hot aq., m.p. 114°.

Ⓓ **Aceto-*p*-toluidide:** as for acetanilide (above) but substituting pure *p*-toluidine for aniline; m.p. 153° (148°).

Ⓓ **Hydrolysis:** C̄, dislvd. in excess dil. alk., acidified with dil. H_2SO_4, and distd. yields distillate contg. acetic ac. (1:1010), q.v.

1:1015 ⟨1⟩ Timmermans, Hennaut-Roland, *J. chim. phys.* **27,** 418–419 (1930). ⟨2⟩ Walton, Withrow, *J. Am. Chem. Soc.* **45,** 2689–2693 (1923). ⟨3⟩ Whitford, *J. Am. Chem. Soc.* **47,**

2939–2940 (1925). ⟨4⟩ Rosenbaum, Walton, *J. Am. Chem. Soc.* **52,** 3366–3368 (1930). ⟨5⟩ Orton, Bradfield, *J. Chem. Soc.* **1927,** 983–985. ⟨6⟩ Calcott, English, Wilbur, *Ind. Eng. Chem.* **17,** 942–944 (1925). ⟨7⟩ Terlinck, *Chem. Ztg.* **53,** 814–815, 850–851 (1929). ⟨8⟩ Smith, Bryant, *J. Am. Chem. Soc.* **58,** 2452–2454 (1936). ⟨9⟩ Richmond, Eggleston, *Analyst* **51,** 281–283 (1926).

1:1020 ACRYLIC ACID $CH_2{=}CH.COOH$ $C_3H_4O_2$ Beil. II-397

B.P. 140° **Neut. Eq. 72** D_4^{16} **= 1.0621** n_D^{20} **= 1.4224**
M.P. +13°

C̄ has sharp odor like acetic acid — Misc. aq.

C̄ shows profound tendency to polymerize, especially in presence of air, light, peroxides, or on htg. Although C̄ will sometimes remain unchanged for as much as a year, polymerization often begins spontaneously. On warming to 100° C̄ polymerizes rapidly (or even explosively). The resultant mixture of polymers consists of "polyacrylic acids." [For further details see ⟨1⟩ ⟨2⟩ ⟨3⟩.]

C̄ reduces $KMnO_4$ (T 1.34) [dif. from acetic ac. (1:1010) or propionic ac. (1:1025)]. C̄ adds Br_2 (yielding α,β-dibromopropionic ac., m.p. 66.5–67°).

Sodium salt of C̄ (dried at 150°) and htd. with $POCl_3$ gives (60% yield ⟨4⟩) acrylyl chloride, b.p. 75–76° [cf. ⟨5⟩ ⟨11⟩].

Ⓓ **Acrylamide:** from acrylyl chloride in C_6H_6 treated with dry NH_3 gas; cryst. from pet. ether; m.p. 84–85° ⟨6⟩.

Ⓓ **Acrylanilide:** from acrylyl chloride in C_6H_6 treated with aniline; cryst. from hot aq.; m.p. 104–105° ⟨7⟩. [Note that C̄, htd. with excess aniline for 3–4 hrs. at 180–190° does not yield acrylanilide, but β-anilinopropionanilide, cryst. from alc., m.p. 92–93° ⟨8⟩ ⟨9⟩.]

Ⓓ **Acrylo-*p*-toluidide:** prepn. analogous to acrylanilide; cryst. from aq.; m.p. 141° ⟨10⟩.

1:1020 ⟨1⟩ Staudinger, Urech, *Helv. Chim. Acta* **12,** 1107–1133 (1929). ⟨2⟩ Staudinger, Kohlschütter, *Ber.* **64,** 2091–2098 (1931). ⟨3⟩ Staudinger, Trommsdorff, *Ann.* **502,** 201–223 (1933). ⟨4⟩ Moureu, *Ann. chim.* (7) **2,** 161–162 (1894). ⟨5⟩ van der Burg, *Rec. trav. chim.* **41,** 23 (1921). ⟨6⟩ Ref. 4, pages 175–177. ⟨7⟩ Ref. 4, pages 181–183. ⟨8⟩ Autenrieth, Pretzell, *Ber.* **36,** 1264–1265 (1903). ⟨9⟩ Stoermer, Robert, *Ber.* **55,** 1037 (1922). ⟨10⟩ Ref. 4, pages 183–184. ⟨11⟩ Marvel, Levesque, *J. Am. Chem. Soc.* **61,** 3245 (1939).

1:1025 PROPIONIC ACID $CH_3.CH_2.COOH$ $C_3H_6O_2$ Beil. II-234

B.P. 141.35° ⟨1⟩ **Neut. Eq. 74** D_4^{20} **= 0.99336 ⟨1⟩** n_D^{20} **= 1.3868**
M.P. −20.8° ⟨1⟩

Odor like acetic ac. — Misc. with aq. but salted out by $CaCl_2$ [dif. from AcOH (1:1010)] — Volatile with steam (see Duclaux Value below) — Salts all soluble aq.

C̄ does *not* reduce $KMnO_4$ (T 1.34) [dif. from acrylic ac. (1:1020) or acetic ac. (1:1010)].

C̄ with PCl_5 (77% yield ⟨2⟩), or $PCl_3 + ZnCl_2$ (91% yield ⟨2⟩) gives propionyl chloride, b.p. 80°. [Note that although $SOCl_2$ (T 1.37) also yields propionyl chloride the latter boils at practically same temp. as thionyl chloride (b.p. 79°).]

[For detn. of C̄ in presence of formic ac. (1:1005) or acetic acid (1:1010) by controlled oxidn. of C̄ to oxalic ac. (1:0445) via $KMnO_4$ see ⟨3⟩; for identif. of C̄ in presence of acetic ac. (1:1010) or *n*-butyric ac. (1:1035) via microscopic observation of mercurous salts see ⟨4⟩; for detn. of C̄ in presence of other fatty acids via their distribution between immiscible solvents see ⟨5⟩.]

[For study of separation of C̄ from *n*-butyric ac. by distn. with hydrocarbons see ⟨22⟩.]

Ⓓ **Duclaux Value:** 11.9; 11.7; 11.3 [T 1.38). [For application to detn. of C̄ in presence of formic ac., acetic ac., and *n*-butyric acids, see ⟨6⟩.]

Ⓓ **Analysis of silver salt:** %Ag = 59.67 [T 1.36].

Ⓓ ***p*-Nitrobenzyl propionate:** m.p. 31° ⟨7⟩ [cf. T 1.39].

Ⓓ ***p*-Chlorophenacyl propionate:** m.p. 98.2° ⟨8⟩ [cf. T 1.391].

Ⓓ ***p*-Bromophenacyl propionate:** m.p. 63.4° ⟨8⟩; 59.0° ⟨9⟩ [cf. T 1.391].

Ⓓ ***p*-Iodophenacyl propionate:** m.p. 98.0° ⟨8⟩; 94.9° ⟨9⟩ [cf. T 1.391].

Ⓓ ***p*-Phenylphenacyl propionate:** m.p. 102° ⟨10⟩ [cf. T 1.391].

Ⓓ **Propionamide:** m.p. 81.3° ⟨11⟩; 79° ⟨12⟩.

Ⓓ **Propionanilide:** m.p. 105.6° ⟨13⟩; 104.0–104.5° ⟨14⟩; 105° ⟨12⟩. [For f.p. + compn. diagram of system: propionanilide + acetanilide see ⟨13⟩.]

Ⓓ **Propion-*p*-toluidide:** 123° ⟨12⟩.

Ⓓ **2-Ethylbenzimidazole:** from C̄ on htg. with 1 mole *o*-phenylenediamine at b.p. for $\frac{1}{2}$ hr.; m.p. 174.5° cor. ⟨15⟩; or from C̄ + $\frac{2}{3}$ mole *o*-phenylenediamine + 4 *N* HCl boiled for 30–40 min. (70% yield ⟨16⟩); pr. from 50% alc.; m.p. 177° ⟨16⟩; m.p. 174–175° ⟨17⟩. [The picrate of this deriv. has m.p. 120° ⟨18⟩.]

Ⓓ **Piperazonium 1,4-dipropionate:** from C̄ + 0.5 mole piperazine hexahydrate (50% yield); cryst. from dioxane, m.p. 124–125° cor.; Neut. Eq. 234.2 ⟨19⟩.

Ⓓ ***S*-Benzylthiuronium propionate:** m.p. 148° ⟨20⟩; 151–152° ⟨21⟩.

1:1025 ⟨1⟩ Timmermans, Hennaut-Roland, *J. chim. phys.* **27,** 425–427 (1930). ⟨2⟩ Clark, Bell, *Trans. Roy. Soc. Canada* (3) **27,** III, 97–103 (1933). ⟨3⟩ McNair, *J. Am. Chem. Soc.* **54,** 3249–3250 (1932). ⟨4⟩ Musicant, Kaszuba, *J. Am. Chem. Soc.* **61,** 2974–2976 (1939). ⟨5⟩ Osburn, Wood, Werkman, *Ind. Eng. Chem., Anal. Ed.* **8,** 270–275 (1936). ⟨6⟩ McNair, *J. Am. Chem. Soc.* **55,** 1470–1474 (1933). ⟨7⟩ Reid, *J. Am. Chem. Soc.* **39,** 136 (1917). ⟨8⟩ Moses, Reid, *J. Am. Chem. Soc.* **54,** 2101 (1932). ⟨9⟩ Judefind, Reid, *J. Am. Chem. Soc.* **42,** 1055 (1920). ⟨10⟩ Drake, Bronitsky, *J. Am. Chem. Soc.* **52,** 3719 (1930).

⟨11⟩ Mitchell, Reid, *J. Am. Chem. Soc.* **53,** 1881 (1931). ⟨12⟩ Robertson, *J. Chem. Soc.* **93,** 1033 (1908). ⟨13⟩ Skau, Rowe, *J. Am. Chem. Soc.* **57,** 2437 (1935). ⟨14⟩ Underwood, Gale, *J. Am. Chem. Soc.* **56,** 2119 (1934). ⟨15⟩ Pool, Harwood, Ralston, *J. Am. Chem. Soc.* **59,** 178 (1937). ⟨16⟩ Phillips, *J. Chem. Soc.* **1928,** 2395. ⟨17⟩ Weidenhagen, *Ber.* **69,** 2267 (1936). ⟨18⟩ Brown, Campbell, *J. Chem. Soc.* **1937,** 1701. ⟨19⟩ Pollard, Adelson, Bain, *J. Am. Chem. Soc.* **56,** 1759 (1934). ⟨20⟩ Donleavy, *J. Am. Chem. Soc.* **58,** 1005 (1936).

⟨21⟩ Veibel, Lillelund, *Bull. soc. chim.* (5) **5,** 1157 (1938). ⟨22⟩ Axe, Bratton, *J. Am. Chem. Soc.* **59,** 1424–1425 (1937).

1:1030 ISOBUTYRIC ACID $C_4H_8O_2$ Beil. II-288

(2-Methylpropanoic acid-1)

```
        CH3
         |
CH3—C—COOH
         |
         H
```

B.P. 154.7° ⟨1⟩ **Neut. Eq. 88** D_4^{20} **= 0.94791 ⟨1⟩** n_D^{15} **= 1.39525 ⟨1⟩**
M.P. −46.1° ⟨1⟩ n_D^{20} **= 1.39300**

C̄ has unpleasant odor like rancid butter — C̄ is sol. in 5 pts. aq. [dif. from *n*-butyric ac. (1:1035)]; misc. alc., ether — Volatile with steam.

C̄, treated with PCl_5 (81% yield ⟨2⟩), or $PCl_3 + ZnCl_2$ (82% yield ⟨2⟩) or 1.5 moles $SOCl_2$ (44% yield ⟨2⟩; 75% yield ⟨3⟩) [cf. T 1.37] gives isobutyryl chloride, b.p. 92°, n_D^{20} = 1.4070 ⟨3⟩.

C̄ on oxidn. with alk. $KMnO_4$ ⟨4⟩ yields α-hydroxy-isobutyric acid (1:0431) [dif. from *n*-butyric ac. (1:1035) which is destroyed].

Ⓟ **Solubility of CaĀ₂:** an aq. soln. of CaĀ₂ does *not* become turbid on boiling [dif. from *n*-butyric ac. (1:1035), q.v.].

Ⓓ **Duclaux Value:** 25.0; 20.9; 16.0 [T 1.38] [distinguishes from *n*-butyric ac. (1:1035) but not from *n*-valeric (1:1060) or isovaleric (1:1050)].

Ⓓ **Analysis of silver salt:** %Ag = 55.38 [T 1.36].

Ⓓ **p-Bromophenacyl isobutyrate:** m.p. 76.8° ⟨6⟩ [cf. T 1.391] [distinguishes from *n*-butyric ac. (1:1035)].

Ⓓ **p-Iodophenacyl isobutyrate:** m.p. 109.2° ⟨6⟩ [cf. T 1.391] [distinguishes from *n*-butyric ac. (1:1035), *n*-valeric ac. (1:1060) or isovaleric ac. (1:1050)].

Ⓓ **p-Phenylphenacyl isobutyrate:** m.p. 89° ⟨7⟩ [cf. T 1.391].

Ⓓ **Isobutyramide:** m.p. 129° ⟨8⟩; 126.8° ⟨9⟩.

Ⓓ **Isobutyranilide:** m.p. 105° ⟨10⟩; 104–105° ⟨11⟩ ⟨12⟩.

Ⓓ **Isobutyro-p-toluidide:** m.p. 108.5–109.5° ⟨13⟩; 106–106.5° ⟨14⟩.

Ⓓ **2-(Isopropyl)benzimidazole:** from $\bar{C}$ + 1 mole *o*-phenylenediamine on htg. 8 hrs. at 140–150°; cryst. from C_6H_6 on addn. of pet. ether; m.p. 223–225° ⟨15⟩. [The picrate of this deriv. has m.p. 136° ⟨16⟩.]

Ⓓ **S-Benzylthiuronium isobutyrate:** m.p. 143° ⟨17⟩.

1:1030 ⟨1⟩ Timmermans, Delcourt, *J. chim. phys.* **31,** 109–112 (1934). ⟨2⟩ Clark, Bell, *Trans. Roy. Soc. Canada* (3) **27,** III, 97–103 (1933). ⟨3⟩ Whitmore, *Rec. trav. chim.* **57,** 565 (1938). ⟨4⟩ Hutzler, Meyer, *Ber.* **30,** 2525–2526 (1897). ⟨6⟩ Judefind, Reid, *J. Am. Chem. Soc.* **42,** 1055 (1920). ⟨7⟩ Clutterbuck, Raistrick, Reuter, *Biochem. J.* **29,** 880 (1935). ⟨8⟩ Meyer, *Monatsh.* **27,** 43 (1906). ⟨9⟩ Hoffmann, Barbier, *Bull. soc. chim. Belg.* **45,** 570 (1936). ⟨10⟩ Tingle, Blanck, *J. Am. Chem. Soc.* **30,** 1408 (1908).

⟨11⟩ Fieser, Campbell, *J. Am. Chem. Soc.* **60,** 168–169 (1938). ⟨12⟩ Underwood, Gale, *J. Am. Chem. Soc.* **56,** 2119 (1934). ⟨13⟩ von Auwers, Ungemach, *Ber.* **67,** 252 (1934). ⟨14⟩ Fieser, Hartwell, Seligman, *J. Am. Chem. Soc.* **58,** 1226 (1936). ⟨15⟩ Seka, Müller, *Monatsh.* **57,** 104 (1931). ⟨16⟩ Brown, Campbell, *J. Chem. Soc.* **1937,** 1701. ⟨17⟩ Donleavy, *J. Am. Chem. Soc.* **58,** 1005 (1936).

1:1035 *n*-BUTYRIC ACID $CH_3.CH_2.CH_2.COOH$ $C_4H_8O_2$ Beil. II-264

(Butanoic acid)

B.P. 164.05° ⟨1⟩ **Neut. Eq. 88** D_4^{20} **= 0.95790 ⟨1⟩** n_D^{20} **= 1.3979**

M.P. −5.50° ⟨1⟩

$\bar{C}$ has unpleasant odor like rancid butter — $\bar{C}$ is misc. with aq. [dif. from isobutyric ac. (1:1030)]; misc. alc., ether — Volatile with steam. [For study of sepn. from propionic ac. (1:1025) or *n*-valeric ac. (1:1050) via distn. with hydrocarbons see ⟨2⟩.] [For study of distribution of $\bar{C}$ between water and various org. solvents including ether see ⟨20⟩.]

$\bar{C}$ treated with PCl_5 (83% yield ⟨3⟩), or $PCl_3 + ZnCl_2$ (77% yield ⟨3⟩), or 1.5 moles $SOCl_2$ (50% yield ⟨3⟩; 80% yield ⟨4⟩) [cf. T 1.37] gives *n*-butyryl chloride, b.p. 101.0–101.5°_{730} ⟨4⟩, n_D^{20} = 1.4117 ⟨4⟩.

Ⓟ **Solubility of $CaĀ_2$:** $\bar{C}$, neutralized with excess $CaCO_3$; soln. filtered, concentrated, stood in cold, again filtered, gives on warming a white ppt. of $CaĀ_2$ [dif. from isobutyric ac. (1:1030)].

Ⓓ **Duclaux Value:** 17.9; 15.9; 14.6 [T 1.38].

Ⓓ **Analysis of silver salt:** %Ag = 55.38 [T 1.36].

Ⓓ **p-Nitrobenzyl *n*-butyrate:** m.p. 35° ⟨5⟩ [cf. T 1.39].

Ⓓ **p-Chlorophenacyl *n*-butyrate:** m.p. 55.0° ⟨6⟩ [cf. T 1.391].

Ⓓ **p-Bromophenacyl *n*-butyrate:** m.p. 63.0° ⟨6⟩; 63.2° ⟨7⟩ [cf. T 1.391].

Ⓓ **p-Iodophenacyl *n*-butyrate:** m.p. 81.5° ⟨6⟩; 81.4° ⟨7⟩ [cf. T 1.391].

Ⓓ **p-Phenylphenacyl *n*-butyrate:** m.p. 82° ⟨8⟩ ⟨9⟩ [cf. T 1.391].

Ⓓ ***n*-Butyramide:** m.p. 115° ⟨10⟩.

Ⓓ ***n*-Butyranilide:** m.p. 96° ⟨11⟩; 97° ⟨12⟩; 92° ⟨13⟩ ⟨14⟩.

Ⓓ ***n*-Butyro-p-toluidide:** m.p. 75° ⟨11⟩.

Ⓓ **2-(*n*-Propyl)benzimidazole:** from $\bar{C}$ htd. with 1 mole *o*-phenylenediamine at b.p. for ½ hr.; m.p. 157.0–157.5° cor. ⟨15⟩; 152–153° ⟨16⟩ [depresses m.p. of corresp. deriv. of *n*-valeric ac. (1:1060) ⟨15⟩]. [The picrate of this deriv. has m.p. 124° ⟨17⟩.]

Ⓓ **Piperazonium 1,4-di-*n*-butyrate:** from C̄ + 0.5 mole piperazine hexahydrate (88% yield); cryst. from dioxane; m.p. 121–122° cor.; Neut. Eq. 262 ⟨18⟩.

Ⓓ ***S*-Benzylthiuronium *n*-butyrate:** m.p. 146° ⟨19⟩.

1:1035 ⟨1⟩ Timmermans, Hennaut-Roland, *J. chim. phys.* **29,** 550–552 (1932). ⟨2⟩ Axe, Bratton, *J. Am. Chem. Soc.* **59,** 1424–1425 (1939). ⟨3⟩ Clark, Bell, *Trans. Roy. Soc. Canada* (3) **27,** III, 97–103 (1933). ⟨4⟩ Whitmore, *Rec. trav. chim.* **57,** 565 (1938). ⟨5⟩ Reid, *J. Am. Chem. Soc.* **39,** 136 (1917). ⟨6⟩ Moses, Reid, *J. Am. Chem. Soc.* **54,** 2101 (1932). ⟨7⟩ Judefind, Reid, *J. Am. Chem. Soc.* **42,** 1055 (1920). ⟨8⟩ Clutterbuck, Raistrick, Reuter, *Biochem. J.* **29,** 880 (1935). ⟨9⟩ Weizmann, Bergmann, Haskelberg, *Chemistry and Industry* **56,** 589 (1937). ⟨10⟩ Mitchell, Reid, *J. Am. Chem. Soc.* **53,** 1881 (1931).

⟨11⟩ Robertson, *J. Chem. Soc.* **115,** 1220–1221 (1919). ⟨12⟩ Fournier, *Bull. soc. chim.* (4) **7,** 25–26 (1910). ⟨13⟩ Underwood, Gale, *J. Am. Chem. Soc.* **56,** 2119 (1934). ⟨14⟩ Schwartz, Johnson, *J. Am. Chem. Soc.* **53,** 1065 (1931). ⟨15⟩ Pool, Harwood, Ralston, *J. Am. Chem. Soc.* **59,** 178 (1937). ⟨16⟩ Seka, Müller, *Monatsh.* **57,** 101–102 (1931). ⟨17⟩ Brown, Campbell, *J. Chem. Soc.* **1937,** 1701. ⟨18⟩ Pollard, Adelson, Bain, *J. Am. Chem. Soc.* **56,** 1759 (1934). ⟨19⟩ Donleavy, *J. Am. Chem. Soc.* **58,** 1005 (1936). ⟨20⟩ Archibald, *J. Am. Chem. Soc.* **54,** 3180–3181 (1932).

1:1040 PYRUVIC ACID $CH_3.CO.COOH$ $C_3H_4O_3$ Beil. III-608

(Pyroracemic acid;
α-oxopropionic acid)

B.P. 165° sl. dec. **Neut. Eq. 88** D_4^{15} = **1.2668** $n_D^{15.3}$ = **1.43025**
M.P. +13.6°

Sharp odor like acetic acid; misc. aq., alc., ether.

[For prepn. in 50–55% yield by htg. tartaric ac. (1:0525) with $KHSO_4$ see ⟨1⟩.]

C̄ slowly but spontaneously decomposes ⟨2⟩ even at ord. temp. yielding α-keto-γ-valerolactone-γ-carboxylic acid [Beil. XVIII-451], m.p. 116° [which titrates as a dibasic acid ⟨3⟩].

C̄, on warming with conc. H_2SO_4, yields both CO and CO_2 — C̄ reduces NH_4OH / $AgNO_3$ and Tollens' reagt. (T 1.11) — C̄ reduces $KMnO_4$ (T 1.34) — C̄ on treatment with I_2.KI soln. + aq. NaOH (T 1.81) yields CHI_3.

C̄ in ether, treated with ether soln. of 1 mole aniline, yields ppt. of pyruvic ac. anil, $CH_3.C(:N.C_6H_5).COOH$ [Beil. XII-516], which after extraction with $CHCl_3$ and crystn. from hot C_6H_6 has m.p. 127–128° dec. ⟨4⟩.

C̄ with $SOCl_2$ gives no corresp. acid chloride but instead a complex mixt. contg. AcCl, Ac_2O and other products. However, C̄ in dry pyridine, treated with $SOCl_2$ in dry ether, yields a soln. which reacts with aniline to yield pyruvanilide, m.p. 104° ⟨13⟩.

Ⓟ **Sodium nitroprusside color reaction:** C̄, dislvd. in conc. NH_4OH, treated with conc. aq. soln. of sodium nitroprusside slowly gives characteristic violet-blue color; addn. of KOH changes color to dark red; AcOH to blue ⟨5⟩.

Ⓓ **Pyruvic acid phenylhydrazone:** from C̄ mixed with 1 mole phenylhydrazine in ether; cryst. from alc., m.p. 192° rap. htg. dec. ⟨6⟩.

Ⓓ **Pyruvic acid *p*-nitrophenylhydrazone:** m.p. 219–220° ⟨7⟩ [distinguished from methylglyoxal *p*-nitrophenylhydrazone by soly. in dil. NH_4OH ⟨8⟩].

Ⓓ **Pyruvic acid 2,4-dinitrophenylhydrazone:** yel. cryst. from alc., or AcOH; m.p. 218° ⟨9⟩ ⟨10⟩; 213° cor. ⟨11⟩ [cf. T 1.14]. [Use in quant. detn. of C̄ ⟨12⟩.]

Pyruvamide [Beil. III-620]: m.p. 124–125° [prepared indirectly].

Pyruvanilide [Beil. XII-516]: m.p. 104° [prepared indirectly; e.g., by oxidn. of lactanilide ⟨14⟩].

Pyruvic-*p*-toluidide [Beil. XII-969]: m.p. 130° [prepared indirectly].

1:1040 ⟨1⟩ Howard, Fraser, *Organic Syntheses, Coll. Vol.* I, 462–463 (1932). ⟨2⟩ DeJong, *Rec. trav. chim.* **20,** 91 (1901). ⟨3⟩ Wolff, *Ann.* **317,** 8 (1901). ⟨4⟩ Simon, *Ann. chim.* (7) **9,** 463–466 (1896). ⟨5⟩ Simon, *Compt. rend.* **125,** 534–536 (1897). ⟨6⟩ Fischer, *Ber.* **17,** 578 (1884);

41, 76 (1908). ⟨7⟩ Fernbach, Schoen, *Compt. rend.* **158,** 1720 (1914). ⟨8⟩ Neuberg, Gorr, *Biochem. Z.* **166,** 442–443 (1925). ⟨9⟩ Campbell, *Analyst* **61,** 393 (1936). ⟨10⟩ Strain, *J. Am. Chem. Soc.* **57,** 760 (1935).
⟨11⟩ Allen, *J. Am. Chem. Soc.* **52,** 2958 (1930). ⟨12⟩ Case, *Biochem. J.* **26,** 753–758 (1932). ⟨13⟩ Carré, Jullien, *Compt. rend.* **202,** 1521–1523 (1936). ⟨14⟩ Scudi, *J. Am. Chem. Soc.* **59,** 1403 (1937).

1:1042 VINYLACETIC ACID $CH_2{=}CH.CH_2.COOH$ $C_4H_6O_2$ **Beil. II-407**
(Butene-3-oic acid-1)

B.P. 169.0–169.2$^\circ_{764}$ ⟨1⟩ **Neut. Eq. 86** D_4^{20} **= 1.0094 ⟨2⟩** n_D^{15} **= 1.4257 ⟨3⟩**
M.P. −35° ⟨2⟩ n_D^{20} **= 1.4221 ⟨2⟩**

Mobile liq. with odor like *n*-butyric ac. — Misc. with aq.
[For prepn. via hydrolysis of allyl cyanide with conc. H_2SO_4 see ⟨2⟩ ⟨1⟩.]

$\bar{C}$ in CS_2 adds Br_2 yielding β,γ-dibromo-*n*-butyric acid [Beil. II-295], cryst. from CS_2, m.p. 49–50° ⟨2⟩ ⟨3⟩. [Use in quant. detn. of $\bar{C}$ ⟨4⟩.]

$\bar{C}$ under specified conditions adds HBr (gas); without solvent, or in presence of aq., ether, AcOH ⟨5⟩, or benzoyl peroxide ⟨6⟩, yields almost exclusively β-bromo-*n*-butyric ac. [Beil. II-283], m.p. 17–18°; in toluene or pet. ether ⟨5⟩, or in hexane in atm. of H_2 or presence of antioxidants ⟨6⟩ yields almost exclusively γ-bromo-*n*-butyric acid [Beil. II-283], m.p. 31–32°.

$\bar{C}$ on htg. at b.p. for 24 hrs. ⟨1⟩, or htd. with 5% H_2SO_4 for a few hrs. ⟨3⟩, or boiled with 50% H_2SO_4 for 5 min. (98% yield ⟨7⟩) isomerizes to crotonic ac. (1:0425) — Although $\bar{C}$ may be recovered unchanged upon acidification of its neutral salts ⟨1⟩, yet in presence of excess alk. $\bar{C}$ isomerizes to salts of crotonic ac. (1:0425); e.g., $\bar{C}$ stood 48 hrs. with 10% excess NaOH ⟨1⟩ or $\bar{C}$ htd. with 10 equiv. 25% aq. KOH at 100° for 10 min. ⟨8⟩.

$\bar{C}$, htd. with excess aniline 4 hrs. at 180° yields β-anilino-*n*-butyranilide [Beil. XII-558], cryst. from alc., m.p. 93° ⟨9⟩ ⟨10⟩ [does not distinguish from crotonic ac. (1:0425), isocrotonic ac. (1:1045), all of which give same product by same treatment; or from acrylic ac. (1:1020) which gives β-anilino-propionanilide, also m.p. 93°, on similar treatment].

Ⓓ **Vinylacetamide:** m.p. 73° ⟨11⟩ [from allyl cyanide + H_2O_2 in acetone, 80% yield, m.p. 72–72.5° ⟨12⟩].

Ⓓ **Vinylacetanilide:** m.p. 58° ⟨13⟩.

1:1042 ⟨1⟩ Bruylants, *Bull. soc. chim. Belg.* **33,** 334–338 (1924). ⟨2⟩ Linstead, Noble, Boorman, *J. Chem. Soc.* **1933,** 560–561. ⟨3⟩ Fichter, Sonneborn, *Ber.* **35,** 938–942 (1902). ⟨4⟩ Linstead, Noble, *J. Chem. Soc.* **1934,** 617. ⟨5⟩ Boorman, Linstead, Rydon, *J. Chem. Soc.* **1933,** 569, 572–573. ⟨6⟩ Linstead, Rydon, *J. Chem. Soc.* **1934,** 2002. ⟨7⟩ Boorman, Linstead, *J. Chem. Soc.* **1933,** 578. ⟨8⟩ Ref. 4, page 622. ⟨9⟩ Autenrieth, Pretzell, *Ber.* **36,** 1267–1268 (1903). ⟨10⟩ Autenrieth, *Ber.* **38,** 2550–2551 (1905).
⟨11⟩ Stoermer, Robert, *Ber.* **55,** 1034 (1922). ⟨12⟩ Murray, Cloke, *J. Am. Chem. Soc.* **56,** 2751 (1934). ⟨13⟩ Ref. 10, page 2547.

1:1045 ISOCROTONIC ACID $C_4H_6O_2$ **Beil. II-412**
(β-Crotonic acid;
cis-buten-2-oic acid-1)

CH_3—C—H
‖
HOOC—C—H

B.P. 169° **Neut. Eq. 86** D_4^{20} **= 1.0265 ⟨1⟩** n_D^{20} **= 1.4456 ⟨1⟩**
M.P. 15°

Sharp odor — Sol. in 2.5 pts. aq.
[For anal. of mixts. of $\bar{C}$ and crotonic ac. (1:0425) by fractional crystn. of their sodium salts see ⟨2⟩ ⟨3⟩ ⟨4⟩.]
$\bar{C}$ reduces $KMnO_4$ (T 1.34) and adds Br_2 (T 1.91).

C̄ in ether treated with $SOCl_2$ ⟨8⟩ or PCl_5 ⟨9⟩ yields an ether soln. of isocrotonyl chloride, which may be used for prepn. of other derivs. such as amide or anilide; but isocrotonyl chloride cannot be distilled without isomerization to crotonyl chloride ⟨8⟩.

C̄, htd. with excess aniline 4 hrs. at 180°, yields β-anilino-*n*-butyranilide [Beil. XII-558], cryst. from alc., m.p. 93° ⟨5⟩ [does not distinguish from crotonic ac. (1:0425), vinylacetic ac. (1:1042), all of which give same product by same treatment; or from acrylic ac. (1:1020) which gives β-anilino-propionanilide also m.p. 93°].

Ⓓ **Isomerization to α-(*trans*)-crotonic acid:** C̄ (0.5 mole) htd. with I_2 (5 mg.) for 1 hr. at 150° yields α-crotonic ac. (1:0425), m.p. 72° ⟨6⟩.
Ⓓ ***p*-Bromophenacyl isocrotonate:** m.p. 80.5–81.5° ⟨1⟩ [cf. T 1.391].
Ⓓ **Isocrotonamide:** m.p. 101–102°.
Ⓓ **Isocrotonanilide:** m.p. 101–102° ⟨7⟩.

1:1045 ⟨1⟩ von Auwers, *Ann.* **432,** 60–61 (1923). ⟨2⟩ Young, *J. Am. Chem. Soc.* **54,** 2501 (1932). ⟨3⟩ Kaufler, *Monatsh.* **53/54,** 120–121 (1929). ⟨4⟩ Wislicenus, *Cent.* **1897,** II, 259–260. ⟨5⟩ Autenrieth, *Ber.* **38,** 2541, 2550–2551 (1905). ⟨6⟩ Mulliken, "Method" I, 74 (1904). ⟨7⟩ Ref. 5, pages 2542–2543. ⟨8⟩ Jones, Mason, *J. Am. Chem. Soc.* **49,** 2534 (1927). ⟨9⟩ Ref. 5, page 2543.

1:1050 ISOVALERIC ACID (β-Methyl-*n*-butyric acid; 3-methyl-butanoic acid-1) $CH_3.CH(CH_3).CH_2.COOH$ $C_5H_{10}O_2$ **Beil. II-309**

B.P. 176.50° ⟨1⟩ **Neut. Eq. 102** D_4^{20} = **0.92623** ⟨1⟩ n_D^{20} = **1.4043**
M.P. −30.0° ⟨1⟩

C̄ has offensive odor like decayed cheese — C̄ is sol. in 23.6 pts. aq. at 20° (is salted out by $CaCl_2$); misc. with alc. or ether. [For study of sepn. of C̄ from *n*-butyric ac. (1:1035) by distn. with hydrocarbons see ⟨2⟩.]

C̄ treated with $PCl_3 + ZnCl_2$ (79% yield ⟨3⟩) or 1.5 moles $SOCl_2$ (72% yield ⟨3⟩) [cf. T 1.37], gives isovaleryl chloride, b.p. 119.7°_{766} ⟨4⟩, D_4^{20} = 0.9844 ⟨4⟩; n_D^{20} = 1.41488 ⟨4⟩. [Note that use of PCl_5 is inadvisable since by-product $POCl_3$ boils at same b.p. as prod.]

AgĀ; very dif. sol. aq. [cf. T 1.36] — Alk. salts of C̄ give no ppt. with $CaCl_2$ soln.; gelat. ppt. with $ZnSO_4$ in cold or scales if hot.

Ⓓ **Duclaux Value:** 28.7; 23.1; 16.8 [T 1.38].
Ⓓ **Analysis of silver salt:** %Ag = 51.67 [T 1.36].
Ⓓ ***p*-Bromophenacyl isovalerate:** m.p. 68.0° ⟨5⟩ [cf. T 1.391].
Ⓓ ***p*-Iodophenacyl isovalerate:** m.p. 78.8° ⟨5⟩ [cf. T 1.391].
Ⓓ ***p*-Phenylphenacyl isovalerate:** m.p. 78° ⟨6⟩; 76° ⟨7⟩ [cf. T 1.391]. [This deriv. depresses m.p. of corresp. deriv. of α-methyl-*n*-butyric ac. (1:1105) ⟨6⟩.]
Ⓓ **Isovaleramide:** m.p. 135° ⟨8⟩; 137° ⟨9⟩.
Ⓓ **Isovaleranilide:** m.p. 109.5° cor. ⟨10⟩; 109–110° ⟨11⟩; 110° ⟨12⟩.
Ⓓ **Isovalero-*p*-toluidide:** m.p. 106–107° ⟨11⟩.
Ⓓ **2-(Isobutyl)benzimidazole:** should be preparable from C̄ htd. with 1 mole *o*-phenylenediamine according to ⟨13⟩; so far reported only indirectly; m.p. 186–187° ⟨16⟩.
Ⓓ **Piperazonium 1,4-di-isovalerate:** from C̄ + 0.5 mole piperazine hexahydrate (67% yield); cryst. from acetone; m.p. 139–140° cor.; Neut. Eq. 290.2 ⟨14⟩.
Ⓓ ***S*-Benzylthiuronium isovalerate:** m.p. 153° ⟨15⟩.

1:1050 ⟨1⟩ Timmermans, Hennaut-Roland, *J. chim. phys.* **29,** 554–555 (1932). ⟨2⟩ Axe, Bratton, *J. Am. Chem. Soc.* **59,** 1424–1425 (1937). ⟨3⟩ Clark, Bell, *Trans. Roy. Soc. Canada* (3) **27,** III, 97–103 (1933). ⟨4⟩ Leimu, *Ber.* **70,** 1049 (1937). ⟨5⟩ Judefind, Reid, *J. Am. Chem. Soc.* **42,** 1055 (1920). ⟨6⟩ Kögl, Erxleben, *Z. physiol. Chem.* **227,** 71 (1934). ⟨7⟩ Drake, Bronitsky, *J. Am. Chem. Soc.* **52,** 3719 (1930). ⟨8⟩ Schmidt, Sachtleben, *Ann.* **193,** 102

(1878). ⟨9⟩ Fournier, *Bull. soc. chim.* (4) **5,** 924 (1909). ⟨10⟩ Schwartz, Johnson, *J. Am. Chem. Soc.* **53,** 1065 (1931).
⟨11⟩ Underwood, Gale, *J. Am. Chem. Soc.* **56,** 2119 (1934). ⟨12⟩ Crossley, Perkin, *J. Chem. Soc.* **73,** 16 (1898). ⟨13⟩ Seka, Müller, *Monatsh.* **57,** 105 (1931). ⟨14⟩ Pollard, Adelson, Bain, *J. Am. Chem. Soc.* **56,** 1759 (1934). ⟨15⟩ Donleavy, *J. Am. Chem. Soc.* **58,** 1005 (1936). ⟨16⟩ Weidenhagen, *Ber.* **69,** 2268 (1936).

1:1055 DIETHYL OXALATE $\begin{array}{l}COOC_2H_5\\|\\COOC_2H_5\end{array}$ $C_6H_{10}O_4$ Beil. II-535

B.P. 185.4° ⟨1⟩ **Neut. Eq. 146** D_4^{20} **= 1.07846 ⟨1⟩** n_D^{20} **= 1.41043**
M.P. −40.6° ⟨1⟩ **Sap. Eq. 73**

Dif. sol. aq.; eas. sol. ether; misc. with alc. — C̄ with 0.1 *N* aq. alk. titrates (slowly) like *mono*basic acid.

[For prepn. from crystn. oxalic acid + alc. (80–83% yield ⟨2⟩; 85% yield ⟨3⟩; 91% yield ⟨4⟩); from anhydrous oxalic acid (80–90% yield ⟨5⟩, 90–95% yield ⟨4⟩) see cited references; also ⟨6⟩.]

Ⓟ **Oxamide formation:** C̄ shaken with conc. aq. NH_4OH gives immed. ppt. of oxamide. [The m.p. of this product is far too high (417–419° dec.) to use as a real deriv. for identification of C̄.]

Ⓓ **Saponification:** Hydrolysis with alk. (T 1.51) yields ethyl alc. (1:6130) and oxalic ac. (1:0445).

Ⓓ **Oxalic dihydrazide:** from C̄ + 2 moles hydrazine hydrate in a little alc.; ndls. from hot aq.; m.p. 240° ⟨7⟩. [The half hydrazide, $C_2H_5OOC.CO.NH.NH_2$ has m.p. 52–53° ⟨7⟩.]

Ⓓ **Ethyl oxamate:** from C̄ in 3 vols. alc. treated at 0° with 1 mole alc. NH_3; lfts. from hot alc., m.p. 114° ⟨8⟩.

1:1055 ⟨1⟩ Timmermans, Hennaut-Roland, *J. chim. phys.* **27,** 435–436 (1930). ⟨2⟩ Clarke, Davis, *Organic Syntheses, Coll. Vol.* I, 256–258 (1932). ⟨3⟩ Jewel, Butts, *J. Am. Chem. Soc.* **53,** 3560–3561 (1931). ⟨4⟩ Mitchovitch, *Bull. soc. chim.* (5) **4,** 1666–1667 (1937). ⟨5⟩ Kenyon, *Organic Syntheses, Coll. Vol.* I, 257–260 (1932). ⟨6⟩ Thielepape, *Ber.* **66,** 1457–1459 (1933). ⟨7⟩ Tierie, *Rec. trav. chim.* **52,** 358 (1933). ⟨8⟩ Weddige, *J. prakt. Chem.* (2) **10,** 196 (1874).

1:1060 *n*-VALERIC ACID $CH_3.(CH_2)_3.COOH$ $C_5H_{10}O_2$ Beil. II-299
(Pentanoic acid-1)

B.P. 186.35° ⟨1⟩ **Neut. Eq. 102** D_4^{20} **= 0.93922 ⟨1⟩** n_D^{20} **= 1.4086**
M.P. −34.5° ⟨1⟩

Odor of C̄ and solubility of C̄ and its salts nearly same as for isovaleric ac. (1:1050). [For prepn. of C̄ in 72–73% yield from *n*-butyl MgCl + CO_2 see ⟨2⟩.] [For distribution of C̄ between water and various immiscible org. solvents including ether see ⟨3⟩.]

C̄, treated with PCl_5 (60% yield ⟨4⟩), or $PCl_3 + ZnCl_2$ (75% yield ⟨4⟩), or 1.5 moles $SOCl_2$ (77% yield ⟨4⟩) [cf. T 1.37] gives *n*-valeryl chloride, b.p. 127–128°.

Ⓓ **Duclaux Value:** 24.5; 20.6; 17.0 [T 1.38] [dif. from isovaleric ac. (1:1050) but not from isobutyric ac. (1:1030)].

Ⓓ **Analysis of silver salt:** %Ag = 51.67 [T 1.36].

Ⓓ ***p*-Chlorophenacyl *n*-valerate:** m.p. 97.8° ⟨5⟩ [cf. T 1.391].

Ⓓ ***p*-Bromophenacyl *n*-valerate:** m.p. 75.0° ⟨5⟩; 63.6° ⟨6⟩ [cf. T 1.391].

Ⓓ ***p*-Iodophenacyl *n*-valerate:** m.p. 81.0° ⟨5⟩; 78.6° ⟨6⟩ [cf. T 1.391].

Ⓓ ***p*-Phenylphenacyl *n*-valerate:** m.p. 63.5° ⟨7⟩ [cf. T 1.391].

Ⓓ **n-Valeramide:** m.p. 106° ⟨8⟩; 105.8° ⟨9⟩.
Ⓓ **n-Valeranilide:** m.p. 63° ⟨8⟩ ⟨10⟩; 62–63° ⟨11⟩; 61–62° ⟨12⟩.
Ⓓ **n-Valero-p-toluidide:** m.p. 74° ⟨8⟩; 72–73° ⟨11⟩ ⟨12⟩.
Ⓓ **n-Valero-α-naphthalide:** m.p. 109–110° ⟨11⟩.
Ⓓ **2-(n-Butyl)benzimidazole:** from C̄ on htg. with 1 mole *o*-phenylenediamine at b.p. for ½ hr.; m.p. 155.0–155.5° cor. ⟨13⟩ [depresses m.p. of corresp. deriv. of *n*-caproic ac. (1:1130)].
Ⓓ **Piperazonium 1,4-di-n-valerate:** from C̄ + 0.5 mole piperazine hexahydrate; cryst. from dioxane; m.p. 112.5–113° cor.; Neut. Eq. 290.2 ⟨14⟩ [dif. from isovaleric ac. (1:1050) or isobutyric ac. (1:1030)]. [This deriv. depresses m.p. of corresp. deriv. of *n*-caproic ac. (1:1130) ⟨14⟩.]

1:1060 ⟨1⟩ Timmermans, Hennaut-Roland, *J. chim. phys.* **29,** 552–554 (1932). ⟨2⟩ Gilman, Kirby, *Organic Syntheses, Coll. Vol.* I, 355 (1932). ⟨3⟩ Archibald, *J. Am. Chem. Soc.* **54,** 3180–3181 (1932). ⟨4⟩ Clark, Bell, *Trans. Roy. Soc. Canada* (3) **27,** III, 97–103 (1933). ⟨5⟩ Moses, Reid, *J. Am. Chem. Soc.* **54,** 2101 (1932). ⟨6⟩ Judefind, Reid, *J. Am. Chem. Soc.* **42,** 1055 (1920). ⟨7⟩ Drake, Bronitsky, *J. Am. Chem. Soc.* **52,** 3719 (1930). ⟨8⟩ Robertson, *J. Chem. Soc.* **115,** 1220–1221 (1919). ⟨9⟩ Mitchell, Reid, *J. Am. Chem. Soc.* **53,** 1881 (1931). ⟨10⟩ Schwartz, Johnson, *J. Am. Chem. Soc.* **53,** 1065 (1931).

⟨11⟩ Underwood, Gale, *J. Am. Chem. Soc.* **56,** 2119 (1934). ⟨12⟩ Kipping, *J. Chem. Soc.* **1935,** 1146. ⟨13⟩ Pool, Harwood, Ralston, *J. Am. Chem. Soc.* **59,** 178 (1937). ⟨14⟩ Pollard, Adelson, Bain, *J. Am. Chem. Soc.* **56,** 1759 (1934).

1:1065 METHOXYACETIC ACID $CH_3O.CH_2.COOH$ $C_3H_6O_3$ Beil. III-232
(Glycolic acid methyl ether)

B.P. 203° **Neut. Eq. 90** D_4^{20} = **1.1768** n_D^{20} = **1.41677**

Viscous oily liq.; misc. with aq., alc., ether.
C̄, treated with 10% less than 1 mole of $SOCl_2$ [cf. T 1.37] gives (70% yield ⟨1⟩) methoxyacetyl chloride, b.p. 99° ⟨1⟩; D_4^{20} = 1.1871 ⟨7⟩; n_D^{20} = 1.41945 ⟨7⟩.

Ⓓ **Methoxyacetamide:** m.p. 96.5–97° ⟨2⟩; 92–94° ⟨3⟩; 92° ⟨4⟩.
Ⓓ **ω-Methoxyacetanilide:** from C̄ + phenylisocyanate at 130° or aniline at 150°; ndls. from pet. ether; m.p. 58° ⟨5⟩.
Ⓓ **2-(Methoxymethyl)benzimidazole:** from C̄ + 1 mole *o*-phenylenediamine boiled 2 hrs. with 4 *N* HCl (50–60% yield); pale yel. pl. from aq. alc.; m.p. 136° ⟨6⟩.

1:1065 ⟨1⟩ Rothstein, *Bull. soc. chim.* (4) **51,** 840 (1932). ⟨2⟩ Cocker, Lapworth, Walton, *J. Chem. Soc.* **1930,** 454. ⟨3⟩ Dykstra, *J. Am. Chem. Soc.* **58,** 1749 (1936). ⟨4⟩ Gauthier, *Ann. chim.* (8) **16,** 307 (1909). ⟨5⟩ Lambling, *Bull. soc. chim.* (3) **17,** 357 (1897). ⟨6⟩ Hughes, Lions, *J. Proc. Roy. Soc. N. S. Wales* **71,** 209–222 (1938); *Chem. Abs.* **32,** 5831 (1938). ⟨7⟩ Leimu, *Ber.* **70,** 1050 (1937).

1:1070 ETHOXYACETIC ACID $C_2H_5O.CH_2.COOH$ $C_4H_8O_3$ Beil. III-233
(Glycolic acid ethyl ether)

B.P. 206-207° **Neut. Eq. 104** D_4^{20} = **1.1021** n_D^{20} = **1.41937**

[For prepn. in 73–74% yield from chloroacetic ac. + NaOEt see ⟨1⟩; 93% yield see ⟨2⟩.]
C̄, with $SOCl_2$ [cf. T 1.37] gives (73% yield ⟨2⟩) ethoxyacetyl chloride, b.p. 123–124° ⟨2⟩, D_4^{20} = 1.1170 ⟨3⟩, n_D^{20} = 1.42039 ⟨3⟩.

Ⓓ **p-Chlorophenacyl ethoxyacetate:** m.p. 94.4° ⟨4⟩ [cf. T 1.391].
Ⓓ **p-Bromophenacyl ethoxyacetate:** m.p. 104.8° ⟨4⟩ [cf. T 1.391].

Ⓓ **Ethoxyacetamide:** m.p. 80–82°.
Ⓓ **Ethoxyacet-*p*-toluidide** [Beil. XII-960]: pr. from ether, m.p. 32° (formed indirectly).

1:1070 ⟨1⟩ Fuson, Wojick, *Organic Syntheses* **13,** 42–44 (1933). ⟨2⟩ Rothstein, *Bull. soc. chim.* (4) **51,** 841 (1932). ⟨3⟩ Leimu, *Ber.* **70,** 1050 (1937). ⟨4⟩ Judefind, Reid, *J. Am. Chem. Soc.* **42,** 1054–1055 (1920).

—— **LEVULINIC ACID** $CH_3.CO.CH_2.CH_2.COOH$ $C_5H_8O_3$ **Beil. III-672**

B.P. 245-246° **Neut. Eq. 116**

See 1:0405. Genus 3: Division A: Section 1. M.P. 33°.

ORDER I: SUBORDER I: GENUS 3: ACIDS

Division B, Liquids

Section 2: Liquid acids not soluble in 50 parts water

1:1100 PROPIONIC ANHYDRIDE $(CH_3.CH_2.CO)_2O$ $C_6H_{10}O_3$ **Beil. II-242**

B.P. 166° **Neut. Eq. 65** $D^{15} = 1.0169$ $n_D^{20} = 1.4038$
M.P. −45°

Sharp irritating odor — Dif. sol. cold aq. and very slowly decd. by it — For behavior on titration, see Generic Test 3, Note 7 (Manual) — [For quant. detn. by titration with $NaOCH_3$ see ⟨1⟩; via cat. decompn. of oxalic ac. in pyridine ⟨2⟩.]

Ⓓ **Hydrolysis; Duclaux Value of resultant acid:** C̄, dislvd. in a little dil. alk., acidif. with H_2SO_4, distd., yields distillate in which propionic ac. (1:1025) can be identified by Duclaux Value (T 1.38); viz., 11.9; 11.7; 11.3.

Ⓓ **Propion-*p*-toluidide:** from C̄, htd. with *p*-toluidine; cryst. from hot alc. or C_6H_6, m.p. 123–124° u.c.

1:1100 ⟨1⟩ Smith, Bryant, *J. Am. Chem. Soc.* **58,** 2452–2454 (1936). ⟨2⟩ Hurd, Dull, *J. Am. Chem. Soc.* **54,** 2438 (1932).

1:1105 *d,l*-2-METHYLBUTANOIC ACID-1 $C_5H_{10}O_2$ **Beil. II-305**
(Ethyl-methyl-acetic acid; *α*-methyl-*n*-butyric acid)

$$CH_3.CH_2—\underset{\displaystyle H}{\overset{\displaystyle CH_3}{C}}—COOH$$

B.P. 176–177° **Neut. Eq. 102** $D_{20}^{20} = 0.938$ $n_D^{14} = 1.4083$

[For prepn. in 76–86% yield from *sec*-butyl MgCl + CO_2 see ⟨1⟩ ⟨2⟩] — Soly. of $Ca\bar{A}_2$ in aq. reaches max. of 29.9 g. per 100 g. aq. at 36.5°; is less sol. at 100° than at 0° ⟨3⟩.

C̄ dropped slowly into 2 moles $SOCl_2$ (cf. T 1.37) yields ethylmethylacetyl chloride, b.p. 118.0–118.3°, $D_4^{20} = 0.9917$, $n_D^{20} = 1.41464$ ⟨4⟩.

Ⓓ ***p*-Bromophenacyl *α*-methyl-*n*-butyrate:** m.p. 55° ⟨5⟩ ⟨6⟩ [cf. T 1.391].

Ⓓ ***p*-Phenylphenacyl *α*-methyl-*n*-butyrate:** m.p. 70.6° ⟨7⟩; 70–71° ⟨8⟩ [cf. T 1.391]. [This deriv. does depress m.p. of corresp. deriv. of *β*-methyl-*n*-valeric ac. (1:1050) ⟨8⟩.]

Ⓓ ***α*-Methyl-*n*-butyramide:** m.p. 121° ⟨9⟩; 112° ⟨10⟩; 110.9° ⟨7⟩; 111.4° ⟨15⟩.

Ⓓ ***α*-Methyl-*n*-butyranilide:** m.p. 110–111° ⟨11⟩; 108° ⟨12⟩; 105.5–106.5° ⟨13⟩ ⟨14⟩. [This deriv. lowers m.p. of corresp. deriv. of isovaleric ac. (1:1050) ⟨11⟩.]

Ⓓ ***α*-Methyl-*n*-butyro-*p*-toluidide:** m.p. 92.5–93° ⟨13⟩.

1:1105 ⟨1⟩ Gilman, Kirby, *Organic Syntheses, Coll. Vol.* I, 353–356 (1932). ⟨2⟩ Bartlett, Stauffer, *J. Am. Chem. Soc.* **57,** 2582 (1935). ⟨3⟩ Houston, *J. Research Natl. Bur. Standards* **17,** 55–58 (1936). ⟨4⟩ Leimu, *Ber.* **70,** 1049 (1937). ⟨5⟩ Murahashi, *Chem. Abs.* **32,** 3755 (1938). ⟨6⟩ Sjollema, Dienske, *Rec. trav. chim.* **52,** 230, Note 6 (1933). ⟨7⟩ Drake, Veitch, *J. Am. Chem. Soc.* **57,** 2624 (1935). ⟨8⟩ Kögl, Erxleben, *Z. physiol. Chem.* **227,** 70–71 (1934). ⟨9⟩ Hopff, et al., *Ber.* **69,** 2249 (1936). ⟨10⟩ Scheuble, Löbl, *Monatsh.* **25,** 1097 (1904).

⟨11⟩ Verkade, *Rec. trav. chim.* **36,** 204 (1916). ⟨12⟩ Schwartz, Johnson, *J. Am. Chem. Soc.* **53,** 1065 (1931). ⟨13⟩ Underwood, Gale, *J. Am. Chem. Soc.* **56,** 2117 (1934). ⟨14⟩ Ssuknewitsch, Tschilingarjan, *Ber.* **68,** 1216 (1935). ⟨15⟩ Hoffmann, Barbier, *Bull. soc. chim. Belg.* **45,** 570 (1936).

1:1110 ISOBUTYRIC ANHYDRIDE $[(CH_3)_2CH.CO]_2O$ $C_8H_{14}O_3$ **Beil. II-292**

B.P. 182.5° **Neut. Eq. 79** $D^{16.5}$ = **0.9574**

For behavior on titration, see Generic Test 3, Note 7 (Manual).

Ⓓ **Hydrolysis; Duclaux Value of acid:** $\bar{C}$, dislvd. in a little dil. alk., acidif. with H_2SO_4, distd., yields distillate in which isobutyric ac. (1:1030) can be identif. by Duclaux Value (T 1.38); viz., 25.0; 20.9; 16.0.

Ⓓ **Isobutyr-*p*-toluidide:** from $\bar{C}$, htd. with *p*-toluidine; cryst. from aq., m.p. 104–105° u.c.

1:1112 3,3-DIMETHYLBUTANOIC ACID-1 $C_6H_{12}O_2$ **Beil. II-337**
(*ter*-Butylacetic acid; β,β-dimethyl-*n*-butyric acid)

```
      CH3
      |
CH3—C—CH2.COOH
      |
      CH3
```

B.P. 183.0-183.3°$_{739}$ ⟨1⟩ **Neut. Eq. 116** D_4^{20} = **0.9124** ⟨1⟩ n_D^{20} = **1.4096** ⟨1⟩
183.1-183.8°$_{741}$ ⟨2⟩
M.P. +6-7° ⟨1⟩
+5.6° ⟨2⟩

[For prepn. in 80–90% yield by NaOBr oxidation of methyl neopentyl ketone (from oxidn. of di-isobutylene) see ⟨1⟩.]

$\bar{C}$ with $SOCl_2$ (cf. T 1.37) gives 93% yield ⟨1⟩ *ter*-butylacetyl chloride, b.p. 129.9°$_{746}$ ⟨2⟩, D_4^{20} = 0.9696 ⟨2⟩, n_D^{20} = 1.422 ⟨1⟩.

Ⓓ ***p*-Phenylphenacyl *ter*-butylacetate:** m.p. 92° ⟨3⟩ [cf. T 1.391].

Ⓓ ***ter*-Butylacetamide:** from acid chloride + aq. NH_4OH below 10° (82% yield ⟨1⟩) pptd. from AcOEt soln. with pet. ether; m.p. 132° ⟨1⟩ ⟨2⟩ [mixed m.p. with corresp. deriv. of isopropyl-methyl-acetic acid (1:1114) is sharply depressed ⟨2⟩].

Ⓓ ***ter*-Butylacetanilide:** m.p. 131.0° ⟨1⟩; 131.6° ⟨2⟩.

Ⓓ ***ter*-Butylacet-*p*-toluidide:** m.p. 134.4° ⟨2⟩.

1:1112 ⟨1⟩ Homeyer, Whitmore, Wallingford, *J. Am. Chem. Soc.* **55,** 4211–4212 (1933). ⟨2⟩ Hommelen, *Bull. soc. chim. Belg.* **42,** 243–250 (1933). ⟨3⟩ Wrede, Rothhaas, *Ber.* **67,** 740 (1934).

1:1113 2,2-DIMETHYLBUTANOIC ACID-1 $C_6H_{12}O_2$ **Beil. II-335**
(Dimethyl-ethyl-acetic acid)

```
           CH3
           |
CH3.CH2—C—COOH
           |
           CH3
```

B.P. 187.0° ⟨1⟩ **Neut. Eq. 116** D_4^{20} = **0.9276** ⟨1⟩ n_D^{20} = **1.4145** ⟨1⟩
M.P. −15.0° ⟨1⟩

$\bar{C}$ refluxed 3–4 hrs. with 1.5 pts. $SOCl_2$ (T 1.37) yields dimethylethylacetyl chloride, b.p. 132.1°$_{748}$, D_4^{20} = 0.9801 ⟨1⟩.

Ⓓ ***p*-Phenylphenacyl dimethyl-ethyl-acetate:** cryst. from 60% alc.; m.p. 86.5° ⟨2⟩ ⟨3⟩ [cf. T 1.391].

Ⓓ **Dimethyl-ethyl-acetamide:** from acid chloride + NH_3 gas in dry ether; cryst. from pet. ether; m.p. 99.8° ⟨1⟩; 102.7–103.2° ⟨6⟩; 103° ⟨7⟩.

Ⓓ **Dimethyl-ethyl-acetanilide:** from acid chloride + aniline; m.p. 92° ⟨4⟩; 91.4° ⟨1⟩; 90–91° ⟨5⟩.

Ⓓ **Dimethyl-ethyl-acet-*p*-toluidide:** m.p. 83.0–83.5° ⟨5⟩; 83.3° ⟨1⟩.

Ⓓ **Dimethyl-ethyl-acet-α-naphthalide:** m.p. 137–138° ⟨5⟩.

1:1113 ⟨1⟩ Hommelen, *Bull. soc. chim. Belg.* **42,** 243–250 (1933). ⟨2⟩ Drake, Bronitsky, *J. Am. Chem. Soc.* **52,** 3719 (1930). ⟨3⟩ Wrede, Rothhaas, *Ber.* **67,** 740 (1934). ⟨4⟩ Schwartz, Johnson, *J. Am. Chem. Soc.* **53,** 1065 (1931). ⟨5⟩ Underwood, Gale, *J. Am. Chem. Soc.* **56,** 2119 (1934). ⟨6⟩ Whitmore, Baedertscher, *J. Am. Chem. Soc.* **55,** 1565 (1933). ⟨7⟩ Whitmore, Homeyer, *J. Am. Chem. Soc.* **54,** 3437 (1932).

1:1114 ***d,l*-2,3-DIMETHYLBUTANOIC ACID-1** $C_6H_{12}O_2$ **Beil. S.N. 162**

(Isopropyl-methyl-acetic acid; *α,β*-dimethyl-*n*-butyric acid)

```
     CH3 CH3
      |   |
CH3.C----C--COOH
      |   |
      H   H
```

B.P. 191.7° ⟨1⟩ **Neut. Eq. 116** D_4^{20} **= 0.9275 ⟨1⟩** n_D^{20} **= 1.4146 ⟨1⟩**
M.P. −1.5° ⟨1⟩

C̄, refluxed 3–4 hrs. with 1.5 pts. $SOCl_2$ (cf. T 1.37) yields isopropyl-methyl-acetyl chloride, b.p. 136.3°_{751}; D_4^{20} = 0.9795 ⟨1⟩.

Ⓓ ***p*-Iodophenacyl isopropyl-methyl-acetate:** cryst. from 63% alc. or pet. eth.; m.p. 66° ⟨2⟩ [cf. T 1.391].

Ⓓ ***p*-Phenylphenacyl isopropyl-methyl-acetate:** m.p. 73.5° ⟨3⟩ [cf. T 1.391].

Ⓓ **Isopropyl-methyl-acetamide:** m.p. 132° ⟨4⟩; 131° ⟨5⟩; 130.9° ⟨1⟩.

Ⓓ **Isopropyl-methyl-acetanilide:** m.p. 78.4° ⟨1⟩.

Ⓓ **Isopropyl-methyl-acet-*p*-toluidide:** m.p. 112.6° ⟨1⟩.

1:1114 ⟨1⟩ Hommelen, *Bull. soc. chim. Belg.* **42,** 243–250 (1933). ⟨2⟩ Schmidt, *Ann.* **476,** 269 (1929). ⟨3⟩ Wrede, Rothhaas, *Ber.* **67,** 740 (1934). ⟨4⟩ Nenitzescu, Chicos, *Ber.* **68,** 1587 (1935). ⟨5⟩ Reindel, Kipphan, *Ann.* **493,** 189 (1932).

1:1115 **2-ETHYLBUTANOIC ACID-1** $C_6H_{12}O_2$ **Beil. II-333**

(Diethylacetic acid; *α*-ethyl-*n*-butyric acid)

```
          C2H5
           |
CH3.CH2.C.COOH
           |
           H
```

B.P. 192.8°_{754} ⟨1⟩ **Neut. Eq. 116** D_4^{20} **= 0.9239 ⟨1⟩** n_D^{20} **= 1.4132 ⟨1⟩**
M.P. −31.8° ⟨1⟩

C̄ with $SOCl_2$ (T 1.37) yields diethylacetyl chloride, b.p. 138.4°_{750}, D_4^{20} = 0.9825 ⟨1⟩.

Ⓓ ***p*-Iodophenacyl diethylacetate:** lfts. from 63% alc. or pet. eth.; m.p. 54° ⟨2⟩ [cf. T 1.391].

Ⓓ ***p*-Phenylphenacyl diethylacetate:** cryst. from 60% alc.; m.p. 77.5° ⟨3⟩ [cf. T 1.391].

Ⓓ **Diethylacetamide:** m.p. 111.8° ⟨1⟩; 112° ⟨4⟩.

Ⓓ **Diethylacetanilide:** m.p. 127.5° ⟨4⟩; 126.8° ⟨1⟩; 123–124° cor. ⟨5⟩; 121° ⟨6⟩.

Ⓓ **Diethylacet-*p*-toluidide:** m.p. 116.2° ⟨1⟩

1:1115 ⟨1⟩ Hommelen, *Bull. soc. chim. Belg.* **42,** 243–250 (1933). ⟨2⟩ Schmidt, *Ann.* **476,** 268 (1929). ⟨3⟩ Wrede, Rothhaas, *Ber.* **67,** 740 (1934). ⟨4⟩ Tiffeneau, *Compt. rend.* **204,** 592 (1937). ⟨5⟩ Schwartz, Johnson, *J. Am. Chem. Soc.* **53,** 1065 (1931). ⟨6⟩ Lauer, Stodola, *J. Am. Chem. Soc.* **56,** 1218 (1934).

1:1117 ***d,l*-2-METHYLPENTANOIC ACID-1** $C_6H_{12}O_2$ **Beil. II-326**

(Methyl-*n*-propyl-acetic acid; *α*-methyl-*n*-valeric acid)

```
                H
                |
CH3.CH2.CH2.C.COOH
                |
               CH3
```

B.P. $195\text{-}196^{\circ}_{760}$ ⟨1⟩ **Neut. Eq. 116** D_4^{20} **= 0.9230 ⟨2⟩** n_D^{20} **= 1.4136 ⟨2⟩**
$192.0\text{-}193.6^{\circ}_{748}$ ⟨2⟩

C̄ refluxed 3–4 hrs. with 1.5 pts. $SOCl_2$ (T 1.37) yields methyl-*n*-propylacetyl chloride, b.p. 140.4°_{745}, D_4^{20} = 0.9781 ⟨2⟩.

Ⓓ **p-Iodophenacyl methyl-n-propyl-acetate:** cryst. from 63% alc. or pet. ether; m.p. 66° ⟨3⟩ [cf. T 1.391].

Ⓓ **p-Phenylphenacyl methyl-n-propyl-acetate:** m.p. 64–65° ⟨4⟩; 46° ⟨5⟩ [cf. T 1.391].

Ⓓ **Methyl-n-propyl-acetamide:** from acid chloride + NH_3 gas in dry ether; cryst. from pet. ether; m.p. 79.6° ⟨2⟩.

Ⓓ **Methyl-n-propyl-acetanilide:** m.p. 95.2° ⟨2⟩ 92.6° ⟨6⟩. [For m.p.'s of mixts. with diethylacetanilide see ⟨6⟩.]

Ⓓ **Methyl-n-propyl-acet-p-toluidide:** m.p. 80.5° ⟨2⟩.

1:1117 ⟨1⟩ Olivier, *Rec. trav. chim.* **55,** 1030 (1936). ⟨2⟩ Hommelen, *Bull. soc. chim. Belg.* **42,** 243–250 (1933). ⟨3⟩ Schmidt, *Ann.* **476,** 268 (1929). ⟨4⟩ Magnani, McElvain, *J. Am. Chem. Soc.* **60,** 819 (1938). ⟨5⟩ Wrede, Rothhaas, *Ber.* **67,** 740 (1934). ⟨6⟩ Lauer, Stodola, *J. Am. Chem. Soc.* **56,** 1218 (1934).

1:1125 *d,l*-3-METHYLPENTANOIC ACID-1 $C_6H_{12}O_2$ Beil. II-332

(*sec*-Butylacetic acid; β-methyl-n-valeric acid)

$CH_3.CH_2.CH(CH_3).CH_2.COOH$

B.P. 197.5° ⟨1⟩ ⟨2⟩ **Neut. Eq. 116** D_4^{20} = **0.9262** ⟨2⟩ n_D^{20} = **1.4159** ⟨2⟩
M.P. −41.6° ⟨2⟩

[For prepn. in 62–65% yield from diethyl *sec*-butylmalonate see ⟨3⟩.]
$\bar{C}$ with $SOCl_2$ (T 1.37) yields *sec*-butylacetyl chloride, b.p. $142.8°_{749}$, D_4^{20} = 0.9781 ⟨2⟩.

Ⓓ **p-Phenylphenacyl *sec*-butylacetate:** m.p. 47° ⟨4⟩ [cf. T 1.391].

Ⓓ ***sec*-Butylacetamide:** m.p. 124.9° ⟨2⟩.

Ⓓ ***sec*-Butylacetanilide:** m.p. 87.0° ⟨2⟩; 88° ⟨5⟩.

Ⓓ ***sec*-Butylacet-p-toluidide:** m.p. 74.8° ⟨2⟩.

Ⓓ **2-(β-Methylamyl)benzimidazole:** from $\bar{C}$ htd. 8 hrs. at 140–150° with 1 mole o-phenylenediamine; m.p. 158–159° ⟨6⟩.

1:1125 ⟨1⟩ Olivier, *Rec. trav. chim.* **55,** 1033 (1936). ⟨2⟩ Hommelen, *Bull. soc. chim. Belg.* **42,** 243–250 (1933). ⟨3⟩ Vliet, Marvel, Hsueh, *Organic Syntheses* **11,** 76–78 (1931). ⟨4⟩ Wrede, Rothhaas, *Ber.* **67,** 740 (1934). ⟨5⟩ Schwartz, Johnson, *J. Am. Chem. Soc.* **53,** 1065 (1931). ⟨6⟩ Seka, Müller, *Monatsh.* **57,** 185 (1931).

1:1126 n-BUTYRIC ANHYDRIDE $(CH_3.CH_2.CH_2.CO)_2O$ $C_8H_{14}O_3$ Beil. II-274

B.P. 198° **Neut. Eq. 79** D^{15} = **0.978**

For behavior on titration see Generic Test 3, Note 7 (Manual).

Ⓓ **Hydrolysis; Duclaux Value of resultant acid:** $\bar{C}$, dislvd. in a little dil. alk., acidif. with H_2SO_4, distd. yields distillate in which n-butyric ac. (1:1035) can be identif. by Duclaux Value (T 1.38).

Ⓓ **n-Butyro-p-toluidide:** $\bar{C}$, htd. with p-toluidine gives compd., cryst. from dil. alc., m.p. 72.5–73.5° u.c.

1:1127 4-METHYLPENTANOIC ACID-1 $C_6H_{12}O_2$ Beil. II-327

(Isocaproic acid; isobutylacetic acid)

$CH_3.CH(CH_3).CH_2.CH_2.COOH$

B.P. 199.1°$_{752}$ ⟨1⟩ [cf. ⟨2⟩] **Neut. Eq. 116** D_4^{20} = **0.9225** ⟨1⟩ n_D^{20} = **1.4144** ⟨1⟩
M.P. −33° ⟨1⟩

C̄ with PCl_5 (63% yield ⟨3⟩), or $PCl_3 + ZnCl_2$ (68% yield ⟨3⟩) or 1.5 moles $SOCl_2$ (82% yield ⟨3⟩) [cf.T 1.37] gives isocaproyl chloride, b.p. 144.2°, $D_4^{20} = 0.9725$ ⟨1⟩.

Ⓓ ***p*-Bromophenacyl isocaproate:** m.p. 77.3° ⟨4⟩ [cf. T 1.391].

Ⓓ ***p*-Phenylphenacyl isocaproate:** m.p. 70° ⟨5⟩ ⟨6⟩ [cf. T 1.391]. [This deriv. does *not* depress m.p. of corresp. deriv. of *n*-caproic ac. (1:1130) ⟨6⟩.]

Ⓓ **Isocaproamide:** m.p. 120–121° ⟨7⟩ ⟨8⟩; 118.8° ⟨1⟩; 119° ⟨6⟩.

Ⓓ **Isocaproanilide:** m.p. 112.0° ⟨1⟩ ⟨9⟩; 111.5° ⟨10⟩; 110.5° ⟨11⟩ [depresses m.p. of deriv. from isovaleric ac. (1:1050) ⟨10⟩].

Ⓓ **Isocapro-*p*-toluidide:** m.p. 63.0° ⟨1⟩; 61.5–62.5° ⟨11⟩.

1:1127 ⟨1⟩ Hommelen, *Bull. soc. chim. Belg.* **42,** 243–250 (1933). ⟨2⟩ Levene, Allen, *J. Biol. Chem.* **27,** 450 (1916). ⟨3⟩ Clark, Bell, *Trans. Roy. Soc. Can.* (3) **27,** III, 97–103 (1933). ⟨4⟩ Powell, *J. Am. Chem. Soc.* **53,** 1172 (1931). ⟨5⟩ Drake, Sweeney, *J, Am. Chem. Soc.* **54,** 2060 (1932). ⟨6⟩ Wrede, Rothhaas, *Ber.* **67,** 739–740 (1934). ⟨7⟩ Nenitzescu et al., *Ber.* **71,** 2060–2061 (1938). ⟨8⟩ Curtius, Hambsch, *J. prakt. Chem.* (2) **125,** 194 (1930). ⟨9⟩ Brunner, Farmer, *J. Chem. Soc.* **1937,** 1044. ⟨10⟩ Dragendorff, *Ann.* **487,** 76 (1931). ⟨11⟩ Underwood, Gale, *J. Am. Chem. Soc.* **56,** 2119 (1934).

1:1130 HEXANOIC ACID $CH_3.(CH_2)_4.COOH$ $C_6H_{12}O_2$ Beil. II-321
(*n*-Caproic acid)

B.P. 205.35° ⟨1⟩ **Neut. Eq. 116** D_4^{20} **= 0.93568 ⟨1⟩** n_D^{20} **= 1.4163 ⟨1⟩**
M.P. −3.9° ⟨1⟩

Oily liq. of unpleasant odor — Very dif. sol. aq.; volatile with steam.

[For prepn. in 66% yield by $K_2Cr_2O_7 + H_2SO_4$ oxidn. of *n*-hexyl methyl ketone (1:5490) see ⟨2⟩; in 75% yield via diethyl *n*-butylmalonate see ⟨3⟩.]

C̄ with PCl_5 (62% yield ⟨4⟩), or $PCl_3 + ZnCl_2$ (89% yield ⟨4⟩), or 1.5 moles $SOCl_2$ (77% yield ⟨4⟩) [cf. T 1.37] gives *n*-caproyl chloride, b.p. 152.6°, $D_4^{20} = 0.9754$ ⟨5⟩.

$Ag\bar{A}_2$, dif. sol. hot aq. [T 1.36]; $Ca\bar{A}_2.H_2O$, lfts. sol. 37 pts. aq. at 18.5°; $Zn\bar{A}_2.H_2O$, crystn. ppt. when C̄ is poured into $Zn(OAc)_2$ soln. ⟨6⟩ [dif. from *n*-butyric (1:1035) and isovaleric ac. (1:1050)]; $Pb\bar{A}_2$, m.p. 73–74° ⟨7⟩.

Ⓓ **Duclaux Value:** 33; 24; 19 [T 1.38].

Ⓓ ***p*-Chlorophenacyl *n*-caproate:** m.p. 62.0° ⟨8⟩ [cf. T 1.391].

Ⓓ ***p*-Bromophenacyl *n*-caproate:** m.p. 72.0° ⟨8⟩; 71.6° ⟨9⟩ [cf. T 1.391].

Ⓓ ***p*-Iodophenacyl *n*-caproate:** m.p. 84.0° ⟨8⟩; 81.5° ⟨9⟩ [cf. T 1.391].

Ⓓ ***p*-Phenylphenacyl *n*-caproate:** m.p. 65.0° ⟨10⟩; 69–70° ⟨11⟩ [cf. T 1.391].

Ⓓ ***n*-Caproamide:** m.p. 101° ⟨12⟩ ⟨5⟩; 100° ⟨11⟩.

Ⓓ ***n*-Caproanilide:** m.p. 96° cor. ⟨13⟩; 94–95° ⟨14⟩; 92° ⟨12⟩.

Ⓓ ***n*-Capro-*p*-toluidide:** m.p. 74–75° ⟨14⟩; 73° ⟨12⟩.

Ⓓ **2-(*n*-Amyl)benzimidazole:** from C̄ on htg. 8 hrs. at 140–150° with 1 mole *o*-phenylenediamine; m.p. 163.0–163.5° cor. ⟨15⟩; 155–156° ⟨16⟩. [Picrate of this deriv., m.p. 282° ⟨17⟩.]

1:1130 ⟨1⟩ Hommelen, *Bull. soc. chim. Belg.* **42,** 246 (1933). ⟨2⟩ Kao, Chang, *Science Repts. Natl. Tsing Hua Univ., Ser.* **A-4,** 38 (1937); *Chem. Abs.* **31,** 6189 (1937). ⟨3⟩ Vliet, Marvel, Hsueh, *Organic Syntheses* **11,** 78 (1931). ⟨4⟩ Clark, Bell, *Trans. Roy. Soc. Canada* (3) **27,** III, 97–103 (1933). ⟨5⟩ Simon, *Bull. soc. chim. Belg.* **38,** 56 (1929). ⟨6⟩ Freund, *J. prakt. Chem.* (2) **3,** 232 (1871). ⟨7⟩ Neave, *Analyst* **37,** 399 (1912). ⟨8⟩ Moses, Reid, *J. Am. Chem. Soc.* **54,** 2101 (1932). ⟨9⟩ Judefind, Reid, *J. Am. Chem. Soc.* **42,** 1055 (1920). ⟨10⟩ Drake, Bronitsky, *J. Am. Chem. Soc.* **52,** 3718 (1930).

⟨11⟩ Wrede, Rothhaas, *Ber.* **67,** 740 (1934). ⟨12⟩ Robertson, *J. Chem. Soc.* **115,** 1220–1221 (1919). ⟨13⟩ Schwartz, Johnson, *J. Am. Chem. Soc.* **53,** 1065 (1931). ⟨14⟩ Underwood, Gale, *J. Am. Chem. Soc.* **56,** 2119 (1934). ⟨15⟩ Pool, Harwood, Ralston, *J. Am. Chem. Soc.* **59,** 178 (1937). ⟨16⟩ Seka, Müller, *Monatsh.* **57,** 102 (1931). ⟨17⟩ Brown, Campbell, *J. Chem. Soc.* **1937,** 1701.

1:1133 2-ETHYLPENTANOIC ACID-1 C_2H_5 $C_7H_{14}O_2$ **Beil. II-344**

(α-Ethyl-*n*-valeric acid; ethyl-*n*-propylacetic acid)

$CH_3.CH_2.CH_2.C(C_2H_5)(H).COOH$

B.P. 209° **Neut. Eq. 130**

C̄ with PCl_3 ⟨1⟩ or $SOCl_2$ ⟨2⟩ [cf. T 1.37] yields α-ethyl-*n*-valeryl chloride, b.p. 158–160° ⟨1⟩.

Ⓓ **α-Ethyl-*n*-valeramide:** m.p. 104–105° ⟨3⟩; 102.5–103.5° ⟨1⟩.
Ⓓ **α-Ethyl-*n*-valeranilide:** m.p. 94° ⟨4⟩.
Ⓓ **α-Ethyl-*n*-valero-*p*-bromoanilide:** m.p. 148° ⟨4⟩ ⟨2⟩.
Ⓓ **α-Ethyl *n*-valero-*p*-toluidide:** m.p. 129° ⟨4⟩.
Ⓓ **α-Ethyl *n*-valero-*p*-anisidide:** m.p. 120° ⟨4⟩ ⟨2⟩.

1:1133 ⟨1⟩ Rasetti, *Bull. soc. chim.* (3) **33,** 687 (1905). ⟨2⟩ Reichstein, Trivelli, *Helv. Chim. Acta* **16,** 974 (1933). ⟨3⟩ Sutter, Wijkman, *Ann.* **505,** 254 (1933). ⟨4⟩ Reichstein, Trivelli, *Helv. Chim. Acta* **15,** 259 (1932).

1:1134 2-METHYLHEXANOIC ACID-1 $C_7H_{14}O_2$ **Beil. II-342**

(α-Methyl-*n*-caproic acid; *n*-butyl-methyl-acetic acid)

$CH_3.CH_2.CH_2.CH_2.C(CH_3)(H).COOH$

B.P. 209.6° **Neut. Eq. 130**

Ⓓ **α-Methyl-*n*-caproamide:** m.p. 70–72.5° ⟨1⟩; 69.2° ⟨3⟩.
Ⓓ **α-Methyl-*n*-caproanilide:** m.p. 98° ⟨2⟩.
Ⓓ **α-Methyl-*n*-capro-*p*-bromoanilide:** m.p. 114° ⟨2⟩.
Ⓓ **α-Methyl-*n*-capro-*p*-toluidide:** m.p. 85° ⟨2⟩.
Ⓓ **α-Methyl-*n*-capro-*p*-anisidide:** m.p. 103° ⟨2⟩.

1:1134 ⟨1⟩ Rasetti, *Bull. soc. chim.* (3) **33,** 690 (1905). ⟨2⟩ Reichstein, Trivelli, *Helv. Chim. Acta* **15,** 258–259 (1932). ⟨3⟩ Hoffmann, Barbier, *Bull. soc. chim.* **45,** 570 (1936).

1:1135 CITRACONIC ANHYDRIDE $C_5H_4O_3$ **Beil. XVII-440**

(Methylmaleic anhydride)

$CH_3—C—C(=O)$ / $H—C—C(=O)$ (C=C double bond; ring closed through O)

B.P. 213-214° D_4^{25} = **1.2380** $n_D^{21.3}$ = **1.4710**
M.P. +7-8°

[For prepn. in 62–66% yield by rapid distn. of itaconic anhydride (1:0654) or itaconic ac. (1:0515) see ⟨1⟩; also for improvements see ⟨2⟩.]

C̄ is somewhat volatile with steam, but its volatility so diminishes as conc. falls that large quant. of water are necessary, e.g., 6 liters for 5 g. C̄ ⟨3⟩. [Under these conditions itaconic ac. (1:0515) is non-volatile and mesaconic ac. (1:0548) only slightly vol. ⟨3⟩.]

C̄, htd. above 160°, gradually decomposes into CO_2 and diethylmaleic anhydride [Beil. XVII-451], b.p. 242°; eas. volatile with steam — C̄ htd. with dil. HNO_3 gives 43–52% yield mesaconic ac. (1:0548) ⟨4⟩ ⟨5⟩.

C̄, in ether, C_6H_6, or toluene soln., treated with dry NH_3 gas gives ppt. of NH_4 salt of citraconamidic ac., from whose aq. soln. conc. HCl ppts. the free citraconamidic acid, ndls., m.p. 124–125° ⟨6⟩ — C̄ + aniline in ether yields citraconanilic ac., m.p. 153° ⟨6⟩.

Ⓓ **Saponification:** Hydrolysis of C̄ with aq. alk. (T 1.51) gives Sap. Eq. 56 and yields soln. of salts of citraconic ac. (1:0435).

1:1135 ⟨1⟩ Shriner, Ford, Roll, *Organic Syntheses* **11,** 28–29 (1931). ⟨2⟩ van de Straete, *Bull. soc. chim. Belg.* **44,** 315 (1935). ⟨3⟩ Linstead, Mann, *J. Chem. Soc.* **1931,** 727, 734. ⟨4⟩ Shriner, Ford, Roll, *Organic Syntheses* **11,** 74–75 (1931). ⟨5⟩ Mottern, Keenan, *J. Am. Chem. Soc.* **53,** 2348 (1931). ⟨6⟩ Anschütz, *Ann.* **461,** 163–167 (1928).

1:1136 4-METHYLHEXANOIC ACID-1 $C_7H_{14}O_2$ Beil. II-343

(γ-Methyl-*n*-caproic acid)

$$CH_3.CH_2.\overset{\displaystyle CH_3}{\overset{|}{\underset{\underset{\displaystyle H}{|}}{C}}}.CH_2.CH_2.COOH$$

B.P. 217-218°$_{754}$ ⟨1⟩ Neut. Eq. 130 D_4^{20} **= 0.9194 ⟨1⟩** n_D^{20} **= 1.4211 ⟨1⟩**

C̄ with PCl_3 yields γ-methyl-*n*-caproyl chloride, b.p. 167–168°$_{767}$, D_4^{20} = 0.9677 ⟨1⟩.

Ⓓ **γ-Methyl-*n*-caproamide:** m.p. 98° ⟨1⟩.
Ⓓ **γ-Methyl-*n*-caproanilide:** m.p. 76.5° ⟨1⟩.
Ⓓ **Piperazonium di-(γ-methyl-*n*-caproate):** m.p. 109°; Neut. Eq. 346 ⟨2⟩.

1:1136 ⟨1⟩ Dewael, Weckering, *Bull. soc. chim. Belg.* **33,** 501–502 (1924). ⟨2⟩ Powell, Baldwin, *J. Am. Chem. Soc.* **58,** 1872 (1936).

1:1137 *n*-VALERIC ANHYDRIDE $[CH_3.(CH_2)_3.CO]_2O$ $C_{10}H_{18}O_3$ Beil. II-301

B.P. 218° ⟨1⟩ ⟨2⟩ D_4^{17} **= 0.9223 ⟨1⟩**

Responds to Generic Test 3-B (titration in alc.) — Neut. Eq. *in alcohol* (T 1.31) 186; Sap. Eq. in aq. alk. (T 1.51) 93, yielding soln. contg. salt of *n*-valeric ac. (1:1060), q.v.

1:1137 ⟨1⟩ Pickard, Kenyon, *J. Chem. Soc.* **101,** 1432, Note (1912). ⟨2⟩ Backer, van der Baan, *Rec. trav. chim.* **56,** 1166 (1937).

1:1139 δ-VALEROLACTONE $C_5H_8O_2$ Beil. XVII-235

$$\underbrace{CH_2.CH_2.CH_2.CH_2.C{=}O}_{O}$$

B.P. 219-222° ⟨1⟩ D_4^{20} **= 1.0794 ⟨1⟩** n_D^{20} **= 1.4503 ⟨1⟩**
B.P. 215-220° ⟨2⟩ D_4^{20} **= 1.1081 ⟨3⟩** n_D^{20} **= 1.4568 ⟨3⟩**

Colorless mobile liq. — M.p. −12.5° ⟨3⟩ — Fairly dif. sol. aq. [not miscible like γ-butyro- or γ-valerolactones]; eas. sol. alc., ether — On stdg. at room temp., or more rapidly with htg. or cat., C̄ polymerizes to a solid ⟨4⟩ ⟨5⟩ [dif. from γ-butyro- or γ-valerolactones]. The polymer is not homogeneous ⟨4⟩, but nevertheless is hydrolyzed by boilg. few hrs. with excess *N*/10 alk., giving Sap. Eq. of 101.7, calcd. 100 ⟨5⟩.

Monomeric C̄ responds to Generic Test 3-A (titration in water); Sap. Eq. in either aq. or alc. alk. (T 1.51) gives 100. Boilg. with aq. alk. yields soln. contg. salts of δ-hydroxy-*n*-valeric acid [Beil. III-323].

Oxidn. with $Na_2Cr_2O_7 + H_2SO_4$ (T 1.72) for 5 hrs. gives glutaric ac., m.p. 97° (1:0440) ⟨6⟩.

Ⓓ **δ-Hydroxy-*n*-valeric hydrazide:** C̄, pptd. with 3 vols. hydrazine hydrate for 2 hrs. at 120°, gave prod., recrystd. from EtOH—EtOAc, m.p. 105° ⟨1⟩.

1:1139 ⟨1⟩ Coffman, *J. Am. Chem. Soc.* **57,** 1984 (1935). ⟨2⟩ Marvel, Birkhimer, *J. Am. Chem. Soc.* **51,** 261 (1929). ⟨3⟩ Linstead, Rydon, *J. Chem. Soc.* **1933,** 583. ⟨4⟩ Carothers, Dorough, Van Natta, *J. Am. Chem. Soc.* **54,** 761, 769 (1932). ⟨5⟩ Fichter, Beisswenger, *Ber.* **36,** 1200 (1903). ⟨6⟩ Wieland, Fischer, *Ann.* **446,** 74 (1926).

1:1140 **HEPTANOIC ACID** $CH_3.(CH_2)_5.COOH$ $C_7H_{14}O_2$ **Beil. II-338**
(Enanthic acid;
n-heptylic acid;
n-heptoic acid)

B.P. 223.0° ⟨1⟩ **Neut. Eq. 130** D_4^{20} = **0.91808** ⟨1⟩ n_D^{20} = **1.4234** ⟨2⟩
M.P. −7.46° ⟨1⟩

[For prepn. in 76–78% yield by acid $KMnO_4$ oxidn. of *n*-heptaldehyde (1:0183) see ⟨3⟩.]
C̄ with PCl_5 (51% yield ⟨4⟩), or $PCl_3 + ZnCl_2$ (89% yield ⟨4⟩), or with 1.5 moles $SOCl_2$ (80% yield ⟨4⟩) [cf. T 1.37] gives *n*-heptanoyl chloride, b.p. 175.2° ⟨5⟩.

$Hg\bar{A}_2$; anhydrous cryst. from MeOH; m.p. 106.5° ⟨6⟩; $Ba\bar{A}_2$, anhyd. lfts. from aq., m.p. 240° ⟨7⟩; $Zn\bar{A}_2$, m.p. 130° ⟨8⟩; $Pb\bar{A}_2$, m.p. 90.5–91.5° ⟨18⟩.

Ⓓ **Phenacyl *n*-heptylate:** oil; not recommended as deriv. ⟨9⟩.
Ⓓ ***p*-Chlorophenacyl *n*-heptylate:** m.p. 65.0° ⟨10⟩ [cf. T 1.391].
Ⓓ ***p*-Bromophenacyl *n*-heptylate:** m.p. 72.0° ⟨10⟩ [cf. T 1.391].
Ⓓ ***p*-Iodophenacyl *n*-heptylate:** m.p. 78.8° ⟨10⟩ [cf. T 1.391].
Ⓓ ***p*-Phenylphenacyl *n*-heptylate:** m.p. 62° ⟨11⟩ [cf. T 1.391].
Ⓓ **Enanthamide:** m.p. 96° ⟨12⟩; 96.5° ⟨13⟩.
Ⓓ **Enanthanilide:** m.p. 65° ⟨12⟩; 64° ⟨17⟩; 69° ⟨14⟩.
Ⓓ **Enanth-*p*-toluidide:** m.p. 81° ⟨12⟩.
Ⓓ **2-(*n*-Hexyl)benzimidazole:** from C̄ + 1 mole *o*-phenylenediamine htd. at b.p. for 30 min.; cryst. from alc., m.p. 137.5–138.0° cor. ⟨15⟩; 136–138° ⟨16⟩. [This deriv. depresses m.p. of corresp. deriv. of *n*-caprylic ac. (1:1145) ⟨15⟩.]
Ⓓ **Piperazonium 1,4-di-*n*-heptoate:** from C̄ + 0.5 mole piperazine hexahydrate (72% yield); cryst. from acetone, m.p. 95–96° cor.; Neut. Eq. 318.3 ⟨19⟩.

1:1140 ⟨1⟩ Bilterys, Gisseleire, *Bull. soc. chim. Belg.* **44,** 570 (1935). ⟨2⟩ Kunz, Shulnik, *Ind. Eng. Chem., Anal. Ed.* **8,** 485 (1936). ⟨3⟩ Ruhoff, *Organic Syntheses,* **16,** 39–40 (1936). ⟨4⟩ Clark, Bell, *Trans. Roy. Soc. Canada* (3) **27,** III, 97–103 (1933). ⟨5⟩ Deffet, *Bull. soc. chim. Belg.* **40,** 391 (1931). ⟨6⟩ Bornwater, *Rec. trav. chim.* **26,** 413 (1907). ⟨7⟩ Lwow, *Ber.* **20,** 1022 (1877). ⟨8⟩ Darapsky, Engels, *J. prakt. Chem.* (2) **146,** 238 (1936). ⟨9⟩ Lundqvist, *J. Am. Chem. Soc.* **60,** 2000 (1938). ⟨10⟩ Moses, Reid, *J. Am. Chem. Soc.* **54,** 2101 (1932).
⟨11⟩ Drake, Bronitsky, *J. Am. Chem. Soc.* **52,** 3718 (1930). ⟨12⟩ Robertson, *J. Chem. Soc.* **115,** 1220–1221 (1919). ⟨13⟩ Mitchell, Reid, *J. Am. Chem. Soc.* **53,** 1881 (1931). ⟨14⟩ Schwartz, Johnson, *J. Am. Chem. Soc.* **53,** 1065 (1931). ⟨15⟩ Pool, Harwood, Ralston, *J. Am. Chem. Soc.* **59,** 178 (1937). ⟨16⟩ Weidenhagen, *Ber.* **69,** 2268 (1936). ⟨17⟩ Asano, *Cent.* **1922,** I, 1227. ⟨18⟩ Neave, *Analyst* **37,** 399 (1912). ⟨19⟩ Pollard, Adelson, Bain, *J. Am. Chem. Soc.* **56,** 1759 (1931).

1:1143 **α-ETHYL-*n*-CAPROIC ACID** $C_8H_{16}O_2$ **Beil. S.N. 162**
(2-Ethylhexanoic acid-1, $CH_3.(CH_2)_3.CH(C_2H_5).COOH$
n-butyl-ethyl-acetic acid)

B.P. 228° ⟨1⟩ **Neut. Eq. 144**

With $BaCl_2$ yields an amorphous barium salt [dif. from *n*-caprylic ac. (1:1145) whose barium salt is crystn.] ⟨2⟩.

With PCl_3 yields α-ethyl-*n*-caproyl chloride (b.p. 85–90° at 20 mm.) ⟨3⟩ which with excess conc. NH_4OH yields α-ethyl-*n*-caproamide, cryst. from lgr., m.p. 101° ⟨2⟩ ⟨4⟩; 103° ⟨5⟩.

Ⓓ ***p*-Phenylphenacyl α-ethyl-*n*-caproate:** m.p. 49.5–50° ⟨4⟩; 53–54° ⟨5⟩.

1:1143 ⟨1⟩ Levene, Taylor, *J. Biol. Chem.* **54,** 354 (1922). ⟨2⟩ Raper, *J. Chem. Soc.* **91,** 1837 (1907). ⟨3⟩ Tiffeneau, *Bull. soc. chim.* (4) **33,** 186 (1923). ⟨4⟩ Weizmann, Bergmann, Haskelberg, *Chemistry and Industry* **56,** 589 (1937). ⟨5⟩ Magnani, McElvain, *J. Am. Chem. Soc.* **60,** 818–819 (1938).

— CYCLOHEXANECARBOXYLIC ACID $C_6H_{11}.COOH$ $C_7H_{12}O_2$ Beil. IX-7

B.P. 233° **Neut. Eq. 128**

See 1:0575. Genus 3: Division B: Section 2. M.P. 30°.

1:1145 *n*-CAPRYLIC ACID $CH_3.(CH_2)_6.COOH$ $C_8H_{16}O_2$ Beil. II-347
(Octanoic acid)

B.P. 239.3° ⟨1⟩ **Neut. Eq. 144** D_4^{20} = **0.90884** ⟨1⟩ n_D^{20} = **1.4268**
M.P. +16.3° ⟨1⟩ ⟨2⟩

$\bar{C}$ is sol. in abt. 400 pts. aq. at 100° but on cooling seps. out completely — $\bar{C}$ is eas. sol. alc., ether, C_6H_6.

$\bar{C}$ with PCl_5 (64% yield ⟨3⟩), or $PCl_3 + ZnCl_2$ (90% yield ⟨3⟩), or 1.5 moles $SOCl_2$ (90% yield ⟨3⟩) gives *n*-octanoyl chloride, b.p. 195.6°, m.p. −6.0° ⟨1⟩.

$Ag\bar{A}_2$, curdy ppt.; $Ca\bar{A}_2.H_2O$, ndls. very dif. sol. cold aq.; $Zn\bar{A}_2$, scales from aq. or alc., m.p. 135°; $Pb\bar{A}_2$, lfts. from hot alc., m.p. 83.5–84.5° ⟨4⟩.

Ⓓ ***p*-Chlorophenacyl *n*-caprylate:** m.p. 63° ⟨5⟩ [cf. T 1.391].
Ⓓ ***p*-Bromophenacyl *n*-caprylate:** m.p. 67.4° ⟨5⟩; 65.5° ⟨6⟩ [cf. T 1.391].
Ⓓ ***p*-Iodophenacyl *n*-caprylate:** m.p. 79.2° ⟨5⟩ [cf. T 1.391].
Ⓓ ***p*-Phenylphenacyl *n*-caprylate:** m.p. 67° ⟨7⟩ [cf. T 1.391].
Ⓓ ***n*-Caprylamide:** m.p. 106° ⟨8⟩; 105.5° ⟨1⟩; 105° ⟨9⟩.
Ⓓ ***n*-Caprylanilide:** m.p. 55° ⟨9⟩; 57° ⟨10⟩.
Ⓓ ***n*-Capryl-*p*-toluidide:** m.p. 70° ⟨9⟩.
Ⓓ **2-(*n*-Heptyl)benzimidazole:** from $\bar{C}$ on htg. for 8 hrs. at 140–150° with 1 mole *o*-phenylenediamine; m.p. 144.5–145.0° cor. ⟨11⟩; 139–140° ⟨12⟩. [This deriv. depresses m.p. of corresp. deriv. from *n*-nonylic ac. (1:0560) ⟨11⟩.]

1:1145 ⟨1⟩ Deffet, *Bull. soc. chim. Belg.* **40,** 390–391 (1931). ⟨2⟩ Holde, Gentner, *Ber.* **58,** 1422 (1925). ⟨3⟩ Clark, Bell, *Trans. Roy. Soc. Canada* (3) **27,** III, 97–103 (1933). ⟨4⟩ Neave, *Analyst* **37,** 399 (1912). ⟨5⟩ Moses, Reid, *J. Am. Chem. Soc.* **54,** 2101 (1932). ⟨6⟩ Judefind, Reid, *J. Am. Chem. Soc.* **42,** 1055 (1920). ⟨7⟩ Drake, Bronitsky, *J. Am. Chem. Soc.* **52,** 3718 (1903). ⟨8⟩ Mitchell, Reid, *J. Am. Chem. Soc.* **53,** 1881 (1931). ⟨9⟩ Robertson, *J. Chem. Soc.* **115,** 1220–1221 (1919). ⟨10⟩ Schwartz, Johnson, *J. Am. Chem. Soc.* **53,** 1065 (1931). ⟨11⟩ Pool, Harwood, Ralston, *J. Am. Chem. Soc.* **59,** 178 (1937). ⟨12⟩ Seka, Müller, *Monatsh.* **57,** 102 (1931).

1:1150 *n*-CAPROIC ANHYDRIDE $[CH_3.(CH_2)_4.CO]_2O$ $C_{12}H_{22}O_3$ Beil. II-324

B.P. 245° (254) D_4^{20} = **0.91983** ⟨1⟩ n_D^{25} = **1.42971** ⟨1⟩

F.p. is −40.6° ⟨1⟩ — Should respond to Generic Test 3-B (titration in alcohol) reacting as monobasic ac. Neut. Eq. *in alcohol* (T 1.51) gives Sap. Eq. of 107 and yields soln. contg. only salts of *n*-caproic ac. (1:1130), q.v.

1:1150 ⟨1⟩ Simon, *Bull. soc. chim. Belg.* **38,** 56–59 (1929).

1:1155 CROTONIC ANHYDRIDE $(CH_3.CH{=}CH.CO)_2O$ $C_8H_{10}O_3$ Beil. II-411

B.P. 248° D_4^{20} = **1.0397** n_D^{20} = **1.47446**

Not solidified even at −15° — Adds Br_2.

Should respond to Generic Test 3-B (titration in alcohol), reacting as monobasic acid. Neut. Eq. *in alcohol* (T 1.31) = 154. Hydrolysis with aq. alk. (T 1.51) gives Sap. Eq. of 72 and yields soln. contg. only salts of crotonic ac. (1:0425), q.v.

—— **PELARGONIC ACID** $CH_3.(CH_2)_7.COOH$ $C_9H_{18}O_2$ **Beil. II-352**

B.P. 253° **Neut. Eq. 158**

See 1:0560. Genus 3: Division A: Section 2. M.P. +12.

1:1165 ***n*-ENANTHIC ANHYDRIDE** $[CH_3.(CH_2)_5.CO]_2O$ $C_{14}H_{26}O_3$ **Beil. II-340**
(*n*-Heptylic anhydride)

B.P. 258° D_4^{20} = **0.91745** ⟨1⟩ n_D^{15} = **1.43346**

M.p. +17°; f.p. −12.4° ⟨1⟩ — Should respond to Generic Test 3-B (titration in alc.) reacting as monobasic ac. Neut. Eq. *in alcohol* (T 1.31) = 242 — Hydrolysis with aq. alk. (T 1.51) gives Sap. Eq. of 121 and yields soln. contg. only salt of *n*-enanthic ac. (1:1140), q.v.

[For use of titration with $NaOCH_3$ in quant. detn. see ⟨2⟩.]

With conc. NH_4OH immed. solidified to *n*-enanthamide, cryst. from hot aq., m.p. 96°.

1:1165 ⟨1⟩ Deffet, *Bull. soc. chim. Belg.* **40,** 390 (1931). ⟨2⟩ Smith, Bryant, *J. Am. Chem. Soc.* **58,** 2452–2454 (1936).

—— ***d,l*-α-METHYLHYDROCINNAMIC ACID** $C_{10}H_{12}O_2$ **Beil. IX-542**
$C_6H_5.CH_2.CH(CH_3).COOH$

B.P. 272° **Neut. Eq. 164**

See 1:0593. Genus 3: Division A: Section 2. M.P. 36.5°.

—— **UNDECYLENIC ACID** $CH_2{=}CH(CH_2)_8.COOH$ $C_{11}H_{20}O_2$ **Beil. II-458**

B.P. 275° **Neut. Eq. 184**

See 1:0570. Genus 3: Division A: Section 2. M.P. 24.5°.

—— ***n*-UNDECYLIC ACID** $CH_3.(CH_2)_9.COOH$ $C_{11}H_{22}O_2$ **Beil. II-358**

B.P. 280° **Neut. Eq. 186**

See 1:0573. Genus 3: Division A: Section 2. M.P. 28.5°.

1:1175 ***n*-CAPRYLIC ANHYDRIDE** $[CH_3.(CH_2)_6.CO]_2O$ $C_{16}H_{30}O_3$ **Beil. II-348**

M.P. −1° ⟨1⟩ **B.P. 280-290°** 5 mm. $D_4^{17.5}$ = **0.9065** ⟨1⟩ $n_D^{17.5}$ = **1.4358** ⟨1⟩

Prob. responds to Generic Test 3-B (titration in alc.) — Hydrolysis with aq. alk. (T 1.51) gives Sap. Eq. 135 and yields soln. contg. salt of *n*-caprylic acid (1:1145), q.v.

1:1175 ⟨1⟩ Holde, Gentner, *Ber.* **58,** 1418–1424 (1925).

CHAPTER VI

GENUS 4. PHENOLS

1. ALPHABETICAL NAME INDEX*

*For complete alphabetical name index covering all listed names of all numbered compounds in this book see the main alphabetical index.

2. Chemical Type Index

(Names used here are not necessarily same as subject index names)

I. Monohydric Phenols

A. *Alkyl phenols*

Phenol **1:1420**

o-Cresol **1:1400**
m-Cresol **1:1730**
p-Cresol **1:1410**

2,4-Dimethylphenol **1:1740**
2,5-Dimethylphenol **1:1473**
2,6-Dimethylphenol **1:1425**
3,4-Dimethylphenol **1:1453**
3,5-Dimethylphenol **1:1455**

o-Ethylphenol **1:1739**
m-Ethylphenol **1:1744**
p-Ethylphenol **1:1424**

2,4,5-Trimethylphenol **1:1469**
2,4,6-Trimethylphenol **1:1467**

2,3,4,6-Tetramethylphenol **1:1481**
2,3,5,6-Tetramethylphenol **1:1537**

Carvacrol **1:1760**
Thymol **1:1430**

p-*n*-Butylphenol **1:1771**
p-*sec*-Butylphenol **1:1452**
p-*ter*-Butylphenol **1:1510**
p-Isobutylphenol **1:1759**

p-*n*-Amylphenol **1:1773**
p-*ter*-Amylphenol **1:1495**

B. *Alkaryl phenols*

α-Naphthol **1:1500**
β-Naphthol **1:1540**

o-Phenylphenol **1:1440**
m-Phenylphenol **1:1475**
p-Phenylphenol **1:1585**

o-Cyclohexylphenol **1:1441**
p-Cyclohexylphenol **1:1550**

o-Benzylphenol **1:1431**
p-Benzylphenol **1:1485**

C. *Hydroxy derivs. of biphenyl*

2-Hydroxybiphenyl **1:1440**
3-Hydroxybiphenyl **1:1475**
4-Hydroxybiphenyl **1:1585**

o-Cyclohexylphenol **1:1441**
p-Cyclohexylphenol **1:1550**

D. *Phenolic alcohols*

o-Hydroxybenzyl alcohol **1:1490**
Vanillyl alcohol **1:1533**

E. *Half ethers of dihydric phenols*

E_1-Methyl ethers

o-Methoxyphenol **1:1405**
m-Methoxyphenol **1:1765**
p-Methoxyphenol **1:1435**

2-Methoxy-4-allylphenol **1:1775**
2-Methoxy-4-propenylphenol **1:1785**

2-Methoxy-4-formylphenol **1:0050**
Vanillyl alcohol **1:1533**

E_2-Ethyl ethers

o-Ethoxyphenol **1:1745**
m-Ethoxyphenol **1:1770**
p-Ethoxyphenol **1:1461**

2-Ethoxy-4-formylphenol **1:0045**

E_3-Benzyl ethers

Pyrocatechol monobenzyl ether **1:1830**
Resorcinol monobenzyl ether **1:1466**
Hydroquinone monobenzyl ether **1:1539**

F. *Half esters of dihydric phenols*

m-Acetoxyphenol **1:1795**

G. *Phenolic aldehydes*

o-Hydroxybenzaldehyde **1:0205**
m-Hydroxybenzaldehyde **1:0055**
p-Hydrobenzaldehyde **1:0060**

2-Hydroxy-5-methylbenzaldehyde **1:0030**

4-Hydroxy-3-methoxybenzaldehyde **1:0050**
4-Hydroxy-3-ethoxybenzaldehyde **1:0045**

H. *Phenolic acids*

o-Hydroxybenzoic acid **1:0780**
m-Hydroxybenzoic acid **1:0825**
p-Hydroxybenzoic acid **1:0840**

p-Hydroxyphenylacetic acid **1:0500**

3,5-Dimethoxy-4-hydroxybenzoic acid........... **1:0830**

2-Hydroxy-3-naphthoic acid.................. **1:0850**

I. *Esters of phenolic acids*

Methyl *o*-hydroxybenzoate (salicylate)............ **1:1750**
Ethyl *o*-hydroxybenzoate (salicylate)............ **1:1755**
n-Propyl *o*-hydroxybenzoate (salicylate)............ **1:1774**
Isopropyl *o*-hydroxybenzoate (salicylate)......... **1:1763**
n-Butyl *o*-hydroxybenzoate (salicylate)............ **1:1780**
Isobutyl *o*-hydroxybenzoate (salicylate)............ **1:1776**

Isoamyl *o*-hydroxybenzoate (salicylate)............ **1:1790**

Phenyl *o*-hydroxybenzoate (salicylate)............ **1:1415**
β-Naphthyl *o*-hydroxybenzoate (salicylate)......... **1:1505**

Methyl *m*-hydroxybenzoate **1:1468**
Ethyl *m*-hydroxybenzoate.. **1:1471**

Methyl *p*-hydroxybenzoate. **1:1549**
Ethyl *p*-hydroxybenzoate.. **1:1534**

J. *Phenolic ketones*

o-Acetylphenol........... **1:1746**
m-Acetylphenol.......... **1:1506**
p-Acetylphenol........... **1:1527**

o-Benzoylphenol.......... **1:1414**
m-Benzoylphenol......... **1:1535**
p-Benzoylphenol......... **1:1560**

1-Aceto-2-naphthol....... **1:1459**
2-Aceto-1-naphthol....... **1:1515**

II. Dihydric Phenols

A. *Pyrocatechol derivatives*

Pyrocatechol............. **1:1520**
3,4-Dihydroxytoluene..... **1:1460**
3,4-Dihydroxybiphenyl.... **1:1576**
3,4-Dihydroxybenzaldehyde **1:0073**

B. *Resorcinol derivatives*

Resorcinol............... **1:1530**

2,4-Dihydroxytoluene..... **1:1521**
2,6-Dihydroxytoluene..... **1:1536**
3,5-Dihydroxytoluene..... **1:1525**

n-Hexylresorcinol........ **1:1465**

n-Caproylresorcinol....... **1:1443**

2,4-Dihydroxybenzaldehyde **1:0065**

C. *Hydroquinone derivatives*

Hydroquinone........... **1:1590**
2,5-Dihydroxytoluene..... **1:1545**

D. *Biphenyl series*

2,2′-Dihydroxybiphenyl... **1:1529**
2,4′-Dihydroxybiphenyl... **1:1581**
3,3′-Dihydroxybiphenyl... **1:1541**
3,4-Dihydroxybiphenyl.... **1:1576**
4,4′-Dihydroxybiphenyl... **1:1640**

2,2′-Dihydroxy-3,3′-dimethylbiphenyl...... **1:1531**
2,2′-Dihydroxy-4,4′-dimethylbiphenyl....... **1:1538**
2,2′-Dihydroxy-5,5′-dimethylbiphenyl....... **1:1579**
2,2′-Dihydroxy-6,6′-dimethylbiphenyl....... **1:1583**

4,4′-Dihydroxy-2,2′-dimethylbiphenyl....... **1:1532**
4,4′-Dihydroxy-3,3′-dimethylbiphenyl....... **1:1580**

5,5′-Dihydroxy-2,2′-dimethylbiphenyl....... **1:1623**

Bi-*β*-naphthol............ **1:1621**

E. *Dihydroxynaphthalene derivs.*

1,2-Dihydroxynaphthalene **1:1524**
1,3-Dihydroxynaphthalene **1:1544**
1,4-Dihydroxynaphthalene **1:1592**
1,5-Dihydroxynaphthalene **1:1630**
1,8-Dihydroxynaphthalene **1:1572**
2,7-Dihydroxynaphthalene **1:1594**

Di-*β*-naphthol............ **1:1621**

F. *Phenolic acids*

2,4-Dihydroxybenzoic acid. **1:0843**
3,4-Dihydroxybenzoic acid. **1:0545**

III. Trihydric Phenols

1,2,3-Trihydroxybenzene... **1:1555**
1,2,4-Trihydroxybenzene... **1:1570**
1,3,5-Trihydroxybenzene... **1:1620**

3,4,5-Trihydroxybenzoic acid................. **1:0875**
Methyl 3,4,5-trihydroxybenzoate.............. **1:1605**

IV. Miscellaneous Compounds

A. *Enolic compounds*

A_1-Diketones

Acetylacetone............ **1:1700**
Benzoylacetone.......... **1:1450**

Dibenzoylmethane........ **1:1480**
Dimethyldihydroresorcinol **1:0768**

A_2-Esters of β-keto acids

Methyl acetoacetate...... **1:1705**
Ethyl acetoacetate....... **1:1710**

Methyl methylacetoacetate **1:1708**
Ethyl methylacetoacetate.. **1:1712**

Methyl ethylacetoacetate.. **1:1718**
Ethyl ethylacetoacetate.... **1:1723**

Ethyl allylacetoacetate.... **1:1738**
Ethyl *n*-butylacetoacetate . **1:1840**

Methyl benzoylacetate.... **1:1810**
Ethyl benzoylacetate...... **1:1778**

Methyl furoylacetate...... **1:1800**
Ethyl furoylacetate....... **1:1820**

Ethyl acetopyruvate...... **1:1742**

Diethyl acetonedicarboxylate.................. **1:1772**

B. *Glucosides*

Coniferin................ **1:1595**
Esculin.................. **1:1615**
Salicin.................. **1:1610**

C. *Other compounds*

Furoin.................. **1:1565**
Phenolphthalein.......... **1:1635**
Triketohydrindene hydrate **1:1625**

ORDER I: SUBORDER I: GENUS 4: PHENOLS

Division A, Solid Phenolic Compounds

— **ETHYL ACETOPYRUVATE** $C_7H_{10}O_4$ **Beil. III-747**
(Ethyl α,γ-dioxo-*n*-valerate; ethyl acetoneoxalate) $CH_3.CO.CH_2.CO.COOC_2H_5$

M.P. 18°
See 1:1742. Genus 4: Phenols. B.P. 213–215°.

— ***o*-BENZYLPHENOL** $C_{13}H_{12}O$ **Beil. VI-675**
(2-Hydroxy-diphenylmethane)

OH
—$CH_2.C_6H_5$

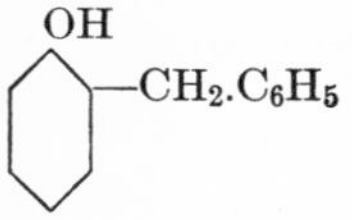

M.P. 21° **B.P. 312°**
Labile form; spontaneously changes to stable form, m.p. 54° (1:1431), q.v.

— ***p*-*n*-BUTYLPHENOL** $C_{11}H_{16}O$ **Beil. S.N. 533**
$CH_3.CH_2.CH_2.CH_2$—⟨ ⟩—OH

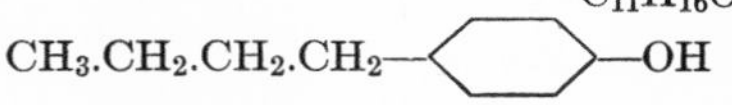

M.P. 22°
See 1:1771. Genus 4: Phenols. B.P. 248°.

— ***p*-*n*-AMYLPHENOL** $C_{11}H_{16}O$ **Beil. S.N. 533**
$CH_3.(CH_2)_3.CH_2$—⟨ ⟩—OH

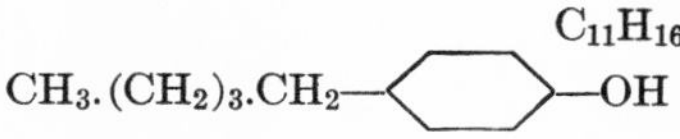

M.P. 23°
See 1:1772. Genus 4: Phenols. B.P. 248–253°.

— **2,4-DIMETHYLPHENOL** $C_8H_{10}O$ **Beil. VI-486**
(*unsym.*-*m*-Xylenol; 1,3,4-xylenol; 4-hydroxy-1,3-dimethylbenzene)

OH
—CH_3
CH_3

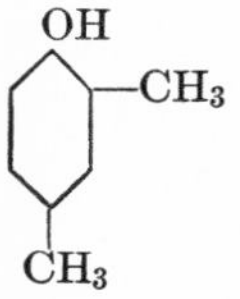

M.P. 27°
See 1:1740. Genus 4: Phenols. B.P. 211.5° cor.

— **PYROCATECHOL MONOETHYL ETHER** $C_8H_{10}O_2$ **Beil. VI-771**
(*o*-Ethoxyphenol; guaethol) $C_2H_5O.C_6H_4.OH$

M.P. 28°
See 1:1745. Genus 4: Phenols. B.P. 217°.

1:1400 ***o*-CRESOL** (*o*-Methylphenol) —CH_3 —OH C_7H_8O **Beil. VI-349**

M.P. 30.75° **B.P. 190.8°**

Abt. 3% sol. in aq. at 35° — Volatile with steam. [For temp.-compn. curve for system C̄ + H_2O see ⟨1⟩.]

C̄ is not dislvd. by 5 pts. NH_4OH [dif. from phenol] — With $FeCl_3$ (T 1.41) C̄ gives VB color on mixing, changing in 5 min. to Y, later to turbid brown — C̄ with Br_2-aq. (2 moles) yields 4,6-dibromo-2-methylphenol, m.p. 56–57°.

C̄ in 50% alc. mixed with conc. soln. of PkOH in 50% alc. yields or.-yel. picrate, C̄.PkOH, ndls., m.p. 88° (89.8° ⟨2⟩). [Dif. from *p*-cresol whose picrate is unstable under these conditions and does not ppt.]

Ⓓ ***o*-Tolyl *p*-nitrobenzoate:** m.p. 94°.
Ⓓ ***o*-Tolyl 3,5-dinitrobenzoate:** pl. from alc., m.p. 138.4° cor. ⟨3⟩ [cf. T 1.47]. [Distinguishes from *p*-cresol (1:1410) but not from guaiacol (1:1405).]
Ⓓ ***o*-Tolyl *p*-toluenesulfonate:** from C̄ + *p*-toluenesulfonyl chloride in aq. NaOH or in pyridine, ndls., m.p. 54–55° ⟨4⟩.
Ⓓ ***o*-Tolyl *p*-nitrobenzyl ether:** cryst. from alc., m.p. 89.7° ⟨5⟩ [cf. T 1.44].
Ⓓ ***o*-Tolyl 2,4-dinitrophenyl ether:** faintly yel. pr. from alc., m.p. 90° ⟨6⟩.
Ⓓ ***o*-Methylphenoxyacetic acid:** cryst. from aq., m.p. 151–152°; Neut. Eq. 166 ⟨7⟩ [cf. T 1.46].
Ⓓ ***o*-Tolyl *N*-phenylcarbamate:** from C̄ + phenylisocyanate in boilg. lgr., cryst. from alc., m.p. 141° ⟨8⟩; 143° ⟨9⟩.
Ⓓ ***o*-Tolyl *N*-α-naphthylcarbamate:** cryst. from lgr., m.p. 141–142° ⟨10⟩ [cf. T 1.45]. [Distinguishes from guaiacol (1:1405) but not from *p*-cresol (1:1410).]
Ⓓ ***o*-Tolyl *N*-*p*-xenylcarbamate:** m.p. 151° ⟨11⟩.
Ⓓ ***o*-Tolyl *N,N*-diphenylcarbamate:** m.p. 72–73° ⟨12⟩ [cf. T 1.43].

1:1400 ⟨1⟩ Sedgwick, Spurrell, Davies, *J. Chem. Soc.* **107,** 1203 (1915). ⟨2⟩ Kendall, *J. Am. Chem. Soc.* **38,** 1319 (1916). ⟨3⟩ Phillips, Keenan, *J. Am. Chem. Soc.* **53,** 1926 (1931). ⟨4⟩ Reverdin, Crépieux, *Ber.* **35,** 1443 (1902); *Bull. soc. chim.* (3) **27,** 745 (1902). ⟨5⟩ Reid, *J. Am. Chem. Soc.* **39,** 308 (1917). ⟨6⟩ Bost, Nicholson, *J. Am. Chem. Soc.* **57,** 2369 (1935). ⟨7⟩ Koelsch, *J. Am. Chem. Soc.* **53,** 305 (1931). ⟨8⟩ Weehuizen, *Rec. trav. chim.* **37,** 267 (1918). ⟨9⟩ Fromm, Eckard, *Ber.* **56,** 953 (1923). ⟨10⟩ French, Wirtel, *J. Am. Chem. Soc.* **48,** 1737 (1926).
⟨11⟩ Morgan, Pettet, *J. Chem. Soc.* **1931,** 1125. ⟨12⟩ Herzog, *Ber.* **40,** 1833 (1907).

1:1405 **GUAIACOL** (Pyrocatechol monomethyl ether; *o*-methoxyphenol; *o*-hydroxyanisole) —OH —OCH_3 $C_7H_8O_2$ **Beil. VI-768**

M.P. 28.2° ⟨1⟩ (32° ⟨2⟩) **B.P. 205°** $D^{20.4}_{(vac.)}$ = **1.1287** n^{20}_{D} = **1.5441** ⟨3⟩

Liq. with characteristic agreeable aromat. odor — Sol. in 60 vols. aq. at 15°; eas. sol. org. solv. — Volatile with steam.

C̄ in 1% aq. soln. gives with $FeCl_3$ (T 1.41) R-OR color slowly fading to yield turbid soln.; C̄ in 1% alc. soln. with $FeCl_3$ (T 1.41) gives G-B very rapidly fading to Y-T_2 — Alk. soln. from phthalic anhyd. fusion (T 1.42) has VB-BV color.

C̄ htd. 2 hrs. at 210° with eq. wt. $AlCl_3$ followed by soln. in dil. HCl and extractn. with ether gives (70% yield) pyrocatechol (1:1520) ⟨4⟩ — C̄ htd. with HBr (48%) gives (85–87%) pyrocatechol (1:1520) ⟨5⟩.

Ⓓ **4,5,6-Tribromoguaiacol:** To 0.31 g. $\bar{C}$ dislvd. in 3 ml. alc. is added during 8 min. 1.5. g. Br_2 dislvd. in 3 ml. alc. The mixt. is heated 20 min. on water bath, alc. removed by distn., and 1 ml. AcOH added. The resultant solid is then recrystd. from 3 ml. alc., yielding 0.7 g. ndls., m.p. 116° u.c. ⟨6⟩. [Evidence ⟨7⟩ indicates that product is 2-methoxy-4,5,6-tribromophenol.]

Ⓓ **Guaiacol picrate:** $\bar{C}$.PkOH. To mixt. of 0.1 g. $\bar{C}$ in 1 ml. aq. add hot soln. of 0.2 g. picric ac. in 5 ml. aq.; shake well, and cool slowly. O-YO cryst., m.p. 86–87° sep. ⟨8⟩; m.p. 88° ⟨9⟩. [Does not distinguish from *o*-cresol (1:1400).]

Ⓓ ***o*-Methoxyphenyl benzoate:** pr. from aq. alc., m.p. 57° ⟨10⟩.

Ⓓ ***o*-Methoxyphenyl *p*-nitrobenzoate:** m.p. 93°.

Ⓓ ***o*-Methoxyphenyl 3,5-dinitrobenzoate:** cryst. from alc., m.p. 141.2° cor. ⟨11⟩ [cf. T 1.47].

Ⓓ ***o*-Methoxyphenyl benzenesulfonate:** from $\bar{C}$ + benzenesulfonyl chloride + aq. alk., cryst. from alc., m.p. 51–52° ⟨12⟩.

Ⓓ ***o*-Methoxyphenyl *p*-toluenesulfonate:** from $\bar{C}$ + *p*-toluenesulfonyl chloride + dil. aq. alk.; ndls. from lgr., m.p. 85° ⟨13⟩.

Ⓓ ***o*-Methoxyphenyl *p*-nitrobenzyl ether:** m.p. 63.6° ⟨14⟩. [Distinguishes from *o*- or *p*-cresol.] [Cf. T 1.44.]

Ⓓ ***o*-Methoxyphenyl 2,4-dinitrophenyl ether:** ndls. from alc., m.p. 97° ⟨15⟩.

Ⓓ ***o*-Methoxyphenoxyacetic acid:** m.p. 116°; Neut. Eq. 182 ⟨16⟩ [cf. T 1.46].

Ⓓ ***o*-Methoxyphenyl *N*-phenylcarbamate:** ndls. from alc. or ether, m.p. 136° ⟨17⟩.

Ⓓ ***o*-Methoxyphenyl *N*-α-naphthylcarbamate:** m.p. 118° ⟨18⟩ [cf. T 1.45].

1:1405 ⟨1⟩ Carswell, *J. Am. Pharm. Assoc.* **18,** 995–997 (1929). ⟨2⟩ Jaeger, *Z. anorg. allgem. Chem.* **101,** 134 (1917). ⟨3⟩ Puschin, Matavulj, *Z. physik. Chem.* **A-158,** 293 (1931). ⟨4⟩ Hartmann, Gattermann, *Ber.* **25,** 3532 (1892). ⟨5⟩ Clarke, Taylor, *Organic Syntheses, Coll. Vol.* I, 144–147 (1932). ⟨6⟩ Underwood, Baril, Toone, *J. Am. Chem. Soc.* **52,** 4090 (1930). ⟨7⟩ Zagirolami, *Gazz. chim. ital.* **62,** 570–575 (1932). ⟨8⟩ Mulliken "Method" I, 91 (1904). ⟨9⟩ Baril, Megrdichian, *J. Am. Chem. Soc.* **58,** 1415 (1936). ⟨10⟩ Brüggemann, *J. prakt. Chem.* (2) **53,** 254 (1896).

⟨11⟩ Phillips, Keenan, *J. Am. Chem. Soc.* **53,** 1926 (1931). ⟨12⟩ Beil. XI-32. ⟨13⟩ Reverdin, Crépieux, *Ber.* **34,** 2998 (1901); *Bull. soc. chim.* (3) **25,** 1046 (1901). ⟨14⟩ Lyman, Reid, *J. Am. Chem. Soc.* **42,** 616 (1920). ⟨15⟩ Bost, Nicholson, *J. Am. Chem. Soc.* **57,** 2369 (1935). ⟨16⟩ Koelsch, *J. Am. Chem. Soc.* **53,** 305 (1931). ⟨17⟩ Morel, *Bull. soc. chim.* (3) **21,** 827 (1899). ⟨18⟩ French, Wirtel, *J. Am. Chem. Soc.* **48,** 1738 (1926).

1:1410 ***p*-CRESOL** $CH_3.C_6H_4.OH$ CH_3—⟨ ⟩—OH C_7H_8O **Beil. VI-389**
(*p*-Methylphenol)

M.P. 36° **B.P. 202.32° ⟨1⟩**

Abt. 2.3% sol. in aq. at 40°. [For temp.-compn. curve for system $\bar{C}$ + H_2O, see ⟨2⟩.] Volatile with steam.

$\bar{C}$ (1% aq. soln.) with $FeCl_3$ (T 1.41) gives BV-T_1 to BV-T_2 color on mixing, later becomes turbid — $\bar{C}$ with Br_2-aq. (2 moles) yields 2,6-dibromo-4-methylphenol, ndls. from pet., m.p. 48–49° ⟨3⟩. [$\bar{C}$ with a large excess of Br_2-aq. yields ppt. which after washing with $NaHSO_3$ soln. yields 2,4,6-tribromophenol, cryst. from 40% alc., m.p. 92.5–93.5 u.c. ⟨3⟩.]

Ⓓ ***p*-Tolyl benzoate:** m.p. 70° ⟨4⟩.

Ⓓ ***p*-Tolyl *p*-nitrobenzoate:** m.p. 98°.

Ⓓ ***p*-Tolyl 3,5-dinitrobenzoate:** cryst. from alc., m.p. 188.6° cor. ⟨5⟩ [cf. T 1.47].

Ⓓ ***p*-Tolyl *p*-toluenesulfonate:** from $\bar{C}$ + *p*-toluenesulfonyl chloride in aq. alk. or in pyridine, ndls. from alc., m.p. 69–70° ⟨6⟩.

Ⓓ ***p*-Tolyl *p*-nitrobenzyl ether:** cryst. from alc., m.p. 88° ⟨7⟩ [cf. T 1.44]. [Does not distinguish from *o*-cresol (1:1400).]

Ⓓ ***p*-Tolyl 2,4-dinitrophenyl ether:** faintly yel. flat ndls. from alc., m.p. 93.5° ⟨8⟩.
Ⓓ ***p*-Methylphenoxyacetic acid:** m.p. 135° ⟨4⟩, 134–136° ⟨9⟩; Neut. Eq. 166 [cf. T 1.46].
Ⓓ ***p*-Tolyl *N*-phenylcarbamate:** m.p. 115° ⟨10⟩.
Ⓓ ***p*-Tolyl *N*-α-naphthylcarbamate:** m.p. 146° ⟨11⟩ [cf. T 1.45].
Ⓓ ***p*-Tolyl *N*-*p*-xenylcarbamate:** m.p. 198° ⟨12⟩.
Ⓓ ***p*-Tolyl *N,N*-diphenylcarbamate:** m.p. 93–94° ⟨13⟩ [cf. T 1.43].

1:1410 ⟨1⟩ Gibb, *J. Am. Chem. Soc.* **49,** 839–844 (1927). ⟨2⟩ Sedgwick, Spurrell, Davies, *J. Chem. Soc.* **107,** 1203 (1915). ⟨3⟩ Werner, *Bull. soc. chim.* (2) **46,** 278 (1886). ⟨4⟩ Sherwood, Short, *J. Chem. Soc.* **1938,** 1013. ⟨5⟩ Phillips, Keenan, *J. Am. Chem. Soc.* **53,** 1926 (1931). ⟨6⟩ Reverdin, Crépieux, *Ber.* **35,** 1444 (1902); *Bull. soc. chim.* (3) **27,** 746 (1902). ⟨7⟩ Reid, *J. Am. Chem. Soc.* **39,** 308 (1917). ⟨8⟩ Bost, Nicholson, *J. Am. Chem. Soc.* **57,** 2369 (1935). ⟨9⟩ Koelsch, *J. Am. Chem. Soc.* **53,** 305 (1931). ⟨10⟩ Fromm, Eckard, *Ber.* **56,** 953 (1923). ⟨11⟩ French, Wirtel, *J. Am. Chem. Soc.* **48,** 1736 (1926). ⟨12⟩ Morgan, Pettet, *J. Chem. Soc.* **1931,** 1125. ⟨13⟩ Herzog, *Ber.* **40,** 1833 (1907).

1:1414 *o*-HYDROXYBENZOPHENONE $C_{13}H_{10}O_2$ Beil. VIII-155

(*o*-Benzoylphenol)

M.P. 41°

Pl. from alc. by addn. of aq. — Insol. aq.; very sol. alc., ether, AcOH, C_6H_6; spar. sol. pet. ether — Easily volatile with steam.

C̄ dis. readily in aq. alk. giving deep yel. solns.; insol. in aq. Na_2CO_3.

Ⓓ ***o*-Benzoylphenyl *p*-nitrobenzyl ether:** from C̄ + equiv. amt. *p*-nitrobenzyl bromide in acetone, htd. 1 hr. at 100° with equiv. amt. aq. NaOH; cryst. from acetone, m.p. 124–125° ⟨1⟩.

Ⓓ ***o*-Hydroxybenzophenone oxime:** C̄ forms two stereoisomeric ketoximes which melt at closely adjacent temperatures. Both can be obtained directly from C̄ by treatment with NH_2OH in alk. At ord. temp. the product is almost pure *h*-oxime, plates from C_6H_6 + pet. ether, m.p. 142–143°; in boiling solns. the product is a mixture in which the proportion of *n*-oxime increases with time of boiling. The *n*-oxime cryst. in needles from C_6H_6 + pet. ether, m.p. 141–142°. A mixture of the *h* and *n* forms melts 115–120°. For directions see ⟨2⟩. [For dif. in soly. of Cu salts of these stereoisomers see ⟨5⟩.]

Ⓓ ***o*-Hydroxybenzophenone phenylhydrazone:** m.p. 155° ⟨3⟩; 153.5° ⟨4⟩.

1:1414 ⟨1⟩ Blicke, Weinkauff, *J. Am. Chem. Soc.* **54,** 1448 (1932). ⟨2⟩ Kohler, Bruce, *J. Am. Chem. Soc.* **53,** 1572–1574 (1931). ⟨3⟩ Cohn, *Monatsh.* **17,** 108 (1896). ⟨4⟩ Pfeiffer, Loewe, *J. prakt. Chem.* (2) **147,** 299 (1936). ⟨5⟩ Blatt, *J. Am. Chem. Soc.* **61,** 214 (1939).

1:1415 PHENYL SALICYLATE $C_{13}H_{10}O_3$ Beil. X-76

(Salol)

OH / $CO.O.C_6H_5$

M.P. 42°

Crystallizes in three dif. modifications: stable (ordinary form), m.p. 42.0°; second form, m.p. 38.8°; third, obtd. by supercooling liq. C̄ to −20°, m.p. 28.5° ⟨1⟩.

Odor faintly aromatic — Alm. insol. hot aq. (dif. from phenol): eas. sol. MeOH, alc., or ether.

With $FeCl_3$ in alcohol gives violet red with $FeCl_3$ — Distn. of C̄ at ord. pressure yields CO_2, phenol (1:1420), and xanthone (1:7275) ⟨2⟩.

Ⓓ **Saponification:** $\bar{C}$ on alk. hydrolysis (T 1.51) gives Sap. Eq. of 214 and yields salicylic ac. (1:0780) and phenol (1:1420).

Ⓓ **Phenyl *o*-acetoxybenzoate** (Salol acetate): from $\bar{C}$ in ice cold dil. alk. by shaking with Ac_2O; pr. from alc., m.p. 99.5° ⟨3⟩. [Salicylic acid itself is not acetylated by this procedure.]

Ⓓ **Phenyl *o*-benzoxybenzoate** (Salol benzoate): from $\bar{C}$ in cold dil. alk. by shaking with BzCl; cryst. from alc., m.p. 80.5–81° ⟨4⟩.

Ⓓ **Phenyl *o*-(*p*-nitrobenzoxy)benzoate** (Salol *p*-nitrobenzoate): m.p. 111° [cf. T 1.47].

Ⓓ **Phenyl *o*-(*p*-nitrobenzyloxy)benzoate** (Salol *p*-nitrobenzyl ether): m.p. 87° ⟨5⟩ [cf. T 1.44].

Ⓓ **Phenyl salicylate *N*-phenylcarbamate:** from $\bar{C}$ + phenylisocyanate in C_6H_6; m.p. 111–112° ⟨6⟩; m.p. 242° ⟨7⟩.

Ⓓ **Phenyl salicylate *N,N*-diphenylcarbamate:** m.p. 143–144.5° ⟨7⟩ [cf. T 1.44].

1:1415 ⟨1⟩ Tamman, *Z. physik. Chem.* **29,** 71 (1899). ⟨2⟩ Holleman, *Organic Syntheses, Coll. Vol.* I, 537–538 (1932). ⟨3⟩ Chattaway, *J. Chem. Soc.* **1931,** 2496. ⟨4⟩ Purgotti, Monti, *Gazz. chim. ital.* **34,** I, 269 (1904). ⟨5⟩ Lyman, Reid, *J. Am. Chem. Soc.* **42,** 617–619 (1920). ⟨6⟩ Humnicki, *Chem. Abs.* **26,** 5556 (1932). ⟨7⟩ Herzog, *Ber.* **40,** 1834 (1907). ⟨7⟩ Eckenroth, Wolf, *Ber.* **26,** 1466 (1893).

1:1420 PHENOL —OH C_6H_6O **Beil. VI-110**

(" Carbolic acid ")

M.P. 42° **B.P. 183°**

Sol. in 15 pts. aq. at 16°; alm. insol. in Na_2CO_3 soln.; misc. with alc. or ether — Sol. in less than 5 pts. conc. NH_4OH [dif. from cresols] — Volat. with steam.

$\bar{C}$ in 1% aq. soln. gives with $FeCl_3$ (T 1.41) a violet (V) color, permanent for more than 15 min. — $\bar{C}$ htd. with phthalic anhydride (T 1.42) yields phenolphthalein, whose soln. in dil. alk. is VR, fading with large excess conc. alk. — With Br_2-aq. $\bar{C}$ yields ppt. of 2,4,6-tribromophenol, which after $NaHSO_3$ washing, and recrystn. from 40% alc. melts 92.5–93.5° u.c. [Also given by salicylic ac. (1:0780).] [This test sensitive to 1 pt. $\bar{C}$ in 50,000 aq. ⟨1⟩.] [Action of I_2 + Na_2CO_3 on $\bar{C}$ yields 2,4,6-triiodophenol, ndls. from dil. alc., m.p. 157°, and is even more delicate ⟨1⟩.]

$\bar{C}$ with PkOH yields mol. cpd., $\bar{C}$.PkOH, yel. cryst., m.p. 83.1° ⟨2⟩.

Ⓓ **Picric acid (2,4,6-trinitrophenol):** Pour a soln. of 0.05 g. $\bar{C}$ in 1 ml. conc. H_2SO_4 into a mixt. of 1 ml. each of conc. H_2SO_4 and conc. HNO_3. Heat 5–10 min. on aq. bath; pour slowly into 10 ml. cold aq.; cool; filter; wash ppt. with cold mixture of 2 ml. aq. + 0.5 ml. conc. HCl. Cryst. from boilg. mixt. of 4 ml. aq. + 1 ml. conc. HCl. Filter; wash with dil. HCl as before, and dry at 100°. M.p. 122.5° cor. ⟨3⟩.

Ⓓ **Phenyl benzoate:** from $\bar{C}$ + BzCl + aq. NaOH, pr. from ether + alc., m.p. 69° ⟨4⟩.

Ⓓ **Phenyl *p*-nitrobenzoate:** from $\bar{C}$ + *p*-nitrobenzoyl chloride on htg.; cryst. from C_6H_6, m.p. 127° ⟨5⟩.

Ⓓ **Phenyl 3,5-dinitrobenzoate:** from $\bar{C}$ + 3,5-dinitrobenzoyl chloride in pyridine, cryst. from alc., m.p. 145.8° cor. ⟨6⟩ [cf. T 1.47].

Ⓓ **Phenyl *p*-toluenesulfonate:** from $\bar{C}$ + *p*-toluenesulfonyl chloride in pyridine; ndls. from alc., m.p. 95–96° ⟨7⟩.

Ⓓ **Phenyl *p*-nitrobenzyl ether:** cryst. from dil. alc., m.p. 91° ⟨8⟩ [cf. T 1.44].

Ⓓ **Phenyl 2,4-dinitrophenyl ether:** ndls. from alc., m.p. 69° ⟨9⟩.

Ⓓ **Phenoxyacetic acid:** cryst. from aq., m.p. 88–89°; Neut. Eq. 152 ⟨10⟩ [cf. T 1.46].

Ⓓ **Phenyl *N*-phenylcarbamate:** from $\bar{C}$ + phenylisocyanate htd. several hours at 100° ⟨11⟩ or more readily in presence of a little $AlCl_3$ ⟨12⟩; ndls. from C_6H_6, m.p. 126°.

Ⓓ **Phenyl *N*-(*p*-nitrophenyl)carbamate:** pale yel. ndls. from alc., m.p. 161° ⟨13⟩.

Ⓓ **Phenyl *N*-(α-naphthyl)carbamate:** cryst. from lgr., m.p. 132–133° ⟨14⟩ [cf. T 1.45].
Ⓓ **Phenyl *N*-(*p*-xenyl)carbamate:** cryst. from alc., C_6H_6 or C_6H_6 + pet.; m.p. 173° ⟨15⟩.
Ⓓ **Phenyl *N,N*-diphenylcarbamate:** m.p. 104–105° ⟨16⟩ [cf. T 1.43].

1:1420 ⟨1⟩ Wilkie, *J. Soc. Chem. Ind.* **30,** 403 (1911). ⟨2⟩ Baril, Hauber, *J. Am. Chem. Soc.* **53,** 1090 (1931). ⟨3⟩ Mulliken, "Method" I, 108–109 (1904). ⟨4⟩ Garelli, Gorni, *Gazz. chim. ital.* **34,** II, 106 (1904). ⟨5⟩ Meijer, *Rec. trav. chim.* **53,** 394 (1934). ⟨6⟩ Phillips, Keenan, *J. Am. Chem. Soc.* **53,** 1926 (1931). ⟨7⟩ Reverdin, Crépieux, *Ber.* **35,** 1443 (1902); *Bull. soc. chim.* (3) **27,** 745 (1902). ⟨8⟩ Reid, *J. Am. Chem. Soc.* **39,** 306 (1917). ⟨9⟩ Bost, Nicholson, *J. Am. Chem. Soc.* **57,** 2369 (1935). ⟨10⟩ Koelsch, *J. Am. Chem. Soc.* **53,** 305 (1931).
⟨11⟩ Eckenroth, *Ber.* **18,** 517, Note (1885). ⟨12⟩ Leuckart, *J. prakt. Chem.* (2) **41,** 318 (1890). ⟨13⟩ van Hoogstraten, *Rec. trav. chim.* **51,** 427 (1932). ⟨14⟩ French, Wirtel, *J. Am. Chem. Soc.* **48,** 1737 (1926). ⟨15⟩ Morgan, Pettet, *J. Chem. Soc.* **1931,** 1125. ⟨16⟩ Herzog, *Ber.* **40,** 1833 (1907).

1:1424 ***p*-ETHYLPHENOL** C_2H_5—⟨ ⟩—OH $C_8H_{10}O$ **Beil. VI-472**
(*p*-Hydroxyethylbenzene)

M.P. 47° **B.P. 219°** D^{20}_{20} = **1.0123** n^{25}_D = **1.5239** (supercooled liquid)

Very sl. sol. aq.; misc. alc., ether; sl. sol. C_6H_6, CS_2 — Volatile with steam. $FeCl_3$ (T 1.41) gives deep blue color.

From its 1 *N* alk. soln. two vols. of ether at 15° extract 25% C̄ ⟨1⟩.

[For prepn. (100% yield) by reduction of *p*-hydroxyacetophenone (1:1527) with Zn + HCl see ⟨2⟩.]

Ⓓ ***p*-Ethylphenyl benzoate:** from C̄ + BzCl + cold aq. NaOH (cf. T 2.26-B); cryst. from alc., m.p. 59–60° ⟨3⟩ ⟨4⟩.
Ⓓ ***p*-Ethylphenyl *p*-nitrobenzoate:** m.p. 80–81° ⟨1⟩.
Ⓓ ***p*-Ethylphenyl 3,5-dinitrobenzoate:** m.p. 132–133° ⟨1⟩.
Ⓓ ***p*-Ethylphenoxyacetic acid:** m.p. 96–97° ⟨5⟩ ⟨4⟩; Neut. Eq. 180 [cf. T 1.46].
Ⓓ ***p*-Ethylphenyl *N*-phenylcarbamate:** m.p. 120° ⟨5⟩ ⟨4⟩.
Ⓓ ***p*-Ethylphenyl *N*-α-naphthylcarbamate:** m.p. 128° ⟨6⟩.

1:1424 ⟨1⟩ Vavon, Mitchovitch, *Bull. soc. chim.* (4) **45,** 963 (1929). ⟨2⟩ Clemmensen, *Ber.* **47,** 53 (1914). ⟨3⟩ Béhal, Choay, *Bull. soc. chim.* (3) **11,** 209 (1894). ⟨4⟩ Kruber, Schmitt, *Ber.* **64,** 2272 (1931). ⟨5⟩ Steinkopf, Höpner, *J. prakt. Chem.* (2) **113,** 151, 154 (1926). ⟨6⟩ Walbaum, Rosenthal, *J. prakt. Chem.* (2), **117,** 230 (1927).

1:1425 **2,6-DIMETHYLPHENOL** (*vic.-m*-Xylenol; 1,3,2-xylenol; 2-hydroxy-1,3-dimethylbenzene) [OH; H_3C, CH_3] $C_8H_{10}O$ **Beil. VI-485**

M.P. 49° **B.P. 203°** (212°)

Volatile with steam.

C̄ with Br_2 yields smoothly 3,4,5-tribromo-2,6-dimethylphenol, cryst. from pet. ether, m.p. 201° ⟨1⟩ — C̄ with PkOH yields mol. cpd., C̄.PkOH, or.-yel. cryst., m.p. 50–53° ⟨2⟩.

Ⓓ **2,6-Dimethylphenyl 3,5-dinitrobenzoate:** tbls. from alc., m.p. 158.8° cor. ⟨3⟩ [cf. T 1.47].
Ⓓ **2,6-Dimethylphenoxyacetic acid:** ndls. from aq., m.p. 139.5°; Neut. Eq. 180 ⟨4⟩.
Ⓓ **2,6-Dimethylphenyl *N*-phenylcarbamate:** from C̄ htd. 1 hr. with slight excess phenylisocyanate in 3–4 vols. high boilg. (170–200°) pet.; m.p. 133° ⟨4⟩.

Ⓓ **2,6-Dimethylphenyl *N*-α-naphthylcarbamate:** from C̄ + equal wt. α-naphthylisocyanate + trace of trimethylamine in dry ether; cryst. from pet. ether or alc., m.p. 176.5° ⟨1⟩ [cf. T 1.45].

Ⓓ **2,6-Dimethylphenyl *N*-*p*-xenylcarbamate:** m.p. 198° ⟨5⟩.

1:1425 ⟨1⟩ Hurd, Pollack, *J. Am. Chem. Soc.* **58,** 181 (1936). ⟨2⟩ Baril, Hauber, *J. Am. Chem. Soc.* **53,** 1090 (1931). ⟨3⟩ Phillips, Keenan, *J. Am. Chem. Soc.* **53,** 1926 (1931). ⟨4⟩ Steinkopf, Höpner, *J. prakt. Chem.* (2) **113,** 150–154 (1926). ⟨5⟩ Morgan, Pettet, *J. Chem. Soc.* **1931,** 1125.

1:1430 THYMOL (3-Hydroxy-*p*-cymene; 3-methyl-6-isopropylphenol) $C_{10}H_{14}O$ **Beil. VI-532**

HO
$(CH_3)_2CH$—⟨ring⟩—CH_3

M.P. 51.5° **B.P. 233.5°**

Strong odor of thyme — Pl. from AcOEt, AcOH or acetone; very sol. alc., ether, AcOH, $CHCl_3$, C_6H_6 — Sol. in 1200 pts. aq. at 15°, or in 900 pts. at 100° — Volatile with steam and extd. by ether, both even from alk. soln.

C̄ with $FeCl_3$ (T 1.41) gives no color except in conc. (1:2) alc. soln. when trace of very dil. reagt. gives transient green. [Dif. from guaiacol (1:1405).] — C̄ fused with phthalic anhydride (T 1.42) gives intense VR-R, dislvg. in dil. NaOH to intense blue B (thymolphthalein).

Ⓓ **2,4,6-Trinitro-*m*-cresol:** Dis. 0.1 g. powd. C̄ in 1 ml. conc. H_2SO_4 and stir into mixt. of 1 ml. each of conc. HNO_3 and conc. H_2SO_4 contd. in small glass evap. dish. Heat on aq. bath 3–4 min.; pour into 20 ml. cold aq.; cool, shake, and filter. Wash ppt. with 10 ml. aq., and recryst. from boilg. mixt. of 10 ml. aq., and recryst. from boilg. mixt. of 10 ml. aq., 4 ml. alc., and 0.5 ml. conc. HCl. Filter and wash with aq. Dry below 100°. M.p. 109–110° u.c. ⟨1⟩. [Under these cond. the isopropyl group is eliminated and same prod. results as from *m*-cresol: cf. ⟨2⟩.]

Ⓓ **Thymyl benzoate:** m.p. 33° ⟨3⟩.

Ⓓ **Thymyl *p*-nitrobenzoate:** m.p. 70°.

Ⓓ **Thymyl 3,5-dinitrobenzoate:** cryst. from alc., m.p. 103.2° cor. ⟨4⟩ [cf. T 1.47].

Ⓓ **Thymyl *p*-toluenesulfonate:** m.p. 71°.

Ⓓ **Thymyl *p*-nitrobenzyl ether:** cryst. from 80% alc., m.p. 85.5° ⟨5⟩ [cf. T 1.44].

Ⓓ **Thymyl 2,4-dinitrophenyl ether:** ndls. from alc., m.p. 67° ⟨6⟩.

Ⓓ **Thymoxyacetic acid:** cryst. from aq., m.p. 148–149°; Neut. Eq. 208 ⟨7⟩ [cf. T 1.46]. [Better yield (75%) by rubbing together 3 g. C̄, 2.3 g. chloroacetic ac., 3 g. powd. NaOH, working up product ⟨8⟩.] [For m.p.-compn. curve with *m*-cresoxyacetic ac. see ⟨9⟩.]

Ⓓ **Thymyl *N*-phenylcarbamate:** from C̄ + phenylisocyanate htd. in high boilg. pet., m.p. 107° ⟨10⟩.

Ⓓ **Thymyl *N*-α-naphthylcarbamate:** cryst. from lgr., m.p. 160° ⟨11⟩ [cf. T 1.45].

Ⓓ **Thymyl *N*-*p*-xenylcarbamate:** cryst. from alc., C_6H_6, or lt. pet., m.p. 194° ⟨12⟩.

1:1430 ⟨1⟩ Mulliken, " Method " I, 92 (1904). ⟨2⟩ Giua, *Gazz. chim. ital.* **49,** II, 158–166 (1919); *Chem. Abs.* **14,** 1532 (1920). ⟨3⟩ Peratoner, *Gazz. chim. ital.* **28,** I, 215 (1898). ⟨4⟩ Phillips, Keenan, *J. Am. Chem. Soc.* **53,** 1926 (1931). ⟨5⟩ Reid, *J. Am. Chem. Soc.* **39,** 307 (1917). ⟨6⟩ Bost, Nicholson, *J. Am. Chem. Soc.* **57,** 2369 (1935). ⟨7⟩ Koelsch, *J. Am. Chem. Soc.* **53,** 305 (1931). ⟨8⟩ Steinkopf, Höpner, *J. prakt. Chem.* (2) **113,** 153 (1926). ⟨9⟩ Ono, Imoto, *J. Soc. Chem. Ind. Japan*, Suppl. **39,** 215 B (1936). ⟨10⟩ Weehuizen, *Rec. trav. chim.* **37,** 268 (1918).

⟨11⟩ French, Wirtel, *J. Am. Chem. Soc.* **48,** 1738 (1926). ⟨12⟩ Morgan, Pettet, *J. Chem. Soc.* **1931,** 1125.

1:1431 o-BENZYLPHENOL (o-Hydroxydiphenylmethane) $C_{13}H_{12}O$ **Beil. VI-675**

OH —$CH_2.C_6H_5$

M.P. 54° (52°) **B.P. 312°**

Occurs in two dif. crystn. modifications: labile form, m.p. 21–22° and stable form, m.p. 54° (52°) — The lower melting form changes spontaneously into the higher, and once latter is obtd., the lower m.p. form is difficult to obt. ⟨1⟩.

C̄ is volatile with steam — C̄ may be sepd. from p-benzylphenol (1:1485) by fact that it seps. as a heavy oil on cooling hot lgr. soln. of mixture ⟨2⟩.

Ⓓ **o-Benzylphenyl benzyl ether:** from C̄ + benzyl chloride + NaOEt in alc. for 3 hrs. at 100°; cryst. from warm MeOH, m.p. 38° ⟨2⟩. [M.p. corresp. deriv. of p-benzylphenol, 49.5°.]

Ⓓ **o-Benzylphenyl N-phenylcarbamate:** ndls. from hot lgr., m.p. 117.5–118° ⟨1⟩ ⟨3⟩.

1:1431 ⟨1⟩ Claisen, *Ann.* **442,** 239–240 (1925). ⟨2⟩ Short, Stewart, *J. Chem. Soc.* **1929,** 556. ⟨3⟩ Short, *J. Chem. Soc.* **1928,** 528.

—— **p-HOMOSALICYLALDEHYDE** (2-Hydroxy-5-methylbenzaldehyde) $C_8H_8O_2$ **Beil. VIII-100**

CHO —OH H_3C—

M.P. 56° **B.P. 217-218°**

See 1:0030. Genus 1: Aldehydes.

1:1435 HYDROQUINONE MONOMETHYL ETHER (p-Methoxyphenol; p-hydroxyanisole) $C_7H_8O_2$ **Beil. VI-843**

CH_3O— —OH

M.P. 56° ⟨1⟩ **B.P. 243-244°** ⟨1⟩

Crystd. from lt. pet. has m.p. 56°; after heating to 200° and quickly cooling m.p. is 53°, changing in a week or two to 55°. The 56° crystals also change on keeping to m.p. 55° ⟨1⟩.

Volatile with steam [dif. and sepn. from hydroquinone dimethyl ether (1:7160)] — C̄ reduces $AgNO_3$ yielding odor of quinone but does not reduce Fehling's soln. (T 1.22) — Alk. soln. of C̄ does not turn brown in air.

For prepn. of C̄ from hydroquinone by methylation with dimethyl sulfate + alk. see ⟨1⟩ ⟨2⟩ ⟨3⟩.

C̄ in $CHCl_3$ treated with $CHCl_3$ soln. of PkOH yields picrate, C̄.PkOH, long flat or.-yel. ndls., m.p. 43–44° ⟨4⟩ — C̄ rubbed with Br_2 yields 2,3,6-tribromo-4-methoxyphenol, long white ndls. from AcOH, m.p. 145° ⟨5⟩.

Ⓓ **p-Methoxyphenyl acetate:** from C̄ + Ac_2O + trace conc. H_2SO_4; m.p. 31–32° ⟨6⟩.

Ⓓ **p-Methoxyphenyl benzoate:** from C̄ + dil. alk. + BzCl; cryst. from alc. or lgr., m.p. 87° ⟨7⟩.

Ⓓ **p-Methoxyphenoxyacetic acid:** m.p. 110–112°; Neut. Eq. 182 ⟨8⟩ [cf. T 1.46].

1:1435 ⟨1⟩ Robinson, Smith, *J. Chem. Soc.* **1926,** 393–394. ⟨2⟩ Kohn, Steiner, *Monatsh.* **58,** 97 (1931). ⟨3⟩ Kohn, Guttmann, *Monatsh.* **45,** 581–582 (1924). ⟨4⟩ Baril, Megrdichian, *J. Am. Chem. Soc.* **58,** 1415 (1936). ⟨5⟩ Kohn, Grün, *Monatsh.* **45,** 665 (1924). ⟨6⟩ Klemenc, *Monatsh.* **35,** 90 (1914). ⟨7⟩ Irvine, Smith, *J. Chem. Soc.* **1927,** 75. ⟨8⟩ Koelsch, *J. Am. Chem. Soc.* **53,** 305 (1931).

1:1440 2-HYDROXYBIPHENYL $C_{12}H_{10}O$ **Beil. VI-672**
(*o*-Phenylphenol; *o*-xenol)

OH

M.P. 56° **B.P. 275°**
67.5° cor. ⟨1⟩

With $FeCl_3$ (T 1.41) gives only brownish red turbidity.

For detn. of C̄ via react. of alk. soln. with I_2—KI see ⟨2⟩. C̄ with C_2H_5Br + NaOH in acetone gives (87% yield) *o*-xenyl ethyl ether, m.p. 34° ⟨9⟩.

Ⓓ **o-Xenyl acetate:** from C̄ + AcOH + $POCl_3$ ⟨3⟩ or from C̄ + Ac_2O + fused NaOAc on htg. ⟨4⟩; ndls. from pet. ether, m.p. 62.5–63° ⟨3⟩, 63–63.5° ⟨10⟩.

Ⓓ **o-Xenyl benzoate:** from C̄ + BzOH + $POCl_3$ in toluene; pr. from MeOH, m.p. 75–76° ⟨5⟩.

Ⓓ **o-Xenyl benzenesulfonate:** from C̄ + benzenesulfonyl chloride in pyridine (93% yield); ndls. from dil. alc., m.p. 66–68° ⟨6⟩.

Ⓓ **o-Xenyl p-toluenesulfonate:** from C̄ + *p*-toluenesulfonyl chloride in pyridine (100% yield); ndls. from dil. alc. or lgr., m.p. 64–66° ⟨6⟩.

Ⓓ **3,5-Dinitro-2-hydroxybiphenyl:** C̄ (0.4 g.) dislvd. in AcOH (5 ml.) is treated with conc. HNO_3 (2.5 ml.); after initial reaction ceases, mixt. is htd. a few min. at 100°, poured into aq., filtered, and recrystd. from $CHCl_3$; yield 85%, m.p. 203–204° ⟨7⟩ ⟨8⟩.

1:1440 ⟨1⟩ Mikeska, Bogert, *J. Am. Chem. Soc.* **57,** 2122 (1935). ⟨2⟩ Emery, Fuller, *Ind. Eng. Chem., Anal. Ed.* **7,** 248 (1935). ⟨3⟩ von Auwers, Wittig, *J. prakt. Chem.* (2) **108,** 105 (1924). ⟨4⟩ Hönigschmid, *Monatsh.* **22,** 569 (1901). ⟨5⟩ Harris, Christiansen, *J. Am. Pharm. Assoc.* **24,** 553–557 (1935). ⟨6⟩ Hazlet, *J. Am. Chem. Soc.* **59,** 287 (1937). ⟨7⟩ Borsche, *Ann.* **312,** 226 (1900). ⟨8⟩ Borsche, Scholten, *Ber.* **50,** 602 (1917). ⟨9⟩ Brewster, Putnam, *J. Am. Chem. Soc.* **61,** 3084 (1939). ⟨10⟩ Harris, Pierce, *J. Am. Chem. Soc.* **62,** 2224 (1940).

1:1441 o-CYCLOHEXYLPHENOL $C_{12}H_{16}O$ **Beil. S.N. 534**
(Hexahydro-*o*-hydroxy-biphenyl)

OH
$—C_6H_{11}$

M.P. 56-57°

Cryst. from lgr.

Ⓓ **4,6-Dinitro-2-cyclohexylphenol:** from C̄ in 20 pts. $CHCl_3$ nitrated below 30° with 3 pts. conc. HNO_3 (93% yield) ⟨1⟩ or from C̄ by nitration in dry EtOAc with fumg. HNO_3 + P_2O_5 (65% yield) ⟨2⟩; cryst. from alc., m.p. 106° ⟨1⟩; 106.5–107.5° ⟨2⟩.

1:1441 ⟨1⟩ Baroni, Kleinau, *Monatsh.* **68,** 257 (1936). ⟨2⟩ Bartlett, Garland, *J. Am. Chem. Soc.* **55,** 2066–2067 (1933).

1:1443 n-CAPROYLRESORCINOL $C_{12}H_{16}O_3$ **Beil. S.N. 775**
(2,4-Dihydroxy-l-*n*-caproyl-benzene)

$CH_3.(CH_2)_4.CO.$ —OH
OH

M.P. 56-57° **B.P. 343-345°** dec. at 760 mm.
B.P. 217-218° at 14 mm.

White pl. from mixt. of toluene + pet. ether — Sol. in ord. org. solvents except pet. ether — Crystals turn brown on long exposure to light.

Sol. in aq. alk., Na_2CO_3, borax — Sol. in cold conc. H_2SO_4 and pptd. unchanged on immediate diln.; sulfonates on stdg.

C̄ with $FeCl_3$ (T 1.41) gives red color either in aq. or alc. soln.

C̄ dis. in AcCl with absorption of heat and without evoln. of HCl to give dark red soln. which turns yel. on htg. [Dif. from *n*-hexylresorcinol (1:1465) where evoln. of HCl is immediate ⟨1⟩.]

C̄ poured over with 4 pts. conc. HNO_3 gives (52% yield) mononitro deriv.; pl. from alc., m.p. 73–74°. [Dif. from *n*-hexylresorcinol (1:1465) which is completely destroyed.] ⟨1.⟩

C̄ reduced with amalgamated or mossy zinc + HCl gives (76% yield) *n*-hexylresorcinol (1:1465) ⟨1⟩.

Ⓓ **3-Hydroxy-4-*n*-caproylphenyl *p*-nitrobenzoate:** from C̄ + *p*-nitrobenzoyl chloride + aq. NaOH (56% yield); pale yel. cryst. from alc., m.p. 89–91° ⟨1⟩.

Ⓓ ***n*-Amyl 2,4-dihydroxyphenyl ketoxime:** from C̄ + $NH_2OH.HCl$ + KOAc in abs. alc., (65% yield); cryst. from 50% alc., m.p. 190–191° dec. ⟨1⟩.

1:1443 ⟨1⟩ Twiss, *J. Am. Chem. Soc.* **48,** 2209–2210 (1926).

1:1445 **ORCINOL** (hydrated) (5-Methylresorcinol; 3,5-dihydroxytoluene) $C_7H_{10}O_3$ **Beil. VI-882**

OH

H_3C — $OH.H_2O$

M.P. 56-58°

Cryst. from aq., melting range somewhat variable ⟨1⟩ — Loses aq. on distg. or long drying in vac. over H_2SO_4 — See orcinol (anhydrous) (1:1525).

1:1445 ⟨1⟩ Nevile, Winther, *Ber.* **15,** 2992 (1882).

1:1450 **BENZOYLACETONE** $C_6H_5.CO.CH_2.CO.CH_3$ $C_{10}H_{10}O_2$ **Beil. VII-680**
(1-Phenylbutandione-1,3; methyl phenacyl ketone)

M.P. 60-61° **B.P. 261°**

Pr. of agreeable but penetrating and persistent odor — Dif. sol. cold aq., eas. sol. alc., ether. Eas. sol. aq. NaOH; dif. sol. aq. Na_2CO_3; insol. aq. $NaHCO_3$.

With $FeCl_3$ (T 1.41) C̄ gives intense red color [the solid C̄ contains 98% enol form, the alc. soln. 94%, probably mainly in form $C_6H_5.C(OH){=}CH.CO.CH_3$ ⟨1⟩ ⟨2⟩]. Alc. or ether soln. of C̄, shaken with aq. soln. of $Cu(OAc)_2$ gives alm. quant. ppt. of $Cu(O.C_{10}H_9O)_2$, sol. in $CHCl_3$, pale green cryst. from C_6H_6, m.p. 195–196° ⟨3⟩. [Use in quant. detn. of C̄ ⟨8⟩.] — C̄ with $I_2{\cdot}KI$ soln. + alk. yields CHI_3 (T 1.81).

C̄ with 1 mole phenylhydrazine in dry ether 2–3 hrs. at room temp. gives benzoylacetone phenylhydrazone, m.p. varying acc. to rate of htg. 150–153° ⟨4⟩; but on further htg. or treatment with acids ring closure occurs yielding 1,5-diphenyl-3-methylpyrazole ⟨4⟩ ⟨5⟩.

Ⓓ **Hydrolysis:** Alk. hydrolysis (T 1.51) yields acetophenone (1:5515) and acetic ac. (1:1010).

Ⓓ ***N*-(*p*-Nitrophenyl-3 (or 5)-methyl-5 (or 3)-phenylpyrazole):** from C̄ by boiling with equal wt. *p*-nitrophenylhydrazine.HCl in aq. alc. for two hrs.; ndls. from MeOH, m.p. 100–101° ⟨4⟩ ⟨6⟩.

Ⓓ ***N*-(2,4-Dinitrophenyl-3 (or 5)-methyl-5 (or 3)-phenylpyrazole:** from C̄ + 2,4-dinitrophenylhydrazine in 2 *N* HCl; pale yel. lfts. from alc., m.p. 151° ⟨7⟩.

1:1450 ⟨1⟩ Meyer, *Ann.* **380,** 242 (1911), *Ber.* **45,** 2846 (1912). ⟨2⟩ Scheiber, Herold, *Ann.* **405,** 318 (1914). ⟨3⟩ Wislicenus, Stoeber, *Ber.* **35,** 545 (1902). ⟨4⟩ von Auwers, Stuhlmann, *Ber.* **59,** 1053–1054 (1926). ⟨5⟩ Drumm, *Proc. Roy. Irish Acad.* **40B,** 106–108 (1931); *Chem. Abs.* **26,** 452 (1932). ⟨6⟩ Reilly, Daly, Drumm, *Proc. Roy. Irish Acad.* **40B,** 94–101 (1931); *Chem. Abs.* **26,** 452 (1932). ⟨7⟩ Brady, *J. Chem. Soc.* **1931,** 759. ⟨8⟩ Hieber, *Ber.* **54,** 909 (1921).

1:1452 p-sec-BUTYLPHENOL $C_{10}H_{14}O$ **Beil. VI-522**

$CH_3.CH_2.CH(CH_3)$—C_6H_4—OH

M.P. 61-62° ⟨1⟩ **B.P. 240-242° ⟨1⟩** D^{25}_{25} = **0.9659 ⟨2⟩** n^{25}_{D} = **1.5150 ⟨2⟩**

Cryst. from lgr. or dil. alc. — Insol. aq.; sol. alc., ether. Volatile with steam.

With $FeCl_3$ (T 1.41) gives no coloration — Pract. insol. in 4% aq. NaOH, but sol. in 40% KOH or in Claisen soln. ⟨3⟩.

The acetate and benzoate of C̄ both are oils.

1:1452 ⟨1⟩ Read, Miller, *J. Am. Chem. Soc.* **54,** 1196 (1932). ⟨2⟩ Croxall, Sowa, Nieuwland, *J. Org. Chem.* **2,** 254 (1937). ⟨3⟩ Sprung, Wallis, *J. Am. Chem. Soc.* **56,** 1718 (1934).

1:1453 3,4-DIMETHYLPHENOL (*unsym.-o*-Xylenol; 1,2,4-xylenol; 4-hydroxy-1,2-dimethylbenzene) $C_8H_{10}O$ **Beil. VI-480**

M.P. 62.5° **B.P. 225°**

[Must not be confused with "*sym.*-xylenol" (3-5-dimethylphenol) (1:1455).]

Ndls. from aq., rhombic octahedra from alc.

C̄ with $FeCl_3$ (T 1.41) gives green color either in aq. or alc.

C̄ fused with equiv. amt. PkOH yields chrome yel. mol. cpd., C̄.PkOH, which can be recrystd. from alc., m.p. 83.8° ⟨1⟩.

Ⓓ **3,4-Dimethylphenyl benzoate:** from C̄ + BzCl + dil. aq. alk., m.p. 58.5° ⟨2⟩.

Ⓓ **3,4-Dimethylphenyl 3,5-dinitrobenzoate:** rods or ndls. from alc., m.p. 181.6° ⟨3⟩ [cf. T 1.47].

Ⓓ **3,4-Dimethylphenoxyacetic acid:** from C̄ + chloroacetic acid + 25% NaOH htd. 2 hrs., ndls. from C_6H_6, pl. from alc. + acetone, m.p. 162.5° ⟨4⟩; Neut. Eq. 180 [cf. T 1.46].

Ⓓ **3,4-Dimethylphenyl N-phenylcarbamate:** from C̄ htd. with sl. excess of $C_6H_5.N{=}C{=}O$ in high boilg. pet. (b.p. 170–200°) for ½ hr.; cryst. from dil. alc., m.p. 120° ⟨5⟩.

Ⓓ **3,4-Dimethylphenyl N-α-naphthylcarbamate:** from C̄ + α-naphthylisocyanate + trace of trimethylamine, boiled for a few moments; cryst. from lgr., m.p. **141–142°** ⟨6⟩ [cf. T 1.45].

Ⓓ **3,4-Dimethylphenyl N-(p-xenyl)carbamate:** cryst. from alc., C_6H_6, or C_6H_6 + lgr., m.p. 183° ⟨7⟩.

1:1453 ⟨1⟩ Baril, Hauber, *J. Am. Chem. Soc.* **53,** 1090 (1931). ⟨2⟩ Béhal, Choay, *Bull. soc. chim.* (3) **11,** 603 (1894). ⟨3⟩ Phillips, Keenan, *J. Am. Chem. Soc.* **53,** 1926 (1931). ⟨4⟩ Gluud, Breuer, *Cent.* **1919,** I, 626. ⟨5⟩ Steinkopf, Höpner, *J. prakt. Chem.* (2) **113,** 150–151 (1926). ⟨6⟩ French, Wirtel, *J. Am. Chem. Soc.* **48,** 1738 (1926). ⟨7⟩ Morgan, Pettet, *J. Chem. Soc.* **1931,** 1125.

1:1455 3,5-DIMETHYLPHENOL (*sym.-m*-Xylenol; *m*-5-xylenol; 5-hydroxy-1,3-dimethylbenzene) $C_8H_{10}O$ **Beil. VI-492**

M.P. 63.2° ⟨1⟩ **B.P. 220.2° ⟨1⟩**
68° ⟨2⟩

[Must not be confused with " *unsym.-o*-xylenol " (3,4-dimethylphenol) (1:1453).]

Ndls. from aq. — Subl. — Volatile with steam — For data + bibliography see ⟨1⟩.

C̄ with $FeCl_3$ (T 1.41) gives no coloration — C̄ on treatment of aq. ⟨3⟩ or AcOH ⟨4⟩ soln. with 3 moles Br_2 yields 2,4,6-tribromo-3,5-dimethylphenol, ndls. from CCl_4, m.p. 166° ⟨4⟩.

Ⓓ **3,5-Dimethylphenyl benzoate:** from C̄ + BzCl + dil. aq. alk., m.p. 24° ⟨5⟩.

Ⓓ **3,5-Dimethylphenyl 3,5-dinitrobenzoate:** from C̄ + 3,5-dinitrobenzoyl chloride in pyridine, rods from alc., m.p. 195.4° cor. ⟨6⟩ [cf. T 1.47].

Ⓓ **3,5-Dimethylphenyl *p*-toluenesulfonate:** from C̄ + *p*-toluenesulfonyl chloride in pyridine (87.5% yield) flat ndls. from AcOH, m.p. 83° ⟨2⟩.

Ⓓ **3,5-Dimethylphenoxyacetic acid:** from C̄ + alk. + chloroacetic acid; cryst. from aq. as monohydrate, m.p. 81° ⟨7⟩; on stdg. over P_2O_5 in vac. desic. for few days yields anhydrous form, m.p. 111° ⟨7⟩; Neut. Eq. 180 [cf. T 1.46].

Ⓓ **3,5-Dimethylphenyl *N*-phenylcarbamate:** m.p. 148° ⟨8⟩ ⟨9⟩.

Ⓓ **3,5-Dimethylphenyl *N*-(*p*-xenyl)carbamate:** cryst. from alc., C_6H_6, or C_6H_6 + lgr., m.p. 150° ⟨9⟩.

1:1455 ⟨1⟩ Kester, *Ind. Eng. Chem.* **24,** 770–771 (1932). ⟨2⟩ Rowe, Bannister, Seth, Storey, *J. Soc. Chem. Ind.*, **49T,** 471 (1930). ⟨3⟩ Nölting, Forel, *Ber.* **18,** 2679 (1885). ⟨4⟩ Raiford, Scott, *J. Org. Chem.* **2,** 216 (1937). ⟨5⟩ Béhal, Choay, *Bull. soc. chim.* (3) **11,** 603 (1894). ⟨6⟩ Phillips, Keenan, *J. Am. Chem. Soc.* **53,** 1926 (1931). ⟨7⟩ Albright, *J. Am. Chem. Soc.* **55,** 1736 (1933). ⟨8⟩ Carlinfanti, Germain, *Rend. Accad. Lincei* [5] **19,** II, 237 (1910). ⟨9⟩ Morgan, Pettet, *J. Chem. Soc.* **1931,** 1125.

1:1459 1-ACETO-2-NAPHTHOL $C_{12}H_{10}O_2$ Beil. S.N. 751

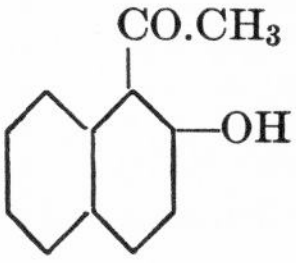

M.P. 64°

Rhomb. pr. from lgr.; ndls. or tbls. (often pale yellow) from gasoline — Volatile with steam.

C̄ readily sol. in aq. alk. or conc. H_2SO_4 yielding intensely yellow solns.

C̄ in dil. aq. alk. undergoes autoxidation in air giving definite but complex products; for structures see ⟨1⟩.

Ⓓ **1-Acetyl-2-naphthyl benzoate:** from C̄ + BzCl in pyridine, colorless pl., m.p. 85–86° ⟨2⟩.

Ⓓ **1-Acetyl-2-naphthoxyacetic acid:** from C̄ + dil. aq. NaOH + chloroacetic acid refluxed for 2 hrs.; white lfts. from C_6H_6, m.p. 145° ⟨3⟩ [cf. T 1.46].

1:1459 ⟨1⟩ Fries, Ehlers, *Ber.* **56,** 1304–1308 (1923). ⟨2⟩ Bhalla, Mahal, Venkataraman, *J. Chem. Soc.* **1935,** 870. ⟨3⟩ Fries, *Ber.* **54,** 714 (1921).

1:1460 3,4-DIHYDROXYTOLUENE $C_7H_8O_2$ Beil. VI-878

(4-Methylpyrocatechol; homopyrocatechol)

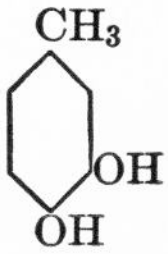

M.P. 65° **B.P. 251-252°**

Pr. from C_6H_6 or lfts. from C_6H_6 + lgr. — Eas. sol. aq.; sol. alc., ether; spar. sol. lgr. — Sublimable.

C̄ in alc. gives with $FeCl_3$ (T 1.41) a green color, becoming red on addn. of NH_4OH —C̄ as solid is stable in air but alk. soln. turns red or brown in air — C̄ reduces $AgNO_3$ soln. or Fehling's soln. (T 1.22) even in cold.

- Ⓓ **4-Methylpyrocatechol diacetate:** from C̄ + Ac_2O + NaOAc htd. 4 hrs. at 140–150°, cryst. from alc., m.p. 57–58° ⟨3⟩.
- Ⓓ **4-Methylpyrocatechol dibenzoate:** from C̄ htd. with BzCl; m.p. 58° ⟨1⟩.
- Ⓓ **3,4-Dihydroxytoluene bis-[*N*-phenylcarbamate]:** m.p. 166° ⟨2⟩.
- Ⓓ **3,4-Dihydroxytoluene bis-[(*N-p*-xenyl)carbamate]:** from C̄ + *p*-xenylisocyanate in pyridine; m.p. 193° ⟨2⟩.

1:1460 ⟨1⟩ Cousin, *Ann. chim.* (7) **13,** 529 (1898). ⟨2⟩ Morgan, Pettet, *J. Chem. Soc.* **1931,** 1125. ⟨3⟩ Ono, Imoto, *Bull. Chem. Soc. Japan* **11,** 131 (1936).

1:1461 HYDROQUINONE MONOETHYL ETHER $C_8H_{10}O_2$ Beil. VI-843

(*p*-Ethoxyphenol; *p*-hydroxyphenetole) $C_2H_5O.C_6H_4.OH$

M.P. 66° **B.P. 247°**

Lfts. from aq. — Fairly eas. sol. cold aq.; eas. sol. hot aq., alc., ether.

1:1465 *n*-HEXYLRESORCINOL $C_{12}H_{18}O_2$ Beil. S.N. 557

(2,4-Dihydroxy-1-*n*-hexylbenzene; "caprokol," "alkorcin")

$CH_3.(CH_2)_4.CH_2.C_6H_3(OH)_2$ [ring structure: hexyl chain on ring, OH para and ortho]

M.P. 67.5-69.0° **B.P. 333-335°** sl. dec. at 760 mm.
198-200° at 13–14 mm.

White ndls. from C_6H_6, pl. from lgr. turning brown on long exposure to light — Dif. sol. in aq. (0.05% at 18°) — Sol. alc., ether, $CHCl_3$, acetone; spar. sol. pet. ether.

Sol. in aq. alk., Na_2CO_3 or borax — Sol. in cold concd. H_2SO_4 and repptd. unchanged on immediate diln.; sulfonates on stdg. ⟨1⟩.

C̄ in alc. soln. gives with $FeCl_3$ (T 1.41) greenish yel. color ⟨1⟩.

Attempts to prepare from C̄ the benzoate, *p*-nitrobenzoate, or 3,5-dinitrobenzoate derivatives gave only non-crystallizable or tarry products ⟨1⟩.

C̄ is completely destroyed by conc. HNO_3 [dif. from *n*-caproylresorcinol (1:1443)] which gives mononitro deriv. ⟨1⟩.

For detn. of C̄ see ⟨2⟩. [For survey of color tests differentiating C̄ from resorcinol (1:1530) see ⟨3⟩.]

1:1465 ⟨1⟩ Twiss, *J. Am. Chem. Soc.* **48,** 2207–2211 (1926). ⟨2⟩ Robbins, Wesson, *J. Pharmacol.* **43,** 335–337 (1931). ⟨3⟩ Revillon, *Bull. soc. chim. biol.* **16,** 305–306 (1934).

1:1466 RESORCINOL MONOBENZYL ETHER $C_{13}H_{12}O_2$ Beil. S.N. 554

(Benzyl *m*-hydroxyphenyl ether)

$C_6H_5—CH_2—O—C_6H_4—OH$ [ring structure]

M.P. 69.2° ⟨1⟩ **B.P. 200°** at 5 mm. ⟨1⟩

Cryst. from CCl_4 — For prepn. see ⟨1⟩ — Gives faint green color with $FeCl_3$ ⟨2⟩.

Sol. in 5% aq. KOH [dif. and sepn. from resorcinol dibenzyl ether, m.p. 73–74°].

1:1466 ⟨1⟩ Klarmann, Gatyas, Shternov, *J. Am. Chem. Soc.* **53,** 3404–3405 (1931). ⟨2⟩ Druey, *Bull. soc. chim.* (5) **2,** 1740 (1935).

1:1467 MESITOL (2,4,6-Trimethylphenol; hydroxymesitylene) $C_9H_{12}O$ **Beil. VI-518**

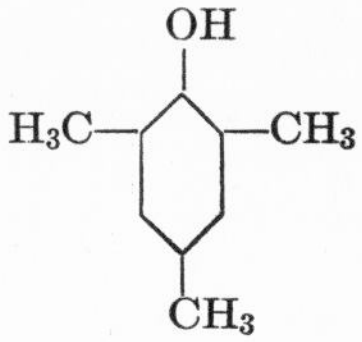

OH; H_3C—; —CH_3; CH_3

M.P. 70° **B.P. 220°**

Sublimes in ndls. even below m.p. — Eas. volatile with steam — Spar. sol. aq., eas. sol. alc., ether — Sol. in caustic alk. but largely extracted from alk. solns. by org. solv.; insol. NH_4OH or alk. carbonates.

C̄ gives no color with $FeCl_3$ (T 1.41) either in aq. or in alc. soln.

Ⓓ **Mesityl benzoate:** from C̄ + BzCl + aq. alk. (cf. T 2.26-B); cryst. from pet. ether, m.p. 61.5–62.5° ⟨1⟩.

Ⓓ **Mesitoxyacetic acid:** m.p. 139.5° ⟨2⟩; Neut. Eq. 194 [cf. T 1.46].

Ⓓ **Mesityl *N*-phenylcarbamate:** ndls. from lgr., m.p. 141–142° ⟨3⟩.

1:1467 ⟨1⟩ von Auwers, Mauss, *Ann.* **464,** 306 Note (1928). ⟨2⟩ Steinkopf, Höpner, *J. prakt. Chem.* (2) **113,** 154 (1926). ⟨3⟩ Hey, *J. Chem. Soc.* **1931,** 1590.

1:1468 METHYL *m*-HYDROXYBENZOATE $C_8H_8O_3$ **Beil. X-139**

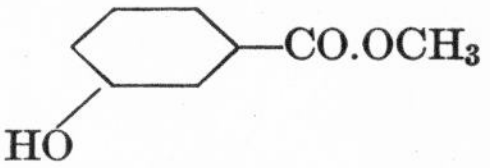

—CO.OCH$_3$; HO

M.P. 70° **B.P. 280°**

Ndls. from C_6H_6 + pet. ether.

Ⓓ **Saponification:** C̄ on alk. hydrolysis (T 1.51) gives Sap. Eq. 152 and yields *m*-hydroxybenzoic acid (1:0825) and methyl alc. (1:6120).

Ⓓ ***m*-Carbomethoxyphenyl *N*-phenylcarbamate:** from C̄ in dry ether + equiv. phenylisocyanate, stood 20 hrs. at room temp., cryst. from C_6H_6, m.p. 115–116° ⟨1⟩.

1:1468 ⟨1⟩ Michael, Cobb, *Ann.* **363,** 88–89 (1908).

1:1469 PSEUDOCUMENOL (2,4,5-Trimethylphenol) $C_9H_{12}O$ **Beil. VI-509**

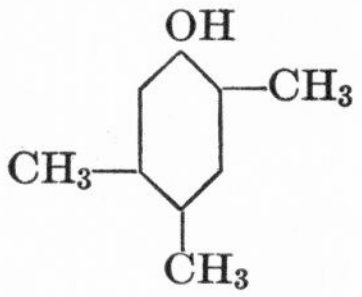

OH; —CH_3; CH_3—; CH_3

M.P. 71° **B.P. 232°**

Ndls. from aq. — Insol. cold aq.; sol. alc., ether.

Ⓓ ***s*-Pseudocumyl acetate:** ndls. from pet. ether, m.p. 34–34.5° ⟨1⟩.

Ⓓ ***s*-Pseudocumyl benzoate:** from C̄ by warming with BzCl, cryst. from alc., m.p. 63° ⟨2⟩.

Ⓓ **2,4,5-Trimethylphenoxyacetic acid:** m.p. 132° ⟨3⟩; Neut. Eq. 194 [cf. T 1.46].

Ⓓ ***s*-Pseudocumyl *N*-phenylcarbamate:** m.p. 110° ⟨4⟩.

Ⓓ ***s*-Pseudocumyl *N*-*p*-xenylcarbamate:** m.p. 196° ⟨4⟩.

1:1469 ⟨1⟩ von Auwers, Bundesmann, Wieners, *Ann.* **447,** 183 (1926). ⟨2⟩ Stohman, Rodatz, Herzberg, *J. prakt. Chem.* (2) **36,** 8 (1887). ⟨3⟩ Steinkopf, Höpner, *J. prakt. Chem.* (2) **113,** 154 (1926). ⟨4⟩ Morgan, Pettet, *J. Chem. Soc.* **1931,** 1125.

—— **PHTHALIDE** $C_8H_6O_2$ **Beil. XVII-310**

M.P. 73° (stable form) **B.P. 290°** cor.
66° (unstable form)

See 1:4920. Genus 6: Anhydrides, etc.

1:1471 ETHYL *m*-HYDROXYBENZOATE $C_9H_{10}O_3$ **Beil. X-139**

M.P. 73.8° ⟨1⟩ **B.P. 295°** (282°)

Tbls. from aq. or ether, lfts. from C_6H_6 — Very sol. alc., ether; spar. sol. aq.—$\bar{C}$ with $FeCl_3$ (T 1.41) gives violet color.

Ⓓ **Saponification:** Hydrolysis with aq. alk. (T 1.51) gives Sap. Eq. of 166 and yields *m*-hydroxybenzoic acid (1:0825) and ethyl alcohol (1:6130).

Ⓓ **Ethyl *m*-acetoxybenzoate:** m.p. 35°. [Has been reported only indirectly via actn. of ketene on $\bar{C}$ ⟨2⟩.]

Ⓓ **Ethyl *m*-benzoxybenzoate:** from $\bar{C}$ or its K deriv. + BzCl + $AlCl_3$; ndls. from alc., m.p. 58° ⟨3⟩. [$\bar{C}$ cannot be benzoylated by Schotten-Baumann reaction (T 2.25-B) because of its rapid hydrolysis with aq. alk. ⟨4⟩.]

Ⓓ ***m*-Hydroxybenzamide:** from $\bar{C}$ by shaking with conc. aq. NH_4OH ⟨5⟩; lfts. from aq., m.p. 170.5° cor.

1:1471 ⟨1⟩ Kohlrausch, Stockmair, *Monatsh.* **66,** 324 (1935). ⟨2⟩ van Alphen, *Rec. trav. chim.* **44,** 839 (1925). ⟨3⟩ Limpricht, *Ann.* **290,** 170 (1896). ⟨4⟩ Lassar-Cohn, Löwenstein, *Ber.* **41,** 3364 (1908). ⟨5⟩ Schulerud, *J. prakt. Chem.* (2) **22,** 290 (1880).

1:1473 2,5-DIMETHYLPHENOL $C_8H_{10}O$ **Beil. VI-494**
(*p*-Xylenol; 1,4,2-xylenol; 2-hydroxy-1,4-dimethylbenzene)

M.P. 74.5° **B.P. 212°**

Pr. from alc. — Volatile with steam.
$\bar{C}$ with $FeCl_3$ (T 1.41) gives no color with $FeCl_3$; only sl. sol. in conc. NaOH.
$\bar{C}$ fused with equiv. amt. PkOH yields orange mol. cpd., $\bar{C}$ PkOH, m.p. 81–82° ⟨1⟩.

Ⓓ **2,5-Dimethylphenyl benzoate:** from $\bar{C}$ + BzCl + dil. aq. alk.; m.p. 61° ⟨2⟩.

Ⓓ **2,5-Dimethylphenyl *p*-nitrobenzoate:** m.p. 87°.

Ⓓ **2,5-Dimethylphenyl 3,5-dinitrobenzoate:** cryst. from alc., m.p. 137.2° cor. ⟨3⟩ [cf. T 1.47].

Ⓓ **2,5-Dimethylphenoxyacetic acid:** from $\bar{C}$ + chloroacetic ac. + 25% NaOH htd. for 2 hrs. (37.5% yield), ndls. from lgr., m.p. 118° ⟨4⟩ [cf. T 1.46].

Ⓓ **2,5-Dimethylphenyl *N*-phenylcarbamate:** from $\bar{C}$ + equiv. $C_6H_5.N{:}C{:}O$ in C_6H_6 htd. in s.t. at 100°; cryst. from C_6H_6, m.p. 160–161° ⟨5⟩.

Ⓓ **2,5-Dimethylphenyl** ***N*-(α-naphthyl)carbamate:** from C̄ + α-naphthylisocyanate + trace trimethylamine boiled for a few moments; cryst. from lgr., m.p. 172–173° ⟨6⟩ [cf. T 1.45].

Ⓓ **2,5-Dimethylphenyl** ***N*-(*p*-xenyl)carbamate:** cryst. from alc., C_6H_6, or C_6H_6 + lgr., m.p. 162° ⟨7⟩.

1:1473 ⟨1⟩ Baril, Hauber, *J. Am. Chem. Soc.* **53,** 1090 (1931). ⟨2⟩ Béhal, Choay, *Bull. soc. chim.* (3) **11,** 603 (1894). ⟨3⟩ Phillips, Keenan, *J. Am. Chem. Soc.* **53,** 1926 (1931). ⟨4⟩ Gluud, Breuer, *Cent.* **1919,** I, 626. ⟨5⟩ von Auwers, *Ber.* **32,** 19 (1899). ⟨6⟩ French, Wirtel, *J. Am. Chem. Soc.* **48,** 1738 (1926). ⟨7⟩ Morgan, Pettet, *J. Chem. Soc.* **1931,** 1125.

—— **PROTOCATECHUALDEHYDE 3-ETHYL ETHER** $C_9H_{10}O_5$ **Beil. VIII-256**
(" Bourbonal "; " Ethylvanillin ")

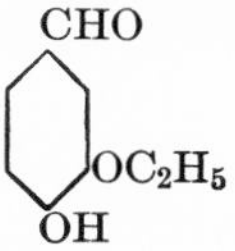

CHO / OC_2H_5 / OH

M.P. 77°

See 1:0045. Genus 1: Aldehydes.

1:1475 3-HYDROXYBIPHENYL $C_{12}H_{10}O$ **Beil. VI-673**
(*m*-Phenylphenol; *m*-xenol)

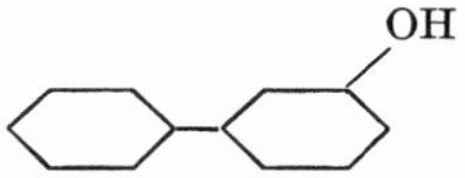

OH

M.P. 78° **B.P. > 300°**

Ndls. from aq. or pet. ether — Spar. sol. even in hot aq.; volatile with steam — Sol. alc., C_6H_6, ether, $CHCl_3$, AcOH — Sol. in aq. alk. and warm alkali carbonate solns.
With $FeCl_3$ (T 1.41) aq. soln. gives no color.

Ⓓ ***m*-Xenyl benzoate:** from C̄ + BzCl + aq. alk., cryst. from alc., m.p. 60–61° ⟨1⟩ m.p. 57–58° ⟨2⟩.

Ⓓ ***m*-Xenyl, 2,4-dinitrophenyl ether:** from C̄ + 2,4-dinitrochlorobenzene + KOH + pyridine (90% yield), m.p. 100° ⟨3⟩.

Ⓓ ***m*-Xenyl 2,4,6-trinitrophenyl ether (*m*-xenyl picryl ether):** from C̄ + picryl chloride + KOH (92% yield), m.p. 143° ⟨3⟩.

1:1475 ⟨1⟩ Errera, La Spada, *Gazz. chim. ital.* **35,** II, 553 (1905). ⟨2⟩ Harris, Christiansen, *J. Am. Pharm. Assoc.* **24,** 553–557 (1935). ⟨3⟩ Colbert, Meigs, Jenkins, *J. Am. Chem. Soc.* **59,** 1123–1124 (1937).

1:1480 DIBENZOYLMETHANE $C_{15}H_{12}O_2$ **Beil. VII-769**
(ω-Benzoylacetophenone, phenyl phenacyl ketone, β-hydroxychalcone)

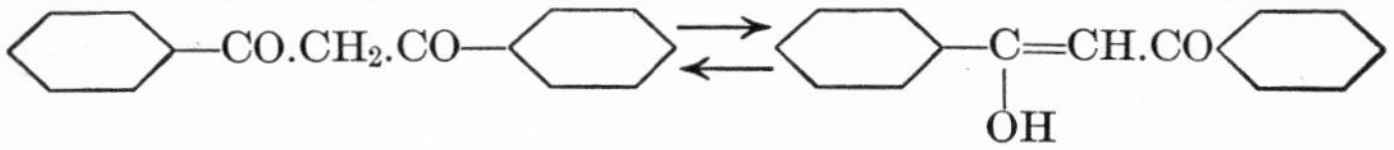

—$CO.CH_2.CO$— ⇄ —C=CH.CO / OH

M.P. 78°

C̄ exists in 4 isomeric forms ⟨1⟩ ⟨2⟩ ⟨3⟩, the common one m.p. 77–78° — Cryst. from alc., MeOH, ether or pet. ether almost always in tbls.; rarely in pr. — Slow recrystn. from alc. gave large prisms, m.p. 78°; rapid crystn. from more concd. solns. gave ndls., m.p. 71° ⟨4⟩; latter changes over to the 78° form on standing overnight ⟨5⟩.

Solid C̄ is alm. entirely in enol form ⟨6⟩ ⟨7⟩ ⟨8⟩ — Very eas. sol. in aq. NaOH but insol. in aq. Na_2CO_3 — C̄ in alc. gives with $FeCl_3$ (T 1.41) intense red-violet color — C̄ in ether soln. shaken with satd. aq. $Cu(OAc)_2$ yields quant. $Cu(OC_{15}H_{11})_2$ ⟨9⟩, green ndls. from C_6H_6, m.p. 325° dec. ⟨10⟩; from this copper salt of the enol C̄ can be recovered by acidification and ether extn. ⟨5⟩.

[For prepn. of C̄ from benzalacetophenone dibromide + NaOMe (74–81% yield) see ⟨5⟩.]

Ⓓ **Alkali cleavage:** C̄ boiled with 50% aq. KOH yields in distillate acetophenone (1:5515) and in residual liq., salt of benzoic acid (1:0715) ⟨11⟩ ⟨13⟩.

Ⓓ **Dibenzoyl-dibromo-methane:** from C̄ + 2 moles Br_2 in 93% yield; pr. from ether, m.p. 94–95° ⟨12⟩ ⟨13⟩. [With 1 mole Br_2 in $CHCl_3$ or CS_2 C̄ yields dibenzoyl monobromomethane, m.p. 92–93° ⟨12⟩.]

Ⓓ **3,5-Diphenylisoxazole** [Beil. XXVII-77]:

```
HC════C—C6H5
 ‖       ‖
C6H5—C     N
     \   /
       O
```

from C̄ with NH_2OH. HCl in boilg. alc., tbls. from alc., m.p. 140.5–141° ⟨14⟩. [With free NH_2OH (not hydrochloride) 75% yield of a true monoxime, m.p. 165°, can be obtd. ⟨14⟩.]

Ⓓ **1,3,5-Triphenylpyrazole** [Beil. XXIII-254]:

```
     HC════C—C6H5
      ‖      ‖
C6H5—C       N
      \    /
        N
        |
       C6H5
```

from C̄ + phenylhydrazine in AcOH in alm. 100% yield on stdg. 2 days at room temp. ⟨15⟩, or from C̄ + phenylhydrazine on warming in alc. ⟨16⟩, cryst. m.p. 137° ⟨13⟩.

1:1480 ⟨1⟩ Dufraisse, Gillett, *Ann. chim.* (10) **6,** 311 (1926). ⟨2⟩ Weygand, *Ber.* **60,** 2428–2432 (1927). ⟨3⟩ Weygand, Bauer, Hennig, *Ber.* **62,** 562–573 (1929). ⟨4⟩ Morton, Hassan, Calloway, *J. Chem. Soc.* **1934,** 891. ⟨5⟩ Allen, Abell, Normington, *Organic Syntheses, Coll. Vol.* I, 199–201 (1932). ⟨6⟩ Meyer, *Ann.* **380,** 242 (1911). ⟨7⟩ Meyer, *Ber.* **45,** 2846, 2859 (1912). ⟨8⟩ Scheiber, Herold, *Ann.* **405,** 323 (1914). ⟨9⟩ Wislicenus, *Ann.* **308,** 231 (1898). ⟨10⟩ André, *Ann. chim.* (8) **29,** 582 (1913).

⟨11⟩ Ref. 9, page 246. ⟨12⟩ Ref. 9, pages 247–248. ⟨13⟩ Magnani, McElvain, *J. Am. Chem. Soc.* **60,** 818 (1938). ⟨14⟩ Ref. 9, pages 248–253. ⟨15⟩ Ref. 9, pages 253–254. ⟨16⟩ Knorr, Laubmann, *Ber.* **21,** 1206 (1888).

1:1481 ISODURENOL (2,3,4,6-Tetramethylphenol) $C_{10}H_{14}O$ Beil. VI-546

```
         OH
   H3C /  \ CH3
      |    |
       \  / CH3
        CH3
```

M.P. 79-81° **B.P. 230-250°**

Cryst. from lt. pet.

C̄ in AcOH, treated with Br_2 at room temp., gives bromoisodurenol, long white ndls. from aq. alc., m.p. 135° ⟨1⟩.

Ⓓ **2,3,4,6-Tetramethylphenyl benzoate** (**isodurenyl benzoate**)**:** from C̄ + BzCl + aq. alk.; white pl. from aq. alc., m.p. 71–72° ⟨1⟩.

Ⓓ **2,3,4,6-Tetramethylphenyl *N*-phenylcarbamate:** from C̄ (slight excess) htd. with phenyl isocyanate at 90–100° for 3–4 hrs.; white pr. from aq. alc., m.p. 178–179° ⟨1⟩.

1:1481 ⟨1⟩ Hey, *J. Chem. Soc.* **1931,** 1590.

—— **VANILLIN** (4-Hydroxy-3-methoxybenzaldehyde; protocatechualdehyde 3-methyl ether) CHO / OCH$_3$ / OH $C_8H_8O_2$ **Beil. VIII-247**

M.P. 80-81° **B.P. 285°**

See 1:0050. Genus 1: Aldehydes.

1:1485 *p*-BENZYLPHENOL $C_{13}H_{12}O$ **Beil. VI-675**

p-Hydroxydiphenyl-(methane) $C_6H_5.CH_2$—⬡—OH

M.P. 84° **B.P. 321°** (308°)

Cryst. from alc., pet. ether, or C_6H_6 + pet. ether — Sol. alc., ether, $CHCl_3$, C_6H_6, AcOH — Moderately sol. hot aq.

With $FeCl_3$ (T 1.41) aq. soln. gives no color, but $\bar{C}$ is sol. in caustic alk.

$\bar{C}$ on methylation yields *p*-benzylphenol methyl ether, m.p. 20–21°, which on oxidn. with $Na_2Cr_2O_7$ + H_2SO_4 gives *p*-methoxybenzophenone (1:5170), cryst. from lt. pet., m.p. 61–62° ⟨1⟩.

Ⓓ ***p*-Benzylphenyl benzoate:** from $\bar{C}$ + Bz_2O at 180°; ndls. from pet., m.p. 87° ⟨2⟩. [Requires mixed m.p. to distinguish from $\bar{C}$.]

Ⓓ ***p*-Benzylphenyl benzyl ether:** from $\bar{C}$ + benzyl chloride + alc. NaOEt 3 hrs. at 100°; ndls. from alc., m.p. 49.5° ⟨1⟩.

1:1485 ⟨1⟩ Short, Stewart, *J. Chem. Soc.* **1929,** 556–557. ⟨2⟩ Zincke, Walter, *Ann.* **334,** 373 (1904).

1:1490 *o*-HYDROXYBENZYL ALCOHOL $C_7H_8O_2$ **Beil. VI-891**

(Saligenin; salicyl alcohol) ⬡ —CH_2OH / —OH

M.P. 86-87°

Rhomb. tbls. or ndls. from aq.; tbls. from ether — Sol. in 15 pts. aq. at 22°, very sol. hot aq., alc., ether — Subl. easily in lfts.; resinified on htg. above 100°.

$\bar{C}$ in 0.5% alc. soln. gives with $FeCl_3$ (T 1.41) an RV color, soon changing to YO-T_2 — With conc. H_2SO_4, $\bar{C}$ gives red color (RT_1—VR-T_1).

$\bar{C}$ htd. with powd. KOH at 200–240° yields H_2 gas (93% theory) and salicylic acid (1:0780) (88% theory) ⟨1⟩ — $\bar{C}$ htd. with phenylhydrazine at 160° for 5–10 min. yields salicylaldehyde phenylhydrazone, m.p. 142–143° ⟨2⟩ — $\bar{C}$ htd. 30–45 min. with phenacyl bromide + K_2CO_3 in acetone gives (50% yield) phenacylsaligenin, pr. from MeOH + aq., m.p. 86–87° ⟨9⟩.

$\bar{C}$ under protracted action of excess Br_2-aq. gives (96–97% yield) 2,4,6-tribromophenol bromide, m.p. 133°, which after washing with $NaHSO_3$ soln. is converted to 2,4,6-tribromophenol, m.p. 93° ⟨3⟩.

[For prepn. of $\bar{C}$ by reductn. of salicylaldehyde (1:0205) with Na—Hg (70% yield) see ⟨4⟩ — For detn. and sepn. of $\bar{C}$, salicylic acid, and salicyaldehyde see ⟨5⟩.]

Ⓓ ***o*-Benzoxybenzyl benzoate (saligenin dibenzoate):** from $\bar{C}$ + BzCl + $CaCO_3$ in pyridine (67% yield); cryst. from 70% alc., m.p. 51° ⟨6⟩.

Ⓓ ***o*-Hydroxymethylphenoxyacetic acid:** from $\bar{C}$ + chloroacetic acid + aq. NaOH; tbls. from aq., m.p. 120° ⟨7⟩.

Ⓓ ***N*-(*o*-Hydroxybenzyl)aniline:** from C̄ in quant. yield on boilg. with 5 pts. aniline for 10 min.; pouring into dilute acetic acid; lfts. from dil. alc., m.p. 108° ⟨8⟩.

1:1490 ⟨1⟩ Lock, *Ber.* **63,** 557 (1930). ⟨2⟩ Oddo, Giacolone, *Gazz. chim. ital.* **58,** 298–300 (1928). ⟨3⟩ Autenrieth, Beuttel, *Arch. Pharm.* **248,** 122 (1910); cf. Wieland, *Ber.* **47,** 2093 (1914). ⟨4⟩ Lapworth, Shoesmith, *J. Chem. Soc.* **121,** 1396 (1922). ⟨5⟩ Berg, Grimmer, Müller, *Chem. Ztg.* **55,** 975 (1931). ⟨6⟩ Hart, Hirschfelder, *J. Am. Chem. Soc.* **43,** 1691 (1921). ⟨7⟩ Biginelli, *Gazz. chim. ital.* **21,** I, 257 (1891). ⟨8⟩ Paal, Senniger, *Ber.* **27,** 1802 (1894). ⟨9⟩ Freudenberg, Fikentscher, Harder, *Ann.* **441,** 176 (1924).

1:1495 *p-ter*-AMYLPHENOL

$CH_3.CH_2—C(CH_3)_2—C_6H_4—OH$

$C_{11}H_{16}O$ **Beil. VI-548**

M.P. 93° (95°) **B.P. 260-265°**

Ndls. from aq. or pet. ether — Sol. alc., ether.

With $FeCl_3$ (T 1.41) gives only rusty ppt., but C̄ is eas. sol. in dil. alk.

Ⓓ ***p-ter*-Amylphenyl benzoate:** m.p. 60–61° ⟨1⟩.

Ⓓ ***p-ter*-Amylphenyl *p*-toluenesulfonate:** m.p. 54–55° ⟨1⟩.

1:1495 ⟨1⟩ Huston, Hsieh, *J. Am. Chem. Soc.* **58,** 440–441 (1936).

1:1500 α-NAPHTHOL

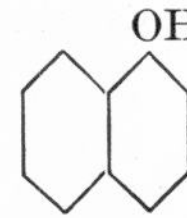

$C_{10}H_8O$ **Beil. VI-596**

M.P. 94° **B.P. 278-280°**

Phenolic odor — Sparingly volatile with steam — Insol. cold aq.; spar. sol. hot aq.; eas. sol. alc., ether, $CHCl_3$, C_6H_6.

With $FeCl_3$ (T 1.41) gives scanty white turbidity of di-α-naphthol [Beil. VI-1053] [cf. ⟨1⟩] but soln. then passes through red to violet with sepn. of violet flocks — C̄ is sol. in aq. alk. but pptd. by CO_2 — C̄ reduces Tollens' reagt. (T 1.11), and alk. $KMnO_4$.

C̄ in 5 pts. AcOH treated in cold with calcd. amt. Br_2 in AcOH ppts. 2,4-dibromo-α-naphthol, cryst. from pet. ether, m.p. 107–108° ⟨2⟩.

Ⓟ **Color test with $CHCl_3$ and alkali:** To 0.05 g. C̄ in 10 ml. 1% NaOH soln., add 5 drops $CHCl_3$ and boil 20 sec.; first gives clear blue (B); in 15 min. color changes to bluish green GB-BG; in 4½ hrs. to Y-G [dif. from β-naphthol (1:1540)] ⟨3⟩.

Ⓓ **α-Naphthol picrate:** $C_{10}H_7.OH.PkOH$ — Dis. 0.10 g. C̄ and 0.15 g. PkOH in 10 ml. boilg. 50% alc. Cool slowly; filter off orange ndls.; wash with 2 ml. 50% alc.; dry on porous tile. M.p. picrate 188.5–189.5° u.c., rap. htg. ⟨3⟩ [cf. ⟨4⟩].

Ⓓ **α-Naphthyl acetate:** from C̄ in ice cold alk. soln. by shaking with Ac_2O (92% yield); ndls. or tbls. from alc., m.p. 48–49° ⟨5⟩. [Distn. of α-naphthyl acetate with steam causes quant. hydrolysis to α-naphthol and acetic acid.]

Ⓓ **α-Naphthyl benzoate:** from C̄ by shaking aq. alk. soln. with BzCl; cryst. from alc., m.p. 56° ⟨6⟩.

Ⓓ **α-Naphthyl *p*-nitrobenzoate:** m.p. 143°.

Ⓓ **α-Naphthyl 3,5-dinitrobenzoate:** from C̄ + 3,5-dinitrobenzoyl chloride in pyridine; yel. ndls. from alc., m.p. 217.4° cor. ⟨7⟩ [cf. T 1.47].

Ⓓ **α-Naphthyl *p*-toluenesulfonate:** m.p. 89°.

Ⓓ **α-Naphthyl *p*-nitrobenzyl ether:** m.p. 140° ⟨8⟩ [cf. T 1.44].

Ⓓ **α-Naphthyl 2,4-dinitrophenyl ether:** fine pale yel. ndls. from alc., m.p. 128° ⟨9⟩.
Ⓓ **α-Naphthoxyacetic acid:** m.p. 191–192° ⟨10⟩; 193.5° ⟨11⟩; Neut. Eq. 202 [cf. T 1.46].
Ⓓ **α-Naphthyl *N*-phenylcarbamate:** from C̄ + phenylisocyanate on htg. (espec. in pres. of $AlCl_3$); ndls. from alc., m.p. 177–178° ⟨12⟩.
Ⓓ **α-Naphthyl *N*-(α-naphthyl)carbamate:** from C̄ + α-naphthylisocyanate in presence of trace of trimethylamine, cryst. from lgr., m.p. 152° ⟨13⟩ [cf. T 1.45].
Ⓓ **α-Naphthyl *N*-(*p*-xenyl)carbamate:** m.p. 190° ⟨14⟩.

1:1500 ⟨1⟩ Clemo, Cockburn, Spence, *J. Chem. Soc.* **1931,** 1267. ⟨2⟩ Dahmer, *Ann.* **333,** 367–368 (1904). ⟨3⟩ Mulliken, " Method " I, 108 (1904). ⟨4⟩ Baril, Hauber, *J. Am. Chem. Soc.* **53,** 1090 (1931). ⟨5⟩ Chattaway, *J. Chem. Soc.* **1931,** 2495–2496. ⟨6⟩ Autenrieth, Mühlinghaus, *Ber.* **40,** 748 (1907). ⟨7⟩ Phillips, Keenan, *J. Am. Chem. Soc.*, **53,** 1926 (1931). ⟨8⟩ Lyman, Reid, *J. Am. Chem. Soc.* **42,** 615–619 (1920). ⟨9⟩ Bost, Nicholson, *J. Am. Chem. Soc.* **57,** 2369 (1935). ⟨10⟩ Koelsch, *J. Am. Chem. Soc.* **53,** 305 (1931).
⟨11⟩ Shibata, Okuyama, *Cent.* **1936,** II, 617. ⟨12⟩ Leuckart, *J. prakt. Chem.* (2) **41,** 320 (1890). ⟨13⟩ French, Wirtel, *J. Am. Chem. Soc.* **48,** 1738 (1926). ⟨14⟩ Morgan, Pettet, *J. Chem. Soc.* **1931,** 1125.

1:1505 β-NAPHTHYL SALICYLATE $C_{17}H_{12}O_3$ Beil. X-80

(" Betol ")

—O.CO.— HO

M.P. 95.5° (stable form) ⟨1⟩ ⟨2⟩
M.P. 93.5° (metastable form) ⟨1⟩ ⟨2⟩

With $FeCl_3$ (T 1.41) gives violet color.

Ⓓ **Saponification:** Hydrolysis with alk. (T 1.51) gives Sap. Eq. 264 and yields β-naphthol (1:1540) [pptd. from titration soln. by passing in CO_2] and salicylic acid (1:0780), pptd. (after removal of β-naphthol) by addn. of minl. acid.
Ⓓ **β-Naphthyl *o*-acetoxybenzoate:** from C̄ by refluxing 3–4 hrs. with equiv. amts. Ac_2O + fused NaOAc; ndls. from alc., m.p. 136° ⟨3⟩.
Ⓓ **β-Naphthyl salicylate *N*-phenylcarbamate:** from C̄ + phenylisocyanate, htd. in s.t. at 160°, yel. lfts. from AcOH, m.p. 268° ⟨3⟩.

1:1505 ⟨1⟩ Schaum, *Ann.* **462,** 205 (1928). ⟨2⟩ Tamman, *Z. physik. Chem.* **29,** 72–74 (1899). ⟨3⟩ Eckenroth, Wolf, *Ber.* **26,** 1468 (1893).

1:1506 *m*-HYDROXYACETOPHENONE $C_8H_8O_2$ Beil. VIII-86

(*m*-Acetylphenol)

OH —CO.CH_3

M.P. 96° **B.P. 296°**

Ndls. or lfts.; sol. alc., ether, $CHCl_3$, C_6H_6, hot aq.; spar. sol. cold aq.; insol. lgr.

C̄ is sol. in conc. H_2SO_4 with deep yel. color [dif. from *p*-hydroxyacetophenone (1:1527) which gives colorless soln. ⟨1⟩]. C̄ dissolves in aq. alk. or NH_4OH with yel. color [dif. from *p*-hydroxyacetophenone (1:1527) which yields colorless solns. ⟨1⟩].

C̄ with excess Br_2-aq. yields 2,4,6-tribromo-3-hydroxyacetophenone, cryst. from MeOH, m.p. 127.5° ⟨2⟩.

[For prepn. from *m*-aminoacetophenone via diazo react. (78.5% yield) see ⟨2⟩.]

Ⓓ ***m*-Hydroxyacetophenone semicarbazone:** m.p. 194–196° ⟨3⟩. [This prod. fused with KOH at 190° gives quant. yield of *m*-ethylphenol (1:1744) ⟨3⟩.]

1:1506 ⟨1⟩ Pfeiffer, *Ann.* **393,** 104 (1911). ⟨2⟩ Fuson, Lewis, Du Puis, *J. Am. Chem. Soc.* **54,** 1118 (1932). ⟨3⟩ Kenner, Statham, *J. Chem. Soc.* **1935,** 302.

1:1510 ***p-ter*-BUTYLPHENOL** $(CH_3)_3C—\langle\ \rangle—OH$ $C_{10}H_{14}O$ **Beil. VI-524**

M.P. 99-100° **B.P. 236-238°**

Ndls. from aq. — Volatile with steam, even from alk. soln.
C̄ + $AlCl_3$ refluxed 8 hrs. in C_6H_6 gives 70% yield *ter*-butylbenzene (1:7460) ⟨1⟩.

Ⓓ ***p-ter*-Butylphenyl benzoate:** from C̄ + BzCl + pyridine, m.p. 81–82° ⟨2⟩.

Ⓓ ***p-ter*-Butylphenyl benzenesulfonate:** from C̄ + benzenesulfonyl chloride + pyridine, m.p. 70–71° ⟨2⟩.

Ⓓ ***p-ter*-Butylphenyl *p*-toluenesulfonate:** from C̄ + *p*-toluenesulfonyl chloride + pyridine, m.p. 109–110° ⟨2⟩.

Ⓓ ***p-ter*-Butylphenoxyacetic acid:** m.p. 86.5°; Neut. Eq. 150 ⟨3⟩ [cf. T 1.46].

1:1510 ⟨1⟩ Smith, *J. Am. Chem. Soc.* **59,** 899 (1937). ⟨2⟩ Huston, Hsieh, *J. Am. Chem. Soc.* **58,** 440–441 (1936). ⟨3⟩ Bradley, Kniffen, *Am. Chem. J.* **19,** 70 (1897).

1:1515 **2-ACETO-1-NAPHTHOL** $C_{12}H_{10}O_2$ **Beil. VIII-149**

OH
—CO.CH₃

M.P. 102° **B.P. 325°** sl. dec.

C̄ exists in two forms: pale greenish yel. ndls. from alc., m.p. 102–103°; bright yel. pl. from C_6H_6 or lgr., m.p. 98°. The lower melting form is more sol. than the other into which it gradually changes on repeated recrystn. from alc. ⟨1⟩ ⟨2⟩.

Sol. ether, AcOH, $CHCl_3$, C_6H_6, CS_2; spar. sol. alc.; insol. aq.; solns. are yellow except in lgr. which is colorless.

C̄ with $FeCl_3$ (T 1.41) gives green color in alc. soln. — C̄ is sol. in aq. alk. or in conc. H_2SO_4 yielding yellow solns.

C̄ in hot dil. alc. NaOH exposed to stream of air (free from CO_2) yields a magma of black ndls.; for structure of product see ⟨3⟩.

Ⓓ **2-Acetyl-1-naphthyl acetate:** from dry Na salt of C̄ + AcCl in ether or $CHCl_3$; colorless pr. from alc. or tbls. from AcOH, m.p. 107.5° ⟨4⟩ ⟨5⟩.

Ⓓ **2-Acetyl-1-naphthyl benzoate:** from C̄ in warm 10% NaOH + BzCl (yield 92%); colorless pr. from alc., m.p. 128° ⟨6⟩.

Ⓓ **2-Acetyl-1-naphthoxyacetic acid:** lfts. from dil. alc., m.p. 130° ⟨7⟩ [prepd. indirectly] [cf. T 1.46].

Ⓓ **Methyl 1-hydroxy-2-naphthyl ketoxime:** from C̄ + aq. alk. + excess NH_2OH, m.p. 168–169° ⟨8⟩.

Ⓓ **Methyl 1-hydroxy-2-naphthyl ketone phenylhydrazone:** from C̄ in alc. htd. 2 hrs. with phenylhydrazine + a little AcOH, white ndls. from dil. alc., m.p. 136–137° ⟨9⟩.

Ⓓ **Methyl 1-hydroxy-2-naphthyl ketone semicarbazone:** pale yel. powder, m.p. 245–250° ⟨10⟩.

1:1515 ⟨1⟩ Torrey, Brewster, *J. Am. Chem. Soc.* **35,** 429 (1913). ⟨2⟩ Witt, Braun, *Ber.* **47,** 3219–3220 (1914). ⟨3⟩ Fries, Leue, *Ber.* **55,** 753–757 (1922). ⟨4⟩ Hantzsch, *Ber.* **39,** 3096 (1906). ⟨5⟩ Fries, *Ber.* **54,** 711–714 (1921). ⟨6⟩ Bhullar, Venkataraman, *J. Chem. Soc.* **1931,** 1168. ⟨7⟩ von Kostanecki, Tambor, *Ber.* **42,** 907 (1909). ⟨8⟩ Friedländer, *Ber.* **28,** 1947 (1895). ⟨9⟩ Torrey, Brewster, *J. Am. Chem. Soc.* **31,** 1324 (1909). ⟨10⟩ Ref. 1, page 432.

— **m-HYDROXYBENZALDEHYDE** (*m*-Aldehydophenol; *m*-formylphenol) $C_7H_6O_2$ **Beil. VIII-58**

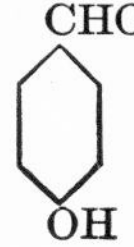

M.P. 104° (108° cor.) **B.P. abt. 240°**

See 1:0055. Genus 1: Aldehydes.

1:1520 PYROCATECHOL (Catechol; 1,2-dihydroxybenzene) $C_6H_6O_2$ **Beil. VI-759**

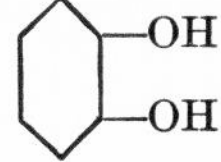

M.P. 104-105° **B.P. 245°** (240°)

Subl. in vac. — Volat. with st. — Eas. sol. aq., alc., ether; dif. sol. cold C_6H_6 (abt. 1%) — $\bar{C}$ is sol. at room temp. in 97.5 pts. dichloroethylene [dif. and sepn. from hydroquinone which requires 20,000 pts. ⟨1⟩]. [For optical data see ⟨13⟩.]

$\bar{C}$ (in 0.4% aq. soln.) gives with $FeCl_3$ (T 1.41) a green color (G) which on addn. of Na_2CO_3 changes to R, becoming OR within 15 min. — Alkn. soln. browns in air — Red. $NH_4OH/AgNO_3$ in cold; Fehling's soln. (T 1.22) on warming.

$Pb(OAc)_2$ soln. gives white ppt. of $Pb\bar{A}$, easily sol. in AcOH [dif. from hydroquinone] — With excess $Ba(OH)_2$ soln. in cold even 0.5% pyrocatechol soln. gives turbidity due to $Ba\bar{A}.3\frac{1}{2}H_2O$ [dif. from resorcinol and hydroquinone] ⟨12⟩ — $\bar{C}$ with $CaCl_2$ + NH_4OH solns. gives immediate ppt. of acid calcium salt [dif. from resorcinol or hydroquinone] ⟨2⟩ — $\bar{C}$ gives no ppt. with Br_2-aq. — $\bar{C}$ with excess I_2 + NaOH (T 1.81) gives CHI_3 [dif. from resorcinol (1:1530) ⟨3⟩]. [Use in quant. detn. ⟨3⟩.]

$\bar{C}$ with its two position isomers forms a ternary eutectic, m.p. 58.7°, contg. 36% $\bar{C}$, 49% resorcinol, and 15% hydroquinone ⟨4⟩.

With PkOH, $\bar{C}$ forms a picrate, $\bar{C}$.PkOH, or. ndls., m.p. 122° ⟨5⟩.

Ⓓ **Tetrabromopyrocatechol:** Dis. 0.05 g. $\bar{C}$ in 2.5 ml. warm $CHCl_3$, add 0.4 ml. Br_2, and evap. to dryness on aq. bath. Dis. residue in 5 ml. cold alc., add 20 ml. aq., shake, and filter, washing ppt. with a little cold aq. Reppt. from 5 ml. alc. with 20 ml. cold aq., and dry on tile. White ndls., tinged with violet, melting about 192–193° u.c., after softening at 185–187° ⟨6⟩.

Ⓓ **Pyrocatechol diacetate:** from $\bar{C}$ in dil. aq. alk. on shaking with Ac_2O in cold, 98% yield, m.p. 64–65° ⟨7⟩.

Ⓓ **Pyrocatechol dibenzoate:** from $\bar{C}$ by htg. with 2 moles BzCl; lfts. from alc. + ether, m.p. 84° ⟨8⟩. [The monobenzoate melts 130–131°.]

Ⓓ **Pyrocatechol di-*p*-nitrobenzoate:** woolly ndls. from alc., m.p. 169° ⟨9⟩ ⟨10⟩.

Ⓓ **Pyrocatechol di-(3,5-dinitrobenzoate):** m.p. 152° [cf. T 1.47].

Ⓓ **Pyrocatechol bis-(*N*-phenylcarbamate):** m.p. 169° ⟨11⟩.

1:1520 ⟨1⟩ Mann, *Chem. Ztg.* **56**, 452 (1932). ⟨2⟩ Boettinger, *Chem. Ztg.* **19**, 23 (1895). ⟨3⟩ Slotta, Neiser, *Ber.* **71**, 1611 (1938). ⟨4⟩ Hrynakowski, *Z. physik. Chem.* **A-171**, 113 (1934). ⟨5⟩ Baril, Hauber, *J. Am. Chem. Soc.* **53**, 1090 (1931). ⟨6⟩ Mulliken, " Method " I, 109 (1904). ⟨7⟩ Chattaway, *J. Chem. Soc.* **1931**, 2496. ⟨8⟩ Döbner, *Ann.* **210**, 261 (1881). ⟨9⟩ Meijer, *Rec. trav. chim.* **53**, 395 (1934). ⟨10⟩ Barnett, Nixon, *Chem. News* **129**, 190-191 (1924).

⟨11⟩ Morgan, Pettet, *J. Chem. Soc.* **1931**, 1125. ⟨12⟩ Elsner, *Monatsh.* **40**, 361–362 (1919). ⟨13⟩ Hendricks, Jefferson, *J. Optical Soc. Am.* **23**, 302 (1933).

1:1521 2,4-DIHYDROXYTOLUENE $C_7H_8O_2$ **Beil. VI-872**
(Cresorcinol, 4-methylresorcinol)

CH_3 OH OH

M.P. 104-105° **B.P. 267-270°**

Cryst. from C_6H_6 + pet. ether, or toluene — Eas. sol. aq., alc., ether; spar. sol. C_6H_6, lgr. $\bar{C}$ with $FeCl_3$ (T 1.41) gives blue color — Alk. soln. turns red in air, becoming brown — $\bar{C}$ with $Ca(OCl)_2$ soln. gives yellow color.

1:1524 1,2-DIHYDROXYNAPHTHALENE $C_{10}H_8O_2$ **Beil. VI-975**
(β-Naphthohydroquinone)

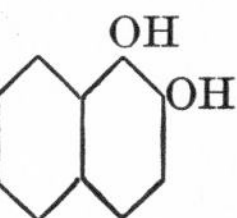

M.P. 108° ⟨1⟩
105.5° ⟨2⟩

Cryst. as colorless pl. from aq. contg. $SnCl_2$ + HCl ⟨1⟩ or from oxygen-free HCl ⟨2⟩. $\bar{C}$ yields a monohydrate, m.p. 59–60° when dried in air; this cryst. aq. is lost on drying in vac. ⟨3⟩.

Soln. of $\bar{C}$ in alk. is yellow and turns green in air — $\bar{C}$ is quant. oxid. to β-naphthoquinone (1:9030) by Ag_2O or PbO_2 in boilg. C_6H_6 ⟨4⟩ or by $FeCl_3$ at 0° under carefully controlled cond. ⟨2⟩.

$\bar{C}$ in soln. of alk. + $NaHCO_3$ shaken with $(CH_3)_2SO_4$ yields 1,2-dimethoxynaphthalene, m.p. 31°, b.p. 278–280° ⟨5⟩.

Ⓓ **1,2-Diacetoxynaphthalene:** from $\bar{C}$ + Ac_2O + anhyd. NaOAc; cryst. from AcOH, m.p. 104–106° ⟨6⟩. [For prepn. from β-naphthoquinone (1:9030) in very pure state, cryst. from alc., m.p. 109.5° and alc. alk. hydrol. in absence of air as means of prepn. of pure $\bar{C}$ see ⟨2⟩.]

1:1524 ⟨1⟩ Fieser, Fieser, *J. Am. Chem. Soc.* **56,** 1575 (1934). ⟨2⟩ Fieser, Peters, *J. Am. Chem. Soc.* **53,** 803–804 (1931). ⟨3⟩ Straus, Bernoully, Mautner, *Ann.* **444,** 186 (1925). ⟨4⟩ Ingold, *J. Chem. Soc.* **123,** 2087 (1923). ⟨5⟩ Bezdzik, Friedländer, *Monatsh.* **30,** 283 (1909). ⟨6⟩ Korn, *Ber.* **17,** 3025 (1884).

1:1525 ORCINOL $C_7H_8O_2$ **Beil. VI-882**
(5-Methylresorcinol;
3,5-dihydroxytoluene)

CH_3 HO OH

M.P. 106.5-108° **B.P. 287-290°**

Cryst. from aq. with 1 H_2O, m.p. 56–58° (1:1445); aq. readily lost on htg. — Cryst in. anhydrous lfts. from $CHCl_3$; ndls. or pr. from C_6H_6 — Sublimes as ndls. in CO_2 or vac. — Eas. sol. aq., alc., ether; dif. sol. pet. ether, lgr., $CHCl_3$.

$\bar{C}$ in 1% aq. soln. gives with $FeCl_3$ (T 1.41) a VB-T_1 to BV-T_1 color, slowly fading to light tint of same hue — $\bar{C}$ in NH_4OH soln. turns red on stdg. in air, faster with H_2O_2 — $\bar{C}$ with $Ca(OCl)_2$ soln. gives intense red color.

$\bar{C}$ reduces $NH_4OH/AgNO_3$ on warming — Alk. soln. of melt with phthalic anhydride (T 1.42) gives pure OR color — $\bar{C}$ with excess Br_2-aq. ppts. 2,4,6-tribromoorcinol, ndls. from dil. alc.; m.p. 103° ⟨1⟩; 108° ⟨2⟩.

$\bar{C}$ with PkOH yields picrate, $\bar{C}$.PkOH, orange-yel. cryst., m.p. 92° ⟨3⟩.

Ⓟ **Color test with $CHCl_3$ and alkali:** Dis. 0.05 g. $\bar{C}$ in 5 ml. 1% NaOH contg. 5 drops $CHCl_3$. An O-OR color is prod., which on diln. to 50 ml. gives intense VG fluoresc. ⟨4⟩.

Ⓓ **Orcinol diacetate:** from C̄ + AcCl, m.p. 25° ⟨5⟩.
Ⓓ **Orcinol dibenzoate:** from C̄ + BzCl + aq. Na_2CO_3; ndls. from alc.; m.p. 87–88° ⟨2⟩ ⟨7⟩.
Ⓓ **Orcinol bis-(*p*-nitrobenzoate):** m.p. 214°.
Ⓓ **Orcinol bis-(3,5-dinitrobenzoate):** m.p. 190° [cf. T 1.47].
Ⓓ **Orcinol diglycolic acid:** from C̄ + chloroacetic acid + aq. alk.; ndls. from aq., m.p. 216–217° ⟨6⟩; Neut. Eq. 229 [cf. T 1.46].
Ⓓ **Orcinol bis-(*N*-phenylcarbamate):** m.p. 154° ⟨8⟩.
Ⓓ **Orcinol bis-(*N*-α-naphthylcarbamate):** from C̄ + α-naphthylisocyanate (2 equiv.) htd. with trace anhydrous dimethylamine (or triethylamine); cryst. from lgr., m.p. 160° ⟨9⟩ [cf. T 1.45].
Ⓓ **Orcinol bis-(*N*-*p*-xenylcarbamate):** m.p. 196° ⟨8⟩.

1:1525 ⟨1⟩ Lamparter, *Ann.* **134,** 257–259 (1865). ⟨2⟩ Simon, *Arch. Pharm.* **240,** 550–551 (1902). ⟨3⟩ Baril, Hauber, *J. Am. Chem. Soc.* **53,** 1090 (1931). ⟨4⟩ Mulliken, " Method " I, 95 (1904); Nevile, Winther, *Ber.* **15,** 2990 (1882). ⟨5⟩ de Luynes, *Ann. chim.* (4) **6,** 195 (1865). ⟨6⟩ Saarbach, *J. prakt. Chem.* (2) **21,** 162 (1880). ⟨7⟩ Lipp, Scheller, *Ber.* **42,** 1972 (1909). ⟨8⟩ Morgan, Pettet, *J. Chem. Soc.* **1931,** 1125. ⟨9⟩ French, Wirtel, *J. Am. Chem. Soc.* **48,** 1738 (1926).

1:1527 *p*-HYDROXYACETOPHENONE $C_8H_8O_2$ Beil. VIII-87

(*p*-Acetylphenol)

HO—⟨C₆H₄⟩—CO.CH₃

M.P. 109°

Ndls. from ether, dil. alc., C_6H_6 + pet. ether, or aq. — C̄ sol. in 100 pts. aq. at 22° and in 14 pts. at 100° — Not volatile with steam [dif. from *o*-isomer (1:1746)].

With dil. aq. NaOH or NH_4OH C̄ dissolves yielding colorless solns. [dif. from *o*- or *m*-isomers which yield yel. solns.] — Sol. in conc. H_2SO_4 yielding colorless soln. [dif. from *o*- or *m*-isomers which give yel. solns.].

C̄ with $FeCl_3$ (T 1.41) gives red-violet coloration.

Ⓓ ***p*-Acetoxyacetophenone:** from C̄ + Ac_2O + NaOAc; m.p. 54° ⟨1⟩.
Ⓓ ***p*-Benzoxyacetophenone:** cryst. from alc., m.p. 134–135° ⟨2⟩.
Ⓓ ***p*-Hydroxyacetophenone oxime:** from C̄ in conc. alc. soln., refluxed with theoret. quant. $NH_2OH.HCl$ + AcONa dislvd. in minimum amt. aq.; the resultant oil solidifies and is recrystd. from hot C_6H_6, m.p. 143–144 ⟨3⟩; 145–146° ⟨4⟩.
Ⓓ ***p*-Hydroxyacetophenone phenylhydrazone:** C̄ htd. with aq. soln. of phenylhydrazine acetate rapidly gives ppt., white ndls., m.p. 151°, rapidly turning yel. and resinifying in air ⟨3⟩.
Ⓓ ***p*-Hydroxyacetophenone 2,4-dinitrophenylhydrazone:** maroon cryst. from alc., m.p. 261.5° cor. ⟨5⟩ [cf. T 1.14].
Ⓓ ***p*-Hydroxyacetophenone semicarbazone:** m.p. 199° ⟨3⟩.

1:1527 ⟨1⟩ Hayashi, *Cent.* **1933,** II, 2009. ⟨2⟩ Baker, *J. Chem. Soc.* **1933,** 1387. ⟨3⟩ Charon, Zamanos, *Compt. rend.* **133,** 743 (1901). ⟨4⟩ Cope, *J. Am. Chem. Soc.* **57,** 574 (1935). ⟨5⟩ Ferrante, Bloom, *Am. J. Pharm.* **105,** 383 (1933).

1:1529 2,2′-DIHYDROXYBIPHENYL $C_{12}H_{10}O_2$ Beil. VI-989

(*o*,*o*′-Biphenol)

OH OH

M.P. 109-110° **B.P. 325-326°**

Cryst. from boilg. aq. in lfts. of hydrate, m.p. 73–75°; these readily lose aq. on stdg. over conc. H_2SO_4 yielding anhydrous form.

Anhydrous $\bar{C}$ is sol. alc., ether, C_6H_6, AcOH; spar. sol. pet. ether.

$\bar{C}$ with $FeCl_3$ (T 1.41) gives dark reddish violet color — $\bar{C}$ is sol. in aq. alk. and even in aq. Na_2CO_3, but is partially extd. from alk. soln. by ether — $\bar{C}$ on fusion with phthalic anhydride (+ $ZnCl_2$) (T 1.42) yields a phthalein whose alk. soln. is blue-violet.

$\bar{C}$, fused with $ZnCl_2$ ⟨1⟩, or htd. 50 hrs. at b.p. (90% yield) ⟨2⟩, or htd. 26 hrs. at 300° with P_2O_5 (95% yield) ⟨2⟩, loses H_2O and gives diphenylene oxide (dibenzofuran) [Beil. XVII-70], lfts. from alc., m.p. 86–87° — $\bar{C}$ distd. with P_2S_5 yields diphenylene sulfide (dibenzothiophene) [Beil. XVII-72], ndls. from alc., m.p. 97° ⟨3⟩.

Ⓓ **2,2′-Diacetoxybiphenyl:** from $\bar{C}$ by boilg. with Ac_2O; cryst. from xylene, m.p. 95° ⟨4⟩.

Ⓓ **2,2′-Dimethoxybiphenyl:** from $\bar{C}$ in 10% aq. NaOH by shaking at room temp. with dimethyl sulfate (84% yield); pr. from alc., m.p. 154–155° ⟨5⟩ ⟨8⟩.

Ⓓ **2,2′-(Dibenzyloxy)biphenyl:** from $\bar{C}$ in alc. htd. with calcd. amts. benzyl chloride + NaOH in s.t. at 100° for 5 hrs.; needles from alc., m.p. 101° ⟨6⟩.

Ⓓ ***o,o′*-Diphenol bis-(*N*-phenylcarbamate):** from $\bar{C}$ + $C_6H_5.N{:}C{:}O$ in C_6H_6 htd. in s.t. 15 hrs. at 100°; ndls. from dil. alc., m.p. 144–145° cor. ⟨7⟩.

1:1529 ⟨1⟩ Kraemer, Weissgerber, *Ber.* **34,** 1663 (1901). ⟨2⟩ Cullinane, Davies, *Rec. trav. chim.* **55,** 882 (1936). ⟨3⟩ Kruber, *Ber.* **53,** 1566, Note 2 (1920). ⟨4⟩ Ref. 1, page 1667. ⟨5⟩ Borsche, Scholten, *Ber.* **50,** 607 (1917). ⟨6⟩ van Alphen, *Rec. trav. chim.* **51,** 457 (1932). ⟨7⟩ Diels, Bibergeil, *Ber.* **35,** 305 (1902). ⟨8⟩ Gilman, Swiss, Cheney, *J. Am. Chem. Soc.* **62,** 1964 (1940).

1:1530 RESORCINOL (1,3-Dihydroxybenzene) $C_6H_6O_2$ Beil. VI-796

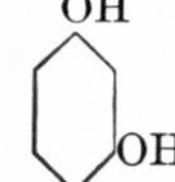

M.P. 110° (stable form) **B.P. 280.8°** cor.
108-108.5° (labile form)

Very eas. sol. aq., alc., ether; sol. at 24° in 380 pts. by wt. C_6H_6; insol. $CHCl_3$ or CS_2 — Slowly volat. with steam. [For optical data see ⟨20⟩.]

$\bar{C}$ in 1% aq. soln. with $FeCl_3$ (T 1.41) gives strong clear BV color, permanent for more than 15 min. — Using Poirrier's blue as indicator, titrates as dibasic acid (Neut. Eq. 55) ⟨1⟩ — Alk. soln. of fusion product with phthalic anhydride (T 1.42) is red by transmitted light, with intense green-yellow fluorescence (fluorescein) by reflected light.

$\bar{C}$ is not pptd. by NH_4OH + $CaCl_2$ soln. or by $Pb(OAc)_2$ soln. [dif. from pyrocatechol] — $\bar{C}$ with NH_4OH + Co^{++} soln. yields characteristic green color. [Use in detectn. of $\bar{C}$ in presence of other phenols ⟨2⟩.] — $\bar{C}$ reduces Tollens' reagt. (T 1.11) in cold and Fehling's soln. (T 1.22) on warming — $\bar{C}$ with 3 moles Br_2-aq. ppts. 2,4,6-tribromoresorcinol, cryst. from aq., m.p. 111° ⟨3⟩. [Excess Br_2 may lead to formation of much "pentabromoresorcinol" [Beil. VII-573], m.p. 113.5°.]

$\bar{C}$ with its two position isomers forms a ternary eutectic, m.p. 58.7° contg. 49% $\bar{C}$, 36% pyrocatechol, and 15% hydroquinone ⟨4⟩ — $\bar{C}$ with picric acid forms a picrate, orange-yel. cryst., m.p. 89–90°, dec. by aq., alc., or ether ⟨5⟩.

Ⓓ **2,4,6-Trinitroresorcinol (styphnic acid):** m.p. 175° u.c. — Dis. 0.1 g. $\bar{C}$ in 1 ml. conc. H_2SO_4 and pour slowly with const. stirring into a cold mixt. of 1 ml. conc. H_2SO_4 + 1 ml. conc. HNO_3, contd. in a small dish floating on cold water. Avoid adding the resorcinol soln. so fast that a *perm.* brown coloration results. Remove from aq., stand 3 min., then pour mixt. of liq. and yel. cryst. into 10 ml. cold water, with external cooling. Filter, wash with 5 ml. cold aq. and recryst. from boilg. mixt. of 10 ml. aq., 4 ml. alc., and 0.4 ml. conc. HCl — Cool, shake, filter; wash cryst. with 5 ml. cold aq. and dry at 100° ⟨6⟩.

Ⓓ **Resorcinol dibenzoate:** from $\bar{C}$ by htg. with 2 moles BzCl till evoln. of HCl ceases ⟨7⟩, or by shaking alk. soln. of C̄ with excess BzCl ⟨8⟩, or from C̄ + 2 moles BzCl in pyridine ⟨9⟩; lfts. from dil. alc., m.p. 117°. [*m*-Hydroxyphenyl benzoate (resorcinol monobenzoate), resulting from incomplete benzoylation has m.p. 135°; for prepn. from dibenzoate by boiling with aq. alc. soln. of Na_2HPO_4 + formalin (90% yield) see ⟨10⟩.]

Ⓓ **Resorcinol di-*p*-nitrobenzoate:** m.p. 182° (175°) ⟨11⟩.

Ⓓ **Resorcinol bis-(3,5-dinitrobenzoate):** m.p. 201° [cf. T 1.47].

Ⓓ **Resorcinol dibenzenesulfonate:** from C̄ in aq. alk. + 2 moles benzenesulfonyl chloride; ndls. from hot alc., m.p. 69–70° ⟨12⟩.

Ⓓ **Resorcinol di-*p*-toluenesulfonate:** from C̄ + aq. Na_2CO_3 htd. 2½ hrs. with 2 moles *p*-toluenesulfonyl chloride in ether; cryst. from acetone + dil. alc., m.p. 80–81° ⟨13⟩.

Ⓓ **Resorcinol diglycolic acid:** from C̄ + 2 moles chloroacetic acid + excess NaOH; ndls. from aq. or AcOH, m.p. 195° ⟨14⟩ ⟨15⟩; Neut. Eq. 113. [*m*-Hydroxyphenoxyacetic acid (the half reaction product) forms pr. from aq., m.p. 158–159° ⟨15⟩.]

Ⓓ **Resorcinol bis-(2,4-dinitrophenyl) ether:** buff granules from alc., m.p. 194° ⟨16⟩.

Ⓓ **Resorcinol bis-[(*N*-phenyl)carbamate]:** tbls. from alc.; ndls. from $CHCl_3$, m.p. 164° ⟨17⟩.

Ⓓ **Resorcinol bis-[(*N*-*p*-nitrophenyl)carbamate]:** m.p. 232° ⟨18⟩.

Ⓓ **Resorcinol bis-[(*N,N*-diphenyl)carbamate]:** m.p. 129–130° ⟨19⟩.

1:1530 ⟨1⟩ Engel, *Ann. chim.* (6) **8,** 569 (1880). ⟨2⟩ Krauskopf, Ritter, *J. Am. Chem. Soc.* **38,** 2182–2187 (1916). ⟨3⟩ Jackson, Dunlap, *Am. Chem. J.* **18,** 123–125 (1896). ⟨4⟩ Hrynakowski, *Z. physik. Chem.* **A171,** 113 (1934). ⟨5⟩ Baril, Hauber, *J. Am. Chem. Soc.* **53,** 1090 (1931). ⟨6⟩ Mulliken, "Method" I, 110 (1904). ⟨7⟩ Döbner, *Ann.* **210,** 256 (1881). ⟨8⟩ Skraup, *Monatsh.* **10,** 390 (1889). ⟨9⟩ Einhorn, Hollandt, *Ann.* **301,** 104 (1898). ⟨10⟩ Benet, *Bull. soc. chim.* (4) **51,** 963–964 (1932).

⟨11⟩ Meijer, *Rec. trav. chim.* **53,** 394 (1934). ⟨12⟩ Georgescu, *Ber.* **24,** 416–417 (1891). ⟨13⟩ Reverdin, Crépieux, *Ber.* **34,** 2997 (1901); *Bull. soc. chim.* (3) **25,** 1045 (1901). ⟨14⟩ Gabriel, *Ber.* **12,** 1640 (1879). ⟨15⟩ Carter, Lawrence, *J. Chem. Soc.* **77,** 1225 (1900). ⟨16⟩ Bost, Nicholson, *J. Am. Chem. Soc.* **57,** 2369 (1935). ⟨17⟩ Snape, *Ber.* **18,** 2429 (1885). ⟨18⟩ van Hoogstraten, *Rec.* **51,** 427 (1932). ⟨19⟩ Herzog, *Ber.* **40,** 1833 (1907). ⟨20⟩ Hendricks, Jefferson, *J. Optical Soc. Am.* **23,** 302 (1933).

1:1531 2,2′-DIHYDROXY-3,3′-DIMETHYLBIPHENYL $C_{14}H_{14}O_2$ Beil. S.N. 563

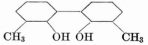

CH_3 OH OH CH_3

M.P. 113° ⟨2⟩

Ndls. from pet. ether — Sol. alc., ether, C_6H_6; spar. sol. pet. ether — Sol. in hot aq. NaOH; spar. sol. cold aq. NaOH — Sublimes.

C̄ on htg. with $ZnCl_2$ yields 1,8-dimethyldiphenylene oxide, volatile with steam, ndls. from alc., m.p. 89° ⟨1⟩.

The corresponding diacetate is an oil.

Ⓓ **2,2′-Dibenzoxy-3,3′-dimethylbiphenyl:** pr. from MeOH, m.p. 147° ⟨1⟩.

1:1531 ⟨1⟩ Sugii, Shindo, *J. Pharm. Soc. Japan* **54,** 149–153 (1934); *Cent.* **1935,** I, 698; *Chem. Abs.* **29,** 791 (1935). ⟨2⟩ Goldschmidt, Schön, *Ber.* **59,** 955 (1926).

1:1532 4,4′-DIHYDROXY-2,2′-DIMETHYLBIPHENYL $C_{14}H_{14}O_2$ Beil. VI-1009

(2,2′-Bi-*m*-cresol)

HO OH
CH_3 CH_3

M.P. 114°

Ⓓ **4,4′-Diacetoxy-2,2′-dimethylbiphenyl:** m.p. 75° ⟨1⟩.

Ⓓ **4,4′-Dibenzoxy-2,2′-dimethylbiphenyl:** m.p. 127° ⟨1⟩.

1:1532 ⟨1⟩ Schultz, Rhode, *Cent.* **1902,** II, 1447.

1:1533 VANILLYL ALCOHOL (4-Hydroxy-3-methoxybenzyl alcohol) CH_2OH / OCH_3 / OH $C_8H_{10}O_3$ **Beil. VI-1113**

M.P. 115°

Pr. from aq.,; ndls. from C_6H_6 — Sol. alc., ether, warm aq. — Cannot be distd. without decompn. at ord. press.

$\bar{C}$ resinifies with minl. ac.; sol. in conc. H_2SO_4 with red-violet color.

Ⓓ **4-Benzoxy-3-methoxybenzyl alcohol:** from $\bar{C}$ + 1 equiv. BzCl on shak. with dil. alk.; exists in two forms: monoclin. (from AcOEt + alc.), m.p. 90° rap. htg., and triclinic (from AcOEt + alc.), m.p. 99° ⟨1⟩.

Ⓓ **4-Benzoxy-3-methoxybenzyl benzoate:** from $\bar{C}$ + large excess BzCl + dil. aq. NaOH, cryst., m.p. 121° ⟨1⟩.

1:1533 ⟨1⟩ Vavon, *Ann. chim.* (9) **1,** 160–161 (1914).

1:1534 ETHYL *p*-HYDROXYBENZOATE $C_9H_{10}O_3$ **Beil. X-159**

$HO\langle\ \rangle CO.OC_2H_5$

M.P. 116° **B.P. 297-298°**

Cryst. from aq. — Very sol. alc., ether; spar. sol. aq., $CHCl_3$, CS_2, pet. ether. Eas. sol. aq. alk.

$\bar{C}$ nitrated with fumg. HNO_3 (D = 1.52) at 10–20° yields ethyl 3,5-dinitro-4-hydroxybenzoate, m.p. 87° ⟨1⟩.

$\bar{C}$ gives Millon's test (T 2.11) — For microchemical detn. see ⟨2⟩.

Ⓓ **Saponification:** Hydrolysis with aq. alk. (T 1.51) gives Sap. Eq. of 166 and yields *p*-hydroxybenzoic acid (1:0840) and ethyl alcohol (1:6130).

Ⓓ **Ethyl *p*-benzoxybenzoate:** from $\bar{C}$ + BzCl + aq. alk.; cryst. from ether, m.p. 94° ⟨3⟩.

1:1534 ⟨1⟩ Reverdin, *Bull. soc. chim.* (4) **3,** 592 (1908). ⟨2⟩ Fischer, Stauder, *Mikrochemie* **8,** 330–336 (1930). ⟨3⟩ Lassar-Cohn, Löwenstein, *Ber.* **41,** 3364 (1908).

1:1535 *m*-HYDROXYBENZOPHENONE (*m*-Benzoylphenol) $C_{13}H_{10}O_2$ **Beil. VIII-157**

O / OH / —C—

M.P. 116°

Pl. from alc. — Very sol. alc., ether.

Ⓓ ***m*-Benzyloxybenzophenone:** from $\bar{C}$ htd. with benzyl chloride + $NaOC_2H_5$; cryst. from alc., m.p. 62–63° ⟨1⟩.

Ⓓ ***anti-m*-Hydroxybenzophenone oxime:** from $\bar{C}$ in alc. with $NH_2OH.HCl$ + aq. Na_2CO_3 on boiling 2 hrs. (under these conditions this isomer forms exclusively), ndls. from C_6H_6, m.p. 76° ⟨2⟩. [On htg. at 80–90° or with HCl gas at ord. temp. isomerizes to *syn.*-isomer, ndls., m.p. 126° ⟨2⟩.]

1:1535 ⟨1⟩ Valette, *Bull. soc. chim.* (4) **47,** 292 (1930). ⟨2⟩ Smith, *Ber.* **24,** 4045 (1891).

— **p-HYDROXYBENZALDEHYDE** $C_7H_6O_2$ **Beil. VIII-64**
(p-Aldehydophenol; p-formylphenol)

HO—⟨benzene ring⟩—CHO

M.P. 116–117°

See 1:0060. Genus 1: Aldehydes.

1:1536 2,6-DIHYDROXYTOLUENE $C_7H_8O_2$ **Beil. VI-878**
(2-Methylresorcinol)

M.P. 117° **B.P. 271°** cor.

Pr. from C_6H_6 or toluene — Readily sol. aq., alc., ether, acetone, $CHCl_3$, AcOH; insol. lgr., pet. ether, CS_2.

With $FeCl_3$ (T 1.41) C̄ gives faint dark violet color, fading with excess reagent.

Ⓓ **2,6-Dibenzoxytoluene (2-methylresorcinol dibenzoate):** ndls. from MeOH, m.p. 105–106° ⟨1⟩.

1:1536 ⟨1⟩ Jones, Robertson, *J. Chem. Soc.* **1932,** 1690.

1:1537 DURENOL $C_{10}H_{14}O$ **Beil. VI-547**
(2,3,5,6-Tetramethylphenol)

M.P. 118° **B.P. 249°**

White ndls. from pet. — Eas. volatile with steam — Does not give color with $FeCl_3$ ⟨1⟩.

C̄ treated with Br_2 in AcOH yields 4-bromo-2,3,5,6-tetramethylphenol, pr. from dil. alc., m.p. 118° ⟨2⟩ ⟨3⟩.

1:1537 ⟨1⟩ von Auwers, Bundesmann, Wieners, *Ann.* **447,** 184 (1926). ⟨2⟩ Jacobsen, Schnapauff, *Ber.* **18,** 2844 (1885). ⟨3⟩ Kruber, Schmitt, *Ber.* **64,** 2277 (1931).

1:1538 2,2′-DIHYDROXY-4,4′-DIMETHYLBIPHENYL $C_{14}H_{14}O_2$ **Beil. S.N. 563**

M.P. 120° ⟨1⟩

Pl. from pet.

C̄ on htg. with $ZnCl_2$ yields 2,7-dimethyldiphenylene oxide, volatile with steam; ndls. from MeOH, m.p. 81° ⟨1⟩.

The corresponding diacetate is an oil.

Ⓓ **2,2′-Dibenzoxy-4,4′-dimethylbiphenyl:** pr. from alc. + acetone, m.p. 148° ⟨1⟩.

1:1538 ⟨1⟩ Sugii, Shindo, *J. Pharm. Soc. Japan* **54,** 149–153 (1934); *Cent.* **1935,** I, 698; *Chem. Abs.* **29,** 791 (1935).

1:1539 HYDROQUINONE MONOBENZYL ETHER $C_{13}H_{12}O_2$ **Beil. VI-845**
(Benzyl p-hydroxyphenyl ether)

⟨benzene ring⟩—CH_2—O—⟨benzene ring⟩—OH

M.P. 122° ⟨1⟩ ⟨2⟩

Pl. from aq. 50% alc. or CCl_4 — Sol. alc., ether, C_6H_6, hot aq.; spar. sol. cold aq.

Sol. in aq. alk. [dif. and sepn. from hydroquinone dibenzyl ether (1:7255), m.p. 129–130°].

1:1539 ⟨1⟩ Druey, *Bull. soc. chim.* (5) **2,** 1740–1741 (1935). ⟨2⟩ Klarmann, Gatyas, Shternov, *J. Am. Chem. Soc.* **54,** 303 (1932).

1:1540 **β-NAPHTHOL** $C_{10}H_8O$ **Beil. VI-627**

M.P. 123° **B.P. 285-286°**

Subl. in lfts.; dif. volatile with steam — Eas. sol. alc., ether, $CHCl_3$, C_6H_6 — Dif. sol. hot aq., pet. ether.

C̄ with $FeCl_3$ (T 1.41) in aq. or ether soln. gives pale green color, then white opalescence due to formation of β-dinaphthol (2,2′-dihydroxybinaphthyl-1,1′) [Beil. VI-1051], ndls. from alc., m.p. 218° cor. — C̄ with $Ca(OCl)_2$ soln. gives pale yellow color fading with excess reagent — C̄ in alk. soln. reduces $KMnO_4$.

C̄ with H.CHO soln. + HCl yields methylene di-β-naphthol (for details see 1:0145); C̄ with CH_3CHO + HCl yields ethylidene di-β-naphthyl oxide (for details see 1:0100).

Ⓟ **Color reaction with $CHCl_3$ and alkali:** Dis. 0.05 g. C̄ in 10 ml. 1% NaOH soln., add 5 drops $CHCl_3$, boil 20 sec. Initial color is blue (B), but unlike that from α-naphthol (1:1500) fades to colorless in 10 min. ⟨1⟩.

Ⓓ **β-Naphthol picrate:** $C_{10}H_7OH.PkOH$ — Dis. 0.10 g. C̄ and 0.15 g. PkOH in 6 ml. boilg. 50% alc., cool slowly, filter off yel.-or. cryst.; wash with 2 ml. 50% alc., dry on porous tile. M.p. 155.5–156.8° rap. htg. ⟨1⟩ [cf. ⟨2⟩].

Ⓓ **β-Naphthyl acetate:** from C̄ in ice cold alk. soln. by shaking with Ac_2O (100% yield); m.p. 71–72° ⟨3⟩.

Ⓓ **β-Naphthyl benzoate:** from C̄ by shaking alk. soln. with BzCl; m.p. 106–107° ⟨4⟩.

Ⓓ **β-Naphthyl *p*-nitrobenzoate:** m.p. 169° ⟨5⟩ ⟨6⟩.

Ⓓ **β-Naphthyl 3,5-dinitrobenzoate:** from C̄ + 3,5-dinitrobenzoyl chloride + pyridine; ndls. from alc., m.p. 210.2° cor. ⟨7⟩ [cf. T 1.47].

Ⓓ **β-Naphthyl benzenesulfonate:** from C̄ + benzenesulfonyl chloride in aq. alk.; ndls. from alc., m.p. 105–107° ⟨8⟩.

Ⓓ **β-Naphthyl *p*-toluenesulfonate:** from C̄ + *p*-toluenesulfonyl chloride + aq. alk.; lfts. from alc., m.p. 125° ⟨9⟩.

Ⓓ **β-Naphthyl *p*-nitrobenzyl ether:** m.p. 106° ⟨10⟩ [cf. T 1.44].

Ⓓ **β-Naphthyl 2,4-dinitrophenyl ether:** colorless hair-like ndls. from alc., m.p. 95° ⟨11⟩.

Ⓓ **β-Naphthoxyacetic acid:** cryst. from aq., m.p. 153–154.5° ⟨12⟩; Neut. Eq. 202 [cf. T 1.46].

Ⓓ **β-Naphthyl *N*-phenylcarbamate:** lfts. from alc., m.p. 155–156° ⟨13⟩.

Ⓓ **β-Naphthyl *N*-(α-naphthyl)carbamate:** from C̄ + α-naphthylisocyanate htd. with trace of anhydrous trimethyl (or triethyl)amine; cryst. from lgr., m.p. 156–157° ⟨14⟩ [cf. T 1.45].

Ⓓ **β-Naphthyl *N,N*-diphenylcarbamate:** m.p. 140.5–141.5° ⟨15⟩ [cf. T 1.43].

1:1540 ⟨1⟩ Mulliken, " Method " I, 108 (1904). ⟨2⟩ Baril, Hauber, *J. Am. Chem. Soc.* **53,** 1090 (1931). ⟨3⟩ Chattaway, *J. Chem. Soc.* **1931,** 2496 . ⟨4⟩ Autenrieth, Mühlinghaus, *Ber.* **40,** 749 (1907). ⟨5⟩ Meijer, *Rec. trav. chim.* **53,** 396 (1934). ⟨6⟩ Barnett, Nixon, *Chem. News* **129,** 190 (1924). ⟨7⟩ Phillips, Keenan, *J. Am. Chem. Soc.* **53,** 1926 (1931). ⟨8⟩ Georgescu, *Ber.* **24,** 417 (1891). ⟨9⟩ Reverdin, Crépieux, *Ber.* **34,** 2999 (1901); *Bull. soc. chim.* (3) **25,** 1047 (1901). ⟨10⟩ Lyman, Reid, *J. Am. Chem. Soc.* **42,** 615–619 (1920).

⟨11⟩ Bost, Nicholson, *J. Am. Chem. Soc.* **57,** 2369 (1935). ⟨12⟩ Koelsch, *J. Am. Chem. Soc.* **53,** 305 (1931). ⟨13⟩ Leuckart, *J. prakt. Chem.* (2) **41,** 320 (1890). ⟨14⟩ French, Wirtel, *J. Am. Chem. Soc.* **48,** 1738 (1926). ⟨15⟩ Herzog, *Ber.* **40,** 1834 (1907).

1:1541 3,3′-DIHYDROXYBIPHENYL $C_{12}H_{10}O_2$ **Beil. VI-991**
(m,m'-Biphenol)

M.P. 123-124°

Ndls. from hot aq.; sol. alc., ether, $CHCl_3$, C_6H_6.
$\bar{C}$ with $FeCl_3$ (T 1.41) gives a blue-violet color.

Ⓓ **3,3′-Diacetoxybiphenyl:** from $\bar{C}$ by htg. with Ac_2O + NaOAc; lfts. from dil. alc., m.p. 82.5° ⟨1⟩ ⟨2⟩.

Ⓓ **3,3′-Dimethoxybiphenyl:** from $\bar{C}$ in alk. soln. by shaking with dimethyl sulfate; ndls. from 45% alc., m.p. 36° ⟨1⟩ ⟨2⟩.

Ⓓ **3,3′-Dibenzoxybiphenyl:** from $\bar{C}$ in alk. soln. by shaking with BzCl; ndls. m.p. 92° ⟨2⟩.

1:1541 ⟨1⟩ Haeussermann, Teichmann, *Ber.* **27,** 2109 (1894). ⟨2⟩ Schultz, Kohlhaus, *Ber.* **39,** 3343–3344 (1906).

1:1544 1,3-DIHYDROXYNAPHTHALENE $C_{10}H_8O_2$ **Beil. VI-978**
(Naphthoresorcinol)

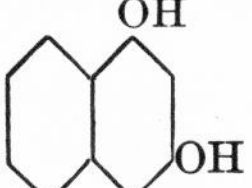

M.P. 124°

Lfts., sol. in aq., alc., ether, AcOH; spar. sol. C_6H_6, lgr.
$\bar{C}$ with $FeCl_3$ (T 1.41) gives milky turbidity, then a yel. ppt. — Alk. solns. of $\bar{C}$ turn brown in air.

Ⓓ **1,3-Diacetoxynaphthalene:** $\bar{C}$ with Ac_2O + AcONa at 100° gives prod., ndls. from AcOH, m.p. 55° ⟨1⟩.

1:1544 ⟨1⟩ Metzner, *Ann.* **298,** 390 (1897).

1:1545 *p*-TOLUHYDROQUINONE $C_7H_8O_2$ **Beil. VI-874**
(2-Methylhydroquinone;
toluquinol;
2,5-dihydroxytoluene)

M.P. 124-125°

Pl. from C_6H_6, xylene, toluene; or cryst. from aq. contg. $NaHSO_3$ — Very sol. aq., alc., ether — Spar. sol. C_6H_6, lgr.; insol. CS_2 — Subl. (on careful htg.) but not volatile with steam [dif. and sepn. from *p*-toluquinone (1:9007)].
$\bar{C}$ reduces NH_4OH + $AgNO_3$, Tollens' reagt. (T 1.11) and Fehling's soln. (T 1.22). $\bar{C}$ with alk. absorbs oxygen from air and gives blue-green color, turning dark brown — $\bar{C}$ in aq. NH_4OH turns red in air and shows orange fluorescence.
With $FeCl_3$ $\bar{C}$ yields corresp. quinhydrone (fine black ndls. from ether, m.p. 52°); but with excess reagt. gives *p*-toluquinone (1:9007) — With $Ca(OCl)_2$ soln. $\bar{C}$ gives blue-green color turning brown.
$\bar{C}$ oxidized with $Na_2Cr_2O_7$ + H_2SO_4 ⟨1⟩ yields *p*-toluquinone, m.p. 68° (1:9007).

Ⓓ **2-Methylhydroquinone diacetate:** from $\bar{C}$ boiled with Ac_2O for an hour; 100% yield; cryst. from hot aq. or AcOH, m.p. 49° ⟨2⟩. [The *mono* acetate, obtd. from $\bar{C}$ + Ac_2O at 0°, forms ndls. from pet. ether, m.p. 92°; sol. alk. ⟨2⟩.]

1:1545 ⟨1⟩ Kumagai, Wolffenstein, *Ber.* **41,** 299 (1908). ⟨2⟩ Schmid, *Monatsh.* **32,** 437–438 (1911).

1:1549 METHYL *p*-HYDROXYBENZOATE $C_8H_8O_3$ **Beil. X-158**

HO—⟨ ⟩—CO.OCH₃

M.P. 131°

With $FeCl_3$ (T 1.41) C̄ gives violet color.
For microchem. detectn. see ⟨1⟩.

Ⓓ **Saponification:** Hydrolysis with aq. alk. (T 1.51) gives Sap. Eq. of 152 and yields *p*-hydroxybenzoic acid (1:0840) and methyl alc. (1:6120).

Ⓓ **Methyl *p*-acetoxybenzoate:** from C̄ by warming with Ac_2O; cryst., m.p. 85° ⟨2⟩.

Ⓓ **Methyl *p*-benzoxybenzoate:** from C̄ by warming with BzCl, m.p. 135° ⟨2⟩. [This deriv. requires a mixed m.p. with original C̄ to be sure reaction has occurred.]

Ⓓ ***p*-Carbomethoxyphenyl *N*-phenylcarbamate:** from C̄ + $C_6H_5.N{=}C{=}O$ in ether; cryst. from C_6H_6, m.p. 134–135° ⟨2⟩. [This deriv. requires a mixed m.p. with original C̄ to be sure reaction has occurred.]

1:1549 ⟨1⟩ Fischer, Stauder, *Mikrochemie* **8,** 330–335 (1930). ⟨2⟩ von Hoessle, *J. prakt. Chem.* (2) **99,** 502 (1894). ⟨3⟩ Michael, Cobb, *Ann.* **363,** 88 (1908).

1:1550 *p*-CYCLOHEXYLPHENOL $C_{12}H_{16}O$ **Beil. VI-583**
(Hexahydro-*p*-hydroxy-biphenyl)

C_6H_{11}—⟨ ⟩—OH

M.P. 132°

Cryst. from C_6H_6 — Insol. cold aq.; dif. sol. hot aq. from which C̄ seps. in hair-like ndls. — Eas. sol. ether, fairly dif. sol. C_6H_6, lgr. — Volatile with steam.

C̄ is sol. in dil. NaOH or KOH but salts readily ppt. from conc. solns.

C̄ in 20 pts. $CHCl_3$ nitrated below 30° with 3 pts. conc. HNO_3 gave 94% yield ⟨1⟩, or C̄ in dry AcOEt nitrated with fumg. HNO_3 + P_2O_5 gave 73% yield ⟨2⟩ of 2,6-dinitro-4-cyclohexylphenol, cryst. from alc., m.p. 86.5–87° ⟨1⟩; 84–85° ⟨2⟩.

Ⓓ ***p*-Cyclohexylphenyl acetate:** from C̄ + Ac_2O in pyridine, m.p. 35° ⟨3⟩.

Ⓓ ***p*-Cyclohexylphenyl benzoate:** cryst. from MeOH, m.p. 118.5° ⟨4⟩.

Ⓓ ***p*-Cyclohexylphenyl *p*-nitrobenzoate:** from C̄ htd. with *p*-nitrobenzoic acid + $SOCl_2$ + $POCl_3$ (yield 15%); cryst. from alc., m.p. 137° ⟨5⟩.

Ⓓ ***p*-Cyclohexyl 3,5-dinitrobenzoate:** m.p. 168° cor. ⟨6⟩ [cf. T 1.47].

Ⓓ ***p*-Cyclohexylphenyl methyl ether:** from C̄ + dimethyl sulfate + alk.; cryst. from MeOH; m.p. 57–58° ⟨7⟩, m.p. 58° ⟨3⟩, 59° ⟨4⟩.

1:1550 ⟨1⟩ Baroni, Kleinau, *Monatsh.* **68,** 258 (1936). ⟨2⟩ Bartlett, Garland, *J. Am. Chem. Soc.* **55,** 2066–2067 (1933). ⟨3⟩ von Braun, *Ann.* **472,** 56 (1929). ⟨4⟩ Meyer, Bernhauer, *Monatsh.* **53**/**54,** 734 (1929). ⟨5⟩ Lilly, Garland, *J. Am. Chem. Soc.* **52,** 2114 (1930). ⟨6⟩ Phillips, Keenan, *J. Am. Chem. Soc.* **53,** 1926 (1931). ⟨7⟩ Bodroux, *Ann. chim.* (10) **11,** 559–560 (1929).

1:1555 PYROGALLOL $C_6H_6O_3$ **Beil. VI-1071**
(1,2,3-Trihydroxybenzene; pyrogallic acid)

OH
OH
OH

M.P. 133° **B.P. 309°**

Subl. undecomposed — Sol. in 2¼ pts. aq. at 13°; sol. alc., ether; spar. sol. C_6H_6, $CHCl_3$, CS_2.

C̄ in alk. soln. rapidly absorbs oxygen from air. [Use in gas anal.] [C̄ in aq. KOH absorbs O_2 more rapidly than in aq. NaOH ⟨1⟩ ⟨2⟩.]

C̄ in 1% aq. soln. gives with $FeCl_3$ (T 1.41) an OY-S_1 color, changing in 15 min. to OY-S_2; with dil. $FeCl_3$ gives bluish soln. — C̄ in alk. soln. gives with $FeCl_3$ a deep red complex ⟨3⟩.

C̄ reduces $NH_4OH + AgNO_3$ in cold.

C̄ with PkOH yields a picrate, C̄.PkOH, lemon-yel. cryst., m.p. 128–129° ⟨4⟩.

C̄ htd. with $Ac_2O + ZnCl_2$ in AcOH for 45 min. at 140–145° gives (54–57% yield) of gallacetophenone (2,3,4-trihydroxyacetophenone); cryst. from satd. aq. soln. of SO_2, straw colored ndls., m.p. 171–172° ⟨5⟩.

Ⓟ **Color reaction with glycerol-sulfuric acid:** To 2 ml. aq. add 5 drops 1% aq. soln. C̄, then 1 drop glycerol, then 2 ml. conc. H_2SO_4. Boil 20–25 sec. and *immediately* compare color against white background. Pyrogallol gives clear tint of violet red (VR-T_{1-2}). On contd. boiling or stdg. color intensifies but later becomes impure ⟨6⟩.

Ⓓ **Pyrogallol triacetate:** from C̄ in dil. aq. alk. on shaking ice cold soln. with Ac_2O; 92% yield; m.p. 172–173° ⟨7⟩.

Ⓓ **Pyrogallol tribenzoate:** from C̄ in dil. aq. alk. + excess BzCl (preferably in inert atmosphere to avoid darkening); pr. from alc., m.p. 89–90° ⟨8⟩. [Note that C̄ + BzCl in pyridine gives much monobenzoate, m.p. 140° but no dibenzoate, m.p. 108° along with the tribenzoate ⟨9⟩.]

Ⓓ **Pyrogallol tri-(*p*-nitrobenzoate):** m.p. 230°.

Ⓓ **Pyrogallol tri-(3,5-dinitrobenzoate):** m.p. 205° [cf. T 1.47].

Ⓓ **Pyrogallol tribenzenesulfonate:** from C̄ + BzCl in dil. aq. alk. ⟨10⟩ or in pyridine ⟨11⟩; cryst. from alc., m.p. 140–142° ⟨10⟩; 146° ⟨11⟩.

Ⓓ **Pyrogallol triglycolic acid:** from C̄ + 3 moles chloroacetic acid + aq. alk.; cryst. from hot aq., m.p. 198° ⟨14⟩ [cf. T 1.46].

Ⓓ **Pyrogallol tris-(*N*-phenylcarbamate):** m.p. 173° ⟨12⟩.

Ⓓ **Pyrogallol tris-(*N,N*-diphenylcarbamate):** m.p. 212° ⟨13⟩ [cf. T 1.43].

1:1555 ⟨1⟩ Henrich, *Ber.* **48,** 2006–2008 (1915). ⟨2⟩ Henrich, *Z. angew. Chem.* **29,** 149–152 (1916). ⟨3⟩ Weinland, Binder, *Ber.* **45,** 151 (1912). ⟨4⟩ Baril, Hauber, *J. Am. Chem. Soc.* **53,** 1090 (1931). ⟨5⟩ Badhwar, Venkataraman, *Organic Syntheses* **14,** 40–41 (1934). ⟨6⟩ Mulliken, "Method" I, 110 (1904). ⟨7⟩ Chattaway, *J. Chem. Soc.* **1931,** 2496. ⟨8⟩ Skraup, *Monatsh.* **10,** 391 (1889). ⟨9⟩ Einhorn, Hollandt, *Ann.* **301,** 105–107 (1898). ⟨10⟩ Georgescu, *Ber.* **24,** 418 (1891).
⟨11⟩ von Wacek, *Oesterr. Chem. Ztg.* **40,** 63–64 (1937). ⟨12⟩ Snape, *Ber.* **18,** 2480 (1885). ⟨13⟩ Herzog, *Ber.* **40,** 1833 (1907). ⟨14⟩ Giacosa, *J. prakt. Chem.* (2) **19,** 398–399 (1879).

1:1560 *p*-HYDROXYBENZOPHENONE $C_{13}H_{10}O_2$ Beil. VIII-158

(*p*-Benzoylphenol)

C_6H_5–CO–C_6H_4–OH

M.P. 134-135°

Cryst. from aq., dil. MeOH, or C_6H_6 + lgr. — Very sol. alc., ether, AcOH; spar. sol. aq.

C̄ reduced with amalgamated Zn + HCl gives nearly quant. yield of *p*-benzylphenol (1:1485), m.p. 83–84° ⟨1⟩.

[For prepn. of C̄ from phenyl benzoate by htg. with $AlCl_3$ at 140° for 15 min. (quant. yield) see ⟨2⟩.]

Ⓓ ***p*-Acetoxybenzophenone:** from C̄ + Ac_2O in pyridine; ndls. from MeOH, m.p. 81° ⟨3⟩.

Ⓓ ***p*-Benzoxybenzophenone:** m.p. 114–115° ⟨4⟩.

Ⓓ **p-Hydroxybenzophenone oxime:** from C̄ on boiling 4–5 hrs. with an alc. soln. of $NH_2OH.HCl$ + aq. NaOH; upon passing in CO_2 a mixt. of two stereoisomers is pptd. as an oil which solidifies on stdg. By fractional pptn. from AcOH soln. this may be separated into a low melting form, m.p. 81°, and a higher melting form, m.p. 152°. The former rapidly changes to latter on warming at 80° ⟨5⟩.

Ⓓ **p-Hydroxybenzophenone phenylhydrazone:** from C̄ in least possible alc. by htg. with phenylhydrazine 1 hr. at 160°; cryst. from pet. ether, m.p. 144° ⟨6⟩.

Ⓓ **p-Hydroxybenzophenone 2,4-dinitrophenylhydrazone:** or. cryst., m.p. 242.4° cor. ⟨7⟩ [cf. T 1.14].

Ⓓ **p-Hydroxybenzophenone semicarbazone:** from C̄ in alc. htd. at 100° with an aq. soln. of semicarbazide HCl + KOAc; cryst. from C_6H_6, m.p. 194° ⟨6⟩.

1:1560 ⟨1⟩ Clemmensen, *Ber.* **47,** 682 (1914). ⟨2⟩ Rosenmund, Schnurr, *Ann.* **460,** 89 (1928). ⟨3⟩ Blakey, Jones, Scarborough, *J. Chem. Soc.* **1927,** 2867. ⟨4⟩ Adickes, von Müllenheim, Simson, *Ber.* **66,** 1904 (1933). ⟨5⟩ Smith, *Ber.* **24,** 4040–4041 (1891). ⟨6⟩ Huber, Brunner, *Monatsh.* **66,** 328–329 (1930). ⟨7⟩ Ferrante, Bloom, *Am. J. Pharm.* **105,** 383 (1933).

1:1565 FUROIN $C_{10}H_8O_4$ Beil. XIX-204

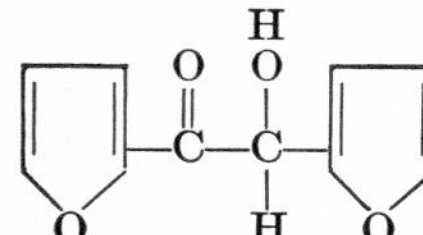

M.P. 135°; 138-139° cor.

Nearly colorless cryst. (about Y-T_3) — Dif. sol. aq., alc., ether; sol. warm alc., toluene. Crude product is apt to be dark brown and sticky but can be purified by air drying and stdg. with ether which removes a black tar. After several such treatments C̄ is further purified by soln. in hot alc. (3–4 pts.) and pptd. by slowly pouring into 5 vols. aq. with rapid stirring ⟨1⟩.

C̄ with $FeCl_3$ (T 1.41) gives no coloration, but is eas. sol. in cold NaOH to deep bluish green soln., very deep violet red by transmitted light; color discharged on diln. after first changing to green — C̄ is sol. in conc. H_2SO_4 with deep blue-green color.

C̄, rapidly cooled from its soln. in 12 pts. hot alc., and the resultant cryst. mass. redissolved by addn. of min. amt. aq. NaOH, gives green soln.; on addn. of equal vol. of aq. and leading through a stream of air at 0°, the green color disappears and is replaced by a smutty brown, together with a ppt. of furil. On further addn. of aq. the pptn. of furil is nearly quant.; recrystd. from alc., golden ndls., m.p. 162° (165°) ⟨2⟩.

C̄ (5 g.) + nitrobenzene (4 g.) in alc. (50 ml.) boiled 2–3 min. with 2 ml. 6% NaOEt gives on cooling 94% yield furil (1:9065), m.p. 162° ⟨3⟩ — C̄ on treatment at 100° for 2 hrs. with aq. soln. of $CuSO_4$ + pyridine gives (63% yield) furil (1:9065), yel. ndls. from MeOH, m.p. 165–166° ⟨4⟩ — C̄ in MeOH treated with NaOMe + I_2 gives (80% yield) furil (1:9065), yel. cryst. from C_6H_6, m.p. 164–165° cor. ⟨1⟩.

[For prepn. of C̄ from furfural (1:0185) + alc. KCN in 37.5% yield see ⟨4⟩.]

Ⓟ **Color test:** C̄ in MeOH added to NaOMe soln. gives navy blue color, much intensified if furil is also present ⟨1⟩.

Ⓓ **Furoin acetate:** from C̄ on boiling with Ac_2O; ndls., m.p. 76–77° ⟨2⟩.

Ⓓ **Furoin benzoate:** m.p. 92–93°.

Ⓓ **Furoin oxime:** C̄ in 4 pts. alc. + 6 pts. aq. shaken 2–3 hrs. with 1 mole NaOH + excess NH_2OH gives pale yel. soln. from which CO_2 ppts. 50% yield of furoin α-oxime, pr. from alc., m.p. 160–161° — From the filtrate ether extracts (25% yield) furoin β-oxime, pale yel. cryst., m.p. 102° ⟨5⟩ ⟨6⟩.

Ⓓ **Furoin phenylhydrazone:** from C̄ in 2 pts. alc. on warming 30 min. with slight excess phenylhydrazine + few drops AcOH; ndls. from lgr. + C_6H_6, m.p. 79–81° ⟨6⟩.
Ⓓ **Furoin 2,4-dinitrophenylhydrazone:** orange-red cryst. from alc., m.p. 216–217° ⟨7⟩.

1:1565 ⟨1⟩ Corson, McAllister, *J. Am. Chem. Soc.* **51,** 2824–2825 (1929). ⟨2⟩ Fischer, *Ann.* **211,** 221 (1882). ⟨3⟩ Nisbet, *J. Chem. Soc.* **1928,** 3124. ⟨4⟩ Hartmann, Dickey, *J. Am. Chem. Soc.* **55,** 1229 (1933). ⟨5⟩ Werner, Detscheff, *Ber.* **38,** 79 (1905). ⟨6⟩ Macnair, *Ann.* **258,** 222–223 (1890). ⟨7⟩ Campbell, *Analyst* **61,** 393 (1936).

—— **β-RESORCYLALDEHYDE** (2,4-Dihydroxybenzaldehyde) CHO, OH, OH $C_7H_6O_3$ **Beil. VIII-241**

M.P. 135-136°

See 1:0065. Genus 1: Aldehydes.

1:1570 HYDROXYHYDROQUINONE (1,2,4-Trihydroxybenzene) OH, OH, OH $C_6H_6O_3$ **Beil. VI-1087**

M.P. 140.5°

Pl. from ether — Very eas. sol. aq., alc., ether, AcOEt; insol. $CHCl_3$, CS_2, C_6H_6, lgr.

C̄ in aq. soln. rapidly turns brown in air — C̄ in alk. or NH_4OH soln. turns violet in air. [Alk. soln. of C̄ absorbs oxygen as well as alk. pyrogallol; reagt. prepd. by making alk. soln. of hydroxyhydroquinone triacetate (see below) which is usual comml. form ⟨1⟩ ⟨2⟩.]

C̄ in very dil. aq. soln. gives with $FeCl_3$ (T 1.41) transient green, which on addn. of Na_2CO_3 changes first to dark blue, then to wine red; C̄ in conc. aq. soln. gives with $FeCl_3$ dark floc. ppt. — C̄ with conc. H_2SO_4 gives green soln. grad. changing to violet; on warming soln. becomes dark cherry red.

C̄ after fusion with phthalic anhydride (T 1.42) gives alk. soln. showing strong greenish fluorescence ⟨3⟩ but on further addn. of alk. fluores. disappears.

C̄ rubbed with excess dry Br_2 in porcelain dish, excess reagt. evapd., and residue recrystd. first from alc., then from $CHCl_3$, yields or.-red. granules of tribromohydroxybenzoquinone [Beil. VIII-240], m.p. 206–207° ⟨4⟩.

C̄ with PkOH yields picrate, C̄.PkOH, or.-red cryst., m.p. 96° ⟨5⟩.

Ⓓ **1,2,4-Triacetoxybenzene (hydroxyhydroquinone triacetate):** from C̄ on refluxing several hrs. with equal wt. fused NaOAc + 10 pts. Ac_2O; crude prod. pptd. by pouring into aq.; then dried and recrystd. from abs. alc., white ndls., m.p. 96–97° ⟨4⟩. [For prepn. in 86–87% yield from benzoquinone + Ac_2O see ⟨6⟩; for hydrolysis to C̄ by htg. in 2 pts. MeOH with 0.2 pt. conc. HCl for 1 hr. (80% yield) see ⟨7⟩.]

Ⓓ **1,2,4-Tribenzoxybenzene (hydroxyhydroquinone tribenzoate):** from C̄ + BzCl in presence of dil. alk., or alk. carbonates, or pyridine; lfts. from alc., m.p. 120° ⟨8⟩ [much less easily saponified than triacetate].

1:1570 ⟨1⟩ Henrich, *Ber.* **48,** 2008 (1915). ⟨2⟩ Henrich, *Z. angew. Chem.* **29,** 152 (1916). ⟨3⟩ Formânek, Knop, *Z. anal. Chem.* **56,** 294 (1917). ⟨4⟩ Barth, Schreder, *Monatsh.* **5,** 593–594 (1884). ⟨5⟩ Baril, Hauber, *J. Am. Chem. Soc.* **53,** 1090 (1931). ⟨6⟩ Vliet, *Organic Syntheses, Coll. Vol.* I, 310–311 (1932). ⟨7⟩ Healey, Robinson, *J. Chem. Soc.* **1934,** 1626–1627. ⟨8⟩ Thiele, Jaeger, *Ber.* **34,** 2837 (1901).

1:1572 1,8-DIHYDROXYNAPHTHALENE $C_{10}H_8O_2$ **Beil. VI-981**

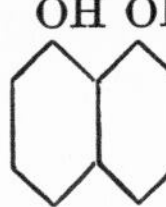

M.P. 142° ⟨2⟩

Crystals from AcOH by diln. with aq. — Spar. sol. aq. or lgr.; sol. ether, C_6H_6.

$FeCl_3$ (T 1.41) yields white flocks becoming dark green — C̄ with HNO_2 yields yellow flocks, sol. in alk. or NH_4OH with intense orange color — C̄ dis. in cold conc. H_2SO_4 with greenish gold color.

C̄ shaken with aq. Na_2CO_3 + $(CH_3)_2SO_4$ yields 1,8-dimethoxynaphthalene, lfts. from pet. ether, m.p. 50° ⟨1⟩.

Ⓓ **1,8-Diacetoxynaphthalene:** from C̄ with hot Ac_2O + pyridine; pl. from Ac_2O, m.p. 155° ⟨2⟩. [Use in purifn. of comml. C̄ via hydrolysis with HCl in AcOH ⟨2⟩.]

Ⓓ **1,8-Dibenzoxynaphthalene:** from C̄ + BzCl + pyridine (cf. T 1.47); m.p. 174–175°.

1:1572 ⟨1⟩ Heller, Kretzschmann, *Ber.* **54,** 1106 (1921). ⟨2⟩ Green, *J. Chem. Soc.* **1927,** 2342–2343.

1:1576 3,4-DIHYDROXYBIPHENYL $C_{12}H_{10}O_2$ **Beil. VI-990**
(Phenylpyrocatechol)

M.P. 145° ⟨2⟩

Sol. alc., acetone, $CHCl_3$, C_6H_6; cold satd. aq. soln. conts. 1.6 g./liter.

C̄ with $FeCl_3$ (T 1.41) gives light green color, changing to reddish brown on stdg., or to deep violet on addn. of Na_2CO_3 — C̄ reduces Tollens' soln. (T 1.11) and gives ppt. with $Pb(NO_3)_2$ soln. or Br_2-aq. ⟨1⟩.

Ⓓ **3,4-Diacetoxybiphenyl:** m.p. 77.5–78° ⟨1⟩.

1:1576 ⟨1⟩ Norris, Macintire, Corse, *Am. Chem. J.* **29,** 128 (1903). ⟨2⟩ Harvey, U. S. 1,952,755 (March 27, 1934).

—— ***p*-HYDROXYPHENYLACETIC ACID** $C_8H_8O_3$ **Beil. X-190**

HO—C_6H_4—$CH_2.COOH$

M.P. 148°

See 1:0500. Genus 3: Acids.

—— **DIMETHYLDIHYDRORESORCINOL** $C_8H_{12}O_2$ **Beil. VII-559**
(" Methone "; " Dimedone ")

$(CH_3)_2$ C.CH_2.CO.CH_2.CO.CH_2

M.P. 148-150° dec.

See 1:0768. Genus 3: Acids.

—— **PROTOCATECHUALDEHYDE** $C_7H_6O_2$ **Beil. VIII-246**
(3,4-Dihydroxybenzaldehyde)

M.P. 153-154° dec.

See 1:0073. Genus 1: Aldehydes.

1:1579 2,2′-DIHYDROXY-5,5′-DIMETHYLBIPHENYL $C_{14}H_{14}O_2$ **Beil. VI-1010**
(3,3′-Bi-*p*-cresol)

H_3C CH_3 OH OH

M.P. 153-154°

Cryst. from aq., C_6H_6 or toluene — Sublimable.
$\bar{C}$ with $FeCl_3$ (T 1.41) gives no color either in aq. or alc., but $\bar{C}$ is sol. in aq. NaOH.
$\bar{C}$ htd. with 3 pts. $ZnCl_2$ for $1\frac{1}{2}$ hrs. at 270–280° yields 3,6-dimethyldiphenylene oxide, volatile with steam; scales from dil. alc., m.p. 64° ⟨1⟩ ⟨2⟩.

Ⓓ **2,2′-Diacetoxy-5,5′-dimethylbiphenyl:** m.p. 88° ⟨3⟩ ⟨4⟩.
Ⓓ **2,2′-Dimethoxy-5,5′-dimethylbiphenyl:** ndls. from 70% alc., m.p. 61° u.c. ⟨4⟩.

1:1579 ⟨1⟩ Sugii, Shindo, *J. Pharm. Soc. Japan* **53,** 97–99 (1933); *Cent.* **1933,** II, 1678. ⟨2⟩ Sugii, Shindo, *J. Pharm. Soc. Japan* **53,** 571–579 (1933); *Chem. Abs.* **28,** 151 (1934). ⟨3⟩ Fichter, Ackerman, *Helv. Chim. Acta* **2,** 597 (1919). ⟨4⟩ Pummerer, Puttfarcken, Schopflocker, *Ber.* **58,** 1815–1816 (1925).

—— **SALICYCLIC ACID** $C_7H_6O_3$ **Beil. X-43**
(*o*-Hydroxybenzoic acid)

—OH —COOH

M.P. 158° cor.

See 1:0780. Genus 3: Acids.

1:1580 4,4′-DIHYDROXY-3,3′-DIMETHYLBIPHENYL $C_{14}H_{14}O_2$ **Beil. VI-1009**

HO OH CH_3 CH_3

M.P. 160-161° ⟨1⟩ ⟨2⟩

Ndls. from hot aq. or aq. alc.; cryst. from CCl_4, toluene or C_6H_6 — Eas. sol. alc., ether, AcOH, boil. C_6H_6; dif. sol. aq.
$\bar{C}$ with $FeCl_3$ (T 1.41) gives grass green flocks ⟨2⟩.

Ⓓ **4,4′-Diacetoxy-3,3′-dimethylbiphenyl:** from K salt on boilg. with AcOH; ndls. from alc., m.p. 131° ⟨3⟩; 135.5° ⟨2⟩.
Ⓓ **4,4′-Dibenzoxy-3,3′-dimethylbiphenyl:** from $\bar{C}$ + BzCl in alk. soln., ndls. from AcOH, m.p. 185° ⟨3⟩.

1:1580 ⟨1⟩ Goldschmidt, Schulz, Bernard, *Ann.* **478,** 20 (1930). ⟨2⟩ Fichter, Ackerman, *Helv. Chim. Acta* **2,** 596 (1919). ⟨3⟩ Hobbs, *Ber.* **21,** 1067 (1888).

1:1581 2,4′-DIHYDROXYBIPHENYL $C_{12}H_{10}O_2$ **Beil. VI-990**
(*o,p′*-Biphenol)

OH OH

M.P. 162-163° B.P. 342°

Eas. sol. alc., ether; insol. toluene; spar. sol. hot aq.
$\bar{C}$ in aq. soln. gives with $FeCl_3$ (T 1.41) a faint brown color followed by pptn. of flocks.
$\bar{C}$ dis. in pure conc. H_2SO_4 yielding colorless soln.

C̄ in abs. MeOH htd. 45 min. with 2 moles KOH + 2 moles CH_3I yields 2,4′-dimethoxybiphenyl, cryst. from alc., m.p. 70° ⟨1⟩.

Ⓓ **2,4′-Diacetoxybiphenyl:** from C̄ on boiling with Ac_2O; lfts. from alc., m.p. 94° ⟨2⟩.

1:1581 ⟨1⟩ Finzi, Mangini, *Gazz. chim. ital.* **62,** 1202 (1932). ⟨2⟩ Schultz, Schmidt, Strasser, *Ann.* **207,** 358 (1881).

1:1583 2,2′-DIHYDROXY-6,6′-DIMETHYLBIPHENYL $C_{14}H_{14}O_2$ Beil. S.N. 563

CH_3 CH_3

OH OH

M.P. 164° ⟨1⟩

Pl. from dil. alc. — Sublimable.

C̄ htd. with $ZnCl_2$ yields 4,5-dimethyldiphenylene oxide, volatile with steam, pl. from alc., m.p. 62° ⟨1⟩.

Ⓓ **2,2′-Diacetoxy-6,6′-dimethylbiphenyl:** pr. from alc., m.p. 87° ⟨1⟩.

Ⓓ **2,2′-Dibenzoxy-6,6′-dimethylbiphenyl:** ndls. from alc., m.p. 136° ⟨1⟩.

1:1583 ⟨1⟩ Sugii, Shindo, *J. Pharm. Soc. Japan* **54,** 149–153 (1934); *Cent.* **1935,** I, 698; *Chem. Abs.* **29,** 791 (1935).

1:1585 4-HYDROXYBIPHENYL $C_{12}H_{10}O$ Beil. VI-674

(*p*-Phenylphenol; *p*-xenol)

—OH

M.P. 164-165° B.P. 305-308° (319°)

Lfts. from dil. alc., C_6H_6, or toluene — Only slightly volatile with steam — Eas. sol. alc., ether, $CHCl_3$; dif. sol. cold pet. ether.

Sol. in hot NH_4OH or Na_2CO_3 but is extracted even from alk. solns. by ether. Gives no coloration with $FeCl_3$ (T 1.41).

C̄ in $CHCl_3$ treated with 1 mole Br_2 (in $CHCl_3$) gives 3-bromo-4-hydroxybiphenyl, m.p. 96° ⟨1⟩; C̄ in $CHCl_3$ treated with 2 moles Br_2 (in $CHCl_3$) gives 100% yield 3,5-dibromo-4-hydroxybiphenyl, ndls. from $CHCl_3$ + lt. pet., m.p. 91–94° (96) ⟨1⟩.

Ⓓ ***p*-Xenyl acetate:** from C̄ by refluxing with Ac_2O + drop of conc. H_2SO_4 (100% yield) ⟨2⟩ or by refluxing with Ac_2O + NaOAc (alm. 100% yield) ⟨3⟩; cryst. from EtOH or MeOH, m.p. 87–88°.

Ⓓ ***p*-Xenyl benzoate:** from C̄ on htg. with BzCl ⟨4⟩; or by shaking with BzCl + aq. alk. ⟨5⟩; cryst. from alc., m.p. 150–151° ⟨4⟩ ⟨6⟩; 148.5–149.5° ⟨7⟩; 147–148° ⟨5⟩ [a m.p. of 121° has also been reported ⟨8⟩].

Ⓓ ***p*-Xenyl benzenesulfonate:** from C̄ + benzenesulfonyl chloride in pyridine (66% yield); cryst. from MeOH or dil. alc., m.p. 104–105° ⟨9⟩.

Ⓓ ***p*-Xenyl *p*-toluenesulfonate:** from C̄ + *p*-toluenesulfonyl chloride in pyridine (75% yield); pl. from 1:1 alc. + acetone or C_6H_6 + lgr.; m.p. 178.5–179.5° ⟨9⟩; cryst. from AcOH, m.p. 177° ⟨9⟩ ⟨10⟩.

Ⓓ ***p*-Xenyl 2,4-dinitrophenyl ether:** from C̄ + equiv. aq. NaOH + 2,4-dinitrochlorobenzene; faintly greenish yel. ndls. from alc., m.p. 118° ⟨11⟩.

1:1585 ⟨1⟩ Bell, Robinson, *J. Chem. Soc.* **1927,** 1132. ⟨2⟩ Cheetham, Hey, *J. Chem. Soc.* **1937,** 771. ⟨3⟩ Hazlet, Kornberg, *J. Am. Chem. Soc.* **61,** 3037 (1939). ⟨4⟩ Blicke, Weinkauff, *J. Am. Chem. Soc.* **54,** 331 (1932). ⟨5⟩ Friebel, Rassow, *J. prakt. Chem.* (2) **63,** 455 (1901).

⟨6⟩ Kaiser, *Ann.* **257**, 101 (1890). ⟨7⟩ Harris, Christiansen, *J. Am. Pharm. Assoc.* **24**, 553–557 (1935). ⟨8⟩ Raiford, Colbert, *J. Am. Chem. Soc.* **47**, 1456 (1925). ⟨9⟩ Hazlet, *J. Am. Chem. Soc.* **59**, 287 (1937). ⟨10⟩ Bell, Kenyon, *J. Chem. Soc.* **1926**, 3049.
⟨11⟩ Bost, Nicholson, *J. Am. Chem. Soc.* **57**, 2369 (1935).

1:1590 HYDROQUINONE HO—⟨ ⟩—OH $C_6H_6O_2$ **Beil. VI-836**
(1,4-Dihydroxybenzene; quinol)

M.P. 171° **B.P. 286°**

Subl. undecomposed 10° below m.p. — At 15° 100 pts. satd. aq. soln. conts. 5.8 pts. $\bar{C}$; eas. sol. alc., ether; very dif. sol. cold C_6H_6 (0.2 g. per liter) [sepn. from pyrocatechol (**1**:1520)].

$\bar{C}$ in cold satd. aq. soln. gives with excess $FeCl_3$ (T 1.41) a YO color [green ndls. of quinhydrone (see below) may separate as intermediate, but excess $FeCl_3$ yields quinone (1:9025)] — $\bar{C}$ in alk. soln. turns brown in air — $\bar{C}$ reduces Fehling's soln. (T 1.22) in cold; ammoniacal $AgNO_3$ on warming.

$\bar{C}$ with PkOH yields a picrate, light yel. cryst., m.p. 115–117° ⟨1⟩.

$\bar{C}$ shaken with excess dimethyl sulfate + 5 N aq. NaOH yields hydroquinone dimethyl ether (1:7160), m.p. 56° ⟨2⟩. [Hydroquinone monomethyl ether (1:1435) also has m.p. 56° but is sol. in alk.]

Ⓟ **Quinhydrone formation:** HO—⟨ ⟩—OH.O=⟨ ⟩=O: To 0.1 g. $\bar{C}$ in 3 ml. aq. slowly add 2–3 ml. 10% $FeCl_3$ soln.; ppt. of green ndls. of the quinhydrone separates.

Ⓓ **1,4-Diacetoxybenzene (hydroquinone diacetate):** from $\bar{C}$ in 98% yield on shaking ice cold alk. soln. with Ac_2O; lfts. from aq. or alc., m.p. 123° ⟨3⟩. [Hydroquinone monoacetate; pr. from pet. eth., m.p. 62–63° ⟨15⟩.]

Ⓓ **1,4-Dibenzoxybenzene (hydroquinone dibenzoate):** from $\bar{C}$ + 2 moles BzCl + aq. alk. ⟨4⟩, or by htg. $\bar{C}$ with BzCl ⟨5⟩ ⟨6⟩; m.p. 199°; cryst. from toluene, m.p. 204° cor. ⟨6⟩. [Hydroquinone monobenzoate: cryst. from boilg. aq. or dry MeOH, m.p. 163° ⟨14⟩.]

Ⓓ **Hydroquinone di-(*p*-nitrobenzoate):** cryst. from alc., m.p. 258° ⟨7⟩ ⟨8⟩ [cf. T 1.47].

Ⓓ **Hydroquinone bis-(3,5-dinitrobenzoate):** m.p. 317°.

Ⓓ **Hydroquinone di-(benzenesulfonate):** from $\bar{C}$ + benzenesulfonyl chloride + alk.; pale yel. cryst., m.p. 120–121° ⟨9⟩.

Ⓓ **Hydroquinone di-(*p*-toluenesulfonate):** from $\bar{C}$ + *p*-toluenesulfonyl chloride in pyridine in cold (26% yield); lfts. from 25 pts. alc., m.p. 159° ⟨10⟩. [The mono-*p*-toluenesulfonate forms ndls. from C_6H_6, m.p. 98–99° ⟨10⟩.]

Ⓓ **Hydroquinone diglycolic acid:** HOOC.CH_2O—⟨ ⟩—O.CH_2.COOH: from $\bar{C}$ + 2 moles chloroacetic acid + aq. alk.; cryst. from AcOH, m.p. 250–251° ⟨11⟩ [cf. T 1.46].

Ⓓ **Hydroquinone bis-(*N*-phenylcarbamate):** from $\bar{C}$ + phenylisocyanate; pr. browning at 200° and melting 205–207° ⟨12⟩; m.p. 224° ⟨13⟩.

1:1590 ⟨1⟩ Baril, Hauber, *J. Am. Chem. Soc.* **53**, 1090 (1931). ⟨2⟩ Vermeulen, *Rec. trav. chim.* **25**, 28 (1906). ⟨3⟩ Chattaway, *J. Chem. Soc.* **1931**, 2496. ⟨4⟩ Echtermeier, *Arch. Pharm.* **244**, 55 (1906). ⟨5⟩ Doebner, Wolff, *Ber.* **12**, 661 (1879). ⟨6⟩ Bogert, Howells, *J. Am. Chem. Soc.* **52**, 846 (1930). ⟨7⟩ Barnett, Nixon, *Chem. News* **129**, 191 (1924). ⟨8⟩ Meijer, *Rec. trav. chim.* **53**, 394 (1934). ⟨9⟩ Georgescu, *Ber.* **24**, 418 (1891). ⟨10⟩ Borsche, Frank, *Ann.* **450**, 84 (1926).
⟨11⟩ Bischoff, Fröhlich, *Ber.* **40**, 2797 (1907). ⟨12⟩ Snape, *Ber.* **18**, 2429 (1885). ⟨13⟩ Morgan, Pettet, *J. Chem. Soc.* **1931**, 1125. ⟨14⟩ Kehrmann, Sandoz, Monnier, *Helv. Chim. Acta* **4**, 943 (1921). ⟨15⟩ Olcott, *J. Am. Chem. Soc.* **59**, 393 (1937).

1:1592 1,4-DIHYDROXYNAPHTHALENE $C_{10}H_8O_2$ **Beil. VI-979**
(α-Naphthohydroquinone)

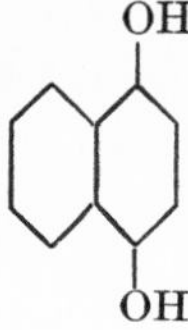

M.P. 176° (192° ⟨3⟩)

Sol. alc., ether, AcOH; mod. sol. hot aq.; insol. CS_2, lgr., cold C_6H_6.

$\bar{C}$, with conc. H_2SO_4, gives violet color — $\bar{C}$ turns red or blue in air — $\bar{C}$ with boiling $FeCl_3$ gives α-naphthoquinone, m.p. 125°.

[For prepn. via reduction of α-naphthoquinone (1:9040) with $SnCl_2$ + HCl see ⟨1⟩.]

Ⓓ **1,4-Diacetoxynaphthalene:** from $\bar{C}$ + Ac_2O; tbls. from alc., m.p. 128–130° ⟨2⟩; 128° ⟨3⟩.

Ⓓ **1,4-Dibenzoxynaphthalene:** from $\bar{C}$ + Bz_2O on htg.; cryst. from AcOH, m.p. 169° ⟨4⟩.

1:1592 ⟨1⟩ Russig, *J. prakt. Chem.* (2) **62,** 32–33 (1900). ⟨2⟩ Korn, *Ber.* **17,** 3025 (1884). ⟨3⟩ Wolff, *Ann.* **399,** 279 (1913). ⟨4⟩ Panizzon-Favre, *Gazz. chim. ital.* **54,** 833 (1924).

1:1594 2,7-DIHYDROXYNAPHTHALENE $C_{10}H_8O_2$ **Beil. VI-985**

HO— —OH

M.P. 185-186°

Ndls. from aq. — Sublimes (with some decompn.) in lfts. — Practically non-volatile with steam — Eas. sol. hot aq., sol. alc., ether; mod. sol. $CHCl_3$, C_6H_6; insol. lgr., CS_2.

Alkali or even ether solns. rapidly darken in air — With $FeCl_3$ (T 1.41) shows transient blue or blue green color. [With $FeCl_3$ under carefully controlled conditions $\bar{C}$ gives 68% yield of 2,2′,7,7′-tetrahydroxybinaphthyl-1,1′, cryst. with 2 H_2O from aq. contg. SO_2, m.p. 114°; air dried anhydrous prod. m.p. 214° ⟨1⟩] — $\bar{C}$ with $Ca(OCl)_2$ soln. gives dark red color changing to brown.

$\bar{C}$ with aq. KOH + dimethyl sulfate gives 2,7-dimethoxynaphthalene, ndls. from alc., m.p. 138° ⟨2⟩. [The monomethyl deriv., 7-methoxy-2-hydroxynaphthalene, ndls. from alc., m.p. 113–114°, has also been reported ⟨3⟩.]

Ⓓ **2,7-Diacetoxynaphthalene:** from $\bar{C}$ + AcCl; cryst. from AcOH, m.p. 136° ⟨4⟩. [The monoacetyl cpd., ndls. from MeOH, m.p. 171–172°, has been obtd. from $\bar{C}$ by actn. of Ac_2O on warm alk. soln. ⟨5⟩.]

Ⓓ **2,7-Dibenzoxynaphthalene:** from $\bar{C}$ by htg. with Bz_2O at 150°; cryst. from alc., m.p. 139° ⟨4⟩. [The monobenzoyl cpd., ndls. from xylene or MeOH, m.p. 199° has been obtd. from $\bar{C}$ by actn. of BzCl on warm alk. soln. ⟨5⟩.]

Ⓓ **2,7-Di-*p*-toluenesulfonyloxynaphthalene:** from $\bar{C}$ + *p*-toluenesulfonyl chloride + aq. alk.; cryst. from AcOEt or CCl_4; m.p. 150° ⟨6⟩.

Ⓓ **2,7-Dihydroxynaphthalene bis-(*N,N*-diphenylcarbamate):** m.p. 176° ⟨5⟩ [cf. T 1.43]. [The corresponding mono-derivative (7-hydroxynaphthyl *N,N*-diphenylcarbamate), cryst. from xylene + *p*-dichlorobenzene, m.p. 261°, has been obtd. from $\bar{C}$ by actn. of diphenylcarbamyl chloride + KOH in acetone ⟨5⟩.]

1:1594 ⟨1⟩ Brass, Patzelt, *Ber.* **70,** 1344–1345 (1937). ⟨2⟩ Fischer, Kern, *J. prakt. Chem.* (2) **94,** 34–35 (1916). ⟨3⟩ Bünzly, Decker, *Ber.* **38,** 3272 (1905). ⟨4⟩ Clausius, *Ber.* **23,** 520 (1890). ⟨5⟩ Lesser, Kranepuhl, Gad, *Ber.* **58,** 2122–2123 (1925). ⟨6⟩ Reverdin, Crépieux, *Ber.* **34,** 3000 (1901); *Bull. soc. chim.* (3) **25,** 1047 (1901).

1:1595 CONIFERIN $C_{16}H_{22}O_8$ **Beil. XXXI-221**

(Coniferyl β-*d*-glucopyranoside)

HO.CH₂.C.C.C.C—C—O—⟨ring⟩—CH:CH.CH₂OH (H, H, OH, H, H above; OH, H, OH below; ring O bridge; OCH₃ on ring)

M.P. 185.5°

Colorless ndls. with 2 H_2O from aq. becoming anhydrous in dry air or at 100° — Sol. in 200 pts. cold aq.; spar. sol. alc., insol. ether. $[\alpha]_D^{20} = -70.1°$ based on anhydrous C̄ in water at $c = 0.4$; $-40.8°$ in pyridine at $c = 1.5$ ⟨1⟩.

C̄ gives Molisch carbohydrate test (Generic Test 2) but is excluded from Genus 2 by its coloration in supplementary test 2 with conc. H_2SO_4 — C̄ with warm conc. H_2SO_4 gives violet soln. changing to deep red, and giving a blue ppt. on addn. of a little water — C̄ on warming with conc. HCl gives an intense cobalt blue.

C̄ gives no color with $FeCl_3$ nor any ppt. with $Pb(OAc_2)_2$.

C̄ on boiling with dil. H_2SO_4 hydrolyzes to *d*-glucose (1:0305) and an amorph. polymerization prod. of coniferyl alc. (Beil. VI-1131) — On distn. of acid, neutral, or alk. soln. C̄ splits off H.CHO, especially after hydrolysis ⟨2⟩.

Ⓓ **Tetraacetylconiferin:** from anhyd. C̄ on htg. 5–6 hrs. at 100° with 7 pts. Ac_2O, shaking with aq. to destroy excess Ac_2O, and purifying resinous prod. by pptn. from alc. soln. with aq.; m.p. 125–126° after softening at 90° ⟨3⟩.

Ⓓ **Tribenzoylconiferin:** from C̄ by shaking with 10% NaOH + BzCl; prod. purified by pptn. from alc. soln. with aq.; amorphous ppt., m.p. 80° after softening at 58° ⟨2⟩.

1:1595 ⟨1⟩ Zemplén, *Z. physiol. Chem.* **85,** 418 (1913). ⟨2⟩ Klein, *Biochem. Z.* **169,** 132 (1926). ⟨3⟩ Tiemann, Nagai, *Ber.* **8,** 1140–1141 (1875). ⟨4⟩ Kueny, *Z. physiol. Chem.* **14,** 367 (1890).

—— **PROTOCATECHUIC ACID** $C_7H_6O_4$ **Beil. X-389**

(3,4-Dihydroxybenzoic acid)

(HO)₂C₆H₃—COOH

M.P. 197-198° dec.

See 1:0545. Genus 3: Acids.

—— ***m*-HYDROXYBENZOIC ACID** $C_7H_6O_3$ **Beil. X-134**

(COOH, OH on ring)

M.P. 200°

See 1:0825. Genus 3: Acids.

1:1605 METHYL GALLATE $C_8H_8O_5$ **Beil. X-483**

(Methyl 3,4,5-trihydroxybenzoate)

(HO)₃C₆H₂—COOCH₃

M.P. 200-201°

With $FeCl_3$ (T 1.41) gives dark green coloration — On alk. sapon. (T 1.51) gives discolored soln. which interferes with titration for Sap. Eq. but from which CH_3OH (1:6120) can be distilled.

[For prepn. from gallic acid (1:0875) + MeOH + H_2SO_4 see ⟨3⟩.]

Ⓓ **Methyl 3,4,5-triacetoxybenzoate:** from C̄ + Ac_2O by refluxing 3 hrs., pouring into aq., recryst. from alc. (85% yield), m.p. 120–122° ⟨1⟩.

Ⓓ **Methyl 3,4,5-tribenzoxybenzoate:** from C̄ + BzCl in pyridine, cryst. from alc., m.p. 139° ⟨2⟩.

1:1605 ⟨1⟩ Schwenk, *J. prakt. Chem.* (2) **90,** 57–58 (1914). ⟨2⟩ Einhorn, Hollandt, *Ann.* **301,** 110 (1898). ⟨3⟩ Mauthner, *J. prakt. Chem.* (2) **133,** 121 (1932).

1:1610 SALICIN $C_{13}H_{18}O_7$ **Beil. XXXI-214**

(Saligenin β-*d*-glucopyranoside)

HO.CH₂.C.C . C . C . C—O—C₆H₄(CH₂OH) [ring C–O–C; substituents H H OH H H above; OH H OH below]

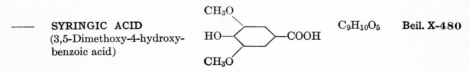

M.P. 200-201° cor.

Colorless cryst. sol. in 28 pts. aq. at 15°; in 0.68 pts. aq. at 102°; sol. alc., insol. ether; sol. in alk. or in AcOH — $[\alpha]_D^{20} = -63.6°$ in aq. at C = 4 ⟨1⟩; −45.6° in abs. alc. at C = 0.6 ⟨4⟩ — Subl. undec. at 190–195° at 12 mm. ⟨2⟩.

C̄ with $FeCl_3$ (T 1.41) gives no color — C̄ gives with conc. H_2SO_4 a bright scarlet (OR) color — C̄ reduces Tollens' reagt. (T 1.11) — C̄ treated with slight excess Br_2-aq. yields ppt. of bromosalicin, ndls. from hot aq., m.p. 170° ⟨3⟩, 171° ⟨4⟩.

Hydrolysis with hot dil. H_2SO_4 yields *d*-glucose (1:0305) and saliretin [Beil. VI-891] (an indef. polymer of *o*-hydroxybenzyl alc. (1:1490)). On distn. of acid, neut. or alk. soln., C̄ splits off H.CHO espec. after hydrolysis ⟨5⟩.

For study of detectn. and detn. see ⟨6⟩ ⟨7⟩.

Ⓓ **Penta-acetylsalicin:** from C̄ in 100% yield on htg. 1 hr. at 100° with 6 pts. Ac_2O + 3 pts. pyridine and pouring into aq.; cryst. from alc., m.p. 130° ⟨8⟩, 131–132° ⟨4⟩; $[\alpha]_D^{23.5} = -18.5°$ ⟨8⟩.

Ⓓ **Monobenzoylsalicin (Populin):** from C̄ + BzCl + aq. alk. in 30% yield; cryst. from alc., m.p. 178–179° after sintering a few degrees lower; $[\alpha]_D = -2.0°$ in pyridine at C = 5 ⟨9⟩.

Ⓓ **Salicin penta-(*N*-phenylcarbamate):** from C̄ + phenylisocyanate in cold anhydrous pyridine; amorph. pdr., m.p. 204° (not sharp) dec. ⟨10⟩.

1:1610 ⟨1⟩ Zemplén, *Z. physiol. Chem.* **85,** 420 (1913). ⟨2⟩ Fischer, *Arch. Pharm.* **276,** 524 (1938). ⟨3⟩ Visser, *Arch. Pharm.* **235,** 550 (1897). ⟨4⟩ Brauns, *J. Am. Chem. Soc.* **47,** 1292–1294 (1925). ⟨5⟩ Klein, *Biochem. Z.* **169,** 132 (1926). ⟨6⟩ Jacobs, Farinacci, *Ind. Eng. Chem., Anal. Ed.* **8,** 279–281 (1936). ⟨7⟩ Jackson, Dehn, *Ind. Eng. Chem., Anal. Ed.* **6,** 382 (1934). ⟨8⟩ Kunz, *J. Am. Chem. Soc.* **48,** 266 (1926). ⟨9⟩ Richtmyer, Yeakel, *J. Am. Chem. Soc.* **56,** 2495 (1934). ⟨10⟩ Jolles, *Gazz. chim. ital.* **65,** 1200 (1935).

—— **SYRINGIC ACID** $C_9H_{10}O_5$ **Beil. X-480**

(3,5-Dimethoxy-4-hydroxybenzoic acid)

[structure: ring with CH_3O, HO—, CH_3O and —COOH]

M.P. 202° (209°)

See 1:0830. Genus 3: Acids.

1:1615 ESCULIN $C_{15}H_{16}O_9$ **Beil. XXXI-246**

(6-Glucosidoxy-7-hydroxycoumarin; esculetin-[*β*-*d*-glucopyranoside]-6) ⟨1⟩ ⟨2⟩

M.P. 204-205° (rap. htg.)
abt. 160° (slow htg.)

White lustrous ndls. with 2 H_2O, losing cryst. aq. at 120–130° — Sol. in 576 pts. aq. at 25° and in abt. 13 pts. at 100°; sol. in MeOH, AcOEt, AcOH, pyridine; dif. sol. cold alc. (but eas. in hot), insol. ether — $[\alpha]_D^{22} = -37.7°$ in pyridine at $p = 2$ ⟨1⟩ — On subl. at 190–200° at 12 mm. dec. yielding esculetin (see below) ⟨3⟩.

With $FeCl_3$ (T 1.41) cold satd. aq. soln. of $\bar{C}$ gives blue-green (B-G) color; $\bar{C}$ is sol. in aq. alk. — $\bar{C}$ with *α*-naphthol (in $CHCl_3$) + conc. H_2SO_4 gives Molisch carbohydrate react. (Generic Test 2) — $\bar{C}$ reduces Fehling's soln. (T 1.22) on long boiling — $\bar{C}$ shaken with a little HNO_3 yields a yellow soln. becoming blood red on addn. of NH_4OH — On warming with dil. HCl or H_2SO_4 $\bar{C}$ hydrolyzes to 1 mole of esculetin (see below) and 1 mole *d*-glucose (1:0305) — $\bar{C}$ in AcOH treated with Br_2 in small portions gives cryst. ppt. of *x*,*x*-dibromoesculin, m.p. 193–195° dec. ⟨4⟩.

Ⓟ **Fluorescence of aq. soln.:** In very dil. aq. soln. $\bar{C}$ shows magnificent light blue fluorescence, extinguished by acids, intensified by traces of alk.; effect is even more brilliant in filtered ultra-violet light (perceptible to 1 part $\bar{C}$ in 1×10^{10} pts. aq.).

Ⓓ **Esculetin (6,7-dihydroxycoumarin):** from $\bar{C}$ on htg. with dil. H_2SO_4; seps. from yel. soln. as cryst. ppt.; ndls. from dil. alc., m.p. 272° dec. ⟨5⟩.

Ⓓ **Penta-acetylesculin:** from $\bar{C}$ + Ac_2O; ndls. from alc., m.p. 166° ⟨6⟩.

Ⓓ **Esculin tetra-[*N*-phenylcarbamate]:** from $\bar{C}$ + phenylisocyanate (6 moles) in anhydrous pyridine; m.p. 270° dec. ⟨7⟩.

1:1615 ⟨1⟩ Seka, Kallir, *Ber.* **64,** 622–627 (1931). ⟨2⟩ Macbeth, *J. Chem. Soc.* **1931,** 1288–1290 ⟨3⟩ Fischer, *Arch. Pharm.* **276,** 516–517 (1938). ⟨4⟩ Liebermann, Knietsch, *Ber.* **13,** 1594 (1880). ⟨5⟩ Zellner, Stein, *Monatsh.* **47,** 674–675 (1927). ⟨6⟩ Merz, *Arch. Pharm.* **270,** 491 (1932). ⟨7⟩ Jolles, *Gazz. chim. ital.* **65,** 1219 (1935).

— ***p*-HYDROXYBENZOIC ACID** $C_7H_6O_3$ **Beil. X-149**

M.P. 210°

See 1:0840. Genus 3: Acids.

— **2-HYDROXY-3-NAPHTHOIC ACID** $C_{11}H_8O_3$ **Beil. X-333**

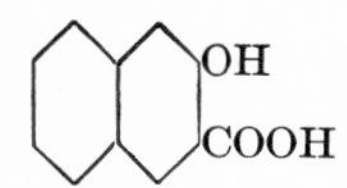

M.P. 216°

See 1:0850. Genus 3: Acids.

1:1620 PHLOROGLUCINOL (1,3,5-Trihydroxybenzene) $C_6H_6O_3$ **Beil. VI-1092**

HO— —OH
OH

M.P. 217-219° (rap. htg.)
200-209° (sl. htg.)

Tbls. and lfts. with 2 H_2O from aq.; m.p. 117°; losing aq. above 100° — Hydrated cryst. sol. in 93 pts. aq. at room temp.; anhydrous C̄ sol. in 118 pts. aq. at room temp. — C̄ largely pptd. from aq. solns. by NaCl — Eas. sol. alc., ether, pyridine — C̄ is extracted from weakly alk. sol. by ether.

[For prepn. (46–53% yield) via reduction and decarboxylation of 2,4,6-trinitrobenzoic acid see ⟨1⟩.]

C̄ (1% aq. soln.) gives with $FeCl_3$ (T 1.41) a BV-V color, rapidly fading — C̄ reduces Fehling's soln. (T 1.22) — C̄ in alk. soln. absorbs oxygen from air but less rapidly than pyrogallol (1:1555) — C̄ in aq. soln. gives deep red color (R-VR) with pine splinter soaked in conc. HCl.

C̄ treated with Br_2-aq. (not excess) gives ppt. of 2,4,6-tribromophloroglucinol, cryst. with 3 H_2O from aq.; m.p. anhyd. cpd., 152–153° sl. htg. ⟨2⟩ — C̄ with PkOH gives brown picrate; C̄.PkOH, m.p. 101–103° ⟨3⟩.

Ⓓ **2,4,6-Trinitrophloroglucinol:** Pour a soln. of 0.1 g. C̄ in conc. H_2SO_4 into a mixt. of 1 ml. each conc. H_2SO_4 and conc. HNO_3 with cooling and stirring until ppt. appears. Stand 5–6 min., then pour into 10 ml. cold water, cool, and filter. Wash ppt. with 2 ml. aq. contg. 0.5 ml. conc. HCl, recryst. from boilg. mixt. of 3 ml. aq. and 1 ml. conc. HCl. Cool, filter, wash with 2 ml. aq. contg. 0.5 ml. conc. HCl and dry at 100°. The prod. cryst. in pale yel. ndls., melting 165–166° u.c. It stains skin yellow, and when htd. on Pt foil deflagrates like picric acid ⟨4⟩.

Ⓓ **1,3,5-Triacetoxybenzene (phloroglucinol triacetate):** from C̄ refluxed 1 hr. with equal wt. fused AcONa + 5 pts. Ac_2O (85% yield ⟨5⟩) or in 100% yield from anhydrous C̄ stood 1 hr. with 6 pts. dry pyridine + 7 pts. Ac_2O, poured into aq. ⟨10⟩; cryst. from alc., m.p. 104–106° ⟨5⟩. [Note that with less Ac_2O a diacetate, also having m.p. 104° but depressing m.p. of triacetate, can be obtd.]

Ⓓ **1,3,5-Tribenzoxybenzene (phloroglucinol tribenzoate):** from C̄ in aq. alk. on shaking with excess BzCl; ndls. from alc., m.p. 173–174° ⟨6⟩.

Ⓓ **Phloroglucinol tri-*p*-nitrobenzoate:** m.p. 283°.

Ⓓ **Phloroglucinol tri-(3,5-dinitrobenzoate):** m.p. 162° [cf. T 1.47].

Ⓓ **Phloroglucinol tri-benzenesulfonate:** from C̄ in dil. alk. on shaking with benzenesulfonyl chloride; cryst. from dil. alc., m.p. 115–117° ⟨7⟩.

Ⓓ **Phloroglucinol tris-(*N*-phenylcarbamate):** from C̄ + phenylisocyanate + trace alk. at 100° ⟨8⟩ or in s.t. at 100° in quant. yield ⟨9⟩; cryst. from alc. or AcOH, m.p. 190–191°.

1:1620 ⟨1⟩ Clarke, Hartmann, *Organic Syntheses, Coll. Vol.* I, 444–446 (1932). ⟨2⟩ Zincke, Kegel, *Ber.* **23,** 1732 (1890). ⟨3⟩ Baril, Hauber, *J. Am. Chem. Soc.* **53,** 1090 (1931). ⟨4⟩ Mulliken, "Method" I, 109 (1904). ⟨5⟩ Heller, Kretzschmar, *Ber.* **45,** 421 (1912). ⟨6⟩ Skraup, *Monatsh.* **10,** 722 (1889). ⟨7⟩ Georgescu, *Ber.* **24,** 418 (1891). ⟨8⟩ Dieckmann, Hoppe, Stein, *Ber.* **37,** 4631, 4637 (1904). ⟨9⟩ Michael, *Ber.* **38,** 48 (1905). ⟨10⟩ Freudenberg, *Ann.* **433,** 237 (1923).

1:1621 BI-β-NAPHTHOL (2,2′-Dihydroxybinaphthyl-1,1′) $C_{20}H_{14}O_2$ **Beil. VI-1051**

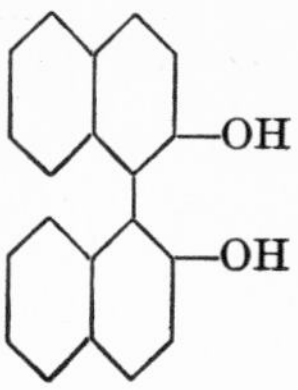

M.P. 218°

Ndls. from alc.; lfts. from toluene — Mod. sol. alc., sol. ether, spar. sol. $CHCl_3$, insol. aq. — Subl. in ndls.

C̄ with $FeCl_3$ (T 1.41) gives a pale greenish yel. color which on htg. turns red, then brown.

C̄ on htg. with 4 pts. $ZnCl_2$ for 6–8 hrs. at 270° ⟨1⟩, or with $\frac{1}{3}$ pt. P_2O_5 ⟨2⟩ or with a slightly more than equal wt. $POCl_3$ ⟨3⟩ or on boiling with 4% V_2O_5 for 7 hrs. (yield 50%) ⟨4⟩, or on distn. with 15 pts. Zn dust ⟨5⟩ gives β-binaphthylene oxide, cryst. from C_6H_6, m.p. 156°.

Ⓓ **2,2′-Diacetoxybinaphthyl-1,1′:** from C̄ + AcCl at 100°; cryst. from alc., m.p. 109° ⟨6⟩.

Ⓓ **2,2′-Dibenzoxybinaphthyl-1,1′:** from C̄ + BzCl (together with some monobenzoate); m.p. 160° ⟨7⟩ [monobenzoate: m.p. 204° ⟨7⟩].

Ⓓ **2,2′-Dimethoxybinaphthyl-1,1′:** from C̄ in alc. NaOH with dimethyl sulfate (94% yield); m.p. 190° ⟨8⟩.

Ⓓ **Bi-β-naphthol bis-(triphenylmethyl) ether:** from C̄ + 3 pts. triphenylchloromethane boiled 20 min. with 5 pts. dry pyridine (100% yield); scales from $CHCl_3$, m.p. 289° u.c. ⟨9⟩.

1:1621 ⟨1⟩ Walder, *Ber.* **15,** 2171 (1882). ⟨2⟩ Dianin, *Ber.* **15,** 1194 (1882). ⟨3⟩ Eckstein, *Ber.* **38,** 3668 (1905). ⟨4⟩ Clemo, Spence, *J. Chem. Soc.* **1928,** 2815. ⟨5⟩ Schoepfle, *J. Am. Chem. Soc.* **45,** 1568 (1923). ⟨6⟩ Fosse, *Bull. soc. chim.* (3) **19,** 612 (1898). ⟨7⟩ Dianin, *Ber.* **7,** 125 (1874). ⟨8⟩ Korczynski, Tucholski, *Chem. Abs.* **26,** 4044 (1932). ⟨9⟩ Pummerer, Luther, *Ber.* **61,** 1105 (1928).

1:1623 5,5′-DIHYDROXY-2,2′-DIMETHYLBIPHENYL (2,2′-Bi-*p*-cresol) $C_{14}H_{14}O_2$ **Beil. S.N. 563**

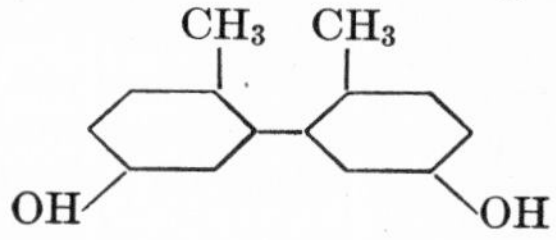

M.P. 228-229° ⟨1⟩

Pr. from dil. alc. — Eas. sol. alc., ether; dif. sol. hot C_6H_6; insol. cold aq., pet. ether — Nat. volatile with steam — Sublimable.

Sol. in 8% aq. NaOH — Gives colorless soln. in 98% H_2SO_4.

1:1623 ⟨1⟩ Pummerer, Puttfarcken, Schopflocker, *Ber.* **58,** 1817 (1925).

— **GALLIC ACID** (3,4,5-Trihydroxybenzoic acid) $C_7H_6O_5$ **Beil. X-470**

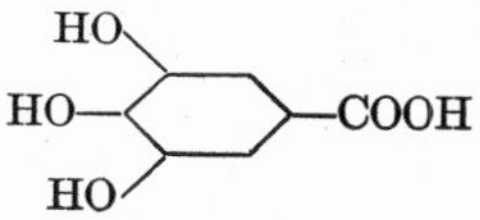

M.P. 222-240° dec.

See 1:0875. Genus 3: Acids.

— **β-RESORCYLIC ACID** (2,4-Dihydroxybenzoic acid) $C_7H_6O_4$ **Beil. X-377**

M.P. 226° dec. (**213°**)

See 1:0855. Genus 3: Acids.

1:1625 TRIKETOHYDRINDENE HYDRATE ("Ninhydrin") $C_9H_6O_4$ **Beil. VII-867**

M.P. 241° dec.

Crude prod. often pink in color, white after recrystn. — On htg. turns red (with loss of aq.) abt. 125–130°, later melting 241° dec. — Eas. sol. boilg. aq., dif. sol. ether. [For prepn. see ⟨1⟩.]

In Generic Test 3 neutralizes 3–4 ml. $N/10$ alk. with indef. end-point. In Generic Test 4 gives no color with $FeCl_3$ but soly. in alk. (Part 2) causes classification with phenols.

Reduces $NH_4OH/AgNO_3$ (T 1.11) or Fehling's soln. (T 1.22) — Soln. in dil. NH_4OH turns reddish-violet on stdg. and then no longer reduces $AgNO_3$ — Aq. soln. colors skin purple.

Ⓟ **Color reaction with alkali:** on addn. of alk. to solid $\bar{C}$, cryst. turn yellow and dis. forming yel. soln. which subsequently turns blue on warming (even at ord. temp. if alk. is concd.) and becoming colorless on dilution. With dil. alk. (15% KOH) blue color does not appear unless soln. is htd. immed. after addn. of alk. to $\bar{C}$ ⟨2⟩. [The colorless diluted alkali soln. no longer reduces Fehling's soln. and conts. salt of *o*-carboxymandelic ac. By acidifying with excess dil. H_2SO_4, htg. 1 hr., extracting with ether, evapg., this acid is quant. converted to phthalidecarboxylic acid [Beil. XVIII-418], cryst. (from hot aq.), m.p. 150–151° ⟨2⟩.]

Ⓟ **Ninhydrin color reaction for α-amino acids:** warm aq. soln. of $\bar{C}$ + any α-amino acid (e.g., glycine) yields intense blue color. [For study of use in detectn. of α-amino acids see ⟨2⟩ ⟨3⟩ ⟨4⟩ ⟨5⟩ ⟨6⟩: for study of mechanism see ⟨4⟩ ⟨7⟩; for comparison of color intensity with various amino acids see ⟨9⟩.]

Ⓓ **Triketohydrindene bis-phenylhydrazone:** $\bar{C}$, in AcOH, treated with phenylhydrazine immed. gives red cryst. ppt.; prod. filtered and recrystd. from much alc. yields orange-red ndls., m.p. 207–208° ⟨8⟩.

Ⓓ **Ketohydrindene phenazine:** Equal wts. $\bar{C}$ + *o*-phenylenediamine, dislvd. in hot dil. AcOH give quant. yield yel. ppt., recrystd. from alc. as yel. pr., m.p. 218–219° ⟨8⟩.

1:1625 ⟨1⟩ Teeters, Shriner, *J. Am. Chem. Soc.* **55,** 3026–3028 (1933). ⟨2⟩ Ruhemann, *J. Chem. Soc.* **97,** 2026, 2030 (1910). ⟨3⟩ Harding, MacLean, *J. Biol. Chem.* **20,** 217–230 (1915). ⟨4⟩ Harding, Warneford, *J. Biol. Chem.* **25,** 319–335 (1916). ⟨5⟩ Harding, MacLean, *J. Biol. Chem.* **25,** 337–350 (1916). ⟨6⟩ Herzfeld, *Biochem. Z.* **59,** 249–259 (1914). ⟨7⟩ Retinger, *J. Am. Chem. Soc.* **39,** 1059–1066 (1917). ⟨8⟩ Ruhemann, *J. Chem. Soc.* **97,** 1448–1449 (1910). ⟨9⟩ Abderhalden, *Z. physiol. Chem.* **252,** 88–89 (1938).

1:1630 1,5-DIHYDROXYNAPHTHALENE $C_{10}H_8O_2$ **Beil. VI-980**

OH

HO

M.P. 258° (265°)

Pr. from aq. containing SO_2; sol. ether, acetone; mod. sol. alc., AcOH; spar. sol. aq.; insol. C_6H_6, pet. ether — For purification of tech. prod. see ⟨1⟩ ⟨2⟩.

Alk. solns. of C̄ turn brown in air; solns. in NH_4OH or Na_2CO_3 turn rose-red — C̄ reduces Fehling's soln. (T 1.22) and even neutral $AgNO_3$.

C̄ in aq. soln. with $FeCl_3$ (T 1.41) gives white ppt. — For action of Br_2 see ⟨2⟩.

Ⓓ **1,5-Diacetoxynaphthalene:** from C̄ + Ac_2O; colorless lfts. from dil. alc., m.p. 159–160° ⟨1⟩.

Ⓓ **1,5-Dibenzoxynaphthalene:** from C̄ + excess BzCl in pyridine at 100° for 1 hr. (98% yield); cryst. from pyridine, m.p. 235° ⟨1⟩ ⟨3⟩.

Ⓓ **1,5-Dimethoxynaphthalene:** from C̄ + dimethyl sulfate + aq. alk.; ndls. from alc., m.p. 181–182° ⟨1⟩, 182–183° ⟨4⟩.

1:1630 ⟨1⟩ Fischer, Bauer, *J. prakt. Chem.* (2) **94,** 13–14 (1916). ⟨2⟩ Wheeler, Ergle, *J. Am. Chem. Soc.* **52,** 4872–4880 (1930). ⟨3⟩ Leman, *Compt. rend.* **202,** 580 (1936). ⟨4⟩ Bentley, Robinson Weizmann, *J. Chem. Soc.* **91,** 106–107 (1907).

1:1635 PHENOLPHTHALEIN $C_{20}H_{14}O_4$ **Beil. XVIII-143**

HO— —OH

C

O

C

O

M.P. 261°

White pdr. insol. aq., sol. alc. — Sol. in dil. alk. hydroxide or carbonate with intense RV color, discharged by large excess NaOH (for discussion of cause see ⟨1⟩ ⟨2⟩) — Acidification of alk. soln. ppts. C̄ in amorphous form very sol. ether; cryst. form is dif. sol. ether.

C̄ on warm. with dil. NaOH + Zn dust discharges color and on acidifn. ppts. phenolphthalin [Beil. X-455] (1:0873), readily reoxidized (e.g., by $K_3Fe(CN)_6$ or $KMnO_4$) to original C̄ — C̄ is sol. in cold conc. H_2SO_4 with yellowish red color and ppts. unchanged on dilution.

C̄ (1 pt.) in boilg. alc. (4 pts.) treated with Br_2 (2 pts.) in AcOH (2 pts.) yields 3′,5′,3″,5″-tetrabromophenolphthalein ⟨3⟩, colorless pdr. from acetone + AcOH, m.p. 293° cor. ⟨4⟩. [For action of Br from KBr/$KBrO_3$ mixt. see ⟨5⟩.]

Ⓓ **Diacetylphenolphthalein:** from C̄ htd. with 5 pts. Ac_2O at 150–160° for 18 hrs. (or perhaps less); cryst. from hot alc., m.p. 143° ⟨6⟩.

Ⓓ **Dibenzoylphenolphthalein:** from C̄ in large excess cold 10% KOH on shaking with BzCl. The resultant white ppt. is filtered, washed with alk., twice extracted with boilg.

alc., and residual solid dislvd. in hot C_6H_6 and repptd. by addn. of lgr. After drying above 100° (to remove cryst. C_6H_6), m.p. 169° ⟨7⟩.

Ⓓ **Phenolphthalein dibenzenesulfonate:** from C̄ in dil. alk. shaken with benzenesulfonyl chloride; colorless cryst. from alc., m.p. 112–113° ⟨8⟩.

Ⓓ **Phenolphthalein bis-(*N*-phenylcarbamate):** from C̄ + 2 moles phenylisocyanate at 130°; ndls. from C_6H_6, m.p. 135° ⟨9].

1:1635 ⟨1⟩ Lund, *J. Chem. Soc.* **1930,** 1844–1852. ⟨2⟩ Amis, LaMer, *J. Am. Chem. Soc.* **61,** 907 (1939). ⟨3⟩ Baeyer, *Ann.* **202,** 77–80 (1880). ⟨4⟩ Thiel, Diehl, *Cent.* **1927,** II, 2672. ⟨5⟩ Day, *J. Am. Chem. Soc.* **52,** 646–650 (1930). ⟨6⟩ Ref. 3, pages 74–75. ⟨7⟩ Bistrzycki, Nencki, *Ber.* **29,** 132 (1896). ⟨8⟩ Georgescu, *Cent.* **1900,** I, 543. ⟨9⟩ Haller, Guyot, *Compt. rend.* **116,** 480 (1893).

1:1640 4,4′-DIHYDROXYBIPHENYL $C_{12}H_{10}O_2$ Beil. VI-991

(*p,p′*-Biphenol)

HO—⟨ ⟩—⟨ ⟩—OH

M.P. 274–275°

Ndls. or pl. from alc.; sol. alc., ether; spar. sol. aq., C_6H_6. Subl. in scales.
C̄ with $FeCl_3$ (T 1.41) gives no color — C̄ with $Ca(OCl)_2$ soln. gives transient violet.

Ⓓ **4,4′-Diacetoxybiphenyl:** from C̄ on refluxing with Ac_2O; cryst. from dil. alc., m.p. 160–161° ⟨1⟩, 163–164° cor. ⟨2⟩.

Ⓓ **4,4′-Dibenzoxybiphenyl:** from C̄ + BzCl + dil. aq. alk.; cryst. from boilg. AcOH, m.p. 241° ⟨3⟩.

Ⓓ **4,4′-Dibenzenesulfonyloxybiphenyl:** from C̄ + benzenesulfonyl chloride (2.1 moles) in pyridine (88% yield ⟨5⟩); cryst. from *n*-PrOH, m.p. 148° ⟨5⟩.

Ⓓ **4,4′-Di-*p*-toluenesulfonyloxybiphenyl:** from C̄ + *p*-toluenesulfonyl chloride + dil. aq. alk. (21% yield ⟨4⟩), or from C̄ + *p*-toluenesulfonyl chloride (2.1 moles) in pyridine (100% yield ⟨5⟩); cryst. from C_6H_6, m.p. 189–190° ⟨4⟩, or from *n*-PrOH, m.p. 187–188° ⟨5⟩.

Ⓓ **4,4′-Dihydroxybiphenyl-*O,O*-diacetic acid:**

[HOOC.CH_2.O⟨ ⟩—⟨ ⟩—O.CH_2.COOH]

from C̄ + chloroacetic acid + aq. NaOH on htg. 1 hr.; ndls. from dil. acetone, m.p. 274° (block) ⟨1⟩; Neut. Eq. 151.

1:1640 ⟨1⟩ van Alphen, *Rec. trav. chim.* **50,** 416–417 (1931). ⟨2⟩ Courtot, Geoffroy, *Compt. rend.* **178,** 2261 (1924). ⟨3⟩ Moir, *J. Chem. Soc.* **91,** 1305 (1907). ⟨4⟩ Gilman, Beaber, Myers, *J. Am. Chem. Soc.* **47,** 2050 (1925). ⟨5⟩ Hazlet, *J. Am. Chem. Soc.* **61,** 1921 (1939).

ORDER I: SUBORDER I: GENUS 4: PHENOLS

Division B, Liquid Phenolic Compounds

—— **BIACETYL** $CH_3.CO.CO.CH_3$ $C_4H_6O_2$ **Beil. I-769**

B.P. 89°

Yellow liq. of peculiar sweetish pung. odor — See Suborder 2, Division B. Liquids (1:9500).

With alk. in Generic Test 4-B gives opaque brown soln.

1:1700 **ACETYLACETONE** (Pentanedione-2,4) $CH_3.CO.CH_2.CO.CH_3 \rightleftarrows CH_3.C(OH){=}CH.CO.CH_3$ $C_5H_8O_2$ **Beil. I-777**

B.P. 139° ⟨1⟩ **M.P. −30° ⟨2⟩** D_4^{20} **= 0.976** $n_D^{25.6}$ **= 1.4465**

Soly. in aq. 15% at 30°; 34% at 80°; misc. alc., ether, $CHCl_3$ — Odor like acetone + AcOH — [For study of prepn. see ⟨3⟩.]

Ord. equilibrium mixt. contains very high proportion of enol form; variously estimated at 76% ⟨4⟩ ⟨5⟩ ⟨6⟩; 80% ⟨7⟩; 97% ⟨8⟩ ⟨9⟩.

$\bar{C}$ in 1% aq. soln. gives with $FeCl_3$ (T 1.41) a permanent OR-RO color — $\bar{C}$ with aq. $Cu(OAc)_2$ soln. gives heavy blue ppt. of Cu enolate, sol. in $CHCl_3$. [For use in detn. of enol content see ⟨6⟩ ⟨10⟩.]

$\bar{C}$ with Poirrier's blue as indicator titrates as monobasic acid — $\bar{C}$ with alk. + I_2.KI soln. (T 1.81) yields CHI_3; $\bar{C}$ with $Ca(OCl)_2$ gives $CHCl_3$ + AcOH ⟨11⟩.

$\bar{C}$ with hydrazine hydrate, or with hydrazine sulfate + 10% aq. NaOH reacts vigorously pptg. alm. quant. yield of 3,5-dimethylpyrazole [Beil. XXIII-75], lfts. from aq., ether, or lgr., m.p. 107°; b.p. 220° cor. ⟨12⟩ [cf. ⟨18⟩].

[$\bar{C}$ htd. at 100° with excess phenylhydrazine yields 1-phenyl-3,5-dimethylpyrazole [Beil. XXIII-75], liquid, b.p. 273°] — $\bar{C}$ mixed with aq. soln. of *p*-nitrophenylhydrazine.HCl immed. ppts. yel. ppt. (86% yield) of 1-(*p*-nitrophenyl)-3,5-dimethylpyrazole, yel. ndls. from dil. alc., m.p. 99.5–100.5° ⟨13⟩ — $\bar{C}$ with 2,4-dinitrophenylhydrazine in dil. alc. H_2SO_4 gives 1-(2′,4′-dinitrophenyl)-3,5-dimethylpyrazole, pale lemon lfts. from alc., m.p. 122° ⟨14⟩. [By same process the (intermediate) acetylacetone 2,4-dinitrophenylhydrazone, yel. cryst. from alc., m.p. 209°, has also been reported ⟨15⟩.]

Addn. of $\bar{C}$ to excess of neutralized $NH_2OH.HCl$ soln. and stdg. yields acetylacetone dioxime, cryst. from alc. or aq., m.p. 149–150° ⟨16⟩. [Note that use of only 1 mole NH_2OH or reversal of order of mixing yields α,γ-dimethylisoxazole ⟨16⟩, which is liquid.]

$\bar{C}$ in alc. treated with semicarbazide HCl + NaOAc soln. yields ppt. of 3,5-dimethylpyrazole-1-carbonamide [Beil. XXIII-76], cryst. from dil. alc., m.p. 111–112° after sintering at 109°; warming with HCl converts latter to 3,5-dimethylpyrazole, m.p. 107° (see above) ⟨17⟩.

Ⓓ **"Ketone splitting":** $\bar{C}$, on hydrolysis with 1 *N* alk. (T 1.51), yields acetone (1:5400), acetic acid (1:1010), and CO_2.

1:1700 ⟨1⟩ Claisen, *Ann.* **277,** 170 (1893). ⟨2⟩ Jaeger, *Z. anorg. allgem. Chem.* **101,** 85 (1917). ⟨3⟩ Sprague, Beckham, Adkins, *J. Am. Chem. Soc.* **56,** 2666 (1934). ⟨4⟩ Meyer, *Ber.* **45,** 2857 (1912). ⟨5⟩ Conant, Thompson, *J. Am. Chem. Soc.* **54,** 4043 (1932). ⟨6⟩ Hieber, *Ber.* **54,** 912 (1921). ⟨7⟩ Meyer, *Ann.* **380,** 242 (1911). ⟨8⟩ von Auwers, Jacobsen, *Ann.* **426,** 187 (1922). ⟨9⟩ von Auwers, *Ann.* **415,** 189 (1918). ⟨10⟩ Dieckmann, *Ber.* **54,** 2254 (1921).
⟨11⟩ Ssuknewitsch, Tschilingarjan, *Ber.* **69,** 1542 (1936). ⟨12⟩ Rosengarten, *Ann.* **279,** 237 (1894). ⟨13⟩ von Auwers, Kreuder, *Ber.* **58,** 1981 (1925). ⟨14⟩ Brady, *J. Chem. Soc.* **1931,** 759. ⟨15⟩ Campbell, *Analyst* **61,** 393 (1936). ⟨16⟩ Harries, Haga, *Ber.* **32,** 1192 (1889). ⟨17⟩ Posner, *Ber.* **34,** 3980 (1901). ⟨18⟩ von Auwers, Daniel, *J. prakt. Chem.* (2) **110,** 248 (1925).

1:1705 METHYL ACETOACETATE $C_5H_8O_3$ Beil. III-632

$CH_3.CO.CH_2.COOCH_3$
↓ ↑
$CH_3.C{=}CH.COOCH_3$
|
OH

B.P. 170° D_4^{20} = **1.0765** n_D^{20} = **1.41964**

Colorless liq., misc. with aq. — C̄ conts. 4.7% enol at 16° by $Cu(OAc)_2$ method ⟨1⟩ ⟨2⟩; 4.1%–5.0% by Br_2 titration ⟨3⟩ ⟨4⟩; 5.7% by gas method ⟨6⟩.

C̄ with $FeCl_3$ (T 1.41) gives dark cherry red color.

C̄ in 2 vols. dry ether, treated with NH_3 gas and stood 2 days at 0°, yields on evapn. of solvent 80–90% methyl β-aminocrotonate, cryst. from alc., m.p. 85° ⟨7⟩ — C̄ dislvd. in 5 pts. 15% aq. NH_4OH and stood 24 hrs. deposits abt. 7% yield of methyl β-aminocrotonate, m.p. 84°; conc. of the residual soln. in vac. and stdg. deposits good yield of acetoacetamide, cryst. from warm aq., m.p. 50° ⟨8⟩.

C̄ in MeOH refluxed 1 hr. with 1 mole $NH_2.NH_2.HCl$ in 0.1 *N* HCl, then made alkn. yields 20–30% 3-methyl-5-methoxypyrazole, ndls. from dil. MeOH, m.p. 49–50° ⟨9⟩.

Ⓓ **Methyl acetoacetate semicarbazone:** from C̄ htd. with satd. soln. of semicarbazide hydrochloride; ndls. from MeOH; m.p. 152.5° ⟨10⟩; 151–152° ⟨11⟩.

Ⓓ "**Ketone splitting**": C̄ hydrolyzed with 1 *N* alk. (T 1.51) yields acetone (1:5400), methyl alc. (1:6120), and CO_2.

1:1705 ⟨1⟩ Hieber, *Ber.* **54,** 912 (1921). ⟨2⟩ Dieckmann, *Ber.* **54,** 2251–2254 (1921). ⟨3⟩ Meyer, *Ann.* **380,** 241 (1911). ⟨4⟩ Meyer, *Ber.* **45,** 2852 (1912). ⟨5⟩ Dieckmann, *Ber.* **55,** 2478 (1922). ⟨6⟩ Conant, Thompson, *J. Am. Chem. Soc.* **54,** 4043 (1932). ⟨7⟩ Mumm, Gottschaldt, *Ber.* **55,** 2068 (1922). ⟨8⟩ Meyer, *Monatsh.* **28,** 4 (1907). ⟨9⟩ Backer, Meijer, *Rec. trav. chim.* **45,** 429 (1926). ⟨10⟩ Backer, Meyer, *Rec. trav. chim.* **45,** 93 (1926).
⟨11⟩ Staudinger, Becker, *Ber.* **50,** 1021 (1917).

1:1708 METHYL METHYLACETOACETATE $C_6H_{10}O_3$ Beil. III-679

(Methyl α-acetopropionate)

CH_3
|
$CH_3.CO.CH.COOCH_3$

B.P. 177.4° D_{25}^{25} = **1.0247** $n_D^{23.8}$ = **1.416**

C̄ with $FeCl_3$ (T 1.41) gives violet red color.

C̄ treated with equiv. amt. hydrazine hydrate yields 3,4-dimethylpyrazolone-5 [Beil. XXIV-63], lfts. or pr. from aq., m.p. 269° rap. htg. ⟨1⟩. [C̄ with equiv. hydrazine hydrochloride in HCl soln. gives 3,4-dimethyl-5-methoxypyrazole, ndls. from dil. MeOH, m.p. 85° ⟨3⟩.] — C̄ htd. with phenylhydrazine at 140° should give 1-phenyl-3,4-dimethylpyrazolone-5 [Beil. XXIV-64], m.p. 117–120° [cf. ethyl methylacetoacetate (1:1712)].

Ⓓ **Methyl methylacetoacetate semicarbazone:** from C̄ + 1 mole of semicarbazide on stdg. conc. soln. overnight; cryst. from alc., m.p. 138° ⟨2⟩. [With semicarbazide.HCl, the semicarbazone (sol. in ether) is main product but is accompanied by 3,4-dimethylpyrazolone-5-carbonamide-1 (insol. ether), ndls. from aq., m.p. 194° dec. on rap. htg. — on slow htg. the carbonamide dec. at 194° without melting yielding 3,4-dimethylpyrazolone-5, m.p. 268° ⟨2⟩.]

1:1708 ⟨1⟩ Backer, Meyer, *Rec. trav. chim.* **45,** 85–86 (1926). ⟨2⟩ Ref. 1, page 94. ⟨3⟩ Backer, Meyer, *Rec. trav. chim.* **45,** 430 (1926).

1:1710 ETHYL ACETOACETATE $C_6H_{10}O_3$ Beil. III-632

$CH_3.CO.CH_2.COOC_2H_5$

↓ ↑

$CH_3.C(OH)=CH.COOC_2H_5$

B.P. 181° ⟨1⟩ D_4^{20} **= 1.025** n_D^{20} **= 1.41976 ⟨1⟩** [cf. ⟨2⟩]

Liq.; at 16° 100 ml. aq. dissolves 12.5 g. C̄; misc. with most org. solv. — Ordinary equil. mixt. of C̄ conts. abt. 7.7% enol form ⟨3⟩ ⟨4⟩. [For prepn. of C̄ from ethyl acetate + Na (28–29% yield) see ⟨5⟩; for increase of yield to 75–76% see ⟨6⟩.]

C̄ is sol. in aq. alk. but pptd. by CO_2; not extracted by ether from soln. in 2% aq. NaOH.

C̄ with $FeCl_3$ (T 1.41) yields clear permanent R-T color [cf. Beil. III-650].

C̄ shaken with satd. aq. $NaHSO_3$ soln. yields ppt. of $NaHSO_3$ addn. cpd. from which K_2CO_3 regenerates C̄ ⟨7⟩ ⟨8⟩. [Use in purification of C̄ ⟨7⟩.] — C̄ with $Ca(OCl)_2$ soln. yields 60% dichloroacetic acid ⟨9⟩.

C̄ with aq. $Cu(OAc)_2$ soln. yields Cu enolate, sol. in $CHCl_3$.

C̄ suspended in aq. and warmed with repeated portions of hydrazine hydrate soln. until liq. remains alk. ppts. 90–100% yield 3-methylpyrazolone-5 [Beil. XXIV-19], pr. from aq., ndls. from alc., m.p. 216° ⟨10⟩ ⟨11⟩. [Same prod. also results from mixing C̄ with equal wt. powd. hydrazine sulfate, adding 8 pts. 2 *N* KOH, evapg. to dryness and extg. prod. with boilg. MeOH ⟨12⟩.]

C̄ + equal wt. hydrazine sulfate dislvd. in 15 pts. aq. and htd. ½ hr. at 100° yields 3-methyl-5-ethoxypyrazole [Beil. XXIII-354], obt. by making alk. and extg. with ether; ndls. from hot dil. alc., m.p. 66–67° ⟨13⟩.

C̄ mixed with precisely 1 equiv. of phenylhydrazine, resultant aq. separated, and oily product (intermediate phenylhydrazone ?) htd. 2 hrs. at 100° gives quant. yield of 1-phenyl-3-methylpyrazolone-5 [Beil. XXIV-20]; cryst. from aq. or hot alc., m.p. 127° ⟨14⟩ ⟨15⟩. [Same product results from C̄ + exactly 1 mole phenylhydrazine htd. in AcOH ⟨15⟩, or from C̄ + exactly 1 mole phenylhydrazine HCl in presence of few drops conc. HCl ⟨16⟩.] — C̄ htd. with 1 mole *p*-nitrophenylhydrazine at 100° yields 1-(*p*-nitrophenyl)-3-methylpyrazolone [Beil. XXIV-24]; yel. cryst. from alc., m.p. 218° ⟨17⟩ — C̄ with 2,4-dinitrophenylhydrazine yields ethyl acetoacetate 2,4-dinitrophenylhydrazone; yel. cryst. from alc., m.p. 93° ⟨18⟩; 96° ⟨19⟩.

C̄ shaken with aq. soln. of 1 mole semicarbazide HCl + AcONa yields ppt. of ethyl acetoacetate semicarbazone, ndls. from ether, m.p. 129° ⟨20⟩, 133° ⟨21⟩.

C̄ warmed with alk. NH_2OH soln. at 40–50° yields 3-methylisoxazolone-5 [Beil. XXVII-157], ndls. m.p. 169–170° ⟨22⟩. [Preparation is difficult ⟨23⟩ ⟨24⟩.]

Ⓓ **"Ketone splitting":** Hydrolysis with 1 *N* alk. (T 1.51) yields acetone (1:5400), ethyl alc. (1:6130) and CO_2.

1:1710 ⟨1⟩ Brühl, *Ann.* **203,** 27 (1880). ⟨2⟩ Falk, *J. Am. Chem. Soc* **31,** 106 (1909). ⟨3⟩ Meyer, *Ann.* **380,** 222 (1911). ⟨4⟩ Meyer, Willson, *Ber.* **47,** 841 (1914). ⟨5⟩ Inglis, Roberts, *Organic Syntheses, Coll. Vol.* I, 230–231 (1932). ⟨6⟩ Roberts, McElvain, *J. Am. Chem. Soc.* **59,** 2007 (1937). ⟨7⟩ Elion, *Rec. trav. chim.* **3,** 245–246 (1884). ⟨8⟩ Stewart, *J. Chem. Soc.* **87,** 187 (1905). ⟨9⟩ Hurd, Thomas, *J. Am. Chem. Soc.* **55,** 1648 (1933). ⟨10⟩ Curtius, Jay, *J. prakt. Chem.* (2) **39,** 52 (1889).

⟨11⟩ von Auwers, Niemyer, *J. prakt. Chem.* (2) **110,** 178–179 (1925). ⟨12⟩ Knorr, *Ber.* **29,** 253, Note 1 (1896). ⟨13⟩ Wolff, *Ber.* **37,** 2834 (1904). ⟨14⟩ Knorr, *Ber.* **16,** 2597 (1883). ⟨15⟩ Knorr, *Ann.* **238,** 146–148 (1887). ⟨16⟩ Michael, *Am. Chem. J.* **14,** 517 (1892). ⟨17⟩ Altschul, *Ber.* **25,** 1853 (1892). ⟨18⟩ Campbell, *Analyst* **61,** 393 (1936). ⟨19⟩ Strain, *J. Am. Chem. Soc.* **57,** 760 (1935). ⟨20⟩ Thiele, Stange, *Ann.* **283,** 29 (1894).

⟨21⟩ Backer, Meyer, *Rec. trav. chim.* **45,** 93 (1926). ⟨22⟩ Hantzsch, *Ber.* **24,** 497 (1891). ⟨23⟩ Uhlenhuth, *Ann.* **296,** 46 (1897). ⟨24⟩ Rose, Scott, *J. Am. Chem. Soc.* **39,** 278 (1917).

1:1712 ETHYL METHYLACETOACETATE CH_3 $C_7H_{12}O_3$ **Beil. III-679**

(Ethyl α-acetopropionate) $CH_3.CO.CH(CH_3).COOC_2H_5$

B.P. 180.8° cor. D_4^{20} = **1.0191** $n_D^{15.3}$ = **1.42178**

C̄ with $FeCl_3$ (T 1.41) gives blue color.

C̄, emulsified with aq. and treated either in cold or at 100° with 1 mole hydrazine hydrate gives alm. quant. yield of 3,4-dimethylpyrazolone-5 [Beil. XXIV-63], lfts. or pr. from aq., m.p. 269° rap. htg. ⟨1⟩.

C̄, htd. with *exactly* 1 equiv. of phenylhydrazine at 140° yields 1-phenyl-3,4-dimethylpyrazolone-5 [Beil. XXIV-64], m.p. 117–120° ⟨2⟩.

Ⓓ **"Ketone splitting":** Hydrolysis with alk. (T **1.51**) yields ethyl methyl ketone (1:5405), ethyl alc. (1:6130) and CO_2.

Ⓓ **Ethyl methylacetoacetate 2,4-dinitrophenylhydrazone:** from C̄ (0.5 g.) + 2,4-dinitrophenylhydrazine (0.7 g.) in alc. (25 ml.) contg. 0.5 ml. conc. HCl on refluxing for 10 min., 82% yield; fine yel.-or. ndls. from alc., m.p. 56–57° cor. ⟨6⟩.

Ⓓ **Ethyl methylacetoacetate semicarbazone:** from C̄ on treatment with conc. soln. of semicarbazide; the sepg. oil crystallizes after stdg. a few hours and yields to ether the soluble semicarbazone, m.p. 86° ⟨3⟩. [The small residue insol. in ether is the by-product 3,4-dimethylpyrazolone-5-carbonamide-1; ndls. from aq., m.p. 194° dec. rap. htg. On slow htg. the carbonamide dec. at 194° without melting, yielding 3,4-dimethylpyrazolone-5, m.p. 268°. The carbonamide is the sole product from react. of C̄ with semicarbazide.HCl ⟨3⟩.]

Ⓓ **α-Methylacetoacetamide:** from C̄ on shaking with 3 vols. conc. aq. NH_4OH; evap. aq. layer; ndls. from ether, m.p. 73° ⟨4⟩.

Ⓓ **α-Methylacetoacetanilide:** from C̄ + 1 mole aniline htd. some time in s.t. at 150–160°; m.p. 138–140° ⟨5⟩.

1:1712 ⟨1⟩ Backer, Meyer, *Rec. trav. chim.* **45,** 85–86 (1926). ⟨2⟩ Knorr, *Ann.* **238,** 162 (1887). ⟨3⟩ Ref. 1, pages 94–95. ⟨4⟩ Peters, *Ann.* **257,** 347–348 (1890). ⟨5⟩ Knorr, *Ann.* **245,** 358 (1888). ⟨6⟩ Adams, Long, *J. Am. Chem. Soc.* **62** 2293 (1940).

—— **PHENOL** $C_6H_5.OH$ C_6H_6O **Beil. VI-110**

("Carbolic acid")

B.P. 183°

See 1:1420. Genus 4: Phenols. M.P. 42°.

1:1718 METHYL ETHYLACETOACETATE C_2H_5 $C_7H_{12}O_3$ **Beil. III-691**

(Methyl α-aceto-*n*-butyrate) $CH_3.CO.CH(C_2H_5).COOCH_3$

B.P. 189.7° cor. D^{14} = **0.995**

C̄ with $FeCl_3$ (T 1.41) gives violet red color.

C̄ htd. with 1 mole hydrazine hydrate in aq. yields 3-methyl-4-ethylpyrazolone-5 [Beil. XXIV-68], pl. from aq., m.p. 227.5° ⟨1⟩. [C̄ with 1 mole hydrazine hydrochloride in dil.

HCl gives 20–30% yield of 3-methyl-4-ethyl-5-methoxypyrazole, ndls. from dil. MeOH, m.p. 106–107° ⟨4⟩.]

C̄ on shaking 1 day with conc. aq. soln. of semicarbazide, yields cryst. ppt.; by repeated crystn. from boilg. ether this may be separated into the more sol. methyl ethylacetoacetate semicarbazone, m.p. 98° (no color with $FeCl_3$), and the less sol. 3-methyl-4-ethylpyrazolone-5-carbonamide-1, pr. from MeOH, m.p. 161–162° (alc. soln. blue with $FeCl_3$). With semicarbazide.HCl, the latter becomes the principal reaction prod. ⟨2⟩.

Ⓓ **"Ketone splitting":** Hydrolysis with alk. (T 1.51) yields methyl *n*-propyl ketone (1:5415), methyl alc. (1:6120), and CO_2.

Ⓓ **α-Ethylacetoacetamide:** from C̄ on dislvg. in 10 vols. conc. aq. NH_4OH, stdg. a few hrs., and evaporating; ndls. from C_6H_6 or alc., m.p. 95–96° ⟨3⟩.

1:1718 ⟨1⟩ Backer, Meyer, *Rec. trav. chim.* **45**, 86 (1926). ⟨2⟩ Ref. 1, pages 95–96. ⟨3⟩ Meyer, *Monatsh.* **27**, 1089 (1906). ⟨4⟩ Backer, Meijer, *Rec. trav. chim.* **45**, 430 (1926).

—— **o-CRESOL** $CH_3.C_6H_4.OH$ C_7H_8O **Beil. VI-349**
(*o*-Methylphenol)

B.P. 190.8°

See 1:1400. Genus 4: Phenols. M.P. 30.75°.

—— **SALICYLALDEHYDE** (benzene ring with CHO and OH ortho) $C_7H_6O_2$ **Beil. VIII-31**
(*o*-Hydroxybenzaldehyde; *o*-aldehydophenol; *o*-formylphenol)

B.P. 197° cor. **F.P. +1.6°** D^{20}_{20} = **1.1690** n^{20}_{D} = **1.574**

See 1:0205. Genus 1: Aldehydes.

1:1723 ETHYL ETHYLACETOACETATE $C_8H_{14}O_3$ **Beil. III-691**
(Ethyl α-aceto-*n*-butyrate)

$$CH_3.CO.\underset{\displaystyle C_2H_5}{CH}.COOC_2H_5 \rightleftarrows CH_3.\underset{OH}{C}{=}\underset{C_2H_5}{C}.COOC_2H_5$$

B.P. 198° D^{20}_{4} = **0.9856** $n^{18.7}_{D}$ = **1.42256**

Liq. mod. sol. aq.; cold satd. soln. is abt. 0.04 *N*; more sol. cold aq. than in hot — Misc. alc., ether.

C̄ with $FeCl_3$ (T 1.41) gives blue color — C̄ is sol. in aq. alk. but extracted by ether from alk. solns.

C̄ (15.5 g.) treated with conc. aq. KOH (8 g. K in 8 ml. aq.) at 0° gives ppt. of K enolate from which dil. HCl regenerates C̄ ⟨1⟩ — C̄ in dry ether treated with 1 mole Na evolves H and yields soluble Na enolate; on addn. of slightly less than 1 mole H_2O, a solid hydrate seps. from which acids regenerate C̄ ⟨1⟩ — C̄ in abs. alc. treated with $NaOC_2H_5$ to yield Na enolate, then with alc. $CuCl_2$ yields Cu enolate as green cryst. ⟨1⟩. [Use of these methods in purification of C̄ ⟨1⟩.]

C̄ in aq. alc. treated with aq. $Cu(OAc)_2$ soln. yields Cu enolate, quant. extd. by $CHCl_3$ ⟨2⟩. [Application to detn. of amt. of enolization ⟨2⟩ ⟨3⟩.]

C̄ treated with aq. hydrazine hydrate ⟨3⟩ or with dil. alc. semicarbazide HCl + AcONa ⟨4⟩ yields 3-methyl-4-ethylpyrazolone-5 [Beil. XXIV-68], pl. from aq., m.p. 226–227° ⟨3⟩ ⟨4⟩. [C̄ in alc. htd. with 1 mole hydrazine hydrochloride in dil. HCl gives 20–30% yield

3-methyl-4-ethyl-5-ethoxypyrazole, ndls. from alc., m.p. 86° ⟨8⟩.] —C̄, htd. with 1 mole phenylhydrazine at 140° yields 1-phenyl-3-methyl-4-ethylpyrazolone-5 [Beil. XXIV-68]; ndls. with 1 H_2O from aq. losing it at 50°; anhydrous cryst. from ether, m.p. 108° ⟨5⟩ — C̄ on shaking with a soln. of semicarbazide yields an oil which slowly cryst.; by recryst. from ether this may be separated into the more sol. ethyl ethylacetoacetate semicarbazone, m.p. 80° and the less sol. 3-methyl-4-ethylpyrazolone-5-carbonamide-1, pr. from MeOH, m.p. 161–162° (alc. soln. blue with $FeCl_3$) ⟨6⟩.

Ⓓ **"Ketone splitting":** Hydrolysis of C̄ with 1 *N* alk. (T 1.51) yields methyl *n*-propyl ketone (1:5415), ethyl alc. (1:6130) and CO_2 [cf. ⟨7⟩].

1:1723 ⟨1⟩ Michael, *Ber.* **38**, 2093–2096 (1905). ⟨2⟩ Hieber, *Ber.* **54**, 905–912 (1921); Dieckmann, *Ber.* **54**, 2251–2254 (1921). ⟨3⟩ Backer, Meyer, *Rec. trav. chim.* **45**, 86 (1926). ⟨4⟩ De, Dutt, *J. Indian Chem. Soc.* **7**, 478–479 (1930). ⟨5⟩ Knorr, Blank, *Ber.* **17**, 2051 (1884). ⟨6⟩ Ref. 3, pages 95–96. ⟨7⟩ Lauer, Lones, *J. Am. Chem. Soc.* **59**, 233 (1937). ⟨8⟩ Backer, Meijer, *Rec. trav. chim.* **45**, 431 (1926).

—— ***p*-CRESOL** $CH_3.C_6H_4.OH$ C_7H_8O **Beil. VI-389**
(*p*-Methylphenol)

B.P. 202.3°

See 1:1410. Genus 4: Phenols. M.P. 36°.

1:1730 ***m*-CRESOL** (*m*-Methylphenol) [ring structure: –OH, with CH_3 in meta position] C_7H_8O **Beil. VI-373**

B.P. 202.7° ⟨15⟩ **M.P. +11.95°** ⟨15⟩ D_4^{20} = **1.03401** ⟨15⟩ n_D^{15} = **1.54318** ⟨15⟩
n_D^{20} = **1.540**

C̄ is not sol. in 5 pts. conc. NH_4OH [dif. from phenol (1:1420)].

C̄ in 1% aq. soln. gives with $FeCl_3$ (T 1.41) a BV-BV-T_1 color of considerable permanence ⟨1⟩.

C̄ treated with Br_2-aq. (3 moles) yields 2,4,6-tribromo-3-methylphenol, cryst. from alc., m.p 84° ⟨2⟩. [With excess Br_2-aq. complications result.]

Ⓓ **2,4,6-Trinitro-3-methylphenol (2,4,6-trinitro-*m*-cresol):** C̄, nitrated by procedure given for prepn. of picric ac. from phenol (1:1420), yields prod.; cryst. from dil. HCl, m.p. 106.5° u.c. ⟨3⟩.

Ⓓ ***m*-Tolyl benzoate:** from C̄ by warm. with BzCl or by shaking with BzCl + aq. alk., cryst. m.p. 55°.

Ⓓ ***m*-Tolyl *p*-nitrobenzoate:** mp. 90° ⟨4⟩.

Ⓓ ***m*-Tolyl 3,5-dinitrobenzoate:** cryst. from alc., m.p. 165.4° cor. ⟨5⟩ [cf. T 1.47].

Ⓓ ***m*-Tolyl benzenesulfonate:** from C̄ + benzenesulfonyl chloride + aq. alk., cryst. from alc., m.p. 45°.

Ⓓ ***m*-Tolyl *p*-toluenesulfonate:** from C̄ + *p*-toluenesulfonyl chloride in aq. alk. or in pyridine, m.p. 51° ⟨6⟩.

Ⓓ ***m*-Tolyl *p*-nitrobenzyl ether:** m.p. 51° ⟨7⟩ [cf. T 1.44].

Ⓓ ***m*-Tolyl 2,4-dinitrophenyl ether:** pale greenish yel. ndls. from alc., m.p. 74° ⟨8⟩.

Ⓓ ***m*-Methylphenoxyacetic acid:** m.p. 102–103°; Neut. Eq. 166 ⟨9⟩ [cf. T 1.46].

Ⓓ ***m*-Tolyl *N*-phenylcarbamate:** from C̄ + phenylisocyanate in boilg. pet., ndls. from lgr. + alc., m.p. 121–122° ⟨10⟩; 125° ⟨11⟩.

Ⓓ ***m*-Tolyl *N*-α-naphthylcarbamate:** m.p. 127–128° ⟨12⟩ [cf. T 1.45].

Ⓓ ***m*-Tolyl *N*-*p*-xenylcarbamate:** m.p. 164° ⟨13⟩.

Ⓓ ***m*-Tolyl *N,N*-diphenylcarbamate:** m.p. 100–101.5° ⟨14⟩ [cf. T 1.43].

1:1730 ⟨1⟩ Clemmensen, *Ber.* **47,** 61 (1914). ⟨2⟩ Baeyer, Seuffert, *Ber.* **34,** 45 (1901). ⟨3⟩ Mulliken, " Method " I, 104 (1904). ⟨4⟩ Barnett, Nixon, *Chem. News* **129,** 190–191 (1924). ⟨5⟩ Phillips, Keenan, *J. Am. Chem. Soc.* **53,** 1926 (1931). ⟨6⟩ Reverdin, Crépieux, *Ber.* **35,** 1444 (1902); *Bull. soc. chim.* (3) **27,** 746 (1902). ⟨7⟩ Reid, *J. Am. Chem. Soc.* **39,** 308 (1917). ⟨8⟩ Bost, Nicholson, *J. Am. Chem. Soc.* **57,** 2369 (1935). ⟨9⟩ Koelsch, *J. Am. Chem. Soc.* **53,** 305 (1931). ⟨10⟩ Weehuizen, *Rec. trav. chim.* **37,** 268 (1918).

⟨11⟩ Fromm, Eckard, *Ber.* **56,** 953 (1923). ⟨12⟩ French, Wirtel, *J. Am. Chem. Soc.* **48,** 1738 (1926). ⟨13⟩ Morgan, Pettet, *J. Chem. Soc.* **1931,** 1125. ⟨14⟩ Herzog, *Ber.* **40,** 1833 (1907). ⟨15⟩ Timmermans, Hennaut-Roland, *J. chim. phys.* **34,** 707–711 (1937).

—— **GUAIACOL** $CH_3O.C_6H_4.OH$ $C_7H_8O_2$ **Beil. VI-768**
(Pyrocatechol monomethyl ether;
o-methoxyphenol)

B.P. 205°

See 1:1405. Genus 4: Phenols. M.P. 28.2°.

1:1738 ETHYL ALLYLACETOACETATE $C_9H_{14}O_3$ **Beil. III-738**
(Ethyl α-allyl-β-oxo-*n*-butyrate)

$CH_3CO.CH(CH_2—CH{=}CH_2)—COOC_2H_5$

B.P. 206° sl. dec. ⟨1⟩ $D_4^{17.6}$ = **0.9922** ⟨1⟩ $n_D^{17.6}$ = **1.43875** ⟨1⟩
211–212° sl. dec. ⟨2⟩ D_4^{20} = **0.9898** ⟨1⟩

Colorless mobile liq.; insol. aq.; misc. alc., ether, C_6H_6.

$\bar{C}$ with $FeCl_3$ (T 1.41) yields carmine-red color.

$\bar{C}$ in alc. with hydrazine hydrate yields 3-methyl-4-allylpyrazolone-5 [Beil. XXIV-97]; lfts. from alc., m.p. 195° ⟨3⟩; 193–194° ⟨4⟩.

Ⓓ **Saponification:** Hydrolysis with alk. (T 1.51) yields allylacetone, b.p. 129° [Beil. I-734], ethyl alc. (1:6130) and CO_2. [Allylacetone: D_4^{20} = 0.842; n_D^{20} = 1.4199; 2,4-dinitrophenylhydrazone, m.p. 108–108.5° ⟨5⟩.]

Ⓓ **Ethyl allylacetoacetate semicarbazone:** from $\bar{C}$ + 16% soln. of semicarbazide (free base) in good yield on shaking 5 hrs.; cryst. from hot aq., m.p. 125° ⟨6⟩.

1:1738 ⟨1⟩ Brühl, *J. prakt. Chem.* (2) **50,** 142 (1894). ⟨2⟩ Michael, *Ber.* **38,** 2093 (1905). ⟨3⟩ von Rothenburg, *J. prakt. Chem.* (2) **51,** 60 (1895). ⟨4⟩ Lauer, Kilburn, *J. Am. Chem. Soc.* **59,** 2588 (1937). ⟨5⟩ Hurd, Pollack, *J. Am. Chem. Soc.* **60,** 1911 (1938). ⟨6⟩ Michael, *J. Am. Chem. Soc.* **41,** 423 (1919).

1:1739 *o*-ETHYLPHENOL $C_8H_{10}O$ **Beil. VI-470**
(Phlorol; *o*-hydroxyethylbenzene)

(benzene ring with —OH and —C_2H_5 ortho)

B.P. 207° D^0 = **1.0371**

Colorless highly refractive liq. — Very spar. sol. aq.; misc. alc., ether; eas. sol. C_6H_6, AcOH — With $FeCl_3$ (T 1.41) gives blue color.

From its 1 *N* alk. soln. two vols. ether at 15° extract 45% $\bar{C}$ ⟨1⟩.

Ⓓ ***o*-Ethylphenyl benzoate:** from $\bar{C}$ + BzCl + cold aq. NaOH (cf. T 2.26-B), cryst. from alc., m.p. 38–39° ⟨2⟩.

Ⓓ ***o*-Ethylphenyl *p*-nitrobenzoate:** m.p. 56–57° ⟨1⟩.

Ⓓ ***o*-Ethylphenyl 3,5-dinitrobenzoate:** m.p. 108° ⟨1⟩.

Ⓓ ***o*-Ethylphenoxyacetic acid:** ndls., m.p. 140–141°; Neut. Eq. 180 ⟨3⟩ [cf. T 1.46].

Ⓓ ***o*-Ethylphenyl *N*-phenylcarbamate:** m.p. 141° ⟨1⟩.

1:1739 ⟨1⟩ Vavon, Mitchovitch, *Bull. soc. chim.* (4) **45,** 963 (1929). ⟨2⟩ Béhal, Choay, *Bull. soc. chim.* (3) **11,** 210 (1894). ⟨3⟩ Steinkopf, Höpner, *J. prakt. Chem.* (2) **113,** 140–141, 153 (1926).

1:1740 2,4-DIMETHYLPHENOL $C_8H_{10}O$ **Beil. VI-486**

(*unsym.-m*-Xylenol;
1,3,4-xylenol;
4-hydroxy-1,3-dimethylbenzene)

OH / —CH_3 / CH_3

B.P. 211.5° cor. **M.P. 27°** D_4^{14} = **1.0276** (supercooled liq.) n_D^{14} = **1.5420** (supercooled liq.)

Spar. sol. aq.; misc. alc., ether — Volat. with steam.
$\bar{C}$ with $FeCl_3$ (T 1.41) yields transient green-blue in alc.; transient blue-violet in aq.

Ⓓ **2,4-Dimethylphenyl benzoate:** cryst. from 75% acetic ac.; m.p. 37–38° ⟨1⟩.

Ⓓ **2,4-Dimethylphenyl *p*-nitrobenzoate:** m.p. 105°.

Ⓓ **2,4-Dimethylphenyl 3,5-dinitrobenzoate:** from $\bar{C}$ + 3,5-dinitrobenzoyl chloride in pyridine; colorless rods or pl. from 95% alc., m.p. 164.6° cor. ⟨2⟩.

Ⓓ **2,4-Dimethylphenoxyacetic acid:** from $\bar{C}$ on rubbing together with chloroacetic ac. + powdered NaOH (79% yield); m.p. 141.6° ⟨3⟩; 140.5° ⟨1⟩; Neut. Eq. 180 [cf. T 1.46].

Ⓓ **2,4-Dimethylphenyl *N*-phenylcarbamate:** from $\bar{C}$ in quant. yield on htg. ½ hr. with sl. excess phenylisocyanate in 3–4 vols. pet. (b.p. 170–200°); cryst. from CCl_4, m.p. 112° ⟨4⟩; white ndls. from CCl_4 + pet. eth., m.p. 111.8–112.2° ⟨5⟩.

Ⓓ **2,4-Dimethylphenyl *N*-α-naphthylcarbamate:** m.p. 134–135° ⟨6⟩; 135–136° ⟨5⟩ [cf. T 1.45].

Ⓓ **2,4-Dimethylphenyl *N*-(*p*-xenyl)carbamate:** m.p. 184° ⟨7⟩.

1:1740 ⟨1⟩ Palfray, Duboc, *Compt. rend.* **185,** 1480–1481 (1927). ⟨2⟩ Phillips, Keenan, *J. Am. Chem. Soc.* **53,** 1926 (1931). ⟨3⟩ Steinkopf, Höpner, *J. prakt. Chem.* (2) **113,** 141, 153 (1926). ⟨4⟩ Ref. 3, pages 141, 151. ⟨5⟩ Fichter, Schetty, *Helv. Chim. Acta* **20,** 154 (1937). ⟨6⟩ French, Wirtel, *J. Am. Chem. Soc.* **48,** 1738 (1926). ⟨7⟩ Morgan, Pettet, *J. Chem. Soc.* **1931,** 1125.

1:1742 ETHYL ACETOPYRUVATE $C_7H_{10}O_4$ **Beil. III-747**

(Ethyl α,γ-dioxo-*n*-valerate; ethyl acetoneoxalate)

$CH_3.CO.CH_2.CO.COOC_2H_5$
↓ ↑
$CH_3.C{=}CH.CO.COOC_2H_5$ (OH on C)

B.P. 213–215° **M.P. 18°** D_4^{20} = **1.1251** n_D^{17} = **1.4757**

[For prepn. from diethyl oxalate + acetone + NaOEt (61–66% yield) see ⟨1⟩.]

$\bar{C}$ with $FeCl_3$ (T 1.41) gives deep dark red color.

$\bar{C}$ with alc. NaOEt yields Na enolate; $\bar{C}$ in alc. treated with conc. aq. $Cu(OAc)_2$ yields Cu enolate, green ndls., sol. $CHCl_3$, m.p. 207–208° ⟨2⟩.

$\bar{C}$ (as Na enolate) stood 30 min. in 1.3 *N* aq. KOH, then treated with 1 mole hydrazine sulfate gives on stirring abt. 90% yield of 5-methylpyrazolecarboxylic acid-3 [Beil. XXV-119], pr. from aq., m.p. 236° dec. ⟨3⟩ — $\bar{C}$ (as Na enolate) dislvd. in 5 pts. aq. and treated first with 1 mole hydrazine sulfate, then with 1 mole NaOH (conc. aq. soln.) yields ethyl 5-methylpyrazolecarboxylate-3, tbls. from lgr., m.p. 82–83° ⟨3⟩.

$\bar{C}$ + 1 mole phenylhydrazine in AcOH, boiled under reflux, poured into aq. and the resultant oil saponified with alc. NaOH yields on acidification 1-phenyl-5-methylpyrazolecarboxylic acid-3 [Beil. XXV-120], ndls. with 1 H_2O from aq.; m.p. anhydrous product 136° ⟨4⟩ ⟨5⟩.

Ⓟ **Color reaction with AcOH + NaOAc:** $\bar{C}$ on boilg. with AcOH + solid NaOAc gives a blue-violet color similar to permanganate ⟨6⟩ ⟨7⟩.

1:1742 ⟨1⟩ Marvel, Dreger, *Organic Syntheses, Coll. Vol.* I, 233–235 (1932). ⟨2⟩ Michael, Smith, *Ann.* **363,** 51 (1908). ⟨3⟩ Knorr, Macdonald, *Ann.* **279,** 217–219 (1894). ⟨4⟩ Claisen, Roosen, *Ann.* **278,** 278–279 (1893). ⟨5⟩ von Auwers, Hollmann, *Ber.* **59,** 1302 (1926). ⟨6⟩ Claisen, Stylos, *Ber.* **21,** 1141–1142 (1888). ⟨7⟩ Claisen, *Ber.* **24,** 128–130 (1891).

1:1744 ***m*-ETHYLPHENOL** (*m*-Hydroxyethylbenzene) —OH, C_3H_5 $C_8H_{10}O$ **Beil. VI-471**

B.P. 217° **M.P. −4°** D^0 = **1.0250**

With $FeCl_3$ (T 1.41) gives violet coloration.

[Can be prepd. in quant. yield by KOH fusion of *m*-hydroxyacetophenone semicarbazone at 190° ⟨1⟩.]

Ⓓ ***m*-Ethylphenyl benzoate:** from C̄ + BzCl + cold aq. NaOH (cf. T 2.26-B); ndls. from 95% alc., m.p. 52° ⟨3⟩ ⟨4⟩; 50° ⟨1⟩.

Ⓓ ***m*-Ethylphenyl *p*-nitrobenzoate:** m.p. 68° ⟨1⟩.

Ⓓ ***m*-Ethylphenoxyacetic acid:** m.p. 75–75.5° ⟨5⟩; 76–77° ⟨4⟩; Neut. Eq. 180 [cf. T 1.46].

Ⓓ ***m*-Ethylphenyl *N*-phenylcarbamate:** m.p. 138.8° ⟨5⟩ ⟨4⟩.

1:1744 ⟨1⟩ Kenner, Statham, *J. Chem. Soc.* **1935,** 302. ⟨3⟩ Béhal, Choay, *Bull. soc. chim.* (3) **11,** 212 (1894). ⟨4⟩ Kruber, Schmitt, *Ber.* **64,** 2273 (1931). ⟨5⟩ Steinkopf, Höpner, *J. prakt. Chem.* (2) **113,** 151 (1926).

1:1745 **PYROCATECHOL MONOETHYL ETHER** $C_8H_{10}O_2$ **Beil. VI-771**
(*o*-Ethoxyphenol; guaethol) —OH, —OC_2H_5

B.P. 217° **M.P. 28°** n_D^{30} = **1.5224** ⟨1⟩

Ⓓ ***o*-Ethoxyphenyl benzoate:** m.p. 31°.

1:1745 ⟨1⟩ Parvatiker, McEwen, *J. Chem. Soc.* **125,** 1490 (1924).

1:1746 ***o*-HYDROXYACETOPHENONE** (*o*-Acetylphenol) —OH, —$CO.CH_3$ $C_8H_8O_2$ **Beil. VIII-85**

B.P. 218° **M.P. 28°** D_4^{20} = **1.131** n_D^{20} = **1.5590**
n_D^{25} = **1.5559**

Oil, dif. sol. aq.; misc. with alc., ether, AcOH — Volatile with steam [dif. from *p*-isomer (1:1527)].

With $FeCl_3$ (T 1.41) gives intense reddish violet color — With dil. NaOH C̄ yields deep yel. soln. [dif. from *p*-isomer (1:1527) whose alk. solns. are colorless] from which small excess NaOH ppts. Na salt [dif. from *p*-isomer] — C̄ dissolves in conc. H_2SO_4 yielding yel. soln. [dif. from *p*-isomer whose solns. are colorless].

For sepn. from phenol via Cu deriv. see ⟨1⟩.

Ⓓ ***o*-Acetoxyacetophenone:** from Na salt of C̄ + AcCl in dry ether ⟨2⟩, or from C̄ + Ac_2O in s.t. at 150°, or from C̄ + Ac_2O + NaOAc on short boiling ⟨3⟩, or from C̄ + Ac_2O + pyridine at 100° ⟨4⟩; tbls. from alc., m.p. 89°.

Ⓓ ***o*-Benzoxyacetophenone:** from C̄ + BzCl + pyridine at 100° for 15 min. (54% yield) ⟨5⟩, or from C̄ + BzCl + dil. aq. alk. ⟨6⟩; cryst. from alc., m.p. 87–88°.

Ⓓ ***o*-Hydroxyacetophenone oxime:** m.p. 116–117° ⟨7⟩ ⟨8⟩; 112° ⟨9⟩.
Ⓓ ***o*-Hydroxyacetophenone semicarbazone:** m.p. 209–210° ⟨1⟩.
Ⓓ ***o*-Hydroxyacetophenone phenylhydrazone:** m.p. 109–110° ⟨10⟩, 108–108.5° cor. ⟨11⟩.

1:1746 ⟨1⟩ Pauly, Lockemann, *Ber.* **48,** 30 (1915). ⟨2⟩ Tahara, *Ber.* **25,** 1310 (1892). ⟨3⟩ Friedländer, Neudorfer, *Ber.* **30,** 1080 (1897). ⟨4⟩ Hayashi, *Cent.* **1933,** II, 2009. ⟨5⟩ Baker, *J. Chem. Soc.* **1933,** 1386. ⟨6⟩ Anschütz, Scholl, *Ann.* **379,** 338 (1911). ⟨7⟩ von Auwers, Lechner, Bundesmann, *Ber.* **58,** 41 (1925). ⟨8⟩ Cope, *J. Am. Chem. Soc.* **57,** 574 (1935). ⟨9⟩ Coulthard, Marshall, Pyman, *J. Chem. Soc.* **1930,** 284. ⟨10⟩ Torrey, Brewster, *J. Am. Chem. Soc.* **35,** 441 (1913).
⟨11⟩ Bogert, Marcus, *J. Am. Chem. Soc.* **41,** 97 (1919).

—— ***p*-ETHYLPHENOL** $C_2H_5.C_6H_4.OH$ $C_8H_{10}O$ **Beil. VI-472**
(*p*-Hydroxyethylbenzene)

B.P. 219°

See 1:1424. Genus 4: Phenols. M.P. 47°.

1:1750 METHYL SALICYLATE (Methyl *o*-hydroxybenzoate) —OH, —$CO.OCH_3$ $C_8H_8O_3$ **Beil. X-70**

B.P. 224° **M.P. −8°** D_4^{20} **= 1.184** n_D^{20} **= 1.5369**

Liq. with odor of oil of wintergreen — Dif. sol. aq.
With $FeCl_3$ (T 1.41) cold satd. aq. soln. gives RV color, perm. for at least 15 min.
$\bar{C}$ is sol. in dil. aq. NaOH; with 3% NaOH (or stronger) gives ppt. of Na salt.

Ⓓ **Saponification:** Alk. hydrolysis (T 1.51) with 1 *N* alk. gives Sap. Eq. of 152 and yields salicylic ac. (1:0780) and methyl alc. (1:6120).

Ⓓ **Methyl *o*-acetoxybenzoate:** from $\bar{C}$ by shaking ice cold alk. soln. with Ac_2O; m.p. 52–52.5° ⟨1⟩.

Ⓓ **Methyl *o*-benzoxybenzoate:** from $\bar{C}$ by shaking cold dil. alk. soln. with BzCl ⟨2⟩; pr. from alc. or ether, m.p. 92°.

Ⓓ **Methyl *o*-(*p*-nitrobenzyloxy)benzoate** (methyl salicylate *p*-nitrobenzyl ether); m.p. 128.2° ⟨3⟩ [cf. T 1.44]. [Does not distinguish from ethyl salicylate (1:1755).]

Ⓓ ***o*-Carbomethoxyphenyl *N*-phenylcarbamate:** from $\bar{C}$ + equal wt. phenylisocyanate + trace NaOAc in 4 days at room temp. or 5 hrs. at 100°, cryst. from C_6H_6 or high boilg. lgr., m.p. 117° ⟨4⟩.

Ⓓ **Methyl 3,5-dinitrosalicylate:** from $\bar{C}$ by nitration at 0° with 5 pts. mixt. of equal vols. fumg. HNO_3 + fumg. H_2SO_4; cryst. from alc., m.p. 126–127° ⟨5⟩.

1:1750 ⟨1⟩ Chattaway, *J. Chem. Soc.* **1931,** 2495–2496. ⟨2⟩ Lassar-Cohn, Löwenstein, *Ber.* **41,** 3363 (1908). ⟨3⟩ Lyman, Reid, *J. Am. Chem. Soc.* **42,** 617–619 (1920). ⟨4⟩ Michael, Cobb, *Ann.* **363,** 86 (1908). ⟨5⟩ Sah, Ma, *Science Repts. Natl. Tsing Hua Univ.*, Ser. **A-1,** 203–204 (1932).

1:1755 ETHYL SALICYLATE (Ethyl *o*-hydroxybenzoate) —OH, —$CO.OC_2H_5$ $C_9H_{10}O_3$ **Beil. X-73**

B.P. 234° **M.P. +1.3°** D_4^{20} **= 1.1396 ⟨1⟩** n_D^{20} **= 1.52542 ⟨1⟩**

Liq. with odor of oil of wintergreen — Dif. sol. aq.
With $FeCl_3$ (T 1.41) cold satd. aq. soln. gives RV color immed.; VR-T_2 to RV-T_1 after 15 min.
$\bar{C}$ is sol. in dil. aq. NaOH (6% or less); with more conc. NaOH ppts. Na salt.

Ⓓ **Saponification:** Alk. hydrolysis (T 1.51) with 1 *N* alk. gives Sap. Eq. of 166 and yields salicylic ac. (1:0780) and ethyl alc. (1:6130).

Ⓓ **Ethyl *o*-benzoxybenzoate:** from Na salt of C̄ + BzCl; lfts. from alc., m.p. 87° ⟨2⟩. [Does not distinguish from methyl salicylate (1:1750).]

Ⓓ **Ethyl *o*-(*p*-nitrobenzoxy)benzoate:** from C̄ + *p*-nitrobenzoyl chloride in pyridine on stdg. overnight at room temp.; yellowish tbls. from C_6H_6, m.p. 107–108° ⟨3⟩ [cf. T 1.47].

Ⓓ **Ethyl *o*-(*p*-nitrobenzyloxy)benzoate** (ethyl salicylate *p*-nitrobenzyl ether): m.p. 125° ⟨4⟩ [cf. T 1.44]. [Does not distinguish from methyl salicylate (1:1750).]

Ⓓ ***o*-Carbethoxyphenyl *N*-phenylcarbamate:** from C̄ + equal wt. phenylisocyanate + trace NaOAc in 2 hrs.; cryst. from CS_2, m.p. 98–100° ⟨5⟩.

Ⓓ **Ethyl 3,5-dinitrosalicylate:** from C̄ by nitration at 0° with 5 pts. mixt. of equal vols. fumg. HNO_3 + fumg. H_2SO_4; cryst. from alc., m.p. 92–93° ⟨1⟩.

1:1755 ⟨1⟩ Sah, Ma, *Science Repts. Natl. Tsing Hua Univ.* Ser. **A-1,** 203–204 (1932). ⟨2⟩ Limpricht, *Ann.* **290,** 169 (1896). ⟨3⟩ Einhorn, von Bagh, *Ber.* **43,** 329 (1910). ⟨4⟩ Lyman, Reid, *J. Am. Chem. Soc.* **42,** 617–619 (1920). ⟨5⟩ Michael, Cobb, *Ann.* **363,** 87 (1908).

1:1759 *p*-ISOBUTYLPHENOL $C_{10}H_{14}O$ Beil. S.N. 530a

$(CH_3)_2.CH.CH_2$—⟨ ⟩—OH

B.P. 235-239°$_{760}$ ⟨1⟩ D^{20}_{20} = **0.9796** ⟨1⟩ n^{25}_{D} = **1.5319** ⟨1⟩

Ⓓ ***p*-Isobutylphenoxyacetic acid:** m.p. 124–125°; Neut. Eq. 208 ⟨1⟩ [cf. T 1.46].

1:1759 ⟨1⟩ Niederl, Niederl, Shapiro, McGreal, *J. Am. Chem. Soc.* **59,** 1114 (1937).

1:1760 CARVACROL $C_{10}H_{14}O$ Beil. VI-527

(2-Hydroxy-*p*-cymene;
2-methyl-5-isopropylphenol)

$(CH_3)_2$>CH—⟨ ⟩(OH)—CH_3

B.P. 237.5° ⟨1⟩ **M.P. +1°** ⟨1⟩ D^{20}_{4} = **0.9760** n^{20}_{D} = **1.524**

Viscous oil, solidifying at −20° — Scarcely sol. aq.; eas. sol. alc., ether — Sol. in alk. but extd. by ether — Volat. with steam, even from strongly alk. soln. — Sol. in conc. H_2SO_4 with sulfonation.

C̄ with $FeCl_3$ (T 1.41) gives impure transient green color, but only in very conc. alc. soln.

C̄ dislvd. in 4 pts. alc. satd. with HCl gas at 0°, and treated with conc. $NaNO_2$ soln. yields thick cream of 4-nitrosocarvacrol (thymoquinone oxime) [Beil. VII-664]; yellowish ndls. from dil. alc., m.p. 153° ⟨2⟩.

C̄ dislvd. in conc. H_2SO_4 soln. diluted and oxid. with MnO_2 ⟨3⟩, $KMnO_4$ ⟨4⟩, or $K_2Cr_2O_7$ (68–70% yield) ⟨5⟩ gives thymoquinone (1:9003), volatile with steam, m.p. 45.5°.

Carvacryl acetate and benzoate are both liquids.

Ⓓ **Carvacryl *p*-nitrobenzoate:** m.p. 51°.

Ⓓ **Carvacryl 3,5-dinitrobenzoate:** m.p. 83° [cf. T 1.47]; 76–77° ⟨6⟩.

Ⓓ **2-Methyl-5-isopropylphenoxyacetic acid:** from C̄ + chloroacetic ac. + aq. NaOH; cryst. from aq., m.p. 150–151° ⟨7⟩; Neut. Eq. 208 [cf. T 1.46].

Ⓓ **Carvacryl *N*-phenylcarbamate:** from C̄ + phenylisocyanate in high boilg. pet.; m.p. 134–135° ⟨8⟩.

Ⓓ **Carvacryl *N*-(α-naphthyl)carbamate:** from C̄ + α-naphthylisocyanate on htg.; cryst. from lgr., m.p. 116° ⟨9⟩ [cf. T 1.45].

Ⓓ **Carvacryl *N*-(*p*-xenyl)carbamate:** from C̄ + *p*-xenylisocyanate, cryst. from alc. or C_6H_6, m.p. 166° ⟨10⟩.

1:1760 ⟨1⟩ John, Beetz, *J. prakt. Chem.* (2) **143,** 256 (1935). ⟨2⟩ Klages, *Ber.* **32,** 1518 (1899). ⟨3⟩ Carstanjen, *J. prakt. Chem.* (2) **15,** 410 (1877). ⟨4⟩ Claus, Fahrion, *J. prakt. Chem.* (2) **39,** 360 (1889). ⟨5⟩ Reychler, *Bull. soc. chim.* (3) **7,** 34 (1892). ⟨6⟩ Brown, Kremers, *J. Am. Pharm. Assoc.* **11,** 607 (1922). ⟨7⟩ Koelsch, *J. Am. Chem. Soc.* **53,** 305 (1931). ⟨8⟩ Weehuizen, *Rec. trav. chim.* **37,** 356 (1917). ⟨9⟩ French, Wirtel, *J. Am. Chem. Soc.* **48,** 1738 (1926). ⟨10⟩ Morgan, Pettet, *J. Chem. Soc.* **1931,** 1125.

1:1763 ISOPROPYL SALICYLATE

—OH
—$CO.OC_3H_7$

$C_{10}H_{12}O_3$ **Beil. S.N. 1061**

B.P. 240–242° ⟨1⟩ D_4^{20} = **1.0729** ⟨1⟩ n_D^{20} = **1.50650** ⟨1⟩
118° at 17 mm. ⟨2⟩ D_{25}^{25} = **1.0781** ⟨2⟩ n_D^{25} = **1.5090** ⟨2⟩

Oil with oil of wintergreen odor — Insol. aq.; misc. alc., ether.

With $FeCl_3$ (T 1.41) satd. aq. soln. gives violet color — C̄ is sol. in NaOH solns. of 5% or less; with 10% aq. NaOH sodium salt of C̄ separates as an oil.

Ⓓ **Saponification:** Alk. hydrolysis (T 1.51) gives Sap. Eq. of 180 and yields salicylic acid (1:0780) and isopropyl alcohol (1:6135).

Ⓓ **Isopropyl 3,5-dinitrosalicylate:** from C̄ by nitration at 0° with 5 pts. mixt. of equal vols. fumg. HNO_3 + fumg. H_2SO_4; cryst. from alc., m.p. 101–102° ⟨1⟩.

1:1763 ⟨1⟩ Sah, Ma, *Science Repts. Natl. Tsing Hua Univ.* Ser. **A-1,** 203–204 (1932). ⟨2⟩ Croxall, Sowa, Nieuwland, *J. Org. Chem.* **2,** 254 (1937).

1:1765 RESORCINOL MONOMETHYL ETHER
(*m*-Methoxyphenol)

OH
—OCH_3

$C_7H_8O_2$ **Beil. VI-813**

B.P. 244° **M.P. −17.5°**

C̄ is volatile with steam ⟨1⟩ [but this has been denied ⟨2⟩] — C̄ spar. sol. aq.; misc. alc., ether.

C̄ in aq. soln. gives with $FeCl_3$ (T 1.41) a pale violet color — Sol. in 10% aq. NaOH [sepn. from resorcinol dimethyl ether (1:7570)].

C̄ + phenacyl bromide htd. in acetone for $1\frac{1}{2}$ hrs. with K_2CO_3 ⟨3⟩ or with aq. NaOH (66% yield) ⟨4⟩ gives ω-(*m*-methoxyphenoxy)acetophenone (resorcinol methyl phenacyl ether), pr. from MeOH, ndls. from alc., m.p. 85–86°.

C̄ in $CHCl_3$ treated with PkOH in $CHCl_3$ yields a picrate, C̄.PkOH; long or. blades, unstable in air, m.p. 68–69.5° ⟨5⟩.

C̄ in ether or AcOH treated with excess Br_2 to perm. color and soln. evapd. yields (80%) 2,4,6-tribromoresorcinol methyl ether, cryst. from lgr. or alc., m.p. 104–105° ⟨6⟩.

[For prepn. of C̄ by monomethylation of resorcinol see ⟨7⟩ ⟨2⟩ ⟨8⟩.]

Ⓓ ***m*-Methoxyphenoxyacetic acid:** cryst. from aq., m.p. 116–116.5°; Neut. Eq. 182 ⟨9⟩ [cf. T 1.46].

Ⓓ ***m*-Methoxyphenyl *N*-α-naphthylcarbamate:** m.p. 128–129° ⟨10⟩ [cf. T 1.45].

1:1765 ⟨1⟩ Ott, Nauen, *Ber.* **55,** 928 (1922). ⟨2⟩ Dey, *J. Indian Chem. Soc.* **12,** 685 (1935). ⟨3⟩ Freudenberg, Fikentscher, Harder, *Ann.* **441,** 177 (1924). ⟨4⟩ Baker, Pollard, Robinson, *J. Chem. Soc.* **1929,** 1470. ⟨5⟩ Baril, Megrdichian, *J. Am. Chem. Soc.* **58,** 1415 (1936). ⟨6⟩ Raiford, Scott, *J. Org. Chem.* **2,** 220 (1937). ⟨7⟩ Perkin, Ray, Robinson, *J. Chem. Soc.* **1926,** 945. ⟨8⟩ Pfeiffer, Oberlin, *Ber.* **57,** 209 (1924). ⟨9⟩ Koelsch, *J. Am. Chem. Soc.* **53,** 305 (1931). ⟨10⟩ French, Wirtel, *J. Am. Chem. Soc.* **48,** 1738 (1926).

1:1770 RESORCINOL MONOETHYL ETHER (*m*-Ethoxyphenol) $C_8H_{10}O_2$ **Beil. VI-814**

[Structure: benzene ring with OH and, in meta position, $-OC_2H_5$]

B.P. 246–247° ⟨1⟩
254–258° ⟨2⟩

Pale yel. liq., rapidly darkening on stdg. — Sl. sol. aq.; eas. sol. alc., ether.

For nitration and nitrosation see ⟨3⟩ — C̄ with $CHCl_3$ soln. of PkOH yields *m*-ethoxyphenol picrate, C̄.PkOH, red ndls. from $CHCl_3$, m.p. 105–106° ⟨4⟩.

1:1770 ⟨1⟩ Einhorn, Rothlauf, *Ann.* **382,** 250 (1911). ⟨2⟩ Doran, *J. Am. Chem. Soc.* **51,** 3449 (1929). ⟨3⟩ Hodgson, Clay, *J. Chem. Soc.* **1930,** 964–967. ⟨4⟩ Baril, Megrdichian, *J. Am. Chem. Soc.* **58,** 1415 (1936).

1:1771 *p*-*n*-BUTYLPHENOL $C_{10}H_{14}O$ **Beil. S.N. 530a**

$CH_3.CH_2.CH_2.CH_2—C_6H_4—OH$

B.P. 248° **M.P. 22°** ⟨4⟩ ⟨5⟩ D_4^{20} = **0.978** ⟨1⟩ n_D^{25} = **1.4981** ⟨3⟩
D^{22} = **0.976** ⟨2⟩ n_D^{22} = **1.5165** ⟨2⟩

Volatile with steam — Sol. in 10% aq. NaOH.

Ⓓ ***p*-*n*-Butylphenyl benzoate:** m.p. 27° ⟨4⟩.
Ⓓ ***p*-*n*-Butylphenyl *p*-nitrobenzoate:** yel. ndls. from alc., m.p. 67–68° ⟨1⟩.
Ⓓ ***p*-*n*-Butylphenoxyacetic acid:** m.p. 81°; Neut. Eq. 208 ⟨3⟩ [cf. T 1.46].
Ⓓ ***p*-*n*-Butylphenyl *N*-phenylcarbamate:** ndls. from alc., m.p. 115° ⟨6⟩; 113° ⟨5⟩.

1:1771 ⟨1⟩ Read, Mullin, *J. Am. Chem. Soc.* **50,** 1764 (1928). ⟨2⟩ Smith, *J. Am. Chem. Soc.* **56,** 1419 (1934). ⟨3⟩ Niederl, Niederl, Shapiro, McGreal, *J. Am. Chem. Soc.* **59,** 1114 (1937). ⟨4⟩ Sandulesco, Girard, *Bull. soc. chim.* (4) **47,** 1310 (1930). ⟨5⟩ Rice, Harden, *J. Am. Pharm. Assoc.* **25,** 7–9 (1936). ⟨6⟩ Reilly, Hickinbottom, *J. Chem. Soc.* **117,** 115 (1920).

1:1772 DIETHYL ACETONEDICARBOXYLATE $C_9H_{14}O_5$ **Beil. III-791**
(Diethyl *β*-oxoglutarate)

$C_2H_5O.OC.CH_2.CO.CH_2.COOC_2H_5$
⇅
$C_2H_5.O.OC.CH_2—C(OH)=CH.COOC_2H_5$

B.P. 250° D_4^{20} = **1.113**

Spar. sol. aq., sol. alc. — C̄ conts. abt. 17% enol form ⟨1⟩ — [For prepn. by esterification of acetonedicarboxylic acid (1:0485) (39–43% yield) see ⟨2⟩.]

C̄ treated with 1 mole KOH in alc. ppts. K enolate, ndls. which can be recrystd. from alc. and dried at 100°; on acidification they regenerate C̄ but on boilg. with aq. yield ethyl acetoacetate (1:1710) ⟨3⟩ — C̄ treated with 2 moles KOH in alc. yields di K di-enolate, cryst. which cannot be recrystd. and are decomp. by acids ⟨3⟩.

C̄ as such or in dil. alc. shaken with $Cu(OAc)_2$ yields green cryst. of Cu enolate, $Cu(C_9H_{13}O_5)_2$, eas. sol. in cold $CHCl_3$ or hot C_6H_6; m.p. 142–143° ⟨3⟩.

$\bar{C}$ treated with $\frac{1}{4}$ wt. of pure hydrazine hydrate at 0° and stood 24 hrs. yields ethyl pyrazolone-3-acetate [Beil. XXV-213], lfts. from warm. aq., m.p. 189–190° ⟨4⟩ — $\bar{C}$ htd. at 100° for 1 hr. with 1 mole phenylhydrazine, then diluted with ether, ppts. ethyl 1-phenylpyrazolone-5-acetate-3 [Beil. XXV-213], pr. from dil. alc., m.p. 85° ⟨5⟩.

$\bar{C}$ in alc. treated with semicarbazide HCl + AcONa yields in $\frac{1}{2}$ hr. diethyl acetonedicarboxylate semicarbazone, cryst. from boilg. alc., m.p. 94–95° ⟨6⟩.

1:1772 ⟨1⟩ Meyer, *Ann.* **380,** 242 (1911). ⟨2⟩ Adams, Chiles, *Organic Syntheses, Coll. Vol.* I, 232–233 (1932). ⟨3⟩ Dünschmann, Pechmann, *Ann.* **261,** 175–177 (1891). ⟨4⟩ Kufferath, *J. prakt. Chem.* (2) **64,** 338 (1891). ⟨5⟩ Pechmann, *Ann.* **261,** 171 (1891). ⟨6⟩ Haller, March, *Bull. soc. chim.* (3) **31,** 442 (1904).

1:1773 *p-n*-AMYLPHENOL $C_{11}H_{16}O$ Beil. S.N. 533

$CH_3.(CH_2)_3.CH_2$—⟨ring⟩—OH

B.P. 248-253°$_{760}$ ⟨1⟩ **M.P. 23°** ⟨2⟩ D^{20}_{20} = **0.9621** ⟨1⟩ n^{25}_{D} = **1.5272** ⟨1⟩

Very sol. org. solvents except cold pet. ether.

Ⓓ ***p-n*-Amylphenyl benzoate:** cryst. from alc., m.p. 51–51.5° ⟨2⟩.

Ⓓ ***p-n*-Amylphenoxyacetic acid:** m.p. 90°; Neut. Eq. 222 ⟨1⟩ [cf. T 1.46].

1:1773 ⟨1⟩ Niederl, Niederl, Shapiro, McGreal, *J. Am. Chem. Soc.* **59,** 1114 (1937). ⟨2⟩ Sandulesco, Girard, *Bull. soc. chim.* (4) **47,** 1310–1311 (1930).

1:1774 *n*-PROPYL SALICYLATE $C_{10}H_{12}O_3$ Beil. X-75

⟨ring⟩ —OH, —$COOC_3H_7$

B.P. 249-251° ⟨1⟩ D^{20}_{4} = **1.0979** ⟨1⟩ n^{20}_{D} = **1.51610** ⟨1⟩

D^{25}_{25} = **1.005** ⟨2⟩ n^{25}_{D} = **1.5100** ⟨2⟩

Oil with oil of wintergreen odor — Insol. aq.; misc. alc., ether.
With $FeCl_3$ (T 1.41) satd. aq. soln. gives faint violet color.

Ⓓ **Saponification:** Alk. hydrolysis (T 1.51) gives Sap. Eq. of 180 and yields salicylic acid (1:0780) and *n*-propyl alc. (1:6150).

Ⓓ ***n*-Propyl 3,5-dinitrosalicylate:** from $\bar{C}$ by nitration at 0° with 5 pts. mixt. of equal vols. fumg. HNO_3 + fumg. H_2SO_4; cryst. from alc., m.p. 67–68° ⟨1⟩.

1:1774 ⟨1⟩ Sah, Ma, *Science Repts. Natl. Tsing Hua Univ.* Ser. **A-1,** 203–204 (1932). ⟨2⟩ Croxall, Sowa, Nieuwland, *J. Org. Chem.* **2,** 254 (1937).

1:1775 EUGENOL $C_{10}H_{12}O_2$ Beil. VI-961

(4-Allyl-2-methoxyphenol)

CH_2=$CH.CH_2$—⟨ring⟩—OH, OCH_3

B.P. 253° **M.P. −9.1°** ⟨1⟩ D^{20}_{4} = **1.0664** ⟨1⟩ n^{20}_{D} = **1.5410** ⟨1⟩

Oil with odor of cloves — Distils at ord. press. without decomposition — Spar. sol. aq.; eas. sol. alc., ether, AcOH.

$\bar{C}$ in cold satd. aq. soln. gives with $FeCl_3$ (T 1.41) a turbid YG-T_2 color; C, 2% in alc. soln., gives B fading in 15 min. to GY-T_2.

$\bar{C}$ reduces $KMnO_4$ (T 1.34); adds Br_2.

$\bar{C}$ in $CHCl_3$ with PkOH in $CHCl_3$ yields picrate, $\bar{C}$.PkOH, long brown-red blades, m.p. 62–63° ⟨14⟩.

Ⓓ **Eugenol acetate:** from C̄ on boilg. for 3–4 hrs. with equal wt. Ac_2O; tbls. from alc., m.p. 29° ⟨2⟩.

Ⓓ **Eugenol benzoate:** from C̄ + BzCl; cryst. from alc.; m.p. 70° ⟨3⟩. [For m.p. + composition curve for mixt. with isoeugenol benzoate (1:1785) see ⟨12⟩.]

Ⓓ **Eugenol *p*-nitrobenzoate:** m.p. 81° ⟨13⟩.

Ⓓ **Eugenol 3,5-dinitrobenzoate:** from C̄ + 3,5-dinitrobenzoyl chloride in pyridine; cryst. from 95% alc.; m.p. 130.8° cor. ⟨4⟩ [cf. T 1.47].

Ⓓ **Eugenol *p*-nitrobenzyl ether:** m.p. 53.6° ⟨5⟩ [cf. T 1.44].

Ⓓ **Eugenol 2,4-dinitrophenyl ether:** from C̄ in alk. + 2,4-dinitrochlorobenzene; fine yel. ndls. from alc., m.p. 114–115° ⟨6⟩.

Ⓓ **Eugenolglycolic acid** (4-allyl-2-methoxyphenoxyacetic acid): cryst. from aq. with 1 H_2O, m.p. 81° ⟨7⟩ ⟨8⟩; cryst. anhydrous from ether or C_6H_6; m.p. 100° ⟨7⟩ ⟨8⟩ [cf. T 1.46].

Ⓓ **Eugenol *N*-phenylcarbamate:** m.p. 95° ⟨9⟩ ⟨13⟩.

Ⓓ **Eugenol *N*-(α-naphthyl)carbamate:** from C̄ htd. with α-naphthylisocyanate; cryst. from lgr.; m.p. 122° ⟨10⟩ [cf. T 1.45].

Ⓓ **Eugenol *N,N*-diphenylcarbamate:** from C̄ + *N,N*-diphenylcarbamyl chloride in pyridine; cryst. from lgr., m.p. 107–108° ⟨1⟩ [cf. T 1.43].

1:1775 ⟨1⟩ Waterman, Priester, *Rec. trav. chim.* **48,** 1272–1277 (1929). ⟨2⟩ Tiemann, Nagai, *Ber.* **10,** 202 (1877). ⟨3⟩ Tiemann, Kraaz, *Ber.* **15,** 2067 (1882). ⟨4⟩ Phillips, Keenan, *J. Am. Chem. Soc.* **53,** 1926 (1931). ⟨5⟩ Reid, *J. Am. Chem. Soc.* **39,** 309 (1917). ⟨6⟩ Bost, Nicholson, *J. Am. Chem. Soc.* **57,** 2369 (1935). ⟨7⟩ Clauser, *Monatsh.* **22,** 123 (1901). ⟨8⟩ Lambling, *Bull soc. chim.* (3) **17,** 360 (1897). ⟨9⟩ Weehuizen, *Rec. trav. chim.* **37,** 268 (1917). ⟨10⟩ French, Wirtel, *J. Am. Chem. Soc.* **48,** 1738 (1926).
⟨11⟩ Herzog, *Ber.* **40,** 1834 (1907). ⟨12⟩ McKie, *J. Chem. Soc.* **119,** 777–779 (1921). ⟨13⟩ Claisen, *Ann.* **418,** 120 (1919). ⟨14⟩ Baril, Megrdichian, *J. Am. Chem. Soc.* **58,** 1415 (1936).

1:1776 ISOBUTYL SALICYLATE $C_{11}H_{14}O_3$ Beil. X-76

$C_6H_4(OH)$—$CO.O.CH_2.CH(CH_3)_2$

B.P. 260-262° ⟨1⟩ D_4^{20} = **1.0639** ⟨1⟩ n_D^{20} = **1.50872** ⟨1⟩
D_{25}^{25} = **1.0681** ⟨2⟩ n_D^{25} = **1.5075** ⟨2⟩

Liq. with oil of wintergreen odor — Dif. sol. aq.; misc. alc., ether.

Ⓓ **Saponification:** Alk. hydrolysis (T 1.51) gives Sap. Eq. of 194 and yields salicylic acid (1:0780) and isobutyl alc. (1:6165).

Ⓓ **Isobutyl 3,5-dinitrosalicylate:** from C̄ by nitration at 0° with 5 pts. mixt. of equal vols. fumg. HNO_3 + fumg. H_2SO_4; cryst. from alc., m.p. 72–73° ⟨1⟩.

1:1776 ⟨1⟩ Sah, Ma, *Science Repts. Natl. Tsing Hua Univ.*, Ser. **A-1,** 203–204 (1932). ⟨2⟩ Croxall, Sowa, Nieuwland, *J. Org. Chem.* **2,** 254 (1937).

1:1778 ETHYL BENZOYLACETATE $C_{11}H_{12}O_3$ Beil. X-674

C_6H_5—$CO\ .\ CH_2.COOC_2H_5$
↓↑
C_6H_5—$C(OH)$=$CH.COOC_2H_5$

$n_D^{15.4}$ = **1.53165** ⟨1⟩

B.P. 265-270° sl. dec. D_4^{20} = **1.116** ⟨1⟩ n_D^{20} = **1.5498** ⟨9⟩

Dif. sol. aq.; eas. sol. alc. or ether — Volatile with steam — C̄ conts. abt. 21% enol form ⟨1⟩ ⟨2⟩; 1% alc. soln. of C̄ at 20° conts. abt. 24% enol form ⟨2⟩.

C̄ in alc. with $FeCl_3$ (T 1.41) gives red-violet color — C̄ is sol. in cold aq. NaOH without decompn. — C̄ treated with 1 mole conc. alc. NaOEt soln. or C̄ in ether treated with 1 mole $NaOC_2H_5$ ppts. Na enolate ⟨3⟩ — C̄ in ether shaken with aq. soln. of $Cu(OAc)_2$ yields ppt. of Cu enolate ⟨4⟩ sol. in $CHCl_3$; green cryst. from hot C_6H_6, m.p. 180–181° ⟨5⟩, 175° ⟨6⟩. [For use in detn. of enol content see ⟨7⟩ ⟨8⟩.]

[For prepn. of C̄ from ethyl acetoacetate + BzCl + Na via hydrol. of intermediate ethyl benzoylacetoacetate (48–58% yield) see ⟨9⟩ ⟨10⟩ ⟨11⟩; from ethyl benzoate + ethyl acetate + Na (37% yield ⟨12⟩; 77% yield ⟨13⟩.]

C̄ (2 pts.) in alc. (1 pt.) + 50% hydrazine hydrate soln. (1 pt.) in stoppered flask, shaken occasionally during 4 hrs. then htd. ½ hr., gives alm. quant. yield 3-phenylpyrazolone-5 [Beil. XXIV-148], lfts. from boilg. alc., m.p. 236° ⟨19⟩ ⟨20⟩.

C̄ warmed with 1 mole phenylhydrazine gives on addn. of ether 1, 3-diphenylpyrazolone-5 cryst. from alc., m.p. 137° ⟨14⟩. [For ketonic splitting of C̄ with phenylhydrazine and resultant formn. of acetophenone phenylhydrazone + oxalic bis-(*N*-phenylhydrazide) see ⟨15⟩.] — C̄ + 1 mole *p*-nitrophenylhydrazine in alc. refluxed 1 hr. gives 1-[*p*-nitrophenyl]-3-phenylpyrazolone-5, ndls. and lfts. from AcOH, m.p. 202–203° ⟨16⟩ — C̄. with 2,4-dinitrophenylhydrazine yields 1-(2,4-dinitrophenyl)-3-phenylpyrazolone-5 [C̄.2,4-dinitrophenylhydrazone ?], orange cryst. from AcOH, m.p. 222–223° ⟨17⟩.

C̄ + 1 mole $NH_2OH.HCl$ mixed in aq., then dislvd. by addn. of alc. gives alm. quant. yield of 3-phenylisoxazolone-5 [Beil. XXVII-200]; ndls. from alc. or C_6H_6, m.p. 151–152° dec. ⟨18⟩.

C̄ shaken 4 hrs. with 13 vols. conc. aq. NH_4OH + trace acacia gum, resultant emulsion stood 6 days, gives yellow cryst. of β-iminohydrocinnamide [Beil. III-679], which on boilg. with aq. gives (80–81% yield) benzoylacetamide, cryst. from aq., m.p. 112–113° ⟨11⟩.

Ⓓ **"Ketonic splitting":** Hydrolysis with alk. (T 1.51) yields acetophenone (1:5515), ethyl alc. (1:6130), and CO_2 [same products also obtd. on boilg. with dil. H_2SO_4 ⟨3⟩].

1:1778 ⟨1⟩ von Auwers, Jacobsen, *Ann.* **426,** 235 (1922). ⟨2⟩ Dieckmann, *Ber.* **55,** 2478 (1922). ⟨3⟩ Perkin, *J. Chem. Soc.* **45,** 175–176 (1884). ⟨4⟩ Wislicenus, *Ber.* **31,** 3153–3154 (1898). ⟨5⟩ Spassow, *Ber.* **70,** 2385 (1937). ⟨6⟩ Sommelet, Hamel, *Bull. soc. chim.* (4) **29,** 551 (1921). ⟨7⟩ Hieber, *Ber.* **54,** 905–912 (1921). ⟨8⟩ Dieckmann, *Ber.* **54,** 2251–2254 (1921). ⟨9⟩ Shriner, Schmidt, *J. Am. Chem. Soc.* **51,** 3636–3638 (1929). ⟨10⟩ Shriner, Schmidt, Roll, *Organic Syntheses* **18,** 33–35 (1938).

⟨11⟩ Abrams, Kipping, *J. Chem. Soc.* **1934,** 1989–1990. ⟨12⟩ Dorsch, McElvain, *J. Am. Chem. Soc.* **54,** 2960–2964 (1932). ⟨13⟩ Chi, Lee, *Trans. Science Soc. China* **8,** 87–89 (1934). ⟨14⟩ Knorr, Klotz, *Ber.* **20,** 2546 (1887). ⟨15⟩ Feist, *Ann.* **428,** 57–58 (1922). ⟨16⟩ von Auwers, Mauss, *Ann.* **452,** 207 (1927). ⟨17⟩ Campbell, *Analyst* **61,** 393 (1936). ⟨18⟩ Hantzsch, *Ber.* **24,** 502 (1891). ⟨19⟩ Michaelis, Rassmann, *Ann.* **352,** 158–159 (1907). ⟨20⟩ von Auwers, Mauss, *J. prakt. Chem.* (2) **110,** 219 (1925).

1:1780 *n*-BUTYL SALICYLATE

(benzene ring) —OH; —CO.O.CH₂.CH₂.CH₂.CH₃ $C_{11}H_{14}O_3$ **Beil. S.N. 1061**

B.P. 270-272° ⟨1⟩ **M.P. −5.9° ⟨2⟩** D_4^{20} = **1.0728** ⟨1⟩ n_D^{20} = **1.51148** ⟨1⟩
259-260° ⟨2⟩ D_{25}^{25} = **1.0681** ⟨3⟩ n_D^{25} = **1.5095** ⟨3⟩

Oil with oil of wintergreen odor — Dif. sol. aq.; sol. alc., ether.

With $FeCl_3$ (T 1.41) satd. aq. soln. gives faint violet color — C̄ is sol. in dil. (1% or less) NaOH; with more conc. NaOH gives gel of Na salt.

Ⓓ **Saponification:** Alk. hydrolysis (T 1.51) gives Sap. Eq. of 194 and yields salicylic ac. (1:0780) and *n*-butyl alc. (1:6180).

Ⓓ ***n*-Butyl *o*-(*p*-nitrobenzyloxy)benzoate** (*n*-butyl salicylate *p*-nitrobenzyl ether): m.p. 92° ⟨4⟩ [cf. T 1.44].

Ⓓ ***n*-Butyl 3,5-dinitrosalicylate:** from C̄ by nitration at 0° with 5 pts. mixt. of equal vols. fumg. HNO_3 + fumg. H_2SO_4; cryst. from alc., m.p. 60–61° ⟨1⟩. [Does not distinguish from isoamyl salicylate (1:1790).]

1:1780 ⟨1⟩ Sah, Ma, *Science Repts. Natl. Tsing Hua Univ.*, Ser. **A-1,** 203–204 (1932). ⟨2⟩ Timmermans, *Bull. soc. chim. Belg.* **36,** 507 (1927). ⟨3⟩ Croxall, Sowa, Nieuwland, *J. Org. Chem.* **2,** 254 (1937). ⟨4⟩ Lyman, Reid, *J. Am. Chem. Soc.* **42,** 617–619 (1920).

1:1785 ISOEUGENOL $C_{10}H_{12}O_2$ Beil. VI-955

(2-Methoxy-4-propenylphenol)

$CH_3.CH{=}CH{-}C_6H_3(OCH_3){-}OH$

B.P. 267.5° D_4^{20} = **1.0851** n_D^{20} = **1.5782**

Dif. sol. aq.; eas. sol. alc., ether.

Comml. C̄ freezes 0°–5° and is mixt. of *cis* and *trans* isomers ⟨1⟩ ⟨2⟩ — Comml. C̄, dislvd. in 1.7 pts. warm 15% NaOH, gives on cooling a Na salt which can be recrystd. from 2 pts. aq. and on acidifn. with dil. AcOH yields *trans*-isoeugenol, m.p. 33° ⟨1⟩.

C̄ with $FeCl_3$ (T 1.41) in alc. gives transient olive-green color.

C̄ on treatment with acids or acid reagents yields diisoeugenol [Beil. VI-955]; for study of structure cf. ⟨3⟩ ⟨12⟩ ⟨14⟩.

C̄ in $CHCl_3$ with PkOH in $CHCl_3$ yields picrate, C̄.PkOH; dark red silky ndl. clusters, unstable in air, m.p. 46–47.5° ⟨13⟩.

Ⓓ **Isoeugenol acetate:** from C̄ on refluxing with Ac_2O, pouring into aq., washing with Na_2CO_3 soln.; cryst. from C_6H_6 by addn. of lgr.; m.p. 79–80° ⟨4⟩. [Also obtd. in quant. yield from *trans*-isoeugenol by htg. with Ac_2O + AcONa for 3 hrs. at 135–140°; *cis*-isoeugenol acetate is liq. ⟨1⟩.]

Ⓓ **Isoeugenol benzoate:** from C̄ in alk. soln. on shaking with BzCl; pr. from alc., m.p. 103–104° ⟨4⟩, 106° ⟨5⟩ [m.p. of *cis*-isoeugenol benzoate is 68° ⟨15⟩].

Ⓓ **Isoeugenol *p*-nitrobenzoate:** m.p. 109°.

Ⓓ **Isoeugenol 3,5-dinitrobenzoate:** from C̄ + 3,5-dinitrobenzoyl chloride in pyridine; cryst. from *n*-butyl alc., m.p. 158.4° cor. ⟨6⟩ [cf. T 1.47].

Ⓓ **Isoeugenol 2,4-dinitrophenyl ether:** from C̄ in aq. NaOH + 2,4-dinitrochlorobenzene; yel. ndls. from alc., m.p. 129–130° ⟨7⟩.

Ⓓ **Isoeugenolglycolic acid** (2-methoxy-4-propenylphenoxyacetic acid): from C̄ + chloroacetic ac. + aq. NaOH; cryst. from dil. alc.; m.p. 92–94° ⟨8⟩; 116° ⟨9⟩.

Ⓓ **Isoeugenol *N*-phenylcarbamate:** *cis* form, m.p. 118°; *trans* form, m.p. 152° ⟨15⟩.

Ⓓ **Isoeugenol *N*-(α-naphthyl)carbamate:** from C̄ + α-naphthylisocyanate in pres. of trace of anhydrous trimethyl (or ethyl) amine; cryst. from lgr., m.p. 149–150° ⟨10⟩ [cf. T 1.45].

1:1785 ⟨1⟩ Boedecker, Volk, *Ber.* **64,** 62–64 (1931). ⟨2⟩ von Auwers, *Ber.* **68,** 1346–1347 (1935). ⟨3⟩ Haworth, Marvin, *J. Chem. Soc.* **1931,** 1363–1366. ⟨4⟩ Tiemann, *Ber.* **24,** 2873–2874 (1891). ⟨5⟩ Barnett, Nixon, *Chem. News* **129,** 190 (1924). ⟨6⟩ Phillips, Keenan, *J. Am. Chem. Soc.* **53,** 1926 (1931). ⟨7⟩ Bost, Nicholson, *J. Am. Chem. Soc.* **57,** 2369 (1935). ⟨8⟩ Gassmann, Krafft, *Ber.* **28,** 1870 (1895). ⟨9⟩ Denozza, *Gazz. chim. ital.* **23,** I, 553 (1893). ⟨10⟩ French, Wirtel, *J. Am. Chem. Soc.* **48,** 1738 (1926).

⟨11⟩ Funakubo, Imoto, Imoto, *Ber.* **71,** 954 (1938). ⟨12⟩ Puxeddu, Rattu, *Gazz. chim. ital.* **67,** 654–659 (1937). ⟨13⟩ Baril, Megrdichian, *J. Am. Chem. Soc.* **58,** 1415 (1936). ⟨14⟩ Puxeddu, *Gazz. chim. ital.* **66,** 710–717 (1936). ⟨15⟩ Junge, *Cent.* **1932,** II, 2818.

1:1790 ISOAMYL SALICYLATE $C_{12}H_{16}O_3$ **Beil. X-76**

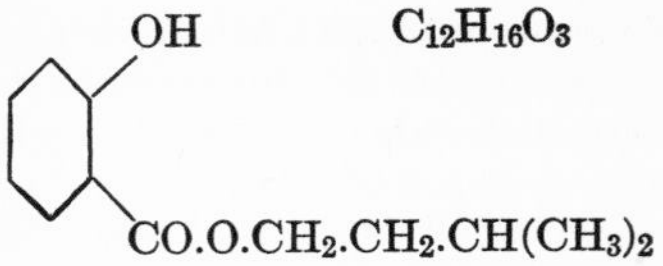

OH

$CO.O.CH_2.CH_2.CH(CH_3)_2$

B.P. 276–278° ⟨1⟩ D_4^{20} = **1.0535** ⟨1⟩ n_D^{20} = **1.50799** ⟨1⟩

Oil with floral odor — Soly. in aq. at 22° = 0.004% — Sol. alc., ether, $CHCl_3$.

With $FeCl_3$ (T 1.41) satd. aq. soln. gives faint violet color — Sol. in dil. NaOH (1% or less); with more conc. alk. soln. gives ppt. of Na salt.

Ⓓ **Saponification:** Alk. hydrolysis (T 1.51) gives Sap. Eq. of 208 and yields salicylic acid (1:0780) and isoamyl alc. (1:6200).

Ⓓ **Isoamyl 3,5-dinitrosalicylate:** from C̄ by nitration at 0° with 5 pts. mixt. of equal vols. fumg. HNO_3 + fumg. H_2SO_4; cryst. from alc., m.p. 61–62° ⟨1⟩. [Does not distinguish from *n*-butyl salicylate (1:1780).]

1:1790 ⟨1⟩ Sah, Ma, *Science Repts. Natl. Tsing Hua Univ.*, Ser. **A-1,** 203–204 (1932).

1:1795 RESORCINOL MONOACETATE $C_8H_8O_3$ **Beil. VI-816**
(*m*-Acetoxyphenol)

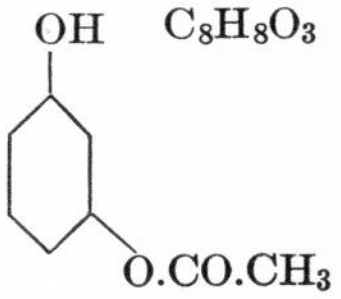

OH

$O.CO.CH_3$

B.P. 283°

Eas. sol. dil. alk.

Ⓓ **Saponification:** Hydrolysis with 1 *N* alk. (T 1.51) gives Sap. Eq. 152 and yields resorcinol (1:1530) and acetic ac. (1:1010).

—— ***o*-BENZYLPHENOL** $C_{13}H_{12}O$ **Beil. VI-675**
(2-Hydroxydiphenylmethane)

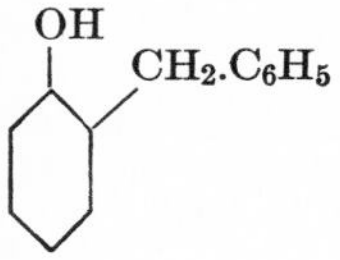

OH $CH_2.C_6H_5$

B.P. 312°

See 1:1431. Genus 4: Phenols. M.P. 54°.

IMPORTANT PHENOLS THAT CAN BE DISTILLED ONLY UNDER REDUCED PRESSURE

1:1800 METHYL FUROYLACETATE $C_8H_8O_4$ **Beil. S.N. 2619**

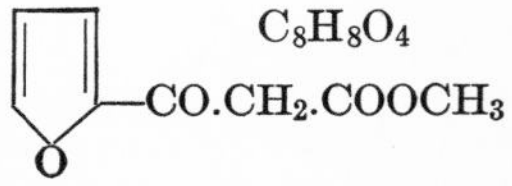

$—CO.CH_2.COOCH_3$

O

B.P. 144–145° at 20 mm. ⟨1⟩
96–98° at 1 mm. ⟨1⟩

Colorless oily liq. which turns yel. on stdg.

C̄ with $NaOC_2H_5$ in abs. alc. rapidly ppts. mono Na salt of enol; C̄ with alc. KOH seps. mono K salt of enol on stdg. 3–4 hrs.; C̄ in ether shaken with conc. aq. soln. of $Cu(OAc)_2$ yields green ndls. of Cu salt of enol.; all of which regenerate to C̄ on treatment with dil. acid.

C̄ with 1 mole phenylhydrazine at 100° yields 1-phenyl-3-furylpyrazolone-5; lfts. from abs. alc., m.p. 179° ⟨1⟩.

Ⓓ **Methyl furoylacetate oxime:** from C̄ + $NH_2OH.HCl$ + AcONa in dil. alc. on stdg. 4 hrs. and pptg. with aq.; cryst. from C_6H_6, dec. at 124–125° (when htd. at 4° per min. from room temp.) and yielding furylisoxazolone, m.p. 147–148° ⟨1⟩.

Ⓓ **Methyl furoylacetate semicarbazone:** from C̄ + semicarbazide.HCl + AcONa in dil. alc. (as above); cryst. from C_6H_6 + alc. (3:1); m.p. 141–142° dec. ⟨1⟩.

1:1800 ⟨1⟩ Zanetti, Beckmann, *J. Am. Chem. Soc.* **50,** 1438–1441 (1928).

1:1810 METHYL BENZOYLACETATE $C_{10}H_{10}O_3$ Beil. S.N. 1316

C_6H_5—CO.CH_2.$COOCH_3$ ⇅ C_6H_5—C(OH)=CH.CO.OCH_3

B.P. 151.5-151.8° at 13 mm. ⟨1⟩ D_4^{20} = **1.158** ⟨1⟩ n_D^{20} = **1.5394** ⟨1⟩

Equilibrium mixt. at 20° conts. 18.5% enol form ⟨2⟩ [for data on solution in org. solv. see ⟨2⟩].

C̄ in alc. gives with $FeCl_3$ (T 1.41) a strong color; C̄ is readily sol. in aq. alk.

C̄ in alc. shaken with aq. $Cu(OAc)_2$ soln. gives Cu salt of enol form, readily extracted by $CHCl_3$ or C_6H_6 and regenerating C̄ on treatment with dil. minl. acid. [Use in purification of C̄ ⟨1⟩; in detn. of enol content of C̄ ⟨3⟩ ⟨4⟩.]

[For prepn. of C̄ from ω-cyanoacetophenone with HCl + MeOH see ⟨5⟩.]

Ⓓ **Saponification:** Hydrolysis with dil. alk. (T 1.51) yields acetophenone (1:5515), methyl alcohol (1:6120) and CO_2.

1:1810 ⟨1⟩ von Auwers, Jacobsen, *Ann.* **426,** 234–235 (1922). ⟨2⟩ Dieckmann, *Ber.* **55,** 2478 (1922). ⟨3⟩ Hieber, *Ber.* **54,** 905, 912 (1921). ⟨4⟩ Dieckmann, *Ber.* **54,** 2253 (1921). ⟨5⟩ Arndt, Loewe, *Ber.* **71,** 1639 (1938).

1:1820 ETHYL FUROYLACETATE $C_9H_{10}O_4$ Beil. XVIII-408

C_4H_3O—CO.CH_2.$COOC_2H_5$ ⇅ C_4H_3O—C(OH)=CH.$COOC_2H_5$

B.P. 170° at 20 mm. ⟨1⟩
143° at 10 mm. ⟨1⟩
113-114° at 1 mm. ⟨2⟩ D_{17}^{17} = **1.165** ⟨1⟩ n_D^{17} = **1.5055** ⟨2⟩

Pale yel. oil; when pure darkens only on long stdg. — Insol. aq., sol. alc., ether; eas. sol. NH_4OH — C̄ reduces NH_4OH + $AgNO_3$ — [For prepn. from ethyl furoate + ethyl acetate in 93% yield see ⟨2⟩.]

C̄ in alc. treated with 50% aq. NaOH at 0° ppts. Na enolate; C̄ in alc. shaken with aq. $Cu(OAc)_2$ soln. yields Cu enolate, sol. $CHCl_3$, m.p. 175° ⟨3⟩.

C̄, dislvd. in excess conc. NH_4OH, evapd. yields α-furoylacetamide, cryst. from alc., m.p. 159° ⟨4⟩ — C̄ in dil. alc. htd. with 1 mole hydrazine sulfate + 1 mole NaOAc yields 3-(α-furyl)pyrazolone-5, pl. from dil. MeOH, beginning to dec. abt. 200°, finally melt. 223° ⟨1⟩ — C̄, htd. with 1 mole phenylhydrazine at 100° yields 1-phenyl-3-(α-furyl)pyrazolone-5, lfts. from abs. alc., m.p. 179° ⟨1⟩ ⟨3⟩.

C̄ with 1 mole $NH_2OH.HCl$ + 1 mole NaOAc in dil. alc. stood 3 hrs. yields ethyl furoylacetate oxime; ndls. from dil. alc., m.p. 131–132° ⟨1⟩ [with alk. NH_2OH, C̄ yields 3-(α-furyl)-isoxazolone, ndls. from alc., m.p. 148–149° (block) dec. ⟨1⟩].

Ⓓ **" Ketone splitting ":** C̄ boiled with 1:25 H_2SO_4 yields α-furyl methyl ketone (2-acetylfuran) [Beil. XVII-286], ethyl alc. (1:6130), and CO_2 ⟨3⟩.

Ⓓ **" Acid splitting ":** C̄ boiled with conc. KOH yields furoic acid (1:0475), acetic ac. (1:1010) and ethyl alc. (1:6130) ⟨1⟩.

1:1820 ⟨1⟩ Torrey, Zanetti, *Am. Chem. J.* **44,** 405–416 (1910). ⟨2⟩ Barger, Robinson, Smith, *J. Chem. Soc.* **1937,** 721. ⟨3⟩ Sandelin, *Ber.* **33,** 492–494 (1900). ⟨4⟩ Mironescu, Ioanid, *Bull. soc. chim. România* **17,** 107–129 (1935); *Cent.* **1935,** II, 3652.

1:1830 PYROCATECHOL MONOBENZYL ETHER $C_{13}H_{12}O_2$ Beil. S.N. 553

(Benzyl *o*-hydroxyphenyl ether)

C_6H_5—CH_2—O—C_6H_4(HO)

B.P. 157° at 6 mm. ⟨1⟩
173–174° at 13 mm. ⟨2⟩ D^{22} = **1.154** ⟨2⟩ n^{22} = **1.1588** ⟨2⟩

C̄ with $FeCl_3$ (T 1.41) gives green color becoming red violet on addition of Na_2CO_3.

C̄ is sol. in alk. with brown-red color [dif. and sepn. from pyrocatechol dibenzyl ether, m.p. 63–64° (1:7172)].

1:1830 ⟨1⟩ Klarmann, Gates, Shternov, *J. Am. Chem. Soc.* **54,** 1210 (1932). ⟨2⟩ Druey, *Bull. soc. chim.* (5) **2,** 1738 (1935).

1:1840 ETHYL *n*-BUTYLACETOACETATE $C_{10}H_{18}O_3$ Beil. III-706

$CH_3.CO.CH(C_4H_9).CO.OC_2H_5$

B.P. 104–104.5° at 12 mm. ⟨1⟩ D_4^{20} = **0.95227** ⟨1⟩ n_D^{20} = **1.43006** ⟨1⟩

[For prepn. from ethyl acetoacetate, EtONa, + *n*-BuBr (69–72% yield) see ⟨2⟩.]

C̄ refluxed with 10% aq. NaOH for 4–5 hrs. gives alm. quant. yield ⟨1⟩ or saponified at room temp. with 5% NaOH for 4 hrs., then made slightly acid and distilled ⟨3⟩ gives 52–61% yield of *n*-amyl methyl ketone (1:5460), b.p. 150°. [For study of influence of conditions on " ketone splitting " *vs.* " acid splitting " see ⟨4⟩.]

C̄ with phenylhydrazine in AcOH at 100° for 10 min. yields 1-phenyl-3-methyl-4-*n*-butylpyrazolone-5, m.p. 95–96° ⟨5⟩.

1:1840 ⟨1⟩ Ceuterick, *Bull. soc. chim. Belg.* **44,** 89–90 (1935). ⟨2⟩ Marvel, Hager, *Organic Syntheses, Coll. Vol.* I, 243–244 (1932). ⟨3⟩ Johnson, Hager, *Organic Syntheses, Coll. Vol.* I, 343–345 (1932). ⟨4⟩ Drake, Riemenschneider, *J. Am. Chem. Soc.* **52,** 5005–5008 (1930). ⟨5⟩ Giacolone, *Gazz. chim. ital.* **67,** 463 (1937).

CHAPTER VII

GENUS 5. ESTERS

(Classified according to acid radicals; for classification according to **alkyl radicals** see General Compound Index)

Names used in this index are not necessarily same as compound index **names**

I. Esters of Aliphatic Saturated Acids

A. *Esters of monobasic acids*

1. Esters of formic acid

Allyl formate............ **1:3035**

Methyl formate.......... **1:1000**
Ethyl formate........... **1:3000**

n-Propyl formate......... **1:3030**
Isopropyl formate........ **1:3010**

n-Butyl formate.......... **1:3090**
sec-Butyl formate........ **1:3055**
ter-Butyl formate......... **1:3033**
Isobutyl formate......... **1:3065**

n-Amyl formate.......... **1:3166**
Isoamyl formate......... **1:3142**

n-Hexyl formate......... **1:3313**
n-Heptyl formate......... **1:3422**
n-Octyl formate.......... **1:3576**

Ethylene glycol monoformate............... **1:3447**
Ethylene glycol diformate **1:3402**

Benzyl formate.......... **1:3596**
Cyclohexyl formate....... **1:3348**
Trimethyl orthoformate ... **1:3087**
Triethyl orthoformate..... **1:3241**

2. Esters of acetic acid

(*a*) *with monohydric alcohols*

Allyl acetate............. **1:3085**
Geranyl acetate.......... **1:3997**

Methyl acetate........... **1:3005**
Ethyl acetate............ **1:3015**

n-Propyl acetate......... **1:3075**
Isopropyl acetate......... **1:3041**

n-Butyl acetate.......... **1:3145**
sec-Butyl acetate......... **1:3105**
ter-Butyl acetate......... **1:3057**
Isobutyl acetate.......... **1:3115**

n-Amyl acetate.......... **1:3276**
sec-Amyl (-2) acetate..... **1:3171**
sec-Amyl (-3) acetate..... **1:3168**
ter-Amyl acetate......... **1:3134**
Isoamyl acetate.......... **1:3221**

n-Hexyl acetate.......... **1:3427**
n-Heptyl acetate......... **1:3521**

n-Octyl acetate.......... **1:3676**
sec-Octyl (-2) acetate..... **1:3541**

Cetyl acetate............ **1:2038**
n-Octadecyl acetate....... **1:2066**

Benzyl acetate........... **1:3751**
β-Phenylethyl acetate..... **1:3922**
l-Linalyl acetate......... **1:3776**

(*b*) *with dihydric alcohols*

Ethylene glycol diacetate.. **1:3511**
Ethylene glycol monoacetate.................. **1:3486**

Trimethylene glycol diacetate.................. **1:3671**
Diethylene glycol diacetate. **1:4076**
β-Ethoxyethyl acetate..... **1:3323**

Pentaerythritol tetraacetate **1:2355**

(*c*) *with alicyclic alcohols*

Cyclohexyl acetate....... **1:3412**
d-Bornyl acetate......... **1:3832**
Cholesteryl acetate....... **1:2475**

(*d*) *with alcohols containing heterocyclic rings*

Furfuryl acetate......... **1:3417**
α-Tetrahydrofurfuryl acetate.................. **1:3551**

(*e*) *with miscellaneous compounds*

Benzoin acetate.......... **1:2350**
Ethylidene diacetate...... **1:3383**
Phenacyl acetate......... **1:2132**
Salicylaldehyde triacetate.. **1:2420**

(*f*) *with phenols*

Phenyl acetate........... **1:3571**

o-Tolyl acetate	**1:3646**
m-Tolyl acetate	**1:3706**
p-Tolyl acetate	**1:3716**
2,4-Dimethylphenyl acetate	**1:3822**
2,5-Dimethylphenyl acetate	**1:3801**
2,6-Dimethylphenyl acetate	**1:3741**
3,4-Dimethylphenyl acetate	**1:3952**
3,5-Dimethylphenyl acetate	**1:4510**
2,4,5-Trimethylphenyl acetate	**1:4041**
2,4,6-Trimethylphenyl acetate	**1:3957**
Thymyl acetate	**1:4026**
Carvacryl acetate	**1:4031**
α-Naphthyl acetate	**1:2124**
β-Naphthyl acetate	**1:2273**
Resorcinol diacetate	**1:4251**
Resorcinol monoacetate	**1:1795**
Hydroquinone diacetate	**1:2520**
Pyrogallol triacetate	**1:2585**
Hydroxyhydroquinone triacetate	**1:2400**
Phloroglucinol triacetate	**1:2430**
Guaiacol acetate	**1:3987**
Eugenol acetate	**1:4266**
Isoeugenol acetate	**1:2340**

3. Esters of propionic acid

Allyl propionate	**1:3140**
Methyl propionate	**1:3020**
Ethyl propionate	**1:3070**
n-Propyl propionate	**1:3130**
Isopropyl propionate	**1:3100**
n-Butyl propionate	**1:3256**
Isobutyl propionate	**1:3211**
n-Amyl propionate	**1:3378**
Isoamyl propionate	**1:3343**
n-Hexyl propionate	**1:3506**
n-Heptyl propionate	**1:3681**
n-Octyl propionate	**1:3877**
Ethylene glycol dipropionate	**1:3691**
α-Tetrahydrofurfuryl propionate	**1:3611**
Cyclohexyl propionate	**1:3526**
Phenyl propionate	**1:3696**

4. Esters of *n*-butyric acid

Allyl *n*-butyrate	**1:3216**
Methyl *n*-butyrate	**1:3080**
Ethyl *n*-butyrate	**1:3127**
n-Propyl *n*-butyrate	**1:3231**
Isopropyl *n*-butyrate	**1:3160**
n-Butyl *n*-butyrate	**1:3358**
ter-Butyl *n*-butyrate	**1:3251**
Isobutyl *n*-butyrate	**1:3328**
n-Amyl *n*-butyrate	**1:3476**
Isoamyl *n*-butyrate	**1:3432**
n-Hexyl *n*-butyrate	**1:3636**
n-Heptyl *n*-butyrate	**1:3817**
n-Octyl *n*-butyrate	**1:4011**
Ethylene glycol di-*n*-butyrate	**1:3962**
Benzyl *n*-butyrate	**1:3977**
Cyclohexyl *n*-butyrate	**1:3711**

5. Esters of isobutyric acid

Allyl isobutyrate	**1:3181**
Methyl isobutyrate	**1:3050**
Ethyl isobutyrate	**1:3095**
n-Propyl isobutyrate	**1:3191**
Isopropyl isobutyrate	**1:3125**
ter-Butyl isobutyrate	**1:3147**
Isobutyl isobutyrate	**1:3271**
Isoamyl isobutyrate	**1:3388**
Cyclohexyl isobutyrate	**1:3601**

6. Esters of *n*-valeric acid

Methyl *n*-valerate	**1:3155**
Ethyl *n*-valerate	**1:3246**
n-Propyl *n*-valerate	**1:3353**
Isopropyl *n*-valerate	**1:3296**
n-Butyl *n*-valerate	**1:3481**
sec-Butyl *n*-valerate	**1:3407**
Isobutyl *n*-valerate	**1:3442**
n-Amyl *n*-valerate	**1:3621**
n-Hexyl *n*-valerate	**1:3847**
n-Heptyl *n*-valerate	**1:4046**
n-Octyl *n*-valerate	**1:4161**

7. Esters of isovaleric acid

Methyl isovalerate	**1:3110**
Ethyl isovalerate	**1:3186**

n-Propyl isovalerate...... **1:3318**
Isopropyl isovalerate...... **1:3226**

Isobutyl isovalerate....... **1:3393**
Isoamyl isovalerate....... **1:3516**

7-A. Esters of pivalic acid
Methyl pivalate.......... **1:3072**
Ethyl pivalate........... **1:3117**

8. Esters of *n*-caproic acid
Methyl *n*-caproate........ **1:3291**
Ethyl *n*-caproate......... **1:3363**

n-Propyl *n*-caproate...... **1:3491**

n-Butyl *n*-caproate....... **1:3631**

n-Amyl *n*-caproate....... **1:3837**

n-Hexyl *n*-caproate....... **1:4061**
n-Heptyl *n*-caproate...... **1:4156**
n-Octyl *n*-caproate....... **1:4236**

9. Esters of enanthic (*n*-heptylic) acid
Methyl enanthate........ **1:3398**
Ethyl enanthate......... **1:3496**
n-Propyl enanthate....... **1:3651**

n-Butyl enanthate........ **1:3842**
Isobutyl enanthate....... **1:3661**

n-Amyl enanthate........ **1:4051**

n-Hexyl enanthate........ **1:4141**
n-Heptyl enanthate....... **1:4241**
n-Octyl enanthate........ **1:4301**

10. Esters of *n*-caprylic acid
Methyl *n*-caprylate....... **1:3546**
Ethyl *n*-caprylate........ **1:3656**
n-Propyl *n*-caprylate...... **1:3852**

n-Butyl *n*-caprylate....... **1:4036**

n-Amyl *n*-caprylate....... **1:4136**

n-Hexyl *n*-caprylate...... **1:4246**
n-Heptyl *n*-caprylate..... **1:4296**
n-Octyl *n*-caprylate....... **1:4351**

11. Esters of pelargonic acid
Methyl pelargonate....... **1:3736**
Ethyl pelargonate........ **1:3867**

12. Esters of *n*-capric acid
Methyl *n*-caprate......... **1:3827**
Ethyl *n*-caprate.......... **1:4016**

13. Esters of lauric acid
Ethyl laurate............ **1:4196**
Ethylene glycol dilaurate.. **1:2157**

14. Esters of myristic acid
Methyl myristate......... **1:2013**
Ethyl myristate.......... **1:4316**
Ethylene glycol dimyristate **1:2233**

15. Esters of pentadecylic acid
Methyl pentadecylate..... **1:2009**

16. Esters of palmitic acid
Methyl palmitate........ **1:2055**
Ethyl palmitate.......... **1:2034**
Cetyl palmitate.......... **1:2153**
Ethylene glycol dipalmitate **1:2269**

17. Esters of margaric acid
Methyl margarate........ **1:2054**
Ethyl margarate......... **1:2017**

18. Esters of stearic acid
Methyl stearate.......... **1:2095**
Ethyl stearate........... **1:2078**

n-Butyl stearate.......... **1:2046**
Isobutyl stearate......... **1:2026**

n-Amyl stearate.......... **1:2061**
Isoamyl stearate......... **1:2030**

Cetyl stearate............ **1:2193**
Ethylene glycol distearate. **1:2320**
Phenyl stearate.......... **1:2161**

19. Esters of aryl-substituted aliphatic acids
Methyl phenylacetate..... **1:3771**
Ethyl phenylacetate...... **1:3872**

Methyl diphenylacetate... **1:2213**
Ethyl diphenylacetate..... **1:2201**

Methyl β-phenylpropionate **1:3982**
Ethyl β-phenylpropionate.. **1:4081**

Methyl α-phenyl-*n*-butyrate **1:2325**
Methyl dibenzylacetate.... **1:2098**

Methyl hexahydrobenzoate **1:3467**
Ethyl hexahydrobenzoate.. **1:3566**

B. *Esters of aliphatic saturated dibasic acids*

1. Esters of carbonic acid
Dimethyl carbonate...... **1:3046**
Diethyl carbonate........ **1:3150**

Di-*n*-propyl carbonate..... **1:3373**
Diisopropyl carbonate..... **1:3261**

Di-*n*-butyl carbonate..... **1:3626**
Diisobutyl carbonate...... **1:3501**

Diisoamyl carbonate...... **1:3937**

Di-(β-methoxyethyl) carbonate **1:3932**
Di-(β-ethoxyethyl) carbonate **1:4066**
Di-(β-*n*-butoxyethyl) carbonate **1:4326**

Ethyl β-methoxyethyl carbonate **1:3462**
Ethyl β-ethoxyethyl carbonate **1:3536**
Ethyl β-*n*-butoxyethyl carbonate **1:3806**

Diphenyl carbonate **1:2335**
Di-*o*-tolyl carbonate **1:2217**
Di-*m*-tolyl carbonate **1:2136**
Di-*p*-tolyl carbonate **1:2470**
Diguaiacyl carbonate **1:2370**

2. Esters of oxalic acid

Dimethyl oxalate **1:0415**
Diethyl oxalate **1:1055**

Di-*n*-propyl oxalate **1:3726**
Diisopropyl oxalate **1:3531**

Di-*n*-butyl oxalate **1:4071**
Diisobutyl oxalate **1:3897**

Diisoamyl oxalate **1:4181**
Dicyclohexyl oxalate **1:2110**

Di-*o*-tolyl oxalate **1:2390**
Di-*m*-tolyl oxalate **1:2435**
Di-*p*-tolyl oxalate **1:2570**

3. Esters of malonic acid

Dimethyl malonate **1:3457**
Diethyl malonate **1:3581**

4. Esters of succinic acid

Dimethyl succinate **1:3556**
Diethyl succinate **1:3756**

Di-*n*-propyl succinate **1:4086**
Di-*n*-butyl succinate **1:4211**
Dibenzyl succinate **1:2145**

Diphenyl succinate **1:2500**
Di-*p*-tolyl succinate **1:2510**

5. Esters of glutaric acid

Dimethyl glutarate **1:3731**
Diethyl glutarate **1:3967**

6. Esters of adipic acid

Dimethyl adipate **1:2005**
Diethyl adipate **1:4056**
Di-*n*-propyl adipate **1:4560**

Diphenyl adipate **1:2440**

7. Esters of pimelic acid

Dimethyl pimelate **1:4500**
Diethyl pimelate **1:4530**

8. Esters of suberic acid

Dimethyl suberate **1:4186**
Diethyl suberate **1:4261**

9. Esters of azelaic acid

Dimethyl azelate **1:4540**
Diethyl azelate **1:4306**

10. Esters of sebacic acid

Dimethyl sebacate **1:2042**
Diethyl sebacate **1:4366**
Di-*n*-butyl sebacate **1:4444**

II. Esters of Aliphatic Unsaturated Acids

A. *Esters of monobasic acids*

Methyl acrylate **1:3025**
Ethyl acrylate **1:3071**

Ethyl methacrylate **1:3118**

Methyl crotonate **1:3121**
Ethyl crotonate **1:3196**

Methyl isocrotonate **1:3088**
Ethyl isocrotonate **1:3144**

Methyl undecylenate **1:4093**
Ethyl undecylenate **1:4176**

Methyl β-(α-furyl)acrylate. **1:3857**
Ethyl β-(α-furyl)acrylate.. **1:3927**

Methyl cinnamate **1:2090**
Ethyl cinnamate **1:4206**
β-Phenylethyl cinnamate.. **1:2120**

B. *Esters of dibasic acids*

Dimethyl maleate **1:3606**
Diethyl maleate **1:3791**
Di-*n*-propyl maleate **1:4520**

Dimethyl fumarate **1:2415**
Diethyl fumarate **1:3761**

Dimethyl citraconate **1:3686**
Diethyl citraconate **1:3912**

Dimethyl itaconate **1:3641**
Diethyl itaconate **1:3885**

Dimethyl mesaconate **1:3591**
Diethyl mesaconate **1:3892**

C. *Esters of tribasic acids*

Trimethyl aconitate **1:4201**
Triethyl aconitate **1:4216**

III. Esters of Aliphatic (or Aryl-Substituted) Saturated Acids Containing also other Functional Groups

A. *Esters of hydroxy acids (ether acids; ester acids)*

1. Esters of monobasic acids

Methyl hydroxyacetate.... **1:3286**
Methyl methoxyacetate... **1:3162**
Methyl ethoxyacetate..... **1:3266**
Methyl phenoxyacetate... **1:4021**

Ethyl hydroxyacetate..... **1:3338**
Ethyl methoxyacetate..... **1:3164**
Ethyl ethoxyacetate...... **1:3333**
Ethyl acetoxyacetate..... **1:3437**
Ethyl phenoxyacetate..... **1:4106**

Methyl α-hydroxypropionate (lactate)........... **1:3236**
Ethyl α-hydroxypropionate (lactate).............. **1:3303**
Isopropyl α-hydroxypropionate (lactate)......... **1:3368**

Methyl α-hydroxyisobutyrate.................. **1:3206**
Ethyl α-hydroxyisobutyrate.................. **1:3281**

Methyl *d,l*-mandelate..... **1:2166**
Ethyl *d,l*-mandelate...... **1:2049**

Methyl benzilate......... **1:2310**
Ethyl benzilate.......... **1:2086**

2. Esters of dibasic acids

Dimethyl tartronate...... **1:2171**
Diethyl tartronate........ **1:3796**

Dimethyl *l*-malate........ **1:3992**
Diethyl *l*-malate......... **1:4116**

Dimethyl *d*-tartrate...... **1:2227**
Diethyl *d*-tartrate........ **1:4256**
Di-*n*-propyl *d*-tartrate..... **1:4321**
Diisopropyl *d*-tartrate **1:4221**
Di-*n*-butyl *d*-tartrate...... **1:2021**
Diisobutyl *d*-tartrate **1:2263**
Dibenzyl *d*-tartrate....... **1:2141**

Dimethyl *d,l*-tartrate...... **1:2385**
Di-*n*-propyl *d,l*-tartrate.... **1:4281**
Diisopropyl *d,l*-tartrate ... **1:4226**
Di-*n*-butyl *d,l*-tartrate..... **1:4401**
Diisobutyl *d,l*-tartrate **1:2197**

Dimethyl *meso*-tartrate.... **1:2460**
Diethyl *meso*-tartrate...... **1:2179**

Dimethyl mucate........ **1:2580**
Diethyl mucate.......... **1:2575**

3. Esters of tribasic acids

Trimethyl citrate......... **1:2315**
Triethyl citrate.......... **1:4311**

B. *Esters of keto acids*

1. Esters of α-keto acids

Methyl pyruvate......... **1:3201**
Ethyl pyruvate.......... **1:3308**
Ethyl acetopyruvate...... **1:1742**

2. Esters of β-keto acids

Methyl acetoacetate...... **1:1705**
Ethyl acetoacetate....... **1:1710**

Methyl methylacetoacetate **1:1708**
Ethyl methylacetoacetate.. **1:1712**

Methyl ethylacetoacetate . **1:1718**
Ethyl ethylacetoacetate... **1:1723**

Ethyl allylacetoacetate.... **1:1738**

Ethyl *n*-butylacetoacetate. **1:1840**

Methyl benzoylacetate.... **1:1810**
Ethyl benzoylacetate..... **1:1778**

Methyl furoylacetate...... **1:1800**
Ethyl furoylacetate....... **1:1820**

Diethyl acetonedicarboxylate.................. **1:1772**

3. Esters of γ-keto acids

Methyl levulinate........ **1:3561**
Ethyl levulinate.......... **1:3616**
n-Propyl levulinate....... **1:3786**
Isopropyl levulinate...... **1:3666**
n-Butyl levulinate........ **1:3972**
Isobutyl levulinate....... **1:3907**
sec-Butyl levulinate....... **1:3812**
n-Amyl levulinate........ **1:4121**
Isoamyl levulinate........ **1:4096**

IV. Esters of Aromatic Acids

A. *Esters of monobasic acids*

1. Esters of benzoic acid

Allyl benzoate........... **1:3902**

Methyl benzoate......... **1:3586**
Ethyl benzoate........... **1:3721**

n-Propyl benzoate........ **1:3917**
Isopropyl benzoate....... **1:3766**
n-Butyl benzoate......... **1:4104**
Isobutyl benzoate........ **1:4006**

Isoamyl benzoate......... **1:4166**

β-Methoxyethyl benzoate.. **1:4126**
β-Ethoxyethyl benzoate... **1:4146**
β-*n*-Butoxyethyl benzoate.. **1:4570**

Benzyl benzoate.......... **1:4422**
α-Tetrahydrofurfuryl benzoate................ **1:4336**

Ethylene glycol dibenzoate. **1:2293**
Glyceryl tribenzoate...... **1:2287**

Phenyl benzoate......... **1:2257**
o-Tolyl benzoate......... **1:4371**
m-Tolyl benzoate......... **1:2183**
p-Tolyl benzoate......... **1:2279**
α-Naphthyl benzoate..... **1:2187**
β-Naphthyl benzoate...... **1:2450**

Pyrocatechol dibenzoate... **1:2360**
Resorcinol dibenzoate..... **1:2485**
Hydroquinone dibenzoate.. **1:2590**

2. Esters of toluic acids

Methyl o-toluate......... **1:3746**
Ethyl o-toluate........... **1:3862**

Methyl m-toluate......... **1:3781**
Ethyl m-toluate.......... **1:3942**

Methyl p-toluate......... **1:2071**
Ethyl p-toluate.......... **1:3947**

3. Esters of naphthoic acids

Ethyl α-naphthoate....... **1:4376**

Methyl β-naphthoate...... **1:2330**
Ethyl β-naphthoate....... **1:4341**

B. *Esters of dibasic aromatic acids*

1. Esters of phthalic acid

Dimethyl phthalate....... **1:4271**
Diethyl phthalate........ **1:4331**
Di-n-butyl phthalate...... **1:4433**
Di-(β-ethoxyethyl) phthalate **1:2074**
Dibenzyl phthalate....... **1:2102**
Dicyclohexyl phthalate.... **1:2239**
Diphenyl phthalate....... **1:2300**

2. Esters of isophthalic acid

Dimethyl isophthalate.... **1:2244**
Diethyl isophthalate...... **1:4276**

3. Esters of terephthalic acid

Dimethyl terephthalate... **1:2550**
Diethyl terephthalate..... **1:2106**

4. Esters of naphthalic acid

Dimethyl naphthalate..... **1:2425**
Diethyl naphthalate...... **1:2209**

5. Esters of d-camphoric acid

Dimethyl d-camphorate... **1:4171**
Diethyl d-camphorate..... **1:4286**

C. *Esters of polybasic aromatic acids*

1. Esters of tribasic acids

Trimethyl trimesate...... **1:2565**
Triethyl trimesate........ **1:2540**

2. Esters of tetrabasic acids

Tetramethyl pyromellitate **1:2555**
Tetraethyl pyromellitate .. **1:2175**

V. Esters of Aromatic Acids Containing also Functional Groups

A. *Esters of phenolic acids*

1. Esters of hydroxybenzoic acids (or their ethers)

Methyl o-hydroxybenzoate. **1:1750**
Ethyl o-hydroxybenzoate.. **1:1755**
n-Propyl o-hydroxybenzoate.................. **1:1774**
Isopropyl o-hydroxybenzoate.................. **1:1763**
n-Butyl o-hydroxybenzoate **1:1780**
Isobutyl o-hydroxybenzoate **1:1776**
Isoamyl o-hydroxybenzoate **1:1790**
Phenyl o-hydroxybenzoate. **1:1415**
β-Naphthyl o-hydroxybenzoate................ **1:1505**

Methyl o-methoxybenzoate **1:4091**
Ethyl o-methoxybenzoate.. **1:4151**

Methyl m-hydroxybenzoate **1:1468**
Ethyl m-hydroxybenzoate . **1:1471**

Methyl m-methoxybenzoate.................. **1:4111**
Ethyl m-methoxybenzoate. **1:4131**

Methyl p-hydroxybenzoate **1:1549**
Ethyl p-hydroxybenzoate.. **1:1534**
n-Propyl p-hydroxybenzoate.................. **1:2410**

Methyl p-methoxybenzoate **1:2128**
Ethyl p-methoxybenzoate.. **1:4191**

Ethyl p-ethoxybenzoate... **1:4231**

Methyl 2-hydroxy-3-naphthoate............... **1:2305**
Ethyl 2-hydroxy-3-naphthoate............... **1:2365**

Methyl gallate........... **1:1605**

2. Esters of keto acids

Methyl o-benzoylbenzoate. **1:2345**
Ethyl o-benzoylbenzoate... **1:2206**

Methyl o-(p-toluyl)benzoate.................. **1:2222**
Ethyl o-(p-toluyl)benzoate. **1:2251**

3. Esters of acids containing heterocyclic nuclei

Methyl furoate........... **1:3452**
Ethyl furoate............ **1:2082**
n-Propyl furoate......... **1:3701**

Methyl piperonylate...... **1:2149**
Ethyl piperonylate **1:4291**

ORDER I: SUBORDER I: GENUS 5: ESTERS

Division A, Solid Esters

—— **DIETHYL FUMARATE** $C_8H_{12}O_4$ **Beil. II-742**

M.P. +0.2° **Sap. Eq. 86** D_4^{15} = **1.05721** $n_D^{20.1}$ = **1.44103**

See 1:3761. Genus 5: Esters. B.P. 218.4°.

—— **DIETHYL SEBACATE** $C_{14}H_{26}O_4$ **Beil. II-719**

M.P. +1.3° **Sap. Eq. 129** D_4^{20} = **0.9631** n_D^{20} = **1.43657**

See 1:4366. Genus 5: Esters. B.P. 307°.

—— **ETHYL CINNAMATE** $C_{11}H_{12}O_2$ **Beil. IX-581**

M.P. +6.5° **Sap. Eq. 176** D_4^{20} = **1.0490** n_D^{20} = **1.55982**

See 1:4206. Genus 5: Esters. B.P. 271°.

—— **ETHYL *p*-METHOXYBENZOATE** $C_{10}H_{12}O_3$ **Beil. X-159**

M.P. +7° **Sap. Eq. 180** D_4^{20} = **1.1038** n_D^{20} = **1.5254**

See 1:4191. Genus 5: Esters. B.P. 269°.

—— **DIMETHYL MALEATE** $C_6H_8O_4$ **Beil. II-751**

M.P. +7.6° **Sap. Eq. 72** D_4^{15} = **1.14513** $n_D^{19.9}$ = **1.44156**

See 1:3606. Genus 5: Esters. B.P. 204.4°.

1:2005 **DIMETHYL ADIPATE** $C_8H_{14}O_4$ **Beil. II-652**

M.P. +8.5° **Sap. Eq. 87** D_4^{20} = **1.0625** ⟨2⟩ n_D^{20} = **1.42835** ⟨2⟩
B.P. 107.6$^{\circ}_{11}$ ⟨1⟩

Ⓓ **Saponification:** Hydrolysis with alk. (T 1.51) yields methyl alc. (1:6120) and adipic ac. (1:0775).

1:2005 ⟨1⟩ Verkade, Coops, Hartman, *Rec. trav. chim.* **45,** 590 (1926). ⟨2⟩ Vogel, *J. Chem. Soc.* **1934,** 1765.

—— **DIETHYL ISOPHTHALATE** $C_{12}H_{14}O_4$ **Beil. IX-834**

M.P. +11.5° **Sap. Eq. 111**

See 1:4276. Genus 5: Esters. B.P. 286°.

—— **ETHYL MYRISTATE** $C_{16}H_{32}O_2$ **Beil. II-365**

M.P. +11.9° **Sap. Eq. 256** D_4^{25} = **0.8573** n_D^{20} = **1.4362**

See 1:4316. Genus 5: Esters. B.P. 295°.

—— *m*-TOLYL ACETATE $C_9H_{10}O_2$ **Beil. VI-379**

M.P. +12° **Sap. Eq. 150** $D^{26} = $ **1.043** $n_D^{20} = $ **1.4978**

See 1:3706. Genus 5: Esters. B.P. 212°.

—— **ETHYL** β-[α-**FURYL]ACRYLATE** $C_9H_{10}O_3$ **Beil. XVIII-300**

M.P. +14° **Sap. Eq. 166**

See 1:3927. Genus 5: Esters. B.P. 232°.

1:2009 METHYL PENTADECYLATE $C_{16}H_{32}O_2$ **Beil. II-369**

M.P. +15.5° ⟨1⟩ **Sap. Eq. 256** $D_4^{25} = $ **0.8618 ⟨1⟩** $n_D^{20} = $ **1.4390 ⟨1⟩**

Ⓓ **Saponification:** Hydrolysis with alk. (T 1.51) yields methyl alc. (1:6120) and pentadecylic ac. (1:0620).

1:2009 ⟨1⟩ Ruhoff, Reid, *J. Am. Chem. Soc.* **55,** 3825 (1933).

—— **DIMETHYL SUCCINATE** $C_6H_{10}O_4$ **Beil. II-609**

M.P. +18.2° **Sap. Eq. 73** $D_4^{20} = $ **1.1192** $n_D^{20} = $ **1.41965**

See 1:3556. Genus 5: Esters. B.P. 196.0°.

—— **ETHYL PIPERONYLATE** $C_{10}H_{10}O_4$ **Beil. XIX-270**

M.P. +18.5° **Sap. Eq. 194**

See 1:4291. Genus 5: Esters. B.P. 286°.

1:2013 METHYL MYRISTATE $C_{15}H_{30}O_2$ **Beil. II-365**

M.P. +18.5° **Sap. Eq. 242** $n_D^{45} = $ **1.428 ⟨1⟩**

[For sepn. by fractnl. distn. from mixts. with methyl laurate, methyl palmitate (1:2055), or both, methyl palmitate + methyl stearate (1:2095), or methyl *n*-caprate (1:3827) + methyl palmitate + methyl stearate, see **⟨1⟩**.]

Ⓓ **Saponification:** Hydrolysis with alk. (T 1.51) yields methyl alc. (1:6120) and myristic ac. (1:0630)

1:2013 ⟨1⟩ Wyman, Barkenbus, *Ind. Eng. Chem., Anal. Ed.* **12,** 658–661 (1940).

—— **DIETHYL** *d*-**TARTRATE** $C_8H_{14}O_6$ **Beil. III-513**

M.P. +18.6° **Sap. Eq. 103** $D_4^{20} = $ **1.2028** $n_D^{20} = $ **1.44677**

See 1:4256. Genus 5: Esters. B.P. 280°.

—— **PHENYL PROPIONATE** $C_9H_{10}O_2$ **Beil. VI-154**

M.P. +20° **Sap. Eq. 150** $D_{25}^{25} = $ **1.0467**

See 1:3696. Genus 5: Esters. B.P. 211°.

1:2017 ETHYL MARGARATE $C_{19}H_{38}O_2$ **Beil. II-377**

M.P. +20.6° (β-form) **⟨1⟩** **Sap. Eq. 298**

Ⓓ **Saponification:** Hydrolysis with alk. (T 1.51) yields ethyl alc. (1:6130) and margaric ac. (1:0635).

1:2017 ⟨1⟩ Phillips, Mumford, *Rec. trav. chim.* **52,** 175–180 (1933).

—— **BENZYL BENZOATE** $C_{14}H_{12}O_2$ **Beil. IX-121**

M.P. 21° **Sap. Eq. 212** D^{19} = **1.1224** n_D^{21} = **1.5681**

See 1:4422. Genus 5: Esters. B.P. 323°.

1:2021 DI-*n*-BUTYL *d*-TARTRATE $C_{12}H_{22}O_6$ **Beil. III-518**

M.P. 22° **Sap. Eq. 131** D_4^{18} = **1.0886 ⟨1⟩** $[\alpha]_D^{14}$ = **+10.09° ⟨1⟩**

Ⓓ **Saponification:** Hydrolysis with alk. (T 1.51) yields *n*-butyl alc. (1:6180) and *d*-tartaric ac. (1:0525).

1:2021 ⟨1⟩ Campbell, *J. Chem. Soc.* **1929,** 1116, 1118.

—— **3,4-DIMETHYLPHENYL ACETATE** $C_{10}H_{12}O_2$ **Beil. S.N. 529**

M.P. 22° **Sap. Eq. 164**

See 1:3952. Genus 5: Esters. B.P. 235°.

1:2026 ISOBUTYL STEARATE $C_{22}H_{44}O_2$ **Beil. II₁-(173)**

M.P. 22.5° and **28-29° ⟨1⟩** **Sap. Eq. 340**

Dimorphous forms.

Ⓓ **Saponification:** Hydrolysis with alk. (T 1.51) yields isobutyl alc. (1:6165) and stearic ac. (1:0660).

1:2026 ⟨1⟩ Vorländer, Selke, *Z. physik. Chem.* **A-129,** 455 (1927).

1:2030 ISOAMYL STEARATE $C_{23}H_{46}O_2$ **Beil. II-380**

M.P. 23° ⟨1⟩ **Sap. Eq. 354**

Ⓓ **Saponification:** Hydrolysis with alk. (T 1.51) yields isoamyl alc. (1:6200) and stearic ac. (1:0660).

1:2030 ⟨1⟩ Whitby, *J. Chem. Soc.* **1926,** 1458.

1:2034 ETHYL PALMITATE $C_{18}H_{36}O_2$ **Beil. II-372**

M.P. β-form 24.2° ⟨1⟩ **Sap. Eq. 284**
α-form 19.4° ⟨1⟩

Liquid $\bar{C}$ on cooling cryst. in α-form, but on stirring these change rapidly to β-form ⟨1⟩. For m.p. + compn. diagram of $\bar{C}$ + ethyl stearate see ⟨2⟩.

Ⓓ **Saponification:** Hydrolysis with alk. (T 1.51) yields ethyl alc. (1:6130) and palmitic ac. (1:0650).

1:2034 ⟨1⟩ Mumford, Phillips, *Rec. trav. chim.* **52,** 183 (1933). **⟨2⟩** Smith, *J. Chem. Soc.* **1931,** 803

1:2038 CETYL ACETATE $C_{18}H_{36}O_2$ **Beil. II-136**
(*n*-Hexadecyl acetate)

M.P. β-form 24.2° ⟨1⟩ ⟨2⟩ **Sap. Eq. 284**
M.P. α-form 18.5° ⟨1⟩ ⟨2⟩

Ⓓ **Saponification:** Hydrolysis with alk. (T 1.51) yields cetyl alc. (1:5945) and acetic ac. (1:1010).

1:2038 ⟨1⟩ Phillips, Mumford, *J. Chem. Soc.* **1934,** 1657–1665. **⟨2⟩** Meyer, Reid, *J. Am. Chem. Soc.* **55,** 1577 (1933).

—— **DI-*n*-PROPYL *d,l*-TARTRATE** $C_{10}H_{18}O_6$ **Beil. S.N. 250**

M.P. 25° **Sap. Eq. 117** $D_4^{20} = 1.1256$

See 1:4281. Genus 5: Esters. B.P. 286°.

1:2042 DIMETHYL SEBACATE $C_{12}H_{22}O_4$ **Beil. II-719**

M.P. 26.6° ⟨1⟩ **Sap. Eq. 115** $D_4^{28} = 0.98818$ $n_D^{28} = 1.43549$
27–28° ⟨2⟩

Ⓓ **Saponification:** Hydrolysis with alk. (T 1.51) yields methyl alc. (1:6120) and sebacic acid (1:0730).

1:2042 ⟨1⟩ Verkade, Coops, Hartman, *Rec. trav. chim.* **45,** 591–592 (1926). ⟨2⟩ Grün, Wirth, *Ber.* **55,** 2214 (1922).

—— **METHYL β-[α-FURYL]ACRYLATE** $C_8H_8O_3$ **Beil. XVIII-301**

M.P. 27° **Sap. Eq. 152**

See 1:3857. Genus 5: Esters. B.P. 227°.

1:2046 *n*-BUTYL STEARATE $C_{22}H_{44}O_2$ **Beil. S.N. 162**

M.P. 27.5° ⟨1⟩; 28° ⟨2⟩ **Sap. Eq. 340**

Ⓓ **Saponification:** Hydrolysis with alk. (T 1.51) yields *n*-butyl alc. (1:6180) and stearic ac. (1:0660).

1:2046 ⟨1⟩ Whitby, *J. Chem. Soc.* **1926,** 1464. ⟨2⟩ Vorländer, Selke, *Z. physik. Chem.* **A-129,** 453 (1927).

1:2049 ETHYL *d,l*-MANDELATE $C_{10}H_{12}O_3$ **Beil. X-202**

M.P. 28.1° ⟨1⟩ **Sap. Eq. 180**

Ⓓ **Saponification:** Hydrolysis with alk. (T 1.51) yields ethyl alc. (1:6130) and *d,l*-mandelic acid (1:0465).

1:2049 ⟨1⟩ Ross, *J. Chem. Soc.* **1936,** 720–721.

—— ***d*-BORNYL ACETATE** $C_{12}H_{20}O_2$ **Beil. VI-78**

M.P. 29° **Sap. Eq. 196**

See 1:3832. Genus 5: Esters. B.P. 226°.

1:2054 METHYL MARGARATE $C_{18}H_{36}O_2$ **Beil. II-377**

M.P. 29° **Sap. Eq. 284**

Ⓓ **Saponification:** Hydrolysis with alk. (T 1.51) yields methyl alc. (1:6120) and margaric ac. (1:0635).

—— **EUGENOL ACETATE** $C_{12}H_{14}O_3$ **Beil. VI-965**

M.P. 30° **Sap. Eq. 206** $D_{15}^{15} = 1.087$ $n_D^{20} = 1.52069$

See 1:4266. Genus 5: Esters. B.P. 282°.

1:2055 METHYL PALMITATE $C_{17}H_{34}O_2$ **Beil. II-372**

M.P. 30° **Sap. Eq. 270** n_D^{45} **= 1.4317 ⟨1⟩**

[For sepn. by fractnl. distn. from mixts. with methyl myristate (1:2013), methyl stearate (1:2095), or both, methyl laurate + methyl myristate, or methyl *n*-caprate (1:3827) + methyl myristate + methyl stearate see **⟨1⟩**.]

Ⓓ **Saponification:** Hydrolysis with alk. (T 1.51) yields methyl alc. (1:6120) and palmitic ac. (1:0650).

1:2055 ⟨1⟩ Wyman, Barkenbus, *Ind. Eng. Chem., Anal. Ed.* **12,** 658–661 (1940).

1:2061 *n*-AMYL STEARATE $C_{23}H_{46}O_2$ **Beil. S.N. 162**

M.P. 30° ⟨1⟩ **Sap. Eq. 354**

Ⓓ **Saponification:** Hydrolysis with alk. (T 1.51) yields *n*-amyl alc. (1:6205) and stearic ac. (1:0660).

1:2061 ⟨1⟩ Whitby, *J. Chem. Soc.* **1926,** 1464.

1:2066 *n*-OCTADECYL ACETATE $C_{20}H_{40}O_2$ **Beil. II-136**

M.P. β-form 31.95° ⟨1⟩ **Sap. Eq. 312**
α-form 29.97° ⟨1⟩

The transparent α-form, when seeded with crysts. recrystd. from alc., or cooled below 0°, changes slowly to pearly white mass of β-form **⟨2⟩**.

Ⓓ **Saponification:** Hydrolysis with alk. (T 1.51) yields stearyl alc. (1:5953) and acetic ac. (1:1010).

1:2066 ⟨1⟩ Meyer, Reid, *J. Am. Chem. Soc.* **55,** 1577 (1933). ⟨2⟩ Phillips, Mumford, *J. Chem. Soc.* **1932,** 1735.

—— ETHYL β-NAPHTHOATE $C_{13}H_{12}O_2$ **Beil. IX-657**

M.P. +32° **Sap. Eq. 200** D_4^{20} **= 1.117** n_D^{20} **= 1.596**

See 1:4341. Genus 5: Esters. B.P. 304°.

1:2071 METHYL *p*-TOLUATE $C_9H_{10}O_2$ **Beil. IX-484**

M.P. 33° **Sap. Eq. 150**
B.P. 222.5°

Ⓓ **Saponification:** Hydrolysis with alk. (T 1.51) yields methyl alc. (1:6120) and *p*-toluic ac. (1:0795).

1:2074 DI-(β-ETHOXYETHYL) PHTHALATE $C_{16}H_{22}O_6$ **Beil. S.N. 972**

M.P. 33° **Sap. Eq. 155**

Ⓓ **Saponification:** Hydrolysis with alk. (T 1.51) yields ethylene glycol monoethyl ether (1:6410) and phthalic ac. (1:0820).

1:2078 ETHYL STEARATE $C_{20}H_{40}O_2$ **Beil. II-379**

M.P. β-form 33.5° ⟨1⟩ **Sap. Eq. 312**
M.P. α-form 30.9° ⟨1⟩

The α-form cryst. unchanged from alc. or lgr.; but if rubbed changes slowly to β-form **⟨2⟩**. For m.p. + compn. diagram of $\bar{C}$ + ethyl palmitate see **⟨2⟩**.

Ⓓ **Saponification:** Hydrolysis with alk. (T 1.51) yields ethyl alc. (1:6130) and stearic ac. (1:0660).

1:2078 ⟨1⟩ Mumford, Phillips, *Rec. trav. chim.* **52,** 183 (1933). ⟨2⟩ Smith, *J. Chem. Soc.* **1931,** 803–805.

—— **DIISOPROPYL *d,l*-TARTRATE** $C_{10}H_{18}O_6$ **Beil. S.N. 250**

M.P. 34° **Sap. Eq. 117** D_4^{20} = **1.1166**

See 1:4226. Genus 5: Esters. B.P. 275°.

1:2082 ETHYL PYROMUCATE $C_7H_8O_3$ **Beil. XVIII-275**
(Ethyl furoate)

M.P. 34° **Sap. Eq. 140** $D_4^{20.8}$ = **1.1174** (supercooled) n_D = **1.4797** (supercooled)
B.P. 197°

Ⓓ **Saponification:** Hydrolysis with alk. (T 1.51) yields ethyl alc. (1:6130) and furoic ac. (1:0475).

—— **2,4,5-TRIMETHYLPHENYL ACETATE** $C_{11}H_{14}O_2$ **Beil. S.N. 510**

M.P. 34° **Sap. Eq. 178**

See 1:4041. Genus 5: Esters. B.P. 245°.

1:2086 ETHYL BENZILATE $C_{16}H_{16}O_3$ **Beil. X-345**

M.P. 34° **Sap. Eq. 256**

Ⓓ **Saponification:** Hydrolysis with alk. (T 1.51) yields ethyl alc. (1:6130) and benzilic ac. (1:0770).

1:2090 METHYL CINNAMATE $C_{10}H_{10}O_2$ **Beil. IX-581**

M.P. 36° **Sap. Eq. 162**
B.P. 261°

Ⓓ **Saponification:** Hydrolysis with alk. (T 1.51) yields methyl alc. (1:6120) and cinnamic ac. (1:0735).

—— **DIMETHYL ITACONATE** $C_7H_{10}O_4$ **Beil. II-762**

M.P. 38° **Sap. Eq. 79** D_4^{18} = **1.12410** n_D^{20} = **1.44413**

See 1:3641. Genus 5: Esters. B.P. 208°.

1:2095 METHYL STEARATE $C_{19}H_{38}O_2$ **Beil. II-379**

M.P. 38.8° ⟨1⟩ **Sap. Eq. 298** n_D^{45} = **1.4346 ⟨2⟩**

[For sepn. by fractnl. distn. from mixts. with methyl palmitate (1:2055), methyl myristate (1:2013) + methyl palmitate, or methyl *n*-caprate (1:3827) + methyl myristate (1:2013) + methyl palmitate see ⟨2⟩.]

Ⓓ **Saponification:** Hydrolysis with alk. (T 1.51) yields methyl alc. (1:6120) and stearic ac. (1:0660).

1:2095 ⟨1⟩ Whitby, *J. Chem. Soc.* **1926,** 1464. ⟨2⟩ Wyman, Barkenbus, *Ind. Eng. Chem., Anal. Ed.* **12,** 658–661 (1940).

1:2098 METHYL DIBENZYLACETATE $C_{17}H_{18}O_2$ **Beil. IX-683**

M.P. 41° ⟨1⟩ **Sap. Eq. 254**

Ⓓ **Saponification:** Hydrolysis with alk. (T 1.51) yields methyl alc. (1:6120) and dibenzylacetic ac. (1:0668).

1:2098 ⟨1⟩ Hill, *J. Chem. Soc.* **1926,** 956.

—— **PHENYL SALICYLATE** $C_{13}H_{10}O_3$ **Beil. X-76**
(Salol)

M.P. 42° **Sap. Eq. 214**

See 1:1415. Genus 4: Phenols.

1:2102 DIBENZYL PHTHALATE $C_{22}H_{18}O_4$ **Beil. IX-802**

M.P. 43° **Sap. Eq. 173**

Ⓓ **Saponification:** Hydrolysis with alk. (T 1.51) yields benzyl alc. (1:6480) and phthalic ac. (1:0820).

1:2106 DIETHYL TEREPHTHALATE $C_{12}H_{14}O_4$ **Beil. IX-844**

M.P. 44° **Sap. Eq. 111**
B.P. 302°

Ⓓ **Saponification:** Hydrolysis with alk. (T 1.51) yields ethyl alc. (1:6130) and terephthalic ac. (1:0910).

1:2110 DICYCLOHEXYL OXALATE $C_{14}H_{22}O_4$ **Beil. VI_1-(6)**

M.P. 47° **Sap. Eq. 127**

Ⓓ **Saponification:** Hydrolysis with alk. (T 1.51) yields cyclohexanol (1:6415) and oxalic ac. (1:0445).

1:2120 β-PHENYLETHYL CINNAMATE $C_{17}H_{16}O_2$ **Beil. S.N. 948**

M.P. 47-48° **Sap. Eq. 252**

Ⓓ **Saponification:** Hydrolysis with alk. (T 1.51) yields β-phenylethyl alc. (1:6505) and cinnamic ac. (1:0735).

1:2124 α-NAPHTHYL ACETATE $C_{12}H_{10}O_2$ **Beil. VI-608**

M.P. 48° **Sap. Eq. 186**

Readily hydrolyzed even by distn. with steam.

Ⓓ **Saponification:** Hydrolysis with alk. (T 1.51) yields α-naphthol (1:1500) and acetic ac. (1:1010).

1:2128 METHYL *p*-METHOXYBENZOATE $C_9H_{10}O_3$ **Beil. X-159**

M.P. 49° **Sap. Eq. 166**
B.P. 255°

Ⓓ **Saponification:** Hydrolysis with alk. (T 1.51) yields methyl alc. (1:6120) and *p*-methoxybenzoic ac. (1:0805).

1:2132 PHENACYL ACETATE $C_{10}H_{10}O_3$ **Beil. VIII-92**
(Benzoylcarbinyl acetate; ω-acetoxyacetophenone)

M.P. 49° **Sap. Eq. 178**

Ⓓ **Saponification:** Hydrolysis with alk. (T 1.51) yields phenacyl alc. (1:5180) and acetic ac. (1:1010).

1:2136 DI-*m*-TOLYL CARBONATE $C_{15}H_{14}O_3$ **Beil. VI-379**
(Di-" *m*-cresyl " carbonate)

M.P. 49° **Sap. Eq. 242**

C̄ with NH_3 gas splits quant. yielding *m*-cresol (1:1730) and urea ⟨1⟩.

Ⓓ **Saponification:** Hydrolysis with alk. (T 1.51) yields *m*-cresol (1:1730) and carbon dioxide.

1:2136 ⟨1⟩ Sabawin, *Cent.* **1934,** II, 3463.

1:2141 DIBENZYL *d*-TARTRATE $C_{18}H_{18}O_6$ **Beil. VI₁-(221)**

M.P. 50° **Sap. Eq. 165**

Ⓓ **Saponification:** Hydrolysis with alk. (T 1.51) yields benzyl alc. (1:6480) and *d*-tartaric ac. (1:0525).

1:2145 DIBENZYL SUCCINATE $C_{18}H_{18}O_4$ **Beil. VI-436**

M.P. 51-52° ⟨1⟩ **Sap. Eq. 149**

[For prepn. from sodium succinate + benzyl chloride (35% yield) see ⟨1⟩; from benzyl alc. + succinic acid see ⟨2⟩.]

Ⓓ **Saponification:** Hydrolysis with alk. (T 1.51) yields benzyl alc. (1:6480) and succinic ac. (1:0530).

1:2145 ⟨1⟩ Howard, *J. Am. Chem. Soc.* **44,** 1763–1764 (1922). ⟨2⟩ Thompson, Leuck, *J. Am. Chem. Soc.* **44,** 2894–2896 (1922).

1:2149 METHYL PIPERONYLATE $C_9H_8O_4$ **Beil. XIX-269**

M.P. 51-52° ⟨1⟩ **Sap. Eq. 180**
B.P. 270-271°/777 mm. ⟨1⟩.

Ⓓ **Saponification:** Hydrolysis with alk. (T 1.51) yields methyl alc. (1:6120) and piperonylic ac. (1:0865).

1:2149 ⟨1⟩ Mauthner, *J. prakt. Chem.* (2) **116,** 322 (1927).

1:2153 CETYL PALMITATE $C_{32}H_{64}O_2$ **Beil. II-37**
(*n*-Hexadecyl palmitate)

M.P. 51.6° ⟨1⟩ **Sap. Eq. 480**

Ⓓ **Saponification:** Hydrolysis with alk. (T 1.51) yields cetyl alc. (1:5945) and palmitic ac. (1:0650).

1:2153 ⟨1⟩ Whitby, *J. Chem. Soc.* **1926,** 1463.

—— FURFURAL DIACETATE $C_9H_{10}O_5$ **Beil. XVII-27**

M.P. 52° **B.P. 220°**

See 1:0020. Genus 1: Aldehydes.

1:2157 ETHYLENE GLYCOL DILAURATE $C_{26}H_{50}O_4$ **Beil. II-361**

M.P. 52° ⟨1⟩ **Sap. Eq. 213**

Ⓓ **Saponification:** Hydrolysis with alk. (T 1.51) yields ethylene glycol (1:6465) and lauric ac. (1:0605).

1:2157 ⟨1⟩ Staudinger, Schwalenstöcker, *Ber.* **68,** 733 (1935).

1:2161 PHENYL STEARATE $C_{24}H_{40}O_2$ **Beil. VI-155**

M.P. 52° **Sap. Eq. 360**

Ⓓ **Saponification:** Hydrolysis with alk. (T 1.51) yields phenol (1:1420) and stearic ac. (1:0660).

1:2166 METHYL *d,l*-MANDELATE $C_9H_{10}O_3$ **Beil. X-202**

M.P. 53.3° ⟨1⟩ **Sap. Eq. 166**
B.P. 250° sl. dec.

Ⓓ **Saponification:** Hydrolysis with alk. (T 1.51) yields methyl alc. (1:6120) and *d,l*-mandelic ac. (1:0465).

1:2166 ⟨1⟩ Ross, *J. Chem. Soc.* **1936,** 720–721.

1:2171 DIMETHYL TARTRONATE $C_5H_8O_5$ **Beil. III$_1$-(148)**

M.P. 53.4° cor. ⟨1⟩ **Sap. Eq. 74**

Ⓓ **Saponification:** Hydrolysis with alk. (T 1.51) yields methyl alc. (1:6120) and tartronic ac. (1:0510).

1:2171 ⟨1⟩ Fisher, Simons, *J. Am. Chem. Soc.* **43,** 628–629 (1921).

—— DIMETHYL OXALATE $C_4H_6O_4$ **Beil. II-534**

M.P. 54° **Sap. Eq. 59**
See 1:0415. Genus 3: Acids.

1:2175 TETRAETHYL PYROMELLITATE $C_{18}H_{22}O_8$ **Beil. IX-998**

M.P. 54° ⟨1⟩ **Sap. Eq. 91.5**

Ⓓ **Saponification:** Hydrolysis with alk. (T 1.51) yields ethyl alc. (1:6130) and pyromellitic ac. (1:0557).

1:2175 ⟨1⟩ von Braun, Lemke, *Ber.* **57,** 682 (1924).

1:2179 DIETHYL MESOTARTRATE $C_8H_{14}O_6$ **Beil. III-530**

M.P. 55° **Sap. Eq. 103**

Ⓓ **Saponification:** Hydrolysis with alk. (T 1.51) yields ethyl alc. (1:6130) and *meso*-tartaric ac. (1:0490).

1:2183 *m*-TOLYL BENZOATE $C_{14}H_{12}O_2$ **Beil. IX-120**
(" *m*-Cresyl " benzoate)

M.P. 55° **Sap. Eq. 212**
B.P. 314°

Ⓓ **Saponification:** Hydrolysis with alk. (T 1.51) yields *m*-cresol (1:1730) and benzoic ac. (1:0715).

1:2187 α-NAPHTHYL BENZOATE $C_{17}H_{12}O_2$ **Beil. IX-125**

M.P. 56° **Sap. Eq. 248**

Ⓓ **Saponification:** Hydrolysis with alk. (T 1.51) yields α-naphthol (1:1500) and benzoic ac. (1:0715).

1:2193 CETYL STEARATE $C_{34}H_{68}O_2$ **Beil. II-380**
(*n*-Hexadecyl stearate)

M.P. 56.6° ⟨1⟩ **Sap. Eq. 508**

Ⓓ **Saponification:** Hydrolysis with alk. (T 1.51) yields cetyl alc. (1:5945) and stearic ac. (1:0660).

1:2193 ⟨1⟩ Whitby, *J. Am. Chem. Soc.* **1926,** 1463.

1:2197 DIISOBUTYL *d,l*-TARTRATE $C_{12}H_{22}O_6$ **Beil. S.N. 250**
(Diisobutyl racemate)

M.P. 58° ⟨1⟩ **Sap. Eq. 131**
B.P. 311°

Ⓓ **Saponification:** Hydrolysis with alk. (T 1.51) yields isobutyl alc. (1:6165) and *d,l*-tartaric ac. (1:0550).

1:2197 ⟨1⟩ Campbell, *J. Chem. Soc.* **1929,** 1113.

1:2201 ETHYL DIPHENYLACETATE $C_{16}H_{16}O_2$ **Beil. IX-673**

M.P. 58° **Sap. Eq. 240**

Ⓓ **Saponification:** Hydrolysis with alk. (T 1.51) yields ethyl alc. (1:6130) and diphenylacetic ac. (1:0765).

1:2206 ETHYL *o*-BENZOYLBENZOATE $C_{16}H_{14}O_3$ **Beil. X-749**

M.P. 58° **Sap. Eq. 254**

Ⓓ **Saponification:** Hydrolysis with alk. (T 1.51) yields ethyl alc. (1:6130) and *o*-benzoylbenzoic ac. (1:0720).

1:2209 DIETHYL NAPHTHALATE $C_{16}H_{16}O_4$ **Beil. IX-919**

M.P. 58-60° ⟨1⟩ **Sap. Eq. 136**

Ⓓ **Saponification:** Hydrolysis with alk. (T 1.51) yields ethyl alc. (1:6130) and naphthalic ac. (1:0890).

1:2213 METHYL DIPHENYLACETATE $C_{15}H_{14}O_2$ **Beil. IX-673**

M.P. 60° **Sap. Eq. 226**

Ⓓ **Saponification:** Hydrolysis with alk. (T 1.51) yields methyl alc. (1:6120) and diphenylacetic ac. (1:0765).

1:2217 DI-*o*-TOLYL CARBONATE $C_{15}H_{14}O_3$ **Beil. VI-356**
(Di-" *o*-cresyl " carbonate)

M.P. 60° **Sap. Eq. 242**

$\bar{C}$ with gas NH_3 splits quant. yielding *o*-cresol (1:1400) and urea ⟨1⟩.

Ⓓ **Saponification:** Hydrolysis with alk. (T 1.51) yields *o*-cresol (1:1400) and CO_2.

1:2217 ⟨1⟩ Sabawin, *Cent.* **1934,** II, 3463.

1:2222 METHYL *o*-(*p*-TOLUYL)BENZOATE $C_{16}H_{14}O_3$ **Beil. X-759**

M.P. 61° **Sap. Eq. 254**

Ⓓ **Saponification:** Hydrolysis with alk. yields methyl alc. (1:6120) and *p*-toluyl-*o*-benzoic acid (1:0750).

1:2227 DIMETHYL *d*-TARTRATE $C_6H_{10}O_6$ **Beil. III-510**

M.P. 61.5° **Sap. Eq. 89**

Exists also in two other crystn. forms, m.p. 48° and m.p. 50° ⟨1⟩.

Ⓓ **Saponification:** Hydrolysis with alk. (T 1.51) yields methyl alc. (1:6120) and *d*-tartaric ac. (1:0525).

1:2227 ⟨1⟩ Weygand, Weissberger, Baumgärtel, *Ber.* **65,** 696–701 (1932).

1:2233 ETHYLENE GLYCOL DIMYRISTATE $C_{30}H_{58}O_4$ **Beil. II-366**

M.P. 63.0° ⟨1⟩ **Sap. Eq. 241**

Ⓓ **Saponification:** Hydrolysis with alk. (T 1.51) yields ethylene glycol (1:6465) and myristic ac. (1:0630).

1:2233 ⟨1⟩ Staudinger, Schwalenstöcker, *Ber.* **68,** 733 (1935).

1:2239 DICYCLOHEXYL PHTHALATE $C_{20}H_{26}O_4$ **Beil. IX-799**

M.P. 66° **Sap. Eq. 165**

Ⓓ **Saponification:** Hydrolysis with alk. (T 1.51) yields cyclohexanol (1:6415) and phthalic ac. (1:0820).

1:2244 DIMETHYL ISOPHTHALATE $C_{10}H_{10}O_4$ **Beil. IX-834**

M.P. 67-68° **Sap. Eq. 97**

Ⓓ **Saponification:** Hydrolysis with alk. (T 1.51) yields methyl alc. (1:6120) and isophthalic ac. (1:0900).

1:2251 ETHYL *o*-(*p*-TOLUYL)BENZOATE $C_{17}H_{16}O_3$ **Beil. X-759**

M.P. 68° **Sap. Eq. 268**

Ⓓ **Saponification:** Hydrolysis with alk. (T 1.51) yields ethyl alc. (1:6130) and *p*-toluyl-*o*-benzoic ac. (1:0750).

1:2257 PHENYL BENZOATE $C_{13}H_{10}O_2$ **Beil. IX-116**

M.P. 69° (**71°**) **Sap. Eq. 198**
B.P. 314°

Ⓓ ***p*-Hydroxybenzophenone:** from 5 pts. $\bar{C}$ on htg. with 4 pts. $AlCl_3$ for 15 min. at 140°; yield quantitative; cryst. from aq., dil. MeOH, or C_6H_6 + lgr.; m.p. 135° ⟨1⟩ ⟨2⟩.

Ⓓ **Saponification:** Hydrolysis with alk. (T 1.51) yields phenol (1:1420) and benzoic ac. (1:0715).

1:2257 ⟨1⟩ Rosenmund, Schnurr, *Ann.* **460,** 89 (1928). ⟨2⟩ Blicke, Weinkauff, *J. Am. Chem. Soc.* **54,** 332 (1932).

1:2263 DIISOBUTYL *d*-TARTRATE $C_{12}H_{22}O_6$ **Beil. III-518**

M.P. 70° ⟨1⟩ **Sap. Eq. 131**
73-74° ⟨2⟩

For nature of green color observed on htg. C̄ and lost on cooling see ⟨3⟩.

Ⓓ **Saponification:** Hydrolysis with alk. (T 1.51) yields isobutyl alc. (1:6165) and *d*-tartaric ac. (1:0525).

1:2263 ⟨1⟩ Campbell, *J. Chem. Soc.* **1929,** 1114. ⟨2⟩ Patterson, *J. Chem. Soc.* **103,** 174 (1913). ⟨3⟩ Patterson, Lamberton, *J. Chem. Soc.* **1937,** 964.

—— **METHYL *m*-HYDROXYBENZOATE** $C_8H_{10}O_3$ **Beil. X-139**

M.P. 70° **Sap. Eq. 152**

See 1:1468. Genus 4: Phenols.

1:2269 ETHYLENE GLYCOL DIPALMITATE $C_{34}H_{66}O_4$ **Beil. II-373**

M.P. 70.5° ⟨1⟩ **Sap. Eq. 269**
69° ⟨2⟩

Ⓓ **Saponification:** Hydrolysis with alk. (T 1.51) yields ethylene glycol (1:6465) and palmitic ac. (1:0650).

1:2269 ⟨1⟩ Staudinger, Schwalenstöcker, *Ber.* **68,** 733 (1935). ⟨2⟩ Bhattacharya, Hilditch, *J. Chem. Soc.* **1931,** 907.

1:2273 β-NAPHTHYL ACETATE $C_{12}H_{10}O_2$ **Beil. VI-644**

M.P. 71° **Sap. Eq. 186**

Ⓓ **Saponification:** Hydrolysis with alk. (T 1.51) yields β-naphthol (1:1540) and acetic ac. (1:1010).

• **1:2279 *p*-TOLYL BENZOATE** $C_{14}H_{12}O_2$ **Beil. IX-120**
(" *p*-Cresyl " benzoate)

M.P. 71° **Sap. Eq. 212**
B.P. 316°

Ⓓ **Saponification:** Hydrolysis with alk. (T 1.51) yields *p*-cresol (1:1410) and benzoic ac. (1:0715).

1:2287 GLYCERYL TRIBENZOATE $C_{24}H_{20}O_6$ **Beil. IX-140**

M.P. 72° (**76°**) (see below). **Sap. Eq. 135**

C̄ when crystd. from lgr. has m.p. 72°; when crystd. from alc. has m.p. 76°; crystn. of material of m.p. 72° from alc. raises m.p. to 76° — Slow solidification of fused material yields prod. of m.p. 72° ⟨1⟩.

Ⓓ **Saponification:** Hydrolysis with alk. (T 1.51) yields glycerol (1:6540) and benzoic ac. (1:0715).

1:2287 ⟨1⟩ Fairbourne, Foster, *J. Chem. Soc.* **127,** 2763 (1925).

1:2293 ETHYLENE GLYCOL DIBENZOATE $C_{16}H_{14}O_4$ **Beil. IX-129**

M.P. 73° **Sap. Eq. 135**

Ⓓ **Saponification:** Hydrolysis with alk. (T 1.51) yields ethylene glycol (1:6465) and benzoic ac. (1:0715).

—— **ETHYL *m*-HYDROXYBENZOATE** $C_9H_{10}O_3$ **Beil. X-139**

M.P. 73.8° **Sap. Eq. 166**

See 1:1471. Genus 4: Phenols.

1:2300 DIPHENYL PHTHALATE $C_{20}H_{14}O_4$ **Beil. IX-801**
(" Phenyl phthalate ")

M.P. 74-75° **Sap. Eq. 159**

Ⓓ **Saponification:** Hydrolysis with alk. (T 1.51) yields **phenol** (**1:1420**) and phthalic ac. (1:0820).

1:2305 METHYL 2-HYDROXY-3-NAPHTHOATE $C_{12}H_{10}O_3$ **Beil. X-335**

M.P. 75° cor. **⟨1⟩** **Sap. Eq. 202**

Ⓓ **Saponification:** Hydrolysis with alk. (T 1.51) yields methyl alc. (1:6120) and 2-hydroxy-3-naphthoic ac. (1:0850). [Cf. **⟨1⟩**.]

1:2305 **⟨1⟩** Lesser, Kranepuhl, Gad, *Ber.* **58,** 2115 (1925).

1:2310 METHYL BENZILATE $C_{15}H_{14}O_3$ **Beil. X-344**

M.P. 75° **Sap. Eq. 242**

Ⓓ **Saponification:** Hydrolysis with alk. (T 1.51) yields methyl alc. (1:6120) and benzilic ac. (1:0770).

Ⓓ **Benzilamide:** from $\bar{C}$ in conc. alc. soln. treated with NH_3 gas, first at room temp., then below 0°, and stood 3 days; m.p. 155° **⟨1⟩**.

1:2310 **⟨1⟩** Burton, *J. Chem. Soc.* **1930,** 2400.

1:2315 TRIMETHYL CITRATE $C_9H_{14}O_7$ **Beil. III-567**

M.P. 76° ⟨1⟩ **Sap. Eq. 78**

Ⓓ **Saponification:** Hydrolysis with alk. (T 1.51) yields methyl alc. (1:6120) and citric ac. (1:0455).

1:2315 **⟨1⟩** Donaldson, McCleary, Degering, *J. Am. Chem. Soc.* **56,** 459 1934).

1:2320 ETHYLENE GLYCOL DI-*n*-STEARATE $C_{38}H_{74}O_4$ **Beil. II-380**

M.P. 76° ⟨1⟩ **Sap. Eq. 297.5**
(73°) ⟨2⟩

Ⓓ **Saponification:** Hydrolysis with alk. (T1.51) yields ethylene glycol (1:6465) and stearic ac. (1:0660).

1:2320 **⟨1⟩** Vorländer, Selke, *Z. physik. Chem.* **129,** 455 (1927). **⟨2⟩** Bhattacharya, Hilditch, *J. Chem. Soc.* **1931,** 907.

1:2325 METHYL *α*-PHENYL-*n*-BUTYRATE $C_{11}H_{14}O_2$ **Beil. IX-541**

M.P. 77-78° ⟨1⟩ **Sap. Eq. 178**

Ⓓ **Saponification:** Hydrolysis with alk. (T 1.51) yields methyl alc. (1:6120) and *α*-phenyl-*n*-butyric ac. (1:0594).

1:2325 **⟨1⟩** Rising, Zee, *J. Am. Chem. Soc.* **50,** 1211 (1928).

1:2330 METHYL β-NAPHTHOATE $C_{12}H_{10}O_2$ **Beil. IX-657**

M.P. 77° **Sap. Eq. 186**
B.P. 290°

Ⓓ **Saponification:** Hydrolysis with alk. (T 1.51) yields methyl alc. (1:6120) and β-naphthoic ac. (1:0800).

1:2335 DIPHENYL CARBONATE $C_{13}H_{10}O_3$ **Beil. VI-158**

M.P. 78° **Sap. Eq. 214**

C̄ htd. at 160–170° for 1 hr. with 4 moles phenylhydrazine yields *N,N′*-diphenylcarbazide, cryst. from dil. alc., m.p. 175–175.5° cor. ⟨1⟩ ⟨2⟩.

Ⓓ **Saponification:** Hydrolysis with alk. (T 1.51) yields phenol (1:1420) and CO_2.

1:2335 ⟨1⟩ Cazeneuve, Moreau, *Bull. soc. chim.* (3) **23,** 52–53 (1900). ⟨2⟩ Noller, *J. Am. Chem. Soc.* **52,** 1134 (1930).

1:2340 ISOEUGENOL ACETATE $C_{12}H_{14}O_3$ **Beil. VI-958**

M.P. 79° **Sap. Eq. 206**
B.P. 283°

C̄ in $CHCl_3$ treated at −10° with 1 mole Br_2 in $CHCl_3$ yields C̄ dibromide, cryst. from AcOH or AcOEt, m.p. 132–133° ⟨1⟩.

Ⓓ **Saponification:** Hydrolysis with alk. (T 1.51) yields isoeugenol (1:1785) and acetic ac. (1:1010).

1:2340 ⟨1⟩ Boedecker, Volk, *Ber.* **64,** 64 (1931).

1:2345 METHYL *o*-BENZOYLBENZOATE $C_{15}H_{12}O_3$ **Beil. X-748**

M.P. 79–80° ⟨1⟩ **Sap. Eq. 240**

Ⓓ **Saponification:** Hydrolysis with alk. (T 1.51) yields methyl alc. (1:6120) and *o*-benzoylbenzoic ac. (1:0720).

1:2345 ⟨1⟩ Smith, Hanson, *J. Am. Chem. Soc.* **57,** 1327 (1935).

1:2350 BENZOIN ACETATE $C_{16}H_{14}O_3$ **Beil. VIII-174**

M.P. 83° **Sap. Eq. 254**

[For prepn. in 86–90% yield from benzoin and Ac_2O see ⟨1⟩.]

Ⓓ **Saponification:** Hydrolysis with alk. (T 1.51) yields benzoin (1:5210) and acetic ac. (1:1010).

1:2350 ⟨1⟩ Corson, Saliani, *Organic Syntheses* **12,** 1–2 (1932).

1:2355 PENTAERYTHRITOL TETRAACETATE $C_{13}H_{20}O_8$ **Beil. S.N. 47**

M.P. 84° ⟨1⟩ **Sap. Eq. 76**

Ⓓ **Saponification:** Hydrolysis with alk. (T 1.51) yields pentaerythritol (1:5850) and acetic ac. (1:1010).

1:2355 ⟨1⟩ Perkin, Simonsen, *J. Chem. Soc.* **87,** 860 (1905).

1:2360 PYROCATECHOL DIBENZOATE $C_{20}H_{14}O_4$ **Beil. IX-130**

M.P. 84° **Sap. Eq. 159**

Ⓓ **Saponification:** Hydrolysis with alk. (T 1.51) yields pyrocatechol (1:1520) and benzoic ac. (1:0715)

1:2365 ETHYL 2-HYDROXY-3-NAPHTHOATE $C_{13}H_{12}O_3$ **Beil. X-335**

M.P. 85° **Sap. Eq. 216**
B.P. 291°

Ⓓ **Saponification:** Hydrolysis with alk. (T 1.51) yields ethyl alc. (1:6130) and 2-hydroxy-3-naphthoic ac. (1:0850).

1:2370 DI-GUAIACYL CARBONATE $C_{15}H_{14}O_5$ **Beil. VI-776**
(Di-[*o*-methoxyphenyl]carbonate; "guaiacol carbonate")

M.P. 87° **Sap. Eq. 274**

C̄ in MeOH treated with Br_2 yields monobromo deriv.; ndls. from alc., m.p. 178° [use in quant. detn. ⟨1⟩] — C̄ htd. 2 hrs. at 160° with 4 moles phenylhydrazine yields 70–72% *N*, *N'*-diphenylcarbazide, m.p. 175–175.5° cor. ⟨2⟩.

Ⓓ **Saponification:** Hydrolysis with alk. (T 1.51) yields guaiacol (1:1405) and carbonic ac.

1:2370 ⟨1⟩ Chernoff, *J. Am. Chem. Soc.* **51,** 3072–3074 (1929). ⟨2⟩ Noller, *J. Am. Chem. Soc.* **52,** 1134 (1930).

1:2385 DIMETHYL *d,l*-TARTRATE $C_6H_{10}O_6$ **Beil. III-527**
(Dimethyl racemate)

M.P. 90° (stable form) ⟨1⟩ **Sap. Eq. 89**
84° (metastable form) ⟨1⟩
B.P. 282° cor.

Ⓓ **Saponification:** Hydrolysis with alk. (T 1.51) yields methyl alc. (1:6120) and *d,l*-tartaric ac. (1:0550).

1:2385 ⟨1⟩ Weygand, Weissberger, Baumgärtel, *Ber.* **65,** 700–701 (1932).

1:2390 DI-*o*-TOLYL OXALATE $C_{16}H_{14}O_4$ **Beil. VI-355**
(Di-"*o*-cresyl" oxalate)

M.P. 91° ⟨1⟩ **Sap. Eq. 135**

Ⓓ **Saponification:** Hydrolysis with alk. (T 1.51) yields *o*-cresol (1:1400) and oxalic ac. (1:0445).

1:2390 ⟨1⟩ Mikšić, Pinterović, *J. prakt. Chem.* (2) **119,** 233 (1928).

—— β-NAPHTHYL SALICYLATE $C_{17}H_{12}O_3$ **Beil. X-80**

M.P. 95.5° (93.5°) **Sap. Eq. 264**

See 1:1505. Genus 4: Phenols.

1:2400 HYDROXYHYDROQUINONE TRIACETATE $C_{12}H_{12}O_6$ **Beil. VI-1089**
(1,2,4-Triacetoxybenzene)

M.P. 96-97° **Sap. Eq. 76**

White ndls. from abs. alc. — Readily hydrolyzed by acids or alk. but owing to oxidation of the resultant hydroxyhydroquinone in alk. soln., detn. of Sap. Eq. via alk. hydrolysis is difficult or impossible.

For hydrolysis of C̄ to hydroxyhydroquinone (1:1570) and acetic ac. (1:1010) by htg. in 2 pts. MeOH with 0.2 pt. conc. HCl for 1 hr. see ⟨1⟩ — [For prepn. of C̄ in 86–87% yield from benzoquinone + Ac_2O see ⟨2⟩.]

1:2400 ⟨1⟩ Healey, Robinson, *J. Chem. Soc.* **1934,** 1626–1627. ⟨2⟩ Vliet, *Organic Syntheses, Coll. Vol.* I, 310–311 (1932).

1:2410 *n*-PROPYL *p*-HYDROXYBENZOATE $C_{10}H_{12}O_3$ **Beil. X-160**

M.P. 96° **Sap. Eq. 180**

[For reviews of use and detection see ⟨1⟩ ⟨2⟩.]

Ⓓ **Saponification:** Hydrolysis with alk. (T 1.51) yields *n*-propyl alc. (1:6150) and *p*-hydroxybenzoic ac. (1:0840).

1:2410 ⟨1⟩ Sabalitschka, *Z. angew. Chem.* **42,** 936–939 (1929). ⟨2⟩ Fischer, Stauder, *Mikrochemie* **8,** 330–336 (1930).

1:2415 DIMETHYL FUMARATE $C_6H_8O_4$ **Beil. II-741**

M.P. 101.7° ⟨1⟩ **Sap. Eq. 72**
B.P. 193.3° ⟨1⟩

[For m.p. + compn. data on system: C̄ + dimethyl maleate (1:3606) see ⟨2⟩.]

Ⓓ **Saponification:** Hydrolysis with alk. (T 1.51) yields methyl alc. (1:6120) and fumaric ac. (1:0895).

1:2415 ⟨1⟩ Viseur, *Bull. soc. chim. Belg.* **35,** 428 (1926). ⟨2⟩ Ref. 1, page 431.

1:2420 SALICYLALDEHYDE TRIACETATE $C_{13}H_{14}O_6$ **Beil. VIII-45**
(Acetylsalicylaldehyde diacetate)

M.P. 103° ⟨1⟩ **Sap. Eq. 89**
107° ⟨2⟩

Ⓓ **Saponification:** Hydrolysis with alk. (T 1.51) yields salicylaldehyde (1:0205) and acetic ac. (1:1010). [Cf. ⟨3⟩.]

1:2420 ⟨1⟩ Knoevenagel, *Ann.* **402,** 124 (1914). ⟨2⟩ Malkin, Nierenstein, *J. Am. Chem. Soc.* **53** 241 (1931). ⟨3⟩ Wegscheider, Späth, *Monatsh.* **30,** 851–854 (1909).

1:2425 DIMETHYL NAPHTHALATE $C_{14}H_{12}O_4$ **Beil. IX-919**

M.P. 104° ⟨1⟩ **Sap. Eq. 122**

Ⓓ **Saponification:** Hydrolysis with alk. (T 1.51) yields methyl alc. (1:6120) and naphthalic ac. (1:0890).

1:2425 ⟨1⟩ Bradbrook, Linstead, *J. Chem. Soc.* **1936,** 1743.

1:2430 PHLOROGLUCINOL TRIACETATE $C_{12}H_{12}O_6$ **Beil. VI-1104**
(1,3,5-Triacetoxybenzene)

M.P. 105-106° **Sap. Eq. 76**

Ⓓ **Saponification:** Hydrolysis with alk. (T 1.51) yields phloroglucinol (1:1620) and acetic ac. (1:1010). Owing to oxidation of the resulting phloroglucinol (1:1620), detn. of Sap. Eq. of C̄ is difficult.

1:2435 DI-*m*-TOLYL OXALATE $C_{16}H_{14}O_4$ **Beil. VI-379**
(Di-" *m*-cresyl " oxalate)

M.P. 105° ⟨1⟩ **Sap. Eq. 135**

Ⓓ **Saponification:** Hydrolysis with alk. (T 1.51) yields *m*-cresol (1:1730) and oxalic ac. (1:0445).

1:2435 ⟨1⟩ Mikšić, Pinterović, *J. prakt. Chem.* (2) **119,** 234 (1928).

1:2440 DIPHENYL ADIPATE $C_{18}H_{18}O_4$ **Beil. S.N. 516**

M.P. 106° ⟨1⟩ **Sap. Eq. 149**

Ⓓ **Saponification:** Hydrolysis with alk. (T 1.51) yields phenol (1:1420) and adipic ac. (1:0775).

1:2440 ⟨1⟩ Hill, *J. Am. Chem. Soc.* **52,** 4113 (1930).

1:2450 β-NAPHTHYL BENZOATE $C_{17}H_{12}O_2$ **Beil. IX-125**

M.P. 107° **Sap. Eq. 248**

[For prepn. of C̄ from β-naphthol (1:1540) + BzCl + pyridine (81% yield) see ⟨1⟩.]

Ⓓ **Saponification:** Hydrolysis with alk. (T 1.51) yields β-naphthol (1:1540) and benzoic ac. (1:0715).

1:2450 ⟨1⟩ Hazlet, *J. Am. Chem. Soc.* **62,** 2156 (1940).

1:2460 DIMETHYL MESOTARTRATE $C_6H_{10}O_6$ **Beil. III-530**

M.P. 111° ⟨1⟩ **Sap. Eq. 89**

Ⓓ **Saponification:** Hydrolysis with alk. (T 1.51) yields methyl alc. (1:6120) and *meso*-tartaric ac. (1:0490).

1:2460 ⟨1⟩ Weygand, Weissberger, Baumgärtel, *Ber.* **65,** 701 (1932).

1:2470 DI-*p*-TOLYL CARBONATE $C_{15}H_{14}O_3$ **Beil. VI-398**
(Di-" *p*-cresyl " carbonate)

M.P. 114° **Sap. Eq. 242**

C̄ with gas. NH_3 splits quant. to *p*-cresol (1:1410) and urea ⟨1⟩.

Ⓓ **Saponification:** Hydrolysis with alk. (T 1.51) yields *p*-cresol (1:1410) + carbon dioxide.

1:2470 ⟨1⟩ Sabawin, *Cent.* **1934,** II, 3463.

1:2475 CHOLESTERYL ACETATE $C_{29}H_{48}O_2$ **Beil. S.N. 4729-C**

M.P. 114° **Sap. Eq. 416**

Ⓓ **Saponification:** Hydrolysis with alk. (T 1.51) yields cholesterol (1:5975) and acetic ac. (1:1010).

— ETHYL *p*-HYDROXYBENZOATE $C_9H_{10}O_3$ **Beil. X-159**

M.P. 116° **Sap. Eq. 166**

See 1:1534. Genus 4: Phenols.

1:2485 RESORCINOL DIBENZOATE $C_{20}H_{14}O_4$ **Beil. IX-131**

M.P. 117° **Sap. Eq. 159**

Ⓓ **Saponification:** Hydrolysis with alk. (T 1.51) yields resorcinol (1:1530) and benzoic ac. (1:0715).

1:2500 DIPHENYL SUCCINATE $C_{16}H_{14}O_4$ **Beil. VI-155**

M.P. 121° **Sap. Eq. 135**
B.P. 330°

Ⓓ **Saponification:** Hydrolysis with alk. (T 1.51) yields phenol (1:1420) and succinic ac. (1:0530).

1:2510 DI-*p*-TOLYL SUCCINATE $C_{18}H_{18}O_4$ **Beil. VI-398**
(Di-" *p*-cresyl " succinate)

M.P. 121° **Sap. Eq. 149**

Ⓓ **Saponification:** Hydrolysis with alk. (T 1.51) yields *p*-cresol (1:1410) and succinic ac. (1:0530).

1:2520 HYDROQUINONE DIACETATE $C_{10}H_{10}O_4$ **Beil. VI-846**

M.P. 124° **Sap. Eq. 97**

Ⓓ **Saponification:** Hydrolysis with alk. (T 1.51) yields hydroquinone (1:1590) and acetic ac. (1:1010).

— METHYL *p*-HYDROXYBENZOATE $C_8H_8O_3$ **Beil. X-158**

M.P. 131° **Sap. Eq. 152**

See 1:1549. Genus 4: Phenols.

1:2540 TRIETHYL TRIMESATE $C_{15}H_{18}O_6$ **Beil. IX-980**

M.P. 133° **Sap. Eq. 98**

Ⓓ **Saponification:** Hydrolysis with alk. (T 1.51) yields ethyl alc. (1:6130) and trimesic ac. (1:0559).

1:2550 DIMETHYL TEREPHTHALATE $C_{10}H_{10}O_4$ **Beil. IX-843**

M.P. 141° **Sap. Eq. 97**

Ⓓ **Saponification:** Hydrolysis with alk. (T 1.51) yields methyl alc. (1:6120) and terephthalic acid (1:0910).

1:2555 TETRAMETHYL PYROMELLITATE $C_{14}H_{14}O_8$ **Beil. IX-998**

M.P. 142° ⟨1⟩ **Sap. Eq. 77.5**

Ⓓ **Saponification:** Hydrolysis with alk. (T 1.51) yields methyl alc. (1:6120) and pyromellitic ac. (1:0557).

1:2555 ⟨1⟩ Ruzicka, Schinz, Meyer, *Helv. Chim. Acta* **6,** 1095 (1923).

1:2565 TRIMETHYL TRIMESATE $C_{12}H_{12}O_6$ **Beil. IX-979**

M.P. 144° **Sap. Eq. 84**

Ⓓ **Saponification:** Hydrolysis with alk. (T 1.51) yields methyl alc. (1:6120) and trimesic ac. (1:0559).

1:2570 DI-*p*-TOLYL OXALATE $C_{16}H_{14}O_4$ **Beil. VI-398**
(Di-" *p*-cresyl " oxalate)

M.P. 148-149° ⟨1⟩ **Sap. Eq. 135**

Ⓓ **Saponification:** Hydrolysis with alk. (T 1.51) yields *p*-cresol (1:1410) and oxalic ac. (1:0445).

1:2570 ⟨1⟩ Mikšić, Pinterović, *J. prakt. Chem.* (2) **119,** 234 (1928).

1:2575 DIETHYL MUCATE $C_{10}H_{18}O_8$ **Beil. III-585**

M.P. 163-164° ⟨1⟩ **Sap. Eq. 133**

Ⓓ **Saponification:** Hydrolysis with alk. (T 1.51) yields ethyl alc. (1:6130) and mucic ac. (1:0845).

1:2575 ⟨1⟩ Behrend, Heyer, *Ann.* **418,** 312–313 (1919).

1:2580 DIMETHYL MUCATE $C_8H_{14}O_8$ **Beil. III-584**

M.P. 165-167° dec. **Sap. Eq. 119**

Ⓓ **Saponification:** Hydrolysis with alk. (T 1.51) yields methyl alc. (1:6120) and mucic ac. (1:0845).

1:2585 PYROGALLOL TRIACETATE $C_{12}H_{12}O_6$ **Beil. VI-1083**

M.P. 172° ⟨1⟩ (165°) **Sap. Eq. 84**

Ⓓ **Saponification:** Hydrolysis with alk. (T 1.51) yields pyrogallol (1:1555) and acetic ac. (1:1010). [Due to air oxidn. of alk. soln. detn. of Sap. Eq. is difficult.]

1:2585 ⟨1⟩ Chattaway, *J. Chem. Soc.* **1931,** 2496.

1:2590 HYDROQUINONE DIBENZOATE $C_{20}H_{14}O_4$ **Beil. IX-132**

M.P. 199° (204° cor.) **Sap. Eq. 159**

Ⓓ **Saponification:** Hydrolysis with alk. (T 1.51) yields hydroquinone (1:1590) and benzoic ac. (1:0715).

—— **METHYL GALLATE** $C_8H_8O_5$ **Beil. X-483**

M.P. 200-201° **Sap. Eq. 184**

See 1:1605. Genus 4: Phenols.

ORDER I: SUBORDER I: GENUS 5: ESTERS

Division B, Liquid Esters

—— **METHYL FORMATE** $C_2H_4O_2$ **Beil. II-18**

B.P. 31.5° Sap. Eq. **60** D_4^{20} = **0.97421** $n^{15}_{He(yel.)}$ = **1.34648**
M.P. −99.0°

See 1:1000. Genus 3: Acids.

1:3000 ETHYL FORMATE $C_3H_6O_2$ **Beil. II-19**

B.P. 54.2° ⟨1⟩ Sap. Eq. **74** D_4^{20} = **0.92247 ⟨1⟩** $n^{15}_{He(yel.)}$ = **1.36253 ⟨1⟩**
M.P. −79.4° ⟨1⟩ n_D^{20} = **1.3597**

C̄ forms no const. boilg. mixt. either with ethyl alc. or formic ac. — C̄ forms with $CHCl_3$ a binary const. boilg. mixt. (b.p. 62.8°) contg. 13% C̄ + 87% $CHCl_3$ ⟨2⟩.

Ⓓ **Saponification:** Hydrolysis with alk. (T 1.51) yields ethyl alc. (1:6130) and formic ac. (1:1005).

1:3000 ⟨1⟩ Timmermans, Hennaut-Roland, *J. chim. phys.* **29,** 556–557 (1932). ⟨2⟩ Kolossowsky, Alimow, *Bull. soc. chim.* (5) **2,** 688 (1935).

1:3005 METHYL ACETATE $C_3H_6O_2$ **Beil. II-124**

B.P. 57.1° Sap. Eq. **74** D_4^{20} = **0.9274 ⟨1⟩** n_D^{20} = **1.36170 ⟨1⟩**

C̄ forms no const. boilg. mixt. with aq. — C̄ with MeOH forms binary const. boilg. mixt. (b.p. 54°) contg. 81.5 wt. % C̄ + 19.5 wt. % aq. — C̄ with MeOH + aq. forms no ternary const. boilg. mixt. ⟨1⟩.

For study of reaction with 6 *N* aq. alc. NH_3 see ⟨2⟩.

Ⓓ **Saponification:** Hydrolysis with alk. (T 1.51) yields methyl alc. (1:6120) and acetic ac. (1:1010).

1:3005 ⟨1⟩ Hannotte, *Bull. soc. chim. Belg.* **35,** 96 (1926). ⟨2⟩ French, Wrightsman, *J. Am. Chem. Soc.* **60,** 51 (1938).

1:3010 ISOPROPYL FORMATE $C_4H_8O_2$ **Beil. II-21**

B.P. 71° Sap. Eq. **88** D_4^{20} = **0.8728**

Ⓓ **Saponification:** Hydrolysis with alk. (T 1.51) yields isopropyl alc. (1:6135) and formic ac. (1:1005).

1:3015 ETHYL ACETATE $C_4H_8O_2$ **Beil. II-125**

B.P. 77.15° ⟨1⟩ ⟨2⟩ Sap. Eq. **88** D_4^{20} = **0.90055 ⟨1⟩**
M.P. −83.6° ⟨1⟩ D_4^{25} = **0.89453 ⟨1⟩ ⟨2⟩** n_D^{25} = **1.37005**

C̄ forms with aq. a heterogeneous binary const. boilg. mixt., b.p. 70.4°, contg. 91.4% C̄ + 8.6% aq. ⟨3⟩. [For effect of press. on b.p. and compn. see ⟨4⟩.] — C̄ forms with ethyl alc. a homogeneous binary const. boilg. mixt., b.p. 71.8°, contg. 69.4% C̄ + 30.6% ethyl alc. ⟨4⟩. [For effect of press. on b.p. and compn. see ⟨5⟩.] — C̄ forms with both ethyl alc. and aq. a ternary const. boilg. mixt., b.p. 70.3°, contg. 82.6% C̄ + 8.4% ethyl alc. + 9.0% aq. ⟨6⟩. [For effect of press. on b.p. and compn. mixt. see ⟨6⟩.]

For study of quant. anal. of mixts. of C̄, ethyl alc., acetic ac. + aq. see ⟨7⟩. C̄ forms with CCl_4 a binary const.-boilg. mixt. (b.p. 74.75°/760 mm.) contg. 43 mole % C̄ + 57 mole % CCl_4 ⟨8⟩ ⟨9⟩ ⟨10⟩.

1:3015 ⟨1⟩ Timmermans, Hennaut-Roland, *J. chim. phys.* **27,** 429 (1930). ⟨2⟩ Wojciechowski, Smith, *J. Res. Natl. Bur. Stand.* **18,** 503 (1937). ⟨3⟩ Wade, *J. Chem. Soc.* **87,** 1661 (1905). ⟨4⟩ Merriman, *J. Chem. Soc.* **103,** 1793 (1913). ⟨4⟩ Ref. 3, page 1663. ⟨5⟩ Merriman, *J. Chem. Soc.* **103,** 1805 (1913). ⟨6⟩ Ref. 5, page 1814. ⟨7⟩ Poznanski, *J. Am. Chem. Soc.* **50,** 981–988 (1928). ⟨8⟩ Kolossowsky, Alimow, *Bull. soc. chim.* (5) **2,** 688 (1935). ⟨9⟩ Schutz, *J. Am. Chem. Soc.* **61,** 2693 (1939). ⟨10⟩ Schutz, Mallonee, *J. Am. Chem. Soc.*, **62,** 1491–1492 (1940).

1:3020 METHYL PROPIONATE $C_4H_8O_2$ Beil. II-239

B.P. 79.9° **Sap. Eq. 88** D_4^{20} = **0.9151** n_D^{20} = **1.3779**
M.P. −87.5°

Ⓓ **Saponification:** Hydrolysis with alk. (T 1.51) yields methyl alc. (1:6120) and propionic ac. (1:1025).

1:3025 METHYL ACRYLATE $C_4H_6O_2$ Beil. II-399

B.P. 80.3° **Sap. Eq. 86** $D^{19.2}$ = **0.961** n_D^{20} = **1.3984**

On stdg. (especially in light) or on warming polymerizes.

Ⓓ **Saponification:** Hydrolysis with alk. (T 1.51) yields methyl alc. (1:6120) and acrylic ac. (1:1020).

1:3030 *n*-PROPYL FORMATE $C_4H_8O_2$ Beil. II-21

B.P. 80.9° ⟨1⟩ **Sap. Eq. 88** D_D^{20} = **0.9071 ⟨1⟩** n_D^{20} = **1.37789 ⟨1⟩**
M.P. −92.9° ⟨2⟩

C̄ forms with aq. a heterogeneous binary const. boilg. mixt., b.p. 71.6°, contg. 97.7% C̄ + 2.3% aq. — C̄ forms with *n*-propyl alc. a homogeneous binary const. boilg. mixt., b.p. 80.6° contg. 90.2% C̄ + 9.8% aq. — C̄ forms with both *n*-propyl alc. + aq. a ternary const. boilg. mixt., b.p. 70.8°, contg. 82% C̄, 5% *n*-propyl alc. + 13% aq. ⟨1⟩.

Ⓓ **Saponification:** Hydrolysis with alk. (T 1.51) yields *n*-propyl alc. (1:6150) and formic ac. (1:1005).

1:3030 ⟨1⟩ Hannotte, *Bull. soc. chim. Belg.* **35,** 86–87 (1926). ⟨2⟩ Timmermans, *Bull. soc. chim. Belg.* **31,** 391 (1922).

1:3033 *ter*-BUTYL FORMATE $C_5H_{10}O_2$ Beil. S.N. 156

B.P. 83° ⟨1⟩ **Sap. Eq. 114**

Ⓓ **Saponification:** Hydrolysis with alk. (T 1.51) yields *ter*-butyl alc. (1:6140) and formic ac. (1:1005).

1:3033 ⟨1⟩ Taylor, *J. Chem. Soc.* **1937,** 1853.

1:3035 ALLYL FORMATE $C_4H_6O_2$ Beil. II-23

B.P. 83.6° **Sap. Eq. 86** D^{18} = **0.948**

Ⓓ **Saponification:** Hydrolysis with alk. (T 1.51) yields allyl alc. (1:6145) and formic ac. (1:1005).

1:3041 ISOPROPYL ACETATE $C_5H_{10}O_2$ **Beil. II-130**

B.P. 88.9° ⟨1⟩ **Sap. Eq. 102** D_4^{25} **= 0.8690 ⟨2⟩** n_D^{25} **= 1.3740 ⟨2⟩**
M.P. −73.4° ⟨1⟩

Ⓓ **Saponification:** Hydrolysis with alk. (T 1.51) yields isopropyl alc. (1:6135) and acetic ac. (1:1010).

1:3041 ⟨1⟩ Timmermans, *Bull. soc. chim. Belg.* **31,** 391 (1922). ⟨2⟩ Munch, *J. Am. Chem. Soc.* **48,** 997 (1926).

1:3046 DIMETHYL CARBONATE $C_3H_6O_3$ **Beil. III-4**

B.P. 90.5° **Sap. Eq. 90** D_4^{20} **= 1.0694 ⟨1⟩** n_D^{20} **= 1.3687 ⟨1⟩**

Ⓓ **Saponification:** Hydrolysis with alk. (T 1.51) yields methyl alc. (1:6120) and carbonic ac.

1:3046 ⟨1⟩ Kogerman, Kranig, *Cent.* **1927,** I, 2408.

1:3050 METHYL ISOBUTYRATE $C_5H_{10}O_2$ **Beil. II-290**

B.P. 92.6° ⟨1⟩ **Sap. Eq. 102** D_4^{20} **= 0.8906** n_D^{20} **= 1.3840**
M.P. −84.7° ⟨1⟩

Ⓓ **Saponification:** Hydrolysis with alk. (T 1.51) yields methyl alc. (1:6120) and isobutyric ac. (1:1030).

1:3050 ⟨1⟩ Timmermans, *Bull. soc. chim. Belg.* **31,** 391 (1922).

1:3055 *sec*-BUTYL FORMATE $C_5H_{10}O_2$ **Beil. S.N. 156**

B.P. 97° **Sap. Eq. 102** $D_4^{21.5}$ **= 0.8820** $n_D^{25.3}$ **= 1.3812**

Ⓓ **Saponification:** Hydrolysis with alk. (T 1.51) yields *sec*-butyl alc. (1:6155) and formic ac. (1:1005).

1:3057 *ter*-BUTYL ACETATE $C_6H_{12}O_2$ **Beil. II-131**
(Trimethylcarbinyl acetate)

B.P. 97.8° ⟨1⟩ **Sap. Eq. 116** D_4^{25} **= 0.8620 ⟨2⟩** n_D^{25} **= 1.3840 ⟨2⟩**

[For prepn. (94% yield) from *ter*-butyl alc. (1:6140) and Ac_2O see ⟨1⟩.]

Ⓓ **Saponification:** Hydrolysis with alk. (T 1.51) yields *ter*-butyl alc. (1:6140) and acetic ac. (1:1010).

1:3057 ⟨1⟩ Norris, Rigby, *J. Am. Chem. Soc.* **54,** 2097–2098 (1932). ⟨2⟩ Bryant, Smith, *J. Am. Chem. Soc.* **58,** 1016 (1936).

1:3065 ISOBUTYL FORMATE $C_5H_{10}O_2$ **Beil. II-21**

B.P. 98.4° ⟨1⟩ **Sap. Eq. 102** D_4^{20} **= 0.8755 ⟨1⟩** n_D^{20} **= 1.38564 ⟨1⟩**
M.P. −95.8° ⟨2⟩

$\bar{C}$ forms with aq. a heterogeneous binary const. boilg. mixt., b.p. 80.4°, contg. 92.2% $\bar{C}$ + 7.8% aq. — $\bar{C}$ forms with isobutyl alc. a homogeneous binary const. boilg. mixt., b.p. 97.8°, contg. 79.4% $\bar{C}$ + 20.6% isobutyl alc. — $\bar{C}$ forms with both isobutyl alc. and aq. a ternary const. boilg. mixt., b.p. 80.2°, contg. 76% $\bar{C}$, 6.7% isobutyl alc., and 17.3% aq. ⟨1⟩.

Ⓓ **Saponification:** Hydrolysis with alk. (T 1.51) yields isobutyl alc. (1:6165) and formic ac. (1:1005).

1:3065 ⟨1⟩ Hannotte, *Bull. soc. chim. Belg.* **35,** 88–90 (1926). ⟨2⟩ Timmermans, *Bull. soc. chim. Belg.* **36,** 506 (1927).

1:3070 ETHYL PROPIONATE $C_5H_{10}O_2$ **Beil. II-240**

B.P. 99.1° ⟨1⟩ **Sap. Eq. 102** D_4^{20} = **0.8889** ⟨2⟩ n_D^{20} = **1.3853** ⟨2⟩
M.P. −73.9° ⟨1⟩

Ⓓ **Saponification:** Hydrolysis with alk. (T 1.51) yields ethyl alc. (1:6130) and propionic ac. (1:1025). [Cf. ⟨3⟩.]

1:3070 ⟨1⟩ Timmermans, Hennaut-Roland, *J. chim. phys.* **27,** 432–433 (1930). ⟨2⟩ Sobotka, Kahn, *J. Am. Chem. Soc.* **53,** 2937 (1931). ⟨3⟩ Bryant, Smith, *J. Am. Chem. Soc.* **58,** 1015 (1936).

1:3071 ETHYL ACRYLATE $C_5H_8O_2$ **Beil. II-399**

B.P. 101° **Sap. Eq. 100** D^{15} = **0.9136** $n_D^{19.4}$ = **1.4059** ⟨1⟩

On stdg. (especially in light) or on protracted htg. polymerizes.

Ⓓ **Saponification:** Hydrolysis with alk. (T 1.51) yields ethyl alc. (1:6130) and acrylic ac. (1:1020).

1:3071 ⟨1⟩ Kohlrausch, Skrabal, *Monatsh.* **70,** 394 (1937).

1:3072 METHYL PIVALATE $C_6H_{12}O_2$ **Beil. II-320**
(Methyl trimethylacetate)

B.P. 101° ⟨1⟩ **Sap. Eq. 116** D_4^0 = **0.891** n_D^{20} = **1.4228** ⟨2⟩

Ⓓ **Saponification:** Hydrolysis with alk. (T 1.51) yields methyl alc. (1:6120) and trimethylacetic ac. (1:0410).

1:3072 ⟨1⟩ Kohlrausch, Köppl, Pongratz, *Z. physik. Chem.* **B-22,** 370 (1933). ⟨2⟩ Aston, Greenburg, *J. Am. Chem. Soc.* **62,** 2593 (1940).

1:3075 *n*-PROPYL ACETATE $C_5H_{10}O_2$ **Beil. II-129**

B.P. 101.6° ⟨1⟩ ⟨2⟩ **Sap. Eq. 102** D_4^{20} = **0.8834** ⟨1⟩ ⟨2⟩ n_D^{20} = **1.38468** ⟨1⟩

$\bar{C}$ forms with aq. a heterogeneous binary const. boilg. mixt., b.p. 82.4°, contg. 86% $\bar{C}$ + 14% aq. — $\bar{C}$ forms with *n*-propyl alc. a homogeneous binary const. boilg. mixt., b.p. 94.2°, contg. 60% $\bar{C}$ + 40% *n*-propyl alc. — $\bar{C}$ forms with both *n*-propyl alc. and aq. a ternary const. boilg. mixt., b.p. 82.2°, contg. 59.5% $\bar{C}$ + 19.5% *n*-propyl alc. + 21% aq. ⟨1⟩.

For reaction of $\bar{C}$ with aq. alc. NH_3 see ⟨3⟩.

Ⓓ **Saponification:** Hydrolysis with alk. (T 1.51) yields *n*-propyl alc. (1:6150) and acetic ac. (1:1010).

1:3075 ⟨1⟩ Hannotte, *Bull. soc. chim. Belg.* **35,** 97–98 (1926). ⟨2⟩ Wojciechowski, Smith, *J. Research Natl. Bur. Standards* **18,** 502–503 (1937). ⟨3⟩ French, Wrightsman, *J. Am. Chem. Soc.* **60,** 51 (1938).

1:3080 METHYL *n*-BUTYRATE $C_5H_{10}O_2$ **Beil. II-270**

B.P. 102.3° **Sap. Eq. 102** D_4^{20} = **0.8982** n_D^{20} = **1.3879**

Ⓓ **Saponification:** Hydrolysis with alk. (T 1.51) yields methyl alc. (1:6120) and *n*-butyric ac. (1:1035).

1:3085 ALLYL ACETATE $C_5H_8O_2$ **Beil. II-136**

B.P. 104° **Sap. Eq. 100** D_4^{20} = **0.9276** n_D^{20} = **1.40488**

Ⓓ **Saponification:** Hydrolysis with alk. (T 1.51) yields allyl alc. (1:6145) and acetic ac. (1:1010).

1:3087 TRIMETHYL ORTHOFORMATE $C_4H_{10}O_3$ **Beil. II-19**
("Methyl orthoformate"; trimethoxymethane)

B.P. 105° **Sap. Eq. 35** D_4^{20} = **0.9676** ⟨1⟩ n_D^{20} = **1.3793** ⟨1⟩
D_4^{25} = **0.9623** ⟨1⟩ n_D^{25} = **1.3773** ⟨1⟩

Ⓓ **Saponification:** Hydrolysis with alk. (T 1.51) yields methyl **alc.** (**1:**6120) and formic ac. (1:1005).

1:3087 ⟨1⟩ Sah, Ma, *J. Am. Chem. Soc.* **54,** 2965 (1932).

1:3088 METHYL ISOCROTONATE $C_5H_8O_2$ **Beil. II₁-(189)**

B.P. 106.2-108.2° cor. ⟨1⟩ **Sap. Eq. 100**

Ⓓ **Saponification:** Hydrolysis with alk. (T **1.51**) yields methyl alc. (**1:**6120) and isocrotonic ac. (1:1045).

1:3088 ⟨1⟩ Dadieu, Pongratz, Kohlrausch, *Monatsh.* **60,** 211 (1932).

1:3090 *n*-BUTYL FORMATE $C_5H_{10}O_2$ **Beil. II-21**

B.P. 106.6° ⟨1⟩ **Sap. Eq. 102** D_4^{20} = **0.8885** ⟨1⟩ n_D^{20} = **1.38940** ⟨1⟩
M.P. −91.9° ⟨2⟩

C̄ forms with aq. a heterogeneous binary const. boilg. mixt., b.p. 83.8°, contg. 83.5% C̄ + 16.5% aq. — C̄ forms with *n*-butyl alc. a homogeneous const. boilg. mixt., b.p. 105.8°, contg. 76.3% C̄ + 23.7% *n*-butyl alc. — C̄ with both *n*-butyl alc. and aq. forms a ternary const. boilg. mixt., b.p. 83.6°, contg. 68.7% C̄, 10% *n*-butyl alc., + 21.3% aq.

Ⓓ **Saponification:** Hydrolysis with alk. (T 1.51) yields *n*-butyl alc. (1:6180) and formic ac. (1:1005).

1:3090 ⟨1⟩ Hannotte, *Bull. soc. chim. Belg.* **35,** 90–91 (1926). ⟨2⟩ Timmermans, *Bull. soc. chim. Belg.* **36,** 506 (1927).

1:3095 ETHYL ISOBUTYRATE $C_6H_{12}O_2$ **Beil. II-291**

B.P. 111.0° ⟨1⟩ **Sap. Eq. 116** D_4^{20} = **0.86930** n_D^{20} = **1.3903**
M.P. −88.2° ⟨1⟩

C̄ boiled 3 days with hydrazine hydrate yields isobutyrohydrazide, cryst. from ether + alc., m.p. 104° ⟨2⟩ ⟨3⟩.

Ⓓ **Saponification:** Hydrolysis with alk. (T 1.51) yields ethyl alc. (1:6130) and isobutyric ac. (1:1030). [Cf. ⟨4⟩.]

1:3095 ⟨1⟩ Timmermans, *Bull. soc. chim. Belg.* **31,** 391 (1922). ⟨2⟩ Stollé, Gutmann, *J. prakt. Chem.* (2) **69,** 497 (1904). ⟨3⟩ Curtius, Hambsch, *J. prakt. Chem.* (2) **125,** 182 (1930). ⟨4⟩ Bryant, Smith, *J. Am. Chem. Soc.* **58,** 1015 (1936).

1:3100 ISOPROPYL PROPIONATE $C_6H_{12}O_2$ **Beil. II-241**

B.P. 111.3° **Sap. Eq. 116** D^0 = **0.8931**

Ⓓ **Saponification:** Hydrolysis with alk. (T 1.51) yields isopropyl alc. (1:6135) and propionic ac. (1:1025). [Cf. ⟨1⟩.]

1:3100 ⟨1⟩ Bryant, Smith, *J. Am. Chem. Soc.* **58,** 1015 (1936).

1:3105 ***sec*-BUTYL ACETATE** $C_6H_{12}O_2$ **Beil. II-131**

B.P. 112.0° **Sap. Eq. 116** D_4^{25} **= 0.8648** n_D^{25} **= 1.3865** ⟨1⟩

For reaction with 6 *N* alc. NH_3 see ⟨1⟩ ⟨2⟩.

Ⓓ **Saponification:** Hydrolysis with alk. (T 1.51) yields *sec*-butyl alc. (1:6155) and acetic ac. (1:1010). [Cf. ⟨3⟩.]

1:3105 ⟨1⟩ French, Wrightsman, *J. Am. Chem. Soc.* **60,** 51 (1938). ⟨2⟩ French, Johnson, Ratekin, *J. Am. Chem. Soc.* **58,** 1347 (1936). ⟨3⟩ Bryant, Smith, *J. Am. Chem. Soc.* **58,** 1015 (1936).

1:3110 **METHYL ISOVALERATE** $C_6H_{12}O_2$ **Beil. II-311**

B.P. 116.7° **Sap. Eq. 116** D_4^{20} **= 0.8808** n_D^{25} **= 1.3900**

Ⓓ **Saponification:** Hydrolysis with alk. (T 1.51) yields methyl alc. (1:6120) and isovaleric ac. (1:1050). [Cf. ⟨1⟩.]

1:3110 ⟨1⟩ Bryant, Smith, *J. Am. Chem. Soc.* **58,** 1015 (1936).

1:3115 **ISOBUTYL ACETATE** $C_6H_{12}O_2$ **Beil. II-131**

B.P. 117.2° ⟨1⟩ (**118°**) **Sap. Eq. 116** D_4^{20} **= 0.8747** ⟨1⟩ n_D^{20} **= 1.39008** ⟨1⟩

$\bar{C}$ forms with aq. a heterogeneous binary const. boilg. mixt., b.p. 87.4°, contg. 83.4% $\bar{C}$ + 16.6% aq. — $\bar{C}$ forms with isobutyl alc. a homogeneous binary const. boilg. mixt., b.p. 107.4°, contg. 45% $\bar{C}$ + 55% isobutyl alc. — $\bar{C}$ forms with both isobutyl alc. and aq. a ternary const. boilg. mixt., b.p. 86.8°, contg. 46.5% $\bar{C}$, 23.1% isobutyl alc., and 30.4% aq. ⟨1⟩.

For study of reaction of $\bar{C}$ with 6 *N* aq. alc. NH_3 see ⟨2⟩.

Ⓓ **Saponification:** Hydrolysis with alk. (T 1.51) yields isobutyl alc. (1:6165) and acetic ac. (1:1010).

1:3115 ⟨1⟩ Hannotte, *Bull. soc. chim. Belg.* **35,** 98–100 (1926). ⟨2⟩ French, Wrightsman, *J. Am. Chem. Soc.* **60,** 51 (1938).

1:3117 **ETHYL PIVALATE** $C_7H_{14}O_2$ **Beil. II-320**
(Ethyl trimethylacetate)

B.P. 118.1° ⟨1⟩ **Sap. Eq. 130** D_4^{20} **= 0.856** ⟨5⟩ n_D^{20} **= 1.3912** ⟨5⟩

$\bar{C}$ with NH_3 cannot be induced to give trimethylacetamide. [Cf. ⟨2⟩ ⟨3⟩.]

Ⓓ **Saponification:** Hydrolysis with alk. (T 1.51) yields very slowly ethyl alc. (1:6130) and trimethylacetic ac. (1:0410). [Cf. ⟨4⟩.]

1:3117 ⟨1⟩ Olsson, *Z. physik. Chem.* **133,** 234 (1928). ⟨2⟩ Homeyer, Whitmore, Wallingford, *J. Am. Chem. Soc.* **55,** 4211–4212 (1933). ⟨3⟩ Meyer, *Monatsh.* **27,** 36 (1906). ⟨4⟩ Bryant, Smith, *J. Am. Chem. Soc.* **58,** 1015 (1936). ⟨5⟩ Aston, Greenburg, *J. Am. Chem. Soc.* **62,** 2593 (1940).

1:3118 **ETHYL METHACRYLATE** $C_6H_{10}O_2$ **Beil. II-423**

B.P. $\mathbf{118.5^{\circ}_{753}}$ ⟨1⟩ **Sap. Eq. 114** D_4^{20} **= 0.91063** ⟨1⟩ n_D^{20} **= 1.41472** ⟨1⟩

$\bar{C}$ polymerizes rapidly on expos. to heat and/ or light if it has been distilled at ord. press.; if distd. in vac. can be preserved unchanged for at least 5 months ⟨1⟩.

Ⓓ **Saponification:** Hydrolysis with alk. (T 1.51) yields ethyl alc. (1:6130) and methacrylic ac.

1:3118 ⟨1⟩ Bruylants, *Bull. soc. chim. Belg.* **38,** 141–143 (1929).

1:3121 METHYL CROTONATE $C_5H_8O_2$ **Beil. II-410**

B.P. 118.8-119.3° ⟨1⟩ Sap. Eq. 100 D^4 **= 0.9806**

Ⓓ **Saponification:** Hydrolysis with alk. (T 1.51) yields methyl alc. (1:6120) and crotonic ac. (1:0425).

1:3121 ⟨1⟩ Dadieu, Pongratz, Kohlrausch, *Monatsh.* **60,** 211 (1932).

1:3125 ISOPROPYL ISOBUTYRATE $C_7H_{14}O_2$ **Beil. II-291**

B.P. 121° Sap. Eq. 130 D_4^0 **= 0.8687**

Ⓓ **Saponification:** Hydrolysis with alk. (T 1.51) yields isopropyl alc. (1:6135) and isobutyric ac. (1:1030).

1:3127 ETHYL *n*-BUTYRATE $C_6H_{12}O_2$ **Beil. II-270**

B.P. 121.6° ⟨1⟩ Sap. Eq. 116 D_4^{20} **= 0.87917 ⟨1⟩** $n_{\mathrm{He(yel.)}}^{15}$ **= 1.39475 ⟨1⟩**
M.P. −100.8° ⟨1⟩

Ⓓ **Saponification:** Hydrolysis with alk. (T 1.51) yields ethyl alc. (1:6130) and *n*-butyric ac. (1:1035). [Cf. ⟨2⟩.]

1:3127 ⟨1⟩ Timmermans, Hennaut-Roland, *J. chim. phys.* **29,** 558–559 (1932). ⟨2⟩ Bryant, Smith, *J. Am. Chem. Soc.* **58,** 1015 (1936).

1:3130 *n*-PROPYL PROPIONATE $C_6H_{12}O_2$ **Beil. II-240**

B.P. 123.4° ⟨1⟩ Sap. Eq. 116 D^{20} **= 0.8809** n_D^{20} **= 1.39325**
M.P. −75.9° ⟨1⟩

Ⓓ **Saponification:** Hydrolysis with alk. (T 1.51) yields *n*-propyl alc. (1:6150) and propionic ac. (1:1025). [Cf. ⟨2⟩.]

1:3130 ⟨1⟩ Timmermans, *Bull. soc. chim. Belg.* **31,** 391 (1922). ⟨2⟩ Bryant, Smith, *J. Am. Chem. Soc.* **58,** 1015 (1936).

1:3134 *ter*-AMYL ACETATE $C_7H_{14}O_2$ **Beil. II-132**
(Dimethylethylcarbinyl acetate)

B.P. 124° Sap. Eq. 130 D^{19} **= 0.8738** n_D^{20} **= 1.392**

Ⓓ **Saponification:** Hydrolysis with aq. alk. (T 1.51) yields *ter*-amyl alc. (1:6160) and acetic ac. (1:1010).

1:3140 ALLYL PROPIONATE $C_6H_{10}O_2$ **Beil. II-241**

B.P. 124° Sap. Eq. 114

Ⓓ **Saponification:** Hydrolysis with alk. (T 1.51) yields allyl alc. (1:6145) and propionic ac. (1:1025).

1:3142 ISOAMYL FORMATE $C_6H_{12}O_2$ **Beil. II-22**

B.P. 124.2° ⟨1⟩ Sap. Eq. 116 D_4^{20} **= 0.8820 ⟨1⟩** n_D^{20} **= 1.39756 ⟨1⟩**
M.P. −93.5° ⟨2⟩

$\bar{C}$ forms with aq. a heterogeneous binary const. boilg. mixt., b.p. 90.2°, contg. 79% $\bar{C}$ + 21% aq. — $\bar{C}$ forms with isoamyl alc. a homogeneous const. boilg. mixt., b.p. 123.6°, contg. 74% $\bar{C}$ + 26% isoamyl alc. — $\bar{C}$ forms with both isoamyl alc. and aq. a ternary const. boilg. mixt., b.p. 89.8°, contg. 48% $\bar{C}$, 19.6% isoamyl alc., + 32.4% aq. ⟨1⟩.

Ⓓ **Saponification:** Hydrolysis with alk. (T 1.51) yields isoamyl alc. (1:6200) and formic ac. (1:1005).

1:3142 ⟨1⟩ Hannotte, *Bull. soc. chim. Belg.* **35,** 92–93 (1926). ⟨2⟩ Timmermans, *Bull. soc. chim. Belg.* **36,** 506 (1927).

1:3144 ETHYL ISOCROTONATE $C_6H_{10}O_2$ Beil. II-414

B.P. 125.5-126°$_{749}$ ⟨1⟩ **Sap. Eq. 114** D_4^{20} = **0.91820** ⟨1⟩ n_D^{20} = **1.42423** ⟨1⟩

Ⓓ **Saponification:** Hydrolysis with alk. (T 1.51) yields ethyl alc. (1:6130) and isocrotonic ac. (1:1045).

1:3144 ⟨1⟩ Bruylants, *Bull. soc. chim. Belg.* **38,** 140–141 (1929).

1:3145 *n*-BUTYL ACETATE $C_6H_{12}O_2$ Beil. II-130

B.P. 126.1° ⟨1⟩ **Sap. Eq. 116** D_4^{25} = **0.87636** ⟨1⟩ n_D^{15} = **1.39614** ⟨2⟩
126.2° ⟨2⟩

$\bar{C}$ forms with aq. a heterogeneous binary const. boilg. mixt., b.p. 90.2° ⟨2⟩ (90.5° ⟨3⟩), contg. 71.3% $\bar{C}$ + 28.7% aq. [cf. also ⟨3⟩] — $\bar{C}$ forms with *n*-butyl alc. a homogeneous binary const. boilg. mixt., b.p. 117.2° ⟨2⟩ (116.5° ⟨4⟩), contg. 53% $\bar{C}$ + 47% aq. [cf. also ⟨4⟩] — $\bar{C}$ forms with both *n*-butyl alc. and aq. a ternary const. boilg. mixt., b.p. 89.4°, contg. 35.3% $\bar{C}$, 27.4% *n*-butyl alc. + 37.3% aq. ⟨2⟩. [Cf. ⟨3⟩.]

Ⓓ **Saponification:** Hydrolysis with alk. (T 1.51) yields *n*-butyl alc. (1:6180) and acetic ac. (1:1010).

1:3145 ⟨1⟩ Wojciechowski, Smith, *J. Research Natl. Bur. Standards* **18,** 503 (1937). ⟨2⟩ Hannotte, *Bull. soc. chim. Belg.* **35,** 100–101 (1926). ⟨3⟩ Brunjes, Furnas, *Ind. Eng. Chem.* **28,** 573–580 (1936). ⟨4⟩ Brunjes, Furnas, *Ind. Eng. Chem.* **27,** 396–400 (1935).

1:3147 *ter*-BUTYL ISOBUTYRATE $C_8H_{16}O_2$ Beil. S.N. 162

B.P. 126.7° ⟨1⟩ **Sap. Eq. 144** n_D^{20} = **1.3921** ⟨1⟩

Ⓓ **Saponification:** Hydrolysis with alk. (T 1.51) yields *ter*-butyl alc. (1:6140) and isobutyric ac. (1:1030). [Cf. ⟨2⟩.]

1:3147 ⟨1⟩ Kohlrausch, Skrabal, *Monatsh.* **70,** 393 (1937). ⟨2⟩ Bryant, Smith, *J. Am. Chem. Soc.* **58,** 1014–1017 (1936).

1:3150 DIETHYL CARBONATE $C_5H_{10}O_3$ Beil. III-5

B.P. 126.8° ⟨1⟩ **Sap. Eq. 118** D_4^{20} = **0.9752** ⟨2⟩ n_D^{20} = **1.3852** ⟨2⟩
M.P. −43.0° ⟨1⟩

Ⓓ **Saponification:** Hydrolysis with alk. (T 1.51) yields ethyl alc. (1:6130) and carbonic ac.

1:3150 ⟨1⟩ Timmermans, Hennaut-Roland, *J. chim. phys.* **27,** 434–435 (1930). ⟨2⟩ Kogerman, Kranig, *Cent.* **1927,** I, 2408.

1:3155 METHYL *n*-VALERATE $C_6H_{12}O_2$ Beil. II-301

B.P. 127.7° ⟨1⟩ **Sap. Eq. 116** D_4^{15} = **0.8947** ⟨1⟩ n_D^{15} = **1.3993** ⟨1⟩
M.P. −91.0° ⟨1⟩

Ⓓ **Saponification:** Hydrolysis with alk. (T 1.51) yields methyl alc. (1:6120) and *n*-valeric ac. (1:1060).

1:3160 ISOPROPYL *n*-BUTYRATE $C_7H_{14}O_2$ **Beil. II-271**

B.P. 128° **Sap. Eq. 130** $D^{13} = $ **0.8652**

Ⓓ **Saponification:** Hydrolysis with alk. (T 1.51) yields isopropyl alc. (1:6135) and *n*-butyric ac. (1:1035).

1:3162 METHYL METHOXYACETATE $C_4H_8O_3$ **Beil. III-236**

B.P. 130.0° ⟨1⟩ **Sap. Eq. 104** $D_4^{20} = $ **1.0511** $n_D^{20} = $ **1.39636**

Ⓓ **Saponification:** Hydrolysis with alk. (T 1.51) yields methyl alc. (1:6120) and methoxyacetic ac. (1:1065).

1:3162 ⟨1⟩ Pryde, Williams, *J. Chem. Soc.* **1933,** 1627.

1:3164 ETHYL METHOXYACETATE $C_5H_{10}O_3$ **Beil. III-236**

B.P. 132° **Sap. Eq. 118** $D^{15} = $ **1.0118**

Ⓓ **Saponification:** Hydrolysis with alk. (T 1.51) yields ethyl alc. (1:6130) and methoxyacetic ac. (1:1065).

1:3166 *n*-AMYL FORMATE $C_6H_{12}O_2$ **Beil. II-22**

B.P. 132.1° ⟨1⟩ **Sap. Eq. 116** $D_4^{20} = $ **0.8853 ⟨2⟩** $n_D^{20} = $ **1.39916 ⟨2⟩**
M.P. −73.5° ⟨1⟩

$\bar{C}$ forms with aq. a heterogeneous binary azeotrope, b.p. 91.6°, contg. 71.7% wt. $\bar{C}$; $\bar{C}$ forms with *n*-amyl alc. (1:6205) a homogeneous binary azeotrope, b.p. 131.4° contg. 57 wt. % $\bar{C}$; $\bar{C}$ forms with both *n*-amyl alc. and aq. an azeotrope, b.p. 91.4° contg. 41 wt. % $\bar{C}$, 21.5 wt. % *n*-AmOH, and 37.5 wt. % aq. ⟨2⟩.

Ⓓ **Saponification:** Hydrolysis with alk. (T 1.51) yields *n*-amyl alc. (1:6205) and formic ac. (1:1005).

1:3166 ⟨1⟩ Lievens, *Bull. soc. chim. Belg.* **33,** 126–128 (1924). ⟨2⟩ Hannotte, *Bull. soc. chim. Belg.* **35,** 94–96 (1926).

1:3168 *sec*-AMYL(-3) ACETATE $C_7H_{14}O_2$ **Beil. II-131**
(Diethylcarbinyl acetate)

B.P. 133° **Sap. Eq. 130** $n_D^{20} = $ **1.4005**

Ⓓ **Saponification:** Hydrolysis with alk. (T 1.51) yields pentanol-3 (1:6175) and acetic ac. (1:1010).

1:3171 *sec*-AMYL(-2) ACETATE $C_7H_{14}O_2$ **Beil. II-131**
(Methyl-*n*-propyl-carbinyl acetate)

B.P. 133.5° **Sap. Eq. 130** $D_4^{18} = $ **0.8692** $n_D^{20} = $ **1.3960**

Ⓓ **Saponification:** Hydrolysis with alk. (T 1.51) yields pentanol-2 (1:6185) and acetic ac. (1:1010).

1:3181 ALLYL ISOBUTYRATE $C_7H_{12}O_2$ **Beil. II-292**

B.P. 134° **Sap. Eq. 128**

Ⓓ **Saponification:** Hydrolysis with alk. (T 1.51) yields allyl alc. (1:6145) and isobutyric ac. (1:1030).

1:3186 ETHYL ISOVALERATE $C_7H_{14}O_2$ Beil. II-312

B.P. 134.7° **Sap. Eq. 130** $D_4^{20} = \mathbf{0.86565}$ $n_D^{20} = \mathbf{1.4009}$
M.P. −99.3°

Ⓓ **Saponification:** Hydrolysis with alk. (T 1.51) yields ethyl alc. (1:6130) and isovaleric ac. (1:1050). [Cf. ⟨1⟩.]

1:3186 ⟨1⟩ Bryant, Smith, *J. Am. Chem. Soc.* **58,** 1015 (1936).

1:3191 *n*-PROPYL ISOBUTYRATE $C_7H_{14}O_2$ Beil. II-291

B.P. 135° **Sap. Eq. 130** $D_4^{0} = \mathbf{0.8843}$ $n_D^{20} = \mathbf{1.3959}$

Ⓓ **Saponification:** Hydrolysis with alk. (T 1.51) yields *n*-propyl alc. (1:6150) and isobutyric ac. (1:1030) [cf. ⟨1⟩].

1:3191 ⟨1⟩ Bryant, Smith, *J. Am. Chem. Soc.* **58,** 1015 (1936).

1:3196 ETHYL CROTONATE $C_6H_{10}O_2$ Beil. II-411

B.P. $\mathbf{136.7^{\circ}_{749}}$ ⟨1⟩ **Sap. Eq. 114** $D_4^{20} = \mathbf{0.91752}$ ⟨1⟩ $n_D^{20} = \mathbf{1.42524}$ ⟨1⟩

Ⓓ **Saponification:** Hydrolysis with alk. (T 1.51) yields ethyl alc. (1:6130) and crotonic ac. (1:0425).

1:3196 ⟨1⟩ Bruylants, *Bull. soc. chim. Belg.* **38,** 138 (1929).

1:3201 METHYL PYRUVATE $C_4H_6O_3$ Beil. III-616

B.P. 136.8-138° ⟨1⟩ **Sap. Eq. 102** $D^{0} = \mathbf{1.154}$

Ⓓ **Methyl pyruvate 2,4-dinitrophenylhydrazone:** yel. cryst. from dioxane + MeOH, m.p. 186.5–187.5° cor. ⟨2⟩. [Cf. T 1.14.]

Ⓓ **Saponification:** Hydrolysis with alk. (T 1.51) yields methyl alc. (1:6120) and pyruvic acid (1:1040).

1:3201 ⟨1⟩ Kohlrausch, Pongratz, *Ber.* **67,** 985 (1934). ⟨2⟩ Strain, *J. Am. Chem. Soc.* **57,** 760 (1935).

1:3206 METHYL α-HYDROXYISOBUTYRATE $C_5H_{10}O_3$ Beil. III_1-(119)

B.P. 137° **Sap. Eq. 118**

Miscible with aq.

Ⓓ **Saponification:** Hydrolysis with alk. (T 1.51) yields methyl alc. (1:6120) and α-hydroxyisobutyric ac. (1:0431).

1:3211 ISOBUTYL PROPIONATE $C_7H_{14}O_2$ Beil. II-241

B.P. 138.0° ⟨1⟩ **Sap. Eq. 130** $D_4^{0} = \mathbf{0.8876}$ $n_D^{20} = \mathbf{1.3975}$
M.P. −71.4° ⟨1⟩

Ⓓ **Saponification:** Hydrolysis with alk. (T 1.51) yields isobutyl alc. (1:6165) and propionic ac. (1:1025). [Cf. ⟨2⟩.]

1:3211 ⟨1⟩ Timmermans, *Bull. soc. chim. Belg.* **31,** 391 (1922). ⟨2⟩ Bryant, Smith, *J. Am. Chem. Soc.* **58,** 1015 (1936).

—— ACETYLACETONE $C_5H_8O_2$ Beil. I-777

B.P. 139° $D_4^{20} = \mathbf{0.976}$ $n_D^{25.6} = \mathbf{1.4465}$

See 1:1700. Genus 4: Phenols.

1:3216 ALLYL *n*-BUTYRATE $C_7H_{12}O_2$ **Beil. II-272**

B.P. 142° **Sap. Eq. 128**

Ⓓ **Saponification:** Hydrolysis with alk. (T 1.51) yields allyl alc. (1:6145) and *n*-butyric ac. (1:1035).

1:3221 ISOAMYL ACETATE $C_7H_{14}O_2$ **Beil. II-132**

B.P. 142° **Sap. Eq. 130** D_4^{20} = **0.8674** ⟨1⟩ n_D^{20} = **1.40034** ⟨1⟩

$\bar{C}$ forms with aq. a binary heterogeneous const. boilg. mixt., b.p. 93.8°, contg. 63.8% $\bar{C}$ + 36.2% aq. — $\bar{C}$ forms with isoamyl alc. no const. boilg. mixt. — $\bar{C}$ forms with both isoamyl alc. and aq. a ternary const. boilg. mixt., b.p. 93.6°, contg. 24% $\bar{C}$, 31.2% isoamyl alc. + 44.8% aq. ⟨1⟩.

For study of react. with 6 *N* aq. alc. NH_3 see ⟨2⟩.

Ⓓ **Saponification:** Hydrolysis with alk. (T 1.51) yields isoamyl alc. (1:6200) and acetic ac. (1:1010).

1:3221 ⟨1⟩ Hannotte, *Bull. soc. chim. Belg.* **35,** 102–104 (1926). ⟨2⟩ French, Wrightsman, *J. Am. Chem. Soc.* **60,** 51 (1938).

1:3226 ISOPROPYL ISOVALERATE $C_8H_{16}O_2$ **Beil. II-312**

B.P. 142° **Sap. Eq. 144** D^{17} = **0.8538** n_D^{25} = **1.3938**

Ⓓ **Saponification:** Hydrolysis with alk. (T 1.51) yields isopropyl alc. (1:6135) and isovaleric ac. (1:1050).

1:3231 *n*-PROPYL *n*-BUTYRATE $C_7H_{14}O_2$ **Beil. II-271**

B.P. 143.8° ⟨1⟩ **Sap. Eq. 130** D^{15} = **0.8789** n_D^{20} = **1.4005**
M.P. −95.2° ⟨1⟩

Ⓓ **Saponification:** Hydrolysis with alk. (T 1.51) yields *n*-propyl alc. (1:6150) and *n*-butyric ac. (1:1035).

1:3231 ⟨1⟩ Timmermans, *Bull. soc. chim. Belg.* **31,** 391 (1922).

1:3236 METHYL *d,l*-LACTATE $C_4H_8O_3$ **Beil. III-280**

B.P. 144.8° **Sap. Eq. 104** D^{19}_{-} = **1.0898** n_D^{16} = **1.4156**
n_D^{25} = **1.4132** ⟨1⟩

Ⓓ **Saponification:** Hydrolysis with alk. (T 1.51) yields methyl alc. (1:6120) and *d,l*-lactic ac. (1:0400).

1:3236 ⟨1⟩ Smith, Claborn, *Ind. Eng. Chem.* **32,** 693 (1940).

1:3241 TRIETHYL ORTHOFORMATE $C_7H_{16}O_3$ **Beil. II-20**
(" Ethyl orthoformate "; triethoxymethane)

B.P. 145.5° **Sap. Eq. 49** D_4^{20} = **0.8909** ⟨1⟩ n_D^{20} = **1.3922** ⟨1⟩
D_4^{25} = **0.8858** ⟨1⟩ n_D^{25} = **1.3900** ⟨1⟩

[For prepn. in 27–31% yield from $CHCl_3$ + NaOEt see ⟨2⟩ ⟨1⟩.]

Ⓓ **Saponification:** Hydrolysis with alk. (T 1.51) yields ethyl alc. (1:6130) and formic ac. (1:1005).

1:3241 ⟨1⟩ Sah, Ma, *J. Am. Chem. Soc.* **54,** 2965 (1932). ⟨2⟩ Kaufmann, Dreger, *Organic Syntheses, Coll. Vol.* I, 253–256 (1932).

1:3246 ETHYL *n*-VALERATE $C_7H_{14}O_2$ **Beil. II-301**

B.P. 145.5° ⟨1⟩ Sap. Eq. 130 D_4^{20} = **0.8739 ⟨2⟩** n_D^{20} = **1.40094 ⟨2⟩**
M.P. −91.2° ⟨1⟩ D_4^{25} = **0.8690 ⟨2⟩** n_D^{25} = **1.39887 ⟨2⟩**

Ⓓ **Saponification:** Hydrolysis with alk. (T 1.51) yields ethyl alc. (1:6130) and *n*-valeric ac. (1:1060). [Cf. ⟨3⟩.]

1:3246 ⟨1⟩ Lievens, *Bull. soc. chim. Belg.* **33,** 126–128 (1924). ⟨2⟩ Kao, Ma, *Science Repts. Natl. Tsing Hua Univ.*, Ser. **A-1,** 181–183 (1932). ⟨3⟩ Bryant, Smith, *J. Am. Chem. Soc.* **58,** 1015 (1936).

1:3251 *ter*-BUTYL *n*-BUTYRATE $C_8H_{16}O_2$ **Beil. S.N. 162**

B.P. 145-146.6° ⟨1⟩ Sap. Eq. 144 $n_D^{17.5}$ = **1.4001 ⟨1⟩**

Ⓓ **Saponification:** Hydrolysis with alk. (T 1.51) yields *ter*-butyl alc. (1:6140) and *n*-butyric ac. (1:1035). [Cf. ⟨2⟩.]

1:3251 ⟨1⟩ Kohlrausch, Skrabal, *Monatsh.* **70,** 397 (1937). ⟨2⟩ Bryant, Smith, *J. Am. Chem. Soc.* **58,** 1014–1017 (1936).

1:3256 *n*-BUTYL PROPIONATE $C_7H_{14}O_2$ **Beil. II-241**

B.P. 146.8° ⟨1⟩ Sap. Eq. 130 D_4^{15} = **0.8818 ⟨1⟩** n_D^{15} = **1.4038 ⟨1⟩**
M.P. −89.6°

Ⓓ **Saponification:** Hydrolysis with alk. (T 1.51) yields *n*-butyl alc. (1:6180) and propionic ac. (1:1025).

1:3256 ⟨1⟩ Lievens, *Bull. soc. chim. Belg.* **33,** 126–128 (1924).

1:3261 DIISOPROPYL CARBONATE $C_7H_{14}O_3$ **Beil. S.N. 199**

B.P. 147.2° cor. **⟨1⟩ Sap. Eq. 146** D_4^{20} = **0.9162 ⟨1⟩** n_D^{20} = **1.3932 ⟨1⟩**

Ⓓ **Saponification:** Hydrolysis with alk. (T 1.51) yields isopropyl alc. (1:6135) and carbonic ac.

1:3261 ⟨1⟩ Kogerman, Kranig, *Cent.* **1927,** I, 2408.

1:3266 METHYL ETHOXYACETATE $C_5H_{10}O_3$ **Beil. III-236**

B.P. 148° Sap. Eq. 118 D_4^{15} = **1.0112**

Ⓓ **Saponification:** Hydrolysis with alk. (T 1.51) yields methyl alc. (1:6120) and ethoxyacetic ac. (1:1070).

1:3271 ISOBUTYL ISOBUTYRATE $C_8H_{16}O_2$ **Beil. II-291**

B.P. 148.7° ⟨1⟩ Sap. Eq. 144 D_4^{0} = **0.8752** n_D^{20} = **1.3999**
M.P. −80.65° ⟨1⟩

Ⓓ **Saponification:** Hydrolysis with alk. (T 1.51) yields isobutyl alc. (1:6165) and isobutyric ac. (1:1030). [Cf. ⟨2⟩.]

1:3271 ⟨1⟩ Timmermans, *Bull. soc. chim. Belg.* **31,** 391 (1922). ⟨2⟩ Bryant, Smith, *J. Am. Chem. Soc.* **58,** 1015 (1936).

1:3276 *n*-AMYL ACETATE $C_7H_{14}O_2$ **Beil. II-131**

B.P. 149.25° ⟨1⟩; 148.8° ⟨2⟩ D_4^{20} = **0.8756 ⟨2⟩** n_D^{20} = **1.4031 ⟨2⟩**
M.P. −70.8° ⟨1⟩ Sap. Eq. 130 D_4^{15} = **0.8810 ⟨1⟩** n_D^{15} = **1.4044 ⟨1⟩**

$\bar{C}$ forms with aq. a heterogeneous binary const. boilg. mixt., b.p. 95.2°, contg. 59% $\bar{C}$ + 41% aq. — $\bar{C}$ forms no const. boilg. mixt. with *n*-amyl alc. — $\bar{C}$ forms with both *n*-amyl alc. and aq. a const. boilg. mixt., b.p. 94.8°, contg. 10.5% $\bar{C}$, 33.3% *n*-AmOH + 56.2% aq. ⟨2⟩.

For study of $\bar{C}$ with 6 *N* aq. alc. NH_3 see ⟨3⟩.

Ⓓ **Saponification:** Hydrolysis with alk. (T 1.51) yields *n*-amyl alc. (1:6205) and acetic ac. (1:1010).

1:3276 ⟨1⟩ Lievens, *Bull. soc. chim. Belg.* **33,** 126–128 (1924). ⟨2⟩ Hannotte, *Bull. soc.chim. Belg.* **35,** 104–105 (1926). ⟨3⟩ French, Wrightsman, *J. Am. Chem. Soc.* **60,** 51 (1938).

1:3281 ETHYL α-HYDROXYISOBUTYRATE $C_6H_{12}O_3$ **Beil. III-315**

B.P. 150° **Sap. Eq. 132**

Ⓓ **Saponification:** Hydrolysis with alk. (T 1.51) yields ethyl alc. (1:6130) and α-hydroxyisobutyric ac. (1:0431).

1:3286 METHYL GLYCOLATE $C_3H_6O_3$ **Beil. III-236**

B.P. 151.2° **Sap. Eq. 90** D^{18}_{4} = **1.1677**

Ⓓ **Saponification:** Hydrolysis with alk. (T 1.51) yields methyl alc. (1:6120) and hydroxyacetic ac. (1:0430).

1:3291 METHYL *n*-CAPROATE $C_7H_{14}O_2$ **Beil. II-323**

B.P. 151.2° ⟨1⟩ **Sap. Eq. 130** D^{20} = **0.88464 ⟨1⟩** $n^{15}_{He\ (yel.)}$ = **1.40699 ⟨1⟩**
M.P. −71.0° ⟨1⟩

Ⓓ **Saponification:** Hydrolysis with alk. (T 1.51) yields methyl alc. (1:6120) and *n*-caproic ac. (1:1130).

1:3291 ⟨1⟩ Bilterys, Gisseleire, *Bull. soc. chim. Belg.* **44,** 571 (1935).

1:3296 ISOPROPYL *n*-VALERATE $C_8H_{16}O_2$ **Beil. S.N. 162**

B.P. 153.5° ⟨1⟩ **Sap. Eq. 144** D^{20}_{4} = **0.8579 ⟨1⟩** n^{20}_{D} = **1.4009 ⟨1⟩**

Ⓓ **Saponification:** Hydrolysis with alk. (T 1.51) yields isopropyl alc. (1:6135) and *n*-valeric ac. (1:1060).

1:3296 ⟨1⟩ Schjanberg, *Z. physik. Chem.* **A-178,** 276–277 (1937).

1:3303 ETHYL *d,l*-LACTATE $C_5H_{10}O_3$ **Beil. II-280**

B.P. 154.5° **Sap. Eq. 118** D^{19} = **1.0308**
D^{25}_{4} = **1.0299** n^{25}_{D} = **1.4121 ⟨1⟩**

Ⓓ **Saponification:** Hydrolysis with alk. (T 1.51) yields ethyl alc. (1:6130) and *d,l*-lactic ac. (1:0400).

1:3303 ⟨1⟩ Smith, Claborn, *Ind. Eng. Chem.* **32,** 693 (1940).

1:3308 ETHYL PYRUVATE $C_5H_8O_3$ **Beil. III-616**

B.P. 155° ⟨1⟩ **Sap. Eq. 116** $D^{15.6}_{4}$ = **1.0596** $n^{15.6}_{D}$ = **1.408**

Ⓓ **Ethyl pyruvate phenylhydrazone:** from $\bar{C}$ + phenylhydrazine, cryst. from dil. alc., m.p. 118° ⟨1⟩.

Ⓓ **Ethyl pyruvate *p*-nitrophenylhydrazone:** m.p. 185–187° ⟨2⟩.

Ⓓ **Ethyl pyruvate 2,4-dinitrophenylhydrazone:** yel. cryst. from dioxane + EtOH, m.p. 154.5–155° cor. ⟨3⟩ [cf. T 1.14].

Ⓓ **Saponification:** Hydrolysis with alk. (T 1.51) yields ethyl alc. (1:6130) and pyruvic ac. (1:1040).

1:3308 ⟨1⟩ von Braun, Leistner, Münch, *Ber.* **59,** 1953 (1926). ⟨2⟩ Malachowski, Czornodola, *Ber.* **68,** 369 (1935). ⟨3⟩ Strain, *J. Chem. Am. Soc.* **57,** 760 (1935).

1:3313 *n*-HEXYL FORMATE $C_7H_{14}O_2$ Beil. II-22

B.P. 155.5° ⟨1⟩ **Sap. Eq. 130** D^{20} = **0.88133 ⟨1⟩** $n^{15}_{He\ (yel.)}$ = **1.40898 ⟨1⟩**
M.P. −62.7° ⟨1⟩

Ⓓ **Saponification:** Hydrolysis with alk. (T 1.51) yields *n*-hexyl alc. (1:6230) and formic ac. (1:1005).

1:3313 ⟨1⟩ Bilterys, Gisseleire, *Bull. soc. chim. Belg.* **44,** 574–575 (1935).

1:3318 *n*-PROPYL ISOVALERATE $C_8H_{16}O_2$ Beil. II-312

B.P. 155.5° **Sap. Eq. 144** $D_4^{17.8}$ = **0.8643** $n_D^{17.8}$ = **1.40413**

Ⓓ **Saponification:** Hydrolysis with alk. (T 1.51) yields *n*-propyl alc. (1:6150) and isovaleric ac. (1:1050).

1:3323 β-ETHOXYETHYL ACETATE $C_6H_{12}O_3$ Beil. II-141

B.P. 156.2° **Sap. Eq. 132** D_4^{15} = **0.9810**

Ⓓ **Saponification:** Hydrolysis with alk. (T 1.51) yields ethylene glycol monoethyl ether (β-ethoxyethanol) (1:6410) and acetic ac. (1:1010).

1:3328 ISOBUTYL *n*-BUTYRATE $C_8H_{16}O_2$ Beil. II-271

B.P. 157° **Sap. Eq. 144** $D_4^{18.4}$ = **0.8634** $n_D^{18.4}$ = **1.40295**

Ⓓ **Saponification:** Hydrolysis with alk. (T 1.51) yields isobutyl alc. (1:6165) and *n*-butyric ac. (1:1035). [Cf. ⟨1⟩.]

1:3328 ⟨1⟩ Bryant, Smith, *J. Am. Chem. Soc.* **58,** 1015 (1936).

1:3333 ETHYL ETHOXYACETATE $C_6H_{12}O_3$ Beil. III-236

B.P. 158° **Sap. Eq. 132** D_4^{20} = **0.9701** n_D^{20} = **1.40292**

[For prepn. in 55–58% yield from chloroacetic ac. see ⟨1⟩.]

Ⓓ **Saponification:** Hydrolysis with alk. (T 1.51) yields ethyl alc. (1:6130) and ethoxyacetic ac. (1:1070).

1:3333 ⟨1⟩ Fuson, Nojick, *Organic Syntheses* **13,** 42–44 (1933).

1:3338 ETHYL GLYCOLATE $C_4H_8O_3$ Beil. III-236

B.P. 160° **Sap. Eq. 104** D_4^{15} = **1.0869**

Ⓓ **Saponification:** Hydrolysis with alk. (T 1.51) yields ethyl alc. (1:6130) and hydroxyacetic ac. (1:0430).

1:3343 ISOAMYL PROPIONATE $C_8H_{16}O_2$ **Beil. II-241**

B.P. 160.2° **Sap. Eq. 144** $D_{15}^{19.5}$ = **0.8580** n_D^{20} = **1.4065**

Ⓓ **Saponification:** Hydrolysis with alk. (T 1.51) yields isoamyl alc. (1:6200) and propionic ac. (1:1025).

1:3348 CYCLOHEXYL FORMATE $C_9H_{12}O_2$ **Beil. VI-6**

B.P. 162.5°$_{750}$ **Sap. Eq. 128** D_4^0 = **1.0057**

Ⓓ **Saponification:** Hydrolysis with alk. (T 1.51) yields cyclohexanol (1:6415) and formic ac. (1:1005).

1:3353 *n*-PROPYL *n*-VALERATE $C_8H_{16}O_2$ **Beil. II-301**

B.P. 166.2° ⟨1⟩ **Sap. Eq. 144** D_4^{20} = **0.8699** ⟨2⟩ n_D^{20} = **1.4065** ⟨2⟩
M.P. −70.7° ⟨1⟩ D_4^{15} = **0.8741** ⟨1⟩ n_D^{15} = **1.4087** ⟨1⟩

Ⓓ **Saponification:** Hydrolysis with alk. (T 1.51) yields *n*-propyl alc. (1:6150) and *n*-valeric ac. (1:1060).

1:3353 ⟨1⟩ Lievens, *Bull. soc. chim. Belg.* **33,** 126–128 (1924). ⟨2⟩ Schjanberg, *Z. physik. Chem.* **A-178,** 276–277 (1937).

1:3358 *n*-BUTYL *n*-BUTYRATE $C_8H_{16}O_2$ **Beil. II-271**

B.P. 166.6° ⟨1⟩ **Sap. Eq. 144** D_4^{15} = **0.8712** ⟨1⟩ n_D^{15} = **1.4087** ⟨1⟩
M.P. −91.5° ⟨1⟩

Ⓓ **Saponification:** Hydrolysis with alk. (T 1.51) yields *n*-butyl alc. (1:6180) and *n*-butyric ac. (1:1035). [Cf. ⟨2⟩.]

1:3358 ⟨1⟩ Lievens, *Bull. soc. chim. Belg.* **33,** 126–128 (1924). ⟨2⟩ Bryant, Smith, *J. Am. Chem. Soc.* **58,** 1015 (1936).

1:3363 ETHYL *n*-CAPROATE $C_8H_{16}O_2$ **Beil. II-323**

B.P. 167.9° ⟨1⟩ **Sap. Eq. 144** D_4^{20} = **0.8710** ⟨2⟩ ⟨1⟩ n_D^{20} = **1.40727** ⟨2⟩
M.P. −67.5° ⟨1⟩ D_4^{25} = **0.8663** ⟨2⟩ n_D^{25} = **1.40530** ⟨2⟩ ⟨1⟩

Ⓓ **Saponification:** Hydrolysis with alk. (T 1.51) yields ethyl alc. (1:6130) and *n*-caproic ac. (1:1130).

1:3363 ⟨1⟩ Simon, *Bull. soc. chim. Belg.* **38,** 56–59 (1929). ⟨2⟩ Kao, Ma, *Science Repts. Natl. Tsing Hua, Univ.*, Ser. **A-1,** 181–183 (1932).

1:3368 ISOPROPYL *d,l*-LACTATE $C_6H_{12}O_3$ **Beil. III-282**

B.P. 166-168° **Sap. Eq. 132** D_{20}^{20} = **0.998** n_D^{25} = **1.4082** ⟨2⟩

[For prepn. from isopropyl alc. + lactic ac. see ⟨1⟩.]

Ⓓ **Saponification:** Hydrolysis with alk. (T 1.51) yields isopropyl alc. (1:6135) and *d,l*-lactic ac. (1:0400).

1:3368 ⟨1⟩ McDermott, *Organic Syntheses* **10,** 88–89 (1930). ⟨2⟩ Smith, Claborn, *Ind. Eng. Chem.* **32,** 693 (1940).

1:3373 DI-*n*-PROPYL CARBONATE $C_7H_{14}O_3$ **Beil. III-6**

B.P. 168.5° cor. ⟨1⟩ **Sap. Eq. 146** D_4^{20} = **0.9411** ⟨1⟩ n_D^{20} = **1.4014** ⟨1⟩

Ⓓ **Saponification:** Hydrolysis with alk. (T 1.51) yields *n*-propyl alc. (1:6150) and carbonic ac.

1:3373 ⟨1⟩ Kogerman, Kranig, *Cent.* **1927,** I, 2408.

1:3378 ***n*-AMYL PROPIONATE** $C_8H_{16}O_2$ **Beil. S.N. 162**

B.P. 168.7° ⟨1⟩ **Sap. Eq. 144** D_4^{15} **= 0.8761 ⟨1⟩** n_D^{15} **= 1.4096 ⟨1⟩**
M.P. −73.1° ⟨1⟩

Ⓓ **Saponification:** Hydrolysis with alk. (T 1.51) yields *n*-amyl alc. (1:6205) and propionic ac. (1:1025).

1:3378 ⟨1⟩ Lievens, *Bull. soc. chim. Belg.* **33,** 126–128 (1924).

1:3383 **ETHYLIDENE DIACETATE** $C_6H_{10}O_4$ **Beil. II-152**

B.P. 169° **Sap. Eq. 73** D^{12} **= 1.061**

Ⓓ **Saponification:** Hydrolysis with alk. (T 1.51) yields acetaldehyde (1:0100) and acetic ac. (1:1010). [The resultant acetaldehyde may undergo further condensation with itself in alk. soln.]

1:3388 **ISOAMYL ISOBUTYRATE** $C_9H_{18}O_2$ **Beil. II-291**

B.P. 169° **Sap. Eq. 158** D_4^0 **= 0.8760**

Ⓓ **Saponification:** Hydrolysis with alk. (T 1.51) yields isoamyl alc. (1:6200) and isobutyric ac. (1:1030).

—— **METHYL ACETOACETATE** $C_5H_8O_3$ **Beil. III-632**

B.P. 170° D_4^0 **= 1.0765** n_D^{20} **= 1.41964**

See 1:1705. Genus 4: Phenols.

1:3393 **ISOBUTYL ISOVALERATE** $C_9H_{18}O_2$ **Beil. II-312**

B.P. 171° **Sap. Eq. 158** D^{20} **= 0.8534** n_D^{20} **= 1.40569**

Ⓓ **Saponification:** Hydrolysis with alk. (T 1.51) yields isobutyl alc. (1:6165) and isovaleric ac. (1:1050).

1:3398 **METHYL ENANTHATE** $C_8H_{16}O_2$ **Beil. II-339**
(Methyl *n*-heptylate)

B.P. 173.8° ⟨1⟩ **Sap. Eq. 144** D^{20} **= 0.88011 ⟨1⟩** $n_{He\ (yel.)}^{15}$ **= 1.41334 ⟨1⟩**
M.P. −55.8° ⟨1⟩

Ⓓ **Saponification:** Hydrolysis with alk. (T 1.51) yields methyl alc. (1:6120) and enanthic ac. (1:1140).

1:3398 ⟨1⟩ Bilterys, Gisseleire, *Bull. soc. chim. Belg.* **44,** 572 (1935).

1:3402 **ETHYLENE GLYCOL DIFORMATE** $C_4H_6O_4$ **Beil. II-23**

B.P. 174° **Sap. Eq. 59** D^0 **= 1.193**

Ⓓ **Saponification:** Hydrolysis with alk. (T 1.51) yields ethylene glycol (1:6465) and formic ac. (1:1005).

1:3407 ***sec*-BUTYL *n*-VALERATE** $C_9H_{18}O_2$ **Beil. S.N. 162**

B.P. 174.5° ⟨1⟩ **Sap. Eq. 158** D_4^{20} **= 0.8605 ⟨1⟩** n_D^{20} **= 1.4081 ⟨1⟩**

Ⓓ **Saponification:** Hydrolysis with alk. (T 1.51) yields *sec*-butyl alc. (1:6155) and *n*-valeric ac. (1:1060).

1:3407 ⟨1⟩ Schjanberg, *Z. physik. Chem.* **A-178,** 276–277 (1937).

1:3412 CYCLOHEXYL ACETATE $C_8H_{14}O_2$ **Beil. VI-7**

B.P. 175° **Sap. Eq. 142** D_4^0 = **0.9854**

Ⓓ **Saponification:** Hydrolysis with alk. (T 1.51) yields cyclohexanol (1:6415) and acetic ac. (1:1010). [Cf. ⟨1⟩.]

1:3412 ⟨1⟩ Bryant, Smith, *J. Am. Chem. Soc.* **58,** 1015 (1936).

1:3417 FURFURYL ACETATE $C_7H_8O_3$ **Beil. XVII-112**

B.P. 175-177° **Sap. Eq. 140** D_{20}^{20} = **1.1175**

[For prepn. (87–93% yield) from furfuryl alc. (1:6425), Ac_2O + NaOAc see ⟨1⟩.]

Ⓓ **Saponification:** Hydrolysis with alk. (T 1.51) yields furfuryl alc. (1:6425) and acetic ac. (1:1010).

1:3417 ⟨1⟩ Miner Laboratories, *Organic Syntheses, Coll. Vol.* I, 279–280 (1932).

—— METHYL METHYLACETOACETATE $C_6H_{10}O_3$ **Beil. III-679**

B.P. 177.4° D_{25}^{25} = **1.0247** $n_D^{23.3}$ = **1.416**

See 1:1708. Genus 4: Phenols.

1:3422 *n*-HEPTYL FORMATE $C_8H_{16}O_2$ **Beil. S.N. 159**

B.P. 178.1° ⟨1⟩ **Sap. Eq. 144** D^{20} = **0.87841 ⟨1⟩** $n_{He\ (yel.)}^{15}$ = **1.41505 ⟨1⟩**

Ⓓ **Saponification:** Hydrolysis with alk. (T 1.51) yields *n*-heptyl alc. (1:6240) and formic ac. (1:1005).

1:3422 ⟨1⟩ Bilterys, Gisseleire, *Bull. soc. chim. Belg.* **44,** 576–577 (1935).

1:3427 *n*-HEXYL ACETATE $C_8H_{16}O_2$ **Beil. S.N. 159**

B.P. 178.1° ⟨1⟩ **Sap. Eq. 144** D^{20} = **0.87336 ⟨1⟩** $n_{He\ (yel.)}^{15}$ = **1.41122 ⟨1⟩**
M.P. −80.9° ⟨1⟩

Ⓓ **Saponification:** Hydrolysis with alk. (T 1.51) yields *n*-hexyl alc. (1:6230) and acetic ac. (1:1010).

1:3427 ⟨1⟩ Bilterys, Gisseleire, *Bull. soc. chim. Belg.* **44,** 574–575 (1935).

1:3432 ISOAMYL *n*-BUTYRATE $C_9H_{18}O_2$ **Beil. II-271**

B.P. 178.6° **Sap. Eq. 158** D_{15}^{19} = **0.8657**

Ⓓ **Saponification:** Hydrolysis with alk. (T 1.51) yields isoamyl alc. (1:6200) and *n*-butyric ac. (1:1035).

1:3437 ETHYL ACETYLGLYCOLATE $C_6H_{10}O_4$ **Beil. III-237**

B.P. 179° **Sap. Eq. 73** D^{17} = **1.0993**

Ⓓ **Saponification:** Hydrolysis with alk. (T 1.51) yields ethyl alc. (1:6130), acetic ac. (1:1010) and glycolic ac. (1:0430).

1:3442 ISOBUTYL *n*-VALERATE $C_9H_{18}O_2$ **Beil. S.N. 162**

B.P. 179.0° ⟨1⟩ **Sap. Eq. 158** D_4^{20} = **0.8625 ⟨1⟩** n_D^{20} = **1.4099 ⟨1⟩**

Ⓓ **Saponification:** Hydrolysis with alk. (T 1.51) yields isobutyl alc. (1:6165) and *n*-valeric ac. (1:1060).

1:3442 ⟨1⟩ Schjanberg, *Z. physik. Chem.* **A-178,** 276–277 (1937).

1:3447 ETHYLENE GLYCOL MONOFORMATE $C_3H_6O_3$ **Beil. II-23**
(β-Hydroxyethyl formate)

B.P. 180° **Sap. Eq. 90** D_4^{15} = **1.1989**

Ⓓ **Saponification:** Hydrolysis with alk. (T 1.51) yields ethylene glycol (1:6465) and formic ac. (1:1005).

—— ETHYL METHYLACETOACETATE $C_7H_{12}O_3$ **Beil. III-679**

B.P. 180.8° cor. D_4^{20} = **1.0191** $n_D^{15.3}$ = **1.42178**

See 1:1712. Genus 4: Phenols.

—— ETHYL ACETOACETATE $C_6H_{10}O_3$ **Beil. III-632**

B.P. 181° D_4^{20} = **1.025** n_D^{20} = **1.41976**

See 1:1710. Genus 4: Phenols.

1:3452 METHYL PYROMUCATE $C_6H_6O_3$ **Beil. XVIII-274**
(Methyl furoate)

B.P. 181.3° **Sap. Eq. 126** $D_4^{21.4}$ = **1.1786** n_D^{20} = **1.4860**

Ⓓ **Saponification:** Hydrolysis with alk. (T 1.51) yields methyl alc. (1:6120) and furoic ac. (1:0475).

1:3457 DIMETHYL MALONATE $C_5H_8O_4$ **Beil. II-572**
(" Methyl malonate ")

B.P. 181.5° **Sap. Eq. 66** D_4^{20} = **1.1539** n_D^{20} = **1.41398**

Ⓓ **Saponification:** Hydrolysis with alk. (T 1.51) yields methyl alc. (1:6120) and malonic ac. (1:0480).

1:3462 ETHYL β-METHOXYETHYL CARBONATE $C_6H_{12}O_4$ **Beil. S.N. 199**

B.P. 182.6° ⟨1⟩ **Sap. Eq. 148** D_4^{25} = **1.0424 ⟨1⟩** n_D^{25} = **1.4036 ⟨1⟩**

Ⓓ **Saponification:** Hydrolysis with alk. (T 1.51) yields ethyl alc. (1:6130), ethylene glycol monomethyl ether (1:6405) and CO_2. [Cf. ⟨1⟩.]

1:3462 ⟨1⟩ Drake, Carter, *J. Am. Chem. Soc.* **52,** 3722 (1930).

1:3467 METHYL CYCLOHEXANECARBOXYLATE $C_8H_{14}O_2$ **Beil. IX-8**
(Methyl hexahydrobenzoate)

B.P. 183° **Sap. Eq. 142** D_4^{15} = **0.9954** n_D^{15} = **1.45372**

Ⓓ **Saponification:** Hydrolysis with alk. (T 1.51) yields methyl alc. (1:6120) and cyclohexanecarboxylic ac. (1:0575).

—— DIETHYL OXALATE $C_6H_{10}O_4$ **Beil. II-535**

B.P. 186° **Sap. Eq. 73** D_4^{20} = **1.0785** n_D^{20} = **1.41043**

See 1:1055. Genus 3: Acids.

1:3476 n-AMYL n-BUTYRATE $C_9H_{18}O_2$ **Beil. II-271**

B.P. 186.4° ⟨1⟩ **Sap. Eq. 158** D_4^{15} = **0.8713 ⟨1⟩** n_D^{15} = **1.4139 ⟨1⟩**
M.P. −73.2° ⟨1⟩

Ⓓ **Saponification:** Hydrolysis with alk. (T 1.51) yields *n*-amyl alc. (1:6205) and *n*-butyric ac. (1:1035).

1:3476 ⟨1⟩ Lievens, *Bull. soc. chim. Belg.* **33,** 126–128 (1924).

1:3481 n-BUTYL n-VALERATE $C_9H_{18}O_2$ **Beil. II-301**

B.P. 186.9° ⟨1⟩ **Sap. Eq. 158** D_4^{20} = **0.8678 ⟨2⟩** n_D^{20} = **1.4123 ⟨2⟩**
M.P. −92.8° ⟨1⟩ D_4^{15} = **0.8700 ⟨1⟩** n_D^{15} = **1.4126 ⟨1⟩**

Ⓓ **Saponification:** Hydrolysis with alk. (T 1.51) yields *n*-butyl alc. (1:6180) and *n*-valeric ac. (1:1060).

1:3481 ⟨1⟩ Lievens, *Bull. soc. chim. Belg.* **33,** 126–128 (1924). ⟨2⟩ Schjanberg, *Z. physik. Chem.* **A-178,** 276–277 (1937).

1:3486 ETHYLENE GLYCOL MONOACETATE $C_4H_8O_3$ **Beil. II-141**
(β-Hydroxyethyl acetate)

B.P. 187-189° **Sap. Eq. 104**

Ⓓ **Saponification:** Hydrolysis with alk. (T 1.51) yields ethylene glycol (1:6465) and acetic ac. (1:1010).

1:3491 n-PROPYL n-CAPROATE $C_9H_{18}O_2$ **Beil. II-323**

B.P. 187.2° ⟨1⟩ **Sap. Eq. 158** D^{20} = **0.86719 ⟨1⟩** $n_{He\ (yel.)}^{15}$ = **1.41401 ⟨1⟩**
M.P. −74.0° ⟨1⟩

Ⓓ **Saponification:** Hydrolysis with alk. (T 1.51) yields *n*-propyl alc. (1:6150) and *n*-caproic ac. (1:1130).

1:3491 ⟨1⟩ Bilterys, Gisseleire, *Bull. soc. chim. Belg.* **44,** 571 (1935).

1:3496 ETHYL ENANTHATE $C_9H_{18}O_2$ **Beil. II-340**
(Ethyl *n*-heptylate)

B.P. 188.6° ⟨1⟩ **Sap. Eq. 158** D^{20} = **0.86856 ⟨1⟩** $n_{He\ (yel.)}^{15}$ = **1.41537 ⟨1⟩**
M.P. −66.3° ⟨1⟩

Ⓓ **Saponification:** Hydrolysis with alk. (T 1.51) yields ethyl alc. (1:6130) and enanthic ac. (1:1140).

1:3496 ⟨1⟩ Bilterys, Gisseleire, *Bull. soc. chim. Belg.* **44,** 572 (1935).

—— METHYL ETHYLACETOACETATE $C_7H_{12}O_3$ **Beil. III-691**

B.P. 189.7° cor. D^{14} = **0.995**

See 1:1718. Genus 4: Phenols.

1:3501 DIISOBUTYL CARBONATE $C_9H_{18}O_3$ **Beil. III-6**

B.P. 189.8° cor. **⟨1⟩** **Sap. Eq. 174** D_4^{20} = **0.9138 ⟨1⟩** n_D^{20} = **1.4072 ⟨1⟩**

Ⓓ **Saponification:** Hydrolysis with alk. (T 1.51) yields isobutyl alc. (1:6165) and carbonic ac.

1:3501 ⟨1⟩ Kogerman, Kranig, *Cent.* **1927,** I, 2408.

1:3506 n-HEXYL PROPIONATE $C_9H_{18}O_2$ **Beil. S.N. 162**

B.P. 190.0° ⟨1⟩ **Sap. Eq. 158** D^{20} = **0.86980 ⟨1⟩** $n^{15}_{He\ (yel.)}$ = **1.41621 ⟨1⟩**
M.P. −57.5° ⟨1⟩

Ⓓ **Saponification:** Hydrolysis with alk. (T 1.51) yields *n*-hexyl alc. (1:6230) and propionic ac. (1:1025).

1:3506 ⟨1⟩ Bilterys, Gisseleire, *Bull. soc. chim. Belg.* **44,** 574–575 (1935).

1:3511 ETHYLENE GLYCOL DIACETATE $C_6H_{10}O_4$ **Beil. II-142**

B.P. 190.2° ⟨1⟩ **Sap. Eq. 73** D^{20}_4 = **1.1040 ⟨1⟩** n^{20}_D = **1.4150 ⟨1⟩**
M.P. −31° ⟨1⟩

Ⓓ **Saponification:** Hydrolysis with alk. (T 1.51) yields ethylene glycol (1:6465) and acetic ac. (1:1010).

1:3511 ⟨1⟩ Taylor, Rinkenbach, *J. Am. Chem. Soc.* **48,** 1305–1309 (1926).

1:3516 ISOAMYL ISOVALERATE $C_{10}H_{20}O_2$ **Beil. II-312**

B.P. 190.4° **Sap. Eq. 172** $D^{18.7}_4$ = **0.8583** $n^{18.7}_D$ = **1.41300**

Ⓓ **Saponification:** Hydrolysis with alk. (T 1.51) yields isoamyl alc. (1:6200) and isovaleric ac. (1:1050).

1:3521 n-HEPTYL ACETATE $C_9H_{18}O_2$ **Beil. II-134**

B.P. 192.5° ⟨1⟩ **Sap. Eq. 158** D^{15} = **0.87070 ⟨1⟩** $n^{15}_{He\ (yel.)}$ = **1.41653 ⟨1⟩**
M.P. −50.2° ⟨1⟩

Ⓓ **Saponification:** Hydrolysis with alk. (T 1.51) yields *n*-heptyl alc. (1:6240) and acetic ac. (1:1010).

1:3521 ⟨1⟩ Bilterys, Gisseleire, *Bull. soc. chim. Belg.* **44,** 576–577 (1935).

1:3526 CYCLOHEXYL PROPIONATE $C_9H_{16}O_2$ **Beil. VI₁-(6)**

B.P. 193°_{750} **Sap. Eq. 156** D^0_4 = **0.9718**

Ⓓ **Saponification:** Hydrolysis with alk. (T 1.51) yields cyclohexanol (1:6415) and propionic ac. (1:1025).

—— DIMETHYL FUMARATE $C_6H_8O_4$ **Beil. II-741**

B.P. 193.3° **Sap. Eq. 72**
See 1:2415. Genus 5: Esters. **M.P. 101.7°.**

1:3531 DIISOPROPYL OXALATE $C_8H_{14}O_4$ **Beil. II-539**

B.P. 193-194° ⟨1⟩ **Sap. Eq. 87** D^{20}_4 = **1.0097 ⟨1⟩** n^{20}_D = **1.4100 ⟨1⟩**
D^{25}_4 = **0.99635 ⟨1⟩** n^{25}_D = **1.4072 ⟨1⟩**

$\bar{C}$ in alc. stood overnight at 0° with 1 mole conc. aq. NH_4OH yields isopropyl oxamate, cryst. from MeOH or EtOH, m.p. 86–87° ⟨1⟩.

Ⓓ **Saponification:** Hydrolysis with alk. (T 1.51) yields isopropyl alc. (1:6135) and oxalic ac. (1:0445).

1:3531 ⟨1⟩ Sah, Chien, *J. Am. Chem. Soc.* **53,** 3902 (1931).

1:3536 ETHYL β-ETHOXYETHYL CARBONATE $C_7H_{14}O_4$ **Beil. S.N. 199**

B.P. 194.5° ⟨1⟩ **Sap. Eq. 162** D_4^{25} = **1.0115 ⟨1⟩** n_D^{25} = **1.5064 ⟨1⟩**

Ⓓ **Saponification:** Hydrolysis with alk. (T 1.51) yields ethyl alc. (1:6130), ethylene glycol monoethyl ether (1:6410), and CO_2. [Cf. ⟨1⟩.]

1:3536 ⟨1⟩ Drake, Carter, *J. Am. Chem. Soc.* **52,** 3722 (1930).

1:3541 *sec*-OCTYL ACETATE $C_{10}H_{20}O_2$ **Beil. II-134**
(*n*-Hexyl-methyl-carbinyl acetate)

B.P. 194.5° **Sap. Eq. 172** D_4^{19} = **0.8606** n_D^{20} = **1.4141**

Ⓓ **Saponification:** Hydrolysis with alk. (T 1.51) yields octanol-2 (1:6245) and acetic ac. (1:1010).

1:3546 METHYL *n*-CAPRYLATE $C_9H_{18}O_2$ **Beil. II-348**

B.P. 194.6° ⟨1⟩ **Sap. Eq. 158** D_0^0 = **0.8942** n_D^{45} = **1.4069 ⟨2⟩**
F.P. −41°

Ⓓ **Saponification:** Hydrolysis with alk. (T 1.51) yields methyl alc. (1:6120) and *n*-caprylic ac. (1:1145).

1:3546 ⟨1⟩ Kohlrausch, Köppl, Pongratz, *Z. physik. Chem.* **B-22,** 372 (1933). ⟨2⟩ Wyman, Barkenbus, *Ind. Eng. Chem., Anal. Ed.* **12,** 658–661 (1940).

1:3551 α-TETRAHYDROFURFURYL ACETATE $C_7H_{12}O_3$ **Beil. S.N. 2380**

B.P. 195° ⟨1⟩ **Sap. Eq. 144** D_0^{20} = **1.061 ⟨1⟩** n_D^{25} = **1.4350 ⟨2⟩**
Misc. with aq. D_4^{25} = **1.0624 ⟨2⟩**

Ⓓ **Saponification:** Hydrolysis with alk. (T 1.51) yields tetrahydrofurfuryl alc. (1:6445) and acetic ac. (1:1010).

1:3551 ⟨1⟩ Zanetti, *J. Am. Chem. Soc.* **50,** 1821–1822 (1928). ⟨2⟩ Burdick, Adkins, *J. Am. Chem. Soc.* **56,** 441 (1934).

1:3556 DIMETHYL SUCCINATE $C_6H_{10}O_4$ **Beil. II-609**

B.P. 196.0° ⟨1⟩ **Sap. Eq. 73** D_4^{20} = **1.1192 ⟨2⟩** n_D^{20} = **1.41965 ⟨2⟩**
M.P. 18.2° ⟨1⟩

Ⓓ **Saponification:** Hydrolysis with alk. (T 1.51) yields methyl alc. (1:6120) and succinic ac. (1:0530).

1:3556 ⟨1⟩ Viseur, *Bull. soc. chim. Belg.* **35,** 428 (1926). ⟨2⟩ Vogel, *J. Chem. Soc.* **1934,** 338.

1:3561 METHYL LEVULINATE $C_6H_{10}O_3$ **Beil. III-675**

B.P. 196.0° ⟨1⟩ **Sap. Eq. 130** D_4^{20} = **1.04945 ⟨1⟩** n_D^{20} = **1.42333 ⟨1⟩**

Ⓓ **Methyl levulinate semicarbazone:** m.p. 142–143° ⟨2⟩.

Ⓓ **Methyl levulinate phenylhydrazone:** m.p. 94–96° ⟨2⟩.

Ⓓ **Methyl levulinate 2,4-dinitrophenylhydrazone:** YO cryst. from dioxane + alc. or from $CHCl_3$; m.p. 141.5–142.5° cor. ⟨3⟩ ⟨4⟩ [cf. T 1.14].

Ⓓ **Saponification:** Hydrolysis with alk. (T 1.51) yields methyl alc. (1:6120) and levulinic ac. (1:0405).

1:3561 ⟨1⟩ Cox, Dodds, *J. Am. Chem. Soc.* **55,** 3393 (1933). ⟨2⟩ Sah, Ma, *J. Am. Chem. Soc.* **52,** 4882–4883 (1930). ⟨3⟩ Strain, *J. Am. Chem. Soc.* **57,** 760 (1935). ⟨4⟩ Cowley, Schuette, *J. Am. Chem. Soc.* **55,** 3464 (1933).

1:3566 ETHYL CYCLOHEXANECARBOXYLATE $C_9H_{16}O_2$ **Beil. IX-8**
(Ethyl hexahydrobenzoate)

B.P. 196° **Sap. Eq. 156** $D_4^{15} = 0.9672$ $n_D^{15} = 1.45012$

Ⓓ **Saponification:** Hydrolysis with alk. (T 1.51) yields ethyl alc. (1:6130) and cyclohexanecarboxylic ac. (1:0575).

1:3571 PHENYL ACETATE $C_8H_8O_2$ **Beil. VI-152**

B.P. 196.7° **Sap. Eq. 136** $D_{15}^{15} = 1.0809$ $n_D^{20} = 1.503$

Ⓓ **Saponification:** Hydrolysis with alk. (T 1.51) yields phenol (1:1420) and acetic ac. (1:1010).

—— ETHYL PYROMUCATE $C_7H_8O_3$ **Beil. XVIII-275**

B.P. 197° **Sap. Eq. 140**

See 1:2082. Genus 5: Esters. M.P. 34°.

—— ETHYL ETHYLACETOACETATE $C_8H_{14}O_3$ **Beil. III-691**

B.P. 198° $D_4^{20} = 0.9856$ $n_D^{18.7} = 1.42256$

See 1:1723. Genus 4: Phenols.

1:3576 *n*-OCTYL FORMATE $C_9H_{18}O_2$ **Beil. II-22**

B.P. 198.8° ⟨1⟩ **Sap. Eq. 158** $D^{20} = 0.87435$ ⟨1⟩ $n_{He\ (yel.)}^{15} = 1.42082$ ⟨1⟩
M.P. −39.1° ⟨1⟩

Ⓓ **Saponification:** Hydrolysis with alk. (T 1.51) yields *n*-octyl alc. (1:6255) and formic ac. (1:1005).

1:3576 ⟨1⟩ Bilterys, Gisseleire, *Bull. soc. chim. Belg.* **44,** 578–579 (1935).

1:3581 DIETHYL MALONATE $C_7H_{12}O_4$ **Beil. II-573**

B.P. 199.3° ⟨1⟩ **Sap. Eq. 80** $D_4^{20} = 1.05513$ ⟨1⟩ $n_D^{20} = 1.41618$
M.P. −51.5° ⟨1⟩

Ⓓ **Saponification:** Hydrolysis with alk. (T 1.51) yields ethyl alc. (1:5130) and malonic ac. (1:0480).

1:3581 ⟨1⟩ Timmermans, Delcourt, *J. chim. phys.* **31,** 112–113 (1934).

1:3586 METHYL BENZOATE $C_8H_8O_2$ **Beil. IX-109**

B.P. 199.6° **Sap. Eq. 136** $D_4^{15} = 1.0937$ $n_D^{20} = 1.5164$
M.P. −12.5°

Ⓓ **Saponification:** Hydrolysis with alk. (T 1.51) yields methyl alc. (1:6120) and benzoic ac. (1:0715).

1:3591 DIMETHYL MESACONATE $C_7H_{10}O_4$ **Beil. II-765**

B.P. 203.0° ⟨1⟩ **Sap. Eq. 79** $D_4^{20} = 1.0914$ ⟨1⟩ $n_D^{20} = 1.45119$ ⟨1⟩

$\bar{C}$ in alc. treated with hydrazine hydrate yields mesaconic dihydrazide, cryst. from dil. alc., m.p. 215° dec. ⟨2⟩.

Ⓓ **Saponification:** Hydrolysis with alk. (T 1.51) yields methyl alc. (1:6120) and mesaconic ac. (1:0548).

1:3591 ⟨1⟩ van de Straete, *Bull. soc. chim. Belg.* **44,** 318–319 (1935). ⟨2⟩ Freri, *Gazz. chim. ital.* **66,** 26 (1936).

1:3596 BENZYL FORMATE $C_8H_8O_2$ **Beil. VI-435**

B.P. 203° **Sap. Eq. 136** $D_4^{17.2} = 1.083$ $n_D^{19.9} = 1.51537$

Ⓓ **Saponification:** Hydrolysis with alk. (T 1.51) yields benzyl alc. (1:6480) and formic ac. (1:1005).

1:3601 CYCLOHEXYL ISOBUTYRATE $C_{10}H_{18}O_2$ **Beil. VI₁-(6)**

B.P. 204°_{750} **Sap. Eq. 170** $D_4^0 = 0.9489$

Ⓓ **Saponification:** Hydrolysis with alk. (T 1.51) yields cyclohexanol (1:6415) and isobutyric ac. (1:1030).

1:3606 DIMETHYL MALEATE $C_6H_8O_4$ **Beil. II-751**

B.P. 204.4° ⟨1⟩ **Sap. Eq. 72** $D_4^{15} = 1.14513$ ⟨1⟩ $n_D^{19.9} = 1.44156$
M.P. +7.6° ⟨1⟩

[For m.p. + compn. data on system: $\bar{C}$ + dimethyl fumarate (1:2415) see ⟨2⟩.]

Ⓓ **Saponification:** Hydrolysis with alk. (T 1.51) yields methyl alc. (1:6120) and maleic ac. (1:0470).

1:3606 ⟨1⟩ Viseur, *Bull. soc. chim. Belg.* **35,** 428 (1926). ⟨2⟩ Ref. 1, page 431.

1:3611 α-TETRAHYDROFURFURYL PROPIONATE $C_8H_{14}O_3$ **Beil. S.N. 2380**

B.P. 204-207° ⟨1⟩ **Sap. Eq. 158** $D_4^{20} = 1.044$ ⟨1⟩

Ⓓ **Saponification:** Hydrolysis with alk. (T 1.51) yields tetrahydrofurfuryl alc. (1:6445) and propionic ac. (1:1025).

1:3611 ⟨1⟩ Zanetti, *J. Am. Chem. Soc.* **50,** 1822 (1928).

1:3616 ETHYL LEVULINATE $C_7H_{12}O_3$ **Beil. III-675**

B.P. 205.8° ⟨1⟩ **Sap. Eq. 144** $D_4^{20} = 1.01114$ ⟨1⟩ $n_D^{20} = 1.42288$ ⟨1⟩

Ⓓ **Ethyl levulinate semicarbazone:** m.p. 147–148° ⟨2⟩.

Ⓓ **Ethyl levulinate phenylhydrazone:** m.p. 103–104° ⟨2⟩.

Ⓓ **Ethyl levulinate 2,4-dinitrophenylhydrazone:** OY cryst. from dioxane + EtOH; m.p. 101–102° ⟨3⟩ ⟨4⟩. [Cf. T 1.14.]

Ⓓ **Saponification:** Hydrolysis with alk. (T 1.51) yields ethyl alc. (1:6130) and levulinic ac. (1:0405).

1:3616 ⟨1⟩ Cox, Dodds, *J. Am. Chem. Soc.* **55,** 3393 (1933). ⟨2⟩ Sah, Ma, *J. Am. Chem. Soc.* **52,** 4882–4883 (1930). ⟨3⟩ Strain, *J. Am. Chem. Soc.* **57,** 760 (1935). ⟨4⟩ Cowley, Schuette, *J. Am. Chem. Soc.* **55,** 3464 (1933).

—— **ETHYL ALLYLACETOACETATE** $C_9H_{14}O_3$ **Beil. III-738**

B.P. 206° sl. dec. $D_4^{20} = 0.9898$ $n_D^{17.6} = 1.43875$
(211-212°) sl. dec.

See **1:1738** Genus 4: Phenols.

1:3621 *n*-AMYL *n*-VALERATE $C_{10}H_{20}O_2$ **Beil. II-301**

B.P. 207.4° ⟨1⟩ **Sap. Eq. 172** $D_4^0 = 0.8825$ ⟨1⟩ $n_D^{15} = 1.4181$ ⟨1⟩

Ⓓ **Saponification:** Hydrolysis with alk. (T 1.51) yields *n*-amyl alc. (1:6205) and *n*-valeric ac. (1:1060).

1:3621 ⟨1⟩ Lievens, *Bull. soc. chim. Belg.* **33,** 126–128 (1924).

1:3626 DI-*n*-BUTYL CARBONATE $C_9H_{18}O_3$ **Beil. III-6**

B.P. 207.5° cor. ⟨1⟩ **Sap. Eq. 174** D_4^{20} = **0.9238** ⟨1⟩ n_D^{20} = **1.4117** ⟨1⟩

Ⓓ **Saponification:** Hydrolysis with alk. (T 1.51) yields *n*-butyl alc. (1:6180) and CO_2.

1:3626 ⟨1⟩ Kogerman, Kranig, *Cent.* **1927,** I, 2408.

1:3631 *n*-BUTYL *n*-CAPROATE $C_{10}H_{20}O_2$ **Beil. II-323**

B.P. 207.7° ⟨1⟩ **Sap. Eq. 172** D^{20} = **0.86530** ⟨1⟩ $n_{He\ (yel.)}^{15}$ = **1.41877** ⟨1⟩
M.P. −63.1° ⟨1⟩

Ⓓ **Saponification:** Hydrolysis with alk. (T 1.51) yields *n*-butyl alc. (1:6180) and *n*-caproic ac. (1:1130).

1:3631 ⟨1⟩ Bilterys, Gisseleire, *Bull. soc. chim. Belg.* **44,** 571 (1935).

1:3636 *n*-HEXYL *n*-BUTYRATE $C_{10}H_{20}O_2$ **Beil. II-272**

B.P. 207.9° ⟨1⟩ **Sap. Eq. 172** D^{20} = **0.86519** ⟨1⟩ $n_{He\ (yel.)}^{15}$ = **1.41875** ⟨1⟩
M.P. −78.0° ⟨1⟩

Ⓓ **Saponification:** Hydrolysis with alk. (T 1.51) yields *n*-hexyl alc. (1:6230) and *n*-butyric ac. (1:1035).

1:3636 ⟨1⟩ Bilterys, Gisseleire, *Bull. soc. chim. Belg.* **44,** 574–575 (1935).

1:3641 DIMETHYL ITACONATE $C_7H_{10}O_4$ **Beil. II-762**

B.P. 208° **Sap. Eq. 79** D_4^{18} = **1.12410** n_D^{20} = **1.44413**
M.P. 38°

C̄ in alc. treated with hydrazine hydrate (50%) yields itaconic dihydrazide, cryst. from alc. m.p. 150° ⟨1⟩.

Ⓓ **Saponification:** Hydrolysis with alk. (T 1.51) yields methyl alc. (1:6120) and itaconic ac. (1:0515). [Note: alc. alk. isomerizes C̄ to dimethyl citraconate (1:3686).]

1:3641 ⟨1⟩ Freri, *Gazz. chim. ital.* **66,** 25 (1936).

1:3646 *o*-TOLYL ACETATE $C_9H_{10}O_2$ **Beil. VI-355**
(" *o*-Cresyl " acetate)

B.P. 208° **Sap. Eq. 150**

Ⓓ **Saponification:** Hydrolysis with alk. (T 1.51) yields *o*-cresol (1:1400) and acetic ac. (1:1010).

1:3651 *n*-PROPYL *n*-ENANTHATE $C_{10}H_{20}O_2$ **Beil. II-340**
(*n*-Propyl *n*-heptylate)

B.P. 208.0° ⟨1⟩ **Sap. Eq. 172** D^{20} = **0.86556** ⟨1⟩ $n_{He\ (yel.)}^{15}$ = **1.41894** ⟨1⟩
M.P. −64.8° ⟨1⟩ D_4^{15} = **0.8682** ⟨2⟩ n_D^{15} = **1.41835** ⟨2⟩

Ⓓ **Saponification:** Hydrolysis with alk. (T 1.51) yields *n*-propyl alc. (1:6150) and enanthic (*n*-heptylic) ac. (1:1140).

1:3651 ⟨1⟩ Bilterys, Gisseleire, *Bull. soc. chim.* **44,** 572–573 (1935). ⟨2⟩ Lumsden, *J. Chem. Soc.* **87,** 93 (1905).

1:3656 ETHYL *n*-CAPRYLATE $C_{10}H_{20}O_2$ **Beil. II-348**

B.P. 208.5° ⟨1⟩ **Sap. Eq. 172** D_4^{20} = **0.8667 ⟨2⟩ ⟨1⟩** n_D^{20} = **1.41775 ⟨2⟩**
M.P. −43.1° ⟨1⟩ D_4^{25} = **0.8624 ⟨2⟩** n_D^{25} = **1.41576 ⟨2⟩**

Ⓓ **Saponification:** Hydrolysis with alk. (T 1.51) yields ethyl alc. (1:6130) and *n*-caprylic ac. (1:1145).

1:3656 ⟨1⟩ Deffet, *Bull. soc. chim. Belg.* **40,** 390, 393 (1931). ⟨2⟩ Kao, Ma, *Science Repts. Natl. Tsing Hua Univ.*, Ser. **A-1,** 181–183 (1932).

1:3661 ISOBUTYL ENANTHATE $C_{11}H_{22}O_2$ **Beil. II₁-(145)**
(Isobutyl *n*-heptylate)

B.P. 209° **Sap. Eq. 186** D^{20} = **0.8593**

Ⓓ **Saponification:** Hydrolysis with alk. (T 1.51) yields isobutyl alc. (1:6165) and enanthic ac. (1:1140).

1:3666 ISOPROPYL LEVULINATE $C_8H_{14}O_3$ **Beil. S.N. 281**

B.P. 209.3° ⟨1⟩ **Sap. Eq. 158** D_4^{20} = **0.98724 ⟨1⟩** n_D^{20} = **1.42088 ⟨1⟩**

Ⓓ **Isopropyl levulinate semicarbazone:** m.p. 141–142° ⟨2⟩.
Ⓓ **Isopropyl levulinate phenylhydrazone:** m.p. 108–109° ⟨2⟩.
Ⓓ **Isopropyl levulinate 2,4-dinitrophenylhydrazone:** m.p. 90.9° ⟨3⟩; OY cryst. from isopropyl alc., m.p. 88–89° cor. ⟨4⟩. [Cf. T 1.14.]
Ⓓ **Saponification:** Hydrolysis with alk. (T 1.51) yields isopropyl alc. (1:6135) and levulinic ac. (1:0405).

1:3666 ⟨1⟩ Cox, Dodds, *J. Am. Chem. Soc.* **55,** 3393 (1933). ⟨2⟩ Sah, Ma, *J. Am. Chem. Soc.* **52,** 4882–4883 (1930). ⟨3⟩ Cowley, Schuette, *J. Am. Chem. Soc.* **55,** 3464 (1933). ⟨4⟩ Strain, *J. Am. Chem. Soc.* **57,** 760 (1935).

1:3671 TRIMETHYLENE GLYCOL DIACETATE $C_7H_{12}O_4$ **Beil. II-143**
(1,3-Diacetoxypropane)

B.P. 210° **Sap. Eq. 80** D^{19} = **1.070**

Ⓓ **Saponification:** Hydrolysis with alk. (T 1.51) yields trimethylene glycol (1:6490) and acetic ac. (1:1010).

1:3676 *n*-OCTYL ACETATE $C_{10}H_{20}O_2$ **Beil. II-134**

B.P. 210° **Sap. Eq. 172** D_0^0 = **0.8847**

Ⓓ **Saponification:** Hydrolysis with alk. (T 1.51) yields *n*-octyl alc. (1:6255) and acetic ac. (1:1010).

1:3681 *n*-HEPTYL PROPIONATE $C_{10}H_{20}O_2$ **Beil. II-241**

B.P. 210.0° ⟨1⟩ **Sap. Eq. 172** D^{20} = **0.86786 ⟨1⟩** $n_{He\ (yel.)}^{15}$ = **1.42605 ⟨1⟩**
M.P. −50.9° ⟨1⟩

Ⓓ **Saponification:** Hydrolysis with alk. (T 1.51) yields *n*-heptyl alc. (1:6240) and propionic ac. (1:1025).

1:3681 ⟨1⟩ Bilterys, Gisseleire, *Bull. soc. chim. Belg.* **44,** 576–577 (1935).

1:3686 DIMETHYL CITRACONATE $C_7H_{10}O_4$ **Beil. II-770**

B.P. 210.5° ⟨1⟩ **Sap. Eq. 79** D_4^{20} **= 1.11531 ⟨1⟩** n_D^{20} **= 1.44856 ⟨1⟩**

C̄ in abs. alc. treated with hydrazine hydrate yields citraconic dihydrazide, cryst. from aq., m.p. 177° ⟨2⟩.

Ⓓ **Saponification:** Hydrolysis with alk. (T 1.51) yields methyl alc. (1:6120) and citraconic ac. (1:0435).

1:3686 ⟨1⟩ van de Straete, *Bull. soc. chim. Belg.* **44,** 316 (1935). ⟨2⟩ Freri, *Gazz. chim. ital.* **66,** 26–27 (1936).

1:3691 ETHYLENE GLYCOL DIPROPIONATE $C_8H_{14}O_4$ **Beil. II-242**

B.P. 211° **Sap. Eq. 87** D_{15}^{15} **= 1.0544**

Ⓓ **Saponification:** Hydrolysis with alk. (T 1.51) yields ethylene glycol (1:6465) and propionic ac. (1:1025).

1:3696 PHENYL PROPIONATE $C_9H_{10}O_2$ **Beil. VI-154**

B.P. 211° **Sap. Eq. 150** D_{25}^{25} **= 1.0467**
M.P. +20°

Ⓓ **Saponification:** Hydrolysis with alk. (T 1.51) yields phenol (1:1420) and propionic ac. (1:1025).

1:3701 *n*-PROPYL PYROMUCATE $C_8H_{10}O_3$ **Beil. XVIII-275**

B.P. 211° **Sap. Eq. 154** $D_4^{25.9}$ **= 1.0745** $n_D^{25.9}$ **= 1.4737**

Ⓓ **Saponification:** Hydrolysis with alk. (T 1.51) yields *n*-propyl alc. (1:6150) and furoic ac. (1:0475).

1:3706 *m*-TOLYL ACETATE $C_9H_{10}O_2$ **Beil. VI-379**
(" *m*-Cresyl " acetate)

B.P. 212° **Sap. Eq. 150** D^{26} **= 1.043 ⟨1⟩** n_D^{20} **= 1.4978 ⟨1⟩**
M.P. 12°

Ⓓ **Saponification:** Hydrolysis with alk. (T 1.51) yields *m*-cresol (1:1730) and acetic ac. (1:1010).

1:3706 ⟨1⟩ Ono, Imoto, *Bull. Chem. Soc. Japan* **11,** 129–130 (1936).

1:3711 CYCLOHEXYL *n*-BUTYRATE $C_{10}H_{18}O_2$ **Beil. VI₁-(6)**

B.P. 212°_{750} **Sap. Eq. 170** D_4^0 **= 0.9572**

Ⓓ **Saponification:** Hydrolysis with alk. (T 1.51) yields cyclohexanol (1:6415) and *n*-butyric ac. (1:1035).

1:3716 *p*-TOLYL ACETATE $C_9H_{10}O_2$ **Beil. VI-397**
(" *p*-Cresyl " acetate)

B.P. 212.5° **Sap. Eq. 150** D^{23} **= 1.0499** n_D^{23} **= 1.4991**

Ⓓ **Saponification:** Hydrolysis with alk. (T 1.51) yields *p*-cresol (1:1410) and acetic ac. (1:1010).

1:3721 ETHYL BENZOATE $C_9H_{10}O_2$ **Beil. IX-110**

B.P. 213.2° **Sap. Eq. 150** D_4^{15} = **1.0509** n_D^{20} = **1.506**
M.P. −34.2° D_4^{25} = **1.0422**

Ⓓ **Saponification:** Hydrolysis with alk. (T 1.51) yields ethyl alc. (1:6130) and benzoic ac. (1:0715).

1:3726 DI-*n*-PROPYL OXALATE $C_8H_{14}O_4$ **Beil. II-539**

B. P. 213.9° ⟨1⟩ **Sap. Eq. 87** D_4^{20} = **1.0169** ⟨2⟩ n_{Di}^{20} = **1.4168** ⟨2⟩
M.P. −51.7° ⟨1⟩ D_4^{25} = **1.0120** ⟨2⟩ n_D^{25} = **1.4142** ⟨2⟩

$\bar{C}$ in alc. stood overnight at 0° with 1 mole conc. aq. NH_4OH yields *n*-propyl oxamate, cryst. from MeOH or EtOH, m.p. 90–92° ⟨2⟩.

Ⓓ **Saponification:** Hydrolysis with alk. (T 1.51) yields *n*-propyl alc. (1:6150) and oxalic ac. (1:0445).

1:3726 ⟨1⟩ Timmermans, *Bull. soc. chim. Belg.* **36,** 506 (1927). ⟨2⟩ Sah, Chien, *J. Am. Chem. Soc.* **53,** 3902 (1931).

1:3731 DIMETHYL GLUTARATE $C_7H_{12}O_4$ **Beil. II-633**

B.P. 214°/751 mm. **Sap. Eq. 80** D_4^{20} = **1.0874** ⟨1⟩ n_D^{20} = **1.42415** ⟨1⟩
M.P. −37.4°

Ⓓ **Saponification:** Hydrolysis with alk. (T 1.51) yields methyl alc. (1:6120) and glutaric ac. (1:0440).

1:3731 ⟨1⟩ Vogel, *J. Chem. Soc.* **1934,** 338.

1:3736 METHYL PELARGONATE $C_{10}H_{20}O_2$ **Beil. II-353**

B.P. 214° **Sap. Eq. 172** D_0^0 = **1.0384**

Ⓓ **Saponification:** Hydrolysis with alk. (T 1.51) yields methyl alc. (1:6120) and pelargonic ac. (1:0560).

—— **ETHYL ACETOPYRUVATE** $C_7H_{10}O_4$ **Beil. III-747**

B.P. 213-215° D_4^{20} = **1.1251** n_D^{17} = **1.4757**

See 1:1742. Genus 4: Phenols.

1:3741 2,6-DIMETHYLPHENYL ACETATE $C_{10}H_{12}O_2$ **Beil. S.N. 529**
(*vic-m*-Xylenyl acetate)

B.P. 214-216° ⟨1⟩ **Sap. Eq. 164**

Ⓓ **Saponification:** Hydrolysis with alk. (T 1.51) yields 2,6-dimethylphenol (1:1425) and acetic ac. (1:1010).

1:3741 ⟨1⟩ von Auwers, Mauss, *Ann.* **460,** 266 (1928).

1:3746 METHYL *o*-TOLUATE $C_9H_{10}O_2$ **Beil. IX-463**

B.P. 215° ⟨1⟩ **Sap. Eq. 150** D^{15} = **1.073**

Ⓓ **Saponification:** Hydrolysis with alk. (T 1.51) yields methyl alc. (1:6120) and *o*-toluic ac. (1:0690).

1:3746 ⟨1⟩ Kohlrausch, Pongratz, *Monatsh.* **63,** 443 (1934).

1:3751 BENZYL ACETATE $C_9H_{10}O_2$ **Beil. VI-435**

B.P. 217.0° ⟨1⟩ **Sap. Eq. 150** **D_4^{20} = 1.055 ⟨1⟩** **n_D^{20} = 1.5200 ⟨1⟩**

For reactn. with 6 *N* aq. alc. NH_3 see **⟨2⟩**.

Ⓓ **Saponification:** Hydrolysis with alk. yields benzyl alc. (1:6480) and acetic ac. (1:1010).

1:3751 ⟨1⟩ Gardner, Brewer, *Ind. Eng. Chem.* **29,** 179 (1937). ⟨2⟩ French, Wrightsman, *J. Am. Chem. Soc.* **60,** 51 (1938).

1:3756 DIETHYL SUCCINATE $C_8H_{14}O_4$ **Beil. II-609**

B.P. 217.7° **Sap. Eq. 87** **D_4^{20} = 1.0398 ⟨1⟩** **n_D^{20} = 1.41975 ⟨1⟩**
M.P. −21°

Ⓓ **Saponification:** Hydrolysis with alk. (T 1.51) yields ethyl alc. (1:6130) and succinic ac. (1:0530).

1:3756 ⟨1⟩ Vogel, *J. Chem. Soc.* **1934,** 339.

1:3761 DIETHYL FUMARATE $C_8H_{12}O_4$ **Beil. II-742**

B.P. 218.4° ⟨1⟩ **Sap. Eq. 86** **D_4^{15} = 1.05721 ⟨1⟩** **$n_D^{20.1}$ = 1.44103**
M.P. + 0.2 ⟨1⟩

[For prepn. in 80% yield from fumaric ac. + ethyl alc. see **⟨2⟩**.] [For m.p. + compn. data on system: $\bar{C}$ + diethyl maleate (1:3791) see **⟨3⟩**.]

Ⓓ **Saponification:** Hydrolysis with alk. (T 1.51) yields ethyl alc. (1:6130) and fumaric ac. (1:0895).

1:3761 ⟨1⟩ Viseur, *Bull. soc. chim. Belg.* **35,** 429 (1926). ⟨2⟩ Corson, Adams, Scott, *Organic Syntheses,* **10,** 48–52 (1930). ⟨3⟩ Ref. 1, page 432.

1:3766 ISOPROPYL BENZOATE $C_{10}H_{12}O_2$ **Beil. IX-112**

B.P. 218.5° **Sap. Eq. 164** **D_4^{25} = 1.0102 ⟨1⟩** **n_D^{25} = 1.4890 ⟨1⟩**

Ⓓ **Saponification:** Hydrolysis with alk. (T 1.51) yields isopropyl alc. (1:6135) and benzoic ac. (1:0715).

1:3766 ⟨1⟩ Dorris, Sowa, Nieuwland, *J. Am. Chem. Soc.* **56,** 2690 (1934).

1:3771 METHYL PHENYLACETATE $C_9H_{10}O_2$ **Beil. IX-434**

B.P. 220° **Sap. Eq. 150** **D_{16}^{16} = 1.0633** **n_D^{16} = 1.5091**

Ⓓ **Saponification:** Hydrolysis with alk. (T 1.51) yields methyl alc. (1:6120) and phenylacetic ac. (1:0665).

1:3776 *l*-LINALYL ACETATE $C_{12}H_{20}O_2$ **Beil. II-141**

B.P. 220° **Sap. Eq. 196** **D^{20} = 0.8951** **n_D^{20} = 1.4460**
D_4^{25} = 0.8997 **n_D^{25} = 1.4509**

Ⓓ **Saponification:** Hydrolysis with alk. (T 1.51) yields linalool (1:6260) and acetic ac. (1:1010).

1:3781 METHYL *m*-TOLUATE $C_9H_{10}O_2$ **Beil. IX-475**

B.P. 221° **Sap. Eq. 150** D^{15} = **1.066**

Ⓓ **Saponification:** Hydrolysis with alk. (T 1.51) yields methyl alc. (1:6120) and *m*-toluic ac. (1:0705).

1:3786 *n*-PROPYL LEVULINATE $C_8H_{14}O_3$ **Beil. III-675**

B.P. 221.2° ⟨1⟩ **Sap. Eq. 158** D_4^{20} = **0.98955 ⟨1⟩** n_D^{20} = **1.42576 ⟨1⟩**

Ⓓ ***n*-Propyl levulinate semicarbazone:** m.p. 129–130° ⟨2⟩.

Ⓓ ***n*-Propyl levulinate phenylhydrazone:** m.p. 88–90° ⟨2⟩.

Ⓓ ***n*-Propyl levulinate 2,4-dinitrophenylhydrazone:** OY cryst. from *n*-PrOH, m.p. 67–68° cor. ⟨3⟩; cryst. from alc., m.p. 63° ⟨4⟩. [Cf. T 1.14.]

Ⓓ **Saponification:** Hydrolysis with alk. (T 1.51) yields *n*-propyl alc. (1:6150) and levulinic ac. (1:0405).

1:3786 ⟨1⟩ Cox, Dodds, *J. Am. Chem. Soc.* **55,** 3393 (1933). ⟨2⟩ Sah, Ma, *J. Am. Chem. Soc.* **52,** 4882–4883 (1930). ⟨3⟩ Strain, *J. Am. Chem. Soc.* **57,** 760 (1935). ⟨4⟩ Cowley, Schuette, *J. Am. Chem. Soc.* **55,** 3464 (1933).

—— METHYL *p*-TOLUATE $C_9H_{10}O_2$ **Beil. IX-484**

B.P. 222.5° **Sap. Eq. 150**

See 1:2071. Genus 5: Esters. M.P. 33°.

1:3791 DIETHYL MALEATE $C_8H_{12}O_4$ **Beil. II-751**

B.P. 222.7° ⟨1⟩ **Sap. Eq. 86** D_4^{15} = **1.07279 ⟨1⟩** $n_D^{19.9}$ = **1.44156**
M.P. −17° ⟨1⟩

[For m.p. + compn. data on system: $\bar{C}$ + diethyl fumarate (1:3761) see ⟨2⟩.]

Ⓓ **Saponification:** Hydrolysis with alk. (T 1.51) yields ethyl alc. (1:6130) and maleic ac. (1:0470).

1:3791 ⟨1⟩ Viseur, *Bull. soc. chim. Belg.* **35,** 429 (1926). ⟨2⟩ Ref. 1, page 432.

1:3796 DIETHYL TARTRONATE $C_7H_{12}O_5$ **Beil. III-416**

B.P. 222-225° dec. **Sap. Eq. 88** D^{15} = **1.152**

Ⓓ **Saponification:** Hydrolysis with alk. (T 1.51) yields ethyl alc. (1:6130) and tartronic ac. (1:0510).

—— METHYL SALICYLATE $C_8H_8O_3$ **Beil. X-70**

B.P. 224° **Sap. Eq. 152** D_4^{20} = **1.184** n_D^{20} = **1.5369**

See 1:1750. Genus 4: Phenols.

1:3801 2,5-DIMETHYLPHENYL ACETATE $C_{10}H_{12}O_2$ **Beil. VI-495**
(*p*-Xylenyl acetate)

B.P. 224° at 741 mm. **⟨1⟩** **Sap. Eq. 164** D^{15} = **1.0264**
(**237°** at 768 mm.)

Ⓓ **Saponification:** Hydrolysis with alk. (T 1.51) yields 2,5-dimethylphenol (1:1473) and acetic ac. (1:1010).

1:3801 ⟨1⟩ von Auwers, Bundesmann, Wieners, *Ann.* **447,** 179 (1926).

1:3806 ETHYL β-n-BUTOXYETHYL CARBONATE $C_9H_{18}O_4$ **Beil. S.N. 199**

B.P. 224° ⟨1⟩ **Sap. Eq. 190** D_4^{25} **= 0.9756 ⟨1⟩** n_D^{25} **= 1.4143 ⟨1⟩**

Ⓓ **Saponification:** Hydrolysis with alk. (T 1.51) yields ethyl alc. (1:6130), ethylene glycol mono-*n*-butyl ether (1:6430), and CO_2. [Cf. ⟨1⟩.]

1:3806 ⟨1⟩ Drake, Carter, *J. Am. Chem. Soc.* **52,** 3722 (1930).

1:3812 sec-BUTYL LEVULINATE $C_9H_{16}O_3$ **Beil. S.N. 281**

B.P. 225.8° ⟨1⟩ **Sap. Eq. 172** D_4^{20} **= 0.96698 ⟨1⟩** n_D^{20} **= 1.42499 ⟨1⟩**

Ⓓ **Saponification:** Hydrolysis with alk. (T 1.51) yields *sec*-butyl alc. (1:6155) and levulinic ac. (1:0405).

1:3812 ⟨1⟩ Cox, Dodds, *J. Am. Chem. Soc.* **55,** 3393 (1933).

1:3817 n-HEPTYL n-BUTYRATE $C_{11}H_{22}O_2$ **Beil. II-272**

B.P. 225.9° ⟨1⟩ **Sap. Eq. 186** D^{20} **= 0.86371 ⟨1⟩** $n_{He\ (yel.)}^{15}$ **= 1.42279 ⟨1⟩**
M.P. −57.5° ⟨1⟩

Ⓓ **Saponification:** Hydrolysis with alk. (T 1.51) yields *n*-heptyl alc. (1:6240) and *n*-butyric ac. (1:1035).

1:3817 ⟨1⟩ Bilterys, Gisseleire, *Bull. soc. chim. Belg.* **44,** 576–577 (1935).

1:3822 2,4-DIMETHYLPHENYL ACETATE $C_{10}H_{12}O_2$ **Beil. VI-487**
(*unsym.-m*-Xylenyl acetate)

B.P. 226° cor. **Sap. Eq. 164** $D_4^{15.5}$ **= 1.0298 ⟨1⟩** n_D^{15} **= 1.4990 ⟨1⟩**

Ⓓ **Saponification:** Hydrolysis with alk. (T 1.51) yields 2,4-dimethylphenol (1:1740) and acetic ac. (1:1010).

1:3822 ⟨1⟩ Palfray, Duboc, *Compt. rend.* **185,** 1479–1481 (1927).

1:3827 METHYL n-CAPRATE $C_{11}H_{22}O_2$ **Beil. II-356**

B.P. 226° ⟨1⟩ **Sap. Eq. 186** n_D^{45} **= 1.4161 ⟨2⟩**

[For sepn. by fractnl. distn. from mixts. with methyl myristate (1:2013) + methyl palmitate (1:2055) + methyl stearate (1:2095) see ⟨2⟩.]

Ⓓ **Saponification:** Hydrolysis with alk. (T 1.51) yields methyl alc. (1:6120) and *n*-capric ac. (1:0585).

1:3827 ⟨1⟩ Kohlrausch, Köppl, Pongratz, *Z. physik. Chem.* **B-22,** 372 (1933). ⟨2⟩ Wyman, Barkenbus, *Ind. Eng. Chem., Anal. Ed.* **12,** 658–661 (1940).

1:3832 d-BORNYL ACETATE $C_{12}H_{20}O_2$ **Beil. VI-78**

B.P. 226° **Sap. Eq. 196** D^{15} **= 0.991** (supercooled) $n_D^{22.6}$ **= 1.4623** (supercooled)
M.P. 29°

Ⓓ **Saponification:** Hydrolysis with alk. (T 1.51) yields *d*-borneol (1:5990) and acetic ac. (1:1010).

1:3837 ***n*-AMYL *n*-CAPROATE** $C_{11}H_{22}O_2$ **Beil. II-323**

B.P. 226.2° ⟨1⟩ **Sap. Eq. 186** D^{20} = **0.86349 ⟨1⟩** $n^{15}_{\text{He (yel.)}}$ = **1.42280 ⟨1⟩**
M.P. −50.0° ⟨1⟩

Ⓓ **Saponification:** Hydrolysis with alk. (T 1.51) yields *n*-amyl alc. (**1:6205**) and *n*-caproic ac. (1:1130).

1:3837 ⟨1⟩ Bilterys, Gisseleire, *Bull. soc. chim. Belg.* **44,** 571 (1935).

1:3842 ***n*-BUTYL *n*-ENANTHATE** $C_{11}H_{22}O_2$ **Beil. II-340**
(*n*-Butyl *n*-heptylate)

B.P. 226.2° ⟨1⟩ **Sap. Eq. 186** D^{20} = **0.86382 ⟨1⟩** $n^{15}_{\text{He (yel.)}}$ = **1.42280 ⟨1⟩**

Ⓓ **Saponification:** Hydrolysis with alk. (T 1.51) yields *n*-butyl alc. (**1:6180**) and enanthic ac. (1:1140).

1:3842 ⟨1⟩ Bilterys, Gisseleire, *Bull. soc. chim. Belg.* **44,** 572 (1935).

1:3847 ***n*-HEXYL *n*-VALERATE** $C_{11}H_{22}O_2$ **Beil. II-301**

B.P. 226.3° ⟨1⟩ **Sap. Eq. 186** D^{20} = **0.86345 ⟨1⟩** $n^{15}_{\text{He (yel.)}}$ = **1.42286 ⟨1⟩**
M.P. −63.1° ⟨1⟩

Ⓓ **Saponification:** Hydrolysis with alk. (T 1.51) yields *n*-hexyl alc. (1:6230) and *n*-valeric ac. (1:1060).

1;3847 ⟨1⟩ Bilterys, Gisseleire, *Bull. soc. chim. Belg.* **44,** 574–575 (1935).

1:3852 ***n*-PROPYL *n*-CAPRYLATE** $C_{11}H_{22}O_2$ **Beil. II-348**

B.P. 226.4° ⟨1⟩ **Sap. Eq. 186** D^{20} = **0.86591 ⟨1⟩** $n^{15}_{\text{He (yel.)}}$ = **1.42351 ⟨1⟩**
M.P. −46.2° ⟨1⟩

Ⓓ **Saponification:** Hydrolysis with alk. (T 1.51) yields *n*-propyl alc. (1:6150) and *n*-caprylic ac. (1:1145).

1:3852 ⟨1⟩ Bilterys, Gisseleire, *Bull. soc. chim. Belg.* **44,** 573 (1935).

1:3857 **METHYL β-(α-FURYL)ACRYLATE** $C_8H_8O_3$ **Beil. XVIII-301**

B.P. 227° **Sap. Eq. 152**
M.P. 27°

C̄ htd. in s.t. at 100° with conc. aq. NH_4OH readily yields β-(α-furyl)acrylamide, cryst. from hot aq., m.p. 168–169° ⟨1⟩.

Ⓓ **Saponification:** Hydrolysis with alk. (T 1.51) yields methyl alc. (1:6120) and β-(α-furyl)acrylic ac. (1:0760).

1:3857 ⟨1⟩ Gibson, Kahnweiler, *Am. Chem. J.* **12,** 315 (1890).

1:3862 **ETHYL *o*-TOLUATE** $C_{10}H_{12}O_2$ **Beil. IX-463**

B.P. 227° **Sap. Eq. 164** $D_4^{21.5}$ = **1.0325** $n_D^{21.6}$ = **1.507**

Ⓓ **Saponification:** Hydrolysis with alk. (T 1.51) yields ethyl alc. (1:6130) and *o*-toluic ac. (1:0690).

1:3867 ETHYL PELARGONATE $C_{11}H_{22}O_2$ **Beil. II-353**

B.P. 227.0° ⟨1⟩ **Sap. Eq. 186** D_4^{20} = **0.8657** ⟨2⟩ ⟨1⟩ n_D^{20} = **1.42200** ⟨2⟩
M.P. −36.7° ⟨1⟩ D_4^{25} = **0.8616** ⟨2⟩ n_D^{25} = **1,42001** ⟨2⟩

Ⓓ **Saponification:** Hydrolysis with alk. (T 1.51) yields ethyl alc. (1:6130) and pelargonic ac. (1:0560).

1:3867 ⟨1⟩ Deffet, *Bull. soc. chim. Belg.* **40,** 390, 393 (1931). ⟨2⟩ Kao, Ma, *Science Repts. Natl. Tsing Hua Univ.*, Ser. **A-1,** 181–183 (1932).

1:3872 ETHYL PHENYLACETATE $C_{10}H_{12}O_2$ **Beil. IX-434**

B.P. 227.5° **Sap. Eq. 164** D_4^{20} = **1.0333** $n_D^{18.5}$ = **1.49921**

[For prepn. in 83–87% yield from ethyl alc. + benzyl cyanide see ⟨1⟩.]

Ⓓ **Saponification:** Hydrolysis with alk. (T 1.51) yields ethyl alc. (1:6130) and phenylacetic ac. (1:0665).

1:3872 ⟨1⟩ Adams, Thal, *Organic Syntheses, Coll. Vol.* I, 265–268 (1932).

1:3877 *n*-OCTYL PROPIONATE $C_{11}H_{22}O_2$ **Beil. II-241**

B.P. 227.9° ⟨1⟩ **Sap. Eq. 186** D^{20} = **0.86633** ⟨1⟩ $n_{\text{He (yel.)}}^{15}$ = **1.42185** ⟨1⟩
M.P. −41.6° ⟨1⟩

Ⓓ **Saponification:** Hydrolysis with alk. (T 1.51) yields *n*-octyl alc. (1:6255) and propionic ac. (1:1025).

1:3877 ⟨1⟩ Bilterys, Gisseleire, *Bull. soc. chim. Belg.* **44,** 578–579 (1935).

1:3885 DIETHYL ITACONATE $C_9H_{14}O_4$ **Beil. II-762**

B.P. 228° **Sap. Eq. 93** D_4^{20} = **1.0467** ⟨1⟩ n_D^{20} = **1.4377** ⟨1⟩

Ⓓ **Saponification:** Hydrolysis with alk. (T 1.51) yields ethyl alc. (1:6130) and itaconic ac. (1:0515) ⟨1⟩. [Note: alc. alk. isomerizes $\bar{C}$ to diethyl citraconate.]

1:3885 ⟨1⟩ Coulson, Kon, *J. Chem. Soc.* **1932,** 2571.

1:3892 DIETHYL MESACONATE $C_9H_{14}O_4$ **Beil. II-766**

B.P. 229° **Sap. Eq. 93** D_4^{20} = **1.0453** ⟨1⟩ n_D^{20} = **1.4488** ⟨1⟩

Ⓓ **Saponification:** Hydrolysis with alk. (T 1.51) yields ethyl alc. (1:6130) and mesaconic ac. (1:0548). [Cf. ⟨1⟩.]

1:3892 ⟨1⟩ Coulson, Kon, *J. Chem. Soc.* **1932,** 2571.

1:3897 DIISOBUTYL OXALATE $C_{10}H_{18}O_4$ **Beil. II-540**

B.P. 229° **Sap. Eq. 101** D_4^{20} = **0.97373** ⟨1⟩ n_D^{20} = **1.4180** ⟨1⟩
D_4^{25} = **0.97545** ⟨1⟩ n_D^{25} = **1.4160** ⟨1⟩

Ⓓ **Isobutyl oxamate:** from $\bar{C}$ in cold abs. alc. on treatment with 1 mole conc. aq. NH_4OH and stdg. overnight; cryst. from MeOH or EtOH, m.p. 75–76° ⟨1⟩.

Ⓓ **Saponification:** Hydrolysis with alk. (T 1.51) yields isobutyl alc. (1:6165) and oxalic ac. (1:0445).

1:3897 ⟨1⟩ Sah, Chien, *J. Am. Chem. Soc.* **53,** 3902 (1931).

1:3902 ALLYL BENZOATE $C_{10}H_{10}O_2$ **Beil. IX-114**

B.P. 230° **Sap. Eq. 162** D^{15}_{15} = **1.0578**

Ⓓ **Saponification:** Hydrolysis with alk. (T 1.51) yields allyl alc. (1:6145) and benzoic ac. (1:0715).

1:3907 ISOBUTYL LEVULINATE $C_9H_{16}O_3$ **Beil. S.N. 281**

B.P. 230.9° ⟨1⟩ **Sap. Eq. 172** D^{20}_4 = **0.96770 ⟨1⟩** n^{20}_D = **1.42677 ⟨1⟩**

Ⓓ **Isobutyl levulinate semicarbazone:** m.p. 112–113° ⟨2⟩.

Ⓓ **Isobutyl levulinate phenylhydrazone:** m.p. 84–86° ⟨2⟩.

Ⓓ **Isobutyl levulinate 2,4-dinitrophenylhydrazone:** m.p. 55.6° ⟨3⟩.

Ⓓ **Saponification:** Hydrolysis with alk. (T 1.51) yields isobutyl alc. (1:6165) and levulinic ac. (1:0405).

1:3907 ⟨1⟩ Cox, Dodds, *J. Am. Chem. Soc.* **55,** 3393 (1933). ⟨2⟩ Sah, Ma, *J. Am. Chem. Soc.* **52,** 4882–4883 (1930). ⟨3⟩ Cowley, Schuette, *J. Am. Chem. Soc.* **55,** 3464 (1933).

1:3912 DIETHYL CITRACONATE $C_9H_{14}O_4$ **Beil. II-771**

B.P. 231° **Sap. Eq. 93** D^{20}_4 = **1.0491 ⟨1⟩** n^{20}_D = **1.4442 ⟨1⟩**

Ⓓ **Saponification:** Hydrolysis with alk. (T 1.51) yields ethyl alc. (1:6130) and citraconic ac. (1:0435) ⟨1⟩.

1:3912 ⟨1⟩ Coulson, Kon, *J. Chem. Soc.* **1932,** 2571.

1:3917 *n*-PROPYL BENZOATE $C_{10}H_{12}O_2$ **Beil. IX-112**

B.P. 231° **Sap. Eq. 164** D^{25}_4 = **0.9958** n^{25}_D = **1.4959**

D^{15}_4 = **1.0274** $n^{20.3}_D$ = **1.5000**

Ⓓ **Saponification:** Hydrolysis with alk. (T 1.51) yields *n*-propyl alc. (1:6150) and benzoic ac. (1:0715).

1:3922 β-PHENYLETHYL ACETATE $C_{10}H_{12}O_2$ **Beil. VI-479**

B.P. 232° (224°) **Sap. Eq. 164** $D^{22.5}$ = **1.057** n_D = **1.5108**

Ⓓ **Saponification:** Hydrolysis with alk. (T 1.51) yields β-phenylethyl alc. (1:6505) and acetic ac. (1:1010).

1:3927 ETHYL β-(α-FURYL)ACRYLATE $C_9H_{10}O_3$ **Beil. XVIII-300**

B.P. 232° **Sap. Eq. 166** D^{15}_4 = **1.0891** n^{20}_D = **1.5286**

M.P. 14°

Ⓓ **Saponification:** Hydrolysis with alk. (T 1.51) yields ethyl alc. (1:6130) and β-(α-furyl)-acrylic ac. (1:0760).

1:3932 DI-(β-METHOXYETHYL) CARBONATE $C_7H_{14}O_5$ **Beil. S.N. 199**

B.P. 232° ⟨1⟩ **Sap. Eq. 178** D^{25}_4 = **1.0936 ⟨1⟩** n^{25}_D = **1.4193 ⟨1⟩**

Ⓓ **Saponification:** Hydrolysis with alk. (T 1.51) yields ethylene glycol monomethyl ether (1:6405) and CO_2. [Cf. ⟨1⟩.]

1:3932 ⟨1⟩ Drake, Carter, *J. Am. Chem. Soc.* **52,** 3722 (1930).

1:3937 DIISOAMYL CARBONATE $C_{11}H_{22}O_3$ **Beil. III-7**

B.P. 233° cor. ⟨1⟩ **Sap. Eq. 202** D_4^{20} = **0.9067** ⟨1⟩ n_D^{20} = **1.4174** ⟨1⟩

Ⓓ **Saponification:** Hydrolysis with alk. (T 1.51) yields isoamyl alc. (1:6200) and carbonic ac.

1:3937 ⟨1⟩ Kogerman, Kranig, *Cent.* **1927,** I, 2408.

1:3942 ETHYL *m*-TOLUATE $C_{10}H_{12}O_2$ **Beil. IX-476**

BP. 234° **Sap. Eq. 164** $D_4^{21.2}$ = **1.0265** $n_D^{21.6}$ = **1.505**

Ⓓ **Saponfication:** Hydrolysis with alk. (T 1.51) yields ethyl alc. (1:6130) and *m*-toluic ac. (1:0705).

—— **ETHYL SALICYLATE** $C_9H_{10}O_3$ **Beil. X-73**

B.P. 234° **Sap. Eq. 166** D_4^{20} = **1.1396** n_D^{20} = **1.52542**

See 1:1755. Genus 4: Phenols.

1:3947 ETHYL *p*-TOLUATE $C_{10}H_{12}O_2$ **Beil. IX-484**

B.P. 234.5° **Sap. Eq. 164** $D_4^{18.2}$ = **1.0269** $n_D^{18.2}$ = **1.5089**

Ⓓ **Saponification:** Hydrolysis with alk. (T 1.51) yields ethyl alc. (1:6130) and *p*-toluic ac. (1:0795).

1:3952 3,4-DIMETHYLPHENYL ACETATE $C_{10}H_{12}O_2$ **Beil. S.N. 529**
(*unsym.-o*-Xylenyl acetate)

B.P. 235° ⟨1⟩ **Sap. Eq. 164**
M.P. 22-22.5° ⟨1⟩

Ⓓ **Saponification:** Hydrolysis with alk. (T 1.51) yields 3,4-dimethylphenol (1:1453) and acetic ac. (1:1010).

1:3952 ⟨1⟩ von Auwers, Bundesmann, Wieners, *Ann.* **447,** 176 (1926).

1:3957 2,4,6-TRIMETHYLPHENYL ACETATE $C_{11}H_{14}O_2$ **Beil. S.N. 530**
(Mesityl acetate)

B.P. 236° ⟨1⟩ **Sap. Eq. 178**

Ⓓ **Saponification:** Hydrolysis with alk. (T 1.51) yields mesitol (1:1467) and acetic ac. (1:1010).

1:3957 ⟨1⟩ von Auwers, Bundesmann, Wieners, *Ann.* **447,** 193 (1926).

1:3962 ETHYLENE GLYCOL DI-*n*-BUTYRATE $C_{10}H_{18}O_4$ **Beil. II-272**

B.P. 235-237°$_{749}$ ⟨1⟩ **Sap. Eq. 101** D_4^{20} = **1.0005** ⟨1⟩ n_{He}^{20} = **1.42619** ⟨1⟩

Ⓓ **Saponification:** Hydrolysis with alk. (T 1.51) yields ethylene glycol (1:6465) and *n*-butyric ac. (1:1035).

1:3962 ⟨1⟩ von Auwers, Hügel, *Z. physik. Chem.* **A-178,** 318, 320 (1937).

1:3967 DIETHYL GLUTARATE $C_9H_{16}O_4$ **Beil. II-633**

B.P. 237° **Sap. Eq. 94** D_4^{20} = **1.02229 ⟨1⟩** n_D^{20} = **1.42395 ⟨1⟩**
M.P. −24.1°

Ⓓ **Saponification:** Hydrolysis with alk. (T 1.51) yields ethyl alc. (1:6130) and glutaric ac. (1:0440).

1:3967 ⟨1⟩ Vogel, *J. Chem. Soc.* **1934,** 339.

1:3972 *n*-BUTYL LEVULINATE $C_9H_{16}O_3$ **Beil. S.N. 281**

B.P. 237.8° ⟨1⟩ **Sap. Eq. 172** D_4^{20} = **0.97353 ⟨1⟩** n_D^{20} = **1.42905 ⟨1⟩**

Ⓓ ***n*-Butyl levulinate semicarbazone:** m.p. 102–103° ⟨2⟩.
Ⓓ ***n*-Butyl levulinate phenylhydrazone:** m.p. 79–81° ⟨2⟩.
Ⓓ ***n*-Butyl levulinate 2,4-dinitrophenylhydrazone:** m.p. 65.8° ⟨3⟩. [Cf. T 1.14.]
Ⓓ **Saponification:** Hydrolysis with alk. (T 1.51) yields *n*-butyl alc. (1:6180) and levulinic ac. (1:0405).

1:3972 ⟨1⟩ Cox, Dodds, *J. Am. Chem. Soc.* **55,** 3393 (1933). ⟨2⟩ Sah, Ma, *J. Am. Chem. Soc.* **52,** 4882–4883 (1930). ⟨3⟩ Cowley, Schuette, *J. Am. Chem. Soc.* **55,** 3464 (1933).

1:3977 BENZYL *n*-BUTYRATE $C_{11}H_{14}O_2$ **Beil. VI-436**

B.P. 238-240° **Sap. Eq. 178** $D_{17.5}^{16}$ = **1.016**

Ⓓ **Saponification:** Hydrolysis with alk. (T 1.51) yields benzyl alc. (1:6480) and *n*-butyric ac. (1:1035).

1:3982 METHYL HYDROCINNAMATE $C_{10}H_{12}O_2$ **Beil. IX-510**
(Methyl β-phenylpropionate)

B.P. 239° **Sap. Eq. 164** D^0 = **1.0455**

Ⓓ **Saponification:** Hydrolysis with alk. (T 1.51) yields methyl alc. (1:6120) and hydrocinnamic ac. (1:0615).

1:3987 GUAIACOL ACETATE $C_9H_{10}O_3$ **Beil. VI-774**
(*o*-Methoxyphenyl acetate)

B.P. 240° **Sap. Eq. 166** D_4^{25} = **1.1285** n_D^{25} = **1.5101**

Ⓓ **Saponification:** Hydrolysis with alk. (T 1.51) yields guaiacol (1:1405) and acetic ac. (1:1010).

—— **ISOPROPYL SALICYLATE** $C_{10}H_{12}O_3$ **Beil. S.N. 1061**

B.P. 240-242° **Sap. Eq. 180** D_4^{20} = **1.0729** n_D^{20} = **1.50650**

See 1:1763. Genus 4: Phenols.

1:3992 DIMETHYL *l*-MALATE $C_6H_{10}O_5$ **Beil. III-429**

B.P. 242° **Sap. Eq. 81** D_4^{20} = **1.2334** n_D^{20} = **1.4425**

$[\alpha]_D^{20}$ = **−6.85°.**

Ⓓ **Saponification:** Hydrolysis with alk. (T 1.51) yields methyl alc. (1:6120) and *l*-malic ac. (1:0450).

1:3997 GERANYL ACETATE $C_{12}H_{20}O_2$ **Beil. II-140**

B.P. 242° **Sap. Eq. 196** D^{15} = **0.9174** n_D^{20} = **1.4660**

Ⓓ **Saponification:** Hydrolysis with alk. (T 1.51) yields geraniol (1:6270) and acetic ac. (1:1010).

1:4006 ISOBUTYL BENZOATE $C_{11}H_{14}O_2$ **Beil. IX-113**

B.P. 242.2° cor. ⟨1⟩ **Sap. Eq. 178** D_4^{15} = **1.0018**

Ⓓ **Saponification:** Hydrolysis with alk. (T 1.51) yields isobutyl alc. (1:6165) and benzoic ac. (1:0715).

1:4006 ⟨1⟩ Timmermans, *Cent.* **1914,** I, 619.

1:4011 *n*-OCTYL *n*-BUTYRATE $C_{12}H_{24}O_2$ **Beil. II-272**

B.P. 244.1° ⟨1⟩ **Sap. Eq. 200** D^{20} = **0.86288** ⟨1⟩ $n_{He\ (yel.)}^{15}$ = **1.42674** ⟨1⟩
M.P. −55.6° ⟨1⟩

Ⓓ **Saponification:** Hydrolysis with alk. (T 1.51) yields *n*-octyl alc. (1:6255) and *n*-butyric ac. (1:1035).

1:4011 ⟨1⟩ Bilterys, Gisseleire, *Bull. soc. chim. Belg.* **44,** 578–579 (1935).

1:4016 ETHYL *n*-CAPRATE $C_{12}H_{24}O_2$ **Beil. II-356**

B.P. 244.9° ⟨1⟩ **Sap. Eq. 200** D_4^{20} = **0.8650** ⟨2⟩ n_D^{20} = **1.42575** ⟨2⟩
M.P. −19.9° ⟨1⟩ D_4^{25} = **0.8609** ⟨2⟩ n_D^{25} = **1.42376** ⟨2⟩

Ⓓ **Saponification:** Hydrolysis with alk. (T 1.51) yields ethyl alc. (1:6130) and *n*-capric ac. (1:0585).

1:4016 ⟨1⟩ Deffet, *Bull. soc. chim. Belg.* **40,** 391 (1931). ⟨2⟩ Kao, Ma, *Science Repts. Natl. Tsing Hua Univ.*, Ser. **A-1,** 181–183 (1932).

1:4021 METHYL PHENOXYACETATE $C_9H_{10}O_3$ **Beil. VI-162**

B.P. 245° **Sap. Eq. 166** $D^{17.5}$ = **1.150**

Ⓓ **Saponification:** Hydrolysis with alk. (T 1.51) yields methyl alc. (1:6120) and phenoxyacetic ac. (1:0680).

1:4026 THYMYL ACETATE $C_{12}H_{16}O_2$ **Beil. VI-537**

B.P. 245° **Sap. Eq. 192** D^0 = **1.009**

Ⓓ **Saponification:** Hydrolysis with alk. (T 1.51) yields thymol (1:1430) and acetic ac. (1:1010).

1:4031 CARVACRYL ACETATE $C_{12}H_{16}O_2$ **Beil. VI-529**

B.P. 245° cor. ⟨1⟩ **Sap. Eq. 192** D^{25} = **0.98959** n_D^{28} = **1.49128**

Ⓓ **Saponification:** Hydrolysis with alk. (T 1.51) yields carvacrol (1:1760) and acetic ac. (1:1010).

1:4031 ⟨1⟩ Bogert, Goldstein, *Am. Perfumer* **23,** 524–526 (1928).

1:4036 n-BUTYL n-CAPRYLATE $C_{12}H_{24}O_2$ **Beil. II-348**

B.P. 245.0° ⟨1⟩ **Sap. Eq. 200** D^{20} = **0.86278 ⟨1⟩** $n^{15}_{He\ (yel.)}$ = **1.42647 ⟨1⟩**
M.P. −42.9° ⟨1⟩

Ⓓ **Saponification:** Hydrolysis with alk. (T 1.51) yields *n*-butyl alc. (1:6180) and *n*-caprylic ac. (1:1145).

1:4036 ⟨1⟩ Bilterys, Gisseleire, *Bull. soc. chim. Belg.* **44,** 573 (1935).

1:4041 2,4,5-TRIMETHYLPHENYL ACETATE $C_{11}H_{14}O_2$ **Beil. S.N. 510**
(Pseudocumenyl acetate)

B.P. 245-246° ⟨1⟩ **Sap. Eq. 178**
M.P. 34- 34.5° ⟨1⟩

Ⓓ **Saponification:** Hydrolysis with alk. (T 1.51) yields 2,4,5-trimethylphenol (1:1469) and acetic ac. (1:1010).

1:4041 ⟨1⟩ von Auwers, Bundesmann, Wieners, *Ann.* **447,** 183 (1926).

1:4046 n-HEPTYL n-VALERATE $C_{12}H_{24}O_2$ **Beil. II-301**

B.P. 245.2° ⟨1⟩ **Sap. Eq. 200** D^{20} = **0.86225 ⟨1⟩** $n^{15}_{He\ (yel.)}$ = **1.42536 ⟨1⟩**
M.P. −46.4° ⟨1⟩

Ⓓ **Saponification:** Hydrolysis with alk. (T 1.51) yields *n*-heptyl alc. (1:6240) and *n*-valeric ac. (1:1060).

1:4046 ⟨1⟩ Bilterys, Gisseleire, *Bull. soc. chim. Belg.* **44,** 576–577 (1935).

1:4051 n-AMYL n-ENANTHATE $C_{12}H_{24}O_2$ **Beil. S.N. 162**
(*n*-Amyl *n*-heptylate)

B.P. 245.4° ⟨1⟩ **Sap. Eq. 200** D^{20} = **0.86232 ⟨1⟩** $n^{15}_{He\ (yel.)}$ = **1.42627 ⟨1⟩**
M.P. −49.5° ⟨1⟩

Ⓓ **Saponification:** Hydrolysis with alk. (T 1.51) yields *n*-amyl alc. (1:6205) and enanthic ac. (1:1140).

1:4051 ⟨1⟩ Bilterys, Gisseleire, *Bull. soc. chim. Belg.* **44,** 572 (1935).

1:4056 DIETHYL ADIPATE $C_{10}H_{18}O_4$ **Beil. II-652**

B.P. 245° **Sap. Eq. 101** D^{20}_4 = **1.0090 ⟨1⟩** n^{20}_D = **1.42765 ⟨1⟩**
M.P. −21°

Ⓓ **Saponification:** Hydrolysis with alk. (T 1.51) yields ethyl alc. (1:6130) and adipic ac. (1:0775).

1:4056 ⟨1⟩ Vogel, *J. Chem. Soc.* **1934,** 339.

1:4061 n-HEXYL n-CAPROATE $C_{12}H_{24}O_2$ **Beil. II-323**

B.P. 245.4° ⟨1⟩ **Sap. Eq. 200** D^{20} = **0.86216 ⟨1⟩** $n^{15}_{He\ (yel.)}$ = **1.42637 ⟨1⟩**
M.P. −55.3° ⟨1⟩

Ⓓ **Saponification:** Hydrolysis with alk. (T 1.51) yields *n*-hexyl alc. (1:6230) and *n*-caproic ac. (1:1130).

1:4061 ⟨1⟩ Bilterys, Gisseleire, *Bull. soc. chim. Belg.* **44,** 574–575 (1935).

1:4066 DI-(β-ETHOXYETHYL) CARBONATE $C_9H_{18}O_5$ **Beil. S.N. 199**

B.P. 245.5° ⟨1⟩ **Sap. Eq. 206** D_4^{25} = **1.0635** ⟨1⟩ n_D^{25} = **1.4239** ⟨1⟩

Ⓓ **Saponification:** Hydrolysis with alk. (T 1.51) yields ethylene glycol monoethyl ether (1:6410) and CO_2. [Cf. ⟨1⟩.]

1:4066 ⟨1⟩ Drake, Carter, *J. Am. Chem. Soc.* **52,** 3722 (1930).

1:4071 DI-*n*-BUTYL OXALATE $C_{10}H_{18}O_4$ **Beil. II-540**

B.P. 245.5° ⟨1⟩ **Sap. Eq. 101** D_4^{20} = **0.98732** ⟨2⟩ n_D^{20} = **1.4240** ⟨2⟩
M.P. −29.6° ⟨1⟩ D_4^{25} = **0.98157** ⟨2⟩ n_D^{25} = **1.4221** ⟨2⟩

[For prepn. in 90% yield from ord. cryst. oxalic ac. + *n*-butyl alc. see ⟨3⟩.]

C̄ in alc. stood overnight at 0° with 1 mole conc. aq. NH_4OH yields *n*-butyl oxamate, cryst. from MeOH or EtOH, m.p. 82–84° ⟨2⟩.

Ⓓ **Saponification:** Hydrolysis with alk. (T 1.51) yields *n*-butyl alc. (1:6180) and oxalic ac. (1:0445).

1:4071 ⟨1⟩ Timmermans, *Bull. soc. chim. Belg.* **36,** 506 (1927). ⟨2⟩ Sah, Chien, *J. Am. Chem. Soc.* **53,** 3902 (1931). ⟨3⟩ Dutt, *J. Chem. Soc.* **123,** 2715 (1923).

1:4076 DIETHYLENE GLYCOL DIACETATE $C_8H_{14}O_5$ **Beil. II-141**
(β,β′-Diacetoxydiethyl ether)

B.P. 245-251° **Sap. Eq. 95** D_{15}^{15} = **1.1078** ⟨1⟩ n_D^{20} = **1.4348** ⟨2⟩
B.P. 148° at 26 mm. ⟨1⟩ D_{20}^{20} = **1.123** ⟨2⟩

Ⓓ **Saponification:** Hydroysis with alk. (T 1.51) yields diethylene glycol (1:6525) and acetic ac. (1:1010). [C̄ may also be hydrolyzed with MeOH + HCl gas ⟨1⟩.]

1:4076 ⟨1⟩ Cretcher, Pittenger, *J. Am. Chem. Soc.* **47,** 165–166 (1925). ⟨2⟩ Macleod, *J. Chem. Soc.* **1928,** 3092.

1:4081 ETHYL HYDROCINNAMATE $C_{11}H_{14}O_2$ **Beil. IX-511**
(Ethyl β-phenylpropionate)

B.P. 247.2° **Sap. Eq. 178** D_4^{20} = **1.0147** n_D^{20} = **1.49542**

Ⓓ **Saponification:** Hydrolysis with alk. (T 1.51) yields ethyl alc. (1:6130) and hydrocinnamic ac. (1:0615).

1:4086 DI-*n*-PROPYL SUCCINATE $C_{10}H_{18}O_4$ **Beil. II-611**

B.P. 248.0° ⟨1⟩ **Sap. Eq. 101** D_4^{20} = **1.011** ⟨1⟩ n_D^{20} = **1.4252** ⟨1⟩
M.P. −10.4° ⟨1⟩

Ⓓ **Saponification:** Hydrolysis with alk. (T 1.51) yields *n*-propyl alc. (1:6150) and succinic ac. (1:0530).

1:4086 ⟨1⟩ Contzen-Crowet, *Bull. soc. chim. Belg.* **35,** 189 (1926).

1:4091 METHYL *o*-METHOXYBENZOATE $C_9H_{10}O_3$ **Beil. X-71**

B.P. 248° ⟨1⟩ **Sap. Eq. 166** D_4^{19} = **1.1571** $n_D^{19.5}$ = **1.534**

Ⓓ **Saponification:** Hydrolysis with alk. (T 1.51) yields methyl alc. (1:6120) and *o*-methoxybenzoic ac. (1:0685).

1:4091 ⟨1⟩ Kahovec, Kohlrausch, *Z. physik. Chem.* **B-38,** 134 (1937).

1:4093 METHYL UNDECYLENATE $C_{12}H_{22}O_2$ **Beil. II-459**

B.P. 248° **Sap. Eq. 198** $D^{15} = 0.889$ $n_D^{20} = 1.43928$
M.P. −27.5°

Ⓓ **Saponification:** Hydrolysis with alk. (T 1.51) yields methyl alc. (1:6120) and undecylenic ac. (1:0570).

1:4096 ISOAMYL LEVULINATE $C_{10}H_{18}O_3$ **Beil. S.N. 281**

B.P. 248.8° ⟨1⟩ **Sap. Eq. 186** $D_4^{20} = 0.96136$ ⟨1⟩ $n_D^{20} = 1.43102$ ⟨1⟩

Ⓓ **Isoamyl levulinate semicarbazone:** m.p. 91–92° ⟨2⟩.
Ⓓ **Isoamyl levulinate phenylhydrazone:** m.p. 70–72° ⟨2⟩.
Ⓓ **Isoamyl levulinate 2,4-dinitrophenylhydrazone:** m.p. 50.5° ⟨3⟩ [cf. T 1.14].
Ⓓ **Saponification:** Hydrolysis with alk. (T 1.51) yields isoamyl alc. (1:6200) and levulinic ac. (1:0405).

1:4096 ⟨1⟩ Cox, Dodds, *J. Am. Chem. Soc.* **55,** 3393 (1933). ⟨2⟩ Sah, Ma, *J. Am. Chem. Soc.* **52,** 4882–4883 (1930). ⟨3⟩ Cowley, Schuette, *J. Am. Chem. Soc.* **55,** 3464 (1933).

—— **DIETHYL ACETONEDICARBOXYLATE** $C_9H_{14}O_5$ **Beil. III-791**

B.P. 250° $D_4^{20} = 1.113$

See 1:1772. Genus 4: Phenols.

—— **METHYL *d,l*-MANDELATE** $C_9H_{10}O_3$ **Beil. X-202**

B.P. 250° **Sap. Eq. 166**

See 1:2166. Genus 5: Esters. M.P. 53.3°.

1:4104 *n*-BUTYL BENZOATE $C_{11}H_{14}O_2$ **Beil. IX-112**

B.P. 250.3° ⟨1⟩ **Sap. Eq. 178** $D_{15}^{15} = 1.0111$
M.P. −22.4° ⟨1⟩

Ⓓ **Saponification:** Hydrolysis with alk. (T 1.51) yields *n*-butyl alc. (1:6180) and benzoic ac. (1:0715).

1:4104 ⟨1⟩ Timmermans, *Bull. soc. chim. Belg.* **30,** 69 (1921).

—— ***n*-PROPYL SALICYLATE** $C_{10}H_{12}O_3$ **Beil. X-75**

B.P. 249-251° **Sap. Eq. 180** $D_4^{20} = 1.0979$ $n_D^{20} = 1.51610$

See 1:1774. Genus 4: Phenols.

1:4106 ETHYL PHENOXYACETATE $C_{10}H_{12}O_3$ **Beil. VI-162**

B.P. 251° **Sap. Eq. 180** $D^{17.5} = 1.104$

Ⓓ **Saponification:** Hydrolysis with alk. (T 1.51) yields ethyl alc. (1:6130) and phenoxyacetic ac. (1:0680).

1:4111 METHYL *m*-METHOXYBENZOATE $C_9H_{10}O_3$ **Beil. X-139**

B.P. 252° **Sap. Eq. 166** $D^{20} = 1.131$ $n_D = 1.52236$

Ⓓ **Saponification:** Hydrolysis with alk. (T 1.51) yields methyl alc. (1:6120) and *m*-methoxybenzoic ac. (1:0703).

1:4116 DIETHYL *l*-MALATE $C_8H_{14}O_5$ **Beil. III-430**

B.P. 253° **Sap. Eq. 95** D_4^{20} = **1.1290** n_D^{20} = **1.4362**
$[\alpha]_D^{20}$ = **−10.18°**

Ⓓ **Saponification:** Hydrolysis with alk. (T 1.51) yields ethyl alc. (1:6130) and *l*-malic ac. (1:0450).

1:4121 *n*-AMYL LEVULINATE $C_{10}H_{18}O_3$ **Beil. S.N. 281**

B.P. 253.4° ⟨1⟩ **Sap. Eq. 186** D_4^{20} = **0.96136 ⟨1⟩** n_D^{20} = **1.43192 ⟨1⟩**

Ⓓ ***n*-Amyl levulinate 2,4-dinitrophenylhydrazone:** m.p. 84.2° ⟨2⟩.

Ⓓ **Saponification:** Hydrolysis with alk. (T 1.51) yields *n*-amyl alc. (1:6205) and levulinic ac. (1:0405).

1:4121 ⟨1⟩ Cox, Dodds, *J. Am. Chem. Soc.* **55,** 3393 (1933). ⟨2⟩ Cowley, Schuette, *J. Am. Chem. Soc.* **55,** 3464 (1933).

—— **METHYL *p*-METHOXYBENZOATE** $C_9H_{10}O_3$ **Beil. X-159**

B.P. 255° **Sap. Eq. 166**

See 1:2128. Genus 5: Esters. M.P. 49°.

1:4126 β-METHOXYETHYL BENZOATE $C_{10}H_{12}O_3$ **Beil. IX-129**
(Methyl " cellosolve " benzoate)

B.P. 255° **Sap. Eq. 180** D_{25}^{25} = **1.0891 ⟨1⟩** n_D^{25} = **1.5040 ⟨1⟩**
252° at 738.5 mm. ⟨1⟩

Ⓓ **Saponification:** Hydrolysis with alk. (T 1.51) yields β-methoxyethyl alc. (1:6405) and benzoic ac. (1:0715).

1:4126 ⟨1⟩ Conn, Collett, Lazzell, *J. Am. Chem. Soc.* **54,** 4372 (1932).

1:4131 ETHYL *m*-METHOXYBENZOATE $C_{10}H_{12}O_3$ **Beil. X-139**

B.P. 260° **Sap. Eq. 180** D_4^{20} = **1.0993 ⟨1⟩** n_D^{20} = **1.5161 ⟨1⟩**
D_4^{25} = **1.0949 ⟨1⟩**

Ⓓ **Saponification:** Hydrolysis with alk. (T 1.51) yields ethyl alc. (1:6130) and *m*-methoxybenzoic ac. (1:0703).

1:4131 ⟨1⟩ Thompson, *J. Am. Chem. Soc.* **59,** 816 (1937).

1:4136 *n*-AMYL *n*-CAPRYLATE $C_{13}H_{26}O_2$ **Beil. S.N. 162**

B.P. 260.2° ⟨1⟩ **Sap. Eq. 214** D^{20} = **0.86132 ⟨1⟩** $n_{He\,(yel.)}^{15}$ = **1.43019 ⟨2⟩**
M.P. −34.8° ⟨1⟩

Ⓓ **Saponification:** Hydrolysis with alk. (T 1.51) yields *n*-amyl alc. (1:6205) and *n*-caprylic ac. (1:1145).

1:4136 ⟨1⟩ Bilterys, Gisseleire, *Bull. soc. chim. Belg.* **44,** 573 (1935).

1:4141 *n*-HEXYL *n*-ENANTHATE $C_{13}H_{26}O_2$ **Beil. S.N. 162**
(*n*-Hexyl *n*-heptylate)

B.P. 260.9° ⟨1⟩ **Sap. Eq. 214** D^{20} = **0.86114 ⟨1⟩** $n_{He\,(yel.)}^{15}$ = **1.42939 ⟨1⟩**
M.P. −47.9° ⟨1⟩

Ⓓ **Saponification:** Hydrolysis with alk. (T 1.51) yields *n*-hexyl alc. (1:6230) and enanthic ac. (1:1140).

1:4141 ⟨1⟩ Bilterys, Gisseleire, *Bull. soc. chim. Belg.* **44,** 574–575 (1935).

—— **ISOBUTYL SALICYLATE** $C_{11}H_{14}O_3$ **Beil. X-76**

B.P. 260-262° **Sap. Eq. 194** D_4^{20} = **1.0639** n_D^{20} = **1.50872**

See 1:1776. Genus 4: Phenols.

1:4146 β-ETHOXYETHYL BENZOATE $C_{11}H_{14}O_3$ **Beil. S.N. 901**
(" Cellosolve " benzoate)

B.P. 260-261° at 738.5 mm. ⟨1⟩ **Sap. Eq. 194**
D_{25}^{25} = **1.0585 ⟨1⟩** n_D^{25} = **1.4969 ⟨1⟩**

Ⓓ **Saponification:** Hydrolysis with alk. (T 1.51) yields β-ethoxyethyl alc. (1:6410) and benzoic ac. (1:0715).

1:4146 ⟨1⟩ Conn, Collett, Lazzell, *J. Am. Chem. Soc.* **54,** 4372 (1932).

—— **METHYL CINNAMATE** $C_{10}H_{10}O_2$ **Beil. IX-581**

B.P. 261° **Sap. Eq. 162**

See 1:2090. Genus 5: Esters. M.P. 36°.

1:4151 ETHYL *o*-METHOXYBENZOATE $C_{10}H_{12}O_3$ **Beil. X-74**

B.P. 261° **Sap. Eq. 180** D_4^{20} = **1.1124 ⟨1⟩** n_D^{20} = **1.5224 ⟨1⟩**
D_4^{25} = **1.1077 ⟨1⟩**

Ⓓ **Saponification:** Hydrolysis with alk. (T 1.51) yields ethyl alc. (1:6130) and *o*-methoxybenzoic ac. (1:0685).

1:4151 ⟨1⟩ Thompson, *J. Am. Chem. Soc.* **59,** 816 (1937).

1:4156 *n*-HEPTYL *n*-CAPROATE $C_{13}H_{26}O_2$ **Beil. II-323**

B.P. 261.0° ⟨1⟩ **Sap. Eq. 214** D^{20} = **0.86115 ⟨1⟩** $n_{He\ (yel.)}^{15}$ = **1.42934 ⟨1⟩**
M.P. −34.4° ⟨1⟩

Ⓓ **Saponification:** Hydrolysis with alk. (T 1.51) yields *n*-heptyl alc. (1:6240) and *n*-caproic ac. (1:1130).

1:4156 ⟨1⟩ Bilterys, Gisseleire, *Bull. soc. chim. Belg.* **44,** 576–577 (1935).

1:4161 *n*-OCTYL *n*-VALERATE $C_{13}H_{26}O_2$ **Beil. II-301**

B.P. 261.6° ⟨1⟩ **Sap. Eq. 214** D^{20} = **0.86148 ⟨1⟩** $n_{He\ (yel.)}^{15}$ = **1.42727 ⟨1⟩**
M.P. −42.3° ⟨1⟩

Ⓓ **Saponification:** Hydrolysis with alk. (T 1.51) yields *n*-octyl alc. (1:6255) and *n*-valeric ac. (1:1060).

1:4161 ⟨1⟩ Bilterys, Gisseleire, *Bull. soc. chim. Belg.* **44,** 578–579 (1935).

1:4166 ISOAMYL BENZOATE $C_{12}H_{16}O_2$ **Beil. IX-113**

B.P. 262.3° ⟨1⟩ **Sap. Eq. 192** $D_{14.4}^{14.4}$ = **0.9925** n_D^{20} = **1.4950 ⟨2⟩**

Ⓓ **Saponification:** Hydrolysis with alk. (T 1.51) yields isoamyl alc. (1:6200) and benzoic ac. (1:0715).

1:4166 ⟨1⟩ Timmermans, *Cent.* **1914,** I, 619. ⟨2⟩ Hennion, Hinton, Nieuwland, *J. Am. Chem. Soc.* **55,** 2858 (1933).

1:4171 DIMETHYL *d*-CAMPHORATE $C_{12}H_{20}O_4$ **Beil. IX-750**

B.P. 263° **Sap. Eq. 114** D_4^{20} = **1.0747** $n_D^{16.9}$ = **1.46334**

Ⓓ **Saponification:** Hydrolysis with alk. (T 1.51) yields methyl alc. (1:6120) and *d*-camphoric ac. (1:0810).

1:4176 ETHYL UNDECYLENATE $C_{13}H_{24}O_2$ **Beil. II-459**

B.P. 264° **Sap. Eq. 212** D_{15}^{15} = **0.88271** n_D^{23} = **1.4449**
M.P. −37.5°

Ⓓ **Saponification:** Hydrolysis with alk. (T 1.51) yields ethyl alc. (1:6130) and undecylenic ac. (1:0570).

1:4181 DIISOAMYL OXALATE $C_{12}H_{22}O_4$ **Beil. II-540**

B.P. 267-268° ⟨1⟩ **Sap. Eq. 115** D_{11}^{11} = **0.968**

[For prepn. in 85% yield from ord. hydrated oxalic ac. + isoamyl alc. see ⟨2⟩.]

Ⓓ **Saponification:** Hydrolysis with alk. (T 1.51) yields isoamyl alc. (1:6200) and oxalic ac. (1:0445).

1:4181 ⟨1⟩ Adams, Weeks, *J. Am. Chem. Soc.* **38,** 2517 (1916). ⟨2⟩ Dutt, *J. Chem. Soc.* **123,** 2715 (1923).

—— **ETHYL BENZOYLACETATE** $C_{11}H_{12}O_3$ **Beil. X-674**

B.P. 265-270° sl. dec. D_4^{20} = **1.116** n_D^{20} = **1.5498**

See 1:1778. Genus 4: Phenols.

1:4186 DIMETHYL SUBERATE $C_{10}H_{18}O_4$ **Beil. II-693**

B.P. 268° **Sap. Eq. 101** D_4^{20} = **1.0198 ⟨1⟩** n_D^{20} = **1.43326 ⟨1⟩**
M.P. −5°

Ⓓ **Saponification:** Hydrolysis with alk. (T 1.51) yields methyl alc. (1:6120) and suberic ac. (1:0755).

1:4186 ⟨1⟩ Vogel, *J. Chem. Soc.* **1934,** 338.

1:4191 ETHYL *p*-METHOXYBENZOATE $C_{10}H_{12}O_3$ **Beil. X-159**

B.P. 269° **Sap. Eq. 180** D_4^{20} = **1.1038 ⟨1⟩** n_D^{20} = **1.5254 ⟨1⟩**
M.P. +7 D_4^{25} = **1.0994 ⟨1⟩**

Ⓓ **Saponification:** Hydrolysis with alk. (T 1.51) yields ethyl alc. (1:6120) and *p*-methoxybenzoic ac. (1:0805).

1:4191 ⟨1⟩ Thompson, *J. Am. Chem. Soc.* **59,** 817 (1937).

1:4196 ETHYL LAURATE $C_{14}H_{28}O_2$ **Beil. II-361**

B.P. 269° **Sap. Eq. 228** D_{19}^{19} = **0.8671** n_D^{20} = **1.4321**
M.P. −1.7° ⟨1⟩

Ⓓ **Saponification:** Hydrolysis with alk. (T 1.51) yields ethyl alc. (1:6130) and lauric ac. (1:0605).

1:4201 TRIMETHYL ACONITATE $C_9H_{12}O_6$ **Beil. II-852**

B.P. 270° **Sap. Eq. 72**

Ⓓ **Saponification:** Hydrolysis with alk. (T 1.51) yields methyl alc. (1:6120) and aconitic ac. (1:0540).

—— **METHYL PIPERONYLATE** $C_9H_8O_4$ **Beil. XIX-269**

B.P. 270° **Sap. Eq. 180**

See 1:2149. Genus 5: Esters. M.P. 51–52°.

—— ***n*-BUTYL SALICYLATE** $C_{11}H_{14}O_3$ **Beil. S.N. 1061**

B.P. 270-272° **Sap. Eq. 194** D_4^{20} = **1.0728** n_D^{20} = **1.51148**
B.P. (**259-260°**)

See 1:1780. Genus 4: Phenols.

1:4206 ETHYL CINNAMATE $C_{11}H_{12}O_2$ **Beil. IX-581**

B.P. 271° **Sap. Eq. 176** D_4^{20} = **1.0490** n_D^{20} = **1.55982**
M.P. 6.5°

[For prepn. in 68–74% yield from benzaldehyde + AcOEt see ⟨1⟩.]

Ⓓ **Saponification:** Hydrolysis with alk. (T 1.51) yields ethyl alc. (1:6130) and cinnamic ac. (1:0735).

1:4206 ⟨1⟩ Marvel, King, *Organic Syntheses, Coll. Vol.* I, 246–248 (1932).

1:4211 DI-*n*-BUTYL SUCCINATE $C_{12}H_{22}O_4$ **Beil. S.N. 172**

B.P. 274.5° ⟨1⟩ **Sap. Eq. 115** D_4^{20} = **0.9760** ⟨1⟩ n_D^{20} = **1.4298** ⟨1⟩
M.P. −29.3° ⟨2⟩.

Ⓓ **Saponification:** Hydrolysis with alk. (T 1.51) yields *n*-butyl alc. (1:6180) and succinic ac. (1:0530).

1:4211 ⟨1⟩ Contzen-Crowet, *Bull. soc. chim. Belg.* **35,** 189 (1926). ⟨2⟩ Timmermans, *Bull. soc. chim. Belg.* **36,** 507 (1927).

1:4216 TRIETHYL ACONITATE $C_{12}H_{18}O_6$ **Beil. II-852**

B.P. 275° dec. **Sap. Eq. 86** D_4^{20} = **1.1064** n_D^{20} = **1.45562**

Ⓓ **Saponification:** Hydrolysis with alk. (T 1.51) yields ethyl alc. (1:6130) and aconitic ac. (1:0540).

1:4221 DIISOPROPYL *d*-TARTRATE $C_{10}H_{18}O_6$ **Beil. III-517**

B.P. 275°/765 mm. ⟨1⟩ **Sap. Eq. 117** D_4^{17} = **1.1274** ⟨1⟩ $[\alpha]_D^{20}$ = **+14.886°**

Ⓓ **Saponification:** Hydrolysis with alk. (T 1.51) yields isopropyl alc. (1:6135) and *d*-tartaric ac. (1:0525).

1:4221 ⟨1⟩ Campbell, *J. Chem. Soc.* **1929,** 1115–1119.

1:4226 DIISOPROPYL *d,l*-TARTRATE $C_{10}H_{18}O_6$ **Beil. S.N. 250**
(Diisopropyl racemate)

B.P. 275°/765 mm. ⟨1⟩ **Sap. Eq. 117** D_4^{20} = **1.1166** ⟨1⟩
M.P. 34° ⟨1⟩

Ⓓ **Saponification:** Hydrolysis with alk. (T 1.51) yields isopropyl alc. (1:6135) and *d,l*-tartaric ac. (1:0550).

1:4226 ⟨1⟩ Campbell, *J. Chem. Soc.* **1929,** 1113–1116.

1:4231 ETHYL *p*-ETHOXYBENZOATE $C_{11}H_{14}O_3$ **Beil. X-159**

B.P. 275° **Sap. Eq. 194** D^{21} = **1.076**

C̄ boiled with hydrazine hydrate gives 95% yield *p*-ethoxybenzhydrazide, tbls. from alc., m.p. 126–127° ⟨1⟩ ⟨2⟩.

Ⓓ **Saponification:** Hydrolysis with alk. (T 1.51) yields ethyl alc. (1:6130) and *p*-ethoxybenzoic ac. (1:0817).

1:4231 ⟨1⟩ Sah, Chang, *Ber.* **69,** 2763 (1936). ⟨2⟩ Curtius, Ulmer, *J. prakt. Chem.* (2) **125,** 56 (1930).

1:4236 *n*-OCTYL *n*-CAPROATE $C_{14}H_{28}O_2$ **Beil. II-323**

B.P. 275.2° ⟨1⟩ **Sap. Eq. 228** D^{20} = **0.86032** ⟨1⟩ $n^{15}_{He\ (yel.)}$ = **1.43256** ⟨1⟩
M.P. −28.4° ⟨1⟩

Ⓓ **Saponification:** Hydrolysis with alk. (T 1.51) yields *n*-octyl alc. (1:6255) and *n*-caproic ac. (1:1130).

1:4236 ⟨1⟩ Bilterys, Gisseleire, *Bull. soc. chim. Belg.* **44,** 578–579 (1935).

—— **ISOAMYL SALICYLATE** $C_{12}H_{16}O_3$ **Beil. X-76**

B.P. 276-278° **Sap. Eq. 208** D_4^{20} = **1.0535** n_D^{20} = **1.50799**

See 1:1790. Genus 4: Phenols.

1:4241 *n*-HEPTYL *n*-ENANTHATE $C_{14}H_{28}O_2$ **Beil. II-340**
(*n*-Heptyl *n*-heptylate)

B.P. 277.2° ⟨1⟩ **Sap. Eq. 228** D^{20} = **0.86039** ⟨1⟩ $n^{15}_{He\ (yel.)}$ = **1.43183** ⟨1⟩
M.P. −33.3° ⟨1⟩

Ⓓ **Saponification:** Hydrolysis with alk. (T 1.51) yields *n*-heptyl alc. (1:6240) and enanthic ac. (1:1140).

1:4241 ⟨1⟩ Bilterys, Gisseleire, *Bull. soc. chim. Belg.* **44,** 576–577 (1935).

1:4246 *n*-HEXYL *n*-CAPRYLATE $C_{14}H_{28}O_2$ **Beil. S.N. 162**

B.P. 277.4° ⟨1⟩ **Sap. Eq. 228** D^{20} = **0.86033** ⟨1⟩ $n^{15}_{He\ (yel.)}$ = **1.43230** ⟨1⟩
M.P. −30.6° ⟨1⟩

Ⓓ **Saponification:** Hydrolysis with alk. (T 1.51) yields *n*-hexyl alc. (1:6230) and *n*-caprylic ac. (1:1145).

1:4246 ⟨1⟩ Bilterys, Gisseleire, *Bull. soc. chim. Belg.* **44,** 574–575 (1935).

1:4251 RESORCINOL DIACETATE $C_{10}H_{10}O_4$ **Beil. VI-816**

B.P. 278° sl. dec. **Sap. Eq. 97**

Ⓓ **Saponification:** Hydrolysis with alk. (T **1.51**) **yields resorcinol (1:1530) and acetic ac.** (1:1010).

1:4256 DIETHYL *d*-TARTRATE $C_8H_{14}O_6$ **Beil. III-513**

B.P. 280 ° **Sap. Eq. 103** D_4^{20} = **1.2028 ⟨1⟩** n_D^{20} = **1.44677 ⟨1⟩**
M.P. +18.6° ⟨1⟩

$[\alpha]^{20}_{Hg\ (green)}$ = **+7.87°** ⟨1⟩ — [For nature of green color observed when $\bar{C}$ is htd. see ⟨2⟩.]

Ⓓ **Saponification:** Hydrolysis with alk. (T 1.51) yields ethyl alc. (1:6130) and *d*-tartaric ac. (1:0525).

1:4256 ⟨1⟩ Lowry, Cutter, *J. Chem. Soc.* **121,** 532–544 (1922). ⟨2⟩ Patterson, Lamberton, *J. Chem. Soc.* **1937,** 963–964.

—— **DIMETHYL *d,l*-TARTRATE** $C_6H_{10}O_6$ **Beil. III-527**

B.P. 282° **Sap. Eq. 89**

See 1:2385. Genus 5: Esters. M.P. 90°.

1:4261 DIETHYL SUBERATE $C_{12}H_{22}O_4$ **Beil. II-693**

B.P. 282° **Sap. Eq. 115** D_4^{20} = **0.9807 ⟨1⟩** n_D^{20} = **1.43236 ⟨1⟩**

Ⓓ **Saponification:** Hydrolysis with alk. (T 1.51) yields ethyl alc. (1:6130) and suberic ac. (1:0755).

1:4261 ⟨1⟩ Vogel, *J. Chem. Soc.* **1934,** 339.

1:4266 EUGENOL ACETATE $C_{12}H_{14}O_3$ **Beil. VI-965**

B.P. 282° **Sap. Eq. 206** D_{15}^{15} = **1.087** n_D^{20} = **1.52069**
M.P. 30°

Ⓓ **Saponification:** Hydrolysis with alk. (T 1.51) yields eugenol (1:1775) and acetic ac. (1:1010). [$\bar{C}$ boiled with conc. NaOH yields NaOAc + Na eugenolate which seps. as white cryst. mass ⟨1⟩.]

1:4266 ⟨1⟩ Erdmann, *J. prakt. Chem.* (2) **56,** 148–150 (1897).

—— **RESORCINOL MONOACETATE** $C_8H_8O_3$ **Beil. VI-816**

B.P. 283°

See 1:1795. Genus 4: Phenols.

—— **ISOEUGENOL ACETATE** $C_{12}H_{14}O_3$ **Beil. VI-958**

B.P. 283° **Sap. Eq. 206**

See 1:2340. Genus 5: Esters. M.P. 79°.

1:4271 DIMETHYL PHTHALATE $C_{10}H_{10}O_4$ **Beil. IX-797**

B.P. 283.8° ⟨1⟩ **Sap. Eq. 97** D_{25}^{25} = **1.188 ⟨1⟩** n_D^{20} = **1.5138 ⟨1⟩**

Ⓓ **Saponification:** Hydrolysis with alk. (T 1.51) yields methyl alc. (1:6120) and phthalic ac. (1:0820).

1:4271 ⟨1⟩ Gardner, Brewer, *Ind. Eng. Chem.* **29,** 179 (1937).

1:4276 DIETHYL ISOPHTHALATE $C_{12}H_{14}O_4$ **Beil. IX-834**

B.P. 286°/733 mm. **Sap. Eq. 111**
M.P. +11.5°

Ⓓ **Saponification:** Hydrolysis with alk. (T 1.51) yields ethyl alc. (1:6130) and isophthalic ac. (1:0900).

1:4281 DI-*n*-PROPYL *d,l*-TARTRATE $C_{10}H_{18}O_6$ **Beil. S.N. 250**
(Di-*n*-propyl racemate)

B.P. 286°/ 765 mm. ⟨1⟩ **Sap. Eq. 117** D_4^{20} = **1.1256**
M.P. 25° ⟨1⟩

Ⓓ **Saponification:** Hydrolysis with alk. (T 1.51) yields *n*-propyl alc. **(1:6150)** and *d,l*-tartaric ac. (1:0550).

1:4281 ⟨1⟩ Campbell, *J. Chem. Soc.* **1929,** 1113–1116.

1:4286 DIETHYL *d*-CAMPHORATE $C_{14}H_{24}O_4$ **Beil. IX-751**

B.P. 286° **Sap. Eq. 128** D_4^{20} = **1.0298** $n_D^{26.2}$ = **1.45354**

Ⓓ **Saponification:** Hydrolysis with alk. (T 1.51) yields ethyl alc. (1:6130) and *d*-camphoric ac. (1:0810).

1:4291 ETHYL PIPERONYLATE $C_{10}H_{10}O_4$ **Beil. XIX-270**

B.P. 286° **Sap. Eq. 194**
M.P. +18.5°

Ⓓ **Saponification:** Hydrolysis with alk. (T **1.51**) yields ethyl alc. (1:6130) and piperonylic ac. (1:0865).

—— **METHYL β-NAPHTHOATE** $C_{12}H_{10}O_2$ **Beil. IX-657**

B.P. 290° **Sap. Eq. 186**

See 1:2330. Genus 5: Esters. M.P. **77°.**

1:4296 *n*-HEPTYL *n*-CAPRYLATE $C_{15}H_{30}O_2$ **Beil. II-348**

B.P. 290.6° ⟨1⟩ **Sap. Eq. 242** D^{20} = **0.85958** ⟨1⟩ $n_{\mathrm{He\ (yel.)}}^{15}$ = **1.43492** ⟨1⟩
M.P. −10.2° ⟨1⟩

Ⓓ **Saponification:** Hydrolysis with alk. (T 1.51) yields *n*-heptyl alc. (1:6240) and *n*-caprylic ac. (1:1145).

1:4296 ⟨1⟩ Bilterys, Gisseleire, *Bull. soc. chim. Belg.* **44,** 576–577 (1935).

1:4301 *n*-OCTYL *n*-ENANTHATE $C_{15}H_{30}O_2$ **Beil. II-340**
(*n*-Octyl *n*-heptylate)

B.P. 290.8° ⟨1⟩ **Sap. Eq. 242** D^{20} = **0.85961** ⟨1⟩ $n_{\mathrm{He\ (yel.)}}^{15}$ = **1.43488** ⟨1⟩
M.P. −21.5° ⟨1⟩

Ⓓ **Saponification:** Hydrolysis with alk. (T 1.51) yields *n*-octyl alc. (1:6255) and enanthic ac. (1:1140).

1:4301 ⟨1⟩ Bilterys, Gisseleire, *Bull. soc. chim. Belg.* **44,** 578–579 (1935).

1:4306 DIETHYL AZELATE $C_{13}H_{24}O_4$ **Beil. II-709**

B.P. 291° **Sap. Eq. 122** D_4^{20} = **0.97294** n_D^{20} = **1.43509**
M.P. −18.5°

Ⓓ **Saponification:** Hydrolysis with alk. (T 1.51) yields ethyl alc. (1:6130) and azelaic ac. (1:0695).

— **ETHYL 2-HYDROXY-3-NAPHTHOATE** $C_{13}H_{12}O_3$ **Beil. X-335**

B.P. 291° **Sap. Eq. 216**

See 1:2365. Genus 5: Esters. M.P. 85°.

1:4311 TRIETHYL CITRATE $C_{12}H_{20}O_7$ **Beil. III-568**

B.P. 294° **Sap. Eq. 92** D_4^{20} = **1.1369** n_D^{20} = **1.44554**

Ⓓ **Saponification:** Hydrolysis with alk. (T 1.51) yields ethyl alc. (1:6130) and citric ac. (1:0455).

1:4316 ETHYL MYRISTATE $C_{16}H_{32}O_2$ **Beil. II-365**

B.P. 295° **Sap. Eq. 256** D_4^{25} = **0.8573** ⟨1⟩ n_D^{20} = **1.4362** ⟨1⟩
M.P. +11.9° ⟨1⟩

A β-form has m.p. 12.3° ⟨2⟩ ⟨3⟩.

Ⓓ **Saponification:** Hydrolysis with alk. (T 1.51) yields ethyl alc. (1:6130) and myristic ac. (1:0630).

1:4316 ⟨1⟩ Ruhoff, Reid, *J. Am. Chem. Soc.* **55,** 3825 (1933). ⟨2⟩ Phillips, Mumford, *J. Chem. Soc.* **1932,** 902. ⟨3⟩ Mumford, Phillips, *Rec. trav. chim.* **52,** 183 (1933).

1:4321 DI-*n*-PROPYL *d*-TARTRATE $C_{10}H_{18}O_6$ **Beil. III-516**

B.P. 297°/765 mm. ⟨1⟩ **Sap. Eq. 117** D_4^{20} = **1.1390** $[\alpha]_D^{20}$ = **+12.00°**

Ⓓ **Saponification:** Hydrolysis with alk. (T 1.51) yields *n*-propyl alc. (1:6150) and *d*-tartaric ac. (1:0525).

1:4321 ⟨1⟩ Campbell, *J. Chem. Soc.* **1929,** 1115–1119.

1:4326 DI-(β-*n*-BUTOXYETHYL) CARBONATE $C_{13}H_{26}O_5$ **Beil. S.N. 199**

B.P. 297-298° ⟨1⟩ **Sap. Eq. 262** D_4^{25} = **0.9766** ⟨1⟩ n_D^{25} = **1.4279** ⟨1⟩

Ⓓ **Saponification:** Hydrolysis with alk. (T 1.51) yields β-*n*-butoxyethyl alcohol (1:6430) and carbonic ac.

1:4331 DIETHYL PHTHALATE $C_{12}H_{14}O_4$ **Beil. IX-798**
(" Ethyl phthalate ")

B.P. 298° **Sap. Eq. 111** D_4^{20} = **1.1175** n_D^{20} = **1.5019**

Ⓓ **Saponification:** Hydrolysis with alk. (T 1.51) yields ethyl alc. (1:6130) and phthalic ac. (1:0820). [Cf. ⟨1⟩.]

1:4331 ⟨1⟩ Handy, Hogt, *J. Am. Pharm. Assoc.* **16,** 7–18 (1927).

1:4336 α-TETRAHYDROFURFURYL BENZOATE $C_{12}H_{14}O_3$ **Beil. S.N. 2380**

B.P. 300-302°$_{750}$ ⟨1⟩ Sap. Eq. 206 **D_0^{20} = 1.137**

Ⓓ **Saponification:** Hydrolysis with alk. (T 1.51) yields tetrahydrofurfuryl alc. (1:6445) and benzoic ac. (1:0715).

1:4336 ⟨1⟩ Zanetti, *J. Am. Chem. Soc.* **50,** 1822 (1928).

—— **DIETHYL TEREPHTHALATE** $C_{12}H_{14}O_4$ **Beil. IX-844**

B.P. 302° Sap. Eq. 111

See 1:2106. Genus 5: Esters. M.P. 44°.

1:4341 ETHYL β-NAPHTHOATE $C_{13}H_{12}O_2$ **Beil. IX-657**

B.P. 304° Sap. Eq. 200 **D_4^{20} = 1.117 ⟨1⟩** **n_D^{20} = 1.596 ⟨1⟩**
M.P. +32°

Ⓓ **Saponification:** Hydrolysis with alk. (T 1.51) yields ethyl alc. (1:6130) and β-naphthoic ac. (1:0800).

1:4341 ⟨1⟩ Krollpfeiffer, *Ann.* **430,** 184 (1923).

1:4351 n-OCTYL n-CAPRYLATE $C_{16}H_{32}O_2$ **Beil. II-348**

B.P. 306.8° ⟨1⟩ Sap. Eq. 256 **D^{20} = 0.85919 ⟨1⟩** **$n_{He\ (yel.)}^{15}$ = 1.43698 ⟨1⟩**
M.P. −15.1° ⟨1⟩

Ⓓ **Saponification:** Hydrolysis with alk. (T 1.51) yields *n*-octyl alc. (1:6255) and *n*-caprylic ac. (1:1145).

1:4351 ⟨1⟩ Bilterys, Gisseleire, *Bull. soc. chim. Belg.* **44,** 578–579 (1935).

1:4366 DIETHYL SEBACATE $C_{14}H_{26}O_4$ **Beil. II-719**

B.P. 307° Sap. Eq. 129 **D_4^{20} = 0.9631 ⟨1⟩** **n_D^{20} = 1.43657 ⟨1⟩**
M.P. 1.3°

Ⓓ **Saponification:** Hydrolysis with alk. (T 1.51) yields ethyl alc. (1:6130) and sebacic ac. (1:0730).

1:4366 ⟨1⟩ Vogel, *J. Chem. Soc.* **1934,** 339.

1:4371 o-TOLYL BENZOATE $C_{14}H_{12}O_2$ **Beil. IX-119**
(“*o*-Cresyl” benzoate)

B.P. 307° Sap. Eq. 212

Ⓓ **Saponification:** Hydrolysis with alk. (T 1.51) yields *o*-cresol (1:1400) and benzoic ac. (1:0715).

1:4376 ETHYL α-NAPHTHOATE $C_{13}H_{12}O_2$ **Beil. IX-648**

B.P. 309° Sap. Eq. 200 **D_{15}^{15} = 1.1274**

Ⓓ **Saponification:** Hydrolysis with alk. (T 1.51) yields ethyl alc. (1:6130) and α-naphthoic ac. (1:0785).

— **DIISOBUTYL *d,l*-TARTRATE** $C_{12}H_{22}O_6$ **Beil. S.N. 250**

B.P. 311° **Sap. Eq. 131**

See 1:2197. Genus 5: Esters. M.P. 58°.

— **PHENYL BENZOATE** $C_{13}H_{10}O_2$ **Beil. IX-116**

B.P. 314° **Sap. Eq. 198**

See 1:2257. Genus 5: Esters. M.P. 69° (71°).

— ***m*-TOLYL BENZOATE** $C_{14}H_{12}O_2$ **Beil. IX-120**

B.P. 314° **Sap. Eq. 212**

See 1:2183. Genus 5: Esters. M.P. 55°.

— ***p*-TOLYL BENZOATE** $C_{14}H_{12}O_2$ **Beil. IX-120**

B.P. 316° **Sap. Eq. 212**

See 1:2279. Genus 5: Esters. M.P. 71°.

1:4401 DI-*n*-BUTYL *d,l*-TARTRATE $C_{12}H_{22}O_6$ **Beil. S.N. 250**
(Di-*n*-butyl racemate)

B.P. 320° ⟨1⟩ **Sap. Eq. 131** D_4^{18} = **1.0879 ⟨1⟩**

Ⓓ **Saponification:** Hydrolysis with alk. (T 1.51) yields *n*-butyl alc. (1:6180) and *d,l*-tartaric ac. (1:0550).

1:4401 ⟨1⟩ Campbell, *J. Chem. Soc.* **1929,** 1113–1116.

1:4422 BENZYL BENZOATE $C_{14}H_{12}O_2$ **Beil. IX-121**

B.P. 323-324° cor. **Sap. Eq. 212** D^{19} = **1.1224** n_D^{21} = **1.5681**
M.P. 21°

[For prepn. in 90–93% yield from benzaldehyde in pres. of sodium benzylate see ⟨1⟩.]

Ⓓ **Saponification:** Hydrolysis with alk. (T 1.51) yields benzyl alc. (1:6480) and benzoic ac. (1:0715).

1:4422 ⟨1⟩ O. Kamm, W. F. Kamm, *Organic Syntheses, Coll. Vol.* I, 99–101 (1932).

— **DIPHENYL SUCCINATE** $C_{16}H_{14}O_4$ **Beil. VI-155**

B.P. 330° **Sap. Eq. 135**

See 1:2500. Genus 5: Esters. M.P. 121°.

1:4433 DI-*n*-BUTYL PHTHALATE $C_{16}H_{22}O_4$ **Beil. S.N. 970**

B.P. 340.7° ⟨1⟩ **Sap. Eq. 139** D_{20}^{20} = **1.047 ⟨1⟩** n_D^{20} = **1.4900 ⟨1⟩**

Ⓓ **Saponification:** Hydrolysis with alk. (T 1.51) yields *n*-butyl alc. (1:6180) and phthalic ac. (1:0820). [$\bar{C}$ gives Generic Test 5 quant. in ½ hr. but aq. alk. hydrol. for T 1.51 is very slow and requires many hours.] [Cf. ⟨2⟩.]

1:4433 ⟨1⟩ Gardner, Brewer, *Ind. Eng. Chem.* **29,** 179 (1937). ⟨2⟩ Bryant, Smith, *J. Am. Chem. Soc.* **58,** 1015 (1936).

1:4444 DI-*n*-BUTYL SEBACATE $C_{18}H_{34}O_4$ **Beil. II-719**

B.P. 345° **Sap. Eq. 157** D^{15} = **0.9329**

Ⓓ **Saponification:** Hydrolysis with alk. (T 1.51) yields *n*-butyl alc. (1:6180) and sebacic ac. (1:0730).

IMPORTANT ESTERS THAT CAN BE DISTILLED ONLY UNDER REDUCED PRESSURE

(Sequence as in formula index)

— METHYL FUROYLACETATE $C_8H_8O_4$ **Beil. S.N. 2619**

B.P. 144-145°/20 mm.
96-98°/1 mm.

See 1:1800. Genus 4: Phenols.

— ETHYL FUROYLACETATE $C_9H_{10}O_4$ **Beil. XVIII-408**

B.P. 170°/20 mm. D_{17}^{17} = **1.165** n_D^{16} = **1.5055**
143°/10 mm.

See 1:1820. Genus 4: Phenols.

1:4500 DIMETHYL PIMELATE $C_9H_{16}O_4$ **Beil. II₁-(281)**

B.P. 119.3-119.6°/10.0 mm. ⟨1⟩
M.P. −20.6° **Sap. Eq. 94** D_4^{20} = **1.0383** ⟨2⟩ n_D^{20} = **1.43088** ⟨3⟩

Ⓓ **Saponification:** Hydrolysis with alk. (T 1.51) yields methyl alc. (1:6120) and pimelic ac. (1:0456).

1:4500 ⟨1⟩ Verkade, Coops, Hartman, *Rec. trav. chim.* **45,** 590 (1926). ⟨2⟩ Vogel, *J. Chem. Soc.* **1934,** 338. ⟨3⟩ Vogel, *J. Chem. Soc.* **1934,** 1765.

— METHYL BENZOYLACETATE $C_{10}H_{10}O_3$ **Beil. S.N. 1316**

B.P. 151.5-151.8°/13 mm. D_4^{20} = **1.158** n_D^{20} = **1.5394**

See 1:1810. Genus 4: Phenols.

1:4510 3,5-DIMETHYLPHENYL ACETATE $C_{10}H_{12}O_2$ **Beil. VI₁-(244)**
(*sym.-m*-Xylenyl acetate)

B.P. 130°/26 mm. **Sap. Eq. 164**
120°/11 mm.

Ⓓ **Saponification:** Hydrolysis with alk. (T 1.51) yields 3,5-dimethylphenol (1:1455) and acetic ac. (1:1010).

1:4520 DI-*n*-PROPYL MALEATE $C_{10}H_{16}O_4$ **Beil. II-752**

B.P. 114-117°/6 mm. **Sap. Eq. 100** D_4^{20} = **1.026** $n_D^{18.3}$ = **1.444**

Ⓓ **Saponification:** Hydrolysis with alk. (T 1.51) yields *n*-propyl alc. (1:6150) and maleic ac. (1:0470).

—— ETHYL *n*-BUTYLACETOACETATE $C_{10}H_{18}O_3$ **Beil. III-706**

B.P. 104-104.5°/12 mm. D_4^{20} = **0.95227** n_D^{20} = **1.43006**

See 1:1840. Genus 4: Phenols.

1:4530 DIETHYL PIMELATE $C_{11}H_{20}O_4$ **Beil. II-671**

B.P. 149°/18 mm. ⟨1⟩ **Sap. Eq. 108** D_4^{20} = **0.9929** ⟨1⟩ n_D^{20} = **1.42985** ⟨1⟩
M.P. −23.8°

Ⓓ **Saponification:** Hydrolysis with alk. (T 1.51) yields ethyl alc. (1:6130) and pimelic ac. (1:0456).

1:4530 ⟨1⟩ Vogel, *J. Chem. Soc.* **1934,** 339.

1:4540 DIMETHYL AZELATE $C_{11}H_{20}O_4$ **Beil. II₁-(290)**

B.P. 146.2°/10 mm. ⟨1⟩ **Sap. Eq. 108** D_4^{20} = **1.0069** ⟨2⟩ n_D^{20} = **1.43607** ⟨2⟩
156°/20 mm. ⟨2⟩

Ⓓ **Saponification:** Hydrolysis with alk. (T 1.51) yields methyl alc. (1:6120) and azelaic ac. (1:0695).

1:4540 ⟨1⟩ Verkade, Coops, Hartman, *Rec. trav. chim.* **45,** 591 (1926). ⟨2⟩ Vogel, *J. Chem. Soc.* **1934,** 339.

1:4560 DI-*n*-PROPYL ADIPATE $C_{12}H_{22}O_4$ **Beil. S.N. 175**

B.P. 155°/16 mm. ⟨1⟩ **Sap. Eq. 115** D_4^{20} = **0.9790** ⟨1⟩ n_D^{20} = **1.4314** ⟨1⟩
M.P. −20° ⟨1⟩

Ⓓ **Saponification:** Hydrolysis with alk. (T 1.51) yields *n*-propyl alc. (1:6150) and adipic ac. (1:0775).

1:4560 ⟨1⟩ Contzen-Crowet, *Bull. soc. chim. Belg.* **35,** 190 (1926).

1:4570 β-*n*-BUTOXYETHYL BENZOATE $C_{13}H_{18}O_3$ **Beil. S.N. 901**
(Butyl " cellosolve " benzoate)

B.P. 156.5-157°/14.5 mm. ⟨1⟩ **Sap. Eq. 222**
131.6-132.6°/3.0 mm. ⟨1⟩ D_{25}^{25} = **1.0277** ⟨1⟩ n_D^{25} = **1.4925** ⟨1⟩

Ⓓ **Saponification:** Hydrolysis with alk. (T 1.51) yields β-*n*-butoxyethyl alc. (1:6430) and benzoic ac. (1:0715).

1:4570 ⟨1⟩ Conn, Collett, Lazzell, *J. Am. Chem. Soc.* **54,** 4372 (1932).

CHAPTER VIII

ORDER I: SUBORDER I: GENUS 6

ACID ANHYDRIDES AND LACTONES

Division A, Solids

Solid acid anhydrides and lactones which do not neutralize cold sodium hydroxide solution sufficiently readily to give Generic Tests 3 or 4-B.

1:4905 **CHROMONE** (Benzopyrone-1,4) $C_9H_6O_2$ **Beil. XVII-327**

M.P. 59°

Ndls. (from aq. or pet. ether) — Eas. sol. alc., ether, $CHCl_3$, C_6H_6 — Volat. with steam — Sol. in cold conc. H_2SO_4 to yel. soln. with blue-violet fluores. Even from fumg. H_2SO_4 (70%) $\bar{C}$ is repptd. unchanged on diln. ⟨1⟩.

$\bar{C}$ prepd. (50% yield) by dehydrogenation of chromanone ⟨2⟩ ⟨3⟩ with PCl_5 in C_6H_6 ⟨4⟩; or (in 100% yield) by $AcCl.H_2SO_4$ ring closure of *cis*-β-phenoxyacrylic ac. ⟨5⟩.

Fails to respond to Generic Tests 3-A or 3-B — Hydrolysis with alc. alk. (T 1.51) gave Sap. Eq. of 211.5 (theor. 146), i.e., 69% hydrolysis. Upon addn. of alc. alk. $\bar{C}$ dis. to dark red soln. End point of titration given by point at which color disappears and milky yel. soln. obtd. Sapon. products are *o*-hydroxyacetophenone (1:1746) and salt of formic acid (1:1005).

$\bar{C}$, dislvd. in $CHCl_3$, satd. with dry HCl gas, forms hydrochloride, pptd. by addn. of pet. ether, dried in vac., m.p. 101–102° ⟨6⟩.

For discussion of differentiation of chromones from coumarins see ⟨7⟩.

Ⓓ **Chromonehydrazone:** in good yield from $\bar{C}$ + 3 moles hydrazine hydrate in alc. soln. for 10 min., m.p. 96° ⟨8⟩.

1:4905 ⟨1⟩ Krüger, *Ber.* **56,** 487 (1923). ⟨2⟩ Arndt, Källner, *Ber.* **57,** 204 (1924). ⟨3⟩ Krollpfeiffer, Schultze, *Ber.* **57,** 207 (1924). ⟨4⟩ Arndt, *Ber.* **58,** 1621 (1925). ⟨5⟩ Gottesmann, *Ber.* **66,** 1174–1175 (1933). ⟨6⟩ Gomberg, Cone, *Ann.* **376,** 229 (1910). ⟨7⟩ Kelkar, *Chem. Abs.* **31,** 2213 (1937). ⟨8⟩ Schönberg, Stolpp, *Ber.* **63,** 3116 (1930).

1:4910 **COUMARIN** $C_9H_6O_2$ **Beil. XVII-328**

M.P. 67° **B.P. 290°**

Fragrant odor like sweet grass or Tonka beans — Subl. unchanged; eas. volat. with st. — On long illumination either as solid or in soln., $\bar{C}$ changes to a dimer, m.p. 262° ⟨1⟩.

Alm. insol. cold aq. but sol. hot aq.; eas. sol. alc., ether, or $CHCl_3$. (For soly. data in comparison with vanillin see ⟨2⟩.) — Sol. in solns. of $NaHSO_3$ or Na_2SO_3 forming sodium hydrocoumarin sulfonate ⟨3⟩ ⟨4⟩ ⟨5⟩ which on treatment with more than 2 moles 50% alk. is converted to coumaric ac. (1:0835), obtd. on acidification; m.p. 208° — Htg. C̄ with conc. alk. or alc. KOH (as in Generic Test 5) also gives salts of coumaric ac.; but short boilg. with mild alkalies gives solns. of salts of the isomeric coumarinic ac. [Beil. X-291] which even with CO_2 regenerate C̄.

Insol. NH_4OH [use in sepn. from vanillin, salicylic ac. or saccharin ⟨11⟩]. Fusion with 50% KOH at lowest possible temp. yields salicylic ac. (1:0780) ⟨11⟩. Reduces $KMnO_4$ (T 1.34) — Adds Br_2 in CS_2 yielding coumarin dibromide, m.p. 105° ⟨6⟩ which loses Br_2 at 120° — Sol. in cold fumg. HNO_3 yielding mainly 6-nitrocoumarin, ndls., m.p. 183° accompanied by some 8-NO_2 coumarin ⟨7⟩; eutectic mixt. of 6-NO_2 + 8-NO_2 isomer melts 140–141° ⟨7⟩. [For sepn. and detn. in presence of vanillin see ⟨8⟩ ⟨9⟩ ⟨10⟩.]

Ⓟ **I_2 + KI color test:** addn. of few drops of I_2 + KI soln. to aq. soln. of C̄ causes br. floc. ppt., which on shakg. clots to dark green curdy mass leaving clear brown supernatant liq. ⟨12⟩.

1:4910 ⟨1⟩ de Jong, *Rec. trav. chim.* **43,** 320 (1924). ⟨2⟩ Hitchens, *Ind. Eng. Chem.* **24,** 418–419 (1932). ⟨3⟩ Dodge, *J. Am. Chem. Soc.* **38,** 446–457 (1916). ⟨4⟩ Dodge, *J. Am. Chem. Soc.* **52,** 1724 (1930). ⟨5⟩ Dey, Row, *J. Chem. Soc.* **125,** 554–564 (1924). ⟨6⟩ Fittig, Ebert, *Ann.* **216,** 163 (1882). ⟨7⟩ Dey, Krishnamurthi, *J. Indian Chem. Soc.* **4,** 197–199 (1927). ⟨8⟩ Hess, Prescott, *J. Am. Chem. Soc.* **21,** 256–259 (1899). ⟨9⟩ Winton, Silverman, *J. Am. Chem. Soc.* **24,** 1128–1135 (1902). ⟨10⟩ Winton, Bailey, *J. Am. Chem. Soc.* **27,** 719–724 (1905).
⟨11⟩ Dean, *Ind. Eng. Chem.* **7,** 519 (1915). ⟨12⟩ Dox, Gaessler, *J. Am. Chem. Soc.* **39,** 115 (1917).

1:4915 STEARIC ANHYDRIDE $[CH_3.(CH_2)_{16}.CO]_2O$ $C_{36}H_{70}O_3$ **Beil. II-384**

M.P. 71-71.5° ⟨1⟩ D_4^{70} = **0.8443** ⟨1⟩ n_D^{70} = **1.4379** ⟨1⟩

White cryst. from acetone ⟨1⟩ — Fails to respond Generic Test 3-B (titration in alc.). Hydrolysis with aq. alk. (T 1.51) gives Sap. Eq. 275 and yields soln. contg. salt of stearic acid (1:0660), q.v.

C̄ can be freed from stearic acid by repeated washing with cold ether. (100 cc. ether at 15° dis. 0.181 g. C̄; corresp. value for stearic acid is 5.5 g.) ⟨2⟩. [Note that stearic anhydride and stearic acid have nearly same m.p.]

An ether soln. of C̄ shaken with Na_2CO_3 soln. remains clear; similar treatment of stearic acid gives a thick gelatinous ppt. [detectn. of stearic acid in stearic anhydride] ⟨2⟩.

1:4915 ⟨1⟩ Holde, Gentner, *Ber.* **58,** 1418–1424 (1925). ⟨2⟩ Autenrieth, Thomae, *Ber.* **57,** 429 (1924).

1:4920 PHTHALIDE

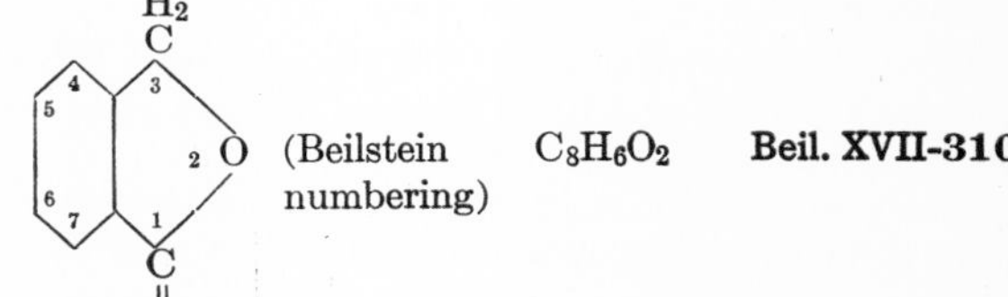

$C_8H_6O_2$ **Beil. XVII-310**

M.P. 73° (stable form) **B.P. 290°** cor.
66° (unstable form) ⟨1⟩ ⟨2⟩)

Ndls. from hot aq.; very dif. sol. cold aq. — Eas. sol. alc., ether — [For prepn. (67–71% yield) from phthalimide see ⟨7⟩.]

[The solid, if finely powdered, dissolves after shakg. 1–2 min. with 5% aq. NaOH in Generic Test 4-B and hence should be detected in Genus 4.] — Sol. in hot alk. giving on acidifn. *o*-hydroxymethylbenzoic ac. [Beil. X-218], m.p. 120° ⟨3⟩.

Does not reduce $NH_3/AgNO_3$ nor combine with $NaHSO_3$ ⟨4⟩ — Eas. oxid. by alk. $KMnO_4$ to phthalic ac. (1:0820) — Nitration gives 6-nitrophthalide (on above numbering system), m.p. 143° ⟨5⟩.

Ⓓ **2-Phenyl-1,3-diketohydrindene:** To abs. alc. soln. of equal moles C̄ and BzH is added 1 mole $NaOC_2H_5$. After 30 min. reflux. the red. soln. is concd., poured into aq., acidif. and extd. with ether to remove impurities. Prod., lfts. from alc., m.p. 146° ⟨6⟩.

1:4920 ⟨1⟩ Müller, *Z. physik. Chem.* **86,** 187 (1913). ⟨2⟩ Beil. XVII-311, footnote. ⟨3⟩ Hjelt, *Ber.* **25,** 524 (1892). ⟨4⟩ Hessert, *Ber.* **11,** 238 (1878). ⟨5⟩ Teppema, *Rec. trav. chim.* **43,** 37 (1923). ⟨6⟩ Dieckmann, *Ber.* **47,** 1439 (1914). ⟨7⟩ Gardner, Naylor, *Organic Syntheses* **16,** 71–72 (1936).

1:4930 DIBENZOYL PEROXIDE $C_{14}H_{10}O_4$ Beil. IX-179

(" Benzoyl peroxide ") $C_6H_5.CO.O.O.CO.C_6H_5$

M.P. 104° dec. (110° on rap. htg.)

Odorless rhomb. cryst.; insol. aq., but eas. sol. acetone, C_6H_6, toluene, ether, or AcOH.

Explodes on htg. or on treat. with conc. H_2SO_4 — Does not react with alc. at 0° ⟨1⟩; stable to even 20% NaOH in the cold ⟨1⟩; but boiling with alk. yields O_2 and soln. of alk. benzoate — Fumg. HNO_3 or H_2SO_4/HNO_3 mixt. gives bis-(3-nitrobenzoyl)peroxide, cryst. from AcOEt, m.p. 139–140° dec. [cf. Beil. IX-381].

Acetone (*but not aqueous*) soln. of C̄, shaken with acidif. KI soln. yields free I_2; used in quant. detn. ⟨2⟩ — Does not decolorize $KMnO_4$ soln. — 2 pts. 10% EtOH/NaOH treated at −5° with 1 pt. finely powd. C̄, then 4 pts. ice aq. added, gives a soln. from which EtOBz is extracted with ether and the residual aq. layer mixed with cold $CHCl_3$ and acid. with 2 pts. cold 4 *N* H_2SO_4, the $CHCl_3$ dried with Na_2SO_4 and evapd. yielding 80–90% perbenzoic ac., m.p. 40° ⟨3⟩ ⟨4⟩. [For alternative methods in which C̄ is dislvd. in C_6H_6 ⟨5⟩ or toluene ⟨6⟩ ⟨7⟩ see indic. ref.]

1:4930 ⟨1⟩ B. T. Brooks, W. B. Brooks, *J. Am. Chem. Soc.* **55,** 4309–4311 (1933). ⟨2⟩ Gelissen, Hermans, *Ber* **59,** 68 (1926). ⟨3⟩ Smit, *Rec. trav. chim.* **49,** 676 (1930). ⟨4⟩ Hibbert, Burt, *J. Am. Chem. Soc.* **47,** 2240–2243 (1925). ⟨5⟩ Wieland, Bergel, *Ann.* **446,** 28 (1926). ⟨6⟩ Levy, Lagrave, *Bull. soc. chim.* (4) **37,** 1597–1600 (1925). ⟨7⟩ Tiffeneau, *Organic Syntheses, Coll. Vol.* I, 422–425 (1932).

1:4970 POLYGLYCOLID $(C_4H_4O_4)_x$ Beil. XIX-153

M.P. 220°

Cryst. (from nitrobenzene) — White pdr., very dif. sol. hot aq. — Fails to respond to Generic Tests 3-A or 3-B; in Generic Test 5-A gives Sap. Eq. 63.5 — On long boilg. with aq. or dil. alk. gives glycolic ac. (1:0430).

Easily prepd. (80% yield) by htg. sodium chloroacetate 2 days at 150° ⟨1⟩ ⟨2⟩.

On distn. in vac. depolymerizes giving good yield (70%) glycolid (1:0667), m.p. 86° ⟨2⟩.

Ⓓ **Glycolanilide:** from C̄ htd. with aniline at 130°, cryst. from aq., m.p. 97° ⟨1⟩ ⟨3⟩. [The m.p. of 108° of ⟨1⟩ could not be confirmed by ⟨3⟩.]

Ⓓ **Glycol α-naphthalide:** from C̄ (1 g.) htd. with α-naphthylamine (2.5 g.); melt dislvd. in hot aq., cooled, prod. recrystd. from acetone, m.p. 128° ⟨4⟩.

1:4970 ⟨1⟩ Norton, Tscherniak, *Bull. soc. chim.* (2) **30,** 102–105 (1878). ⟨2⟩ Bischoff, Walden, *Ann.* **279,** 46 (1894). ⟨3⟩ Ref. 2, page 49. ⟨4⟩ Ref. 2, page 67.

ORDER I: SUBORDER I: GENUS 6

ACID ANHYDRIDES AND LACTONES

Division B, Liquids

1:5070 **γ-BUTYROLACTONE** $H_2C.CH_2.CH_2.C{=}O$ (ring closed through O) $C_4H_6O_2$ **Beil. XVII-234**

B.P. 206° D_4^{20} = **1.1299** ⟨1⟩ n_D^{20} = **1.4354** ⟨1⟩

Colorless mobile liq. of charact. odor — In solid CO_2 + ether mixt. solidifies to lfts., m.p. −48° ⟨1⟩ — Misc. with aq. in all proportions and only very sl. extd. by ether. From not too dil. aq. solns. is salted out by K_2CO_3 — Volatile with steam — Does not polym. on stdg. [dif. from γ- or δ-valerolactones].

Does not respond to Generic Test 3, either in water or in alc. — Hydrolysis with either aq. or alc. alk. (T 1.51) gives Sap. Eq. of 94 (theor. 86). On boilg. with aq. is partially and slowly hydrol. to γ-hydroxy-*n*-butyric ac. [Beil. III-311]; e.g., $\bar{C}$ (0.04 *N* in aq.) boiled 24 hrs. was only 25% conv. to hydroxy ac. ⟨1⟩. Boilg. with alk. carbonates or alk. yields soln. of salts of γ-hydroxy-*n*-butyric ac. [Beil. III-311].

Reduces ammon. $AgNO_3$ (T 1.11) — Oxidn. with $K_2Cr_2O_7$ + H_2SO_4 (T 1.72) gives ⟨4⟩ succinic ac. (1:0530) — With sl. excess liq. NH_3 in s.t. htd. 2 hrs. at 200° gives 64% yield α-pyrrolidone ⟨2⟩.

Ⓓ **γ-Hydroxy-*n*-butyric phenylhydrazide:** $\bar{C}$, htd. at 100° with $1\frac{1}{2}$ parts phenylhydrazine, then treated with two vols. ether, soon separates quant. ppt.; recrystd. from $CHCl_3$, shining tablets, m.p. 94° ⟨3⟩. [The orig. lactone may be regenerated from the phenylhydrazide by warming with conc. HCl ⟨3⟩.]

1:5070 ⟨1⟩ Boorman, Linstead, *J. Chem. Soc.* **1933,** 578–580. ⟨2⟩ Späth, Lintner, *Ber.* **69,** 2728 (1936). ⟨3⟩ Seib, *Ber.* **60,** 1399 (1927). ⟨4⟩ Windaus, Klänhardt, *Ber.* **54,** 585 (1921).

1:5080 **γ-*n*-VALEROLACTONE** $CH_3.CH.CH_2.CH_2.C{=}O$ (ring closed through O) $C_5H_8O_2$ **Beil. XVII-235**

B.P. 206° ⟨1⟩ D_4^{20} = **1.0524** ⟨3⟩ n_D^{20} = **1.4320** ⟨3⟩
206-207° ⟨2⟩ D^{25} = **1.0461** ⟨2⟩ n_D^{25} = **1.4301** ⟨2⟩

Colorless mobile liq. best distd. under red. press. since some decompn. occurs at b.p. under atm. press. ⟨4⟩. F.p. is −37° ⟨3⟩. Completely misc. with aq. [dif. from δ-valerolactone], the soln. reacting neutral. Salted out by K_2CO_3 — Misc. alc., ether — Does not polymerize at room temp. [dif. from δ-valerolactone or γ-butyrolactone] — [For prepn. by cat. reductn. of levulinic acid (1:0405) cf. ⟨5⟩.]

Does not respond to Generic Test 3-A or 3-B — $\bar{C}$ completely unchanged after stdg. 7 days in cold 60% H_2SO_4 ⟨6⟩; $\bar{C}$ only 1% hydrolyzed on boilg. 1 hr. with 50% H_2SO_4 ⟨6⟩. $\bar{C}$ (0.04 *N* in aq.) htd. 24 or 48 hrs. only 7% hydrolyzed ⟨6⟩ — Hydrolysis with aq. or alc. alk. (T 1.51) gives Sap. Eq. 100.

C̄, boiled with dil. HNO_3 to cessation of red fumes, evapd., yields succinic acid (1:0530) ⟨7⟩ — C̄, htd. 3 hrs. in s.t. at 220–230° with $ZnCl_2.6NH_3$ gave 74% 5-methylpyrrolidone ⟨7⟩.

Ⓓ γ-**Hydroxy-*n*-valeric phenylhydrazide**: C̄, htd. 10 hrs. at 100° with $1\frac{1}{2}$ pts. phenylhydrazine gave 80% prod., recrystd. from aq. or $CHCl_3$, ndls. m.p. 76–79° ⟨9⟩.

Ⓓ γ-**Hydroxy-*n*-valeric hydrazide**: 2 pts. C̄, htd. 8 hrs. at 100° with 1 pt. hydrazine hydrate in 20 pts. alc. gave good yield prod., fine ndls. (from $CHCl_3$), m.p. 65° ⟨10⟩ ⟨11⟩.

1:5080 ⟨1⟩ Losanitch, *Monatsh.* **35,** 303 (1914). ⟨2⟩ Schuette, Sah, *J. Am. Chem. Soc.* **48,** 3165 (1926). ⟨3⟩ Linstead, Rydon, *J. Chem. Soc.* **1933,** 583. ⟨4⟩ Thomas, Schuette, *J. Am. Chem. Soc.* **54,** 3008 (1932). ⟨5⟩ Schuette, Thomas, *J. Am. Chem. Soc.* **52,** 3010 (1930). ⟨6⟩ Boorman, Linstead, *J. Chem. Soc.* **1933,** 579–580. ⟨7⟩ Fittig, Messerschmidt, *Ann.* **208,** 99 (1881). ⟨8⟩ Späth, Lintner, *Ber.* **69,** 2729 (1936). ⟨9⟩ Wislicenus, *Ber.* **20,** 402 (1887). ⟨10⟩ Darapsky, Berger, Neuhaus, *J. prakt. Chem.* (2), **147,** 150 (1936).
⟨11⟩ Pummerer, Guyot, Birkofer, *Ber.* **68,** 490 (1935).

CHAPTER IX

GENUS 7. KETONES

1. Alphabetical Name Index*

Name	No.
Acenaphthenone	**1:5200**
d,l-Acetoin	**1:5448**
Acetol	**1:5455**
1-Aceto-2-naphthol	**1:1459**
2-Aceto-1-naphthol	**1:1515**
Acetone	**1:5400**
Acetonedicarboxylic acid	**1:0485**
Acetonylacetone	**1:5495**
Acetophenone	**1:5515**
Acetylacetone	**1:1700**
2-Acetyl-*p*-cymene	**1:5550**
n-Amyl levulinate	**1:4121**
n-Amyl methyl ketone	**1:5460**
n-Amyl phenyl ketone	**1:5111**
Anisoin	**1:5195**
Benzalacetone	**1:5145**
Benzalacetophenone	**1:5155**
Benzil	**1:9015**
d,l-Benzoin	**1:5210**
Benzophenone	**1:5150**
Benzoylacetone	**1:1450**
o-Benzoylbenzoic acid	**1:0720**
Benzyl methyl ketone	**1:5118**
Biacetyl	**1:9500**
n-Butyl levulinate	**1:3972**
sec-Butyl levulinate	**1:3812**
n-Butyl methyl ketone	**1:5435**
sec-Butyl methyl ketone	**1:5431**
Butyrophenone	**1:5535**
d-Camphor	**1:5215**
n-Caproylresorcinol	**1:1443**
d-Carvone	**1:5540**
Cinnamalacetone	**1:5174**
Cyclohexanone	**1:5465**
Cyclopentanone	**1:5446**
n-Decyl methyl ketone	**1:5552**
Desoxybenzoin	**1:5165**
Diacetone alcohol	**1:6423**
Di-*n*-amyl ketone	**1:5532**
Dibenzalacetone	**1:9024**
Dibenzoylmethane	**1:1480**
Dibenzyl ketone	**1:5135**
Di-*n*-butyl ketone	**1:5493**
Diethyl acetonedicarboxylate	**1:1772**
Diethyl ketone	**1:5420**
Diisobutyl ketone	**1:5472**
Diisopropyl ketone	**1:5433**
Di-*n*-propyl ketone	**1:5447**
Di-*p*-tolyl ketone	**1:5185**
n-Dodecyl methyl ketone	**1:5133**
Ethyl acetoacetate	**1:1710**
Ethyl acetopyruvate	**1:1742**
Ethyl allylacetoacetate	**1:1738**
Ethyl benzoylacetate	**1:1778**
Ethyl ethylacetoacetate	**1:1723**
Ethyl levulinate	**1:3616**
Ethyl methylacetoacetate	**1:1712**
Ethyl methyl ketone	**1:5405**
Ethyl *n*-undecyl ketone	**1:5134**
d-Fenchone	**1:7547**
Furoin	**1:1565**
n-Heptyl methyl ketone	**1:5501**
n-Hexyl methyl ketone	**1:5490**
n-Hexyl phenyl ketone	**1:5590**
α-Hydroxyacetophenone	**1:5180**
o-Hydroxyacetophenone	**1:1746**
m-Hydroxyacetophenone	**1:1506**
p-Hydroxyacetophenone	**1:1527**
o-Hydroxybenzophenone	**1:1414**
m-Hydroxybenzophenone	**1:1535**
p-Hydroxybenzophenone	**1:1560**
Indanone-1	**1:5144**
Isoamyl levulinate	**1:4096**
Isobutyl levulinate	**1:3907**
Isobutyl methyl ketone	**1:5430**
Isophorone	**1:5523**
Isopropyl levulinate	**1:3666**
Isopropyl methyl ketone	**1:5410**
Isopropyl phenyl ketone	**1:5528**
Laurone	**1:5175**
Levulinic acid	**1:0405**
l-Menthone	**1:5520**
Mesityl oxide	**1:5445**
o-Methoxyacetophenone	**1:5547**
m-Methoxyacetophenone	**1:5548**
p-Methoxyacetophenone	**1:5140**
o-Methoxybenzophenone	**1:5142**

*For complete alphabetical name index covering all listed names of all numbered compounds in this book see the main alphabetical index.

Compound	No.
m-Methoxybenzophenone	**1:5141**
p-Methoxybenzophenone	**1:5170**
Methyl acetoacetate	**1:1705**
o-Methylacetophenone	**1:5524**
m-Methylacetophenone	**1:5527**
p-Methylacetophenone	**1:5530**
2-Methylcyclohexanone	**1:5470**
d,l-3-Methylcyclohexanone	**1:5480**
4-Methylcyclohexanone	**1:5485**
Methyl ethylacetoacetate	**1:1718**
Methyl levulinate	**1:3561**
Methyl methylacetoacetate	**1:1708**
Methyl α-naphthyl ketone	**1:5600**
Methyl β-naphthyl ketone	**1:5153**
Methyl *n*-nonyl ketone	**1:5531**
Methyl *n*-octyl ketone	**1:5522**
Methyl *n*-propyl ketone	**1:5415**
Methyl *n*-undecyl ketone	**1:5130**
Phenoxyacetone	**1:5534**
p-Phenylacetophenone	**1:5201**
Phenyl *p*-tolyl ketone	**1:5160**
Phenyl *n*-undecyl ketone	**1:5148**
Phorone	**1:5120**
Pinacolone	**1:5425**
Propiophenone	**1:5525**
n-Propyl levulinate	**1:3786**
Pyruvic acid	**1:1040**
o-(*p*-Toluyl)benzoic acid	**1:0750**
Triketohydrindene hydrate	**1:1625**
Valerophenone	**1:5555**
Xanthydrol	**1:5205**

2. Chemical Type Index

(Names used here are not necessarily same as subject index names)

I. Monoketones

A. *Type* $CH_3.CO.R$ (*Alkyl*)

Compound	No.
Acetone	**1:5400**
Methyl ethyl ketone	**1:5405**
Methyl *n*-propyl ketone	**1:5415**
Methyl isopropyl ketone	**1:5410**
Methyl *n*-butyl ketone	**1:5435**
Methyl *sec*-butyl ketone	**1:5431**
Methyl isobutyl ketone	**1:5430**
Methyl *ter*-butyl ketone	**1:5425**
Methyl *n*-amyl ketone	**1:5460**
Methyl *n*-hexyl ketone	**1:5490**
Methyl *n*-heptyl ketone	**1:5501**
Methyl *n*-octyl ketone	**1:5522**
Methyl *n*-nonyl ketone	**1:5531**
Methyl *n*-decyl ketone	**1:5552**
Methyl *n*-undecyl ketone	**1:5130**
Methyl *n*-dodecyl ketone	**1:5133**
Ethyl undecyl ketone	**1:5134**

B. *Type* $CH_3.CO.R$ (*aryl or alkaryl*)

Compound	No.
Methyl phenyl ketone	**1:5515**
Methyl *o*-tolyl ketone	**1:5524**
Methyl *m*-tolyl ketone	**1:5527**
Methyl *p*-tolyl ketone	**1:5530**
Methyl benzyl ketone	**1:5118**
Methyl carvacryl ketone	**1:5550**
Methyl *p*-xenyl ketone	**1:5201**
Methyl α-naphthyl ketone	**1:5600**
Methyl β-naphthyl ketone	**1:5153**

C. *Type* $C_6H_5.CO.R$

Compound	No.
Phenyl methyl ketone	**1:5515**
Phenyl ethyl ketone	**1:5525**
Phenyl *n*-propyl ketone	**1:5535**
Phenyl isopropyl ketone	**1:5528**
Phenyl *n*-butyl ketone	**1:5555**
Phenyl *n*-amyl ketone	**1:5111**
Phenyl *n*-hexyl ketone	**1:5590**
Phenyl *n*-undecyl ketone	**1:5148**
Phenyl phenyl ketone	**1:5150**
Phenyl *p*-tolyl ketone	**1:5160**
Phenyl benzyl ketone	**1:5165**

D. *Type Ar.CO.Ar*

Compound	No.
Diphenyl ketone	**1:5150**
Phenyl *p*-tolyl ketone	**1:5160**
Di-*p*-tolyl ketone	**1:5185**

E. *Symmetrical ketones*

1. Aliphatic

Compound	No.
Dimethyl ketone	**1:5400**
Diethyl ketone	**1:5420**
Di-*n*-propyl ketone	**1:5447**
Diisopropyl ketone	**1:5433**
Di-*n*-butyl ketone	**1:5493**
Diisobutyl ketone	**1:5472**
Di-*n*-amyl ketone	**1:5532**
Di-*n*-undecyl ketone (laurone)	**1:5175**
Diisopropylideneacetone (phorone)	**1:5120**

2. Aromatic

Compound	No.
Diphenyl ketone	**1:5150**
Di-*p*-tolyl ketone	**1:5185**
Dibenzyl ketone	**1:5135**
Dibenzalacetone	**1:9024**

F. *Unsaturated ketones*

Mesityl oxide	**1:5445**
Phorone	**1:5120**
Isophorone	**1:5523**
Benzalacetone	**1:5145**
Dibenzalacetone	**1:9024**
Benzalacetophenone	**1:5155**
Cinnamalacetone	**1:5174**

G. *Hydroxy ketones*

1. Alcohol ketones

d,l-Acetoin	**1:5448**
Acetol	**1:5455**
Diacetone alcohol	**1:6423**
Furoin	**1:1565**
Anisoin	**1:5195**
d,l-Benzoin	**1:5210**
Phenacyl alcohol	**1:5180**

2. Phenolic ketones

o-Hydroxyacetophenone	**1:1746**
m-Hydroxyacetophenone	**1:1506**
p-Hydroxyacetophenone	**1:1527**
o-Hydroxybenzophenone	**1:1414**
m-Hydroxybenzophenone	**1:1535**
p-Hydroxybenzophenone	**1:1560**
1-Aceto-2-naphthol	**1:1459**
2-Aceto-1-naphthol	**1:1515**
n-Caproylresorcinol	**1:1443**

H. *Ether ketones*

o-Methoxyacetophenone	**1:5547**
m-Methoxyacetophenone	**1:5548**
p-Methoxyacetophenone	**1:5140**
o-Methoxybenzophenone	**1:5142**
m-Methoxybenzophenone	**1:5141**
p-Methoxybenzophenone	**1:5170**
Phenoxyacetone	**1:5534**

I. *Cyclic ketones*

Cyclopentanone	**1:5446**
Cyclohexanone	**1:5465**
2 Methylcyclohexanone	**1:5470**
d,l-3-Methylcyclohexanone	**1:5480**
4-Methylcyclohexanone	**1:5485**
Isophorone	**1:5523**
Indanone-1	**1:5144**
Acenaphthenone	**1:5200**
d-Camphor	**1:5215**
d-Carvone	**1:5540**
l-Menthone	**1:5220**
d-Fenchone	**1:7547**

J. *Keto acids*

Pyruvic acid	**1:1040**
Acetonedicarboxylic acid	**1:0485**
Levulinic acid	**1:0405**
o-Benzoylbenzoic acid	**1:0720**
o-(*p*-Toluyl)benzoic acid	**1:0750**

K. *Esters of keto acids*

Ethyl acetopyruvate	**1:1742**
Diethyl acetonedicarboxylate	**1:1772**
Methyl acetoacetate	**1:1705**
Ethyl acetoacetate	**1:1710**
Methyl methylacetoacetate	**1:1708**
Ethyl methylacetoacetate	**1:1712**
Methyl ethylacetoacetate	**1:1718**
Ethyl ethylacetoacetate	**1:1723**
Ethyl allylacetoacetate	**1:1738**
Ethyl benzoylacetate	**1:1778**
Methyl levulinate	**1:3561**
Ethyl levulinate	**1:3616**
n-Propyl levulinate	**1:3786**
Isopropyl levulinate	**1:3666**
n-Butyl levulinate	**1:3972**
sec-Butyl levulinate	**1:3812**
Isobutyl levulinate	**1:3907**
n-Amyl levulinate	**1:4121**
Isoamyl levulinate	**1:4096**

II. Diketones

1. α-Diketones

Biacetyl	**1:9500**
Benzil	**1:9015**

2. β-Diketones

Acetylacetone	**1:1700**
Benzoylacetone	**1:1450**
Dibenzoylmethane	**1:1480**

3. γ-Diketones

Acetonylacetone	**1:5495**

III. Triketones

Triketohydrindene hydrate	**1:1625**

IV. Miscellaneous

Xanthydrol	**1:5205**

(Remember that there are several colored ketones in Suborder II, Colored Compounds.)

ORDER I: SUBORDER I: GENUS 7: KETONES

Division A, Solid Ketones

—— **BUTYROPHENONE** $C_6H_5.CO.CH_2.CH_2.CH_3$ $C_{10}H_{12}O$ **Beil. VII-313**

M.P. 12.2° D_{20}^{20} = **0.989** n_D^{20} = **1.5196**

See 1:5535. Genus 7: Division B. B.P. 230°.

—— **METHYL *n*-NONYL KETONE** $CH_3.CO.C_9H_{19}$ $C_{11}H_{22}O$ **Beil. I-713**

M.P. 12.7° D_4^{20} = **0.82564** n_D^{20} = **1.42899**

See 1:5531. Genus 7: Division B. B.P. 228°.

—— **PROPIOPHENONE** $C_6H_5.CO.CH_2.CH_3$ $C_9H_{10}O$ **Beil. VII-300**

M.P. 18.6° D_4^{20} = **1.0105** n_D^{20} = **1.5269**

See 1:5525. Genus 7: Division B. B.P. 218°.

—— **ACETOPHENONE** $C_6H_5.CO.CH_3$ C_8H_8O **Beil. VII-271**

M.P. 19.6° D_4^{20} = **1.02810** n_D^{20} = **1.5339**

See 1:5515. Genus 7: Division B. B.P. 202°.

1:5111 **_n_-AMYL PHENYL KETONE** (*n*-Caprophenone) $n.C_5H_{11}.C(=O)$—⟨benzene ring⟩ $C_{12}H_{16}O$ **Beil. VII-333**

M.P. 24.7° ⟨1⟩ **B.P. 265.2°** ⟨1⟩ D_4^{25} = **0.95761** ⟨1⟩ n_D^{25} = **1.50272** ⟨1⟩

Ⓓ ***n*-Amyl phenyl ketone 2,4-dinitrophenylhydrazone:** thick red ndls. from AcOH; m.p. 168° cor. ⟨2⟩.

Ⓓ ***n*-Amyl phenyl ketone semicarbazone:** cryst. from 50% alc., m.p. 131.5–132° ⟨3⟩ ⟨4⟩; 133° cor. ⟨2⟩.

1:5119 ⟨1⟩ Simon, *Bull. soc. chim. Belg.* **38,** 57, 59 (1929). ⟨2⟩ Evans, *J. Chem. Soc.* **1936,** 788. ⟨3⟩ Johnson, Schwartz, Jacobs, *J. Am. Chem. Soc.* **60,** 1884 (1938). ⟨4⟩ Roll, Adams, *J. Am. Chem. Soc.* **53,** 3474 (1931).

—— **BENZOPHENONE** (allotropic form) $C_6H_5.CO.C_6H_5$ $C_{13}H_{10}O$ **Beil. VII-410**

M.P. 26°

See 1:5150. Genus 7: Division A. M.P. 48°.

1:5118 **BENZYL METHYL KETONE** (Phenylacetone) ⟨benzene ring⟩—$CH_2.CO.CH_3$ $C_9H_{10}O$ **Beil. VII-303**

M.P. 27° **B.P. 216.5°** cor. D_4^{20} = **1.0157** n_D^{20} = **1.5168** (on supercooled liquid)

[For prepn. (77–86% yield) via H_2SO_4 hydrolysis of α-phenylacetoacetonitrile see ⟨1⟩; for prepn. (55–65% yield) via pyrolysis of phenylacetic acid + acetic ac. over ThO_2 see ⟨2⟩; in 32% yield from C_6H_6, chloroacetone + $AlCl_3$ ⟨12⟩.]

$\bar{C}$, with satd. aq. $NaHSO_3$ soln. (cf. T 1.11) readily forms $NaHSO_3$ addn. cpd. which on treatment with $NaHCO_3$ regenerates $\bar{C}$ (volatile with steam) — $\bar{C}$ with I_2.KI soln. and alk. (T 1.81) yields CHI_3 [cf. ⟨3⟩] — $\bar{C}$ with $Ca(OCl)_2$ soln. yields BzOH (1:0715), BzH (1:0195) and acetic ac. (1:1010) ⟨4⟩.

$\bar{C}$, on oxidation with CrO_3 (T 1.72), yields BzOH (1:0715) and acetic ac. (1:1010) — $\bar{C}$, on reduction with 5% Na/Hg in 50% alc., yields benzyl-methyl-carbinol [Beil. VI-503] ⟨5⟩; $\bar{C}$ reduced with Zn/Hg + HCl gives (90% yield) ⟨6⟩ *n*-propylbenzene (1:7450).

Ⓓ **Benzyl methyl ketoxime:** from $\bar{C}$ + NH_2OH.HCl + NaOAc in dil. alc. (84% yield); m.p. 68–70° ⟨7⟩.

Ⓓ **Benzyl methyl ketone phenylhydrazone:** lfts. from lgr.; m.p. 86–87° ⟨8⟩; 83° ⟨9⟩.

Ⓓ **Benzyl methyl ketone *p*-nitrophenylhydrazone:** m.p. 145–145.5° ⟨10⟩.

Ⓓ **Benzyl methyl ketone semicarbazone:** pr. from alc.; m.p. 199–199.5° (block) ⟨11⟩; 187–190° cor. (rap. htg. by ord. method ⟨11⟩).

1:5118 ⟨1⟩ Julian, Oliver, *Organic Syntheses* **18**, 54–55 (1938). ⟨2⟩ Herbst, Manske, *Organic Syntheses* **16**, 47–50 (1936). ⟨3⟩ Schmidt, *Arch. Pharm.* **252**, 96 (1914). ⟨4⟩ Ssuknewitsch, Tschilingarjan, *Ber.* **69**, 1542 (1936). ⟨5⟩ Errera, *Gazz. chim. ital.* **16**, 315 (1886). ⟨6⟩ Clemmensen, *Ber.* **46**, 1839–1840 (1913). ⟨7⟩ Neber, von Friedolsheim, *Ann.* **449**, 122 (1926). ⟨8⟩ Zincke, Zahn, *Ber.* **43**, 854 (1910). ⟨9⟩ Trenkler, *Ann.* **248**, 110–111 (1888). ⟨10⟩ Dakin, *J. Biol. Chem.* **5**, 173 (1908).

⟨11⟩ Tiffeneau, Cahnmann, *Bull. soc. chim.* (5) **2**, 1880–1881 (1935). ⟨12⟩ Mason, Terry, *J. Am. Chem. Soc.* **62**, 1622 (1940).

1:5120 PHORONE $(CH_3)_2C{=}CH.CO.CH{=}C(CH_3)_2$ $C_9H_{14}O$ **Beil. I-951**
(Diisopropylideneacetone)

M.P. 28° **B.P. 198.5°**

Yel.-green pr. with disagreeable odor, sl. remin. of geraniums — Boiling with dil. H_2SO_4 gives acetone, b.p. 56° (1:5400) + some mesityl oxide, b.p. 129° (1:5445) — $\bar{C}$ with phenylhydrazine yields no phenylhydrazone but only the liq. 1-phenyl-3-isobutenyl-5,5-dimethylpyrazoline ⟨3⟩ — For action of NH_2OH see ⟨4⟩.

Phorone tetrabromide: $\bar{C}$, dislvd. in 10 pts. CS_2 and treated dropwise with 2 moles Br_2 with cooling, yields addn. prod., obt. by evapn. of CS_2 and recrystn. from alc., m.p. 88–89° ⟨1⟩. [Dif. from mesityl oxide (1:5445) which gives liq. dibromide.]

Phorone semicarbazone (?): $\bar{C}$ in alc. soln. reacts with 2 moles semicarbazide HCl in presence of AcOK to give prod., cryst. from aq., m.p. 221° ⟨2⟩.

1:5120 ⟨1⟩ Claisen, *Ann.* **180**, 12 (1875). ⟨2⟩ Rupe, Schlochoff, *Ber.* **36**, 4382 (1903). ⟨3⟩ von Auwers, Kreuder, *Ber.* **58**, 1982 (1925). ⟨4⟩ Harries, Lehmann, *Ber.* **30**, 2730, 230–234 (1897).

—— ***p*-METHYLACETOPHENONE** $CH_3.CO.C_6H_4.CH_3$ $C_9H_{10}O$ **Beil. VII-307**

M.P. 28°

See 1:5530. Genus 7: Division B. B.P. 224°.

1:5130 METHYL UNDECYL KETONE $C_{13}H_{26}O$ **Beil. I-715**
(Tridecanone-2) $CH_3.CO.(CH_2)_{10}.CH_3$

M.P. 28.1° ⟨1⟩ **B.P. 263°** D_4^{30} **= 0.82168 ⟨1⟩** n_D^{30} **= 1.43175 ⟨1⟩**

$\bar{C}$ on oxidn. with $K_2Cr_2O_7$ + dil. H_2SO_4 (cf. T 1.72) gives quant. yield of acetic ac. (1:1010) and undecylic ac. (1:0573) ⟨2⟩.

Ⓓ **Methyl *n*-undecyl ketoxime:** cryst. from alc. + pet. ether; m.p. 56–57° ⟨3⟩.

Ⓓ **Methyl *n*-undecyl ketone *p*-nitrophenylhydrazone:** m.p. 101–102° ⟨4⟩.

Ⓓ **Methyl *n*-undecyl ketone 2,4-dinitrophenylhydrazone:** or.-yel. cryst.; m.p. 69° ⟨5⟩ [cf. T 1.14].

Ⓓ **Methyl *n*-undecyl ketone semicarbazone:** cryst. from alc.; m.p. 123° ⟨2⟩ ⟨6⟩; 126° ⟨7⟩.

1:5130 ⟨1⟩ Ceuterick, *Bull. soc. chim. Belg.* **45,** 545–564 (1936). ⟨2⟩ Krafft, *Ber.* **12,** 1667 (1879). ⟨3⟩ Guérin, *Bull. soc. chim.* (3) **29,** 1130 (1930). ⟨4⟩ Sengoku, *Cent.* **1934,** I, 235. ⟨5⟩ Allen, *J. Am. Chem. Soc.* **52,** 2957 (1930). ⟨6⟩ Wilson, Keenan, *J. Assoc. Official Agr. Chem.* **13,** 390, 395 (1930). ⟨7⟩ Pickard, Kenyon, *J. Chem. Soc.* **99,** 57 (1911).

—— **LEVULINIC ACID** $CH_3.CO.CH_2.CH_2.COOH$ $C_5H_8O_3$ **Beil. III-672**

M.P. 33°

See 1:0405. Genus 3: Acids.

1:5133 ***n*-DODECYL METHYL KETONE** (Tetradecanone-2) $n.C_{12}H_{25}.\overset{\overset{\large O}{\|}}{C}.CH_3$ $C_{14}H_{28}O$ **Beil. I-716**

M.P. 33–34°

Cryst. from dil. alc.

Oxidn. with CrO_3 (T 1.72) yields lauric ac. (1:0605) and acetic acid (1:1010).

Ⓓ ***n*-Dodecyl methyl ketone semicarbazone:** cryst. from alc., m.p. 115–116° ⟨1⟩.

1:5133 ⟨1⟩ Ruzicka, Stoll, Scherrer, *Helv. Chim. Acta* **15,** 1464 (1932).

1:5134 **ETHYL *n*-UNDECYL KETONE** (Tetradecanone-3) $C_2H_5.\overset{\overset{\large O}{\|}}{C}—C_{11}H_{23}$ $C_{14}H_{28}O$ **Beil. I-716**

M.P. 34°

Cryst. from MeOH.

Ⓓ **Ethyl *n*-undecyl ketoxime:** cryst. from MeOH, m.p. 40° ⟨1⟩.

Ⓓ **Ethyl *n*-undecyl semicarbazone:** cryst. from MeOH, m.p. 92° ⟨1⟩.

1:5134 ⟨1⟩ Blaise, Guérin, *Bull. soc. chim.* (3), **29,** 1210–1211 (1903).

1:5135 **DIBENZYL KETONE** (α,α'-Diphenylacetone) $C_6H_5—CH_2.CO.CH_2—C_6H_5$ $C_{15}H_{14}O$ **Beil. VII-445**

M.P. 34° **B.P. 330.6°** cor.

$\bar{C}$ in alc. soln., treated with NaOEt + amyl nitrite at 5–10° yields isonitrosobenzy ketone; ndls., m.p. 116° ⟨1⟩.

Ⓓ **Dibenzylketoxime:** from $\bar{C}$ + hydroxylamine HCl in boilg. 90% alc. + a little HCl; cryst. from alc., m.p. 123° ⟨2⟩; 125° ⟨3⟩.

Ⓓ **Dibenzylketone phenylhydrazone:** eas. obtd. by treating 1 g. $\bar{C}$ in 20 ml. 85% alc. with 1 g. phenylhydrazine in 2 ml. AcOH; lfts. from alc., m.p. 121° ⟨4⟩ ⟨5⟩; 128–129° ⟨3⟩.

Ⓓ **Dibenzylketone 2,4-dinitrophenylhydrazone:** m.p. 100° ⟨6⟩ [cf. T 1.14].

Ⓓ **Dibenzyl ketone semicarbazone:** from $\bar{C}$ + semicarbazide HCl + KOAc in dil. alc.; lfts. from *abs.* alc., m.p. 145–146° ⟨7⟩ ⟨8⟩; from *dil.* alc., m.p. 125–126° ⟨7⟩.

1:5135 ⟨1⟩ Neber, Knoller, Herbst, Tressler, *Ann.* **471,** 122 (1929). ⟨2⟩ Goldschmidt, Krczmar, *Monatsh.* **22,** 664 (1901). ⟨3⟩ Francis, *J. Chem. Soc.* **75,** 868 (1899). ⟨4⟩ Senderens, *Bull. soc. chim.* (4) **7,** 654 (1910). ⟨5⟩ Trenkler, *Ann.* **248,** 112 (1888). ⟨6⟩ Allen, Richmond, *J. Org. Chem.* **2,** 224 (1937). ⟨7⟩ Wedekind, *Ber.* **34,** 2076, Note (1901). ⟨8⟩ Wedekind, *Ann.* **378,** 279 (1910).

1:5140 *p*-METHOXYACETOPHENONE $C_9H_{10}O_2$ Beil. VIII-87

(*p*-Acetylanisole)

$CH_3.CO-C_6H_4-OCH_3$

M.P. 38° **B.P. 257°**

[For prepn. in 90–94% yields from anisole, Ac_2O + $AlCl_3$ see ⟨10⟩.]

C̄, htd. in spacious flask with equal wt. $AlCl_3$ for 1½ hrs. at 140°, evolves CH_3Cl; residue on soln. in dil. HCl, extn. with ether, etc., gives 70% yield *p*-hydroxyacetophenone, m.p. 109° (1:1527) ⟨1⟩.

C̄, in cold MeOH soln., treated with excess alk. NaOCl gives 90% yield *p*-methoxybenzoic ac. (1:0805) ⟨2⟩ — 1 g. C̄ shak. 6 hrs. with soln. of 3 g. $KMnO_4$, and 1 g. KOH in 300 ml. aq.; excess $KMnO_4$ destroyed with alc., MnO_2 filtered, soln. acid. and ether extd.; crude purif. through $NaHCO_3$ gives 91% yield *p*-methoxyphenylglyoxylic ac. [Beil. X-950], anhyd. ndls. from C_6H_6, m.p. 90° ⟨3⟩.

Ⓓ ***p*-Methoxyacetophenone oxime:** white ndls. from pet. ether, m.p. 86–87° ⟨4⟩.

Ⓓ ***p*-Methoxyacetophenone phenylhydrazone:** from C̄ htd. 5 min. with phenylhydrazine (100% yield); yellowish ndls. from alc. or lgr., m.p. 142° ⟨5⟩.

Ⓓ ***p*-Methoxyacetophenone *p*-nitrophenylhydrazone:** or. lfts. from alc.; m.p. 195–195.5° ⟨6⟩.

Ⓓ ***p*-Methoxyacetophenone 2,4-dinitrophenylhydrazone:** red cryst., m.p. 220° cor. ⟨7⟩; 231.8° cor. ⟨9⟩. [Cf. T 1.14.]

Ⓓ ***p*-Methoxyacetophenone semicarbazone:** ndls. from dil. alc., m.p. 197–198° ⟨8⟩; 196.5° ⟨6⟩.

1:5140 ⟨1⟩ Hartmann, Gattermann, *Ber.* **25,** 3533 (1892). ⟨2⟩ Van Arendonk, Cuperey, *J. Am. Chem. Soc.* **53,** 3184–3186 (1931). ⟨3⟩ Kögel, Becker, *Ann.* **465,** 236 (1928). ⟨4⟩ von Auwers, Lechner, Bundesmann, *Ber.* **58,** 41 (1925). ⟨5⟩ Korczynski, Kierzek, *Gazz. chim. ital.* **55,** 365 (1925). ⟨6⟩ Unger, *Ann.* **504,** 279 (1933). ⟨7⟩ Allen, Richmond, *J. Org. Chem.* **2,** 224 (1937). ⟨8⟩ Wahl, Silberzweig, *Bull. soc. chim.* (4) **11,** 69 (1912). ⟨9⟩ Ferrante, Bloom, *Ann. J. Pharm.* **105,** 383 (1933). ⟨10⟩ Adams, Noller, *Organic Syntheses, Coll. Vol.* I, 105 (1932).

1:5141 *m*-METHOXYBENZOPHENONE $C_{14}H_{12}O_2$ Beil. VIII-158

(*m*-Benzoylanisole;
m-anisyl phenyl ketone)

$C_6H_5-CO-C_6H_4(OCH_3)$

M.P. 38° **B.P. 342–343°**/730 mm.

C̄ dislvd. in 4 pts. AcOH and boiled 1½ hrs. with 48% HBr yields *m*-hydroxybenzophenone (1:1535) although much less readily than with corresponding *o*- and *p*-isomers ⟨1⟩ — C̄ in C_6H_6 refluxed 2 hrs. with $AlBr_3$ in C_6H_6 gives 88% yield *m*-hydroxybenzophenone (1:1535) ⟨2⟩.

1:5141 ⟨1⟩ Stoermer, *Ber.* **41,** 323 (1908). ⟨2⟩ Pfeiffer, Loewe, *J. prakt. Chem.* (2) **147,** 299 (1937).

1:5142 o-METHOXYBENZOPHENONE $C_{14}H_{12}O_2$ **Beil. VIII-156**
(o-Benzoylanisole;
o-anisyl phenyl ketone)

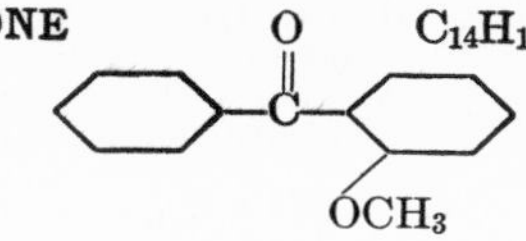

M.P. 39°

C̄ in 4 pts. AcOH + that amt. of 48% HBr just insufficient to ppt. an oil, refluxed 1½ hrs. ⟨1⟩, or C̄ refluxed with 4 pts. $AlBr_3$ in 25 pts. C_6H_6 for 4 hrs. (96% yield) ⟨2⟩ gives o-hydroxybenzophenone (1:1414).

Ⓓ **o-Methoxybenzophenone oxime:** from C̄ + hydroxylamine HCl + NaOAc in dil. alc. refluxed 6 hrs. (100% yield); m.p. 145–148° ⟨3⟩. [After fusion or on recrystallization from AcOH the higher melting form is isomerized to a lower melting form, m.p. 130° ⟨3⟩.]

1:5142 ⟨1⟩ Bonnard, Meyer-Oulif, *Bull. soc. chim.* (4) **49**, 1305 (1931). ⟨2⟩ Pfeiffer, Loewe, *J. prakt. Chem.* (2) **147**, 299 (1937). ⟨3⟩ Billon, *Ann. chim.* (10) **7**, 341 (1927).

—— **o-HYDROXYBENZOPHENONE** $C_{13}H_{10}O_2$ **Beil. VIII-155**
(o-Benzoylphenol)

M.P. 41°

See 1:1414. Genus 4: **Phenols.**

1:5144 INDANONE-1 C_9H_8O **Beil. VII-360**
(α-Hydrindone)

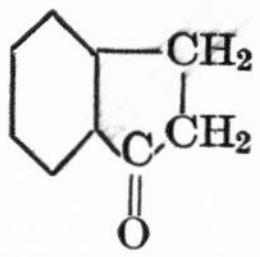

M.P. 42° **B.P. 241–242°**/739 mm.

Tbls. from melt; ndls. from aq.; pl. from pet. ether — Dif. sol. aq.; eas. sol. alc., ether, $CHCl_3$ — Eas. volatile with steam.

C̄ boiled with HNO_3 (D = 1.2) yields smoothly ⟨2⟩ phthalic ac. (1:0820) — C̄, reduced with amalgamated Zn + dil. HCl gives 90% yield hydrindene (1:7511); b.p. 176–176.5° ⟨8⟩.

[For prepn. in 50–60% yield from indene via addn. of HCl and oxidn. of product see ⟨1⟩; in 27% yield from hydrocinnamic acid (1:0615) by ring closure with fumg. H_2SO_4 at 140° for 5 min. ⟨9⟩.]

Ⓓ **α-Hydrindone oxime:** from C̄ in alc. + $NH_2OH.HCl$ + excess alk.; cryst. from 50% alc. ⟨2⟩ or $CHCl_3$ + pet. ether ⟨3⟩, m.p. 144°.

Ⓓ **α-Hydrindone phenylhydrazone:** from C̄ + phenylhydrazine at 100°; m.p. 124–128° ⟨4⟩. [After extraction with 10 pts. hot MeOH, followed by crystn. from MeOH, product melts in evacuated capillary at 134–135°. Cf. ⟨4⟩.]

Ⓓ **α-Hydrindone p-nitrophenylhydrazone:** from C̄ + p-nitrophenylhydrazine.HCl on warm. in dil. alc., or. pdr. from AcOH, m.p. 234–235° ⟨5⟩.

Ⓓ **α-Hydrindone 2,4-dinitrophenylhydrazone:** m.p. 258° ⟨6⟩ [cf. T 1.14].

Ⓓ **α-Hydrindone semicarbazone:** from C̄ in dil. alc. + semicarbazide HCl + KOAc; m.p. 233° after prelim. browning ⟨7⟩ [cf. ⟨5⟩].

1:5144 ⟨1⟩ Pacaud, Allen, *Organic Syntheses* **18**, 47–49 (1938). ⟨2⟩ Wislicenus, *Ann.* **275**, 344–345 (1893). ⟨3⟩ Kipping, *J. Chem. Soc.* **65**, 490 (1894). ⟨4⟩ Leuchs, Kowalski, *Ber.* **58**, 2824 (1925). ⟨5⟩ von Auwers, Auffenberg, *Ber.* **52**, 106 (1919). ⟨6⟩ Allen, *J. Am. Chem. Soc.* **52**, 2958 (1930). ⟨7⟩ Revis, Kipping, *J. Chem. Soc.* **71**, 241–242 (1897). ⟨8⟩ Clemmensen, *Ber.* **47**, 682–683 (1914). ⟨9⟩ Price, Lewis, *J. Am. Chem. Soc.* **61**, 2553–2554 (1939).

1:5145 BENZALACETONE $C_{10}H_{10}O$ **Beil. VII-364**

(Benzylideneacetone; methyl styryl ketone) C_6H_5—CH=CH.CO.CH_3

M.P. 42° **B.P. 262°** cor.

Eas. sol. alc., ether, C_6H_6, $CHCl_3$; spar. sol. lgr. — Sol. in conc. H_2SO_4 with or.-red color; addn. of HNO_3 gives pale yel. — $\bar{C}$ can be purified by steam distn. — [For prepn. in 65–78% yield from benzaldehyde + acetone see ⟨1⟩.]

$\bar{C}$ is sol. in $KHSO_3$ soln. ⟨2⟩; with satd. aq. $NaHSO_3$ soln. (cf. T 1.12) gives insol. $NaHSO_3$ addn. prod. ⟨3⟩ — $\bar{C}$ in 10 pts. $CHCl_3$ adds Br_2 in cold yielding benzalacetone dibromide [Beil. VII-315], ndls. from hot alc., m.p. 124–125° dec. ⟨3⟩ — $\bar{C}$ with NaOCl soln. at 60–70° gives 70% yield cinnamic ac. (1:0735) ⟨4⟩.

$\bar{C}$ + equiv. amt. BzH in alc. soln. treated with a little 10% NaOH, heated and stood, yields dibenzalacetone (1:9024), pale yel. pl. from alc., m.p. 112° u.c. ⟨3⟩.

Ⓓ **Benzalacetone oxime:** from $\bar{C}$ + $NH_2OH.HCl$ + $1\frac{1}{2}$ moles NaOH in dil. alc.; cryst. from 60% alc., m.p. 115–116° ⟨5⟩.

Ⓓ **Benzalacetone phenylhydrazone:** from $\bar{C}$ + 1 equiv. phenylhydrazine in alc.; yel. ndls. from alc., m.p. 156–157° ⟨6⟩. [On htg. to its b.p. the phenylhydrazone is converted to 1,5-diphenyl-3-methylpyrazoline ⟨7⟩.]

Ⓓ **Benzalacetone *p*-nitrophenylhydrazone:** from $\bar{C}$ + *p*-nitrophenylhydrazine.HCl in dil. alc.; cinnabar-red cryst. from alc. or AcOEt, m.p. 165–167° ⟨8⟩. [On boilg. with AcOH this prod. rearr. into yel. 1-(*p*-nitrophenyl)-3-methyl-5-phenyl-pyrazoline, ndls. from alc., m.p. 149° ⟨8⟩.]

Ⓓ **Benzalacetone 2,4-dinitrophenylhydrazone:** red. cryst. from AcOH, m.p. 227° ⟨9⟩; or.-red cryst. from alc., m.p. 223° ⟨10⟩. [Cf. T 1.14.]

Ⓓ **Benzalacetone semicarbazone:** lemon-yel. cryst. from alc., m.p. 186° ⟨11⟩.

1:5145 ⟨1⟩ Drake, Allen, *Organic Syntheses, Coll. Vol.* I, 69–71 (1932). ⟨2⟩ Knoevenagel, *Ber.* **37**, 4044 (1904). ⟨3⟩ Claisen, Ponder, *Ann.* **223**, 140–141 (1884). ⟨4⟩ Schorigin, et al., *Centr.* **1932**, I, 2948. ⟨5⟩ Zelinsky, *Ber.* **20**, 923 (1887). ⟨6⟩ Knorr, *Ber.* **20**, 1099 (1887). ⟨7⟩ Marshall, *J. Chem. Soc.* **107**, 521 (1915). ⟨8⟩ von Auwers, Kreuder, *Ber.* **58**, 1983 (1925). ⟨9⟩ Campbell, *Analyst* **61**, 393 (1936). ⟨10⟩ Allen, *J. Am. Chem. Soc.* **52**, 2958 (1930). ⟨11⟩ Wilson, Keenan, *J. Assoc. Official Agr. Chem.* **13**, 390, 393 (1930).

1:5148 PHENYL UNDECYL KETONE $C_{18}H_{28}O$ **Beil. VII-345**

(Laurophenone) C_6H_5—CO.$C_{11}H_{23}$

M.P. 47°

(No derivatives known.)

1:5150 BENZOPHENONE $C_{13}H_{10}O$ **Beil. VII-410**

(Diphenyl ketone) C_6H_5—CO—C_6H_5

M.P. 48° **B.P. 306°** cor.

[For prepn. in 80–89% yield from C_6H_6, CCl_4 + $AlCl_3$ see ⟨10⟩.]

Pr., insol. aq., eas. sol. alc., ether — Gives yel. soln. in conc. H_2SO_4 — Occurs also in metastable form (m.p. 26°) on cooling after fusion above 100° or evapn. of ether soln.; changes to stable form (m.p. 48°) on seeding with latter.

Htd. gently with metallic Na yields intensely blue product — Reductn. with Mg + MeOH (89% yield) ⟨1⟩ or with Al isopropylate in isopropyl alc. (100% yield) ⟨9⟩ or 2% Na/Hg in abs. alc. + ether + C_6H_6 (98% yield) ⟨11⟩ gives benzohydrol (1:5960), cryst. from lgr., m.p. 67.5°.

Ⓓ **Benzophenone oxime:** from C̄ + $NH_2OH.HCl$ + excess alk., briefly htd. in 80% alc.; after acid. with HCl ppt. recrystd. from MeOH or lgr.; m.p. 142–143° ⟨2⟩.

Ⓓ **Benzophenonephenylhydrazone:** from refluxing dil. alc. soln. of C̄ with phenylhydrazine hydrochloride + AcONa for ½ hr.; the sepg. crude is recrystd. from alc.; colorless ndls., m.p. 137–138° ⟨3⟩. [For study of optim. cond. see ⟨4⟩.]

Ⓓ **Benzophenone-*p*-nitrophenylhydrazone:** from 6 hr. htg. of alc. soln. of C̄ with equiv. amt. *p*-nitrophenylhydrazine; yel. ndls. from alc.; m.p. 154–155° ⟨5⟩.

Ⓓ **Benzophenone 2,4-dinitrophenylhydrazone:** from C̄ + 2,4-dinitrophenylhydrazine; or.-yel. ndls. from AcOH; m.p. 238–239° ⟨6⟩. [Use in quant. detn. of C̄ ⟨7⟩ ⟨12⟩.]

Ⓓ **Benzophenone semicarbazone:** ndls. from alc., m.p. 164–165° ⟨8⟩.

1:5150 ⟨1⟩ Zechmeister, *Rom. Ann.* **468,** 123 (1929). ⟨2⟩ Lachmann, *Organic Syntheses* **10,** 10–11 (1930). ⟨3⟩ Fischer, *Ber.* **17,** 576 (1884). ⟨4⟩ Ardagh, Kellam, Rutherford, Walstaff, *J. Am. Chem. Soc.* **54,** 721–727 (1932). ⟨5⟩ Hyde, *Ber.* **32,** 1814 (1899). ⟨6⟩ Campbell, *Analyst* **61,** 393 (1936). ⟨7⟩ Perkins, Edwards, *Am. J. Pharm.* **107,** 208–209 (1935). ⟨8⟩ Borsche, Merkwitz, *Ber.* **37,** 3180 (1904). ⟨9⟩ Lund, *Ber.* **70,** 1524 (1937). ⟨10⟩ Marvel, Sperry, *Organic Syntheses, Coll. Vol.* I, 89–92 (1932).

⟨11⟩ Bachmann, *J. Am. Chem. Soc.* **55,** 773 (1937). ⟨12⟩ Iddles, Low, Rosen, Hart, *Ind. Eng. Chem., Anal. Ed.* **11,** 102–103 (1939).

1:5153 METHYL β-NAPHTHYL KETONE $C_{12}H_{10}O$ Beil. VII-402

(2-Acetonaphthone;
2-acetylnaphthalene)

CH_3—CO—

M.P. 53-54° B.P. 301°

Cryst. from alc., lgr. or xylene — Spar. sol. cold alc., lgr.; eas. sol. hot alc., or cold CS_2, ether — Alleged to isomerize slowly, particularly in presence of impurities or cat., to α-isomer (1:5600) ⟨1⟩.

[For prepn. from CH_3MgI + β-naphthonitrile see ⟨2⟩.]

Oxidn. with NaOCl yields 98% β-naphthoic ac. (1:0800) ⟨3⟩ — Oxidn. with dil. HNO_3 ⟨4⟩ also yields β-naphthoic ac. (1:0800) — Oxidn. with alk. $KMnO_4$ at 53° yields β-naphthoylformic acid, $C_{10}H_7.CO.COOH$, cryst. from C_6H_6, m.p. 171° ⟨5⟩.

With Al isopropylate in isopropyl alc. C̄ reduces (90% yield) to methyl-β-naphthylcarbinol, cryst. from lgr., m.p. 72° ⟨6⟩.

C̄ in alc. soln., treated with alc. PkOH, yields a dif. sol. picrate, C̄. PkOH, m.p. 85° ⟨7⟩; 82° ⟨8⟩. [Use in distinction or sepn. from more sol. α-isomer.]

Ⓓ **Methyl β-naphthyl ketoxime:** m.p. 145° u.c. ⟨9⟩; 145–146° ⟨8⟩ [cf. also ⟨13⟩].

Ⓓ **Methyl β-naphthyl ketone phenylhydrazone:** m.p. 176–177° ⟨10⟩; 171° u.c. ⟨9⟩.

Ⓓ **Methyl β-naphthyl ketone 2,4-dinitrophenylhydrazone:** red ndls. from AcOH, m.p. 262° dec. ⟨13⟩ [cf. T 1.14].

Ⓓ **Methyl β-naphthyl ketone semicarbazone:** m.p. 234–235° ⟨11⟩; 235–237° ⟨12⟩.

1:5153 ⟨1⟩ Chopin, *Bull. soc. chim.* (4) **45,** 167 (1929). ⟨2⟩ Allen, Hubbard, *J. Am. Chem. Soc.* **52,** 385 (1930). ⟨3⟩ Newman, Holmes, *Organic Syntheses* **17,** 65–67 (1937). ⟨4⟩ Rousset, *Bull. soc. chim.* (3), **15,** 61 (1896). ⟨5⟩ Popovici, *Compt. rend.* **191,** 210–211 (1930). ⟨6⟩ Lund, *Ber.* **70,** 1524 (1937). ⟨7⟩ Stobbé, Lenzner, *Ann.* **380,** 95 (1911). ⟨8⟩ St. Pfau, Ofner, *Helv. Chim. Acta* **9,** 670–671 (1926). ⟨9⟩ Claus, Tersteegen, *J. prakt. Chem.* (2) **42,** 518 (1890). ⟨10⟩ von Braun, Hahn, Seemann, *Ber.* **55,** 1691 (1922).

⟨11⟩ Barbot, *Bull. soc. chim.* (4) **47,** 1319 (1930). ⟨12⟩ Darzens, *Compt. rend.* **145,** 1343 (1907). ⟨13⟩ Campbell, *Analyst* **61,** 393 (1936). ⟨14⟩ Bachmann, Barton, *J. Org. Chem.* **3,** 300–311 (1938).

—— **n-CAPROYLRESORCINOL** $C_{12}H_{16}O_3$ **Beil. S.N. 775**
(2,4-Dihydroxy-1-*n*-caproylbenzene)

M.P. 56-57° **B.P. 343-345°**

See 1:1443. Genus 4: Phenols.

1:5155 BENZALACETOPHENONE $C_{15}H_{12}O$ **Beil. VII-478**
(Chalcone;
phenyl styryl ketone)

C_6H_5—CH=CH—CO—C_6H_5

M.P. 58° **B.P. 345-348°** u.c.

Pale yel. pr. from alc.; eas. sol. ether, $CHCl_3$, CS_2; moderately sol. alc.; dif. sol. pet. ether — Sol. in conc. H_2SO_4 with intense yel. color. [For prepn. in 65–78% yield from benzaldehyde + acetophenone see ⟨11⟩.]

C̄ dissolves in warm 20% $KHSO_3$ soln. and on cooling seps. ppt. of K chalcone hydrosulfonate from which NaOH regenerates C̄ ⟨1⟩ — C̄ dislvd. in Ac_2O, treated with 2 drops of soln. of conc. H_2SO_4 in Ac_2O, stood 24 hrs., poured into aq. gives oil which cryst. on shaking; product is a dimer, cryst. from alc., m.p. 134° ⟨2⟩ — C̄ in ether treated with Br_2 (1 mole) yields chalcone dibromide [Beil. VII-445], cryst. from alc., m.p. 157° ⟨3⟩.

Reaction of C̄ with hydroxylamine is disputed; see Beil. VII-478 and ⟨12⟩ — C̄ in alc. warmed 1 hr. at 100° with 1 mole phenylhydrazine yields 1,3,5-triphenylpyrazoline, yel. ndls. from hot alc., m.p. 134–135° ⟨4⟩ ⟨5⟩ ⟨6⟩ — C̄ in alc. refluxed several hrs. with 1 mole *p*-nitrophenylhydrazine HCl + a little conc. HCl yields 1-(*p*-nitrophenyl)-3,5-diphenylpyrazoline, yel. ndls. from alc., m.p. 177–177.5° ⟨7⟩ — C̄ with 2,4-dinitrophenylhydrazine yields mixt. of chalcone 2,4-dinitrophenylhydrazone, or.-red needles from AcOH, m.p. 244° dec. ⟨8⟩; 245° cor. ⟨9⟩ [use in quant. detn. of C̄ ⟨13⟩] and corresponding 1-(2′,4′-dinitrophenyl)-3,5-diphenylpyrazoline ⟨9⟩; on recrystn. from solvent contg. trace of minl. acid mixt. is converted to latter cpd., m.p. 175° cor. ⟨9⟩.

C̄ in alc. stood 48 hrs. with 2.5 moles semicarbazide acetate in dil. alc. yields white ppt. of α-form of chalcone semicarbazone, purified by soln. in $CHCl_3$ and pptn. with pet. ether; m.p. 168° sl. dec. ⟨10⟩.

1:5155 ⟨1⟩ Knoevenagel, *Ber.* **37**, 4049 (1904). ⟨2⟩ Wieland, *Ber.* **37**, 1147 (1904). ⟨3⟩ Pond, York, Moore, *J. Am. Chem. Soc.* **23**, 790 (1901). ⟨4⟩ Knorr, Laubmann, *Ber.* **21**, 1210 (1888). ⟨5⟩ von Auwers, Voss, *Ber.* **42**, 4422 (1909). ⟨6⟩ Raiford, Davis, *J. Am. Chem. Soc.* **50**, 156–162 (1927). ⟨7⟩ von Auwers, Kreuder, *Ber.* **58**, 1986 (1925). ⟨8⟩ Campbell, *Analyst* **61**, 393 (1936). ⟨9⟩ Allen, Richmond, *J. Org. Chem.* **2**, 224–225 (1937). ⟨10⟩ Heilbron, Wilson, *J. Chem. Soc.* **101**, 1486–1487 (1912).

⟨11⟩ Kohler, Chadwell, *Organic Syntheses, Coll. Vol.* I, 71–73 (1932). ⟨12⟩ von Auwers, Müller, *J. prakt. Chem.* (2) **147**, 57–80 (1933). ⟨13⟩ Iddles, Low, Rosen, Hart, *Ind. Eng. Chem., Anal. Ed.* **11**, 102–103 (1939).

1:5160 PHENYL p-TOLYL KETONE $C_{14}H_{12}O$ **Beil. VII-440**
(*p*-Methylbenzophenone)

C_6H_5—C(=O)—C_6H_4—CH_3

M.P. 60° **B.P. 326° cor.**

Sol. alc., ether, C_6H_6; dif. sol. lgr. — C̄ also known in metastable form, m.p. 55°.

C̄, oxidized for 24 hrs. with $K_2Cr_2O_7$ + dil. H_2SO_4 ⟨1⟩ or better with 4% $KMnO_4$ ⟨2⟩, yields *p*-benzoylbenzoic ac. [Beil. X-753]; cryst. from 30% AcOH, m.p. 194°. C̄, reduced with 2% Na/Hg in abs. alc. + C_6H_6 + ether gives 98% yield ⟨10⟩ phenyl-*p*-tolyl-carbinol (1:5949).

Ⓓ **Phenyl p-tolyl ketoxime:** C̄ (1 pt.) + $NH_2OH.HCl$ (1 pt.) treated with 1.7 pts. NaOH in dil. alc., stood overnight gives mixt. of two stereoisomeric oximes; the mixt. is pptd. with HCl and separated by fractional pptn. with aq. from AcOH soln.; the dif. sol. form has m.p. 154°; the more sol. form, m.p. 115° ⟨3⟩ ⟨4⟩ [cf. ⟨5⟩].

Ⓓ **Phenyl *p*-tolyl ketone phenylhydrazone:** from C̄ + phenylhydrazine in AcOH, on stdg. a few hrs.; white cryst., m.p. 109° ⟨6⟩ [with alc. or dil. AcOH solns. the oil first formed slowly solidifies].

Ⓓ **Phenyl *p*-tolyl ketone 2,4-dinitrophenylhydrazone:** or. cryst., m.p. 199–200° ⟨7⟩; 202.4° cor. ⟨8⟩ [cf. T 1.14].

Ⓓ **Phenyl *p*-tolyl ketone semicarbazone:** from C̄ + semicarbazide HCl + NaOAc in dil. alc. at 100° for 4 hrs.; cryst. from alc., m.p. 121–122° (block) ⟨9⟩.

1:5160 ⟨1⟩ Radziszewski, *Ber.* **6**, 811 (1873). ⟨2⟩ Meyer, *Monatsh.* **28**, 1224 (1907). ⟨3⟩ Hantzsch, *Ber.* **23**, 2325 (1890). ⟨4⟩ Semper, Lichtenstadt, *Ber.* **51**, 936–937 (1918). ⟨5⟩ Bachmann, Barton, *J. Org. Chem.* **3**, 305 (1938). ⟨6⟩ Overton, *Ber.* **26**, 26 (1893). ⟨7⟩ Grieve, Hey, *J. Chem. Soc.* **1934**, 1806. ⟨8⟩ Ferrante, Bloom, *Am. J. Pharm.* **105**, 383 (1933). ⟨9⟩ Bruzau, *Ann. chim.* (11) **1**, 353 (1934). ⟨10⟩ Bachmann, *J. Am. Chem. Soc.* **55** 773 (1937).

1:5165 DESOXYBENZOIN $C_{14}H_{12}O$ Beil. VII-431

(Benzyl phenyl ketone)

C_6H_5—$CH_2.CO$—C_6H_5

M.P. 60° **B.P. 321°** cor.

Tbls. from alc.; eas. sol. cold alc., ether; dif. sol. hot aq. — [For prepn. in 82–83% yield from phenylacetic ac. + C_6H_6 see ⟨7⟩.]

C̄ boiled with 3 pts. 70% aq. KOH splits into toluene (1:7405) and BzOH (1:0715) in good yield ⟨1⟩ — C̄ is readily attacked by nitrous ac. with oxidation and nitration.

Ⓓ **Desoxybenzoin oxime:** from C̄ in alc. on boilg. with NH_2OH, pouring into aq., extg. with ether, evaporating; ndls. from alc., m.p. 98° ⟨2⟩.

Ⓓ **Desoxybenzoin phenylhydrazone:** from C̄ in dil. AcOH on treatment with phenylhydrazine; yel. lfts. from alc., m.p. 116° ⟨3⟩. [On htg. product 1 min. with a little 10% HCl brown oil results which on stirring with AcOH gives quant. yield of 2,3-diphenylindole [Beil. XX-520]; m.p. 123.0–123.5° ⟨3⟩.]

Ⓓ **Desoxybenzoin *p*-nitrophenylhydrazone:** red brown cryst.; m.p. 163° ⟨4⟩.

Ⓓ **Desoxybenzoin 2,4-dinitrophenylhydrazone:** orange cryst., m.p. 204° cor. ⟨5⟩.

Ⓓ **Desoxybenzoin semicarbazone:** from C̄ with semicarbazide HCl + KOAc in dil. alc., m.p. 148° ⟨6⟩.

1:5165 ⟨1⟩ Knoevenagel, Arndts, *Ber.* **35**, 1983, Note (1902). ⟨2⟩ Beckmann, Günther, *Ann.* **252**, 68 (1889). ⟨3⟩ Bodforss, *Ber.* **58**, 782 (1925). ⟨4⟩ Shima, *Cent.* **1930**, II, 2363. ⟨5⟩ Allen, Richmond, *J. Org. Chem.* **2**, 224 (1937). ⟨6⟩ Tiffeneau, *Ann. chim.* (8) **10**, 360 (1907). ⟨7⟩ Allen, Barker, *Organic Syntheses* **12**, 16–18 (1932).

—— BENZOYLACETONE $C_{10}H_{10}O_2$ Beil. VII-680

M.P. 60-61° **B.P. 261°**

See 1:1450. Genus 4: Phenols.

1:5170 *p*-METHOXYBENZOPHENONE $C_{14}H_{12}O_2$ Beil. VIII-159

(*p*-Anisyl phenyl ketone; *p*-benzoylanisole)

C_6H_5—C(=O)—C_6H_4—OCH_3

M.P. 62° **B.P. 354°**

C̄ + 4 pts. 48% HBr dislvd. in AcOH and refluxed 12 hrs. ⟨1⟩ or C̄ + 4 pts. $AlBr_3$ in 30 pts. C_6H_6 refluxed 4 hrs. (95% yield) ⟨2⟩ gives 4-hydroxybenzophenone (1:1560).

C̄ dislvd. in 10 pts. HNO_3 (D = 1.5), kept 12 hrs., poured onto ice, semi-solid ppt. recryst. from alc., gives yel. ndls. of 3-nitro-4-methoxybenzophenone, m.p. 105° ⟨3⟩ — C̄, reduced with Zn dust + dil. aq. alc. NaOH gives (66% yield) *p*-anisyl-phenyl-carbinol (1:5956), cryst. from dil. alc., m.p. 59–60° ⟨9⟩.

Ⓓ ***p*-Methoxybenzophenone oxime:** C̄ with neutral hydroxylamine yields mixt. of stereoisomeric oximes, sepd. by fractional pptn. of AcOH soln. with aq.; higher melting less sol. α-isomer, m.p. 137–138° ⟨4⟩; 146–147° ⟨5⟩; lower melting more sol. β-isomer, m.p. 115–116° ⟨4⟩ ⟨5⟩.

Ⓓ ***p*-Methoxybenzophenone phenylhydrazone:** from C̄ + phenylhydrazine or its acetate in alc. soln.; cryst. from ether, m.p. 132° ⟨6⟩ — [Although two isomeric forms are known [Beil. XV-199] only the higher melting isomer is formed by above method ⟨5⟩.]

Ⓓ ***p*-Methoxybenzophenone *p*-nitrophenylhydrazone:** or. lfts. from alc., m.p. 198–199° ⟨7⟩.

Ⓓ ***p*-Methoxybenzophenone 2,4-dinitrophenylhydrazone:** deep or. cryst., m.p. 180° ⟨8⟩ [cf. T 1.14].

1:5170 ⟨1⟩ Blakey, Jones, Scarborough, *J. Chem. Soc.* **1927**, 2867. ⟨2⟩ Pfeiffer, Loewe, *J. prakt. Chem.* (2) **147**, 300 (1937). ⟨3⟩ Ref. 1, page 2870. ⟨4⟩ Hantzsch, *Ber.* **24**, 54 (1891). ⟨5⟩ Stoermer, *Ber.* **44**, 667 (1911). ⟨6⟩ Hantzsch, Krafft, *Ber.* **24**, 3525 (1891). ⟨7⟩ Unger, *Ann.* **405**, 284 (1933). ⟨8⟩ Ferrante, Bloom, *Am. J. Pharm.* **105**, 383 (1933). ⟨9⟩ Norris, Blake, *J. Am. Chem. Soc.* **50**, 1811 (1928).

—— 1-ACETO-2-NAPHTHOL $C_{12}H_{10}O_2$ Beil. S.N. 751

M.P. 64°

See 1:1459. Genus 4: Phenols.

1:5174 CINNAMALACETONE $C_{12}H_{12}O$ Beil. VII-390

C_6H_5—CH=CH—CH=CH.CO.CH_3

M.P. 68°

Lfts. from ether — Insol. aq.; sol. alc., ether, C_6H_6 — On stdg. even in dark autooxidizes to an oily prod. ⟨1⟩; on illumination or htg. in absence of air polymerizes to a resinous dimer ⟨1⟩. [For prepn. of C̄ from cinnamaldehyde (1:0245) and acetone (1:5400) see ⟨2⟩.]

C̄ is sol. in conc. H_2SO_4 with yel. color which disappears on dilution with aq.

C̄ in alc. treated with BzH + NaOH yields benzal-cinnamal-acetone, pale yel. lfts. from alc., m.p. 106° ⟨3⟩ — C̄ with boilg. NaOH yields cinnamalacetic acid [Beil. IX-638], m.p. 166°, + $CHCl_3$ ⟨4⟩.

Ⓓ **Cinnamalacetone oxime:** from C̄ + $NH_2OH.HCl$ + Na_2CO_3 in dil. alc. at room temp.; ndls. from alc., m.p. 153° ⟨5⟩; 152° ⟨6⟩.

Ⓓ **Cinnamalacetone phenylhydrazone:** from C̄ + phenylhydrazine; citron-yel. lfts. from alc., m.p. 180° ⟨7⟩.

Ⓓ **Cinnamalacetone 2,4-dinitrophenylhydrazone:** purple-red lfts. from AcOH, m.p. 222–223° ⟨8⟩; brown-red lfts. from $CHCl_3$ + MeOH, m.p. 218–220° ⟨9⟩ [cf. T 1.14].

Ⓓ **Cinnamalacetone semicarbazone:** yel. ndls. from alc., m.p. 186° ⟨10⟩.

1:5174 ⟨1⟩ Stobbé, Hensel, Simon, *J. prakt. Chem.* (2) **110**, 148, 152 (1925). ⟨2⟩ Bauer, Dieterle, *Ber.* **44**, 2693 (1911). ⟨3⟩ Scholtz, *Ber.* **29**, 614 (1896). ⟨4⟩ Diel, Einhorn, *Ber.* **18**, 2321 (1885). ⟨5⟩ Scholtz, *Ber.* **28**, 1726 (1895). ⟨6⟩ Batty, et al., *J. Chem. Soc.* **1938**, 178. ⟨7⟩ Ref. 4, page 2323. ⟨8⟩ Campbell, *Analyst* **61**, 393 (1936). ⟨9⟩ Borsche, Peitzsch, *Ber.* **62**, 371 (1929). ⟨10⟩ Rupe, Schlochoef, *Ber.* **36**, 4381 (1903).

1:5175 **LAURONE** $CH_3.(CH_2)_{10}.CO.(CH_2)_{10}.CH_3$ $C_{23}H_{46}O$ **Beil. I-719**
(Di-*n*-undecyl ketone)

M.P. 69.5°

Ⓓ **Laurone oxime:** obtd. by addg. a dil. MeOH soln. of 0.6 g. $NH_2OH.HCl$ + 12 g. KOH to warm MeOH soln. of $\bar{C}$, keeping 4 hrs. at room temp. then htg. at 60–70° for $\frac{1}{2}$ hr. After filt. from sepd. KCl, filtrate acidif. with warm dil. HCl, and after cooling, the pptd. oxime recrystd. from alc., m.p. 39–40° ⟨1⟩ ⟨2⟩.

1:5175 ⟨1⟩ Kipping, *J. Chem. Soc.* **57,** 983 (1890). ⟨2⟩ Petroff, Karasseff, Tschelzowa, *Bull. soc. chim.* (5) **3,** 173 (1936).

—— **DIBENZOYLMETHANE** $C_{15}H_{12}O_2$ **Beil. VII-769**
(ω-Benzoylacetophenone)

M.P. 78°

See 1:1480. Genus 4: Phenols.

1:5180 **α-HYDROXYACETOPHENONE** $C_8H_8O_2$ **Beil. VIII-90**
(Benzoylcarbinol; phenacyl alcohol) ⬡—$CO.CH_2OH$

M.P. 86°

Pr. (from lgr.), hexag. tbls. (from alc. or ether); cryst. from hot aq. with aq. of crystn. and then melts 73–74°.

$\bar{C}$, on htg. alone or with dil. NaOH, decomposes yielding benzaldehyde (1:0195) — $\bar{C}$ reduces ammon. $AgNO_3$ soln. or Fehling's soln. (T 1.22) — Gives dif. sol. $NaHSO_3$ compd. (cf. T 1.12).

$\bar{C}$, in dil. alc. soln., shaken with aq. $Cu(OAc)_2$ gives 60% phenylglyoxal (1:0278) ⟨1⟩ — [For prepn. of $\bar{C}$ by hydrol. of phenacyl bromide, see ⟨2⟩ ⟨3⟩.]

Ⓓ **α-Hydroxyacetophenone oxime:** from 5 g. $\bar{C}$ by warm. several hrs. with mixt. of 5 g. $NH_2OH.HCl$, 10 ml. aq., 29 ml. 2.5 *N* alc. KOH, and 20 ml. alc.; yield 3.9 g. (70%); cryst. from C_6H_6, m.p. 70° ⟨3⟩.

Ⓓ **α-Hydroxyacetophenone phenylhydrazone:** from $\bar{C}$, dislvd. in hot aq., and treated with aq. soln. of 1 pt. phenylhydrazine HCl and $1\frac{1}{2}$ pts. AcONa, gives an oil, which after solid. is dislvd. in ether, lgr. added, and the mixt. conc.; ndls., m.p. 112° ⟨4⟩.

Ⓓ **α-Hydroxyacetophenone semicarbazone:** ndls. from alc., m.p. 146–146.5° ⟨5⟩.

Ⓓ **Phenacyl acetate:** from $\bar{C}$ + Ac_2O at 100°; cryst. from ether, m.p. 49° ⟨6⟩. [Prepd. indirectly from phenacyl Br + NaOAc; m.p. 40° ⟨7⟩.]

Ⓓ **Phenacyl benzoate:** ndls. from dil. alc.; m.p. 118°. [Prepd. indirectly from phenacyl bromide + NaOBz ⟨7⟩.]

Ⓓ **Phenacyl *p*-nitrobenzoate:** m.p. 128.4°. [Prepd. indirectly from phenacyl bromide + sodium *p*-nitrobenzoate ⟨7⟩.]

1:5180 ⟨1⟩ Henze, *Z. physiol. Chem.* **198,** 82–84 (1931). ⟨2⟩ Stoermer, *Ber.* **39,** 2294 (1906). ⟨3⟩ Gabriel, Colman, *Ber.* **47,** 1867 (1914). ⟨4⟩ Laubmann, *Ann.* **243,** 245 (1888). ⟨5⟩ von Auwers, Mauss, *Cent.* **1928,** I, 2607. ⟨6⟩ Nef, *Ann.* **335,** 268 (1904). ⟨7⟩ Rather, Reid, *J. Am. Chem. Soc.* **41,** 83 (1919).

1:5185 **DI-*p*-TOLYL KETONE** $C_{15}H_{14}O$ **Beil. VII-451**
(4,4′-Dimethylbenzophenone) CH_3—⬡—CO—⬡—CH_3

M.P. 95° **B.P. 335°**

Cryst. (from alc.) — Insol. aq.; very eas. sol. alc., ether, $CHCl_3$, CS_2, conc. H_2SO_4.

$\bar{C}$, treated with HNO_3 (D = 1.5), with cooling, yields 3,3′-dinitro-4,4′-dimethylbenzophenone, poured into aq., ppt. recrystd. from alc.; yellow ndls., m.p. 144° ⟨1⟩ — C̄ in mixt. of ether + C_6H_6 shaken with MgI_2 + Mg gives 94% yield 4,4′,4″,4‴-tetramethylbenzopinacol; pr. from $CHCl_3$; m.p. 183–184° rap. htg. ⟨2⟩.

C̄ treated with 2% Na/Hg in abs. alc. + C_6H_6 + ether gives (96% yield) di-*p*-tolylcarbinol (1:5959) ⟨5⟩.

Ⓓ **Di-*p*-tolylketoxime:** by 2 hr. boilg. of a dil. alc. soln. of 1 g. C̄, 1.2 g. $NH_2OH.HCl$, and 2 g. NaOH: colorless lfts. from alc.; m.p. 163° ⟨3⟩.

Ⓓ **Di-*p*-tolylketone phenylhydrazone:** by 2 hr. warming of a soln. of 1 g. C̄, with 1.5 g. phenylhydrazine in some 60% AcOH; the reactn. mixt. is poured into very dil. HCl, the sepg. solid recryst. from alc.; yel. pr., m.p. 100° ⟨3⟩.

Ⓓ **Di-*p*-tolylketone 2,4-dinitrophenylhydrazone:** or. cryst., m.p. 229.4° cor. ⟨4⟩ [cf. T 1.14].

1:5185 ⟨1⟩ Errera, *Gazz. chim. ital.* **21,** I, 99 (1891). ⟨2⟩ Gomberg, Bachmann, *J. Am. Chem. Soc.* **49,** 249–250 (1927). ⟨3⟩ Bistrzycki, Reintke, *Ber.* **38,** 842 (1905). ⟨4⟩ Ferrante, Bloom, *Am. J. Pharm.* **105,** 383 (1933). ⟨5⟩ Bachmann, *J. Am. Chem. Soc.* **55,** 773 (1933); **55,** 2137 (1933).

—— **BENZIL** ⬡—CO.CO—⬡ $C_{14}H_{10}O_2$ **Beil. VII-747**

M.P. 95°

See 1:9015. Suborder II: Colored compounds.

—— ***m*-HYDROXYACETOPHENONE** $C_8H_8O_2$ **Beil. VIII-86**
(*m*-Acetylphenol)

M.P. 96° **B.P. 296°**

See 1:1506. Genus 4: Phenols.

—— **2-ACETO-1-NAPHTHOL** $C_{12}H_{10}O_2$ **Beil. VIII-149**

M.P. 102° **B.P. 325°** sl. dec.

See 1:1515. Genus 4: Phenols.

—— ***p*-HYDROXYACETOPHENONE** $C_8H_8O_2$ **Beil. VIII-87**
(*p*-Acetylphenol)

M.P. 109°

See 1:1527. Genus 4: Phenols.

—— **DIBENZALACETONE** $C_{17}H_{14}O$ **Beil. VII-500**

⬡—CH=CH.CO.CH=CH—⬡

M.P. 112°

See 1:9024. Suborder II: Colored compounds.

1:5195 **ANISOIN** $C_{16}H_{16}O_4$ **Beil. VIII-423**
(4,4′-Dimethoxybenzoin)

CH_3O—⬡—C(H)(OH)—C(=O)—⬡—OCH_3

M.P. 113°

Pr. from dil. alc. — Insol. hot aq.; dif. sol. ether, cold alc.; eas. sol. hot alc. [For prepn. from *p*-methoxybenzaldehyde (1:0240) by act. of KCN in 50–60% yield see ⟨1⟩; in 75% yield see ⟨2⟩.]

C̄ is sol. in conc. H_2SO_4 with pale green color changing to yel. and purple-red on warming — C̄ reduces Fehling's soln. (T 1.22) ⟨1⟩ ⟨3⟩ or alk. $KMnO_4$ (60% yield) ⟨1⟩ giving anisil [Beil. VIII-428]; golden yel. ndls. from alc., m.p. 133°.

C̄ (5 g.) + nitrobenzene (4 g.) in alc. (50 ml.) boiled 2–3 min. with 6% alc. NaOEt gives 80% yield anisil (cf. above) ⟨4⟩.

Ⓓ **Anisoin semicarbazone:** from 2 g. C̄ + 1 g. AcOK in 150 g. alc. treated at room temp. with soln. of 1 g. semicarbazide HCl in 25 ml. aq., and filtered from turbidity. On standing 5 days semicarbazone cryst. out — Recrystn. from alc. + little aq. gives colorless pr., m.p. not sharp but on rap. htg. about 185° cor. ⟨5⟩.

Ⓓ **Anisoin acetate:** from C̄ + AcCl; cryst. from alc. + pet. ether; m.p. 94–95° ⟨6⟩.

1:5195 ⟨1⟩ van Alphen, *Rec. trav. chim.* **48,** 1112–1113 (1929). ⟨2⟩ Dewar, Reid, *Chemistry & Industry* **55**T, 347–348 (1936). ⟨3⟩ Fischer, *Ann.* **211,** 215 (1882). ⟨4⟩ Nisbet, *J. Chem. Soc.* **1928,** 3124. ⟨5⟩ Biltz, Arnd, *Ann.* **339,** 271 (1905). ⟨6⟩ McKenzie, Pirie, *Ber.* **69,** 874 (1936).

—— ***m*-HYDROXYBENZOPHENONE** $C_{13}H_{10}O_2$ **Beil. VIII-157**

M.P. 116°

See 1:1535. Genus 4: Phenols.

1:5200 ACENAPHTHENONE $C_{12}H_8O$ **Beil. VII-410**

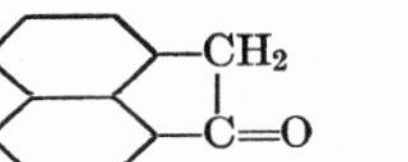

M.P. 121° cor.

Colorless ndls. from alc. — Very eas. sol. alc., $CHCl_3$, C_6H_6; dif. sol. lgr. — Volatile with steam.

C̄ is sol. in alc. KOH with violet color, but ppts. unchanged on acidifn. — C̄ boiled with aq. NaOH in air gives naphthalic ac. (1:0890) — C̄ in alc. + PkOH in alc. yields acenaphthenone picrate; yel. ndls., m.p. 113° ⟨1⟩ — C̄ + equiv. amt. BzH + a little aq. alk. gives alm. quant. yield of benzalacenaphthenone; yel. cryst. from dil. alc., m.p. 107° ⟨2⟩.

Ⓓ **Acenaphthenone oxime:** from C̄ in alc. warmed with $NH_2OH.HCl$ + Na_2CO_3; cryst. from alc., m.p. 175° ⟨3⟩; cryst. from C_6H_6, m.p. 183–184° ⟨4⟩ [m.p. of acenaphthenequinone dioxime is 222° dec.].

Ⓓ **Acenaphthenone phenylhydrazone:** from C̄ in alc. refluxed with equiv. amt. phenylhydrazine; cryst. from alc., m.p. 90° darkening ⟨1⟩. [C̄ (1 g.) + phenylhydrazine (0.65 g.) in 10 ml. AcOH, htd. at 100° for 2–3 hrs. gives yel. ppt. of acenaphthindole, cryst. from dil. alc., m.p. 235° ⟨5⟩.]

1:5200 ⟨1⟩ Graebe, Jequier, *Ann.* **290,** 200 (1896). ⟨2⟩ Ref. 1, page 204. ⟨3⟩ Graebe, Gfeller, *Ann.* **276,** 13 (1892). ⟨4⟩ Morgan, Stanley, *J. Soc. Chem. Ind.* **44**T, 493–496 (1925). ⟨5⟩ Sircar, Gopalan, *J. Indian Chem. Soc.* **9,** 298–299 (1932).

1:5201 *p*-PHENYLACETOPHENONE $C_{14}H_{12}O$ **Beil. VII-443**
(4-Acetylbiphenyl;
methyl *p*-xenyl ketone)

O
‖
$CH_3.C$—⟨ ⟩—⟨ ⟩

M.P. 121° **B.P. 325-327°**

Cryst. from alc. or acetone.

[For prepn. from AcCl + biphenyl + $AlCl_3$ in C_6H_6 (70% yield) see ⟨1⟩; from Ac_2O + biphenyl + $AlCl_3$ in CS_2 (80% yield) see ⟨2⟩.]

Oxidn. with boilg. alk. $KMnO_4$ gives *p*-phenylbenzoic ac. (80% yield) ⟨3⟩ ⟨4⟩, cryst. from alc. (to remove terephthalic ac.), m.p. 228° — Oxidn. with NaOCl yields $CHCl_3$ and *p*-phenylbenzoic ac. ⟨3⟩.

Reductn. with amalgamated zinc + HCl yields 4-ethylbiphenyl, b.p. 280°, cryst. from dil. alc., m.p. 46–47° ⟨5⟩.

C̄ in AcOH treated with equal wt. Br_2 (in AcOH) at 50° yields *p*-phenylphenacyl bromide (cf. T 1.391), lfts. from alc., then from toluene, m.p. 126–127° ⟨6⟩ ⟨2⟩.

C̄ added grad. to fumg. HNO_3 at 0°, stood, poured into aq., gives 2,4′-dinitro-4-acetylbiphenyl, pale yel. ndls. from dil. alc., m.p. 155–156° ⟨1⟩.

Pure C̄ + BzH in alc. htd. 10 min. at 100° with few drops 50% KOH gives 60% yield 4′-phenylchalcone (4-cinnamoylbiphenyl), pale yel. lfts. from C_6H_6, m.p. 156° ⟨7⟩ ⟨8⟩.

C̄ with AcCl + $AlCl_3$ gives 51% yield 4,4′-diacetylbiphenyl, lfts. from alc., m.p. 191° ⟨9⟩.

Ⓓ ***p*-Phenylacetophenone oxime:** from C̄ + $NH_2OH.HCl$ + pyridine in alc., ndls. from EtOH, m.p. 186–187° ⟨10⟩ ⟨11⟩.

1:5201 ⟨1⟩ Grieve, Hey, *J. Chem. Soc.* **1933,** 970. ⟨2⟩ Drake, Bronitsky, *J. Am. Chem. Soc.* **52,** 3718 (1930). ⟨3⟩ Gull, Turner, *J. Chem. Soc.* **1929,** 498. ⟨4⟩ Kindler, *Ann.* **452,** 103 (1927). ⟨5⟩ von Auwers, Jülicher, *Ber.* **55,** 2183 (1922). ⟨6⟩ Carpenter, Turner, *J. Chem. Soc.* **1934,** 870. ⟨7⟩ Dilthey, *J. prakt. Chem.* (2) **101,** 196 (1921). ⟨8⟩ Bachmann, Wiselogle, *J. Am. Chem. Soc.* **56,** 1559 (1934). ⟨9⟩ Silver, Lowy, *J. Am. Chem. Soc.* **56,** 2429–2430 (1934). ⟨10⟩ Bachmann, Barton, *J. Org. Chem.* **3,** 309 (1938).
⟨11⟩ Ingersoll, White, *J. Am. Chem. Soc.* **54,** 279 (1932).

1:5205 XANTHYDROL $C_{13}H_{10}O_2$ **Beil. XVII-129**
(9-Hydroxyxanthene)

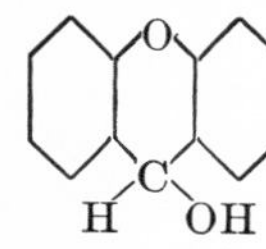

M.P. abt. 122-124° dec. (see text)

M.p. somewhat indefinite owing to conversion by loss of water to dixanthyl ether, m.p. 219° — C̄ must be dried at room temp. owing to disproportionation to xanthone (1:7275) and xanthene [Beil. XVII-73] ⟨1⟩. [For prepn. from xanthone in 91–95% yield by reductn. with Na/Hg + alc. see ⟨2⟩.]

White voluminous ndls. pptd. from alc. by addn. of aq.; can be recrystd. from hot lgr. but on continued boiling dehydrates yielding dif. sol. dixanthyl ether — On htg. in air C̄ gives sublimate of xanthone (1:7275).

C̄ is characterized by extraordinary reactivity of hydroxyl group — C̄, boiled 5 min. with 0.01 *N* HCl, is completely changed to mixt. of equal parts xanthone (1:7275) and xanthene [Beil. XVII-73], but C̄ is not affected by boilg. 0.1 *N* NaOH ⟨3⟩ — C̄ dislvd. in conc. HBr and added dropwise to warm alc. yields AcH + xanthene ⟨4⟩ — C̄ is sol. in conc. H_2SO_4 with yel. color and green fluores. — With alc. NH_2OH C̄ yields xanthylhydroxylamine [Beil. XVIII-638] in cold; similarly C̄ with phenylhydrazine ppts. xanthylphenylhydrazine; and C̄ with semicarbazide gives xanthylsemicarbazide [Beil. XVIII-588] ⟨5⟩.

Ⓓ **Dixanthylurea:** Aq. soln. of urea treated with 5–10% alc. C̄ and 2–3 vols. of AcOH yields quant. ppt. silky ndls., m.p. abt. 260° dec. ⟨6⟩. [Xanthone and xanthene simultaneously formed by disproportionation, remain in soln.]

Ⓓ **Dixanthyl:** 2 g. C̄ in 20 ml. AcOH, treated with 2.25 g. $SnCl_2$ in 5 ml. conc. HCl ppts. or.-red complex salt which on 5–10 min. boilg. changes to white ndls. After treat. with 15 ml. boiling ether and drying, gave 1.4 g. dixanthyl, m.p. after recrystn. from lgr. 204° ⟨7⟩.

1:5205 ⟨1⟩ Kny-Jones, Ward, *Analyst* **54,** 574–575 (1929). ⟨2⟩ Hollemann, *Organic Syntheses, Coll. Vol.* I, 539–540 (1932). ⟨3⟩ Kny-Jones, Ward, *J. Chem. Soc.* **1930,** 535, 539. ⟨4⟩ Fosse, *Compt. rend.* **133,** 881 (1901). ⟨5⟩ Fosse, *Ann. chim.* (9) **6,** 31–32 (1916). ⟨6⟩ Ref. 5, page 66. ⟨7⟩ Wanschiedt, Moldavski, *Ber.* **63,** 1368 (1930).

— *o*-BENZOYLBENZOIC ACID $C_{14}H_{10}O_3$ Beil. X-747

M.P. 127°

See 1:0720. Genus 3: Acids.

1:5210 *d,l*-BENZOIN $C_{14}H_{12}O_2$ Beil. VIII-167

M.P. 133° **B.P. 344°**

Hexag. pr. from alc.; often sulfur yel. in color — Insol. cold aq., dif. sol. cold alc. but very eas. sol. hot alc.; sl. sol. ether.

[For prepn. in 83% yield from BzH + NaCN see ⟨1⟩.]

$\bar{C}$ in alc. soln. reduces Tollens' reagt. (T 1.11) and Fehling's soln. (T 1.22). [Use in quant. detn. of $\bar{C}$ ⟨2⟩.] — $\bar{C}$ on oxidn. with $CuSO_4$ in dil. pyridine gives (86% yield) benzil (1:9015) ⟨3⟩.

$\bar{C}$ in isopropyl alc. treated with Al isopropylate gives (90% yield) *meso*-hydrobenzoin ⟨4⟩ [Beil. VI-1003], pl. from alc., m.p. 138° — $\bar{C}$ with $SOCl_2$ gives (75–79% yield) ⟨5⟩ desyl chloride [Beil. VII-436], ndls. from alc., m.p. 66–67°.

Ⓟ **Color reaction on alk. oxidn.:** $\bar{C}$ boiled with *N* NaOH in stream of air gives RV-T_1 color ⟨6⟩. [For study of this reaction see ⟨7⟩ ⟨8⟩.]

Ⓓ **Benzoin α-oxime:** from $\bar{C}$ in alc. htd. with $NH_2OH.HCl$ + equiv. NaOH; ppt. recrystd. from ether to remove accompanying β-stereoisomer; pr. from C_6H_6, m.p. 151–152° ⟨9⟩ [m.p. β-benzoin oxime, 99°].

Ⓓ **Benzoin α-phenylhydrazone:** from $\bar{C}$ + phenylhydrazine (1 mole) on htg. in alc.; ndls. from C_6H_6 + lgr., m.p. 158–159° ⟨10⟩. [The β-stereoisomer, m.p. 106°, is more sol. in alc. than the α form.] [$\bar{C}$ in AcOH boiled ½ hr. with excess phenylhydrazine yields benzil bisphenylhydrazone, yel. ndls. from AcOH or C_6H_6, m.p. 225° ⟨10⟩.]

Ⓓ **Benzoin 2,4-dinitrophenylhydrazone:** yel. cryst. from alc., m.p. 245° ⟨11⟩; m.p. 234° ⟨12⟩ [cf. T 1.14]. [Use in detn. of $\bar{C}$ ⟨21⟩.]

Ⓓ **Benzoin α-semicarbazone:** from $\bar{C}$ + semicarbazide HCl (1 mole) in pyridine stood at room temp. 6 days; poured into aq.; m.p. 205–206° ⟨13⟩.

Ⓓ **Benzoin acetate:** from $\bar{C}$ with Ac_2O + trace conc. H_2SO_4; yield quant.; cryst. from 90% alc., m.p. 83° ⟨14⟩. [For prepn. on larger scale (86–90% yield) see ⟨15⟩.]

Ⓓ **Benzoin benzoate:** from $\bar{C}$ + BzCl on htg. to 195°; cryst. from 75% alc., m.p. 124–125° ⟨13⟩.

Ⓓ **Benzoin *p*-nitrobenzoate:** from $\bar{C}$ + *p*-nitrobenzoyl chloride htd. in xylene; yellowish pr. from C_6H_6, m.p. 123° ⟨16⟩.

Ⓓ **Benzoin benzenesulfonate:** from $\bar{C}$ + $C_6H_5.SO_2.Cl$ + powd. NaOH in C_6H_6; cryst. from alc., m.p. 99–100° ⟨17⟩.

Ⓓ **Benzoin *N*-phenylcarbamate:** cryst. from C_6H_6; m.p. 165° ⟨18⟩.

Ⓓ **Benzoin *N*-*p*-nitrophenylcarbamate:** yel. ndls. from alc., m.p. 183° ⟨19⟩.

Ⓓ **Benzoin *N*-α-naphthylcarbamate:** m.p. 140° ⟨20⟩.

1:5210 ⟨1⟩ Adams, Marvel, *Organic Syntheses, Coll. Vol.* I, 88–89 (1932). ⟨2⟩ Stern, *Z. physik. Chem.* **50**, 514 (1905). ⟨3⟩ Clarke, Dreger, *Organic Syntheses, Coll. Vol.* I, 80–82 (1932). ⟨4⟩ Lund, *Ber.* **70**, 1524 (1937). ⟨5⟩ Ward, *Organic Syntheses* **12**, 20–21 (1932). ⟨6⟩ Hantzsch,

Glower, *Ber.* **40,** 1519–1523 (1907). ⟨7⟩ Corson, McAllister, *J. Am. Chem. Soc.* **51,** 2824–2825 (1929). ⟨8⟩ Weissberger, Mainz, Strasser, *Ber.* **62,** 1942–1952 (1929). ⟨9⟩ Werner, Detscheff, *Ber.* **38,** 72 (1905). ⟨10⟩ Smith, Ransom, *Am. Chem. J.* **16,** 111–112 (1894).

⟨11⟩ Campbell, *Analyst* **61,** 393 (1936). ⟨12⟩ Allen, *J. Am. Chem. Soc.* **52,** 2958 (1930). ⟨13⟩ Hopper, *J. Chem. Soc.* **127,** 1285 (1925). ⟨14⟩ Madelung, Oberwegner, *Ann.* **490,** 228 (1931). ⟨15⟩ Corson, Saliani, *Organic Syntheses* **12,** 1–2 (1932). ⟨16⟩ Meisenheimer, *Ber.* **38,** 877 (1905). ⟨17⟩ Földi, *Ber.* **60,** 664 (1927). ⟨18⟩ Beckmann, Paul, *Ann.* **266,** 24 (1891). ⟨19⟩ van Hoogstraten, *Rec. trav. chim.* **51,** 427 (1932). ⟨20⟩ Bickel, French, *J. Am. Chem. Soc.* **48,** 749 (1926).

⟨21⟩ Iddles, Low, Rosen, Hart, *Ind. Eng. Chem., Anal. Ed.* **11,** 102–103 (1939).

—— ***p*-HYDROXYBENZOPHENONE** $C_{13}H_{10}O_2$ **Beil. VIII-158**

M.P. 134-135°

See 1:1560. Genus 4: Phenols.

—— **FUROIN** $C_{10}H_8O_4$ **Beil. XIX-204**

M.P. 135°

See 1:1565. Genus 4: Phenols.

—— **ACETONEDICARBOXYLIC ACID** $C_5H_6O_5$ **Beil. III-789**
(β-Ketoglutaric acid) $HOOC.CH_2.CO.CH_2.COOH$

M.P. 135° dec.

See 1:0485. Genus 3: Acids.

—— ***o*-(*p*-TOLUYL)BENZOIC ACID** $C_{15}H_{12}O_3$ **Beil. X-759**

M.P. 139°

See 1:0750. Genus 3: Acids.

1:5215 ***d*-CAMPHOR** $C_{10}H_{16}O$ **Beil. VII-101**

M.P. 179° **B.P. 209°**

Opt. active: $[\alpha]_D^{20}$ in alc. = +44° — Tough, white cryst., translucent, slightly unctuous mass, with peculiar characteristic odor. Small fragments thrown on pure water float about with circular motion, immed. ceasing on addn. of drop of oil — Very volat., sublg. crystn. on sides of container at ord. temp. and in sapon. test depositing in condenser. Sol. unchanged in conc. H_2SO_4 — Very dif. sol. aq.; very sol. alc., ether, acetone, CS_2, C_6H_6.

$\bar{C}$ in boilg. Ac_2O oxidized with SeO_2 gives 90% yield camphorquinone (1:9083), m.p. 198° ⟨8⟩.

Ⓓ *d*-**Camphor oxime:** To 0.1 g. camphor add 0.2 g. powd. NH_2.OH.HCl, 1.5 g. NaOH, trace of aq., then 5 ml. alc., and reflux 1 hr. Cool, add 10 ml. aq., shake and filter, then add dil. HCl till just acid. Wash ppt. with aq., dry at 50°; m.p. 118–119° u.c. ⟨1⟩ [cf. ⟨2⟩].

Ⓓ *d*-**Camphor 2,4-dinitrophenylhydrazone:** or. ndls. from alc., m.p. 177° ⟨3⟩; 175° ⟨4⟩ [cf. T 1.14]. [The 2,4-dinitrophenylhydrazone from synthetic camphor has m.p. 164° ⟨5⟩.]

Ⓓ *d*-**Camphor semicarbazone:** 1.5 g. $\bar{C}$ in 2.0 ml. AcOH are added to a soln. of 1.2 g. semicarbazide HCl and 1.5 g. AcONa in 2.0 ml. aq. After warming, and cooling, pptd. by aq., filtered, and recrystd. from alc. or C_6H_6; m.p. 236–238° ⟨6⟩; 247–248° cor., dec. ⟨7⟩.

1:5215 ⟨1⟩ Mulliken, " Method " I, 150 (1904). ⟨2⟩ Lenz, *Arch. Pharm.* **249,** 292–295 (1911). ⟨3⟩ Campbell, *Analyst* **61,** 393 (1936). ⟨4⟩ Brady, *J. Chem. Soc.* **1931,** 756–759. ⟨5⟩ Janot, Mouton, *J. pharm. chim.* **23,** 547–549 (1936); *Chem. Abs.* **31,** 2750 (1937). ⟨6⟩ Tiemann, *Ber.* **28,** 2191–2192 (1895). ⟨7⟩ Bredt, Perkin, *J. Chem. Soc.* **103,** 2189, Note (1913); *J. prakt. Chem.* (2) **89,** 216, Note (1914). ⟨8⟩ Rupe, Tomassi di Vignano, *Helv. Chim. Acta* **20,** 1081 (1937).

—— **TRIKETOHYDRINDENE HYDRATE** $C_9H_6O_4$ **Beil. VII-867**
(" Ninhydrin ")

M.P. 241° dec.

See 1:1625. Genus 4: Phenols.

ORDER I: SUBORDER I: GENUS 7: KETONES

Division B, Liquid Ketones

1:5400 **ACETONE** $CH_3.CO.CH_3$ C_3H_6O **Beil. I-635**
(Dimethyl ketone)

B.P. 56° **M.P. −95°** D_4^{20} = **0.7912** n_D^{20} = **1.3590**

Alc. ethereal odor — $\bar{C}$ is misc. with aq., alc., ether — $\bar{C}$ is salted out from aq. solns. by addn. of $CaCl_2$, K_2CO_3.

For purification of $\bar{C}$ via cpd. with NaI (3 $\bar{C}$.NaI) see ⟨1⟩ ⟨2⟩ ⟨3⟩. [For extensive survey of methods of purification see ⟨4⟩.]

$\bar{C}$ with satd. aq. $NaHSO_3$ (cf. T 1.12) yields $NaHSO_3$ addn. cpd. — $\bar{C}$ treated with I_2 + KI soln. and alk. (T 1.81) yields CHI_3, m.p. 119° in cold [dif. from ethyl methyl ketone (1:5405)].

$\bar{C}$ in equal vol. $CHCl_3$ treated with a small piece of solid KOH and shaken in cold for a few minutes yields ppt. of 1,1,1-trichloro-*ter*-butyl alc. (chloretone); after evaporation of liq. and washing with aq. prod. is left as cpd. with $\frac{1}{2}$ H_2O; m.p. 80–82° after sintering at 76°. [If prod. is distd. (b.p. 167°) dist. is anhydrous and melts 96–97° after sintering at 89° ⟨5⟩.]

Acetone oxime [Beil. I-649] and acetone phenylhydrazone [Beil. XV-129] are not recommended as derivs. for identification.

Ⓟ **Sodium nitroprusside test (Legal reaction):** To 2 ml. cold aq. add 5 drops $\bar{C}$, then 2 drops 1% aq. soln. of sodium nitroprusside, and finally 2 drops 10% NaOH. Divide soln. into two parts, (a) and (b), adding to latter 3 drops of AcOH. Part (a) is orange (O), but changes to clear yel. (Y-YT_1) in 20 min.; part (b) on acidfn. is red (R-RT_1) with sl. tend. toward purple. This *hue* unchanged after 20 min., although intensity sl. dimin. ⟨6⟩.

Ⓓ **Dibenzalacetone:** To 2 drops $\bar{C}$ add 0.4 ml. aq., 2.0 ml. alc., 0.4 ml. benzaldehyde, and finally 0.5 ml. 10% NaOH. Boil the mixt. one min. over small flame, cool, and shake vigorously. Filter off the product, wash with 2 ml. cold alc., and recryst. from 2 ml. boiling alc. Wash with alc., dry at 100°, m.p. (rap. htg.) is 111–112° u.c. [This test has been employed on aq. solns. contg. as little as 2% of acetone. In such cases emulsions can sometimes be caused to cryst. by addn. of 1 ml. cold alc. Very dilute solns. of acetone should be concd. by distn. ⟨6⟩.]

Ⓓ **Acetone *p*-nitrophenylhydrazone:** yel. ndls. from alc., m.p. 148–149° ⟨7⟩. [Use in quant. detn. of $\bar{C}$ ⟨8⟩.]

Ⓓ **Acetone 2,4-dinitrophenylhydrazone:** yel. ndls. from alc., m.p. 128° ⟨9⟩; 126° ⟨10⟩. [Use in quant. detn. of $\bar{C}$ ⟨11⟩ ⟨12⟩ [cf. T 1.14].]

Ⓓ **Acetone semicarbazone:** ndls. from aq. or acetone; m.p. 190° ⟨13⟩.

1:5400 ⟨1⟩ Shipsey, Werner, *J. Chem. Soc.* **103,** 1255–1257 (1913). ⟨2⟩ Wadsworth, Dawson, *J. Chem. Soc.* **1926,** 2784–2786. ⟨3⟩ Macy, Thomas, *J. Am. Chem. Soc.* **48,** 1547–1550 (1926). ⟨4⟩ Weissberger, Proskauer, " Organic Solvents " (1925). ⟨5⟩ Sah, Lei, Ma, *Science Repts. Natl. Tsing Hua Univ.*, Ser. **A-1,** 209–214 (1932). ⟨6⟩ Mulliken, " Method " I, 148 (1904). ⟨7⟩ Dakin, *J. Biol. Chem.* **4,** 238 (1908). ⟨8⟩ Dehio, *Z. anal. Chem.* **104,** 417–422 (1936). ⟨9⟩ Allen, *J. Am. Chem. Soc.* **52,** 2958 (1930). ⟨10⟩ Campbell, *Analyst* **61,** 393 (1936).

⟨11⟩ Perkins, Edwards, *Am. J. Pharm.* **107,** 209 (1935). ⟨12⟩ Iddles, Jackson, *Ind. Eng. Chem., Anal. Ed.* **6,** 454–456 (1934). ⟨13⟩ Ciamician, Silber, *Ber.* **48,** 186 (1915).

1:5405 ETHYL METHYL KETONE $CH_3.CH_2.CO.CH_3$ C_4H_8O **Beil. I-666**
(Butanone-2)

B.P. 80° **M.P. −86.4°** D_4^{20} = **0.805** n_D^{20} = **1.3791**

C̄ is misc. with aq., alc., ether — C̄ with aq. forms homogeneous binary const. boilg. mixt. (b.p. 73.6°) contg. 88.6% by wt. of C̄ ⟨1⟩ — For purification of C̄ via cpd. with NaI (3 C̄.NaI) see ⟨2⟩ ⟨8⟩. [For soly. data on system: C̄ + aq. see ⟨10⟩.]

C̄ with satd. aq. $NaHSO_3$ soln. (cf. T 1.12) yields $NaHSO_3$ addn. cpd.

C̄ on oxidn. with CrO_3 (T 1.72) yields acetic ac. (1:1010).

Ethyl methyl ketoxime [Beil. I-668] and ethyl methyl ketone phenylhydrazone [Beil. XV-130] are both liquids and not recommended as derivs.

Ⓓ **Ethyl methyl ketone *p*-nitrophenylhydrazone:** yel. ndls. from aq. alc.; m.p. 128–129° ⟨3⟩; 124–125° ⟨4⟩.

Ⓓ **Ethyl methyl ketone 2,4-dinitrophenylhydrazone:** yel. cryst. from alc.; 115° ⟨5⟩; 116–117° ⟨9⟩ [cf. T 1.14]. [Use in quant. detn. of C̄ ⟨6⟩.]

Ⓓ **Ethyl methyl ketone semicarbazone:** cryst. from aq.; m.p. 135–136° ⟨7⟩.

1:5405 ⟨1⟩ Marshall, *J. Chem. Soc.* **89,** 1376 (1906). ⟨2⟩ Lochte, *Ind. Eng. Chem.* **16,** 956 (1924). ⟨3⟩ Dakin, *J. Biol. Chem.* **4,** 238 (1908). ⟨4⟩ Bauer, Strauss, *Ber.* **65,** 312 (1932). ⟨5⟩ Allen, *J. Am. Chem. Soc.* **52,** 2957 (1930). ⟨6⟩ Iddles, Jackson, *Ind. Eng. Chem., Anal. Ed.* **6,** 454–456 (1934). ⟨7⟩ Scholtz, *Ber.* **29,** 610 (1896). ⟨8⟩ Wadsworth, Dawson, *J. Chem. Soc.* **1926,** 2784–2786. ⟨9⟩ Dirscherl, Nahm, *Ber.* **73,** 449 (1940). ⟨10⟩ Ginnings, Plonk, Carter, *J. Am. Chem. Soc.* **62,** 1923 (1940).

—— BIACETYL $C_4H_6O_2$ **Beil. I-769**

B.P. 89°

See 1:9500. Suborder II. Colored compounds.

1:5410 ISOPROPYL METHYL KETONE $C_5H_{10}O$ **Beil. I-682**
(2-Methylbutanone-3) $(CH_3)_2CH.CO.CH_3$

B.P. 94.3° ⟨1⟩ D_4^{20} = **0.8046** ⟨1⟩ n_D^{16} = **1.38788**

[For prepn. (59% yield) from *ter*-amyl alc. (1:6160) + Br_2 see ⟨2⟩.] [For soly. data on system: C̄ + aq. see ⟨8⟩.]

C̄ on oxidn. with CrO_3 + H_2SO_4 (T 1.72) gives acetic ac. (1:1010) and CO_2.

Isopropyl methyl ketoxime [Beil. I-683] and isopropyl methyl ketone phenylhydrazone [Beil. XV-131] are liquids and not recommended as derivs.

Ⓓ **Isopropyl methyl ketone *p*-nitrophenylhydrazone:** or.-yel. ndls. from alc.; m.p. 108–109° ⟨3⟩.

Ⓓ **Isopropyl methyl ketone 2,4-dinitrophenylhydrazone:** or.-yel. cryst. from alc. + $CHCl_3$, m.p. 117° ⟨4⟩; 119–120° ⟨5⟩ [cf. T 1.14].

Ⓓ **Isopropyl methyl ketone semicarbazone:** cryst. from alc.; m.p. 112–113° ⟨6⟩; 113–114.5° ⟨7⟩.

1:5410 ⟨1⟩ Rintelen, Saylor, Gross, *J. Am. Chem. Soc.* **59,** 1129 (1937). ⟨2⟩ Whitmore, Evers, Rothrock, *Organic Syntheses* **13,** 68–70 (1933). ⟨3⟩ Dakin, *J. Biol. Chem.* **4,** 238 (1908). ⟨4⟩ Allen, *J. Am. Chem. Soc.* **52,** 2957 (1930). ⟨5⟩ Lewis, Simonsen, *J. Chem. Soc.* **1936,** 736. ⟨6⟩ Bardan, *Bull. soc. chim.* (4), **49,** 1875–1876 (1931). ⟨7⟩ Whitmore, Evers, *J. Am. Chem. Soc.* **55,** 815 (1933). ⟨8⟩ Ginnings, Plonk, Carter, *J. Am. Chem. Soc.* **62,** 1923 (1940).

1:5415 METHYL *n*-PROPYL KETONE $CH_3.CO.C_3H_7$ $C_5H_{10}O$ **Beil. I-676**
(Pentanone-2)

B.P. 102.3° ⟨1⟩ D_4^{20} = **0.80639** ⟨1⟩ n_D^{20} = **1.39012** ⟨1⟩

[For soly. data on system: $\bar{C}$ + aq. see ⟨11⟩.]

$\bar{C}$ with satd. aq. $NaHSO_3$ soln. yields $NaHSO_3$ addn. cpd. — $\bar{C}$ on oxidn. with CrO_3 + H_2SO_4 (T 1.72) yields propionic ac. (1:1025) and acetic ac. (1:1010).

Methyl *n*-propyl ketoxime [Beil. I-677] and methyl *n*-propyl ketone phenylhydrazone [Beil. XV-130] are liquids and not recommended as derivs.

Ⓓ **Methyl *n*-propyl ketone *p*-nitrophenylhydrazone:** m.p. 117° ⟨2⟩ ⟨3⟩. [For data on mixed m.p. with corresp. deriv. of pentanone-3 see ⟨10⟩.]

Ⓓ **Methyl *n*-propyl ketone 2,4-dinitrophenylhydrazone:** yel.-or. cryst. from alc., m.p. 143–144° ⟨4⟩; 142° ⟨5⟩; 141° ⟨6⟩ [cf. T 1.14]. [Use in quant. detn. of $\bar{C}$ ⟨7⟩.]

Ⓓ **Methyl *n*-propyl ketone semicarbazone:** m.p. 112° ⟨8⟩; 105–106° ⟨9⟩. [For data on mixed m.p. with corresp. deriv. of pentanone-3 see ⟨10⟩.]

1:5415 ⟨1⟩ Ceuterick, *Bull. soc. chim. Belg.* **45,** 555, 558 (1936). ⟨2⟩ Bülow, Deiglmayr, *Ber.* **37,** 4530 (1904). ⟨3⟩ Dakin, *Am. Chem. J.* **44,** 46 (1910). ⟨4⟩ Campbell, *Analyst* **61,** 393 (1936). ⟨5⟩ Morgan, Hardy, *Chemistry & Industry* **52,** 518–519 (1933). ⟨6⟩ Allen, *J. Am. Chem. Soc.* **52,** 2957 (1930). ⟨7⟩ Iddles, Jackson, *Ind. Eng. Chem., Anal. Ed.* **6,** 454–456 (1934). ⟨8⟩ Michael, *J. Am. Chem. Soc.* **41,** 419 (1919). ⟨9⟩ Whitmore, Evers, *J. Am. Chem. Soc.* **55,** 815 (1933). ⟨10⟩ Mowat, Smith, *J. Chem. Soc.* **1938,** 21.
⟨11⟩ Ginnings, Plonk, Carter, *J. Am. Chem. Soc.* **62,** 1923 (1940).

1:5420 DIETHYL KETONE $CH_3.CH_2.CO.CH_2.CH_3$ $C_5H_{10}O$ **Beil. I-679**
(Pentanone-3; propione)

B.P. 102.0° ⟨1⟩ **M.P. −39.8°** ⟨1⟩ D_4^{20} = **0.81425** ⟨1⟩ n_D^{20} = **1.3927**
$n_{He\,(yel.)}^{15}$ = **1.39466** ⟨1⟩

Sol. in 15 vols. cold aq. — $\bar{C}$ with satd. aq. $NaHSO_3$ soln. (T 1.12) adds $NaHSO_3$ only with difficulty — $\bar{C}$ with hot $Ca(OCl)_2$ soln. yields acetic ac. (1:1010), propionic ac. (1:1025), and $CHCl_3$ ⟨2⟩. [For soly. data on system: $\bar{C}$ + aq. see ⟨8⟩.]

$\bar{C}$ on oxidn. with CrO_3 + H_2SO_4 (T 1.72) yields propionic ac. (1:1025) and acetic ac. (1:1010) — $\bar{C}$ reduced with Al isopropylate + isopropyl alc. gives (60% yield) ⟨3⟩ diethylcarbinol (1:6175).

Diethyl ketoxime [Beil. I-680] and diethyl ketone phenylhydrazone [Beil. XV-130] are both liquids and not recommended as derivs.

Ⓓ **Diethyl ketone *p*-nitrophenylhydrazone:** or.-yel. ndls. from 50% alc., m.p. 144° ⟨4⟩. [For data on mixed m.p. with corresp. deriv. of pentanone-2 (1:5415) see ⟨7⟩.]

Ⓓ **Diethyl ketone 2,4-dinitrophenylhydrazone:** pale or. cryst. from alc. or AcOEt + $CHCl_3$; m.p. 156° ⟨5⟩ [cf. T 1.14].

Ⓓ **Diethyl ketone semicarbazone:** m.p. 138–139° ⟨6⟩. [For data on mixed m.p. with corresp. deriv. of pentanone-2 (1:5415) see ⟨7⟩.]

1:5420 ⟨1⟩ Timmermans, Hennaut-Roland, *J. chim. phys.* **29,** 548–550 (1932). ⟨2⟩ Ssuknewitsch, Tschilingarjan, *Ber.* **69,** 1541 (1936). ⟨3⟩ Lund, *Ber.* **70,** 1524 (1937). ⟨4⟩ Boese, Jones, Major, *J. Am. Chem. Soc.* **53,** 3540 (1931). ⟨5⟩ Allen, *J. Am. Chem. Soc.* **52,** 2958 (1930). ⟨6⟩ Schroeter, *Ber.* **49,** 2733 (1916). ⟨7⟩ Mowat, Smith, *J. Chem. Soc.* **1938,** 21. ⟨8⟩ Ginnings, Plonk, Carter, *J. Am. Chem. Soc.* **62,** 1923 (1940).

1:5425 PINACOLONE $(CH_3)_3C.CO.CH_3$ $C_6H_{12}O$ **Beil. I-64**
(" Pinacoline "; *ter*-butyl methyl ketone)

B.P. 106° cor. **M.P. −49.8°** ⟨8⟩ D_4^{20} = **0.8114** n_D^{20} = **1.3956** ⟨9⟩

Oil with peppermint odor — Soly. in aq. at 15° is 2.44% — [For soly. data on system: C̄ + aq. see ⟨10⟩.] — [For prepn. in 65–72% yield via rearr. of pinacol hexahydrate (1:5810) with dil. H_2SO_4 see ⟨1⟩.]

C̄ does not add $NaHSO_3$ (T 1.12) — C̄ with alk. + I_2 (T 1.81) gives no CHI_3 but a yellowish white cryst. cpd., m.p. 68°.

C̄ oxidized with CrO_3 + H_2SO_4 (T 1.72) or with NaOBr at 0° (71–74% yield) ⟨2⟩ gives trimethylacetic ac. (1:0410).

Pinacolone phenylhydrazone [Beil. XV-131] is liquid and not recommended as a deriv.

Ⓓ **Pinacolone oxime:** from C̄ + $NH_2OH.HCl$ + NaOH in dil. alc.; m.p. 77–78° ⟨3⟩, 78.5–79.5° ⟨9⟩.

Ⓓ **Pinacolone 2,4-dinitrophenylhydrazone:** or.-yel. cryst. from alc.; m.p. 125° ⟨4⟩ [cf. T 1.14]. [On fusion this form changes to a second modification, m.p. 131° ⟨5⟩ ⟨6⟩.]

Ⓓ **Pinacolone semicarbazone:** m.p. 157–158° ⟨7⟩.

1:5425 ⟨1⟩ Hill, Flosdorf, *Organic Syntheses, Coll. Vol.* I, 451–452 (1932). ⟨2⟩ Sandborn, Bousquet, *Organic Syntheses, Coll. Vol.* I, 512–513 (1932). ⟨3⟩ Piloty, Stock, *Ber.* **35,** 3097 (1902). ⟨4⟩ Allen, *J. Am. Chem. Soc.* **52,** 2958 (1930). ⟨5⟩ Whitmore, Laughlin, *J. Am. Chem. Soc.* **55,** 3736 (1933). ⟨6⟩ Brunner, Farmer, *J. Chem. Soc.* **1937,** 1043. ⟨7⟩ Gilman, Nelson, *Rec. trav. chim.* **55,** 529 (1936). ⟨8⟩ Hill, Kropa, *J. Am. Chem. Soc.* **55,** 2510 (1933). ⟨9⟩ Whitmore, Noll, Meunier, *J. Am. Chem. Soc.* **61,** 684 (1939). ⟨10⟩ Ginnings, Plonk, Carter, *J. Am. Chem. Soc.* **62,** 1923 (1940).

1:5430 ISOBUTYL METHYL KETONE $C_6H_{12}O$ **Beil. I-691**

(" Hexone ") $(CH_3)_2CH.CH_2.CO.CH_3$

B.P. 116.8° ⟨1⟩ D_4^{20} = **0.8008** ⟨1⟩ $n_D^{17.4}$ = **1.39694**

Strong camphoraceous odor; insol. aq.; misc. alc., ether, C_6H_6. [For soly. data on system: C̄ + aq. see ⟨5⟩.]

C̄ with satd. aq. $NaHSO_3$ soln. (cf. T 1.12) yields $NaHSO_3$ addn. cpd.

C̄ oxidized with CrO_3 (T 1.72) yields isobutyric ac. (1:1030), isovaleric ac. (1:1050), and acetic ac. (1:1010) — C̄, reduced with Na + moist ether, gives 70% yield isobutyl-methyl-carbinol (1:6199) + some isobutyl-methyl-pinacol ⟨2⟩.

Ⓓ **Isobutyl methyl ketone 2,4-dinitrophenylhydrazone:** or.-red cryst. from alc.; m.p. 95° ⟨3⟩ [cf. T 1.14].

Ⓓ **Isobutyl methyl ketone semicarbazone:** m.p. 132° ⟨4⟩.

1:5430 ⟨1⟩ Rintelen, Saylor, Gross, *J. Am. Chem. Soc.* **59,** 1129 (1937). ⟨2⟩ Clarke, Shreve, *Am. Chem. J.* **35,** 515 (1906). ⟨3⟩ Allen, *J. Am. Chem. Soc.* **52,** 2957 (1930). ⟨4⟩ Skita, *Ber.* **41,** 2939 (1908). ⟨5⟩ Ginnings, Plonk, Carter, *J. Am. Chem. Soc.* **62,** 1923 (1940).

1:5431 *sec*-BUTYL METHYL KETONE $C_6H_{12}O$ **Beil. I-693**

(3-Methylpentanone-2; α,α-ethylmethylacetone)

$CH_3.CH_2.CH(CH_3)—C(=O)—CH_3$

B.P. 117.7° ⟨1⟩ D_4^{18} = **0.8145** ⟨1⟩ n_D^{18} = **1.4002** ⟨1⟩

117.8° ⟨2⟩ D_4^{20} = **0.815** ⟨2⟩ n_D^{20} = **1.3990** ⟨2⟩

Liq. with peppermint odor — For toxicity see ⟨3⟩ — Occurs in acetone oil ⟨4⟩. [For soly. data on system: C̄ + aq. see ⟨8⟩.]

Reductn. with Na in moist ether gives 3-methylpentanol-2 (1:6202), accompanied by a smaller quant. of corresp. pinacol ⟨5⟩ ⟨1⟩.

In dioxane soln. yields CHI_3 with NaOH + I_2 (T 1.81) ⟨2⟩ — Oxidn. with NaOBr yields ethyl-methyl-acetic acid (1:1105) ⟨2⟩.

Ⓓ ***sec*-Butyl methyl ketone 2,4-dinitrophenylhydrazone:** m.p. 71.2° ⟨2⟩.

Ⓓ ***sec*-Butyl methyl ketone semicarbazone:** cryst. from pet. ether, m.p. 94–95° ⟨6⟩ 95–96° ⟨7⟩.

1:5431 ⟨1⟩ Zelinsky, Zelikow, *Ber.* **34,** 2865 (1901). ⟨2⟩ Drake, Keitch, *J. Am. Chem. Soc.* **5** 2624 (1935). ⟨3⟩ Specht, *U. S. Pub. Health Repts.* **53,** 292–300 (1938). ⟨4⟩ Suida, Pöll *Monatsh.* **48,** 169 (1927); *Z. angew. Chem.* **40,** 505 (1927). ⟨5⟩ Wislicenus, *Ann.* **219,** 30 (1883). ⟨6⟩ Evers, Rothrock, Woodburn, Stahly, Whitmore, *J. Am. Chem. Soc.* **55,** 113 (1933). ⟨7⟩ Courtot, *Bull. soc. chim.* (3) **35,** 981 (1906). ⟨8⟩ Ginnings, Plonk, Carter, *J. Am. Chem. Soc.* **62,** 1923 (1940).

1:5433 DIISOPROPYL KETONE (2,4-Dimethylpentanone-3; isobutyrone) $(CH_3)_2CH—C(=O)—CH(CH_3)_2$ $C_7H_{14}O$ **Beil. I-70**

B.P. 124° $D_4^{20} = 0.8108$ $n_D^{20} = 1.4001$ ⟨1

Insol. aq. [For soly. data on system: C̄ + aq. see ⟨11⟩.] Misc. alc., ether — Yields n $NaHSO_3$ cpd.

[Prepn.: by oxidation of diisopropylcarbinol with $Na_2Cr_2O_7 + H_2SO_4$ below 35° (74% yield) ⟨1⟩; by action of BF_3 on isobutyric anhydride (81.5% yield) ⟨2⟩.]

Reduction with Na + moist C_6H_6 ⟨3⟩ or with Na/Hg in alc. ⟨4⟩ yields diisopropylcarbinc (1:6215), b.p. 140°. With isopropyl MgBr or with *ter*-butyl MgBr C̄ does not add, but i reduced (78–80% yield) to diisopropylcarbinol ⟨5⟩.

Oxidn. with CrO_3 (T 1.72) yields acetone (1:5400), acetic ac. (1:1010) and isobutyri acid (1:1030) — Oxidn. with $Ca(OCl)_2$ yields $CHCl_3$, much acetic ac. and a smaller amt isobutyric ac. ⟨6⟩. [Dif. from di-*n*-propyl ketone which resists $Ca(OCl)_2$.]

Ⓓ **Diisopropyl ketone 2,4-dinitrophenylhydrazone:** or. cryst., m.p. 85–86° ⟨7⟩; 88° ⟨8⟩.

Ⓓ **Diisopropyl ketone semicarbazone:** reported m.p.'s vary widely: highest is 160° co ⟨9⟩, 149° ⟨10⟩.

1:5433 ⟨1⟩ Whitmore, Stahly, *J. Am. Chem. Soc.* **55,** 4155 (1933). ⟨2⟩ Meerwein, Vosser *J. prakt. Chem.* (2) **141,** 166 (1934). ⟨3⟩ Münch, *Ann.* **180,** 333 (1875). ⟨4⟩ Poletaeff, *Be* **24,** 1309 (1891). ⟨5⟩ Conant, Blatt, *J. Am. Chem. Soc.* **51,** 1235 (1929). ⟨6⟩ Ssuknewitsch Tschilingarjan, *Ber.* **69,** 1541 (1936). ⟨7⟩ Whitmore, Laughlin, *J. Am. Chem. Soc.* **54,** 439 (1932). ⟨8⟩ Allen, Richmond, *J. Org. Chem.* **2,** 222–226 (1937). ⟨9⟩ Spielman, Schmid *J. Am. Chem. Soc.* **59,** 2010 (1937). ⟨10⟩ Hauser, Renfrow, *J. Am. Chem. Soc.* **59,** 1826 (1937) ⟨11⟩ Ginnings, Plonk, Carter, *J. Am. Chem. Soc.* **62,** 1923 (1940).

1:5435 *n*-BUTYL METHYL KETONE $C_4H_9.CO.CH_3$ $C_6H_{12}O$ **Beil. I-68** (Hexanone-2)

B.P. 127.8° ⟨1⟩ $D_4^{20} = 0.81127$ ⟨1⟩ $n_D^{20} = 1.40069$ ⟨1

[For soly. data on system: C̄ + aq. see ⟨8⟩.]

[For prepn. in 50% yield by ketone splitting of ethyl *n*-propylacetoacetate see ⟨2⟩.]

C̄ with satd. aq. $NaHSO_3$ soln. (cf. T 1.12) yields $NaHSO_3$ addn. cpd.

C̄ oxidized with $CrO_3 + H_2SO_4$ (T 1.72) yields *n*-butyric (1:1035), *n*-valeric (1:1060 and acetic (1:1010) acids — C̄ reduced with Na + EtOH gives (33% yield) hexanol- (1:6210) ⟨3⟩.

n-Butyl methyl ketoxime [Beil. I-689] and *n*-butyl methyl ketone phenylhydrazon [Beil. XV-131] are both liquids and not recommended as derivs.

Ⓓ ***n*-Butyl methyl ketone 2,4-dinitrophenylhydrazone:** red-or. cryst. from alc.; m.p 106° ⟨4⟩; gold.-yel. lfts. from MeOH, m.p. 106–109° ⟨7⟩ [cf. T 1.14].

Ⓓ ***n*-Butyl methyl ketone semicarbazone:** m.p. 121° rap. htg. ⟨5⟩; 127° cor., rap. htg ⟨6⟩.

:5435 ⟨1⟩ Ceuterick, *Bull. soc. chim. Belg.* **45,** 553, 555, 558 (1936). ⟨2⟩ Johnson, Hager, *Organic Syntheses, Coll. Vol.* I, 345 (1932). ⟨3⟩ Olivier, *Rec. trav. chim.* **55,** 1029 (1936). ⟨4⟩ Allen, *J. Am. Chem. Soc.* **52,** 2957 (1930). ⟨5⟩ Blaise, Luttringer, *Bull. soc. chim.* (3) **33,** 823 (1905). ⟨6⟩ Bouveault, Locquin, *Bull. soc. chim.* (3) **31,** 1157 (1904). ⟨7⟩ Dirscherl, Nahm, *Ber.* **73,** 450–451 (1940). ⟨8⟩ Ginnings, Plonk, Carter, *J. Am. Chem. Soc.* **62,** 1923 (1940).

1:5445 MESITYL OXIDE $(CH_3)_2CH{=}CH.CO.CH_3$ $C_6H_{10}O$ **Beil. I-736**
(Isopropylideneacetone)

B.P. 130° D_4^{20} = **0.86532** n_D^{20} = **1.44397**

Oil of characteristic odor; dif. sol. aq.; misc. alc., ether. [For prepn. in 65% yield by distn. of diacetone alc. (1:6423) with I_2 see ⟨1⟩.]

C̄ with satd. aq. $NaHSO_3$ soln. (cf. T 1.12) gives quant. yield of $NaHSO_3$ addn. cpd. from which orig. C̄ can be regenerated ⟨2⟩ — C̄ decolorizes Br_2 aq. and reduces alk. $KMnO_4$ (T 1.34) — C̄ with alk. + I_2 (T 1.81) yields CHI_3 [cf. ⟨3⟩].

C̄ boiled with a little H_2SO_4 or alk. yields acetone, b.p. 56° (1:5400).

C̄ with phenylhydrazine gives no phenylhydrazone but instead 60% yield of *liq.* 1-phenyl-3,5,5-trimethylpyrazoline [Beil. XXIII-35] ⟨4⟩.

Ⓓ **Mesityl oxide oxime** (**β-form**): from C̄ + $NH_2OH.HCl$ in MeOH on stdg. 8 days and treating pptd. oxime HCl with Na_2CO_3; m.p. 48–49° ⟨5⟩ ⟨6⟩.

Ⓓ **Mesityl oxide *p*-nitrophenylhydrazone:** from C̄ in alc., mixed with aq. *p*-nitrophenylhydrazine HCl; or.-yel. ndls. from alc., m.p. 132–134° ⟨4⟩. [On boilg. 1 hr. with 3 pts. AcOH this prod. is smoothly converted to 1-(*p*-nitrophenyl)-3,5,5-trimethylpyrazoline, m.p. 205–208°, also formed directly from C̄ + *p*-nitrophenylhydrazine HCl on refluxing ⟨4⟩, and formerly reported ⟨7⟩ as the *p*-nitrophenylhydrazone.]

Ⓓ **Mesityl oxide 2,4-dinitrophenylhydrazone:** red cryst. from AcOH, m.p. 203° ⟨8⟩; carmine cryst. from alc.; m.p. 200° ⟨9⟩ [cf. T 1.14]. [Use in detn. of C̄ ⟨11⟩.]

Ⓓ **Mesityl oxide semicarbazone** (**α-form**): m.p. 164° ⟨10⟩. [The β-form, cryst. from C_6H_6, has m.p. 133–134°.]

1:5445 ⟨1⟩ Conant, Tuttle, *Organic Syntheses, Coll. Vol.* I, 338–339 (1932). ⟨2⟩ Morton, *J. Chem. Soc.* **126,** 719 (1926). ⟨3⟩ Cuculescu, *Cent.* **1931,** I, 589. ⟨4⟩ von Auwers, Kreuder, *Ber.* **58,** 1980–1981 (1925). ⟨5⟩ Harries, Jablonski, *Ber.* **31,** 1382 (1898). ⟨6⟩ Harries, Gley, *Ber.* **32,** 1330 (1899). ⟨7⟩ Harries, *Ann.* **374,** 343 (1910). ⟨8⟩ Campbell, *Analyst* **61,** 393 (1936). ⟨9⟩ Allen, *J. Am. Chem. Soc.* **52,** 2958 (1930). ⟨10⟩ Wilson, Heilbron, *J. Chem. Soc.* **103,** 379 (1913).
⟨11⟩ Iddles, Low, Rosen, Hart, *Ind. Eng. Chem., Anal. Ed.* **11,** 102–103 (1939).

1:5446 CYCLOPENTANONE

```
CH2—CH2
|       \
|        C=O
|       /
CH2—CH2
```

C_5H_8O **Beil. VII-5**

B.P. 130.65° ⟨1⟩ **M.P. −51.3°** ⟨1⟩ D_4^{20} = **0.94869** ⟨1⟩ n_D^{15} = **1.43917** ⟨1⟩
n_D^{20} = **1.4366**

Oil with peppermint odor; dif. sol. aq. — Volatile with steam and even with ether ⟨2⟩ — For prepn. in 75–80% yield by distn. of adipic ac. (1:0775) with $Ba(OH)_2$ see ⟨2⟩.]

C̄ treated with satd. aq. $NaHSO_3$ soln. (cf. T 1.12) readily forms $NaHSO_3$ addn. prod. from which C̄ may be regenerated on warming with Na_2CO_3 soln.

C̄ oxidized with boiling dil. HNO_3 (2:3) gives 44% glutaric ac. (1:0440) accompanied by some succinic ac. (1:0530) ⟨3⟩ ⟨4⟩ — C̄ reduced with Na in moist ether ⟨5⟩ ⟨6⟩ yields cyclopentanol (1:6412).

C̄ dislvd. in 50% alc. and treated with 2 equivs. of BzH + a little 10% NaOH rapid yields yel. ppt. of 1,3-dibenzalcyclopentanone-2; cryst. from boilg. alc., m.p. 189° ⟨7 [Dif. from analogous prod. from cyclohexanone (1:5465).] [For application to quant. det of C̄ see ⟨8⟩.]

Ⓓ **Cyclopentanone oxime:** from C̄ + $NH_2OH.HCl$ + excess aq. Na_2CO_3; pr. from pe ether, m.p. 56.5° ⟨9⟩; 56–57° ⟨10⟩. [For study of reaction velocity see ⟨11⟩.]

Ⓓ **Cyclopentanone phenylhydrazone:** from C̄ + phenylhydrazine with strong evolutic of heat; cryst. from lt. pet., m.p. 55° ⟨12⟩.

Ⓓ **Cyclopentanone 2,4-dinitrophenylhydrazone:** or.-yel. cryst. from alc., m.p. 142° ⟨13 or. cryst. from AcOH, m.p. 145.5–146.5° cor. ⟨14⟩ [cf. T 1.14]. [Use in detn. of C̄ ⟨16⟩

Ⓓ **Cyclopentanone semicarbazone:** cryst. from hot aq.; m.p. varying according to ra of htg. from 209–210° to 216–217° rap. htg. ⟨15⟩.

1:5446 ⟨1⟩ Timmermans, Hennaut-Roland, *J. chim. phys.* **34,** 720–721 (1937). ⟨2⟩ Thorp Kon, *Organic Syntheses, Coll. Vol.* I, 187–188 (1932). ⟨3⟩ Vogel, *J. Chem. Soc.* **1929,** 72 ⟨4⟩ Müller, Rölz, *Monatsh.* **50,** 107 (1928). ⟨5⟩ Hentzschel, Wislicenus, *Ann.* **275,** 322–3 (1893). ⟨6⟩ Harries, Wagner, *Ann.* **410,** 36–37 (1915). ⟨7⟩ Vorländer, Hobohm, *Ber.* **2** 1837, 1840 (1896). ⟨8⟩ Vorländer, Kunze, *Ber.* **59,** 2082–2083 (1926). ⟨9⟩ Ref. 5, page 31 ⟨10⟩ Dieckmann, *Ann.* **317,** 56 (1901).
⟨11⟩ Petrenko-Kritschenko, Kantscheff, *Ber.* **39,** 1455 (1906). ⟨12⟩ Perkin, Plant, *J. Che Soc.* **123,** 3244 (1923). ⟨13⟩ Allen, *J. Am. Chem. Soc.* **52,** 2958 (1930). ⟨14⟩ Strain, *J. A Chem. Soc.* **57,** 760 (1935). ⟨15⟩ Wallach, *Ann.* **414,** 312 (1918). ⟨16⟩ Iddles, Low, Rose Hart, *Ind. Eng. Chem., Anal. Ed.* **11,** 102–103 (1939).

—— **ACETYLACETONE** $CH_3.CO.CH_2.CO.CH_3$ $C_5H_8O_2$ **Beil. I-77**

B.P. 139° D_4^{20} = **0.976** $n_D^{25.6}$ = **1.446**

See 1:1700. Genus 4: Phenols.

1:5447 DI-*n*-PROPYL KETONE $C_3H_7.CO.C_3H_7$ $C_7H_{14}O$ **Beil. I-69**
(Butyrone; heptanone-4)

B.P. 144.1° ⟨1⟩ ⟨2⟩ **M.P. −34.0°** ⟨3⟩ D_4^{20} = **0.8175** ⟨2⟩ $n_{He\ (yel.)}^{20}$ = **1.40719** ⟨

C̄ yields no $NaHSO_3$ addn. cpd. ⟨2⟩ — C̄ is volatile with steam.

C̄, reduced with Al isopropylate + isopropyl alc. gives 92% yield di-*n*-propylcarbin (1:6228) ⟨4⟩.

Di-*n*-propyl ketoxime [Beil. I-700] and di-*n*-propyl ketone phenylhydrazone [Beil. XV (30)] are both liquids and not recommended as derivs.

Ⓓ **Di-*n*-propyl ketone 2,4-dinitrophenylhydrazone:** yel.-or. cryst. from alc.; m.p. 7 ⟨5⟩ [cf. T 1.14].

Ⓓ **Di-*n*-propyl ketone semicarbazone:** cryst. from pet. ether; m.p. 132° ⟨6⟩ ⟨2⟩.

1:5447 ⟨1⟩ Rintelen, Saylor, Gross, *J. Am. Chem. Soc.* **59,** 1129 (1937). ⟨2⟩ Sherrill, *J. Am. Che Soc.* **52,** 1990–1992 (1930). ⟨3⟩ Timmermans, *Bull. soc. chim. Belg.* **36,** 506 (1927 ⟨4⟩ Lund, *Ber.* **70,** 1524 (1937). ⟨5⟩ Allen, *J. Am. Chem. Soc.* **52,** 2958 (1930). ⟨6⟩ Staudi ger, *Ber.* **44,** 528 (1911).

1:5448 *d,l*-ACETOIN $C_4H_8O_2$ **Beil. I-82**
(Acetyl-methyl-carbinol; dimethylketol)

$$CH_3.CO.\overset{\displaystyle H}{\underset{\displaystyle OH}{C}}.CH_3$$

B.P. 145° **M.P. −72°** ⟨1⟩ D_4^{30} = **0.9861** ⟨1⟩ n_D^{20} = **1.4178** ⟨

C̄ is misc. with aq. and very hygroscopic ⟨1⟩; sol. alc. but insol. in dry ether or lgr.

C̄ on stdg. by itself at ord. temp. changes (in 2–9 days) or at −20° ⟨1⟩ (in several week to a white crystn. dimer, cryst. from acetone, m.p. 126–128° ⟨2⟩, 125° ⟨3⟩ both on rapid ht [cf. also ⟨1⟩]. This polymer when pure may be kept unchanged for several months but on melting or soln. in aq. or AcOH regenerates monomeric C̄ ⟨1⟩.

C̄ in contact with granulated Zn at room temp. or even at −10° rapidly polymerizes (within a few hours) to another crystn. dimer, m.p. 96–98° ⟨2⟩, 95° ⟨3⟩, both on rap. htg. [cf. also ⟨1⟩]. This dimer can also be recrystd. from acetone, and on soln. or melting depolymerizes to the original monomeric C̄.

As a consequence of the above equilibrium between C̄ and its polymers, the values observed for *D* and *n* vary according to previous treatment of the sample, both increasing with time ⟨1⟩.

C̄ reduces Tollens' reagent (T 1.11) or Fehling's soln. (T 1.22) in cold, yielding acetic ac.— C̄ with $FeCl_3$ + HCl or on distn. in air yields biacetyl (1:9500) — C̄ with satd. aq. $NaHSO_3$ soln. (T 1.12) yields solid $NaHSO_3$ addn. cpd. ⟨4⟩ — C̄ with I_2 + alk. (T 1.81) yields CHI_3 instantly in cold.

Ⓓ **Biacetyl phenylosazone:** from C̄, warmed with excess phenylhydrazine in either AcOH or alc.; yellowish ndls. from C_6H_6, m.p. 243° dec. ⟨2⟩ ⟨5⟩.

Ⓓ **Biacetyl bis-2,4-dinitrophenylhydrazone:** from C̄ on treatment with excess 2,4-dinitrophenylhydrazine in 2 *N* HCl; an orange turbidity appears at once and on stdg. 6 weeks a quant. yield of prod. is deposited; or. cryst. from nitrobenzene + toluene; m.p. 318° ⟨6⟩ [cf. T 1.14].

Ⓓ **Acetoin semicarbazone:** cryst. from alc. or aq.; m.p. 185° (block) ⟨7⟩ ⟨4⟩.

1:5448 ⟨1⟩ Pound, Wilson, *J. Phys. Chem.* **39,** 1135–1138 (1935). ⟨2⟩ von Pechmann, Dahl, *Ber.* **23,** 2423–2425 (1890). ⟨3⟩ Dirscherl, Braun, *Ber.* **63,** 416–422 (1930). ⟨4⟩ Kling, *Bull. soc. chim.* (3) **35,** 215 (1906); *Ann. chim.* (8) **5,** 552 (1905). ⟨5⟩ Balcom, *J. Am. Chem. Soc.* **39,** 312–315 (1917). ⟨6⟩ Clutterbuck, Raistrick, Reuter, *Biochem. J.* **29,** 313–314 (1935). ⟨7⟩ Béhal, Detoeuf, *Compt. rend.* **153,** 1230 (1911).

1:5455 ACETOL $CH_3.CO.CH_2OH$ $C_3H_6O_2$ **Beil. I-821**

(Hydroxyacetone; acetylcarbinol)

B.P. 146° ⟨1⟩ **M.P. −17°** ⟨1⟩ D^{20}_{20} = **1.0824** ⟨1⟩ n^{20}_{D} = **1.4295** ⟨1⟩

Misc. with aq., alc., or ether — C̄ is volatile with steam — C̄ decomposes on stdg. but is stabilized by addn. of equal vol. MeOH. [For prepn. in 54–58% yield from bromoacetone and K formate see ⟨2⟩.]

C̄ with satd. aq. $NaHSO_3$ soln. yields crystn. $NaHSO_3$ addn. prod. with evol. of ht. C̄ reduces NH_4OH + $AgNO_3$ in cold forming acetic and formic acids; C̄ reduces Fehling's soln. (T 1.22) in cold forming *d,l*-lactic ac. (1:0400).

C̄ with $NH_2OH.HCl$ + K_2CO_3 yields acetol oxime, cryst. from $CHCl_3$, m.p. 71° ⟨3⟩ ⟨4⟩. [This oxime is *not* recommended as a deriv. for identification.]

Ⓟ **Formation and fluorescence of 3-hydroxyquinaldine:** C̄, htd. with *o*-aminobenzaldehyde and a little aq. KOH gives 3-hydroxyquinaldine, easily detectable by strong bluish fluores. after treating soln. with excess solid $NaHCO_3$; specific for acetol ⟨5⟩.

Ⓓ **Methylglyoxal phenylosazone:** from C̄ + excess phenylhydrazine in 50% acetic ac.; yel. ndls. from dil. alc.; m.p. 147–148° ⟨6⟩. [C̄ with 1 mole phenylhydrazine in AcOH yields acetol phenylhydrazone, cryst. from C_6H_6, m.p. 103° ⟨7⟩ ⟨8⟩.]

Ⓓ **Methylglyoxal *p*-nitrophenylosazone:** from C̄, in alc., treated with at least three moles *p*-nitrophenylhydrazine; addition of aq. till clouding occurs, then boiling ppts. long dark red ndls.; m.p. 291° dec. ⟨9⟩; 300° ⟨10⟩; 302–304° according to rate of htg. ⟨11⟩. [C̄ in MeOH, with 1 mole *p*-nitrophenylhydrazine in AcOH, yields acetol *p*-nitrophenylhydrazone; pale yel. pl., m.p. 173° ⟨9⟩.]

Ⓓ **Acetol 2,4-dinitrophenylhydrazone:** or. cryst. from alc.; m.p. 127.5–129.5° cor. ⟨12⟩ [cf. T 1.14].

Ⓓ **Acetol semicarbazone:** from C̄ with 2 pts. semicarbazide HCl + 5 pts. aq. + 1.3 pts. K_2CO_3 ⟨13⟩; ndls. from aq. or alc.; m.p. 196°.

1:5455 ⟨1⟩ Kling, *Ann. chim.* (8) **5,** 496 (1905). ⟨2⟩ Levene, Walti, *Organic Syntheses* **10,** 1–2 (1930). ⟨3⟩ Nef, *Ann.* **335,** 259 (1904). ⟨4⟩ Piloty, Ruff, *Ber.* **30,** 2060 (1897). ⟨5⟩ Baudisch, Deuel, *J. Am. Chem. Soc.* **44,** 1586 (1922). ⟨6⟩ Nef, *Ann.* **335,** 254–255 (1904). ⟨7⟩ Pinkus, *Ber.* **31,** 36 (1898). ⟨8⟩ Nef, *Ann.* **335,** 253–254 (1904). ⟨9⟩ Levene, Walti, *J. Biol. Chem.* **68,** 420 (1926). ⟨10⟩ Bradfield, Francis, Penfold, Simonsen, *J. Chem. Soc.* **1936,** 1623.

⟨11⟩ Dakin, Dudley, *J. Biol. Chem.* **15,** 132–133 (1913). ⟨12⟩ Strain, *J. Am. Chem. Soc.* **57,** 760 (1935). ⟨13⟩ Nef, *Ann.* **335,** 213 (1904).

1:5460 *n*-AMYL METHYL KETONE (Heptanone-2) $C_7H_{14}O$ Beil. I-699

$CH_3.(CH_2)_4.CO.CH_3$

B.P. 151.2° ⟨7⟩ **M.P. −35.5°** D_4^{20} = **0.81536 ⟨1⟩** n_D^{20} = **1.40069 ⟨1⟩**

D_4^{20} = **0.8018 ⟨2⟩**

[For prepn. in 52–61% yield from ethyl acetoacetate via formn. and ketone splitting of ethyl *n*-butylacetoacetate see ⟨3⟩.] [For soly. data on system: C̄ + aq. see ⟨7⟩.]

C̄, with satd. aq. $NaHSO_3$, yields $NaHSO_3$ addn. cpd. [dif. from heptanone-3 or heptanone-4 (1:5447)].

C̄, oxidized with $CrO_3 + H_2SO_4$ (T 1.72), yields ⟨4⟩ *n*-valeric ac. (1:1060) and acetic ac. (1:1010) — C̄ reduced with NaOEt gives 62–65% yield ⟨5⟩ of heptanol-2 (1:6235).

n-Amyl methyl ketoxime [Beil. I_1-(359)] is liq. and not recommended as a deriv.

Ⓓ ***n*-Amyl methyl ketone 2,4-dinitrophenylhydrazone:** yel.-or. cryst. from alc.; m.p. 89° ⟨6⟩ [cf. T 1.14].

Ⓓ ***n*-Amyl methyl ketone semicarbazone:** cryst. from alc.; m.p. 123° ⟨2⟩.

1:5460 ⟨1⟩ Ceuterick, *Bull. soc. chim. Belg.* **45,** 553, 555, 558 (1936). ⟨2⟩ Sherrill, *J. Am. Chem. Soc.* **52,** 1990–1992 (1930). ⟨3⟩ Johnson, Hager, *Organic Syntheses, Coll. Vol.* I, 343–345 (1932). ⟨4⟩ Béhal, *Ann. chim.* (6) **15,** 271–272 (1888). ⟨5⟩ Whitmore, Otterbacher, *Organic Syntheses* **10,** 60–61 (1930). ⟨6⟩ Allen, *J. Am. Chem. Soc.* **52,** 2957 (1930). ⟨7⟩ Ginnings, Plonk, Carter, *J. Am. Chem. Soc.* **62,** 1923 (1940).

1:5465 CYCLOHEXANONE $C_6H_{10}O$ Beil. VII-8

$H_2C<\begin{matrix}CH_2.CH_2\\CH_2.CH_2\end{matrix}>C{=}O$

B.P. 155.7° ⟨1⟩ **M.P. −16.4° ⟨1⟩** D_4^{20} = **0.94653 ⟨1⟩** n_D^{15} = **1.45203 ⟨1⟩**

n_D^{20} = **1.4507**

C̄ is sol. in 27 vols. aq., but is salted out by $(NH_4)_2SO_4$ — C̄ with satd. aq. $NaHSO_3$ soln. (cf. T 1.12) yields $NaHSO_3$ cpd. [cf. ⟨2⟩].

C̄ oxidized with warm dil. HNO_3 undergoes violent react., yielding adipic ac. (1:0775) ⟨3⟩ — C̄, reduced with Al isopropylate in isopropyl alc., gives (95% yield) cyclohexanol (1:6415) ⟨4⟩.

C̄ in alc., treated with at least 2 moles of BzH + a little 10% aq. NaOH, yields on short stdg. 1,3-dibenzalcyclohexanone-2; yel. cryst. from alc., m.p. 118° ⟨5⟩. [For influence of conditions see ⟨6⟩.]

Ⓓ **Cyclohexanone oxime:** from C̄ + $NH_2OH.HCl$ + NaOAc in dil. MeOH (78% yield); hexag. pr. from lgr., m.p. 91° ⟨7⟩ [cf. ⟨8⟩].

Ⓓ **Cyclohexanone phenylhydrazone:** from C̄ + equiv. phenylhydrazine with evol. of ht. (95% yield); cryst. from 50% alc., m.p. 81–82° ⟨9⟩. [This prod. warmed with

10 pts. 10% H_2SO_4 dissolves and on cooling seps. (93% yield) tetrahydrocarbazole, tbls. from 50% alc., m.p. 116–117° ⟨9⟩.]

Ⓓ **Cyclohexanone *p*-nitrophenylhydrazone:** from C̄ + *p*-nitrophenylhydrazine in alc.; cryst. from 90% alc., m.p. 146–147° ⟨10⟩.

Ⓓ **Cyclohexanone 2,4-dinitrophenylhydrazone:** yel. cryst. from alc., m.p. 162° ⟨11⟩; 160° [cf. T 1.14]. [Use in quant. detn. of C̄ ⟨14⟩.]

Ⓓ **Cyclohexanone semicarbazone:** from C̄ + semicarbazide HCl + KOAc in aq.; m.p. 166–167° ⟨13⟩.

1:5465 ⟨1⟩ Timmermans, Hennaut-Roland, *J. chim. phys.* **34,** 722 (1937). ⟨2⟩ Petrenko-Kritschenko, *Ann.* **341,** 164 (1905). ⟨3⟩ Wislicenus, *Ann.* **275,** 362 (1893). ⟨4⟩ Lund, *Ber.* **70,** 1524 (1937). ⟨5⟩ Vorländer, Hobohm, *Ber.* **29,** 1840 (1896). ⟨6⟩ Vorländer, Kunze, *Ber.* **59,** 2082–2083 (1926). ⟨7⟩ Hückel, Sachs, *Ann.* **498,** 182 (1932). ⟨8⟩ Bousquet, *Organic Syntheses* **11,** 56 (1931). ⟨9⟩ Hoshino, Takiura, *Bull. Chem. Soc. Japan* **11,** 218–219 (1936). ⟨10⟩ Borsche, *Ann.* **359,** 67 (1908).

⟨11⟩ Campbell, *Analyst* **61,** 393 (1936). ⟨12⟩ Allen, *J. Am. Chem. Soc.* **52,** 2958 (1930). ⟨13⟩ Zelinsky, *Ber.* **30,** 1541–1544 (1877). ⟨14⟩ Iddles, Low, Rosen, Hart, *Ind. Eng. Chem., Anal. Ed.* **11,** 102–103 (1939).

—— PYRUVIC ACID $CH_3.CO.COOH$ $C_3H_4O_3$ Beil. II-608

B.P. 165° sl. dec.

See 1:1040. Genus 3: Acids.

1:5470 2-METHYLCYCLOHEXANONE $C_7H_{12}O$ Beil. VII-14

```
        CH2—CH2
       /       \
   H2C          C=O
       \       /
        CH2———C—H
              |
              CH3
```

B.P. 165.1° ⟨1⟩ **M.P. −14.0°** ⟨1⟩ D_4^{20} **= 0.92500** ⟨1⟩ n_D^{20} **= 1.4483**

C̄ dis. easily in conc. HCl, and soln. is unchanged on stdg. 24 hrs. at room temp. ⟨2⟩ [dif. from 3-methyl- and 4-methylcyclohexanones] — C̄ with BzH in alk. soln. yields only a yel. oil ⟨2⟩ [dif. from isomers, which give deep yel. colored solids].

C̄ with satd. aq. $NaHSO_3$ soln. (T 1.12) yields $NaHSO_3$ addn. cpd.

C̄ in isopropyl alc. reduced with Al isopropylate gives 90–95% yield 2-methylcyclohexanol (1:6420) ⟨3⟩.

Ⓓ **2-Methylcyclohexanone oxime:** from C̄ + $NH_2OH.HCl$ + solid $NaHCO_3$ in ether; m.p. 43° ⟨4⟩.

Ⓓ **2-Methylcyclohexanone 2,4-dinitrophenylhydrazone:** OY cryst. from alc.; m.p. 135.5–137° cor. ⟨5⟩ [cf. T 1.14].

Ⓓ **2-Methylcyclohexanone semicarbazone:** cryst. from alc., m.p. 197° dec., very rap. htg. ⟨1⟩.

1:5470 ⟨1⟩ Chiurdoglu, *Bull. soc. chim. Belg.* **47,** 244 (1938). ⟨2⟩ Wallach, *Ann.* **346,** 250 (1906). ⟨3⟩ Lund, *Ber.* **70,** 1524 (1937). ⟨4⟩ Skita, *Ber.* **56,** 1021 (1923). ⟨5⟩ Strain, *J. Am. Chem. Soc.* **57,** 760 (1935).

—— DIACETONE ALCOHOL $C_6H_{12}O_2$ Beil. I-836

$CH_3.CO.CH_2.C(OH)(CH_3)_2$

B.P. 166° D^{25} **= 0.931**

See 1:6423. Genus 8: Division B: Section 2.

1:5472 DIISOBUTYL KETONE $C_9H_{18}O$ **Beil. I-710**

(2,6-Dimethylheptanone-4; isovalerone) $[(CH_3)_2.CH.CH_2]_2C{=}O$

B.P. 168.0° ⟨1⟩ D^{20}_{20} = **0.8089** ⟨1⟩

D^{25}_{4} = **0.8279** ⟨2⟩ n^{25}_{D} = **1.4173** ⟨2⟩

Oil, less than 0.1% sol. in aq. at 20°.
Reduced by Na + alc. ⟨3⟩ to diisobutylcarbinol (1:6239-A).

Ⓓ **Diisobutyl ketone 2,4-dinitrophenylhydrazone:** or.-red cryst., m.p. 66° ⟨5⟩; m.p. 92° ⟨4⟩.

Ⓓ **Diisobutyl ketone semicarbazone:** m.p. 122° ⟨6⟩; 121° ⟨7⟩.

1:5472 ⟨1⟩ *Synthetic Organic Chemicals*, 9th Ed. (1938), *Carbide and Carbon Chemicals Corporation.* ⟨2⟩ Araki, *Mem. Coll. Sci. Kyoto Imp. Univ.*, Ser. **A, 16,** 137–159 (1933); *Cent.* **1933,** II, 1860. ⟨3⟩ Freylon, *Ann. chim.* (8), **19,** 572–574 (1910). ⟨4⟩ Morgan, Hardy, *Chemistry & Industry* **52,** 518–519 (1933). ⟨5⟩ Allen, Richmond, *J. Org. Chem.* **2,** 224 (1937). ⟨6⟩ Spielman, Schmidt, *J. Am. Chem. Soc.* **59,** 2010 (1937). ⟨7⟩ Kubota, Yoshikawa, *Chem. Abs.* **20,** 860 (1926).

1:5480 *d,l*-3-METHYLCYCLOHEXANONE $C_7H_{12}O$ **Beil. VII-17**

```
     CH2—CH2
    /       \
 H2C         C=O
    \       /
     CH —CH2
     |
     CH3
```

B.P. 169.58° ⟨1⟩ **M.P. −73.5°** ⟨1⟩ D^{20}_{4} = **0.91535** ⟨1⟩ n^{20}_{D} = **1.4463**

C̄ dis. easily in conc. HCl but on stdg. 24 hrs. at room temp. the soln. crystallizes ⟨2⟩ [dif. from 2-methyl- or 4-methyl isomers] — C̄ with BzH in alc. + few drops aq. alk. ⟨3⟩ or with conc. NaOEt soln. ⟨4⟩ yields 2,4-dibenzal-3-methylcyclohexanone, yel. ndls. from alc., m.p. 122°.

C̄, in isopropyl alc., reduced with Al isopropylate gives 90–95% yield 3-methylcyclohexanol (1:6435) ⟨5⟩.

Ⓓ ***d,l*-3-Methylcyclohexanone 2,4-dinitrophenylhydrazone:** yel. cryst., m.p. 155° ⟨6⟩ [cf. T 1.14].

Ⓓ ***d,l*-3-Methylcyclohexanone semicarbazone:** pl. from MeOH, m.p. 179° ⟨7⟩ ⟨8⟩; m.p. 191–192° ⟨4⟩; 191.4° dec., very rap. htg. ⟨1⟩.

1:5480 ⟨1⟩ Chiurdoglu, *Bull. soc. chim. Belg.* **47,** 244 (1938). ⟨2⟩ Wallach, *Ann.* **346,** 250 (1906). ⟨3⟩ Wallach, *Cent.* **1908,** I, 639. ⟨4⟩ Einhorn, Ehret, *Ann.* **295,** 182–183 (1897). ⟨5⟩ Lund *Ber.* **70,** 1524 (1937). ⟨6⟩ Allen, Richmond, *J. Org. Chem.* **2,** 224 (1937). ⟨7⟩ Knoevenagel, *Ann.* **297,** 156 (1897). ⟨8⟩ Skita, *Ber.* **56,** 1016 (1923). ⟨9⟩ Zelinsky, *Ber.* **30,** 1542 (1897).

—— **METHYL ACETOACETATE** $C_5H_8O_3$ **Beil. III-632**

B.P. 170° D^{20}_{4} = **1.0765** n^{20}_{D} = **1.41964**

See 1:1705. Genus 4: Phenols.

1:5485 4-METHYLCYCLOHEXANONE $C_7H_{12}O$ **Beil. VII-18**

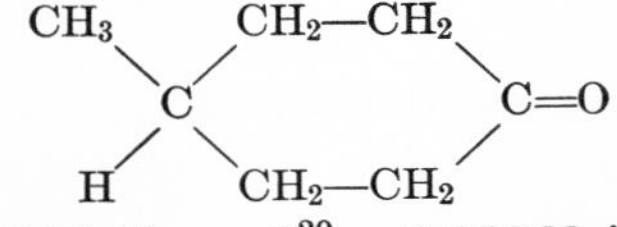

B.P. 171.25° ⟨1⟩ **M.P. −40.6°** ⟨1⟩ D^{20}_{4} = **0.91562** ⟨1⟩ n^{20}_{D} = **1.4445**

C̄ dis. easily in conc. HCl, and on stdg. at room temp. 24 hrs. seps. a viscous oil ⟨2⟩ [dif. from 2-methyl- and 3-methyl isomers] — C̄ + 2 pts. BzH dislvd. in 10 pts. abs. alc. and treated with 5 ml. dil. NaOH yields 2,6-dibenzal-4-methylcyclohexanone, yel. cryst. from alc.; m.p. 98–99° ⟨3⟩; 98–100° ⟨4⟩.

C̄ boiled with conc. HNO_3, evapd. to dryness, triturated with HCl and recrystd. from C_6H_6 gives (56% yield) β-methyladipic acid [Beil. II-675], m.p. 90–91° ⟨5⟩ ⟨6⟩.

C̄ in isopropyl alc., reduced with Al isopropylate, gives 90–95% yield 4-methylcyclohexanol (1:6440) ⟨7⟩.

Ⓓ **4-Methylcyclohexanone oxime:** m.p. 37–39° ⟨3⟩ [dif. to cryst. even from lgr.]

Ⓓ **4-Methylcyclohexanone phenylhydrazone:** from C̄ + phenylhydrazine; the product apparently has not itself been characterized, but on warming 15 min. at 100° with 17% H_2SO_4 yields 3-methyltetrahydrocarbazole; pr. from alc., m.p. 109–110° ⟨8⟩.

Ⓓ **4-Methylcyclohexanone *p*-nitrophenylhydrazone:** from C̄ (1.7 g.) + *p*-nitrophenylhydrazine (1.2 g.) in hot alc.; yel. ndls., m.p. 128.5° ⟨8⟩. [On boiling few minutes with 25% H_2SO_4 it yields 6-nitro-3-methyltetrahydrocarbazole, brown pr. from alc., m.p. 165–166° ⟨8⟩.]

Ⓓ **4-Methylcyclohexanone semicarbazone:** cryst. from MeOH, m.p. 199° ⟨9⟩; 203.5° dec. on very rap. htg. ⟨1⟩.

1:5485 ⟨1⟩ Chiurdoglu, *Bull. soc. chim. Belg.* **47,** 244 (1938). ⟨2⟩ Wallach, *Ann.* **346,** 250 (1906). ⟨3⟩ Ref. 2, page 252. ⟨4⟩ Poggi, Saltini, *Gazz. chim. ital.* **62,** 683 (1932). ⟨5⟩ Desai, *J. Chem. Soc.* **1931,** 1218. ⟨6⟩ Juery, *Bull. soc. chim.* (4) **17,** 173 (1915). ⟨7⟩ Lund, *Ber.* **70,** 1524 (1937). ⟨8⟩ Plant, Rosser, *J. Chem. Soc.* **1928,** 2457. ⟨9⟩ Zelinsky, *Ber.* **30,** 1542 (1897).

1:5490 *n*-HEXYL METHYL KETONE $C_8H_{16}O$ Beil. I-704

(Octanone-2) $CH_3.(CH_2)_4.CH_2.CO.CH_3$

B.P. 173.0° ⟨1⟩ **M.P. −21.5°** ⟨1⟩ D_4^{20} = **0.81853** ⟨1⟩ n_D^{20} = **1.41518** ⟨1⟩

C̄ with satd. aq. $NaHSO_3$ soln. (cf. T 1.12) yields $NaHSO_3$ cpd.

C̄ oxidized with $K_2Cr_2O_7 + H_2SO_4$ (cf. T 1.72) yields *n*-caproic ac. (1:1130) and acetic ac. (1:1010). [Oxidn. of C̄ under specified conditions yields 66% *n*-caproic ac. ⟨5⟩.]

Ⓓ ***n*-Hexyl methyl ketone *p*-nitrophenylhydrazone:** yel. pr. from alc.; m.p. 92–93° ⟨2⟩.

Ⓓ ***n*-Hexyl methyl ketone 2,4-dinitrophenylhydrazone:** or. cryst. from alc.; m.p. 58° ⟨3⟩ [cf. T 1.14].

Ⓓ ***n*-Hexyl methyl ketone semicarbazone:** cryst. from mixt. of pet. ether + alc.; m.p. 122–123° cor. ⟨4⟩.

1:5490 ⟨1⟩ Ceuterick, *Bull. soc. chim. Belg.* **45,** 545–564 (1936). ⟨2⟩ Dakin, *Am. Chem. J.* **44,** 46 (1910). ⟨3⟩ Allen, *J. Am. Chem. Soc.* **52,** 2957 (1930). ⟨4⟩ Bouveault, Locquin, *Bull. soc. chim.* (3) **31,** 1157 (1904). ⟨5⟩ Kao, Chang, *Science Repts. Natl. Tsing Hua Univ.,* Ser. **A-4,** 38 (1937).

—— METHYL METHYLACETOACETATE $C_6H_{10}O_3$ Beil. III-679

B.P. 177.4° D_{25}^{25} = **1.0247** $n_D^{23.8}$ = **1.416**

See 1:1708. Genus 4: Phenols.

—— ETHYL METHYLACETOACETATE $C_7H_{12}O_3$ Beil. III-679

B.P. 180.8° cor. D_4^{20} = **1.0191** $n_D^{15.3}$ = **1.42178**

See 1:1712. Genus 4: Phenols.

—— ETHYL ACETOACETATE $C_6H_{10}O_3$ Beil. III-632

B.P. 181° $D_4^{20} = 1.025$ $n_D^{20} = 1.41976$

See 1:1710. Genus 4: Phenols.

1:5493 DI-*n*-BUTYL KETONE $C_9H_{18}O$ Beil. I_1-(365)
(Nonanone-5; *n*-valerone) $(CH_3.CH_2.CH_2.CH_2)_2C{=}O$

B.P. 187.9° ⟨1⟩ **F.P. −5.9°** ⟨2⟩ $D_4^{20} = 0.8222$ ⟨1⟩ $n_D^{15} = 1.421$
187.65° ⟨2⟩

Ⓓ **Di-*n*-butyl ketone semicarbazone:** pl. from alc., m.p. 90° ⟨3⟩; 89–90° ⟨4⟩.

1:5493 ⟨1⟩ Rintelen, Saylor, Gross, *J. Am. Chem. Soc.* **59,** 1130 (1937). ⟨2⟩ Timmermans, *Bull. soc. chim. Belg.* **36,** 506 (1927). ⟨3⟩ Pickard, Kenyon, *J. Chem. Soc.* **101,** 629 (1912). ⟨4⟩ Vavon, Ivanov, *Compt. rend.* **177,** 453–456 (1923).

—— METHYL ETHYLACETOACETATE $C_7H_{12}O_3$ Beil. III-691

B.P. 189.7° cor. $D^{14} = 0.995$

See 1:1718. Genus 4: Phenols.

1:5495 ACETONYLACETONE $C_6H_{10}O_2$ Beil. I-788
(Hexanedione-2,4) $CH_3.CO.CH_2.CH_2.CO.CH_3$

B.P. 194° **M.P. −9°** $D_4^{20} = 0.97370$ $n_D^{20} = 1.428$

Colorless liq. prod. turning yel. on stdg. — Misc. with aq., alc., ether but insol. in conc. aq. KOH or K_2CO_3 soln. — Eas. volat. with vapors of alc. or ether.

$\bar{C}$, in AcOH, boiled ½ min. with NH_4OAc soln., then treated with dil. H_2SO_4 and boiled with pine splinter gives intense red color ⟨1⟩ [due to formation of 2,5-dimethylpyrrole] — For extensive study of reaction of $\bar{C}$ with other amines see ⟨2⟩.

$\bar{C}$, htd. with $(NH_4)_2CO_3$ at 100° till foaming stops, then at 115°, gives 81–86% yield 2,5-dimethylpyrrole ⟨3⟩.

$\bar{C}$ on boiling with AcOH, or better Ac_2O, yields 2,5-dimethylfuran (1:8080), b.p. 94° ⟨4⟩. [Latter identified by addn. prod. with maleic anhydride (100% yield), m.p. 78° ⟨5⟩.

Ⓓ **Acetonylacetone dioxime:** from $\bar{C}$ on short stdg. with conc. aq. soln. of $NH_2OH.HCl$ + Na_2CO_3, ndls. from small amt. aq., m.p. 137° ⟨6⟩.

Ⓓ **Acetonylacetone bis-phenylhydrazone:** from $\bar{C}$ on short htg. with *excess* phenylhydrazine, or on mixing with (excess) aq. phenylhydrazine acetate ⟨7⟩; alm. white lfts. from dil. alc., m.p. 120°. [In presence of dil. ac. (even acetic) loses 1 mole phenylhydrazine and ring closes to 1-anilino-2,5-dimethylpyrrole, m.p. 90–92° ⟨8⟩ ⟨9⟩.]

Ⓓ **Acetonylacetone bis-2,4-dinitrophenylhydrazone:** cryst. from pyridine, m.p. 257° ⟨10⟩.

1:5495 ⟨1⟩ Knorr, *Ber.* **19,** 46 (1886). ⟨2⟩ Hazlewood, et al., *J. Proc. Roy. Soc., N. S. Wales* **71,** 92–102 (1937); *Chem. Abs.* **32,** 1695–1696 (1938). ⟨3⟩ Young, Allen, *Organic Syntheses* **16,** 25–27 (1936). ⟨4⟩ Benson, Cadenhead, *Chemistry & Industry* **53,** 40–43 (1934). ⟨5⟩ Diels, Alder, *Ber.* **62,** 560–561 (1929). ⟨6⟩ Lipp, Scheller, *Ber.* **42,** 1967 (1909). ⟨7⟩ Paal, *Ber.* **18,** 60 (1885). ⟨8⟩ Smith, Goodell, *Ann.* **289,** 311, Note 4 (1896). ⟨9⟩ Smith, McCoy, *Ber.* **35,** 2169 (1902). ⟨10⟩ Armstrong, Robinson, *J. Chem. Soc.* **1934,** 1650.

—— *d*-FENCHONE $C_{10}H_{16}O$ Beil. VII-96

B.P. 195° $D^{19} = 0.947$ $n_D^{18} = 1.46355$

See 1:7547. Genus 9: Division B: Section 1.

1:5501 **n-HEPTYL METHYL KETONE** (Nonanone-2) $n.C_7H_{15}.C(=O).CH_3$ $C_9H_{18}O$ **Beil. I-709**

B.P. 195.3° ⟨1⟩ **F.P. −7.8° ⟨2⟩ −8.2° ⟨1⟩** D_4^{20} = **0.82133 ⟨2⟩**, D_4^{20} = **0.82217 ⟨1⟩** n_D^{20} = **1.42072 ⟨2⟩**

Insol. aq.; readily forms $NaHSO_3$ cpd.

Oxidn. with CrO_3 yields only acetic ac. (1:1010) and n-heptylic ac. (1:1140) ⟨3⟩.

Reductn. with Na + alc. yields n-heptyl-methyl-carbinol [Beil. I-423], b.p. 193–194° ⟨4⟩ whose α-naphthylcarbamate, cryst. from lt. pet., melts 55.5° ⟨5⟩.

Ⓓ **n-Heptyl methyl ketone semicarbazone:** cryst. from alc., m.p. 118–119° ⟨6⟩.

1:5501 ⟨1⟩ Deffet, *Bull. soc. chim. Belg.* **40,** 391 (1931). ⟨2⟩ Ceuterick, *Bull. soc. chim. Belg.* **45,** 553–558 (1936). ⟨3⟩ van Gysegem, *Cent.* **1907,** I, 530. ⟨4⟩ Thoms, Mannich, *Ber.* **36,** 2548 (1903). ⟨5⟩ Adamson, Kenner, *J. Chem. Soc.* **1934,** 842. ⟨6⟩ Dakin, *Am. Chem. J.* **44,** 46 (1910). ⟨7⟩ Ruzicka, Brugger, *Helv. Chim. Acta* **9,** 353 (1926).

—— **METHYL LEVULINATE** $C_6H_{10}O_3$ **Beil. III-675**

B.P. 196.0° D_4^{20} = **1.04945** n_D^{20} = **1.42333**

See 1:3561. Genus 5: Esters.

—— **ETHYL ETHYLACETOACETATE** $C_8H_{14}O_3$ **Beil. III-691**

B.P. 198° D_4^{20} = **0.9856** $n_D^{18.7}$ = **1.42256**

See 1:1723. Genus 4: Phenols.

—— **PHORONE** $(CH_3)_2C{=}CH.CO.CH{=}C(CH_3)_2$ $C_9H_{14}O$ **Beil. I-751**

B.P. 198.5°

See 1:5120. Genus 7: Division A. M.P. 28°.

1:5515 **ACETOPHENONE** (Methyl phenyl ketone) $CH_3.CO—C_6H_5$ C_8H_8O **Beil. VII-271**

B.P. 202.0° ⟨1⟩ **M.P. +19.6° ⟨1⟩** D_4^{20} = **1.02810 ⟨1⟩** n_D^{15} = **1.53631 ⟨1⟩**, n_D^{20} = **1.5339**

Arom. odor; alm. insol. aq.; sol. alc., ether, C_6H_6, $CHCl_3$ — Volatile with steam — $\bar{C}$ is sol. in conc. H_2SO_4 with or.-yel. soln. — $\bar{C}$ does not add $NaHSO_3$.

[For prepn. in 76–83% yield from C_6H_6, Ac_2O + $AlCl_3$ see ⟨2⟩.] [For extensive survey of phys. consts. see both ⟨1⟩ and ⟨3⟩.]

$\bar{C}$ on oxidn. with $K_2Cr_2O_7$ + H_2SO_4 (cf. T 1.72) or with NaOCl soln. ⟨4⟩ (85% yield) gives BzOH (1:0715) — $\bar{C}$ reduced with Na + alc. ⟨5⟩ gives 40% yield or with Al isopropylate + isopropyl alc. ⟨6⟩ gives 93% yield methyl-phenyl-carbinol (1:6475).

Ⓟ **Sodium nitroprusside color:** To 2 ml. cold satd. aq. soln. of $\bar{C}$ add 2 drops 1% aq. sodium nitroprusside soln. followed by 2 drops 10% NaOH. Divide into two equal parts (a) and (b), adding 3 drops AcOH to (b). Part (a) is R-VR, turning yel. in 20 min.; part (b) on acidfn. turns strong blue B-BV, fading but slightly in 20 min. ⟨7⟩.

Ⓓ **Acetophenone oxime:** m.p. 58–59°.

Ⓓ **Acetophenone phenylhydrazone:** from aq. susp. of $\bar{C}$ on shakg. with aq. soln. of phenylhydrazine.HCl + AcONa; white cryst. from alc., m.p. 105° rapidly darkening in air ⟨8⟩. [For study of optimum cond. for phenylhydrazone pptn. see ⟨9⟩.]

Ⓓ **Acetophenone *p*-nitrophenylhydrazone:** or.-red ndls.; m.p. 184–185° ⟨10⟩.

Ⓓ **Acetophenone 2,4-dinitrophenylhydrazone:** or.-red cryst. from AcOH; m.p. 249–250° ⟨11⟩; 238–240° ⟨15⟩; or. cryst. from alc.; m.p. 237° ⟨12⟩ [cf. T 1.14]. [Use in quant. detn. of $\bar{C}$ ⟨16⟩.]

Ⓓ **Acetophenone semicarbazone:** cryst. from 50% alc., m.p. 198–199° cor. ⟨13⟩ ⟨14⟩.

1:5515 ⟨1⟩ Timmermans, Hennaut-Roland, *J. chim. phys.* **32,** 524 (1935). ⟨2⟩ Adams, Noller, *Organic Syntheses, Coll. Vol.* I, 105 (1932). ⟨3⟩ Morgan, Lammert, *J. Am. Chem. Soc.* **46,** 881–888 (1924). ⟨4⟩ van Arendonk, Cupery, *J. Am. Chem. Soc.* **53,** 3184–3186 (1931). ⟨5⟩ Klages, Allendorff, *Ber.* **31,** 1003 (1898). ⟨6⟩ Lund, *Ber.* **70,** 1524 (1937). ⟨7⟩ Mulliken, " Method " I, 149 (1904). ⟨8⟩ Fischer, *Ber.* **17,** 576 (1884). ⟨9⟩ Ardagh, Kellam, Rutherford, Walstoff, *J. Am. Chem. Soc.* **54,** 721–727 (1932). ⟨10⟩ Hyde, *Ber.* **32,** 1814 (1899).

⟨11⟩ Campbell, *Analyst* **61,** 393 (1936). ⟨12⟩ Allen, *J. Am. Chem. Soc.* **52,** 2958 (1930). ⟨13⟩ Shriner, Turner, *J. Am. Chem. Soc.* **52,** 1269 (1930). ⟨14⟩ Wilson, Keenan, *J. Assoc. Official Agr. Chem.* **13,** 390, 393 (1930). ⟨15⟩ Dirscherl, Nahm, *Ber.* **73,** 450 (1940). ⟨16⟩ Iddles, Low, Rosen, Hart, *Ind. Eng. Chem., Anal. Ed.* **11,** 102–103 (1939).

—— ETHYL LEVULINATE $C_7H_{12}O_3$ Beil. III-675

B.P. 205.8° D_4^{20} = **1.01114** n_D^{20} = **1.42288**

See 1:3616. Genus 5: Esters.

—— ETHYL ALLYLACETOACETATE $C_9H_{14}O_3$ Beil. III-738

B.P. 206° sl. dec. D_4^{20} = **0.9898** $n_D^{17.6}$ = **1.43875**

211-212° sl. dec.

See 1:1738. Genus 4: Phenols.

1:5520 *l*-MENTHONE $C_{10}H_{18}O$ Beil. VII-38

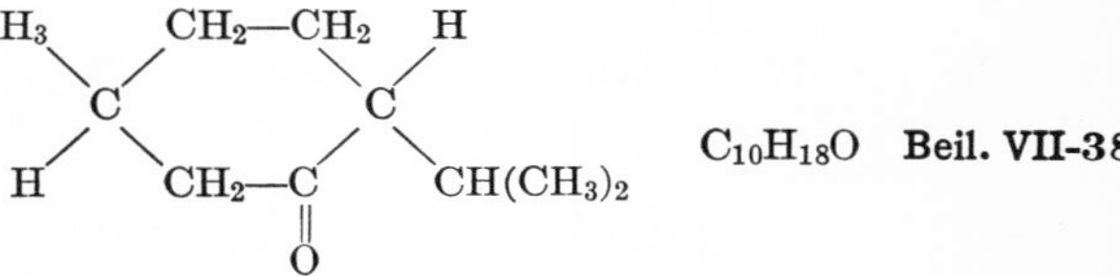

B.P. 209° **M.P. −6.6°** D_4^{20} = **0.8954** n_D^{20} = **1.4505**

Peppermint odor — $[\alpha]_D^{20}$ = −24.8° (in alc.) — Sl. sol. aq.; misc. alc., ether.—$\bar{C}$ does not add $NaHSO_3$.

[For prepn. in 83–85% yield by oxidn. of menthol (1:5940) with $Na_2Cr_2O_7 + H_2SO_4$ see ⟨1⟩.]

Ⓓ ***l*-Menthone oxime:** from $\bar{C}$, dislvd. in 2½ pts. 90% alc. and warmed with 0.6 pt. $NaHCO_3$; addn. of aq. ppts. oil which is extd. by ether, and recrystd. from dil. alc. or ether; m.p. 59° ⟨2⟩ [cf. ⟨3⟩]. [This prod. with conc. H_2SO_4 yields 60% *l*-menthone isoxime, m.p. 119–120° ⟨4⟩.]

Ⓓ ***l*-Menthone phenylhydrazone:** from $\bar{C}$ + phenylhydrazine htd. 2 hrs. at 100°; m.p. 53° ⟨5⟩.

Ⓓ ***l*-Menthone 2,4-dinitrophenylhydrazone:** or. cryst. from alc., m.p. 146° ⟨6⟩; 145° ⟨7⟩ [cf. T 1.14].

Ⓓ ***l*-Menthone semicarbazone:** from $\bar{C}$ in alc. + semicarbazide HCl + NaOAc in aq.; m.p. 189° ⟨8⟩; 184° ⟨9⟩.

1:5520 ⟨1⟩ Sandborn, *Organic Syntheses, Coll. Vol.* I, 333–334 (1932). ⟨2⟩ Beckmann, *Ann.* **250,** 330 (1888). ⟨3⟩ Martine, *Ann. chim.* (8) **3,** 119–120 (1904). ⟨4⟩ Wallach, *Ann.* **278,** 304 (1893). ⟨5⟩ Borsche, *Ann.* **359,** 63 (1908). ⟨6⟩ Campbell, *Analyst* **61,** 393 (1936). ⟨7⟩ Allen, *J. Am. Chem. Soc.* **52,** 2958 (1930). ⟨8⟩ Pickard, Littlebury, *J. Chem. Soc.* **101,** 124 (1912). ⟨9⟩ Wilson, Keenan, *J. Assoc. Official Agr. Chem.* **13,** 390, 395 (1930). ⟨10⟩ Reilly, Noonan, Drumm, *Analyst* **56,** 702–706 (1931).

—— **ISOPROPYL LEVULINATE** $C_8H_{14}O_3$ **Beil. S.N. 281**

B.P. 209.3° D_4^{20} = **0.98724** n_D^{20} = **1.42088**

See 1:3666. Genus 5: Esters.

1:5522 METHYL *n*-OCTYL KETONE (Decanone-2) $CH_3.\overset{\overset{O}{\|}}{C}.C_8H_{17}$ $C_{10}H_{20}O$ **Beil. I-711**

B.P. 211°	**F.P. +3.1°** ⟨1⟩	D_4^{20} = **0.82370** ⟨1⟩	n_D^{20} = **1.42523** ⟨1⟩
215.5° ⟨2⟩	**14°**	D_4^{22} = **0.8230** ⟨3⟩	n_D^{22} = **1.4263** ⟨3⟩

Gives $NaHSO_3$ cpd.

With I_2 + NaOH in MeOH gives alm. quant. yields of CHI_3 and pelargonic ac. (1:0560) ⟨3⟩.

Ⓓ **Methyl *n*-octyl ketone semicarbazone:** m.p. 124° ⟨4⟩; cryst. from pet. ether m.p. 126° ⟨2⟩. [Depresses m.p. of methyl nonyl ketone semicarbazone ⟨4⟩.]

1:5522 ⟨1⟩ Ceuterick, *Bull. soc. chim. Belg.* **45,** 553, 555, 558 (1936). ⟨2⟩ Chavanne, Tock, *Bull. soc. chim. Belg.* **41,** 639 (1932). ⟨3⟩ Ruzicka, Brugger, *Helv. Chim. Acta* **9,** 397–398 (1926). ⟨4⟩ St. Pfau, *Helv. Chim. Acta* **15,** 1270 (1932).

—— **ETHYL ACETOPYRUVATE** $C_7H_{10}O_4$ **Beil. III-747**

B.P. 213-215° D_4^{20} = **1.1251** n_D^{17} = **1.4757**

See 1:1742. Genus 4: Phenols.

1:5523 ISOPHORONE (1,1,3-Trimethylcyclohexene-3-one-5; isoacetophorone) $C_9H_{14}O$ **Beil. VII-65**

```
CH3     CH3
   \   /
     C
   /   \
H2C     CH2
 |       |
O=C      C—CH3
   \   //
     C
     |
     H
```

B.P. 215° $D_4^{20.5}$ = **0.9255** $n_D^{21.5}$ = **1.4789**

Liq. with peppermint-like odor and cooling taste — Alm. insol. in aq.; eas. volatile with steam. [For study of its three types of tautomerism see ⟨1⟩.]

$\bar{C}$ does not add $NaHSO_3$ but dis. very slowly in aq. SO_2 forming 1,1,3-trimethylcyclohexanone-5-sulfonic acid-3 — $\bar{C}$ in ice cold AcOH ⟨2⟩ or $\bar{C}$ in CCl_4 ⟨3⟩ treated with 1 mole Br_2 yields an unstable dibromide, m.p. abt. 40°; with excess of Br_2 yields 1,3,4,5?-tetrabromo-3,3,5-trimethylcyclohexanone-1, cryst. from AcOEt + lgr., m.p. 135° ⟨3⟩.

$\bar{C}$, treated with 1 mole BzH + NaOEt, yields 73% benzalisophorone, m.p. 78.5–79° ⟨4⟩.

Ⓓ **Isophorone oxime:** ndls. or pr. from pet. ether; m.p. 79.5° ⟨3⟩; 78° ⟨5⟩; 60° ⟨6⟩; 58° ⟨7⟩ [cf. ⟨8⟩].

Ⓓ **Isophorone phenylhydrazone:** ndls. from dil. alc., m.p. 68° ⟨9⟩ ⟨7⟩, rapidly dec. on stdg. in air.

Ⓓ **Isophorone semicarbazone:** cryst. from alc., m.p. 199.5° dec. ⟨3⟩; 190–191° dec. at 195° ⟨5⟩ [cf. ⟨8⟩]. [On steam distn. with oxalic ac. this semicarbazone is hydrolyzed to original $\bar{C}$ ⟨3⟩.]

1:5523 ⟨1⟩ Baker, *J. Chem. Soc.* **1926,** 663–670. ⟨2⟩ Kerp, Müller, *Ann.* **299,** 214 (1898). ⟨3⟩ Ref. 1, pages 667–668. ⟨4⟩ Cornubert, Borrel, *Bull. soc. chim.* (4) **45,** 1158 (1929). ⟨5⟩ Crossley, Gilling, *J. Chem. Soc.* **95,** 24–25 (1909). ⟨6⟩ Pringsheim, Bondi, *Ber.* **58,** 1415 (1925). ⟨7⟩ Knoevenagel, *Ann.* **297,** 185–191 (1897). ⟨8⟩ Delacre, *Bull. soc. chim.* (4) **23,** 219–224 (1918). ⟨9⟩ Bredt, *Ann.* **299,** 169 (1898).

1:5524 ***o*-METHYLACETOPHENONE** (Methyl *o*-tolyl ketone; *o*-acetyltoluene) $CH_3.CO$— [benzene ring] —CH_3 $C_9H_{10}O$ **Beil. VII-306**

B.P. 216° D_4^{20} = **1.014** ⟨1⟩ n_D^{20} = **1.5320** ⟨1⟩

C̄ on oxidn. with NaOBr soln. gives *o*-toluic acid (1:0690) ⟨2⟩.

Ⓓ **Methyl *o*-tolyl ketoxime:** rhomb. cryst. from aq. + a little alc.; m.p. 61° ⟨3⟩.

Ⓓ **Methyl *o*-tolyl 2,4-dinitrophenylhydrazone:** yel. cryst. from alc.; m.p. 159°.

Ⓓ **Methyl *o*-tolyl ketone semicarbazone:** cryst. from alc.; m.p. 205° ⟨2⟩; 206° ⟨4⟩; 210° ⟨5⟩.

1:5524 ⟨1⟩ von Auwers, *Ann.* **408,** 242 (1915). ⟨2⟩ Austin, Johnson, *J. Am. Chem. Soc.* **54,** 656 (1932). ⟨3⟩ Posner, Schreiber, *Ber.* **57,** 1134 (1924). ⟨4⟩ Baker, *J. Chem. Soc.* **1938,** 445–448. ⟨5⟩ Mercer, Robinson, Cahn, *J. Chem. Soc.* **1935,** 1000.

—— **BENZYL METHYL KETONE** $C_6H_5.CH_2.CO.CH_3$ $C_9H_{10}O$ **Beil. VII-303** (Phenylacetone)

B.P. 216.5° cor.

See 1:5118. Genus 7: Ketones: Division A. M.P. 27°.

1:5525 **PROPIOPHENONE** (Ethyl phenyl ketone; propionylbenzene) $CH_3.CH_2.CO$— [benzene ring] $C_9H_{10}O$ **Beil. VII-300**

B.P. 218° **M.P. +18.6°** ⟨1⟩ D_4^{20} = **1.0105** ⟨1⟩ n_D^{20} = **1.5269** ⟨1⟩

[For prepn. in 88.5% yield from propionyl chloride, C_6H_6 + $AlCl_3$, see ⟨2⟩.]

C̄ with I_2 + KI soln. + alk. (T 1.81) yields CHI_3 ⟨3⟩ — C̄ does *not* add $NaHSO_3$.

C̄, oxidized with CrO_3 + H_2SO_4 (T 1.72), yields BzOH (1:0715) and acetic ac. (1:1010) ⟨4⟩ — C̄, reduced with Na + EtOH, gives (78% yield) ⟨5⟩ ethyl-phenyl-carbinol (1:6504); Zn + HCl gives (90% yield) ⟨6⟩ ⟨2⟩ *n*-propylbenzene (1:7450).

C̄ with CH_3ONO + dry HCl gas gives 63–66% yield isonitrosopropiophenone; cryst. from toluene, m.p. 112–113° ⟨7⟩.

Ethyl phenyl ketone phenylhydrazone [Beil. XV-142] is liq. and not recommended as deriv.

Ⓓ **Ethyl phenyl ketoxime:** cryst. from pet. ether; m.p. 53° ⟨8⟩ [this product on warming with conc. H_2SO_4 at 100° yields propionanilide, m.p. 105° ⟨3⟩].

Ⓓ **Ethyl phenyl ketone 2,4-dinitrophenylhydrazone:** red lfts. from C_6H_6 or or.-red pl. from AcOH; m.p. 190–191° ⟨9⟩; 191° ⟨10⟩ [cf. T 1.14].

Ⓓ **Ethyl phenyl ketone semicarbazone:** cryst. from alc.; m.p. 173–174° cor. ⟨11⟩ [m.p. much influenced by rate of htg. and has been reported as high as 182° ⟨12⟩].

1:5525 ⟨1⟩ Evans, *J. Chem. Soc.* **1936,** 788. ⟨2⟩ Baddeley, Kenner, *J. Chem. Soc.* **1935,** 307. ⟨3⟩ Schmidt, *Arch. Pharm.* **252,** 105 (1914). ⟨4⟩ Popoff, *Ann.* **161,** 296 (1872). ⟨5⟩ Klages, *Ber.* **35,** 2251 (1902). ⟨6⟩ Clemmensen, *Ber.* **46,** 1839 (1913). ⟨7⟩ Hartung, Crossley, *Organic Syntheses* **16,** 44–46 (1936). ⟨8⟩ Trapesonzjanz, *Ber.* **26,** 1427 (1893). ⟨9⟩ Meisenheimer, *Ann.* **446,** 82 (1926). ⟨10⟩ Ferrante, Bloom, *Am. J. Pharm.* **105,** 383 (1933).

⟨11⟩ Shriner, Turner, *J. Am. Chem. Soc.* **52,** 1269 (1930). ⟨12⟩ Stephens, *J. Am. Chem. Soc.* **50,** 189, Note 4 (1928).

—— **o-HYDROXYACETOPHENONE** $C_8H_8O_2$ **Beil. VIII-85**
(*o*-Acetylphenol)

B.P. 218° **M.P. 28°** $D_4^{20} = 1.131$ $n_D^{20} = 1.5590$

See 1:1746. Genus 4: Phenols.

1:5527 ***m*-METHYLACETOPHENONE** $C_9H_{10}O$ **Beil. VII-307**
(Methyl *m*-tolyl ketone; *m*-acetyltoluene)

$CH_3.CO$—⟨benzene ring⟩—CH_3 (meta)

B.P. 220° $D_4^{20} = 1.007$ ⟨1⟩ $n_D^{20} = 1.5306$ ⟨1⟩

Ⓓ **Methyl *m*-tolyl ketoxime:** cryst. from alc. or pet. ether; m.p. 57° ⟨2⟩.

Ⓓ **Methyl *m*-tolyl ketone semicarbazone:** m.p. 197–198° ⟨1⟩; 202–203° ⟨3⟩.

1:5527 ⟨1⟩ von Auwers, *Ann.* **408,** 243 (1915). ⟨2⟩ Posner, Schreiber, *Ber.* **57,** 1136 (1924). ⟨3⟩ Gilman, Nelson, *Rec. trav. chim.* **55,** 529 (1936).

—— ***n*-PROPYL LEVULINATE** $C_8H_{14}O_3$ **Beil. III-675**

B.P. 221.2° $D_4^{20} = 0.98955$ $n_D^{20} = 1.42576$

See 1:3786. Genus 5: Esters.

1:5528 **ISOPROPYL PHENYL KETONE** $C_{10}H_{12}O$ **Beil. VII-316**
(Isobutyrophenone; α,α-dimethylacetophenone)

$(CH_3)_2.CH.CO$—⟨benzene ring⟩

B.P. 222° $D_{4}^{16.9} = 0.9863$ $n_D^{20} = 1.5190$ ⟨1⟩

C̄ on oxidn. with $CrO_3 + H_2SO_4$ (cf. T 1.72) yields BzOH (1:0715) and AcOH (1:1010); on oxidn. with $Ca(OCl)_2$ ⟨2⟩ yields BzOH, AcOH + $CHCl_3$.

C̄ reduced with excess 3% Na/Hg in dil. alc. yields isopropyl-phenyl-carbinol (1:6515) ⟨3⟩.

Ⓓ **Isopropyl phenyl ketoxime:** from C̄ + $NH_2OH.HCl$ + NaOAc in 95% alc.; tbls. from lt. pet., m.p. 94° ⟨4⟩. [As prepd. by others, m.p. 61–62° ⟨5⟩; 61° ⟨6⟩; 58° ⟨7⟩; perhaps a stereoisomer.]

Ⓓ **Isopropyl phenyl ketone phenylhydrazone:** from C̄ + equiv. phenylhydrazine htd. at 110°; m.p. 73° ⟨8⟩.

Ⓓ **Isopropyl phenyl ketone 2,4-dinitrophenylhydrazone:** or.-yel. pl. from dil. AcOH; m.p. 163° ⟨1⟩ [cf. T 1.14].

Ⓓ **Isopropyl phenyl ketone semicarbazone:** ndls. from alc., m.p. 181° ⟨4⟩; 181.5° ⟨1⟩; 180–181° ⟨5⟩. [A lower m.p. perhaps representing a stereoisomeric form, has also been reported, viz. m.p. 167–168° ⟨9⟩ ⟨10⟩.]

1:5528 ⟨1⟩ Evans, *J. Chem. Soc.* **1936,** 788. ⟨2⟩ Ssuknewitsch, Tschilingarjan, *Ber.* **69,** 1539 (1936). ⟨3⟩ Franke, Klein, *Monatsh.* **33,** 1237 (1912). ⟨4⟩ Lapworth, Steele, *J. Chem. Soc.* **99,** 1885 (1911). ⟨5⟩ Magnani, McElvain, *J. Am. Chem. Soc.* **60,** 819 (1938). ⟨6⟩ Rattner, *Ber.* **20,** 506 (1887). ⟨7⟩ Claus, *J. prakt. Chem.* (2) **46,** 481 (1892). ⟨8⟩ Ramart-Lucas, Hoch, Martynoff, *Bull. soc. chim.* (5) **4,** 494 (1937). ⟨9⟩ Levy, Tabart, *Bull. soc. chim.* (4) **49,** 1784 (1931). ⟨10⟩ Faworski, Tschilingaren, *Compt. rend.* **182,** 221–223 (1926).

1:5530 ***p*-METHYLACETOPHENONE** $C_9H_{10}O$ **Beil. VII-307**
(Methyl *p*-tolyl ketone; *p*-acetyltoluene)

$CH_3.CO$—⟨benzene ring⟩—CH_3

B.P. 224° **M.P. +28°** $D_4^{20} = 1.003$ $n_D^{20} = 1.5332$

[For prepn. in 85–89% yield from toluene, $Ac_2O + AlCl_3$ see ⟨1⟩ cf. ⟨2⟩.]

C̄, in dioxane, treated with I_2 and aq. NaOH (cf. T 1.81) yields CHI_3 ⟨3⟩ — C̄ oxidized with excess alk. NaOCl soln. gives (96% yield) ⟨4⟩ *p*-toluic ac. (1:0795); with $KMnO_4$ gives (95% yield) ⟨5⟩ terephthalic ac. (1:0910).

C̄ reduced with Na + alc. gives (60% yield) ⟨6⟩ methyl-*p*-tolyl-carbinol (1:6502); C̄ reduced with 5% Na/Hg in 70% alc. yields methyl *p*-tolyl pinacone, hexag. tbls. from alc.; m.p. 90° ⟨7⟩.

Ⓓ **Methyl *p*-tolyl ketoxime:** cryst. from pet. ether; m.p. 87–88° ⟨8⟩ ⟨7⟩.

Ⓓ **Methyl *p*-tolyl phenylhydrazone:** pr. from alc., m.p. 97° ⟨8⟩; 95° ⟨7⟩.

Ⓓ **Methyl *p*-tolyl 2,4-dinitrophenylhydrazone:** scarlet pr. from AcOH or toluene; m.p. 260.4° cor. ⟨9⟩; 258° cor. ⟨10⟩ [cf. T 1.14].

Ⓓ **Methyl *p*-tolyl ketone semicarbazone:** ndls. or pl. from alc., m.p. 204–205° slow htg. ⟨11⟩ ⟨12⟩ ⟨13⟩.

1:5530 ⟨1⟩ Adams, Noller, *Organic Syntheses, Coll. Vol.* I, 105 (1932). ⟨2⟩ Groggins, Nagel, *Ind. Eng. Chem.* **26,** 1315 (1934). ⟨3⟩ Fuson, Tullock, *J. Am. Chem. Soc.* **56,** 1638 (1934). ⟨4⟩ van Arendonk, Cupery, *J. Am. Chem. Soc.* **53,** 3184–3186 (1931). ⟨5⟩ Claus, *Ber.* **19,** 234 (1886). ⟨6⟩ Klages, *Ber.* **35,** 2247 (1902). ⟨7⟩ Claus, *J. prakt. Chem.* (2) **41,** 403 (1890). ⟨8⟩ Widman, Bladin, *Ber.* **19,** 587–588 (1886). ⟨9⟩ Ferrante, Bloom, *Am. J. Pharm.* **105,** 383 (1933). ⟨10⟩ Allen, Richmond, *J. Org. Chem.* **2,** 224 (1937).
⟨11⟩ Sorge, *Ber.* **35,** 1070 (1902). ⟨12⟩ Rupe, Steinbach, *Ber.* **43,** 3465 (1910). ⟨13⟩ Wilson, Keenan, *J. Assoc. Official Agr. Chem.* **13,** 390, 395 (1930).

—— ***sec*-BUTYL LEVULINATE** $C_9H_{16}O_3$ **Beil. S.N. 281**

B.P. 225.8° D_4^{20} **= 0.96698** n_D^{20} **= 1.42499**

See 1:3812. Genus 5: Esters.

1:5531 METHYL *n*-NONYL KETONE $CH_3.CO.C_9H_{19}$ $C_{11}H_{22}O$ **Beil. I-713**
(Undecanone-2)

B.P. 228.0° ⟨1⟩ **M.P. +12.1°** ⟨1⟩ D_4^{20} **= 0.82564** ⟨2⟩ n_D^{20} **= 1.42899** ⟨2⟩
+12.7° ⟨2⟩

Chief constituent of oil of rue — C̄ with satd. aq. $NaHSO_3$ soln. (cf. T 1.12) yields $NaHSO_3$ addn. cpd.

C̄, on oxidn. with CrO_3 (cf. T 1.72) yields pelargonic ac. (1:0560) and acetic ac. (1:1010).

Ⓓ **Methyl *n*-nonyl ketoxime:** m.p. 44–45°.

Ⓓ **Methyl *n*-nonyl ketone *p*-nitrophenylhydrazone:** yel. ndls. from alc., m.p. 90–91° ⟨3⟩.

Ⓓ **Methyl *n*-nonyl ketone 2,4-dinitrophenylhydrazone:** OY cryst. from alc., m.p. 63° ⟨4⟩ [cf. T 1.14].

Ⓓ **Methyl *n*-nonyl ketone semicarbazone:** m.p. 122–122.5° ⟨3⟩.

1:5531 ⟨1⟩ Timmermans, *Bull. soc. chim. Belg.* **31,** 391 (1922). ⟨2⟩ Ceuterick, *Bull. soc. chim. Belg.* **45,** 553–558 (1936). ⟨3⟩ Dakin, *Am. Chem. J.* **44,** 47 (1910). ⟨4⟩ Allen, *J. Am. Chem. Soc.* **52,** 2958 (1930).

1:5532 DI-*n*-AMYL KETONE $C_5H_{11}.CO.C_5H_{11}$ $C_{11}H_{22}O$ **Beil. I-714**
(Undecanone-6; caprone)

B.P. 228.0° cor. ⟨1⟩ **M.P. +14.6°** ⟨1⟩ D_4^{20} **= 0.82471** ⟨1⟩ n_D^{20} **= 1.42875** ⟨1⟩
−4° ⟨4⟩

Gives no $NaHSO_3$ cpd.

Oxidn. with $K_2Cr_2O_7 + H_2SO_4$, CrO_3, alk. $KMnO_4$, or ac. $KMnO_4$ gives mixture of *n*-caproic, *n*-valeric, and lower acids ⟨2⟩.

Reductn. with Na + alc. gives 85% yield undecanol-6 ⟨3⟩.

Oxime and semicarbazone of C̄ are both oils and not recommd. as derivs.

1:5532 ⟨1⟩ Simon, *Bull. soc. chim. Belg.* **38,** 57, 59 (1929). ⟨2⟩ Hercz, *Ann.* **186,** 262–265 (1877). ⟨3⟩ Hess, Bappert, *Ann.* **441,** 152 (1924). ⟨4⟩ von Braun, Kröper, *Ber.* **62,** 2885 (1929).

1:5534 PHENOXYACETONE C_6H_5—O.CH$_2$.CO.CH$_3$ $C_9H_{10}O_2$ **Beil. VI-151**

B.P. 230° D_4^{20} = **1.0903** ⟨1⟩ n_D^{20} = **1.5228** ⟨1⟩

C̄ dislvd. in cold conc. H_2SO_4 and poured into aq. gives 2-methylcumarone [Beil. XVII-60], b.p. 193–194° ⟨2⟩.

Ⓓ **Phenoxyacetone semicarbazone:** cryst. from 50% alc., m.p. 176° cor. ⟨1⟩.

1:5534 ⟨1⟩ Whitney, Henze, *J. Am. Chem. Soc.* **60,** 1149 (1938). ⟨2⟩ Stoermer, *Ann.* **312,** 274 (1900).

1:5535 BUTYROPHENONE (Phenyl *n*-propyl ketone) C_6H_5—CO.CH$_2$.CH$_2$.CH$_3$ $C_{10}H_{12}O$ **Beil. VII-313**

B.P. 230° **M.P. +12.2°** ⟨1⟩ D_{20}^{20} = **0.989** n_D^{20} = **1.5196** ⟨1⟩

C̄ yields no $NaHSO_3$ cpd. — C̄ on oxidn. with $CrO_3 + H_2SO_4$ (T 1.72) gives BzOH (1:0715) and propionic ac. (1:1025).

Phenyl *n*-propyl ketone phenylhydrazone [Beil. XV-142] is liq. and not recommended as a deriv. for identification.

Ⓓ **Phenyl *n*-propyl ketoxime:** ndls. from abs. ether; m.p. 49–50° ⟨2⟩.

Ⓓ **Phenyl *n*-propyl 2,4-dinitrophenylhydrazone:** or.-red pl. from dil. AcOH; m.p. 190° ⟨1⟩; 188° ⟨3⟩ [cf. T 1.14].

Ⓓ **Phenyl *n*-propyl ketone semicarbazone:** pr. from alc.; m.p. 187–188° ⟨2⟩ ⟨4⟩; 191.5° ⟨1⟩.

1:5535 ⟨1⟩ Evans, *J. Chem. Soc.* **1936,** 788. ⟨2⟩ Sorge, *Ber.* **35,** 1073–1074 (1902). ⟨3⟩ Ferrante, Bloom, *Am. J. Pharm.* **105,** 383 (1933). ⟨4⟩ Johnson, Schwartz, Jacobs, *J. Am. Chem. Soc.* **60,** 1883 (1938).

1:5540 *d*-CARVONE $C_{10}H_{14}O$ **Beil. VII-153**

CH—CH$_2$ H CH$_2$
CH$_3$—C C—C
C—CH$_2$ CH$_3$
O

B.P. 230° $[\alpha]_D^{20}$ = **+62.9°** D_4^{20} = **0.9608** n_D^{20} = **1.49952**

Oil with caraway odor.

C̄ does not give normal $NaHSO_3$ addn. cpd.; on boiling with $NaHSO_3$ soln. (from which all H_2SO_3 has been removed by addn. of solid Na_2CO_3) C̄ gradually dissolves owing to formation of sodium carvone dihydrosulfonate, from which alk. does *not* regenerate orig. C̄ ⟨1⟩ — C̄ dissolves in aq. Na_2SO_3 soln. forming free alk. whose titration may serve for quant. detn. of C̄ ⟨2⟩ ⟨3⟩.

C̄ adds Br_2 [use in quant. detn. ⟨4⟩].

C̄ refluxed 8 hrs. with equal wt. formic ac. (D = 1.2) ⟨5⟩ or warmed cautiously with 4% of its wt. of $POCl_3$ until vig. spontaneous reactn. occurs ⟨6⟩ gives almost quant. yield of carvacrol (1:1760).

C̄ (5 pts.) in alc. (2 pts.), satd. with H_2S, then treated with an equal vol. of alc. which has been satd. with NH_3 at 0°, and the mixed solns. then treated with H_2S, soon ppts. a compound of compn. 2 C̄ + H_2S ⟨7⟩; silky white ndls. from $CHCl_3$, or alc. + $CHCl_3$; m.p. 211° ⟨8⟩. [The bis-2,4-dinitrophenylhydrazone of this prod. forms or.-yel. cryst. from alc.; m.p. 222° ⟨8⟩.]

Ⓓ ***d*-Carvone oxime:** from C̄ + sl. more than 1 mole $NH_2OH.HCl$ in 4 pts. MeOH on stdg. 3–4 days at room temp. (98–99% yield) ⟨9⟩; or from C̄ + $NH_2OH.HCl$ + NaOAc in EtOH refluxed for 4 hrs. (82% yield) ⟨10⟩; lfts. from alc.; m.p. 72–73°. [Use in quant. detn. of C̄ ⟨11⟩ ⟨12⟩.]

Ⓓ ***d*-Carvone phenylhydrazone:** ndls. from alc.; m.p. 109–110° ⟨13⟩.

Ⓓ ***d*-Carvone *p*-nitrophenylhydrazone:** red.-br. ndls.; m.p. 174–175° ⟨14⟩.

Ⓓ ***d*-Carvone 2,4-dinitrophenylhydrazone:** red cryst. from AcOH ⟨15⟩, alc. + AcOEt ⟨16⟩, or alc. + $CHCl_3$ ⟨16⟩; m.p. 191–191.5° ⟨8⟩, 190° ⟨15⟩, 189° ⟨16⟩ [cf. T 1.14]. [Use in quant. detn. of C̄ ⟨20⟩.]

Ⓓ ***d*-Carvone semicarbazone: higher melting isomer:** from C̄ + semicarbazide.HCl + $NaHCO_3$ in dil. alc.; m.p. 162–163° ⟨17⟩. **Lower melting isomer:** from C̄ in alc. + KOAc + conc. aq. semicarbazide.HCl in the cold; forms slowly; m.p. 141–142° ⟨17⟩; 143° ⟨18⟩. [Use in quant. detn. of C̄ ⟨18⟩ ⟨19⟩.]

1:5540 ⟨1⟩ Labbé, *Bull. soc. chim.* (3) **23,** 281 (1900). ⟨2⟩ Sadtler, *J. Am. Chem. Soc.* **27,** 1323 (1905). ⟨3⟩ Schmallfuss, Werner, Kraul, *Z. anal. Chem.* **87,** 161–164 (1932). ⟨4⟩ Kaufmann, Barich, *Arch. Pharm.* **267,** 25–26 (1929). ⟨5⟩ Klages, *Ber.* **32,** 1517 (1899). ⟨6⟩ Kreysler, *Ber.* **18,** 1704 (1885). ⟨7⟩ Wallach, *Ann.* **305,** 224 (1899). ⟨8⟩ Hooper, Macbeth, Price, *J. Chem. Soc.* **1934,** 1149. ⟨9⟩ Harries, *Ann.* **328,** 322 (1903). ⟨10⟩ Cooke, Macbeth, *J. Chem. Soc.* **1937,** 1596.

⟨11⟩ Bennett, Cocking, *Analyst* **56,** 79–82 (1931). ⟨12⟩ Bennett, Donovan, *Analyst* **47,** 148 (1922). ⟨13⟩ Baeyer, *Ber.* **27,** 811 (1894). ⟨14⟩ Borsche, *Ann.* **359,** 70 (1908). ⟨15⟩ Campbell, *Analyst* **61,** 393 (1936). ⟨16⟩ Allen, *J. Am. Chem. Soc.* **52,** 2958 (1930). ⟨17⟩ Rupe, Dorschky, *Ber.* **39,** 2113 (1906). ⟨18⟩ Wilson, Keenan, *J. Assoc. Official Agr. Chem.* **13,** 390, 394 (1930). ⟨19⟩ Reilly, Drumm, *Analyst* **53,** 209–211 (1928). ⟨20⟩ Iddles, Low, Rosen, Hart, *Ind. Eng. Chem., Anal. Ed.* **11,** 102–103 (1939).

—— ISOBUTYL LEVULINATE $C_9H_{16}O_3$ Beil. S.N. 281

B.P. 230.9° D_4^{20} = **0.96770** n_D^{20} = **1.42677**

See 1:3907. Genus 5: Esters.

—— *n*-BUTYL LEVULINATE $C_9H_{16}O_3$ Beil. S.N. 281

B.P. 237.8° D_4^{20} = **0.97353** n_D^{20} = **1.42905**

See 1:3972. Genus 5: Esters.

1:5547 *o*-METHOXYACETOPHENONE $C_9H_{10}O_2$ Beil. VIII-85

(*o*-Acetylanisole)

$CH_3.CO$—(benzene ring)—CH_3O (ortho)

B.P. 239° ⟨1⟩ D_4^{20} = **1.089** ⟨1⟩ n_D^{20} = **1.5395** ⟨4⟩

Ⓓ ***o*-Methoxyacetophenone oxime:** from C̄ + hydroxylamine.HCl + alk. in dil. alc.; oxime isolated as sodium salt, then regenerated: m.p. 83° ⟨2⟩; 79.5° ⟨1⟩ [after recrystn. from pet.; m.p. 96–96.5° ⟨1⟩].

Ⓓ ***o*-Methoxyacetophenone phenylhydrazone:** tbls. from alc., m.p. 114° ⟨2⟩ ⟨3⟩.

Ⓓ ***o*-Methoxyacetophenone semicarbazone:** from C̄ in alc. + free semicarbazide on stdg. 24 hrs. ⟨2⟩; m.p. 182–183° ⟨4⟩ ⟨3⟩.

1:5547 ⟨1⟩ von Auwers, Lechner, Bundesmann, *Ber.* **58,** 41 (1925). ⟨2⟩ Klages, *Ber.* **36,** 3589 (1903). ⟨3⟩ Wahl, Silberzweig, *Bull. soc. chim.* (4) **11,** 68 (1912). ⟨4⟩ von Auwers, *Ann.* **408,** 246 (1915).

1:5548 **m-METHOXYACETOPHENONE** $C_9H_{10}O_2$ **Beil. VIII-86**
(*m*-Acetylanisole)

$CH_3.CO$—⟨benzene ring⟩ with OCH_3 (meta)

B.P. 240° (252°) $D_4^{15.4}$ = **1.0993** $n_D^{15.4}$ = **1.5583**

Ⓓ ***m*-Methoxyacetophenone semicarbazone:** m.p. 196° ⟨1⟩ ⟨2⟩.

1:5548 ⟨1⟩ Wahl, Silberzweig, *Bull. soc. chim.* (4) **11,** 68 (1912). ⟨2⟩ Levy, Pernot, *Bull. soc. chim.* (4) **49,** 1727 (1931).

—— **INDANONE-1** C_9H_8O **Beil. VII-360**

B.P. 241-242°/739 mm.

See 1:5144. Genus 7: Division A. M.P. 42°.

1:5550 **2-ACETYL-*p*-CYMENE** $C_{12}H_{16}O$ **Beil. VII-336**
(5-Isopropyl-2-methyl-acetophenone; carvacryl methyl ketone)

$CH_3.CO$—⟨benzene ring⟩ with CH_3 and $CH(CH_3)_2$

B.P. 245° D_{20}^{20} = **0.9654** ⟨1⟩ n_D^{20} = **1.51849** ⟨1⟩

[For prepn. in 50–55% yield from *p*-cymene, AcCl + $AlCl_3$ see ⟨2⟩.]

C̄, htd. 24 hrs. at 100° with 100 pts. HNO_3 (D = 1.15), gives on cooling 86% yield of 4-methylisophthalic ac. [Beil. IX-863]; cryst. from dil. alc., m.p. 332° ⟨1⟩.

Ⓓ **Carvacryl methyl ketoxime:** m.p. 91–92.5° ⟨1⟩.

Ⓓ **Carvacryl methyl ketone 2,4-dinitrophenylhydrazone:** incipient melting to a turbid liq. at 140–142° becoming clear at 160° ⟨3⟩ [cf. T 1.14].

Ⓓ **Carvacryl methyl ketone semicarbazone:** m.p. 147° ⟨1⟩.

1:5550 ⟨1⟩ Lacourt, *Bull. soc. chim. Belg.* **38,** 17 (1929). ⟨2⟩ Allen, *Organic Syntheses* **14,** 1–3 (1934). ⟨3⟩ Ferrante, Bloom, *Am. J. Pharm.* **105,** 383–384 (1933).

1:5552 ***n*-DECYL METHYL KETONE** $C_{12}H_{24}O$ **Beil. I-714**
(Dodecanone-2)

$n.C_{10}H_{21}.C(=O).CH_3$

B.P. 246-247° ⟨2⟩ **M.P. 20.5°** ⟨1⟩ D_4^{30} = **0.81982** ⟨1⟩ n_D^{30} = **1.42855** ⟨1⟩

Oxidn. with CrO_3 (T 1.72) yields acetic ac. (1:1010) and *n*-capric ac. (1:0585) ⟨2⟩.

Ⓓ ***n*-Decyl methyl ketone semicarbazone:** ndls. from dil. alc., m.p. 122–123° ⟨3⟩.

1:5552 ⟨1⟩ Ceuterick, *Bull. soc. chim. Belg.* **45,** 545–564 (1936). ⟨2⟩ Krafft, *Ber.* **15,** 1708 (1882). ⟨3⟩ Pickard, Kenyon, *J. Chem. Soc.* **99,** 57 (1911).

1:5555 **VALEROPHENONE** $C_{11}H_{14}O$ **Beil. VII-327**
(*n*-Butyl phenyl ketone)

$n\text{-}C_4H_9.CO$—⟨benzene ring⟩

B.P. 248.5° cor. D_{20}^{20} = **0.988** n_D^{20} = **1.5150** ⟨1⟩

Ⓓ ***n*-Butyl phenyl ketoxime:** ndls. from hot dil. alc. or pet. ether; m.p. 52.0–52.5° ⟨2⟩; 51–52° ⟨3⟩.

Ⓓ ***n*-Butyl phenyl ketone *p*-nitrophenylhydrazone:** or.-red ndls. from alc.; m.p. 161.5–162.5° ⟨4⟩.

Ⓓ ***n*-Butyl phenyl ketone 2,4-dinitrophenylhydrazone:** bright red ndls. from AcOH; m.p. 166° ⟨1⟩ [cf. T 1.14].

Ⓓ ***n*-Butyl phenyl ketone semicarbazone:** ndls. from aq. alc.; m.p. 166° ⟨5⟩ ⟨1⟩.

1:5555 ⟨1⟩ Evans, *J. Chem. Soc.* **1936,** 788. ⟨2⟩ Layraud, *Bull. soc. chim.* (3) **35,** 225 (1906). ⟨3⟩ Haller, Bauer, *Ann. chim.* (8) **28,** 410 (1913). ⟨4⟩ von Auwers, Lämmerhirt, *Ber.* **53,** 441 (1920). ⟨5⟩ Ref. 2, page 227.

—— **ISOAMYL LEVULINATE** $C_{10}H_{18}O_3$ **Beil. S.N. 281**

B.P. 248.8° D_4^{20} = **0.96136** n_D^{20} = **1.43102**

See 1:4096. Genus 5: Esters.

—— ***n*-AMYL LEVULINATE** $C_{10}H_{18}O_3$ **Beil. S.N. 281**

B.P. 253.4° D_4^{20} = **0.96136** n_D^{20} = **1.43192**

See 1:4121. Genus 5: Esters.

—— ***p*-METHOXYACETOPHENONE** $CH_3.CO.C_6H_4.OCH_3$ $C_9H_{10}O_2$ **Beil. VIII-87**

B.P. 257°

See 1:5140. Genus 7: Division A. M.P. 38°.

—— **DIETHYL ACETONEDICARBOXYLATE** $C_9H_{14}O_5$ **Beil. III-791**

B.P. 250° D_4^{20} = **1.113**

See 1:1772. Genus 4. Phenols.

—— **BENZALACETONE** C_6H_5—CH=CH.CO.CH₃ $C_{10}H_{10}O$ **Beil. VII-364**

B.P. 262° cor.

See 1:5145. Genus 7: Division A. M.P. 42°.

—— **METHYL *n*-UNDECYL KETONE** $CH_3.CO.(CH_2)_{10}.CH_3$ $C_{13}H_{26}O$ **Beil. I-715**

B.P. 263°

See 1:5130. Genus 7: Division A. M.P. 28°.

—— ***n*-AMYL PHENYL KETONE** $n.C_5H_{11}.CO.C_6H_5$ $C_{12}H_{16}O$ **Beil. VII-333**

B.P. 265.2°

See 1:5111. Genus 7: Division A. M.P. 24.7°.

—— **ETHYL BENZOYLACETATE** $C_{11}H_{12}O_3$ **Beil. X-674**

B.P. 265-270° sl. dec.

See 1:1778. Genus 4: Phenols.

1:5590 ***n*-HEXYL PHENYL KETONE** $C_{13}H_{18}O$ **Beil. VII-337**

$CH_3.(CH_2)_5.CO$—C_6H_5

B.P. 283.3° ⟨1⟩ **M.P. +16.4°** ⟨1⟩ D_4^{20} = **0.95155** ⟨1⟩ $n_{He\ (yel.)}^{15}$ = **1.50760** ⟨1⟩

Ⓓ ***n*-Hexyl phenyl ketoxime:** m.p. 55° ⟨2⟩.

Ⓓ ***n*-Hexyl phenyl *p*-nitrophenylhydrazone:** m.p. 127–128°.

Ⓓ ***n*-Hexyl phenyl ketone semicarbazone:** ndls. from dil. alc., m.p. 119°.

1:5590 ⟨1⟩ Deffet, *Bull. soc. chim. Belg.* **40,** 391, 394 (1931). ⟨2⟩ Auger, *Bull. soc. chim.* (2) **47** 50 (1887).

—— **METHYL β-NAPHTHYL KETONE** $CH_3.C(=O).C_{10}H_7$ $C_{12}H_{10}O$ **Beil. VII-402**

B.P. 301°

See 1:5153. Genus 7: Division A. M.P. 53–54°.

1:5600 METHYL α-NAPHTHYL KETONE (1-Acetonaphthone; 1-acetylnaphthalene) $CH_3—C(=O)—C_{10}H_7$ $C_{12}H_{10}O$ **Beil. VII-402**

B.P. 302° ⟨1⟩ D_4^{20} = **1.119 ⟨2⟩** n_D^{20} = **1.629 ⟨2⟩**

n_D^{27} = **1.6233 ⟨1⟩**

Prepn. from naphthalene + AcCl or Ac_2O ⟨1⟩ ⟨4⟩.

Oxidn. with warm $KMnO_4$ ⟨3⟩ or with dil. HNO_3 ⟨3⟩ ⟨4⟩ or $Ca(OCl)_2$ (90% yield) ⟨1⟩ gives α-naphthoic ac. (1:0785); oxidn. with alk. $KMnO_4$ at 30–35° gave (51% yield) α-naphthoylformic acid, m.p. 105° ⟨4⟩.

With Al isopropylate in isopropyl alc. C̄ reduces (95% yield ⟨5⟩) to methyl-α-naphthyl-carbinol, ndls. from lt. pet., m.p. 66° ⟨6⟩.

C̄ in alc. soln., treated with alc. PkOH yields a picrate, C̄.PkOH, m.p. 119–120° ⟨1⟩; 118° ⟨7⟩. [Use in sepn. and purifn. of α and β isomers.]

Ⓓ **Methyl α-naphthyl ketoxime:** m.p. 139.5–140.5° ⟨1⟩; 137–138° ⟨7⟩ [cf. ⟨10⟩].

Ⓓ **Methyl α-naphthyl ketone phenylhydrazone:** m.p. 146° u.c. ⟨8⟩.

Ⓓ **Methyl α-naphthyl ketone semicarbazone:** m.p. 228.5–229.5° ⟨1⟩; 232–233° ⟨9⟩.

1:5600 ⟨1⟩ Fieser, Holmes, Newman, *J. Am. Chem. Soc.* **58,** 1055 (1936). ⟨2⟩ von Auwers, Krollpfeiffer, *Ann.* **430,** 233 (1923). ⟨3⟩ Claus, Feist, *Ber.* **19,** 3181 (1886). ⟨4⟩ Darapsky, Beck, *J. prakt. Chem.* (2) **146,** 301–302 (1936). ⟨5⟩ Lund, *Ber.* **70,** 1524 (1937). ⟨6⟩ Pickard, Kenyon, *J. Chem. Soc.* **105,** 1126 (1914). ⟨7⟩ St. Pfau, Ofner, *Helv. Chim. Acta* **9,** 669–671 (1926). ⟨8⟩ Claus, Tersteegen, *J. prakt. Chem.* (2) **42,** 518 (1890). ⟨9⟩ Darzens, *Compt. rend.* **145,** 1342 (1907). ⟨10⟩ Bachmann, Barton, *J. Org. Chem.* **3,** 305 (1938).

—— **BENZOPHENONE** $C_6H_5.CO.C_6H_5$ $C_{13}H_{10}O$ **Beil. VII-410**

B.P. 306°

See 1:5150. Genus 7: Division A. M.P. 48°.

—— **DIBENZYL KETONE** $C_6H_5.CH_2.CO.CH_2.C_6H_5$ $C_{15}H_{14}O$ **Beil. VII-445**

B.P. 330.6°

See 1:5135. Genus 7: Division A. M.P. 34°.

—— ***m*-METHOXYBENZOPHENONE** $C_6H_5—C(=O)—C_6H_4OCH_3$ $C_{14}H_{12}O_2$ **Beil. VIII-158**

B.P. 342-343°/730 mm.

See 1:5141. Genus 7: Division A. M.P. 38°.

CHAPTER X

GENUS 8. ALCOHOLS

1. Alphabetical Name Index*

*For complete alphabetical name index covering all listed names of all numbered compounds in this book see the main alphabetical index.

2. Chemical Type Index

(Names used here are not necessarily same as subject index names)

Undecanol-2 . . . . **1:6268**

2. Containing aromatic nuclei

Phenyl-methyl-carbinol **1:6475**
Phenyl-ethyl-carbinol **1:6504**
Phenyl-*n*-propyl-carbinol . . **1:6700**
Phenyl-isopropyl-carbinol . . **1:6515**
Phenyl-*n*-butyl-carbinol . . . **1:6710**
Phenyl-*n*-amyl-carbinol **1:6720**
Phenyl-*n*-hexyl-carbinol . . . **1:6535**

Phenyl-phenyl-carbinol **1:5960**
Phenyl-*p*-tolyl-carbinol **1:5949**
Phenyl-benzyl-carbinol **1:5958**
Phenyl-*p*-anisyl-carbinol . . . **1:5956**

Di-*p*-tolylcarbinol **1:5959**
p-Tolyl-methyl-carbinol . . . **1:6502**
p-Anisyl-methyl-carbinol . . **1:6550**
α-Naphthyl-methyl-carbinol **1:5957**

3. Cyclanols

Cyclopentanol **1:6412**
Cyclohexanol **1:6415**

2-Methylcyclohexanol **1:6420**
3-Methylcyclohexanol **1:6435**
4-Methylcyclohexanol **1:6440**

d-Borneol **1:5990**
d,l-Fenchyl alcohol **1:5938**
l-Menthol **1:5940**

Cholesterol **1:5975**
Ergosterol **1:5980**

C. *Tertiary alcohols*

1. Aliphatic

Trimethylcarbinol **1:6140**
Dimethyl-ethyl-carbinol . . . **1:6160**

Methyl-diethyl-carbinol . . . **1:6189**
Dimethyl-*n*-propyl-carbinol **1:6190**
Dimethyl-isopropyl-carbinol **1:6187**

Diacetone alcohol **1:6423**

Triethylcarbinol **1:6220**

l-Linalool **1:6260**
α-Terpineol **1:6500**
Terpin hydrate **1:5965**

2. Containing aromatic nuclei

Benzyl-dimethyl-carbinol . . **1:5910**
Diphenyl-α-naphthyl-carbinol **1:5970**
Triphenylcarbinol **1:5985**

II. Dihydric Alcohols

A. *1,2-glycols*

Ethylene glycol **1:6465**
Propylene glycol **1:6455**
Butylene glycol-2,3 . . . . **1:6452**
Isobutylene glycol **1:6446**

Tetramethylethylene glycol (pinacol) **1:5805**

Tetramethylethylene glycol hexahydrate **1:5810**
Glyceryl α-phenyl ether . . . **1:5815**

B. *1,3-Glycols*

Trimethylene glycol **1:6490**
Butylene glycol-1,3 . . . . **1:6482**
2-Methylpentanediol-2,4 . . . **1:6460**

C. *1,4-Glycols*

Tetramethylene glycol **1:6516**

D. *1,5-Glycols*

Pentamethylene glycol **1:6519**

E. *Miscellaneous dihydric alcohols*

Decanediol-1,10 . . . . **1:5961**
Diethylene glycol **1:6525**
Triethylene glycol **1:6538**

III. Trihydric Alcohols

Glycerol **1:6540**

IV. Tetrahydric Alcohols

meso-Erythritol **1:5825**
Pentaerythritol **1:5850**

V. Pentahydric Alcohols

d-Quercitol **1:5845**

VI. Hexahydric Alcohols

Dulcitol **1:5835**
d-Mannitol **1:5830**
d-Sorbitol **1:5820**
d,l-Inositol **1:5840**

VII. Ethers of Genus 8

A. *Ethylene oxides*

Ethylene oxide **1:6105**
Propylene oxide **1:6115**

1,2-Epoxy-2-methylpropane **1:6117**
1,2-Epoxybutane **1:6118**
2,3-Epoxybutane **1:6116**

B. *Ethers (with no other functional group)*

Methyl ethyl ether **1:6100**
Diethyl ether **1:6110**
Diisopropyl ether **1:6125**
1,4-Dioxane **1:6400**
Ethylene glycol dimethyl ether **1:6141**
Ethylene glycol methyl ethyl ether **1:6159**

Ethylene glycol methyl *n*-propyl ether **1:6191**

C. *Ethers containing other functional groups*

Ethylene glycol monomethyl ether **1:6405**
Ethylene glycol monoethyl ether **1:6410**
Ethylene glycol mono-*n*-propyl ether **1:6414**
Ethylene glycol mono-iso-propyl ether **1:6413**
Ethylene glycol mono-*n*-butyl ether **1:6430**
Ethylene glycol mono-*sec*-butyl ether **1:6235-B**
Ethylene glycol mono-iso-butyl ether **1:6235-A**
Ethylene glycol monophenyl ether **1:6518**
Ethylene glycol monobenzyl ether **1:6533**

Diethylene glycol **1:6525**
Diethylene glycol monomethyl ether **1:6458**
Diethylene glycol monoethyl ether **1:6470**
Diethylene glycol mono-*n*-butyl ether **1:6517**

Triethylene glycol **1:6538**

Glyceryl α-phenyl ether **1:5815**

ORDER I: SUBORDER I: GENUS 8: ALCOHOLS

Division A, Solid Alcohols

Section 1. Soluble in less than 50 parts of cold water

—— **1,4-DIOXANE** $O\langle{CH_2.CH_2 \atop CH_2.CH_2}\rangle O$ $C_4H_8O_2$ **Beil. XIX-3**

M.P. 11.8° D_4^{20} = **1.03361** n_D^{20} = **1.4232**

See 1:6400. Genus 8: Division B: Section 2. B.P. 101.3°.

—— **GLYCEROL** $CH_2(OH).CH(OH).CH_2OH$ $C_3H_8O_3$ **Beil. I-502**

M.P. 17.9° D_4^{20} = **1.26134** n_D^{20} = **1.4729**

See 1:6540. Genus 8: Division B: Section 2. B.P. 290°.

—— **TETRAMETHYLENE GLYCOL** $C_4H_{10}O_2$ **Beil. I-478**

$HO.CH_2.CH_2.CH_2.CH_2.OH$

M.P. +19° D_4^{20} = **1.0171** n_D^{20} = **1.4467**

See 1:6516. Genus 8: Division B: Section 2. B.P. 230°.

—— **CYCLOHEXANOL** $C_6H_{11}.OH$ $C_6H_{12}O$ **Beil. VI-5**

M.P. 25.2° D_4^{30} = **0.94155** n_D^{25} = **1.46477**

See 1:6415. Genus 8: Division B: Section 2. B.P. 161.1°.

—— ***d,l*-2,3-BUTYLENE GLYCOL** $C_4H_{10}O_2$ **Beil. I-479**

$CH_3.CH(OH).CH(OH).CH_3$

M.P. 24-27° D_4^{20} = **1.0433** n_D^{25} = **1.43637**

See 1:6452. Genus 8: Division B: Section 2. B.P. 182.5°.

—— ***ter*-BUTYL ALCOHOL** $(CH_3)_3C.OH$ $C_4H_{10}O$ **Beil. I-379**

M.P. 25.5° D_4^{20} = **0.78670** n_D^{20} = **1.38779**

See 1:6140. Genus 8: Division B: Section 1. B.P. 82.5°.

—— ***meso*-BUTYLENE GLYCOL** $CH_3—CH(OH)—CH(OH)—CH_3$ $C_4H_{10}O_2$ **Beil. I-479**

M.P. 34.4°

See 1:6452. Genus 8: Division B: Section 2. B.P. $181.7°_{742}$.

1:5805 PINACOL (Tetramethylethylene glycol) $C_6H_{14}O_2$ **Beil. I-487**

```
      CH3CH3
       |  |
 CH3—C—C—CH3
       |  |
      OH OH
```

M.P. 43° ⟨1⟩ B.P. 173°

Clear cryst. with faint peculiar odor — Observed m.p. often lower than 43° according to previous exposure of sample to moisture — $\bar{C}$ when exposed to aq. vapor gradually shows lower m.p. which falls to 29–30° then rises again to 45–46° when hydration to hexahydrate (1:5810) is complete ⟨1⟩ — $\bar{C}$ is dif. sol. cold aq. but eas. sol. hot aq. from which on cooling the hexahydrate (1:5810) separates; $\bar{C}$ is eas. sol. alc., ether.

$\bar{C}$ on oxidn. with CrO_3 (T 1.72) yields acetone (1:5400) — $\bar{C}$ on treatment with I_2.KI solution + alk. (T 1.81) yields CHI_3 — $\bar{C}$ shaken with alk. NaOBr gives CBr_4 (83% yield) and acetic ac. (1:1010) (89% yield) ⟨2⟩ — $\bar{C}$ boiled with dil. H_2SO_4 gives very strong peppermint-like odor of methyl *ter*-butyl ketone (pinacolone) (1:5425) — $\bar{C}$ htd. at 140° for 4 hrs. with 2 pts. finely powd. B_2O_3 (from freshly fused boric ac.) gives excellent yield pinacolone (1:5425) ⟨3⟩.

$\bar{C}$ boiled with 0.004 pt. of HBr (D = 1.48) gives 55–75% yield of 2,3-dimethylbutadiene-1,3 (1:8050), b.p. 70° ⟨4⟩ — $\bar{C}$, in dry ether, treated with HBr gas gives 21–27% yield 3-bromo-2,3-dimethylbutanol-2, cryst. from lgr., m.p. 70.5° ⟨5⟩ — $\bar{C}$, stood 48 hrs. with 10 pts. HBr (satd. at 0°) gives in good yield ppt. of 2,3-dibromo-2,3-dimethylbutane [Beil. I-152], cryst. from alc. or AcOH, m.p. 192° ⟨6⟩ ⟨7⟩ — $\bar{C}$ treated with dry HCl gas at 65–90° yields 3-chloro-2,3-dimethylbutanol-2 [Beil. I-413], m.p. 65°, b.p. 151–152°.

$\bar{C}$ + 3 moles phenylisocyanate in dry ether, htd. in s.t. 45 hrs. at 100° gives 56% yield pinacol bis-(N-phenylcarbamate), cryst. from alc., m.p. 215° ⟨8⟩.

Ⓟ **Mercuric sulfate test:** $\bar{C}$ (20–25 mg.) + 2 ml. $HgSO_4$ soln. (from 5 g. HgO in mixt. of 100 ml. aq. + 20 ml. conc. H_2SO_4) + 5–6 drops 2% $KMnO_4$ are placed in a tt. standing in a conical flask so as to be heated by water. Decolorization occurs rapidly and after 30–40 secs. pptn. of a characteristic ppt. (interfered with by acetone, isopropyl alc., etc.) ⟨9⟩.

1:5805 ⟨1⟩ Krasuskiĭ, Mamedov, *Chem. Abs.* **32,** 5378 (1938); *Cent.* **1938** II, 4218. ⟨2⟩ Palmén, *J. prakt. Chem.* (2) **141,** 116–118 (1934). ⟨3⟩ Lindner, *Monatsh.* **32,** 413 (1911). ⟨4⟩ Whitby, Crozier, *Can. J. Research* **6,** 213 (1932). ⟨5⟩ Ayers, *J. Am. Chem. Soc.* **60,** 2959 (1938). ⟨6⟩ Wheeler, *Am. Chem. J.* **20,** 150 (1898). ⟨7⟩ Thiele, *Ber.* **27,** 455 (1894). ⟨8⟩ Krasuskiĭ, Movsum-Zade, *Chem. Abs.* **31,** 1377 (1937). ⟨9⟩ Denigès, *Ann. chim.* (8) **18,** 176 (1909).

1:5810 PINACOL (HEXA)HYDRATE $C_6H_{14}O_2.6H_2O$ **Beil. I-488**

M.P. 45-46° ⟨1⟩

Quad. tbls. from hot aq. — [For prepn. in 43–50% yield by reductn. of acetone (1:5400) with Mg + $HgCl_2$ in C_6H_6 see ⟨2⟩ ⟨3⟩.] — Air-dried $\bar{C}$ still contains 4.9% uncombined aq. ⟨3⟩ ⟨4⟩.

$\bar{C}$ on stdg. in vac. (49 mm.) over NaOH loses aq. (8 days) yielding anhydrous pinacol (1:5805) ⟨1⟩ [when mixt. conts. 18.9% pinacol hexahydrate, m.p. passes through a minimum of 29–30°, then rises to that of anhydrous pinacol, m.p. 43° ⟨1⟩] — $\bar{C}$ on distn. gives 75–85% yield ⟨4⟩ anhydrous pinacol (1:5805); $\bar{C}$ on distn. with C_6H_6 gives 96% yield ⟨4⟩ anhydrous pinacol (1:5805).

$\bar{C}$ treated with H_2SO_4 gives 72% yield methyl *ter*-butyl ketone (1:5425) ⟨3⟩ ⟨5⟩ — $\bar{C}$ treated with 70% HBr gives 50–85% yield ⟨6⟩ 2,3-dibromo-2,3-dimethylbutane [Beil. I-152], m.p. 192°.

1:5810 ⟨1⟩ Krasuskiĭ, Mamedov, *Chem. Abs.* **32,** 5378 (1938); *Cent.* **1938,** II, 4218. ⟨2⟩ R. Adams, E. W. Adams, *Organic Syntheses, Coll. Vol.* I, 448–450 (1932). ⟨3⟩ Hill, Kropa, *J. Am. Chem. Soc.* **55,** 2509–2510 (1933). ⟨4⟩ King, Stewart, *Proc. Trans. Nova Scotian Inst. Sci.* **17,** 262–267 (1930); *Chem. Abs.* **25,** 1799 (1931). ⟨5⟩ Hill, Flosdorf, *Organic Syntheses, Coll. Vol.* I, 451–452 (1932). ⟨6⟩ Youtz, Perkins, *J. Am. Chem. Soc.* **51,** 3510 (1929).

1:5812 NEOPENTYL ALCOHOL $(CH_3)_3.C.CH_2OH$ $C_5H_{12}O$ **Beil. I-406**
(*ter*-Butylcarbinol;
2,2-dimethylpropanol-1)

M.P. 52° **B.P. 113°**

Cryst. with peppermint-like odor — F.p. const. is large (11.0); even 5% aq. renders C̄ liq. at room temp. ⟨1⟩ — Dif. sol. aq.; eas. sol. in alc., ether, pet. ether — Very volatile and eas. volat. with steam — Can be salted out from aq. with anhyd. K_2CO_3.

C̄ is stable to heat (240°), dry HCl at 175° ⟨1⟩; does *not* yield corresp. halides with $SOCl_2$, PBr_3 or 48% HBr ⟨1⟩ [cf. ⟨2⟩].

With Na or K evolves H_2 and yields corresp. alcoholates — Sol. in cold conc. H_2SO_4 with formn. of acid ester; on diln. and steam distn. C̄ can be recovered. [The acid ester seps. as crystals on stdg. with conc. H_2SO_4 at 20°; cryst. are sol. in aq., alc., C_6H_6, or ether.] ⟨1.⟩

C̄, in aq. soln., treated with half calcd. amt. of $Na_2Cr_2O_7 + H_2SO_4$, warmed, distilled, yields trimethylacetaldehyde, b.p. 74° (1:0133) and methyl isopropyl ketone, b.p. 94° (1:5410) ⟨3⟩.

Ⓓ **Neopentyl hydrogen phthalate:** m.p. 70–71° ⟨5⟩; Neut. Eq. 236.

Ⓓ **Neopentyl hydrogen tetrachlorophthalate:** m.p. 140–141° ⟨5⟩; Neut. Eq. 374.

Ⓓ **Neopentyl *N*-phenylcarbamate:** from 1 g. C̄ + 1.4 g. $C_6H_5.N{:}C{:}O$ in 10 g. pet. ether stood 1 day at room temp.; solv. evapd. and prod. extd. with dry ether (leaving residue of diphenylurea); evapn. of ether and recrystn. from boilg. lgr. gives cryst., m.p. 144° ⟨4⟩ ⟨1⟩.

Ⓓ **Neopentyl *N*-(α-naphthyl)carbamate:** m.p. 99–100° ⟨5⟩ [cf. T 1.86].

1:5812 ⟨1⟩ Whitmore, Rothrock, *J. Am. Chem. Soc.* **54,** 3431–3435 (1932). ⟨2⟩ Whitmore, Fleming, *J. Am. Chem. Soc.* **55,** 4161–4162 (1933). ⟨3⟩ Samec, *Ann.* **351,** 258 (1907). ⟨4⟩ Richard, *Ann. chim. phys.* (8) **21,** 339 (1910). ⟨5⟩ Rice, Jenkins, Harden, *J. Am. Chem. Soc.* **59,** 2000 (1937).

—— ***d*-SORBITOL HYDRATE** $C_6H_{14}O_6.H_2O$ **Beil. I-533**

M.P. 55°

See *d*-Sorbitol 1:5820.

1:5815 GLYCERYL α-PHENYL ETHER C_6H_5—O—CH_2 / HO—CH / HO—CH_2 $C_9H_{12}O_3$ **Beil. VI-149**

M.P. 69°

Cryst. from anhyd. ether, C_6H_6, or lgr. in long flexible ndls.; after fusion and resolidification m.p. becomes 53–54° but gradually regains higher m.p. on stdg. ⟨1⟩ ⟨3⟩.

Eas. sol. aq.; sol. C_6H_6, alc.; dif. sol. ether, lgr. or pet. ether — Sol. in conc. H_2SO_4 with pale red color turning to green on addn. of $NaNO_2$ soln. — [For prepn. in 61–64% yield from glyceryl α-chlorohydrin see ⟨2⟩.]

1:5815 ⟨1⟩ Fairbourne, Stephens, *J. Chem. Soc.* **1932,** 1972–1973. ⟨2⟩ Wheeler, Willson, *Organic Syntheses, Coll. Vol.* I, 290–291 (1932). ⟨3⟩ Stephens, *J. Soc. Chem. Ind.* **51,** 376–378 (1932).

1:5820 ***d*-SORBITOL, anhydrous** $C_6H_{14}O_6$ **Beil. I-533**

```
        H  H  OH H
        |  |  |  |
HOCH2—C—C—C—C—CH2OH
        |  |  |  |
        OH OH H  OH
```

M.P. 89-93° ⟨1⟩
112° ⟨2⟩

M.p. with 1 H_2O = 55°; in vac. loses $\frac{1}{2}$ H_2O, melts 75°; at 100° becomes anhyd. — $\bar{C}$ cryst. from pyridine as mol. cpd.; $\bar{C}.1C_5H_5N$, m.p. 88–89° cor. ⟨1⟩.

$\bar{C}$ is sol. aq. or warm alc., but sparingly sol. in cold alc. — Sweetish taste — In pure aq. soln. $[\alpha]_D^{15} = -1.75°$ in aq. (C = 4.12); in borax soln. + 1.52° — $\bar{C}$ does not reduce Fehling's soln. (T 1.22).

Ⓓ **Hexaacetyl-*d*-sorbitol** [Beil. II-150]: from $\bar{C}$ on reflux. with Ac_2O + little fused $ZnCl_2$ for 2 hrs., pouring into aq., giving heavy oil, which dis. in ether, gives cryst.; m.p. 99° ⟨3⟩ ⟨4⟩.

Ⓓ **Hexabenzoyl-*d*-sorbitol:** from $\bar{C}$ + BzCl + aq. alk.; cryst. from AcOEt; m.p. 216–217° ⟨5⟩.

Ⓓ **Tribenzal-*d*-sorbitol** [Beil. XIX-464]: from 0.5 g. $\bar{C}$, 1 ml. BzH, and 1.5 ml. conc. HCl, htd. 15 min. on aq. bath, stood at room temp., pptd. with aq., washed with aq., alc., ether, acetone; then recrystd. from $CHCl_3$ + alc.; white amorph. powder, m.p. 190.1–192° ⟨6⟩; 190–191° ⟨7⟩; 184–187° ⟨8⟩ ⟨9⟩.

1:5820 ⟨1⟩ Strain, *J. Am. Chem. Soc.* **56,** 1756–1757 (1934). ⟨2⟩ von Lippmann, *Ber.* **60,** 162 (1927). ⟨3⟩ Vincent, Delachanal, *Compt. rend.* **109,** 676 (1889). ⟨4⟩ Jahr, *Z. Untersuch. Lebensm.* **59,** 285–288 (1930). ⟨5⟩ Kraszewski, Judelowkzowna, *Cent.* **1938,** I, 2080; **1935,** I, 1462. ⟨6⟩ Wolfrom, et al., *J. Am. Chem. Soc.* **60,** 573 (1938). ⟨7⟩ Karrer, Büchi, *Helv. Chim. Acta* **20,** 90 (1937). ⟨8⟩ Zach, *Mitt. Lebensm. Hyg.* **21,** 127 (1930). ⟨9⟩ van Ekenstein, de Bruyn, *Rec. trav. chim.* **19,** 178 (1900).

1:5825 ***meso*-ERYTHRITOL** $C_4H_{10}O_4$ **Beil. I-525**

```
          H  H
          |  |
HOCH2.C—C.CH2OH
          |  |
          OH OH
```

M.P. 120° cor. (126°) **B.P. 330°**

Clear cryst. with sweet taste — Opt. inactive — Soly. at 20–25° in 100 g. aq. is 61.5%; in 100 g. 50% pyridine 8.5%; in pure pyridine 2.5% ⟨1⟩.

$\bar{C}$ does not reduce Fehling's soln. (T 1.22) — Aq. soln. of $\bar{C}$ dis. CaO in cold and coagulates on boiling or on addn. of alc. — $\bar{C}$ gives no ppt. with $Pb(OAc)_2$.

Ⓟ **Color reaction:** By actn. of Br_2-aq. (0.3 g. Br_2 in 100 aq.) or 2% $KMnO_4$ a soln. of erythrulose ($CH_2OH.CHOH.CO.CH_2OH$) is obtd., which with 5% alc. resorcinol soln. and 2 ml. conc. H_2SO_4 yields a cherry-red soln., or with 5% alc. β-naphthol a red soln. with green fluores. ⟨2⟩.

Ⓓ **Tetraacetylerythritol** [Beil. II-149]: from $\bar{C}$ refluxed with Ac_2O and a little fused $ZnCl_2$; m.p. 85° ⟨3⟩, 89° ⟨7⟩.

Ⓓ **Tetrabenzoylerythritol** [Beil. IX-144]: shaking 2 g. $\bar{C}$, 12 g. BzCl, and 75 ml. 10% NaOH at room temp. ppts. a white resin, insol. ether, dif. sol. alc., cryst. from AcOH, m.p. 187° ⟨4⟩; 190° ⟨5⟩. [Use of pyridine gives mixtures of di- (m.p. 154–157°) + tri- (m.p. 108–110°) benzoates which are sol. in ether ⟨5⟩.]

Ⓓ **Dibenzalerythritol** [Beil. XIX–439]: from $\bar{C}$ + 2 pts. BzH, shaken with 3 pts. conc. HCl or 50% H_2SO_4 or P_2O_5 ⟨8⟩ yields solid, washed with aq., cryst. from alc., m.p. 197–198° u.c. (200–201° cor.) ⟨6⟩.

1:5825 ⟨1⟩ Dehn, *J. Am. Chem. Soc.* **39,** 1400 (1917). ⟨2⟩ Denigès, *Ann. chim.* (8) **18,** 169 (1909). ⟨3⟩ Griner, *Bull. soc. chim.* (3) **9,** 219 (1893). ⟨4⟩ Skraup, *Monatsh.* **10,** 393 (1889). ⟨5⟩ Einhorn, Hollandt, *Ann.* **301,** 101–102 (1898). ⟨6⟩ Fischer, *Ber.* **27,** 1535 (1894). ⟨7⟩ Perkin, Simonsen, *J. Chem. Soc.* **87,** 859 (1909). ⟨8⟩ Pette, *Rec. trav. chim.* **53,** 977 (1934).

1:5830 *d*-MANNITOL HO.CH$_2$.C(OH)(H)—C(OH)(H)—C(H)(OH)—C(H)(OH).CH$_2$OH $C_6H_{14}O_6$ **Beil. I-534**

```
      H   H   OH OH
      |   |   |  |
HO.CH2.C—C—C—C.CH2OH
      |   |   |  |
      OH OH  H  H
```

M.P. 166°

Ndls. with sweet taste — Subl. slowly above m.p. — Soly. in 100 g. H_2O: at 0°, 10.36 g.; at 20°, 18.6 g.; at 100°, 197.0 g. [For f.p.-sol. diagram see ⟨1⟩.] — Soly. of C̄ in 100 g. pyridine: 0.47 g. at 20–25°; in 100 g. 50% pyridine, 2.46 g. — C̄ is very dif. sol. in alc.; insol. ether. [For resume of phys. prop. of C̄ see ⟨1⟩.]

C̄ is slightly laevorotatory: $[\alpha]_D^{25} = -0.208°$ ⟨1⟩, but solns. of C̄ in boric ac. or borax become strongly dextrorotatory, e.g., for C̄ in *N*/2 boric acid, $[\alpha]_D^{20} = +28.3°$ ⟨2⟩.

C̄ does not reduce Fehling's soln. (T 1.22) [dif. from mannose (1:0300)] — C̄ prevents pptn. of Fe$(OH)_3$ on addn. of alk. to solns. of ferric salts — C̄, on oxidn. with HNO_3 (T 1.25) gives no saccharic ac. and no mucic ac. [dif. from dulcitol (1:5835)].

Ⓓ **Hexaacetylmannitol** [Beil. II-150]: from C̄ in quant. yield by warming with 4 pts. Ac_2O + a little fused $ZnCl_2$, or with AcCl + pyridine; crude melts 119°; after 2 recrystn. from ether, m.p. 126° ⟨3⟩.

Ⓓ **Hexabenzoylmannitol** [Beil. IX-145]: from C̄ in 65% yield on treat. at 0° with 6 pts. BzCl + large excess 20% aq. NaOH; ndls. from alc., m.p. 147–148° ⟨3⟩; 149° ⟨4⟩. [Note: 4,5-Dibenzoyl-*d*-mannitol, m.p. 183° ⟨5⟩, and tribenzoyl-*d*-mannitol, m.p. 152° ⟨5⟩ on further benzoylation yield the hexabenzoyl deriv. ⟨5⟩.]

Ⓓ **Tribenzal-*d*-mannitol** [Beil. XIX-464]: from C̄ + 2 pts. freshly dist. BzH + 1 pt. P_2O_5; after treatment with aq. and recrystn. from alc., m.p. 223–224° (50% yield) ⟨6⟩ ⟨7⟩. [A less pure product can also be obtd. by shaking together C̄ + 2 pts. BzH + 3 pts. conc. HCl and recrystn. of prod. from alc., white ndls. (70% yield); m.p. 218–219° ⟨3⟩; 222° ⟨7⟩.] [M.p. of tribenzal-*d,l*-mannitol is 192° ⟨8⟩ ⟨9⟩.]

1:5830 ⟨1⟩ Braham, *J. Am. Chem. Soc.* **41,** 1707–1718 (1919). ⟨2⟩ Irvine, Steele, *J. Chem. Soc.* **107,** 1229 (1915). ⟨3⟩ Patterson, Todd, *J. Chem. Soc.* **1929,** 2887–2889. ⟨4⟩ Power, Rogerson, *J. Chem. Soc.* **97,** 1949 (1910). ⟨5⟩ Ohle, Erlbach, Hepp, Toussaint, *Ber.* **62,** 2985–2986 (1929). ⟨6⟩ Pette, *Ber.* **64,** 1568 (1931). ⟨7⟩ Pette, *Rec. trav. chim.* **53,** 970 (1934). ⟨8⟩ Lespieau, Wiemann, *Compt. rend.* **194,** 1947 (1932). ⟨9⟩ Fischer, *Ber.* **27,** 1530 (1894).

1:5835 DULCITOL $C_6H_{14}O_6$ **Beil. I-544**

```
      H  OH  OH  H
      |   |   |   |
HO.CH2.C—C—C—C.CH2OH
      |   |   |   |
      OH  H   H  OH
```

M.P. 188°

Nearly tasteless — Can be sublimed in small vessel — 100 pts. aq. at 15° dis. 3.2 pts.; eas. sol. hot aq.; alm. insol. alc. or ether — Opt. inact. even after addn. of borax — C̄ forms with $CaCl_2$ a non-deliquescent non-efflorescent cpd., C̄.$CaCl_2$.$4H_2O$ ⟨4⟩.

C̄ on oxidn. with HNO_3 (T 1.25) yields mucic ac. (1:0845) ⟨1⟩ — C̄ does *not* reduce Fehling's soln. (T 1.22) — C̄ on shakg. with BzH + conc. HCl (or 50% H_2SO_4) does *not* ppt. dibenzal deriv. at room temp. [dif. from *d*-mannitol (1:5830) or *d*-sorbitol (1:5820) ⟨2⟩].

Ⓓ **Hexaacetyldulcitol** [Beil. II-151]: from $\bar{C}$ on refluxg. with Ac_2O, pouring into aq., recrystn. from abs. alc.; ndls., m.p. 168–169° ⟨3⟩.

Ⓓ **Hexabenzoyldulcitol** [Beil. IX-146]: from 5 g. $\bar{C}$ dislvd. in 70 g. hot pyridine and 30.5 g. BzCl grad. added; after boiling 15 min. poured into aq., ppt. washed and recrystd. from mixt. of eq. vols. ether + $CHCl_3$; m.p. 189–191° ⟨3⟩.

1:5835 ⟨1⟩ von Lippmann, *Ber.* **25,** 3217 (1892). ⟨2⟩ Fischer, *Ber.* **27,** 1534 (1894). ⟨3⟩ Rogerson, *J. Chem. Soc.* **101,** 1043–1044 (1912). ⟨4⟩ Délépine, Horeau, *Bull. soc. chim.* (5) **4,** 1530 (1937).

1:5840 *meso*-INOSITOL (1,2,3,4,5,6-Hexahydroxycyclohexane) $C_6H_{12}O_6$ **Beil. VI-1194**

```
        H      OH
         \    /
           C
   H     /   \     H
    \   /     \   /
 HO—C           C—OH
    |           |
   H|           |H
    \|          |/
 HO—C           C—OH
      \       /
          C
        /   \
      HO     H
```

M.P. 225° cor. ⟨1⟩
(218°)

[For prepn. from starch factory " sweet water " see ⟨2⟩ ⟨3⟩.]

Tastes sweet — Efflores. cryst. with $2H_2O$ from cold aq.; above 50% cryst. in anhyd. form — Sublimes in small quant. — Hydrated cryst. sol. in 5.7 pts. aq. at 24°; insol. abs. alc. or ether.

$\bar{C}$ does not condense with BzH ⟨4⟩ — $\bar{C}$ does not reduce Fehling's soln. (T 1.22) but does reduce Tollens' reagt. (T 1.11).

Ⓟ **Color test on oxidation:** 2 mg. (or more) of $\bar{C}$ are placed on a porcelain crucible cover, treated with a few drops conc. HNO_3, evapd. almost to dryness. On addn. of a few drops NH_4OH followed by an equal amt. $CaCl_2$ soln. and evapn. a rose red color results, probably due to salts of tetrahydroxyquinone and of dihydroxyquinone (rhodizonic acid) [dif. from carbohydrates] ⟨5⟩ ⟨6⟩. The test is improved if carried out on platinum crucible cover or by addition of a drop of 1–2% $PtCl_4$ soln. ⟨7⟩. [For extensive study of oxidn. products, see ⟨8⟩ ⟨11⟩.]

Ⓓ **Hexaacetylinositol:** from $\bar{C}$, refluxed with Ac_2O in pres. of $ZnCl_2$, poured into aq., recrystd. from toluene, m.p. 212° subl. ⟨9⟩ ⟨2⟩; 215° ⟨10⟩.

Ⓓ **Hexabenzoylinositol** [Beil. IX-147]: from 2 g. $\bar{C}$, 10 g. BzCl, and 10 g. quinoline heated half hour at 120°; resultant red syrup dislvd. in 100 ml. $CHCl_3$, washed three times with 10% H_2SO_4, then once with aq. After filtering off ppt. of pentabenzoyl deriv., soln. is concd. to 50 ml. and stood in ice box 12 hrs. Cryst. of hexabenzoyl deriv. sep., cryst. from hot alc., m.p. 258° ⟨1⟩.

Ⓓ **Hexa-(3,5-dinitrobenzoyl)inositol:** from $\bar{C}$ htd. with excess 3,5-dinitrobenzoyl chloride; cryst. from alc., m.p. 86° ⟨2⟩.

1:5840 ⟨1⟩ Griffin, Nelson, *J. Am. Chem. Soc.* **37,** 1562 (1915). ⟨2⟩ Hoglan, Bartow, *Ind. Eng. Chem.* **31,** 749–750 (1939). ⟨3⟩ Bartow, Walker, *Ind. Eng. Chem.* **30,** 300–303 (1938). ⟨4⟩ Karrer, *Helv. Chim. Acta* **9,** 116 (1926). ⟨5⟩ Scherer, *Ann.* **81,** 375 (1852). ⟨6⟩ Seidel, *Chem. Ztg.* **11,** 316, 376 (1887). ⟨7⟩ Salkowski, *Z. physiol. Chem.* **69,** 478–481 (1910). ⟨8⟩ Gelormini, Artz, *J. Am. Chem. Soc.* **52,** 2483–2494 (1930). ⟨9⟩ Maquenne, *Compt. rend.* **104,** 1719 (1887). ⟨10⟩ Sando, *J. Biol. Chem.* **68,** 404 (1926).
⟨11⟩ Hoglan, Bartow, *J. Am. Chem. Soc.* **62,** 2397–2398 (1940).

1:5845 ***d*-QUERCITOL** (1,2,3,4,5-Pentahydroxycyclohexane) $C_6H_{12}O_5$ **Beil. VI-1186**

```
H   OH H      OH
 \  /   \    /
  C--------C     H
 /          \   /
H2C          C—OH
 \          /
  C--------C
 /  \    /   \
H   OH  H     OH
```

Not to be confused with the flavanol quercitin [Beil. XVIII-242] or the rhamnoside of the latter called quercitrin [Beil. XXXI-75].

M.P. 232°

Cryst. sol. in 10 pts. cold aq.; dif. sol. alc.; insol. ether — $[\alpha]_D^{20} = +27.10°$ (C = 3.85 in aq.).

C̄, boiled with dil. H_2SO_4 and MnO_2 gives pungent odor of quinone (1:9025) — C̄, on oxidn. with HNO_3 (T 1.25) yields mucic ac. (1:0845) ⟨1⟩ ⟨2⟩. [For study of oxidn. prod. from use of alk. $KMnO_4$ see ⟨3⟩.] C̄ does not condense with acetone or BzH [dif. from pentaerythritol (1:5850) ⟨2⟩].

1:5845 ⟨1⟩ von Lippmann, *Ber.* **60,** 162 (1927). ⟨2⟩ Karrer, *Helv. Chim. Acta* **9,** 116 (1926.) ⟨3⟩ Posternak, *Helv. Chim. Acta* **15,** 952–954 (1932).

1:5850 **PENTAERYTHRITOL** $C_5H_{12}O_4$ **Beil. I-528**

```
          CH2OH
           |
HOH2C—C—CH2OH
           |
          CH2OH
```

M.P. 253° (see text)

Tetrag. cryst.; sol. 18 pts. aq. at 15° — Ord. prod. conts. dipentaerythritol which cannot be removed by recrystn. ⟨1⟩ — C̄, on sublim. at 130° in high vac. gives pure pentaerythritol, m.p. 259° u.c. ⟨2⟩.

[For prepn. of C̄ in 55–57% yield from acetaldehyde, paraformaldehyde and $Ca(OH)_2$ see ⟨3⟩.]

C̄, htd. with 4 moles PBr_3 for 20 hrs. at 160–180° gives 86% yield pentaerythrityl tetrabromide, m.p. 162–163° ⟨4⟩ ⟨5⟩. [For conv. of this tetrabromide to corresp. tetraiodide (m.p. 233°) by htg. with NaI in MeEt ketone (88–99% yield) see ⟨6⟩.] [For reactn. of pentaerythrityl tetrabromide with various alcoholates and phenolates see ⟨6⟩.]

Ⓓ **Pentaerythrityl tetraacetate** [Beil. II-150]: from C̄ refluxed 2 hrs. with 4 pts. Ac_2O + a small piece $ZnCl_2$ and poured into aq.; white ndls. from alc., m.p. 84° ⟨7⟩ [dipentaerythrityl hexaacetate has m.p. 73° ⟨1⟩].

Ⓓ **Pentaerythrityl tetrabenzoate** [Beil. IX-144]: 5 g. C̄ in 15 ml. aq., shaken with 20 g. BzCl and 120 ml. 10% NaOH yields resin, which ground in mortar with more BzCl and alk. gives a solid powder; washed with water and repeatedly cryst. from alc. yields ndls. m.p. 99–101° ⟨8⟩. [Dipentaerythritol hexabenzoate has m.p. 183° ⟨1⟩.]

Ⓓ **Diacetonepentaerythritol:** from C̄ + 10 pts. anhyd. acetone + 0.5 pt. anhyd. $CuSO_4$ on stdg. 12 hrs.; cryst. from pet. ether, m.p. 117° ⟨9⟩.

1:5850 ⟨1⟩ Friederich, Brün, *Ber.* **63,** 2681–2690 (1930). ⟨2⟩ Ebert, *Ber.* **64,** 114–119 (1931). ⟨3⟩ Schurink, *Organic Syntheses, Coll. Vol.* I, 417–419 (1932). ⟨4⟩ Backer, Schurink, *Rec. trav. chim.* **50,** 924–925 (1931). ⟨5⟩ Schurink, *Organic Syntheses* **17,** 73–75 (1937). ⟨6⟩ Backer, Dijken, *Rec. trav. chim.* **55,** 22–32 (1936). ⟨7⟩ Perkin, Simonsen, *J. Chem. Soc.* **87,** 860 (1905). ⟨8⟩ Rave, Tollens, *Ann.* **276,** 60 (1893). ⟨9⟩ Orthner, *Ber.* **61,** 116 (1928).

ORDER I: SUBORDER I: GENUS 8: ALCOHOLS

Division A, Solid Alcohols

Section 2. Solid alcohols not soluble in 50 parts cold water

—— ***n*-DECYL ALCOHOL** $CH_3.(CH_2)_8.CH_2OH$ $C_{10}H_{22}O$ **Beil. I-425**

M.P. 6° D_4^{20} **= 0.8292** n_D^{20} **= 1.43682**

See 1:6275. Genus 8: Division B: Section 1. B.P. 231°

1:5890 UNDECANOL-1 $CH_3.(CH_2)_9.CH_2OH$ $C_{11}H_{24}O$ **Beil. I-427**
(*n*-Undecyl alcohol; hendecyl alcohol)

M.P. +15.85° ⟨1⟩
+14.3° ⟨2⟩

Oxidn. with $K_2Cr_2O_7 + H_2SO_4$ (cf. T 1.72) yields *n*-undecylic ac. (1:0573) ⟨3⟩.

Ⓓ ***n*-Undecyl *N*-phenylcarbamate:** cryst. from alc., m.p. 62° ⟨3⟩; 52° ⟨7⟩. [For optical data see ⟨7⟩.]

Ⓓ ***n*-Undecyl *N*-(*p*-nitrophenyl)carbamate:** lfts. from alc., m.p. 99.5° ⟨4⟩.

Ⓓ ***n*-Undecyl hydrogen phthalate:** m.p. 43.8–44.1°; Neut. Eq. 320 ⟨6⟩.

Ⓓ **2-(*n*-Undecyl) hydrogen 3-nitrophthalate:** m.p. 123.2°; Neut. Eq. 365 ⟨5⟩.

1:5890 ⟨1⟩ Meyer, Reid, *J. Am. Chem. Soc.* **55,** 1577 (1933). ⟨2⟩ Robinson, *J. Chem. Soc.* **125,** 229 (1924). ⟨3⟩ Jeffreys, *Am. Chem. J.* **22,** 38–39 (1899). ⟨4⟩ Hoppenbrouwers, *Rec. trav. chim.* **51,** 952 (1932). ⟨5⟩ Dickinson, Crosson, Copenhaver, *J. Am. Chem. Soc.* **59,** 1095 (1937). ⟨6⟩ Goggans, Copenhaver, *J. Am. Chem. Soc.* **61,** 2909 (1939). ⟨7⟩ Dewey, Witt, *Ind. Eng. Chem., Anal. Ed.* **12,** 459 (1940).

—— ***d,l*-METHYL-PHENYL-CARBINOL** $C_8H_{10}O$ **Beil. VI-475**
$CH_3.CH(OH).C_6H_5$

M.P. 20.1° D_4^{20} **= 1.0129** n_D^{20} **= 1.5275**

See 1:6475. Genus 8: Division B: Section 2. B.P. 202°.

1:5900 DODECANOL-1 $CH_3.(CH_2)_{10}.CH_2OH$ $C_{12}H_{26}O$ **Beil. I-428**
(*n*-Dodecyl alcohol; lauryl alcohol)

M.P. 23.87° ⟨1⟩ **B.P. 259°**

[For prepn. of C̄ in 65–75% yield by reductn. of ethyl laurate (1:4196) with Na + alc. in toluene see ⟨2⟩.]

C̄, after fusion, seps. on cooling in transparent α-form, at 21.6°; this material on stdg. or rubbing changes to opaque β-form, m.p. 23.8° ⟨3⟩.

Ⓓ **Lauryl *p*-nitrobenzoate:** m.p. 45° [T 1.82].

Ⓓ **Lauryl 3,5-dinitrobenzoate:** m.p. 60° [T 1.82].

Ⓓ **Lauryl hydrogen phthalate:** m.p. 50.2–50.4° cor.; Neut. Eq. 334 ⟨4⟩.

Ⓓ **Lauryl hydrogen 3-nitrophthalate:** m.p. 123.9–124.0°; Neut. Eq. 379 ⟨5⟩ [cf.T 1.83].

Ⓓ **Lauryl *N*-phenylcarbamate:** m.p. 74° ⟨6⟩ ⟨9⟩. [For optical data see ⟨9⟩.]

Ⓓ **Lauryl *N*-(*p*-nitrophenyl)carbamate:** m.p. 117° ⟨7⟩.

Ⓓ **Lauryl *N*-(α-naphthyl)carbamate:** m.p. 80° ⟨8⟩ [cf. T 1.86].

1:5900 ⟨1⟩ Meyer, Reid, *J. Am. Chem. Soc.* **55,** 1577 (1933). ⟨2⟩ Ford, Marvel, *Organic Syntheses* **10,** 62–64 (1930). ⟨3⟩ Phillips, Mumford, *J. Chem. Soc.* **1934,** 1660. ⟨4⟩ Goggans, Copenhaver, *J. Am. Chem. Soc.* **61,** 2909 (1939). ⟨5⟩ Dickinson, Crosson, Copenhaver, *J. Am. Chem. Soc.* **59,** 1095 (1937). ⟨6⟩ Hoeke, *Rec. trav. chim.* **54,** 513 (1935). ⟨7⟩ van Hoogstraten, *Rec. trav. chim.* **51,** 426 (1932). ⟨8⟩ Bickel, French, *J. Am. Chem. Soc.* **48,** 749 (1926). ⟨9⟩ Dewey, Witt, *Ind. Eng. Chem., Anal. Ed.* **12,** 459 (1940).

1:5910 BENZYL-DIMETHYL-CARBINOL C_6H_5—CH_2—C(CH_3)(OH)—CH_3 $C_{10}H_{14}O$ **Beil. VI-523**

M.P. 24° **B.P. 214-216°** D_4^{16} = **0.9790** n_D^{16} = **1.5174**

C̄ htd. 3 hrs. on steam bath with equal wt. Ac_2O and few drops of conc. H_2SO_4, cooled, poured into aq., neutralized, extd. with ether, distd., gives 90% yield β,β-dimethylstyrene, $C_6H_5.CH{=}C(CH_3)_2$, b.p. 180–182° [cf. Beil. V_1-(236)] ⟨1⟩.

1:5910 ⟨1⟩ Tiffeneau, *Bull. soc. chim.* (4) **29,** 814–815 (1921).

1:5915 *p*-ANISYL ALCOHOL (*p*-Methoxybenzyl alcohol) CH_3O—C_6H_4—$CH_2.OH$ $C_8H_{10}O_2$ **Beil. VI-897**

M.P. 25° **B.P. 258°** D_{15}^{15} = **1.1129** n_D^{25} = **1.5422** ⟨1⟩

C̄ readily yields di-*p*-anisyl ether [Beil. VI_1-(440)], m.p. 41°; e.g., on stdg. over conc. H_2SO_4 or on shaking ether soln. of C̄ with aq. $NaHSO_3$ ⟨2⟩, or on stdg. over Na_2SO_4 (contg. a trace of $NaHSO_4$) ⟨3⟩, or on addn. of few drops of conc. HCl to boiling ether soln. (alm. quant. yield) ⟨4⟩.

C̄, at b.p., readily oxidized by air to *p*-anisaldehyde (1:0240); further oxidn. with air or actn. of dil. HNO_3 on C̄ yields *p*-anisic ac. (1:0805).

Ⓓ ***p*-Anisyl *N*-phenylcarbamate:** m.p. 92° cor. ⟨5⟩.

1:5915 ⟨1⟩ Ofner, *Helv. Chim. Acta* **18,** 955–956 (1935). ⟨2⟩ Späth, *Monatsh.* **34,** 2000 (1913). ⟨3⟩ Ofner, *Helv. Chim. Acta* **20,** 53 (1937). ⟨4⟩ Quelet, Allard, *Bull. soc. chim.* (5) **4,** 1469 (1937). ⟨5⟩ Kindler, *Arch. Pharm.* **265,** 401 (1927).

—— **CYCLOHEXANOL** $C_6H_{11}OH$ $C_6H_{12}O$ **Beil. VI-5**

M.P. 25.2° D_4^{30} = **0.94155** n_D^{25} = **1.46477**

See 1:6415. Genus 8: Division B: Section 2. B.P. 161.1°.

1:5917 TRIDECANOL-1 $CH_3.(CH_2)_{11}.CH_2OH$ $C_{13}H_{28}O$ **Beil. I-428**

M.P. 30.63° (α-form) ⟨1⟩ D_4^{31} = **0.8223**
28.35° (β-form) ⟨1⟩

Ⓓ ***n*-Tridecyl hydrogen phthalate:** m.p. 52.4–52.7°; Neut. Eq. 348 ⟨3⟩.

Ⓓ ***n*-Tridecyl hydrogen 3-nitrophthalate:** m.p. 124.0–124.2° cor.; Neut. Eq. 393 ⟨2⟩ [cf. T 1.83].

1:5917 ⟨1⟩ Meyer, Reid, *J. Am. Chem. Soc.* **55,** 1577 (1933). ⟨2⟩ Dickinson, Crosson, Copenhaver, *J. Am. Chem. Soc.* **59,** 1095 (1937). ⟨3⟩ Goggans, Copenhaver, *J. Am. Chem. Soc.* **61,** 2909 (1939).

1:5920 CINNAMYL ALCOHOL $C_9H_{10}O$ **Beil. VI-570**

C_6H_5—CH=CH.CH_2OH

M.P. 33° **B.P. 257°**

Fairly eas. sol. aq.; eas. sol. alc., ether — Ord. comml. C̄ is *trans* isomer ⟨1⟩ — C̄, dislvd. in dry ether and stood for 24 hrs. with powd. anhydrous $CaCl_2$ yields addn. prod. ($CaCl_2$. 1.5 C̄), m.p. 157° u.c. ⟨2⟩ [dif. and sepn. from hydrocinnamyl alc. (1:6520) ⟨3⟩].

C̄ on gentle oxidn. with CrO_3 yields cinnamic ac. (1:0735); on oxidn. with $KMnO_4$ yields benzoic ac. (1:0715).

C̄ in cold $CHCl_3$ ⟨4⟩ or in cold dry ether in dark ⟨5⟩ readily adds Br_2 yielding β,γ-dibromo-γ-phenylpropyl alc. [Beil. VI-504]; ndls. from ether, m.p. 74°.

C̄ shaken 3 hrs. at room temp. with 3 pts. HBr (D = 1.48) yields heavy oil which on chilling gives 80–85% yield cinnamyl bromide, m.p. 28° ⟨6⟩ — C̄ on distn. with 5 moles 6 N HCl gives (79% yield ⟨7⟩; 60% yield ⟨13⟩) cinnamyl chloride; also obtd. (69–75% yield ⟨13⟩) from C̄ + SO_2Cl_2.

Ⓓ **Cinnamyl *p*-nitrobenzoate:** m.p. 78° ⟨8⟩ ⟨3⟩, 76.5° ⟨9⟩ [cf. T 1.82].

Ⓓ **Cinnamyl 3,5-dinitrobenzoate:** m.p. 121° [T 1.82].

Ⓓ **Cinnamyl *N*-phenylcarbamate:** m.p. 90–91.5° ⟨10⟩.

Ⓓ **Cinnamyl *N*-(α-naphthyl)carbamate:** m.p. 114° ⟨11⟩ [cf. T 1.86].

Ⓓ **Cinnamyl *N,N*-diphenylcarbamate:** stable form, m.p. 103.5–104°; metastable form, m.p. 97–98° ⟨12⟩ [cf. T 1.43].

1:5920 ⟨1⟩ Gredy, *Bull. soc. chim.* (5) **3,** 1098 (1936). ⟨2⟩ Endoh, *Rec. trav. chim.* **44,** 871 (1925). ⟨3⟩ Hill, Nason, *J. Am. Chem. Soc.* **46,** 2245 (1924). ⟨4⟩ Grimaux, *Bull. soc. chim.* (2) **20,** 120 (1873). ⟨5⟩ Duquesnois, *Bull. soc. chim.* (5) **4,** 195–196 (1937). ⟨6⟩ Claisen, Tietze, *Ber.* **58,** 279 (1925). ⟨7⟩ Norris, Watt, Thomas, *J. Am. Chem. Soc.* **38,** 1078 (1916). ⟨8⟩ Burton, Ingold, *J. Chem. Soc.* **1928,** 914. ⟨9⟩ Meisenheimer, Schmidt, Schäfer, *Ann.* **501,** 131 (1933). ⟨10⟩ Pauly, Schmidt, Böhme, *Ber.* **57,** 1329 (1924); cf. Schimmel and Co., *Cent.* **1910,** I, 1720.

⟨11⟩ Bickel, French, *J. Am. Chem. Soc.* **48,** 749 (1926). ⟨12⟩ Hoejenbos, Coppens, *Rec. trav. chim.* **50,** 1047 (1931). ⟨13⟩ Young, Ballou, Nozaki, *J. Am. Chem. Soc.* **61,** 14 (1939).

1:5922 *o*-TOLYLCARBINOL (*o*-Xylyl alcohol; *o*-methylbenzyl alcohol) $C_8H_{10}O$ **Beil. VI-484**

C_6H_4(—CH_2OH)(—CH_3)

M.P. 35°

Sol. in 100 pts. cold or 60 pts. boilg. aq.; very sol. alc., ether, $CHCl_3$.

Volatile with steam. [For m.p.'s of mixtures with *p*-tolylcarbinol (1:5954) see ⟨1⟩.]

C̄ on oxidn. with theor. amt. $K_2Cr_2O_7$ + dil. H_2SO_4 ⟨2⟩ yields *o*-tolualdehyde (1:0210); on oxidn. with excess 5% $KMnO_4$ in alk. soln. ⟨3⟩ yields *o*-toluic ac. (1:0690).

Ⓓ ***o*-Tolylcarbinyl *N*-phenylcarbamate:** m.p. 79° cor. ⟨4⟩.

1:5922 ⟨1⟩ Hill, Short, *J. Chem. Soc.* **1935,** 1126. ⟨2⟩ Kröber, *Ber.* **23,** 1029 (1890). ⟨3⟩ Gilman, Breuer, *J. Am. Chem. Soc.* **56,** 1128 (1934). ⟨4⟩ Kindler, *Arch. Pharm.* **265,** 400 (1927).

1:5925 ELAIDYL ALCOHOL (*trans*-Octadecenyl alcohol; *trans*-octadecen-9-ol-1) $C_{18}H_{36}O$ **Beil. S.N. 25**

$CH_3.(CH_2)_7.CH{=}CH.(CH_2)_7.CH_2OH$

M.P. 35° ⟨1⟩ **B.P. abt. 333°**
34° ⟨2⟩

Cryst. from alc. or acetone.

C̄ in AcOH treated with perhydrol at 95° for 2 hrs. gave 9,10-dihydroxystearyl alc., lfts. from EtOAc, m.p. 125–126°. [Dif. from stereoisomeric oleyl alc. (1:6300) ⟨2⟩.]

C̄ in dry pyridine stood for 3 days with phthalic anhydride yields elaidyl hydrogen phthalate as an oil; aq.NaOH soln. of prod., oxid. with $KMnO_4$ at 0° and subsequently hydrolyzed, yields 9,10-dihydroxystearyl alcohol, form of m.p. 81–82° [dif. from oleyl alc. (1:6300) ⟨2⟩].

Ⓓ **Elaidyl *N*-phenylcarbamate:** m.p. 56–57° ⟨3⟩.

Ⓓ **Elaidyl *N*-(β-naphthyl)carbamate:** m.p. 71° ⟨3⟩.

1:5925 ⟨1⟩ Toyama, *Chem. Umschau Fette, Öle, Wachse, Harze,* **31,** 13–16 (1924). ⟨2⟩ Collin, Hilditch, *J. Chem. Soc.* **1933,** 247–248. ⟨3⟩ André, Francois, *Compt. rend.* **185,** 281 (1927).

—— ***d,l*-α-TERPINEOL** $CH_3—C\langle^{CH_2.CH_2}_{CH.CH_2}\rangle C(H)—C(CH_3)(OH)—CH_3$ $C_{10}H_{18}O$ **Beil. VI-56**

M.P. 35° D_4^{20} = **0.9337** n_D^{20} = **1.4834**

See 1:6507. Genus 8: Division B: Section 2. B.P. 221.1°.

1:5935 TETRADECANOL-1 $CH_3.(CH_2)_{12}.CH_2OH$ $C_{14}H_{30}O$ **Beil. I-428**
(*n*-Tetradecyl alcohol;
myristyl alcohol)

M.P. 37.6° ⟨1⟩
37.7° ⟨2⟩

[For prepn. in 70–80% yield by reductn. of ethyl myristate (1:4316) with Na + EtOH in toluene see ⟨3⟩.]

C̄ exhibits dimorphism, changing after solidification at 37.7° a few degrees lower (34.8°) from semitransparent α-form to white opaque β-form ⟨2⟩.

Ⓓ ***n*-Myristyl hydrogen phthalate:** m.p. 59.8–60.0° cor.; Neut. Eq. 362 ⟨4⟩.

Ⓓ ***n*-Myristyl hydrogen 3-nitrophthalate:** m.p. 123.2–123.5° cor.; Neut. Eq. 407 ⟨5⟩ [cf. T 1.83]

Ⓓ ***n*-Myristyl *N*-phenylcarbamate:** m.p. 71° ⟨6⟩.

1:5935 ⟨1⟩ Meyer, Reid, *J. Am. Chem. Soc.* **55,** 1577 (1933). ⟨2⟩ Phillips, Mumford, *J. Chem. Soc.* **1933,** 235–236. ⟨3⟩ Ford, Marvel, *Organic Syntheses* **10,** 62–64 (1930). ⟨4⟩ Goggans, Coppenhaver, *J. Am. Chem. Soc.* **61,** 2909 (1939). ⟨5⟩ Dickinson, Crosson, Copenhaver, *J. Am. Chem. Soc.* **59,** 1095 (1937). ⟨6⟩ Kariyone, Sugino, *Chem. Abs.* **31,** 2583 (1937).

1:5938 *d,l*-FENCHYL ALCOHOL $C_{10}H_{18}O$ **Beil. VI-71**

(Structure: bicyclic; C(CH₃) bridgehead bonded to H_2C, CH_2 bridge, and CH(OH); H_2C—H_2C; $C(CH_3)_2$; bridgehead C–H.)

M.P. 38-39° ⟨1⟩ ⟨2⟩ **B.P. 201.4°** ⟨1⟩

Impt. constituent of American pine oil — Insol. aq.; eas. sol. alc., ether, pet. ether — Eas. volatile with steam.

C̄, htd. with equal wt. crystn. oxalic ac. for 5 hrs. at 125°, prod. washed with aq., then with a little alc., yields di-*d,l*-fenchyl oxalate, cryst. from hot alc., m.p. 101° ⟨3⟩.

- Ⓓ ***d,l*-Fenchyl *p*-nitrobenzoate:** m.p. α-form, 108–109° ⟨4⟩ ⟨5⟩; m.p. β-form, 94–95° ⟨2⟩, 82–83° ⟨4⟩ [cf. T 1.82]. [Recommended as best derivative ⟨2⟩.]
- Ⓓ ***d,l*-Fenchyl hydrogen phthalate:** m.p. 169–169.5° ⟨1⟩.
- Ⓓ ***d,l*-Fenchyl *N*-phenylcarbamate:** m.p. 104° ⟨1⟩.
- Ⓓ ***d,l*-Fenchyl *N*-(α-naphthyl)carbamate:** m.p. 148.5°–149.5° ⟨2⟩ [cf. T 1.86].

1:5938 ⟨1⟩ Zeitschel, Todenhöfer, *J. prakt. Chem.* (2) **133,** 374–376 (1932). ⟨2⟩ Kommpa, Beckmann, *Ber.* **68,** 10–11 (1935). ⟨3⟩ Quist, *Ann.* **417,** 294–296 (1918). ⟨4⟩ Kenyon, Priston, *J. Chem. Soc.* **127,** 1447 (1925). ⟨5⟩ Hintikka, Melander, *Chem. Abs.* **14,** 941 (1920).

1:5940 *l*-MENTHOL

$C_{10}H_{20}O$ **Beil. VI-28**

```
           CH3
            |
            C
          / | \
      H2C   H   CH2
       |         |  H
       |         | /
      H2C   H    C—OH
          \ | /
            C
            |
            CH
          /    \
       CH3      CH3
```

M.P. 43° **B.P. 216°**

Cryst. with strong peppermint odor — Cryst. in 4 forms of which α (stable) has m.p. 42.5° ⟨1⟩ [m.p. of *d,l*-menthol is 35.5–36.5° ⟨2⟩]. [For sepn. and detn. of isomeric menthols see ⟨13⟩.]

C̄ is very dif. sol. aq. (0.04 g. per 100 ml.); very eas. sol. alc., ether, CS_2, AcOH and conc. HCl — $[\alpha]_D^{20} = -48.9°$ (in $CHCl_3$, C = 5).

C̄ on oxidn. with $K_2Cr_2O_7 + H_2SO_4$ (cf. T 1.72) gives alm. quant. yield *l*-menthone (1:5520) ⟨3⟩ ⟨4⟩.

- Ⓓ ***l*-Menthyl benzoate:** from C̄ on htg. with 2 moles Bz_2O for 3 hrs. at 160°; m.p. 53–54° ⟨5⟩ ⟨6⟩ [m.p. of *d,l*-menthyl benzoate is 31.5–32.0° ⟨2⟩].
- Ⓓ ***l*-Menthyl *p*-nitrobenzoate:** m.p. 61–62° ⟨7⟩ [cf. T 1.82] [*d,l*-menthyl *p*-nitrobenzoate, m.p. 91° ⟨7⟩].
- Ⓓ ***l*-Menthyl 3,5-dinitrobenzoate:** m.p. 153° ⟨7⟩ [cf. T 1.82] [*d,l*-menthyl 3,5-dinitrobenzoate, m.p. 121° ⟨7⟩].
- Ⓓ ***l*-Menthyl hydrogen phthalate:** m.p. 110° ⟨8⟩; pr. from AcOH, m.p. 129–131°; Neut. Eq. 304. [After keeping the preliminary 110° prod. in contact with the mother liquor it slowly changes to stable form, m.p. 122° ⟨9⟩.]
- Ⓓ ***l*-Menthyl *N*-phenylcarbamate:** cryst. from C_6H_6 or alc.; m.p. 111–112° ⟨10⟩ [*d,l*-menthyl *N*-phenylcarbamate: m.p. 103–104° ⟨2⟩].
- Ⓓ ***l*-Menthyl *N*-(α-naphthyl)carbamate:** m.p. 119° ⟨11⟩; 126° ⟨12⟩ [cf. T 1.86].

1:5940 ⟨1⟩ Wright, *J. Am. Chem. Soc.* **39,** 1515 (1917). ⟨2⟩ Zeitschel, Eck, *J. prakt. Chem.* (2) **133,** 368 (1932). ⟨3⟩ Beckmann, *Ann.* **250,** 325 (1888). ⟨4⟩ Sandborn, *Organic Syntheses, Coll. Vol.* I, 333–334 (1932). ⟨5⟩ Beckmann, Pleisner, *Ann.* **262,** 31 (1891). ⟨6⟩ Beckmann, *J. prakt. Chem.* (2) **55,** 16 (1897). ⟨7⟩ Read, Grubb, Malcolm, *J. Chem. Soc.* **1933,** 170, 173 ⟨8⟩ Arth, *Ann. chim.* (6) **7,** 487 (1886). ⟨9⟩ Pickard, Littlebury, *J. Chem. Soc.* **101,** 116–117 (1912). ⟨10⟩ Weehuizen, *Rec. trav. chim.* **37,** 268 (1917).

⟨11⟩ Bickel, French, *J. Am. Chem. Soc.* **48,** 749 (1926). ⟨12⟩ Zeitschel, Schmidt, *Ber.* **59,** 2302 (1926). ⟨13⟩ Hall, Holcomb, Griffin, *Ind. Eng. Chem., Anal. Ed.* **12,** 187–188 (1940).

1:5941 PENTADECANOL-1 $CH_3.(CH_2)_{13}.CH_2OH$ $C_{15}H_{32}O$ **Beil. I-429**
(*n*-Pentadecyl alcohol)

M.P. **α-form 44° ⟨1⟩**
β-form 38.9° ⟨1⟩

Ⓓ ***n*-Pentadecyl hydrogen phthalate:** m.p. 60.3–60.5°; Neut. Eq. 376 ⟨2⟩.
Ⓓ ***n*-Pentadecyl hydrogen 3-nitrophthalate:** m.p. 122.4–122.6°; Neut. Eq. 421 ⟨3⟩ [cf. T 1.83].
Ⓓ ***n*-Pentadecyl *N*-phenylcarbamate:** cryst. from lgr. ⟨4⟩ or C_6H_6 ⟨5⟩, m.p. 72°.

1:5941 ⟨1⟩ Phillips, Mumford, *J. Chem. Soc.* **1934**, 1660. ⟨2⟩ Goggans, Copenhaver, *J. Am. Chem. Soc.* **61**, 2909 (1939). ⟨3⟩ Dickinson, Crosson, Copenhaver, *J. Am. Chem. Soc.* **59**, 1095 (1937). ⟨4⟩ Jeffreys, *Am. Chem. J.* **22**, 29 (1899). ⟨5⟩ Landa, Landova, *Collection Czechoslov. Chem. Comm.* **2**, 31–35 (1930); *Chem. Abs.* **24**, 3213 (1930).

1:5945 HEXADECANOL-1 $CH_3.(CH_2)_{14}.CH_2OH$ $C_{16}H_{34}O$ **Beil. I-429**
(Cetyl alcohol)

M.P. 50° ⟨1⟩
49.27° ⟨1⟩ ⟨2⟩

[For prepn. in 70–78% yield by reductn. of ethyl palmitate (1:2034) with Na + EtOH in toluene see ⟨3⟩.]

Lfts. from MeOH, EtOH, AcOEt, or acetone — [For study of m.p.'s of mixts. of C̄ with octadecanol-1 (1:5953) see ⟨1⟩.] — C̄ readily evolves H_2 when *melted* with Na (Generic Test 8).

C̄ on oxidn. with CrO_3 in AcOH yields palmitic ac. (1:0650) ⟨4⟩ — C̄ with PI_3 gives 85% yield cetyl iodide ⟨5⟩.

Ⓓ **Cetyl *p*-nitrobenzoate:** m.p. 52° [T 1.82].
Ⓓ **Cetyl 3,5-dinitrobenzoate:** m.p. 66° [T 1.82].
Ⓓ **Cetyl hydrogen phthalate:** m.p. 66.7–66.9° cor.; Neut. Eq. 390 ⟨6⟩.
Ⓓ **Cetyl hydrogen 3-nitrophthalate:** m.p. 121.4–122.0°; Neut. Eq. 435 ⟨7⟩ [cf. T 1.83].
Ⓓ **Cetyl *N*-phenylcarbamate:** m.p. 73° ⟨8⟩.
Ⓓ **Cetyl *N*-(*p*-nitrophenyl)carbamate:** m.p. 117–118° ⟨9⟩.
Ⓓ **Cetyl *N*-(α-naphthyl)carbamate:** m.p. 82° ⟨10⟩.

1:5945 ⟨1⟩ Smith, *J. Chem. Soc.* **1931**, 802–807. ⟨2⟩ Meyer, Reid, *J. Am. Chem. Soc.* **55**, 1577 (1933). ⟨3⟩ Ford, Marvel, *Organic Syntheses* **10**, 62–64 (1930). ⟨4⟩ Claus, von Dreden, *J. prakt. Chem.* (2) **43**, 149 (1891). ⟨5⟩ Hartmann, Byers, Dickey, *Organic Syntheses* **15**, 29–30 (1935). ⟨6⟩ Goggans, Copenhaver, *J. Am. Chem. Soc.* **61**, 2909 (1939). ⟨7⟩ Dickinson, Crosson, Copenhaver, *J. Am. Chem. Soc.* **59**, 1095 (1937). ⟨8⟩ Bloch, *Bull. soc. chim.* (3) **31**, 52 (1904). ⟨9⟩ Hoppenbrouwers, *Rec. trav. chim.* **51**, 952 (1932). ⟨10⟩ Neuberg, Kansky, *Biochem. Z.* **20**, 445 (1909).

1:5949 PHENYL-*p*-TOLYL-CARBINOL $C_{14}H_{14}O$ **Beil. VI-686**
(4-Methylbenzohydrol)

H
—C—
OH

M.P. 53°

Ndls. from lgr.
C̄ on oxidn. with $CrO_3 + H_2SO_4$ (T 1.72) gives phenyl *p*-tolyl ketone (1:5160).

1:5950 HEPTADECANOL-1 $CH_3.(CH_2)_{15}.CH_2OH$ $C_{17}H_{36}O$ **Beil. I₁-(220)**
(*n*-Heptadecyl alcohol)

M.P. α-form: 54° ⟨1⟩ ⟨2⟩ ⟨3⟩ **B.P. 310°**
β-form: 45.7° ⟨4⟩

Cryst. from acetone ⟨1⟩ or lfts. from 80% alc. ⟨2⟩ — C̄ is dif. sol. cold aq.; sol. cold abs. alc. or ether. [For m.p.'s of mixt. of C̄ with hexadecanol-1 (1:5945) or with octadecanol-1 (1:5953) see ⟨5⟩.]

C̄ htd. with 3 pts. powd. KOH for 15 min. at 240–250° gives good yield margaric ac. (1:0635) ⟨2⟩.

Ⓓ ***n*-Heptadecyl hydrogen phthalate:** m.p. 66.6°–66.8° cor.; Neut. Eq. 404 ⟨6⟩.

Ⓓ ***n*-Heptadecyl hydrogen 3-nitrophthalate:** m.p. 121.0–121.8°; Neut. Eq. 449 ⟨7⟩ [cf. T 1.83].

1:5950 ⟨1⟩ Levene, West, van der Scheer, *J. Biol. Chem.* **20**, 531 (1915). ⟨2⟩ Heiduschka, Ripper, *Ber.* **56**, 1738–1739 (1923). ⟨3⟩ Phillips, Mumford, *J. Chem. Soc.* **1934**, 1660. ⟨4⟩ Meyer, Reid, *J. Am. Chem. Soc.* **55**, 1577 (1933). ⟨5⟩ Carey, Smith, *J. Chem. Soc.* **1933**, 1350. ⟨6⟩ Goggans, Copenhaver, *J. Am. Chem. Soc.* **61**, 2909 (1939). ⟨7⟩ Dickinson, Crosson, Copenhaver, *J. Am. Chem. Soc.* **59**, 1095 (1937).

1:5953 OCTADECANOL-1 $CH_3.(CH_2)_{16}.CH_2OH$ $C_{18}H_{38}O$ **Beil. I-431**
(*n*-Octadecyl alcohol;
stearyl alcohol)

M.P. α-form: 57.95° ⟨1⟩; **57.85°** ⟨2⟩
58.5° ⟨3⟩ ⟨4⟩ ⟨5⟩; **59.5°** ⟨6⟩

C̄ shows dimorphism; the semitransparent α-form changing at 53.5° (a few degrees below its f.p.) into the white opaque β-form ⟨7⟩. [For m.p.'s of mixts. of C̄ with heptadecanol-1 (1:5950) see ⟨8⟩.]

[For prepn. of C̄ in 90% yield by reductn. of ethyl stearate (1:2078) with Na + *n*-butyl alc. see ⟨6⟩.] [For purifn. of comml. C̄ see ⟨9⟩.] — C̄ forms cryst. from MeOH ⟨4⟩, C_6H_6 ⟨4⟩, lgr. ⟨9⟩, ether ⟨5⟩, acetone ⟨3⟩.

Molten C̄ treated with HI gives quant. yield ⟨10⟩ of *n*-octadecyl iodide, m.p. 34.5–35° which yields 66.5% corresp. R.MgI ⟨11⟩.

Ⓓ ***n*-Octadecyl hydrogen phthalate:** m.p. 72.4–72.6° cor.; Neut. Eq. 418 ⟨12⟩.

Ⓓ ***n*-Octadecyl hydrogen 3-nitrophthalate:** m.p. 118.3–119.2° cor.; Neut. Eq. 463 ⟨13⟩ [cf. T 1.83].

Ⓓ ***n*-Octadecyl *N*-phenylcarbamate:** m.p. 79–80°.

Ⓓ ***n*-Octadecyl *N*-(*p*-nitrophenyl)carbamate:** m.p. 115° ⟨14⟩.

1:5953 ⟨1⟩ Phillips, Mumford, *J. Chem. Soc.* **1934**, 1660. ⟨2⟩ Meyer, Reid, *J. Am. Chem. Soc.* **55**, 1577 (1933). ⟨3⟩ Levene, Taylor, *J. Biol. Chem.* **59**, 914 (1924). ⟨4⟩ Smith, *J. Chem. Soc.* **1931**, 805. ⟨5⟩ Gascard, *Ann. chim.* (9) **15**, 348 (1921). ⟨6⟩ Bleyberg, Ulrich, *Ber.* **64**, 2510 (1931). ⟨7⟩ Phillips, Mumford, *J. Chem. Soc.* **1934**, 235–236. ⟨8⟩ Carey, Smith, *J. Chem. Soc.* **1933**, 637, 1350. ⟨9⟩ Woolley, Sandin, *J. Am. Chem. Soc.* **57**, 1078 (1935). ⟨10⟩ Adam, Dyer, *J. Chem. Soc.* **127**, 71 (1925).

⟨11⟩ Oldham, Ubbelohde, *J. Chem. Soc.* **1938**, 202. ⟨12⟩ Goggans, Copenhaver, *J. Am. Chem. Soc.* **61**, 2909 (1939). ⟨13⟩ Dickinson, Crosson, Copenhaver, *J. Am. Chem. Soc.* **59**, 1095 (1937). ⟨14⟩ van Hoogstraten, *Rec. trav. chim.* **51**, 426 (1932).

1:5954 *p*-TOLYLCARBINOL CH_3—⬡—CH_2OH $C_8H_{10}O$ **Beil. VI-498**
(" *p*-Xylyl alcohol ";
p-methylbenzyl alcohol)

M.P. 59° [cf. ⟨1⟩] **B.P. 217°**

Dif. sol. cold aq.; eas. sol. alc. or ether — Volatile with steam.
[For prepn. in 90% yield from *p*-tolualdehyde (1:0215) + HCHO + KOH see ⟨2⟩.]
[For m.p. of mixtures of C̄ with *o*-tolylcarbinol (1:5922) see ⟨1⟩.]

Ⓓ ***p*-Tolylcarbinyl *N*-phenylcarbamate:** m.p. 79° ⟨3⟩.

1:5954 ⟨1⟩ Hill, Short, *J. Chem. Soc.* **1935**, 1126. ⟨2⟩ Davidson, Weiss, *Organic Syntheses*, **18**, 79–81 (1938). ⟨3⟩ Kindler, *Arch. Pharm.* **265**, 401 (1927).

1:5956 *p*-ANISYL-PHENYL-CARBINOL $C_{14}H_{14}O_2$ Beil. S.N. 564

(*p*-Methoxybenzohydrol)

M.P. 60°

[For prepn. in 90% yield from *p*-anisaldehyde + C_6H_5MgBr see ⟨1⟩.]
C̄ on oxidn. with CrO_3 + H_2SO_4 gives *p*-methoxybenzophenone (1:5170).
C̄, in C_6H_6 at 0° + $CaCl_2$, treated with dry HCl gas, gives 85% yield *p*-anisylphenylcarbinyl chloride, colorless ndls. from lgr., m.p. 64° ⟨1⟩.

1:5956 ⟨1⟩ Bachmann, *J. Am. Chem. Soc.* **55**, 2137 (1933).

1:5957 METHYL-α-NAPHTHYL-CARBINOL $C_{12}H_{12}O$ Beil. VI_1-(321)

M.P. 66°

Ndls. from lt. pet.
C̄ htd. with ⅓ wt. $KHSO_4$ for 4 hrs. at 120–130° loses aq., yielding α-vinylnaphthalene ⟨1⟩.
C̄ oxidized with CrO_3 + H_2SO_4 (T 1.72) yields methyl α-naphthyl ketone (1:5600).

Ⓓ **Methyl-α-naphthyl-carbinyl hydrogen phthalate:** from C̄ + equiv. amt. phthalic anhyd. dis. in 10 pts. $CHCl_3$, htd. 6 hrs. at 100°, solv. evapd.; resultant paste poured into aq. Na_2CO_3 and purified in usual way; cryst. from C_6H_6, m.p. 131–132° ⟨2⟩. [C̄ htd. with phthalic anhyd. without solv. is merely dehydrated ⟨2⟩.]

Ⓓ **Methyl-α-naphthylcarbinyl hydrogen tetrachlorophthalate:** from C̄ + tetrachlorophthalic ac. in C_6H_6; m.p. 155.0–155.5° ⟨1⟩ [cf. ⟨3⟩].

1:5957 ⟨1⟩ Zal'kind, Zonis, *J. Gen. Chem.* (*U.S.S.R.*) **6**, 988–998 (1936); *Cent.* **1937**, I, 1934. ⟨2⟩ Pickard, Kenyon, *J. Chem. Soc.* **105**, 1126 (1914). ⟨3⟩ Teterin, Zonis, *J. Gen. Chem.* (*U.S.S.R.*) **6**, 658–662 (1936); *Cent.* **1936**, II, 2347; *Chem. Abs.* **30**, 6354 (1936).

1:5958 *d,l*-BENZYL-PHENYL-CARBINOL $C_{14}H_{14}O$ Beil. VI-683

("Toluylene hydrate")

M.P. 67°

[For prepn. of C̄ in 78% yield from BzH + $C_6H_5.CH_2.MgCl$ see ⟨1⟩.]
C̄ is sol. in 1600 pts. hot aq.; very sol. ether — C̄ is crystd. from lt. pet. contg. 5% C_6H_6 or from 20 pts. alc.

C̄, on distn. at ord. press., or on short boilg. with Ac_2O ⟨2⟩, or on htg. 3–4 hrs. in an oil bath at 220–230° (64% yield ⟨3⟩) gives stilbene (1:7250).

C̄, on treatment with conc. HNO_3 (D = 1.3), yields desoxybenzoin (1:5165) even in cold (more rapidly on warming) ⟨4⟩.

Ⓓ **Benzyl-phenyl-carbinyl hydrogen phthalate:** from C̄ on htg. with ¾ wt. of pure phthalic anhydride (crystd. from dry $CHCl_3$ to remove traces of phthalic acid). Product is treated with 2 equiv. aq. Na_2CO_3, stood at 20° for 1½ hrs. to decompose any unchanged reagt.; extd. with ether to remove any unchanged C̄; aq. layer acidified giving 91% yield prod.; ndls. from mixt. of ether + lt. pet., m.p. 131° cor., Neut. Eq. 346 ⟨1⟩ ⟨5⟩. [Use in resolution of C̄ ⟨1⟩.]

1:5958 ⟨1⟩ Gerrard, Kenyon, *J. Chem. Soc.* **1928,** 2564–2565. ⟨2⟩ Pearl, Dehn, *J. Am. Chem. Soc.* **60,** 58 (1938). ⟨3⟩ Ruggli, Lang, *Helv. Chim. Acta* **21,** 47 (1938). ⟨4⟩ Limpricht, Schwanert, *Ann.* **155,** 64 (1870). ⟨5⟩ Levene, Mikesa, *J. Biol. Chem.* **65,** 510–511 (1925).

1:5959 DI-*p*-TOLYLCARBINOL (4,4′-Dimethylbenzohydrol) $C_{15}H_{16}O$ **Beil. VI-688**

CH_3—⟨ring⟩—C(H)(OH)—⟨ring⟩—CH_3

M.P. 68°

Ndls. from alc.; sol. alc., $CHCl_3$, acetone, AcOH. Insol. aq.

C̄ on oxidation with $CrO_3 + H_2SO_4$ (T 1.72) yields di-*p*-tolyl ketone (1:5185).

C̄ in C_6H_6 + pet. ether + solid $CaCl_2$ treated with HCl gas yields di-*p*-tolylcarbinyl chloride, white pr. from pet. ether, m.p. 45–46° ⟨1⟩ — C̄ htd. with 30% HBr in AcOH for 1 hr., then treated with AcBr, yields 80% di-*p*-tolylcarbinyl bromide, odorless pl. from lgr.; m.p. 48.5–49° ⟨2⟩.

1:5959 ⟨1⟩ Norris, Blake, *J. Am. Chem. Soc.* **50,** 1811 (1927). ⟨2⟩ Bachmann, *J. Am. Chem. Soc.* **55,** 2137 (1933).

1:5960 BENZOHYDROL (Diphenylcarbinol) $C_{13}H_{12}O$ **Beil. VI-678**

⟨ring⟩—C(H)(OH)—⟨ring⟩

M.P. 68° **B.P. 288°**

Ndls. from lgr. — Sol. in 2000 pts. aq. at 20°; eas. sol. alc., ether, CS_2, $CHCl_3$ — C̄ gives deep red color with conc. H_2SO_4.

[For prepn. from benzophenone (1:5150) by reduction with 2% Na/Hg in abs. alc. + ether + C_6H_6 (98% yield) see ⟨1⟩; with Zn dust + alk. (65–99% yield) see ⟨2⟩.]

C̄ is eas. oxid. by $CrO_3 + H_2SO_4$ (cf. T 1.72) yielding benzophenone (1:5150) — C̄, on boilg. with dil. HCl is partially converted to dibenzohydryl ether [Beil. VI-679], m.p. 110° ⟨3⟩ — C̄ in ether or C_6H_6 treated with dry HCl gas gives diphenylchloromethane, m.p. 17–18° ⟨4⟩.

Ⓓ **Diphenylcarbinyl benzoate:** from C̄ on melting with ⅔ wt. of BzOH and htg. to expel water; prod. purified by extn. with dil. alk. and recrystn. from alc.; m.p. 88–89° ⟨5⟩ [Note: this prod. cannot be obtd. via Schotten-Baumann method using BzCl + aq. alk. owing to formn. of dibenzohydryl ether ⟨5⟩.]

Ⓓ **Diphenylcarbinyl *p*-nitrobenzoate:** m.p. 131–132° ⟨6⟩ [cf. T 1.82].

Ⓓ **Diphenylcarbinyl 3,5-dinitrobenzoate:** m.p. 141° [T 1.82].

Ⓓ **Diphenylcarbinyl hydrogen phthalate:** from C̄ in 18% yield on htg. with phthalic anhydride for 15 hrs. at 110°; m.p. 164–165°; Neut. Eq. 332 ⟨7⟩. [If C̄ is first treated with C_2H_5MgBr and resultant prod. treated with phthalic anhydride at 0° for 20 hrs. yield is 74% ⟨7⟩.]

Ⓓ **Diphenylcarbinyl *N*-phenylcarbamate:** from C̄ + equiv. phenylisocyanate in C_6H_6 on stdg. 2 days; ndls. from C_6H_6; m.p. 139–140° ⟨8⟩.

Ⓓ **Diphenylcarbinyl *N*-(α-naphthyl)carbamate:** m.p. 135–136° ⟨9⟩ [cf. T 1.86].

1:5960 ⟨1⟩ Bachmann, *J. Am. Chem. Soc.* **55,** 773 (1937). ⟨2⟩ Marvel, Hansen, *Organic Syntheses, Coll. Vol.* I, 84–85 (1932). ⟨3⟩ Ward, *J. Chem. Soc.* **1928,** 2290, 2295. ⟨4⟩ Norris, Banta, *J. Am. Chem. Soc.* **50,** 1807 (1928). ⟨5⟩ Linneman, *Ann.* **133,** 21 (1865). ⟨6⟩ Meisenheimer, Schmidt, *Ann.* **475,** 177–178 (1929). ⟨7⟩ Fessler, Shriner, *J. Am. Chem. Soc.* **58,** 1385–1389 (1936). ⟨8⟩ Bergmann, Wagenberg, *Ber.* **63,** 2587, Note 7 (1930). ⟨9⟩ Bickel, French, *J. Am. Chem. Soc.* **48,** 749 (1926).

1:5961 DECANEDIOL-1,10 HO.CH$_2$.(CH$_2$)$_8$.CH$_2$OH $C_{10}H_{22}O_2$ Beil. I-494

(Decamethylene glycol)

M.P. 74.5° (**72°**)

Lfts. (from C_6H_6); beautiful long ndls. from aq. or dil. alc. — Eas. sol. alc., warm ether; spar. sol. cold ether, pet. ether, cold aq., $CHCl_3$ — Sol. in cold conc. H_2SO_4 but *not* repptd. on diln. (formation of ester).

[For prepn. by reduction of diethyl sebacate (1:4366) with Na + alc. (73–76% yield) see ⟨1⟩ ⟨2⟩ ⟨3⟩ ⟨4⟩.]

C̄ on oxidn. with slight excess neutral $KMnO_4$ yields sebacic ac., m.p. 133° (1:0730) — C̄ htd. ½ hr. with large excess (12 pts.) Ac_2O + anhyd. AcONa (1 pt.) gives 50% yield decamethylene glycol diacetate, m.p. 25.5° ⟨5⟩.

C̄ htd. with phthalic anhydride at 200° yields polymeric ester ⟨6⟩ — C̄ treated with stream of dry HBr at 130–150° yields 1,10-dibromodecane (85–90%) ⟨3⟩ ⟨4⟩, b.p. 162–165.5° at 10 mm., m.p. 27.4° ⟨7⟩.

1:5961 ⟨1⟩ Manske, Carothers, McEwen, *Organic Syntheses* **14,** 20–22 (1934). ⟨2⟩ Bennett, Mosses, *J. Chem. Soc.* **1931,** 1698. ⟨3⟩ Carothers, Hill, Kirby, Jacobson, *J. Am. Chem. Soc.* **52,** 5287–5288 (1930). ⟨4⟩ Franke, Kroupa, *Monatsh.* **56,** 340 (1930). ⟨5⟩ Scheuble, *Monatsh.* **24,** 630 (1903). ⟨6⟩ Carothers, Arvin, *J. Am. Chem. Soc.* **51,** 2569 (1929). ⟨7⟩ Chuit, *Helv. Chim. Acta* **9,** 266 (1926).

1:5965 TERPIN HYDRATE $C_{10}H_{20}O_2.H_2O$ Beil. VI-745

```
CH3      CH2—CH2   H   CH3
   \    /       \  |   |
     C           C—C—CH3.H2O
   /    \       /      |
HO       CH2—CH2       OH
```

M.P. 116–117° dec. (see text)

Sol. in 250 pts. aq. at 15°; in 32 pts. hot aq.; in 10 pts. alc. at 15°; in 100 pts. ether at 15°; insol. pet. ether.

C̄, on placing in preheated bath, melts 120–121° with loss of 1 mole H_2O and conversion to anhydrous *cis*-terpin; m.p. 105° ⟨1⟩. [The eutectic of C̄ + *cis*-terpin has m.p. 95° ⟨2⟩; for m.p. + compn. curves of system see ⟨2⟩.]

C̄ (4 pts.) on oxidn. with 35 pts. $K_2Cr_2O_7$, 50 pts. conc. H_2SO_4 and 150 ml. aq. (cf. T 1.72) yields terpenylic ac., $C_6H_{12}O_4$ [Beil. XVIII-384]; very sol. aq.; m.p. anhydrous form 90° ⟨3⟩.

C̄ with dry HCl, conc. aq. HCl, or PCl_3 yields dipentene bis-hydrochloride [Beil. V-50], pptd. by aq. from warm alc., m.p. 50° — C̄, shaken with const. boilg. HBr until the initial oily mass becomes crystn., yields dipentene bis-hydrobromide [Beil. V-52], m.p. 64° ⟨4⟩.

Ⓟ **Color test:** With conc. H_2SO_4 gives citron-yel. to salmon color — In presence of $NaHSO_3$ color is blood-red to brown.

Ⓓ **α-Terpineol** (1:6507): from C̄ in 89% yield on boiling with 2 pts. 0.5% oxalic acid soln. ⟨5⟩.

1:5965 ⟨1⟩ Perkin, *J. Chem. Soc.* **85,** 668, Note (1904). ⟨2⟩ Schoorl, *Cent.* **1932,** I, 2950. ⟨3⟩ Hempel, *Ann.* **180,** 78–79 (1875). ⟨4⟩ Wallach, *Ann.* **239,** 18 (1887). ⟨5⟩ Acharya, Wheeler, *Cent.* **1938,** I, 4654.

1:5970 DIPHENYL-α-NAPHTHYLCARBINOL $C_{23}H_{18}O$ Beil. VI-729

M.P. 137°

C̄ with HCl (cf. T 1.85) or with $CH_3.CO.Cl$ should give diphenyl-α-naphthyl-chloromethane, m.p. 169° — Should give micro test for triarylcarbinols ⟨1⟩.

Ⓓ **Diphenyl-α-naphthylmethane** [Beil. V-733]: C̄ (1 g.) htd. to boilg. with 15 ml. AcOH + 2 g. Zn dust, then treated with 1 drop H_2PtCl_6 soln. evolves H_2, turns brown, finally colorless. After filtration and cooling 0.7 g. hydrocarbon seps.; recryst. from AcOH, m.p. 150° ⟨2⟩. [Also obtd. in 96% yield from C̄ in AcOH, treated with NaI + $SnCl_2$ + conc. HCl in stream of CO_2 ⟨4⟩.]

Ⓓ **Phenylchrysofluorene** [Beil. V-736]: 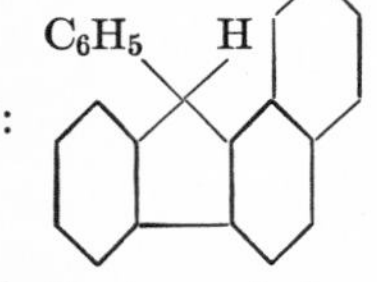

C̄ (2 g.) in 20 ml. AcOH, htd. to b.p., treated with 2 ml. conc. HCl; liq. turns dark green, then brown, and colorless ndls. of hydrocarbon sep. in 70% yield; recryst. from AcOH, m.p. 195.5° ⟨2⟩ confirmed by ⟨3⟩.

1:5970 ⟨1⟩ Morton, Peakes, *Ind. Eng. Chem., Anal. Ed.* **5,** 185 (1933). ⟨2⟩ Ullmann, Mourawiew-Winigradoff, *Ber.* **38,** 2215 (1905). ⟨3⟩ Blicke, *J. Am. Chem. Soc.* **46,** 2570 (1924). ⟨4⟩ Wanscheidt, Moldavski, *Ber.* **64,** 921–922 (1931).

1:5975 CHOLESTEROL $C_{27}H_{46}O$ **Beil. 4729-c**

```
                          CH2  CH3       H  CH3                 CH3
                         /   \  |        |   |                   |
                    H2C        C---------C---C--CH2.CH2.CH2.C--CH3
          H2         |         |         |   H                   |
          C     CH3 C--H       C--H      CH2                     H
        /   \    | /    \     /    \    /
     H2C      C          C          CH2
      |       |          | \
   H--C       C          CH2 H
    /   \   /   \\      /
 HO       C        C
          H2       H
```

M.P. 148.5° (anhydrous)

Subl. at 300° in vac. — Cryst. from ether in anhyd. ndls., from alc. in tbls. with 1 H_2O (lost over H_2SO_4) — Insol. aq., ac., alk., eas. sol. ether, $CHCl_3$, CS_2, C_6H_6, acetone, very sol. pyridine — $[\alpha]^{21}_{D}$ is −38.8°.

C̄ on warming with Na in pet. ether evolves H ⟨1⟩ — C̄ on oxidn. with CrO_3 + AcOH gives much acetone (1:5400) ⟨2⟩. [Does not distinguish C̄ from other sterols.]

Ⓟ **Liebermann-Burchard reaction:** To a few cg. C̄ in 2 ml. $CHCl_3$ in a *dry* tt. add 10 drops Ac_2O, mix, and then add 2–5 drops conc. H_2SO_4 and shake. A violet color changing to blue-green quickly develops. [Cf. ergosterol (1:5980).] [This test is also given by cholesteryl esters ⟨3⟩ and by some but not all (see list) cholesteryl derivatives ⟨4⟩.] [Use in quant. colorimetric detn. of C̄ ⟨3⟩.]

Ⓟ **Salkowski reaction:** Dis. a few cg. C̄ in 2 ml. $CHCl_3$ in a *dry* tt. and add 2 ml. conc. H_2SO_4. After standing a minute or two the $CHCl_3$ layer becomes cherry-red to purple, while the H_2SO_4 has strong green fluores. Shake, and allow layers to sep. for further confirmn. On pouring out $CHCl_3$ layer into dish it soon changes through blue and green to dirty yel. [For impt. study of this test see ⟨5⟩.]

Ⓓ **Cholesterol dibromide:** Addn. of 10% soln. of Br_2 in AcOH to 10% soln. of C̄ in ether rap. gives ppt., m.p. 124–125° [dif. from phytosterol] ⟨6⟩. [Note: addn. of only half necessary Br_2 results in formn. of addn. product containing 1 mole each of C̄ and C̄ dibromide, m.p. 112° dec. ⟨7⟩.]

Ⓓ **Cholesteryl acetate:** Ht. together in a dry tt. for 15 min. at 130° 0.1 g. C̄, 0.1 g. anhydrous sodium acetate, and 1 ml. Ac_2O. Dis. prod. in 5 ml. 80% alc., cool, filter ppt. and wash with 2 ml. same alc. Recryst. from 10 ml. same alc. Recryst. a third time from 3 ml. strong alc. Dry on tile, and then at 100° for 15 min.; m.p. 114° u.c. Play of opalescent colors observed on cooling melt ⟨8⟩. [Use in prepn. of β-cholestanol (dihydrocholesterol) by reductn. with H_2 ⟨9⟩.]

Ⓓ **Cholesteryl benzoate:** Heat 0.1 g. C̄ with 0.5 ml. BzCl in dry tt. at 160° for 5 min. Cool, boil up with 10 ml. alc. and cool again, filtering off the ppt. and washing it with 5 ml. cold alc. Recryst. from 10 ml. hot alc. as before. Repeat the crystn. a third time. Dry 15 min. at 100° and det. m.p. in a wide cap. The prod. melts at 145° to a turbid liq. which changes to a clear liq. at 178° u.c. Finally remove the tube quickly from the htg. bath, hold it in front of a black background, and observe the character. play of opalescent colors during solidfn. ⟨8⟩.

Ⓓ **Cholesteryl *p*-nitrobenzoate:** from C̄ on htg. with *p*-nitrobenzoyl chloride, extn. with alc., recrystn. from acetone; m.p. 185° to turbid liq., dec. at 250°; on cooling charact. play of violet, green, red is observed ⟨6⟩. Also from C̄ + *p*-nitrobenzoyl chloride +

pyridine + $CHCl_3$; m.p. 190–193° cor., becoming clear, then decomp. at 261° cor. ⟨11⟩ [cf. T 1.82].

Ⓓ **Cholesteryl hydrogen phthalate:** from $\bar{C}$ (1 g.) + phthalic anhydride (2 g.) on boiling in pyridine (5 ml.) for 1 hr.; mixt. is poured into aq. and the pptd. deriv. washed with dil. HCl, then crystd. from alc.; white cryst. m.p. 161.0–161.5°, Neut. Eq. 534 ⟨12⟩. [This acid phthalate is eas. sol. ether and not pptd. by addn. of lt. pet. (dif. and sepn. from $\bar{C}$) ⟨12⟩.]

Ⓓ **Cholesteryl *p*-toluenesulfonate:** from $\bar{C}$ + *p*-toluenesulfonyl chloride in pyridine 24 hrs. at 30°; cryst. from acetone or dry ether (89% yield ⟨14⟩); m.p. 131° ⟨13⟩; 131.5–132.5° ⟨14⟩.

Ⓓ **Cholesteryl *N*-(*p*-nitrophenyl)carbamate:** m.p. 204–205° ⟨15⟩.

Ⓓ **Cholesteryl *N*-(α-naphthyl)carbamate:** m.p. 175–176°, after softening at 172° ⟨16⟩ [cf. T 1.86].

1:5975 ⟨1⟩ Reinitzer, *Monatsh.* **9,** 438 (1898). ⟨2⟩ Windaus, *Z. physiol. Chem.* **100,** 167 (1917). ⟨3⟩ Myers, Wardwell, *J. Biol. Chem.* **36,** 147–156 (1918). ⟨4⟩ Eck, Thomas, *J. Biol. Chem.* **128,** 272 (1939). ⟨5⟩ Ref. 4, pages 267–277. ⟨6⟩ Windaus, *Ber.* **39,** 518 (1906); *Chem. Ztg.* **30,** 1011 (1906). ⟨7⟩ Cloez, *Compt. rend.* **124,** 864 (1897). ⟨8⟩ Mulliken, " Method " I, 172 (1904). ⟨9⟩ Ralls, *Organic Syntheses* **17,** 45–47 (1937). ⟨10⟩ Dorée, Orange, *J. Chem. Soc.* **109,** 54 (1916).

⟨11⟩ Sandquist, Gorton, *Ber.* **63,** 1759–1760 (1930). ⟨12⟩ Weidemann, *Biochem. J.* **20,** 688–689 (1926). ⟨13⟩ Freudenberg, Hess, *Ann.* **448,** 128 (1926). ⟨14⟩ Wallis, Fernholz, Gephart, *J. Am. Chem. Soc.* **59,** 139 (1937). ⟨15⟩ Hoppenbrouwers, *Rec. trav. chim.* **51,** 953 (1931). ⟨16⟩ Neuberg, Hirschberg, *Biochem. Z.* **27,** 345 (1910).

1:5980 ERGOSTEROL $C_{28}H_{44}O$ Beil. 4729-b

```
                          CH2 CH3  H   CH3          CH3  CH3
                         /    \|   |    |   H   H    |    |
                     H2C       C---C----C---C===C----C----C---CH3
               H2     |        |        |   H        H    H
               C  CH3 C        CH      CH2
             /   \ | /  \\    /   \    /
        H2C        C      C         CH2
         |         |      |
       H-C         C      CH2
       /   \     /  \\   /
     HO      C         C
             H2        H
```

M.P. 165° (anhydrous) (Maquenne block ⟨1⟩)
162-164° ⟨2⟩

B.p. 185° at 20 mm. — Cryst. from alc. with aq., lost above 105°; from ether anhyd. — Sol. in 500 pts. cold alc. or 32 parts hot 94% alc.; sol. at 20° in 50 pts. abs. ether. $[\alpha]_D = -126°$ (1 g. in 30.5 ml. $CHCl_3$).

$\bar{C}$ slowly oxidizes in air (accelerated by light) becoming yellow [cf. ⟨2⟩].

Ⓟ **Rosenheim color test:** $\bar{C}$ dislvd. in a few drops $CHCl_3$ and treated with a soln. of 9 pts. of trichloroacetic ac. in 1 pt. aq. immediately yields a red soln., which changes gradually to clear blue ⟨3⟩. [This test is not given (at room temp.) by other naturally occurring sterols (when free from $\bar{C}$), such solns. remaining colorless. The test is sensitive to 0.01 mg. $\bar{C}$ within 5 min. and is still just recognizable with 0.005 mg. $\bar{C}$; it will detect as little as 0.1% $\bar{C}$ in cholesterol (1:5975) ⟨3⟩.] [For modifications giving increased sensitivity see ⟨4⟩.]

Ⓟ **Liebermann-Burchard test:** Soln. of $\bar{C}$ in conc. H_2SO_4 is or.-red becoming red, then violet on addn. of water. The orange soln. shaken with $CHCl_3$ does not color latter [dif. from cholesterol]. [For complete study of behavior of C̄ in Liebermann-Burchard test and the influence of conditions upon latter see ⟨5⟩ and ⟨6⟩.]

Ⓓ **Ergosteryl acetate:** from C̄ on refluxing ½ hr. with 10 pts. Ac_2O; cryst. from ether, m.p. 180° ⟨1⟩; 172° ⟨7⟩, 173° ⟨8⟩.

Ⓓ **Ergosteryl benzoate:** m.p. 168°. [Use in purification of C̄ by formn., recrystn. from AcOEt, and hydrolysis ⟨9⟩.]

Ⓓ **Ergosteryl 3,5-dinitrobenzoate:** cryst. from $CHCl_3$, m.p. 202° ⟨8⟩ [cf. T 1.82].

1:5980 ⟨1⟩ Tanret, *Ann. chim.* (8) **15,** 317–318 (1908). ⟨2⟩ Bacharach, Smith, Stevenson, *Analyst* **58,** 128–131 (1933). ⟨3⟩ Rosenheim, *Biochem. J.* **23,** 47–53 (1929). ⟨4⟩ Christiani, Anger, *Ber.* **72,** 1124–1125, 1482 (1939). ⟨5⟩ Meesemaecker, Griffon, *J. pharm. chim.* (8) **11,** 572–580 (1930); *Cent.* **1930,** II, 1994; *Chem. Abs.* **25,** 980 (1931). ⟨6⟩ Meesemaecker, *Compt. rend.* **190,** 216–218 (1930). ⟨7⟩ Marker, et al., *J. Am. Chem. Soc.* **59,** 1840 (1937). ⟨8⟩ Windaus, Bock, *Z. physiol. Chem.* **250,** 260 (1937). ⟨9⟩ Callow, *Biochem. J.* **25,** 79–86 (1931).

1:5985 TRIPHENYLCARBINOL $C_{19}H_{16}O$ **Beil. VI-713**

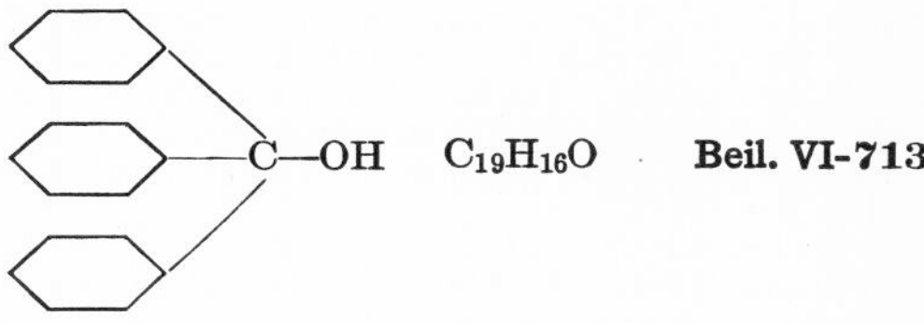

M.P. 161-162° B.P. 380°

Cryst. (from C_6H_6): hexag. tbls. (from alc.) — Insol. aq., eas. sol. alc., ether, C_6H_6 — From hot CCl_4 cryst. on cooling in large flat square cryst. of compn. $[(C_6H_5)_3C.OH]_4.[(CCl_4)]_3$ which effloresce in the air and soon become opaque ⟨1⟩.

C̄ dis. in conc. H_2SO_4 with intense yel. color, sepg. unchanged on diln. with aq., or extn. by C_6H_6.

C̄ is unattacked by dil. mineral acids or by distn. from NaOH — C̄, on treatment with conc. HCl in ether or AcOH, or on passing HCl into C_6H_6 soln., or treatment with AcCl ⟨2⟩ ⟨3⟩ [for execution as microtest see ⟨4⟩] yields triphenylchloromethane, m.p. 108–111°.

Ⓓ **Triphenylmethane:** 1 pt. C̄ dis. in 10 pts. alc., treated with 10 pts. conc. H_2SO_4 so that temp. is 70–80°, gives transitory yel. color, followed by grad. sepn. of triphenylmethane (1:7220) cryst. from C_6H_6, m.p. 92° ⟨5⟩. [Also obt. in 96% yield by treatment of C̄ in AcOH with NaI + $SnCl_2$ + conc. HCl in stream of CO_2 ⟨6⟩.]

1:5985 ⟨1⟩ Norris, *J. Am. Chem. Soc.* **38,** 711 (1916). ⟨2⟩ Gomberg, Davis, *Ber.* **36,** 3925 (1903). ⟨3⟩ Spassow, *Ber.* **70,** 1927 (1937). ⟨4⟩ Morton, Peakes, *Ind. Eng. Chem., Anal. Ed.* **5,** 185 (1933). ⟨5⟩ Schmidlin, Garcia-Banus, *Ber.* **45,** 3189 (1912). ⟨6⟩ Wanscheidt, Moldavski, *Ber.* **64,** 921 (1931).

1:5990 *d*-BORNEOL $C_{10}H_{18}O$ **Beil. VI-75**
("Borneo camphor")

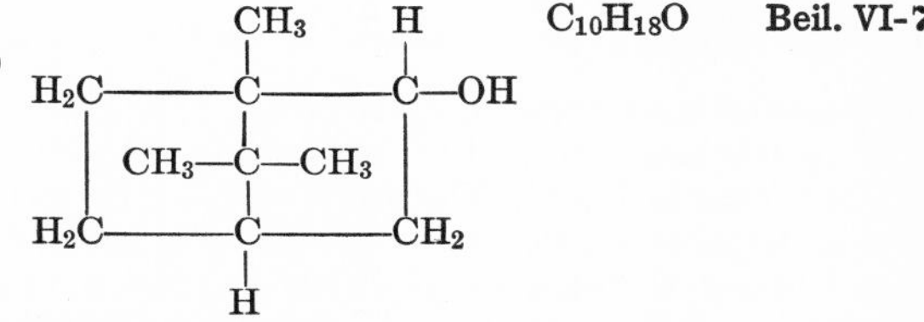

M.P. 204.5-205.5° ⟨1⟩ B.P. 212°

Odor scarcely dif. from ord. *d*-camphor (1:5215) — Subl. slowly at ord. temp. — Very dif. sol. aq.; eas. sol. alc., ether, lgr., C_6H_6 — $[\alpha]_D^{20}$ = +36.37° (in CH_3OH, C = 10). [For further comment and ref. see ⟨2⟩.] [Comml. C̄ consists of mixed cryst. of *d*-borneol and *l*-isoborneol ⟨2⟩.]

Mixts. of C̄ with the *l*-isomer do not show depressed m.p.'s ⟨2⟩; for m.p. of mixts. of C̄ with *d*-camphor see ⟨2⟩ — [M.p. of C̄ higher than 205° indicates presence of isoborneol, m.p. 214° [Beil. VI-87].]

C̄ in xylene htd. with Na evolves H beginning at 80°, becoming vigorous at 100–130° — C̄ yields no oxime [dif. from *d*-camphor (1:5215)].

C̄, boiled with fairly conc. HNO_3 or shaken with 5 pts. 50% HNO_3 for 3 hrs. ⟨3⟩, then diluted with aq., gives *d*-camphor (1:5215), m.p. 179°. [If NO_2 is present in the HNO_3 isoborneol also yields *d*-camphor ⟨4⟩.]

d-Bornyl acetate (1:3832), m.p. 29°, b.p. 226°, and *d*-bornyl benzoa e, m.p. 25.5° [Beil. IX-115] are too low melting to be good derivs. for identification.

Ⓓ ***d*-Bornyl *p*-nitrobenzoate:** m.p. 153° [T 1.82]. [Corresp. deriv. of *d,l*-borneol has m.p. 134° ⟨5⟩; of isoborneol, 129°.]

Ⓓ ***d*-Bornyl 3,5-dinitrobenzoate:** m.p. 154° ⟨6⟩ ⟨7⟩ [cf. T 1.82]. [Corresp. deriv. of active isoborneol has m.p. 133° ⟨8⟩, 138° ⟨6⟩.]

Ⓓ ***d*-Bornyl hydrogen phthalate:** from C̄ htd. with phthalic anhydride; cryst. from AcOH, m.p. 161.4° ⟨2⟩; 164.5–165.5° cor. ⟨9⟩, 165° ⟨10⟩. [The *p*-nitrobenzyl ester (T 1.39) of this acid phthalate has m.p. 100° ⟨11⟩.] [Isobornyl hydrogen phthalate has m.p. abt. 167° dec. ⟨9⟩; its *p*-nitrobenzyl ester (T 1.39) has m.p. 87° ⟨11⟩.]

Ⓓ ***d*-Bornyl benzenesulfonate:** from C̄ in pyridine at 0° + benzenesulfonyl chloride on stdg. 3–4 hrs.; after addn. of aq. the sepg. oil is extracted with C_6H_6, dried, soln. evapd.; m.p. 52° ⟨12⟩. [*d*-Bornyl β-naphthalenesulfonate in analogous fashion, m.p. 76° ⟨12⟩.]

Ⓓ ***d*-Bornyl *N*-phenylcarbamate:** m.p. 138° ⟨13⟩.

Ⓓ ***d*-Bornyl *N*-(α-naphthyl)carbamate:** m.p. 127° ⟨14⟩ [cf. T 1.86]. [Corresp. deriv. of isoborneol has m.p. 130°.]

1:5990 ⟨1⟩ Clarke, Read, *J. Chem. Soc.* **1934,** 1774–1775. ⟨2⟩ Ross, Somerville, *J. Chem. Soc.* **1926,** 2774–2778. ⟨3⟩ Mulaney, Watson, *J. Indian Chem. Soc.* **3,** 254 (1926). ⟨4⟩ Ikeda, Fjuita, *Cent.* **1928,** II, 43. ⟨5⟩ Hintikka, Melander, *Chem. Abs.* **14,** 941 (1920). ⟨6⟩ Asahina, *Ber.* **69,** 346–347 (1936). ⟨7⟩ Alder, Windemuth, *Ann.* **543,** 47 (1939). ⟨8⟩ Bredt-Savelsberg, Bund, *J. prakt. Chem.* (2) **131,** 45 (1931). ⟨9⟩ Vavon, Peignier, *Bull. soc. chim.* (4) **39,** 937 (1926). ⟨10⟩ Sabetay, Naves, *Ann. chim. anal. chim. appl.* (3) **19,** 285–289 (1937); *Cent.* **1938,** I, 1839.

⟨11⟩ Reid, *J. Am. Chem. Soc.* **39,** 1255 (1917). ⟨12⟩ Patterson, McAlpine, *J. Chem. Soc.* **1928,** 2471. ⟨13⟩ Asahina, Ishidate, *Ber.* **67,** 73 (1934). ⟨14⟩ Bickel, French, *J. Am. Chem. Soc.* **48,** 749 (1926).

ORDER I: SUBORDER I: GENUS 8: ALCOHOLS

Division B, Liquid Alcohols (and Soluble Ethers)

Section 1. Specific gravity less than 0.90 at 20°/4°

1:6100 **ETHYL METHYL ETHER** $CH_3.CH_2.O.CH_3$ C_3H_8O **Beil. I-314**

B.P. +10.8° D_0^0 = **0.7260** ⟨1⟩

$\bar{C}$ dis. readily in liq. HBr with large evoln. of ht. yielding oxonium salt $\bar{C}$.HBr; white cryst., m.p. −30° ⟨2⟩; in liq. HI yielding $\bar{C}$.HI; white cryst., m.p. −22° ⟨2⟩.

1:6100 ⟨1⟩ Berthoud, Brum, *J. chim. phys.* **21,** 153 (1924). ⟨2⟩ McIntosh, *J. Am. Chem. Soc.* **30,** 1104 (1908).

1:6105 **ETHYLENE OXIDE** H_2C——CH_2 (bridged by O) C_2H_4O **Beil. XVII-4**

B.P. +10.7° ⟨1⟩ ⟨2⟩ **M.P. −111.7°** ⟨1⟩ ⟨2⟩ D_4^0 = **0.89713** ⟨1⟩

Combustible gas at ord. temp.; comml. fumigant — [For prepn. + purification see ⟨2⟩.] Misc. with aq., alc., ether — $\bar{C}$ cannot be dried by usual chem. means because of ease of hydration. [For study of hydration see ⟨3⟩.]

$\bar{C}$ in aq. soln. stood with small amt. $ZnCl_2$ or KOH, or htd. with a few drops KOH at 55° yields polymeric cryst. form, m.p. 56° — $\bar{C}$ in aq. treated with I_2 + KI soln. + KOH (T 1.81) yields CHI_3 — $\bar{C}$ reduces Tollens' reagt. (T 1.11).

$\bar{C}$ on long stdg. with conc. aq. $MgCl_2$ soln. ppts. $Mg(OH)_2$ ⟨4⟩; reactn. much more sensitive using neut. satd. $MnCl_2$ soln. ⟨5⟩.

$\bar{C}$ passed into cold HBr (D = 1.48) gives 90% yield ethylene bromohydrin [Beil. I-338], b.p. 149° ⟨6⟩ — $\bar{C}$ adds HCl yielding ethylene chlorohydrin [Beil. I-337]; $\bar{C}$ passed into 0.1 N HCl contg. 22% NaCl reacts nearly quant. (method of detn.) ⟨7⟩; for critical study and improvement see ⟨8⟩ ⟨9⟩ — $\bar{C}$ passed into 40% aq. KSCN soln. very rap. yields $HO.CH_2.CH_2.SCN$ + KOH which may be titrated ⟨7⟩.

1:6105 ⟨1⟩ Timmermans, Hennaut-Roland, *J. chim. phys.* **34,** 723–724 (1937). ⟨2⟩ Maas, Boomer, *J. Am. Chem. Soc.* **44,** 1711–1712 (1922). ⟨3⟩ Matignon, Moureu, Dodé, *Bull. soc. chim.* (5) **1,** 1316–1317 (1934). ⟨4⟩ Walker, *Ber.* **34,** 4117 (1901). ⟨5⟩ Lenher, *J. Am. Chem. Soc.* **53,** 3739–3740 (1931). ⟨6⟩ Thayer, Marvel, Hiers, *Organic Syntheses, Coll. Vol.* I, 111–114 (1932). ⟨7⟩ Deckert, *Z. anal. Chem.* **82,** 297–307 (1930). ⟨8⟩ Lubatti, *J. Soc. Chem. Ind.* **51T,** 361–367 (1932). ⟨9⟩ Kerchow, *Z. anal. Chem.* **108,** 249–254 (1937). ⟨10⟩ Deckery, *Angew. Chem.* **45,** 758 (1932).

1:6110 **DIETHYL ETHER** $CH_3.CH_2.O.CH_2.CH_3$ $C_4H_{10}O$ **Beil. I-315**

B.P. 34.60° ⟨1⟩ D_4^{15} = **0.71925** ⟨1⟩ n_D^{15} = **1.35555** ⟨1⟩
M.P. stable form −116.3° ⟨1⟩ D_4^{30} = **0.70205** ⟨1⟩ n_D^{20} = **1.3526**
metastable form −123.3° ⟨1⟩

$\bar{C}$ dis. in aq. at 16° to extent of 7.5 pts. dry $\bar{C}$ to 100 pts. aq. — $\bar{C}$ forms with aq. a const. boilg. mixt., b.p. 34.15°, contg. 1.3% aq. ⟨1⟩.

$\bar{C}$ is sol. in cold conc. H_2SO_4, sepg. unchanged on cautious dilution; $\bar{C}$ is insol. in cold 50% H_2SO_4 — $\bar{C}$ is sol. in cold conc. HCl.

For study of detection of ether peroxides see ⟨2⟩ ⟨3⟩ ⟨4⟩.

C̄ refluxed some hours with HI (D = 1.7) yields ethyl iodide, b.p. 72°, D = 2.285, insol. aq. — C̄ refluxed 1 hr. with 3,5-dinitrobenzoyl chloride + $ZnCl_2$ (T 1.98) yields ⟨5⟩ ethyl 3,5-dinitrobenzoate, m.p. 93°.

1:6110 ⟨1⟩ Timmermans, Martin, *J. chim. phys.* **25,** 433–437 (1928). ⟨2⟩ Middleton, Hyams, *Analyst* **53,** 201–209 (1928). ⟨3⟩ Rieche, Meister, *Angew. Chem.* **49,** 101–103 (1936). ⟨4⟩ Rieche, *Z. angew. Chem.* **44,** 896–899 (1931). ⟨5⟩ Underwood, Baril, Toone, *J. Am. Chem. Soc.* **52,** 4088 (1930).

1:6115 PROPYLENE OXIDE (*d,l*) $CH_3—CH—CH_2$ (epoxide, bridged by O) C_3H_6O **Beil. XVII-6**
(Methylethylene oxide)

B.P. 35° **D^0 = 0.859**

Ether-like odor — Misc. aq., alc., ether.

C̄ htd. with aq. or dil. H_2SO_4 ⟨1⟩ gives *d,l*-propylene glycol (1:6455). [For study see ⟨1⟩.] — C̄ with hot conc. $MgCl_2$ soln. ppts. $Mg(OH)_2$ [cf. ethylene oxide (1:6105)].

1:6115 ⟨1⟩ Moureu, Dodé, *Bull. soc. chim.* (5) **4,** 289–295 (1937).

—— **METHYLAL** $CH_2(OCH_3)_2$ $C_3H_8O_2$ **Beil. I-574**

B.P. 42.3° **F.P. −104.0°** **D_4^{20} = 0.86012** **n_D^{20} = 1.35335**

See 1:0105. Genus 1: Aldehydes.

1:6116 2,3-EPOXYBUTANE $CH_3—CH—CH—CH_3$ (epoxide, bridged by O) C_4H_8O **Beil. XVII-11**
(α,β-Dimethylethylene oxide)

***Trans* isomer:**

B.P. 53.5°$_{742}$ ⟨1⟩ **M.P. abt. −85°** ⟨2⟩ **D_4^{25} = 0.8010** ⟨1⟩ **n_D^{20} = 1.3736** ⟨1⟩
52-53°$_{741}$ ⟨3⟩ **n_D^{25} = 1.3705** ⟨1⟩

***Cis* isomer:**

B.P. 59.7°$_{742}$ ⟨1⟩ **M.P. abt. −80°** ⟨2⟩ **D_4^{25} = 0.8226** ⟨1⟩ **n_D^{20} = 1.3828** ⟨1⟩
58-59°$_{745}$ ⟨3⟩ **n_D^{25} = 1.3802** ⟨1⟩

The crude 2,3-epoxybutane mixt. obtd. from the mixt. of *cis-* and *trans*-butene-2 (from H_2SO_4 dehydration of butanol-1) contains approx. 65% *trans* C̄ and 35% *cis* C̄ ⟨2⟩.

Both forms of C̄ readily hydrate in dil. aq. solns. of strong acids, the *trans* C̄ yielding *meso*-butanediol-1,3 (cf. 1:6452), the *cis* C̄ yielding *d,l*-butanediol-1,3 (cf. 1:6452) ⟨2⟩.

1:6116 ⟨1⟩ Winstein, Lucas, *J. Am. Chem. Soc.* **61,** 1580 (1939). ⟨2⟩ Wilson, Lucas, *J. Am. Chem. Soc.* **58,** 2396–2400 (1936). ⟨3⟩ Norton, Hass, *J. Am. Chem. Soc.* **58,** 2147 (1936).

1:6117 1,2-EPOXY-2-METHYLPROPANE $CH_3—C(CH_3)—CH_2$ (epoxide, bridged by O) C_4H_8O **Beil. XVII-11**
(α,α-Dimethylethylene oxide; isobutylene oxide)

B.P. 56.0-56.5° ⟨1⟩ **(52°)**

C̄ in 0.5% H_2SO_4 at 90° gives 85% yield isobutylene glycol (1:6446) ⟨1⟩ — C̄ htd. above 210° with Al_2O_3 yields isobutyraldehyde (1:0120).

[C̄ with C_2H_5MgBr gives 21% 2-methylpentanol-3 (1:6194); with $(C_2H_5)_2Mg$ gives 27.5% yield of 2-methylpentanol-2 (1:6190).] [For reactn. of C̄ with alcs. see ⟨3⟩.]

1:6117 ⟨1⟩ Moureu, Dodé, *Bull. soc. chim.* (5) **4,** 289 (1937). ⟨2⟩ Norton, Hass, *J. Am. Chem. Soc.* **58,** 2149 (1936). ⟨3⟩ Sparks, Nelson, *J. Am. Chem. Soc.* **58,** 671–672 (1936).

1:6118 1,2-EPOXYBUTANE $CH_3.CH_2.CH{-}CH_2$ (with O bridging the last two carbons) C_4H_8O **Beil. S.N. 2362**
(Butylene oxide-1,2;
α-butylene oxide)

B.P. 61-62° ⟨1⟩ D_4^{17} = **0.837** ⟨1⟩ n_D^{17} = **1.3855** ⟨1⟩

C̄ with 0.5% H_2SO_4 at 90° gives 95% yield butanediol-1,2 [Beil. I-477] ⟨1⟩.

1:6118 ⟨1⟩ Moureu, Dodé, *Bull. soc. chim.* (5) **4,** 289 (1937).

1:6120 METHYL ALCOHOL $CH_3.OH$ CH_4O **Beil. I-273**

B.P. 64.65° ⟨1⟩ **F.P. = −97°** ⟨1⟩ D_4^{20} = **0.7915** n_D^{15} = **1.33066** ⟨1⟩

Misc. with aq., alc., ether — Does *not* form const. boilg. mixt. with aq. — Salted out from aq. soln. with K_2CO_3 — Neither CaO nor BaO effects complete dehydration ⟨1⟩, but this can be effected by simple fractn. ⟨2⟩, or by distn. over Na ⟨3⟩.

For analysis of binary system methyl alc. + ethyl alc. via detn. of refractive index see ⟨4⟩; for analysis of ternary system methyl alc. + ethyl alc. + aq. by detn. of refractive index and density see ⟨5⟩.

Methyl acetate, b.p. 57.1° (1:3005) and methyl benzoate, b.p. 199.6° (1:3586) are both liquids and not recommended as derivs. for identification of C̄.

Ⓟ **Resorcinol-H_2SO_4 color test:** See T 1.84-A of Manual.

Ⓟ **U.S.P. test for MeOH (in pres. of EtOH):** See T 1.84-B of Manual. [For critical study of 58 dif. reactns. for detectn. of MeOH see ⟨6⟩ and ⟨7⟩.]

Ⓓ **Methyl *p*-nitrobenzoate:** cryst. from dil. alc.; m.p. 96°. [Use for detectn. of C̄ in 0.25% aq. soln. ⟨8⟩.]

Ⓓ **Methyl 3,5-dinitrobenzoate:** cryst. from 95% alc. or pet. ether; m.p. 107.5° ⟨9⟩; 107.8° cor. ⟨10⟩; 108° ⟨11⟩; 110° ⟨12⟩ [cf. T 1.82].

Ⓓ **Methyl hydrogen phthalate:** m.p. 82.4–82.7° cor. ⟨13⟩; Neut. Eq. 180. [The *p*-nitrobenzyl ester (cf. T 1.39) of this acid phthalate has m.p. 105.7° ⟨14⟩.]

Ⓓ **Methyl hydrogen 3-nitrophthalate:** cryst. from aq. or C_6H_6 + lgr.; m.p. 152.9–153.4° cor. ⟨15⟩ [cf. T 1.83].

Ⓓ **Methyl *N*-phenylcarbamate:** from C̄ + phenylisocyanate; lfts. from alc.; m.p. 47°. [For optical data see ⟨21⟩.]

Ⓓ **Methyl *N*-(*p*-nitrophenyl)carbamate:** cryst. from CCl_4; m.p. 179.5° ⟨16⟩ [cf. ⟨17⟩].

Ⓓ **Methyl *N*-(α-naphthyl)carbamate:** cryst. from lgr.; m.p. 124° ⟨18⟩ [cf. T 1.86].

Ⓓ **Methyl *N*-(*p*-xenyl)carbamate:** cryst. from alc., C_6H_6, or C_6H_6 + pet.; m.p. 127° ⟨19⟩.

Ⓓ **Methyl *N,N*-diphenylcarbamate:** m.p. 85° ⟨20⟩ [cf. T 1.43].

1:6120 ⟨1⟩ Timmermans, Hennaut-Roland, *J. chim. phys.* **27,** 411–414 (1930). ⟨2⟩ Young, Fortey, *J. Chem. Soc.* **81,** 717 (1902); **83,** 45 (1903). ⟨3⟩ Crismer, *Bull. soc. chim. Belg.* **18,** 42 (1904). ⟨4⟩ Williams, *Ind. Eng. Chem.* **19,** 844–845 (1927). ⟨5⟩ Berl, Ranis, *Ber.* **60,** 2225–2229 (1927). ⟨6⟩ Gettler, *J. Biol. Chem.* **42,** 311–328 (1920). ⟨7⟩ Sumner, *J. Am. Chem. Soc.* **45,** 2378–2380 (1923). ⟨8⟩ Henstock, *J. Chem. Soc.* **1933,** 216. ⟨9⟩ Mulliken, "Method" I, 166 (1904). ⟨10⟩ Malone, Reid, *J. Am. Chem. Soc.* **51,** 3426 (1929).

⟨11⟩ Bryant, *J. Am. Chem. Soc.* **54,** 3760 (1932). ⟨12⟩ Reichstein, *Helv. Chim. Acta* **9,** 802 (1926). ⟨13⟩ Goggans, Copenhaver, *J. Am. Chem. Soc.* **61,** 2909 (1939). ⟨14⟩ Reid, *J. Am. Chem. Soc.* **39,** 1250–1251 (1917). ⟨15⟩ Dickinson, Crosson, Copenhaver, *J. Am. Chem. Soc.* **59,** 1095 (1937). ⟨16⟩ Shriner, Cox, *J. Am. Chem. Soc.* **53,** 1604, 3186 (1931). ⟨17⟩ Hoeke, *Rec. trav. chim.* **54,** 514 (1935). ⟨18⟩ Bickel, French, *J. Am. Chem. Soc.* **48,** 749 (1926). ⟨19⟩ Morgan, Pettet, *J. Chem. Soc.* **1931,** 1125. ⟨20⟩ Melnikov, Vinokurov, *Chem. Abs.* **27,** 965 (1933).

⟨21⟩ Dewey, Witt, *Ind. Eng. Chem., Anal. Ed.* **12,** 459 (1940).

1:6125 DIISOPROPYL ETHER $(CH_3)_2CH.O.CH(CH_3)_2$ $C_6H_{14}O$ **Beil. I-362**

B.P. 67.5° ⟨1⟩ **M.P. <−60° ⟨1⟩** D^{20}_{20} **= 0.7247 ⟨1⟩** n^{23}_{D} **= 1.3678 ⟨1⟩**

C̄, on stdg., is unusually prone to formn. of peroxides which cause explosion on htg. [cf. ⟨2⟩ ⟨3⟩].

C̄ is sol. in conc. H_2SO_4 and repptd. unchanged on immediate diln. [For further data cf. ⟨4⟩.] [For data on solvent power see ⟨1⟩; for use in detn. of fatty acids via distrib. between C̄ + aq. see ⟨5⟩.] [For D^{25}_{4} on mixts. of C̄ with isopropyl alc. see ⟨7⟩.]

C̄, refluxed 1 hr., with 3,5-dinitrobenzoyl chloride + $ZnCl_2$ (T 1.98), yields isopropyl 3,5-dinitrobenzoate, cryst. from CCl_4, m.p. 120–121° ⟨6⟩.

1:6125 ⟨1⟩ Fife, Reid, *Ind. Eng. Chem.* **22,** 513, 515 (1930). ⟨2⟩ Morgan, Pickard, *Chemistry & Industry* **55,** 421–422 (1936). ⟨3⟩ Robertson, *Chemistry & Industry* **52,** 274 (1933). ⟨4⟩ Kirrmann, Graves, *Bull. soc. chim.* (5) **1,** 1497–1498 (1934). ⟨5⟩ Werkman, *Ind. Eng. Chem., Anal. Ed.* **2,** 302–304 (1930). ⟨6⟩ Underwood, Baril, Toone, *J. Am. Chem. Soc.* **52,** 4088 (1930). ⟨7⟩ Miller, Bliss, *Ind. Eng. Chem.* **32,** 123–125 (1940).

1:6130 ETHYL ALCOHOL $CH_3.CH_2OH$ C_2H_6O **Beil. I-292**

B.P. 78.325° ⟨1⟩ **F.P. —117.3°** D^{20}_{4} **= 0.7894** n^{20}_{D} **= 1.3610**

C̄ is misc. with aq., glycerol, ether, pet. ether, etc. — C̄ with aq. forms a binary const. boilg. mixt. (b.p. 78.5°) contg. 95.57% C̄ by wt. ⟨2⟩ — C̄ with C_6H_6 forms a binary const. boilg. mixt. (b.p. 68.25°) contg. 32.4% C̄ + 67.6% benzene ⟨3⟩ — C̄ forms with both aq. and C_6H_6 a ternary const. boilg. mixt. (b.p. 64.85°) contg. 18.5% C̄, 7.4% aq. and 74.1% C_6H_6 ⟨3⟩.

C̄ is oxidized by hot dil. $K_2Cr_2O_7$ + H_2SO_4 to acetaldehyde, b.p. +20° (1:0100); by alk. $KMnO_4$ soln. to acetic ac., b.p. 118° (1:1010) — C̄ warmed with I_2 + KI soln. + dil. NaOH (T 1.81) yields iodoform, m.p. 119°. [For study of influence on sensitivity of conc. of I_2 + KI, of alk. conc. etc. see ⟨4⟩.]

C̄ on slow distn. with HI (D = 1.7) gives ethyl iodide, b.p. 72°; with HBr (D = 1.48) gives ethyl bromide, b.p. 39°. [Use of former for isolation, identification, and detn. of C̄ in extreme diln. (e.g., 0.0025%) see ⟨5⟩.]

Ⓓ **Ethyl *p*-nitrobenzoate:** cryst. from alc.; m.p. 57° [use in detection of C̄ in 1% aq. soln. ⟨6⟩ [cf. T 1.82].

Ⓓ **Ethyl 3,5-dinitrobenzoate:** cryst. from alc. or pet. ether; m.p. 93° ⟨7⟩ ⟨8⟩ ⟨9⟩ [cf. T 1.82].

Ⓓ **Ethyl hydrogen phthalate:** dif. to crystallize; m.p. 47–48° ⟨10⟩ [the *p*-nitrobenzyl ester (cf. T 1.39) of this acid phthalate; cryst. from 63% alc.; m.p. 80° ⟨11⟩].

Ⓓ **Ethyl hydrogen 3-nitrophthalate:** cryst. from aq.; m.p. 157.7–158.3° cor.; Neut. Eq. 239 ⟨12⟩ [cf. T 1.83].

Ⓓ **Ethyl *N*-phenylcarbamate** (*N*-phenylurethane): m.p. 52°. [For optical data see ⟨18⟩.]

Ⓓ **Ethyl *N*-(*p*-nitrophenyl)carbamate:** cryst. from CCl_4; m.p. 129° ⟨13⟩; 130° ⟨14⟩.

Ⓓ **Ethyl *N*-(α-naphthyl)carbamate:** cryst. from lgr.; m.p. 79° ⟨15⟩ [cf. T 1.86].

Ⓓ **Ethyl *N*-(*p*-xenyl)carbamate:** cryst. from alc., C_6H_6 or pet.; m.p. 119° ⟨16⟩.

Ⓓ **Ethyl *N,N*-diphenylcarbamate:** m.p. 84° ⟨17⟩. [Note that this m.p. is close to corresp. deriv. for methyl alc. (1:6120) and *n*-propyl alc. (1:6150).]

1:6130 ⟨1⟩ Wojciechowski, *J. Research Natl. Bur. Standards* **17,** 724 (1936). ⟨2⟩ Young, Fortey, *J. Chem. Soc.* **81,** 719–723 (1902). ⟨3⟩ Young, *J. Chem. Soc.* **81,** 710 (1902). ⟨4⟩ Korenman, *Z. anal. Chem.* **93,** 338 (1933). ⟨5⟩ Gettler, Niederl, Benedetti-Pichler, *J. Am. Chem. Soc.* **54,** 1476–1485 (1932); *Mikrochemie* **11,** 167–199 (1932). ⟨6⟩ Henstock, *J. Chem. Soc.* **1933,** 216. ⟨7⟩ Bryant, *J. Am. Chem. Soc.* **54,** 3760 (1932). ⟨8⟩ Malone, Reid, *J. Am. Chem. Soc.* **51,** 3426 (1929). ⟨9⟩ Reichstein, *Helv. Chim. Acta* **9,** 802 (1926). ⟨10⟩ Goggans, Copenhaver, *J. Am. Chem. Soc.* **61,** 2909 (1939).

⟨11⟩ Reid, *J. Am. Chem. Soc.* **39**, 1251 (1917). ⟨12⟩ Dickinson, Crosson, Copenhaver, *J. Am. Chem. Soc.* **59**, 1095 (1937). ⟨13⟩ Shriner, Cox, *J. Am. Chem. Soc.* **53**, 1604, 3186 (1931). ⟨14⟩ Hoeke, *Rec. trav. chim.* **54**, 514 (1935). ⟨15⟩ Bickel, French, *J. Am. Chem. Soc.* **48**, 749 (1926). ⟨16⟩ Morgan, Pettet, *J. Chem. Soc.* **1931**, 1125. ⟨17⟩ Melnikov, Vinokurov, *Chem. Abs.* **27**, 965 (1933). ⟨18⟩ Dewey, Witt, *Ind. Eng. Chem., Anal. Ed.* **12**, 459 (1940).

1:6135 ISOPROPYL ALCOHOL $(CH_3)_2CH.OH$ C_3H_8O **Beil. I-360**
(Propanol-2)

B.P. 82.4° ⟨1⟩ **M.P. −89.5°** ⟨1⟩ D_4^{20} = **0.78507** ⟨1⟩ n_D^{20} = **1.37927** ⟨1⟩
D_4^{30} = **0.77690** ⟨1⟩ n_D^{25} = **1.3781** ⟨1⟩

C̄ is misc. with aq. and with it forms a binary const. boilg. mixt. (b.p. 80.37°) contg. 87.9% by wt. of C̄ + 12.1% aq. ⟨2⟩ — C̄ forms with C_6H_6 a binary const. boilg. mixt. (b.p. 71.92°) contg. 33.3% by wt. of C̄ + 66.7% by wt. of C_6H_6 ⟨3⟩ — C̄ forms with both aq. and C_6H_6 a ternary const. boilg. mixt. (b.p. 66.5°) contg. 18.7% by wt. of C̄, 7.5% by wt. of aq., and 73.8% by wt. of C_6H_6 ⟨3⟩.

From aq. soln. C̄ is salted out by K_2CO_3 or KF; less effectively by many other salts ⟨4⟩.

For detn. of C̄ in mixts. with aq. by means of immersion refractometer see ⟨5⟩.

C̄ on oxidn. with $CrO_3 + H_2SO_4$ (cf. T 1.72) yields acetone, b.p. 56° (1:5400) — C̄ (even in 1% aq. soln.) treated with I_2 + KI soln. + alk. (T 1.81) rapidly yields iodoform, m.p. 119°, *in cold* — C̄ in resorcinol + H_2SO_4 test (T 1.84-A) gives amber ring.

C̄ refluxed with HI (D = 1.7) yields isopropyl iodide, b.p. 89°; with HBr (D = 1.48) yields isopropyl bromide, b.p. 60° — C̄ with $ZnCl_2$ + HCl (T 1.85) rapidly clouds at room temp. and on stdg. overnight in stoppered tt. separates layer of isopropyl chloride, b.p. 35° ⟨6⟩.

For detn. of C̄ in pres. of acetone see ⟨7⟩ ⟨8⟩; in pres. of EtOH see ⟨9⟩.

Ⓓ **Isopropyl *p*-nitrobenzoate:** cryst. from lt. pet., m.p. 110.5° ⟨10⟩; 111° ⟨11⟩ — [The value of 55.5° given in ⟨12⟩ where the deriv. is used for detect. of C̄ in 1.5% aq. solns. is undoubtedly wrong due to recrystallization of product from ethyl alcohol; cf. ⟨10⟩.]

Ⓓ **Isopropyl 3,5-dinitrobenzoate:** cryst. from pet. ether or 50% alc.; m.p. 123° ⟨13⟩; 122.1° cor. ⟨14⟩; 121–122° ⟨15⟩.

Ⓓ **Isopropyl hydrogen 3-nitrophthalate:** cryst. from aq., m.p. 153.9–154.3° cor. ⟨16⟩; 152–153° ⟨17⟩; Neut. Eq. 253 [cf. T 1.83].

Ⓓ **Isopropyl *N*-phenylcarbamate:** cryst. from lt. pet.; m.p. 75–76° ⟨18⟩.

Ⓓ **Isopropyl *N*-(*p*-nitrophenyl)carbamate:** cryst. from CCl_4; m.p. 116° ⟨19⟩. [Does not distinguish from *n*-propyl alc. (1:6150).]

Ⓓ **Isopropyl *N*-(α-naphthyl)carbamate:** tbls. from lgr., m.p. 105–106° ⟨20⟩ [cf. T 1.86].

Ⓓ **Isopropyl *N*-(*p*-xenyl)carbamate:** cryst. from alc., C_6H_6 or C_6H_6 + pet., m.p. 138° ⟨21⟩.

1:6135 ⟨1⟩ Timmermans, Delcourt, *J. chim. phys.* **31**, 105–106 (1934). ⟨2⟩ Young, Fortey, *J. Chem. Soc.* **81**, 728–729 (1902). ⟨3⟩ Young, Fortey, *J. Chem. Soc.* **81**, 744–746 (1902). ⟨4⟩ Ginnings, Chen, *J. Am. Chem. Soc.* **53**, 3765–3769 (1931). ⟨5⟩ Batscha, Reznek, *J. Assoc. Official Agr. Chem.* **20**, 107–115 (1937). ⟨6⟩ Lucas, *J. Am. Chem. Soc.* **52**, 802–804 (1930). ⟨7⟩ Cassar, *Ind. Eng. Chem.* **19**, 1061–1062 (1927). ⟨8⟩ Cook, Smith, *J. Biol. Chem.* **85**, 251–260 (1929). ⟨9⟩ Archibald, Beamer, *Ind. Eng. Chem., Anal. Ed.* **4**, 18–20 (1932). ⟨10⟩ Adamson, Kenner, *J. Chem. Soc.* **1935**, 287.

⟨11⟩ Brunner, Wöhrl, *Monatsh.* **63**, 377 (1934). ⟨12⟩ Henstock, *J. Chem. Soc.* **1933**, 216. ⟨13⟩ Bryant, *J. Am. Chem. Soc.* **54**, 3760 (1932). ⟨14⟩ Malone, Reid, *J. Am. Chem. Soc.* **51**, 3426 (1929). ⟨15⟩ Reichstein, *Helv. Chim. Acta* **9**, 802 (1926). ⟨16⟩ Dickinson, Crosson, Copenhaver, *J. Am. Chem. Soc.* **59**, 1095 (1937). ⟨17⟩ Nicolet, Sachs, *J. Am. Chem. Soc.* **47**, 2349 (1925). ⟨18⟩ Weizmann, Garrard, *J. Chem. Soc.* **117**, 328 (1920). ⟨19⟩ Shriner, Cox, *J. Am. Chem. Soc.* **53**, 1604, 3186 (1931). ⟨20⟩ Neuberg, Kansky, *Biochem. Z.* **20**, 447 (1909). ⟨21⟩ Morgan, Pettet, *J. Chem. Soc.* **1931**, 1125.

1:6140 *ter*-**BUTYL ALCOHOL** $(CH_3)_3C.OH$ $C_4H_{10}O$ **Beil. I-379**
(Trimethylcarbinol)

B.P. 82.50° ⟨1⟩ **M.P. +25.55° ⟨1⟩** D_4^{20} = **0.78670 ⟨1⟩** n_D^{20} = **1.38779 ⟨2⟩**
D_4^{30} = **0.77620 ⟨1⟩**

C̄ is misc. with aq. and with it forms a binary const. boilg. mixt. (b.p. 79.91°) contg. 88.24% by wt. of C̄ + 11.76% by wt. of aq. ⟨3⟩ — C̄ forms with C_6H_6 a binary const. boilg. mixt. (b.p. 73.95°) contg. 36.6% by wt. of C̄ + 63.4% by wt. of C_6H_6 ⟨4⟩ — C̄ forms with both aq. and C_6H_6 a ternary const. boilg. mixt. (b.p. 67.30°) contg. 21.4% by wt. of C̄, 8.1% by wt. of aq., and 70.5% by wt. of C_6H_6 ⟨4⟩.

For table of sp. gr. at 20° and 25° of system C̄ + aq. see ⟨3⟩; for table of values of n_D^{25} of system C̄ + aq. see ⟨5⟩ — C̄ with aq. forms a dihydrate, C̄.$2H_2O$, m.p. 0° ⟨6⟩.

From aq. soln. C̄ is salted out by K_2CO_3 or KF; less effectively by other salts ⟨7⟩. [For data on system C̄ + various salts see ⟨7⟩ ⟨8⟩.]

C̄, on oxidn. with CrO_3 + H_2SO_4 (T 1.72), yields acetone (1:5400), acetic ac. (1:1010) and CO_2 [cf. ⟨9⟩] — C̄ with resorcinol + H_2SO_4 (T 1.84-A) gives red flocks (like MeOH) — C̄ does *not* give CHI_3 with I_2 + KI soln. + alk. (T 1.81).

C̄ reacts instantly with excess cold conc. HCl (T 1.85) to yield *ter*-butyl chloride, b.p. 52° [use in prepn. of latter ⟨10⟩]; similarly HBr (D = 1.48) yields *ter*-butyl bromide, b.p. 72°.

For formation of *ter*-butyl hydrogen phthalate or substituted hydrogen phthalates see ⟨18⟩.

Ⓓ ***ter*-Butyl *p*-nitrobenzoate:** from C̄ + *p*-nitrobenzoyl chloride in ether (5% yield in 1 hr. diminishing with time ⟨11⟩) or in pyridine (29% yield in 15 hrs. ⟨12⟩); lfts. from alc., m.p. 116° ⟨11⟩; 115–117° ⟨12⟩ [cf. T 1.82].

Ⓓ ***ter*-Butyl 3,5-dinitrobenzoate:** cryst. from pet. ether, m.p. 142° ⟨13⟩; 141.5–142.5° ⟨14⟩ [cf. T 1.82].

Ⓓ ***ter*-Butyl *N*-phenylcarbamate:** from C̄ + phenylisocyanate on warmg.; cryst. from ether or pet. eth.; m.p. 136° ⟨15⟩; 134–135° ⟨16⟩.

Ⓓ ***ter*-Butyl *N*-(α-naphthyl)carbamate:** m.p. 101° (poor yield) ⟨7⟩ [cf. T 1.86].

1:6140 ⟨1⟩ Timmermans, Delcourt, *J. chim. phys.* **31,** 107–108 (1934). ⟨2⟩ Davis, Murray, *Ind. Eng. Chem.* **18,** 844 (1926). ⟨3⟩ Young, Fortey, *J. Chem. Soc.* **81,** 729–732 (1902). ⟨4⟩ Young, Fortey, *J. Chem. Soc.* **81,** 746–747 (1902). ⟨5⟩ French, McShan, Johler, *J. Am. Chem. Soc.* **56,** 1348 (1934). ⟨6⟩ Paterno, Mieli, *Gazz. chim. ital.* **37,** II, 330–338 (1907). ⟨7⟩ Ginnings, Robbins, *J. Am. Chem. Soc.* **52,** 2282–2286 (1930). ⟨8⟩ Ginnings, Herring, Webb, *J. Am. Chem. Soc.* **55,** 875–878 (1933). ⟨9⟩ Semichon, Flanzy, *Compt. rend.* **195,** 255–256 (1932). ⟨10⟩ Norris, *Organic Syntheses, Coll. Vol.* I, 137–138 (1932).

⟨11⟩ Meisenheimer, Schmidt, *Ann.* **475,** 180 (1929). ⟨12⟩ Hückel, Nerdel, Reimer, *J. prakt. Chem.* (2) **149,** 315 (1937). ⟨13⟩ Bryant, *J. Am. Chem. Soc.* **54,** 3760 (1932). ⟨14⟩ Reichstein, *Helv. Chim. Acta* **9,** 802 (1926). ⟨15⟩ Knoevenagel, *Ann.* **297,** 148 (1897). ⟨16⟩ Lambling, *Bull. soc. chim.* (3) **19,** 777 (1898). ⟨17⟩ Neuberg, Kansky, *Biochem. Z.* **20,** 447 (1909). ⟨18⟩ Fessler, Shriner, *J. Am. Chem. Soc.* **58,** 1384–1386 (1936).

1:6141 **ETHYLENE GLYCOL DIMETHYL ETHER** $C_4H_{10}O_2$ **Beil. I-467**
(1,2-Dimethoxyethane) $CH_3O.CH_2.CH_2.O.CH_3$

B.P. 84.7° ⟨1⟩ D_4^{20} = **0.8665 ⟨1⟩** n_D^{20} = **1.37965 ⟨1⟩**

Misc. with aq.

1:6141 ⟨1⟩ Palomaa, Honkanen, *Ber.* **70,** 2203 (1937).

1:6145 **ALLYL ALCOHOL** $CH_2{=}CH.CH_2OH$ C_3H_6O **Beil. I-436**

B.P. 97.1° ⟨1⟩ D_4^{20} = **0.8540** n_D^{20} = **1.41345**

Liq. with penetrating mustard-like odor — C̄ is misc. with aq. and with it forms a binary const. boilg. mixt. (b.p. 88.0°) contg. 72% by wt. of C̄ + 28% by wt. of aq. ⟨2⟩ — C̄ forms with C_6H_6 a binary const. boilg. mixt. (b.p. 76.75°) contg. 17.36% by wt. of C̄ + 82.64% by wt. of C_6H_6 ⟨1⟩ — C̄ forms with both aq. and C_6H_6 a ternary const. boilg. mixt. (b.p. 68.21°) contg. 9.16% by wt. of C̄, 8.58% by wt. of aq., and 82.26% by wt. of C_6H_6 ⟨1⟩.

For graph of density of system: C̄ + aq. see ⟨1⟩; for data on ternary system: C̄ + aq. + salts see ⟨3⟩ — [For prepn. of C̄ in 45–47% yield from glycerol + formic ac. see ⟨4⟩.]

C̄ on oxidn. with dil. $K_2Cr_2O_7 + H_2SO_4$ (cf. T 1.72) yields acrolein (1:0115) — C̄ with resorcinol + H_2SO_4 (T 1.84-A) gives brown ring — C̄ decolorizes Br_2 in CCl_4 (T 1.91) or Br_2 + aq. [Use in quant. detn. ⟨5⟩.] [For use of Br_2 + KBr for anal. see ⟨2⟩.]

C̄ dis. readily in 50–60% H_2SO_4 yielding allyl HSO_4 — C̄ on distn. with large excess (16 pts.) 6 *N* HCl gives (50% yield) ⟨6⟩ allyl chloride, b.p. 46°; C̄ dislvd. in cold conc. HCl and treated with trace CuCl + H_2SO_4 rapidly seps. (95% yield ⟨7⟩) allyl chloride — C̄ on distn. with excess HBr (D = 1.48) yields mainly allyl bromide, b.p. 70°; with excess HI (D = 1.70) yields allyl iodide, b.p. 101°.

Ⓓ **Allyl *p*-nitrobenzoate:** m.p. 28° ⟨8⟩; 29° [cf. T 1.82].

Ⓓ **Allyl 3,5-dinitrobenzoate:** cryst. from pet. ether; m.p. 49–50° ⟨9⟩ [cf. T 1.82].

Ⓓ **Allyl hydrogen 3-nitrophthalate:** m.p. 124° [cf. T 1.83].

Ⓓ **Allyl *N*-phenylcarbamate:** m.p. 70° ⟨10⟩.

Ⓓ **Allyl *N*-(*p*-nitrophenyl)carbamate:** scales from pet. ether; m.p. 108° ⟨11⟩.

Ⓓ **Allyl *N*-(α-naphthyl)carbamate:** cryst. from lgr., m.p. 108° ⟨12⟩ [cf. T 1.86].

1:6145 ⟨1⟩ Wallace, Atkins, *J. Chem. Soc.* **101,** 1958–1964 (1912). ⟨2⟩ Wallace, Atkins, *J. Chem. Soc.* **101,** 1179–1184 (1912). ⟨3⟩ Ginnings, Dees, *J. Am. Chem. Soc.* **57,** 1038–1040 (1935). ⟨4⟩ Kamm, Marvel, *Organic Syntheses, Coll. Vol.* I, 34–37 (1932). ⟨5⟩ Stritar, *Monatsh.* **39,** 617–619 (1918). ⟨6⟩ Norris, Watt, Thomas, *J. Am. Chem. Soc.* **38,** 1075 (1916). ⟨7⟩ Breckpot, *Bull. soc. chim. Belg.* **39,** 462 (1931). ⟨8⟩ Adamson, Kenner, *J. Chem. Soc.* **1935,** 287. ⟨9⟩ Reichstein, *Helv. Chim. Acta* **9,** 802 (1926). ⟨10⟩ Pariselle, *Ann. chim.* (8) **24,** 339 (1911). ⟨11⟩ Hoeke, *Rec. trav. chim.* **54,** 513–514 (1935). ⟨12⟩ Hurd, Lui, *J. Am. Chem. Soc.* **57,** 2657 (1935).

1:6150 *n*-PROPYL ALCOHOL (Propanol-1) $CH_3.CH_2.CH_2.OH$ C_3H_8O Beil. I-350

B.P. 97.15° ⟨1⟩ D_4^{20} = **0.80359** ⟨1⟩ n_D^{20} = **1.38499** ⟨3⟩
97.175° ⟨2⟩ D_4^{25} = **0.79957** ⟨1⟩ n_D^{25} = **1.3834** ⟨2⟩

C̄ is misc. with aq. and with it forms a binary const. boilg. mixt. (b.p. 87.72°) contg. 71.69% by wt. of C̄ + 28.31% by wt. of aq. ⟨4⟩ — C̄ forms with C_6H_6 a binary const. boilg. mixt. (b.p. 77.12°) contg. 16.9% by wt. of C̄ + 83.1% by wt. of C_6H_6 ⟨5⟩ — C̄ forms with both aq. and C_6H_6 a ternary const. boilg. mixt. (b.p. 68.48°) contg. 9.0% by wt. of C̄, 8.6% by wt. of aq., and 82.4% by wt. of C_6H_6 ⟨5⟩.

For table of n_D^{20} for system C̄ + aq. see ⟨3⟩.

C̄ is salted out from aq. solns. by K_2CO_3.

C̄, on oxidn. with $CrO_3 + H_2SO_4$ (T 1.72), yields propionaldehyde (1:0110) [cf. ⟨6⟩] — C̄, on oxidn. with alk. $KMnO_4$, yields propionic ac. (1:1025) — C̄, with resorcinol + H_2SO_4 (T 1.84-A), gives amber-colored ring.

C̄, on distn. with excess HBr (D = 1.48), yields *n*-propyl bromide, b.p. 71°; with excess HI (D = 1.70) yields *n*-propyl iodide, b.p. 102°.

Ⓓ ***n*-Propyl *p*-nitrobenzoate:** cryst. from pet., m.p. 35° ⟨7⟩. [For use in ident. of C̄ in 0.5% aq. solns. see ⟨8⟩ [cf. T 1.82].]

Ⓓ ***n*-Propyl 3,5-dinitrobenzoate:** cryst. from pet. ether; m.p. 74° ⟨9⟩; 73° ⟨10⟩; 74–75° ⟨11⟩ [cf. T 1.82].

Ⓓ ***n*-Propyl hydrogen phthalate:** cryst. from mixt. of 90% pet. ether + 10% C_6H_6; m.p. 54.1–54.4° cor.; Neut. Eq. 208 ⟨12⟩. [For use in prepn. of pure C̄ cf. ⟨13⟩.] [The *p*-nitrobenzyl ester (cf. T 1.39) of this acid phthalate has m.p. 53° ⟨14⟩.]

Ⓓ **n-Propyl hydrogen 3-nitrophthalate:** cryst. from aq.; m.p. 144.9–145.7° cor.; Neut. Eq. 253 ⟨15⟩ [cf. T 1.82].

Ⓓ **Potassium n-propyl xanthate:** from C̄ + powd. KOH + CS_2 in dry ether; purified by soln. in minimum quant. of alc. or acetone, cooling and pptn. with dry ether; m.p. 205.7° cor. ⟨16⟩.

Ⓓ **n-Propyl N-phenylcarbamate:** cryst. from pet.; m.p. 57° ⟨17⟩. [For optical data see ⟨20⟩.]

Ⓓ **n-Propyl N-(p-nitrophenyl)carbamate:** cryst. from CCl_4; m.p. 115° ⟨18⟩; 110° ⟨19⟩.

Ⓓ **n-Propyl N-(α-naphthyl)carbamate:** tbls. from lgr., m.p. 80° [cf. T 1.86].

Ⓓ **n-Propyl N-(p-xenyl)carbamate:** cryst. from alc., C_6H_6, or C_6H_6 + pet.; m.p. 129° ⟨17⟩.

1:6150 ⟨1⟩ Timmermans, Delcourt, *J. chim. phys.* **31**, 102–103 (1934). ⟨2⟩ Brunel, *J. Am. Chem. Soc.* **45**, 1336 (1923). ⟨3⟩ Wrewsky, *Z. physik. Chem.* **81**, 20 (1912). ⟨4⟩ Young, Fortey, *J. Chem. Soc.* **81**, 723–726 (1902). ⟨5⟩ Young, Fortey, *J. Chem. Soc.* **81**, 747–748 (1902). ⟨6⟩ Semichon, Flanzy, *Compt. rend.* **195**, 254–256 (1932). ⟨7⟩ Adamson, Kenner, *J. Chem. Soc.* **1935**, 287. ⟨8⟩ Henstock, *J. Chem. Soc.* **1933**, 216. ⟨9⟩ Bryant, *J. Am. Chem. Soc.* **54**, 3760 (1932). ⟨10⟩ Malone, Reid, *J. Am. Chem. Soc.* **51**, 3426 (1929).

⟨11⟩ Reichstein, *Helv. Chim. Acta* **9**, 802 (1926). ⟨12⟩ Goggans, Copenhaver, *J. Am. Chem. Soc.* **61**, 2909 (1939). ⟨13⟩ Brunel, *J. Am. Chem. Soc.* **45**, 1335 (1923). ⟨14⟩ Reid, *J. Am. Chem. Soc.* **39**, 1251 (1917). ⟨15⟩ Dickinson, Crosson, Copenhaver, *J. Am. Chem. Soc.* **59**, 1095 (1937). ⟨16⟩ Whitmore, Lieber, *Ind. Eng. Chem., Anal. Ed.* **7**, 129 (1935). ⟨17⟩ Morgan, Pettet, *J. Chem. Soc.* **1931**, 1125. ⟨18⟩ Shriner, Cox, *J. Am. Chem. Soc.* **53**, 1604, 3186 (1931). ⟨19⟩ Hoeke, *Rec. trav. chim.* **54**, 514 (1935). ⟨20⟩ Dewey, Witt, *Ind. Eng. Chem., Anal. Ed.* **12**, 459 (1940).

1:6155 d,l-sec-BUTYL ALCOHOL $CH_3.CH_2.CH(OH).CH_3$ $C_4H_{10}O$ Beil. I-371

(Ethyl-methyl-carbinol;
butanol-2)

B.P. 99.5° ⟨1⟩ ⟨2⟩ D_4^{20} = **0.80692** ⟨1⟩ n_D^{15} = **1.39946** ⟨1⟩
D_4^{25} = **0.80235** ⟨2⟩ n_D^{25} = **1.39495** ⟨2⟩

C̄ is sol. in 8 pts. aq. at 20°; salted out by K_2CO_3 — C̄ forms with aq. a binary const. boilg. mixt. (b.p. 88.5°) contg. 32% by wt. of C̄ ⟨3⟩.

C̄ on oxidn. with CrO_3 + H_2SO_4 (cf. T 1.72) yields ethyl methyl ketone (1:5405) and acetic ac. (1:1010) — C̄ with H_2SO_4 + resorcinol (T 1.84-A) gives pale lemon-yel. ring below a pale rose-red ring — C̄ in 1% aq. soln. treated with I_2 + KI soln. + alk. (T 1.81) slowly gives some CHI_3 in cold.

C̄ does not cloud with conc. HCl alone, but with HCl + $ZnCl_2$ reagt. (T 1.85) immed. clouds in cold and on stdg. seps. layer of *sec*-butyl chloride, b.p. 67° — C̄ on distn. with excess HBr (D = 1.48), yields ⟨4⟩ *sec*-butyl bromide, b.p. 91°. [Note that C̄ + *sec*-butyl bromide forms a binary const. boilg. mixt., b.p. 87.2° at 749 mm. ⟨18⟩.] — C̄ on distn. with excess HI (D = 1.70) yields ⟨4⟩ *sec*-butyl iodide, b.p. 119°.

Ⓓ ***d,l-sec*-Butyl p-nitrobenzoate:** from C̄ + *p*-nitrobenzoyl chloride in C_6H_6 + pyridine htd. 2 hrs. at 100°; cryst. from dil. alc., m.p. 25–26° ⟨5⟩ ⟨6⟩ [cf. T 1.82] [m.p. of corresponding *d*- or *l*- deriv. is +17.5–18° ⟨5⟩].

Ⓓ ***d,l-sec*-Butyl 3,5-dinitrobenzoate:** m.p. 76° ⟨7⟩; 75.6° cor. ⟨8⟩ [cf. T 1.82] [m.p. of corresp. deriv. of *l*-alc. is 81° ⟨9⟩].

Ⓓ ***d,l-sec*-Butyl hydrogen phthalate:** m.p. 59–60° ⟨10⟩ ⟨11⟩.

Ⓓ ***d,l-sec*-Butyl hydrogen 3-nitrophthalate:** m.p. 130.6–131.5° cor.; Neut. Eq. 267 ⟨12⟩ [cf. T 1.83].

Ⓓ ***d,l-sec*-Butyl N-phenylcarbamate:** cryst. from pet.; m.p. 64.5° ⟨13⟩. [The eutectic of the *N*-phenylcarbamates of C̄ and of isobutyl alc. (1:6165) melts at 60° and contains 75% of that from C̄ ⟨13⟩.]

Ⓓ ***d,l-sec*-Butyl *N*-(*p*-nitrophenyl)carbamate:** cryst. from CCl_4; m.p. **75°** ⟨**14**⟩ [cf. ⟨**15**⟩].

Ⓓ ***d,l-sec*-Butyl *N*-(α-naphthyl)carbamate:** m.p. 97° ⟨**16**⟩ [cf. T 1.86].

Ⓓ ***d,l-sec*-Butyl *N*-(*p*-xenyl)carbamate:** m.p. 105.5° ⟨**17**⟩.

1:6155 ⟨1⟩ Timmermans, Martin, *J. chim. phys.* **25,** 431–433 (1928). ⟨2⟩ Brunel, *J. Am. Chem. Soc.* **45,** 1337–1338 (1923). ⟨3⟩ Lecat, " L'Azeotropisme " **1918,** page 94. ⟨4⟩ Norris, *Am. Chem. J.* **38,** 640 (1907). ⟨5⟩ Veibel, Lillelund, *Bull. soc. chim.* (5) **5,** 498 (1938). ⟨6⟩ Meisenheimer, Schmidt, *Ann.* **475,** 174 (1929). ⟨7⟩ Bryant, *J. Am. Chem. Soc.* **54,** 3760 (1932). ⟨8⟩ Malone, Reid, *J. Am. Chem. Soc.* **51,** 3426 (1929). ⟨9⟩ Burwell, *J. Chem. Soc.* **59,** 1610 (1937). ⟨10⟩ Lombaers, *Bull. soc. chim. Belg.* **33,** 233–245 (1924).

⟨11⟩ Pickard, Kenyon, *J. Chem. Soc.* **103,** 1939–1940 (1913). ⟨12⟩ Dickinson, Crosson, Copenhaver, *J. Am. Chem. Soc.* **59,** 1095 (1937). ⟨13⟩ Hückel, Ackermann, *J. prakt. Chem.* (2) **136,** 23 (1933). ⟨14⟩ Shriner, Cox, *J. Am. Chem. Soc.* **53,** 1604, 3186 (1931). ⟨15⟩ Hoeke, *Rec. trav. chim.* **54,** 514 (1935). ⟨16⟩ Neuberg, Kansky, *Biochem. Z.* **20,** 447 (1909). ⟨17⟩ Morgan, Hardy, *Chemistry & Industry* **52,** 519 (1933). ⟨18⟩ Houston, *J. Am. Chem. Soc.* **55,** 4131–4132 (1933).

1:6159 ETHYLENE GLYCOL ETHYL METHYL ETHER — Beil. S.N. 30

(1-Ethoxy-2-methoxyethane) $CH_3.CH_2.O.CH_2.CH_2.OCH_3$ $C_5H_{12}O_2$

B.P. 102° ⟨1⟩ D_4^{20} = **0.8529** ⟨1⟩ n_D^{20} = **1.38677** ⟨1⟩

Misc. with aq.

1:6159 ⟨1⟩ Palomaa, Honkanen, *Ber.* **70,** 2204 (1937).

1:6160 *ter*-AMYL ALCOHOL — $C_5H_{12}O$ — Beil. I-338

(Dimethyl-ethyl-carbinol; " amylene hydrate "; 2-methylbutanol-2)

$$CH_3-\underset{\underset{OH}{|}}{\overset{\overset{CH_3}{|}}{C}}-CH_2.CH_3$$

B.P. 102.35° ⟨1⟩ **M.P. −8.55°** ⟨1⟩ D_4^{20} = **0.80889** ⟨1⟩ n_D^{20} = **1.4052** ⟨2⟩ ⟨3⟩

$\bar{C}$ is sol. in 5 pts. aq. at 10°; in 11 pts. at 70° ⟨4⟩ — $\bar{C}$ forms with aq. a binary const. boilg. mixt. (b.p. 87.2°) contg. 78% by wt. of $\bar{C}$ + 22% aq. ⟨4⟩.

$\bar{C}$ on oxidn. with $CrO_3 + H_2SO_4$ (T 1.72) yields acetone (1:5400), and acetic ac. (1:1010) — $\bar{C}$ gives with resorcinol + H_2SO_4 in T 1.84-A a color similar to that from MeOH — $\bar{C}$ does not give CHI_3 test (T 1.81).

$\bar{C}$ treated with excess cold conc. HCl (cf. T 1.85) immed. gives layer of *ter*-amyl chloride, b.p. 86°. [This may be converted to *ter*-amyl MgCl and thence by reactn. with phenylisocyanate to anilide of dimethylethylacetic acid, m.p. 92° cor. ⟨5⟩.] — $\bar{C}$ on distn. with excess HBr (D = 1.48) yields *ter*-amyl bromide, b.p. 107° ⟨6⟩ — $\bar{C}$ on shaking with excess HI (D = 1.7) *in cold* yields *ter*-amyl iodide, b.p. 127° [if reaction is htd. product is trimethylethylene (1:8220), b.p. 38°].

$\bar{C}$ on warming with 46% H_2SO_4 ⟨7⟩, or conc. H_2SO_4 ⟨8⟩, or with anhydrous oxalic ac. ⟨9⟩, or on slow distn. with a small amt. iodine ⟨10⟩ yields mainly trimethylethylene (2-methylbutene-2) (1:8220), b.p. 38° — $\bar{C}$ + Br_2 at 50–60° yields 2,3-dibromo-2-methylbutane (trimethylethylene dibromide) [Beil. I-137] which cannot be distilled without decomp. but which on boilg. with aq. gives 59% yield isopropyl methyl ketone (1:5410) ⟨11⟩.

Ⓓ ***ter*-Amyl *p*-nitrobenzoate:** m.p. 85° [cf. T 1.82].

Ⓓ ***ter*-Amyl 3,5-dinitrobenzoate:** m.p. 116° ⟨12⟩; 117–118° ⟨13⟩ [cf. T 1.82].

Ⓓ ***ter*-Amyl *N*-phenylcarbamate:** cryst. from pet. eth.; m.p. 42° ⟨14⟩.

Ⓓ ***ter*-Amyl *N*-(α-naphthyl)carbamate:** ndls. from lgr., m.p. 71–72° (very poor yield) ⟨15⟩ [cf. T 1.86].

1:6160 ⟨1⟩ Timmermans, Hennaut-Roland, *J. chim. phys.* **29,** 541–542 (1932). ⟨2⟩ Davis, Murray, *Ind. Eng. Chem.* **18,** 844 (1926). ⟨3⟩ Norris, Reuter, *J. Am. Chem. Soc.* **49,** 2633 (1927). ⟨4⟩ Ayres, *Ind. Eng. Chem.* **21,** 903–904 (1929). ⟨5⟩ Schwartz, Johnson, *J. Am. Chem. Soc.* **53,** 1065 (1931). ⟨6⟩ Norris, Watt, Thomas, *J. Chem. Soc.* **38,** 1076 (1916). ⟨7⟩ Ref. 2, page 2630. ⟨8⟩ Adams, Kamm, Marvel, *J. Am. Chem. Soc.* **40,** 1952–1953 (1918). ⟨9⟩ Norris, Thompson, *J. Am. Chem. Soc.* **53,** 3114 (1931). ⟨10⟩ Hickinbottom, *J. Chem. Soc.* **1935,** 1280.

⟨11⟩ Whitmore, Evers, Rothrock, *Organic Syntheses* **13,** 68–70 (1933). ⟨12⟩ Bryant, *J. Am. Chem. Soc.* **54,** 3760 (1932). ⟨13⟩ Reichstein, *Helv. Chim. Acta* **9,** 802 (1926). ⟨14⟩ Lambling, *Bull. soc. chim.* (3) **19,** 777 (1898). ⟨15⟩ Neuberg, Kansky, *Biochem. Z.* **20,** 445 (1909).

1:6165 ISOBUTYL ALCOHOL $(CH_3)_2CH.CH_2OH$ $C_4H_{10}O$ **Beil. I-373**
(Isopropylcarbinol; 2-methylpropanol-1)

B.P. 108.1° ⟨1⟩ D_4^{20} = **0.80196** ⟨1⟩ n_D^{15} = **1.39768** ⟨1⟩
D_4^{25} = **0.79801** ⟨2⟩ n_D^{25} = **1.3939** ⟨2⟩

$\bar{C}$ is sol. in 10 pts. aq. at 15° — $\bar{C}$ forms with aq. a binary const. boilg. mixt. (b.p. 89.82°) contg. 66.8% by wt. of $\bar{C}$ + 33.2% by wt. of aq. ⟨3⟩ — $\bar{C}$ forms with C_6H_6 a binary const. boilg. mixt. (b.p. 79.84°) contg. 9.3% by wt. of $\bar{C}$ + 90.7% by wt. of C_6H_6 ⟨4⟩ — $\bar{C}$ with C_6H_6 + aq. forms no ternary const. boilg. mixt. ⟨4⟩.

$\bar{C}$, on oxidn. with $K_2Cr_2O_7 + H_2SO_4$ (cf. T 1.72), gives complex mixt.; on oxidn. with dil. alk. $KMnO_4$ in cold yields isobutyric ac. (1:1030) ⟨5⟩ — $\bar{C}$ with resorcinol + H_2SO_4 (T 1.84-A) gives amber ring — $\bar{C}$ with I_2 + KI soln. and alk. (T 1.81) gives *no* CHI_3.

$\bar{C}$, on distn. with excess HBr (D = 1.48) ⟨6⟩, yields isobutyl bromide, b.p. 91°; with excess HI (D = 1.70) ⟨6⟩ yields isobutyl iodide, b.p. 120°.

- Ⓓ **Isobutyl *p*-nitrobenzoate:** m.p. 68.5–69° ⟨7⟩; 69° ⟨8⟩ [cf. T 1.82]. [Use for identif. of $\bar{C}$ in 0.25% aq. soln. ⟨9⟩.]
- Ⓓ **Isobutyl 3,5-dinitrobenzoate:** m.p. 87° ⟨10⟩; 86.5° cor. ⟨11⟩; 87–88° ⟨12⟩ [cf. T 1.82].
- Ⓓ **Isobutyl hydrogen phthalate:** cryst. from pet. ether; m.p. 65° ⟨13⟩; Neut. Eq. 222. [For further details of method see ⟨14⟩.]
- Ⓓ **Isobutyl hydrogen 3-nitrophthalate:** m.p. 179.9–180.6° cor. ⟨15⟩; Neut. Eq. 267 [cf. T 1.83].
- Ⓓ **Isobutyl *N*-phenylcarbamate:** ndls. from lgr.; m.p. 86° ⟨16⟩ ⟨13⟩. [The eutectic of the *N*-phenylcarbamates of $\bar{C}$ and of *sec*-butyl alc. (1:6155) melts at 60° and conts. 25% of that from $\bar{C}$ ⟨13⟩.]
- Ⓓ **Isobutyl *N*-(*p*-nitrophenyl)carbamate:** cryst. from CCl_4; m.p. 80° ⟨17⟩ [cf. ⟨18⟩].
- Ⓓ **Isobutyl *N*-(α-naphthyl)carbamate:** m.p. 104° ⟨18⟩ [cf. T 1.86].

1:6165 ⟨1⟩ Timmermans, Martin, *J. chim. phys.* **25,** 429–431 (1928). ⟨2⟩ Brunel, Crenshaw, Tobin, *J. Am. Chem. Soc.* **43,** 575 (1921). ⟨3⟩ Young, Fortey, *J. Chem. Soc.* **81,** 732–733 (1902). ⟨4⟩ Young, Fortey, *J. Chem. Soc.* **81,** 748–749 (1902). ⟨5⟩ Fournier, *Bull. soc. chim.* (4) **5,** 920 (1909). ⟨6⟩ Norris, *Am. Chem. J.* **38,** 640 (1907). ⟨7⟩ Adamson, Kenner, *J. Chem. Soc.* **1935,** 287. ⟨8⟩ Brunner, Wöhrl, *Monatsh.* **63,** 377 (1934). ⟨9⟩ Henstock, *J. Chem. Soc.* **1933,** 216. ⟨10⟩ Bryant, *J. Am. Chem. Soc.* **54,** 3760 (1932).

⟨11⟩ Malone, Reid, *J. Am. Chem. Soc.* **51,** 3426 (1929). ⟨12⟩ Reichstein, *Helv. Chim. Acta* **9,** 802 (1926). ⟨13⟩ Hückel, Ackermann, *J. prakt. Chem.* (2) **136,** 23 (1933). ⟨14⟩ Pickard, Kenyon, *J. Chem. Soc.* **103,** 1937 (1913). ⟨15⟩ Dickinson, Crosson, Copenhaver, *J. Am. Chem. Soc.* **59,** 1095 (1937). ⟨16⟩ Michael, Cobb, *Ann.* **363,** 84 (1908). ⟨17⟩ Shriner, Cox, *J. Am. Chem. Soc.* **53,** 1604; 3186 (1931). ⟨18⟩ Hoeke, *Rec. trav. chim.* **54,** 514 (1935). ⟨19⟩ Neuberg, Kansky, *Biochem. Z.* **20,** 447 (1909).

1:6170 *d,l*-ISOPROPYL-METHYL-CARBINOL $C_5H_{12}O$ **Beil. I-391**
(2-Methylbutanol-3; *sec*-isoamyl alcohol)

```
      CH3   H
      |     |
CH3—C——C—CH3
      |     |
      H     OH
```

B.P. 112° D_4^{20} = **0.8180** ⟨1⟩ n_D^{20} = **1.3973** ⟨1⟩

[For prepn. in 53–54% yield from isopropyl MgBr + acetaldehyde see ⟨2⟩.] — [For soly. in aq. and soly. of aq. in C̄ cf. ⟨3⟩.]

C̄ on oxidn. with $K_2Cr_2O_7$ + H_2SO_4 (T 1.72) yields isopropyl methyl ketone (1:5410) ⟨4⟩.

C̄ with conc. H_2SO_4 or weak HI yields trimethylethylene (1:8220), b.p. 38° ⟨5⟩. [C̄ htd. with $1\frac{1}{2}$ moles 75% H_2SO_4 at 80% for 20 min. gives 55–60% yield ⟨6⟩ of a mixture (b.p. 149–169°) of two isomeric decenes, viz., 3,5,5-trimethylheptene-2 and 3,4,5,5-tetramethylhexene-2.]

Ⓓ ***d,l*-Isopropyl-methyl-carbinyl hydrogen phthalate:** m.p. 38–40° ⟨7⟩ ⟨8⟩ [m.p. of active isomer, 44–45° ⟨7⟩].

Ⓓ ***d,l*-Isopropyl-methyl-carbinyl *N*-phenylcarbamate:** m.p. 68° ⟨9⟩.

Ⓓ ***d,l*-Isopropyl-methyl-carbinyl *N*-(α-naphthyl)carbamate:** m.p. 108–109° ⟨9⟩ [cf. T 1.86].

1:6170 ⟨1⟩ Pickard, Kenyon, *J. Chem. Soc.* **101,** 625 (1912). ⟨2⟩ Drake, Cooke, *Organic Syntheses* **12,** 48–50 (1932). ⟨3⟩ Ginnings, Baum, *J. Am. Chem. Soc.* **59,** 1112 (1937). ⟨4⟩ Allen, Spanagel, *J. Am. Chem. Soc.* **54,** 4345–4346 (1932). ⟨5⟩ Michael, Zeidler, *Ann.* **385,** 262–263 (1911). ⟨6⟩ Drake, Kline, Rose, *J. Am. Chem. Soc.* **56,** 2077 (1934). ⟨7⟩ Ref. 1, page 633. ⟨8⟩ Pickard, Kenyon, *J. Chem. Soc.* **99,** 58 (1911). ⟨9⟩ Cottle, Powell, *J. Am. Chem. Soc.* **58,** 2270 (1936).

1:6175 PENTANOL-3 $C_5H_{12}O$ Beil. I-385

(Diethylcarbinol; *sym. sec*-amyl alcohol)

$$CH_3.CH_2—\underset{OH}{\overset{H}{C}}—CH_2.OH_3$$

B.P. 116.1° ⟨1⟩
115.9° ⟨2⟩
114.4°$_{741.5}$ ⟨15⟩

D_4^{20} = **0.82037** ⟨1⟩ n_D^{20} = **1.4103** ⟨15⟩
D_4^{25} = **0.8154** ⟨2⟩ n_D^{25} = **1.0479** ⟨1⟩

C̄ is sol. in 18 vols. aq. at 30°; in 24 vols. at 70° ⟨4⟩ — C̄ forms with aq. a binary const. boilg. mixt. (b.p. 91.4°) contg. 67.8% by wt. of C̄ + 32.2% by wt. of aq. ⟨4⟩.

C̄ with $ZnCl_2$ + conc. HCl (T 1.85) rapidly clouds and yields 3-chloropentane, b.p. 97.2°. [For use in prepn. of latter (70% yield) see ⟨5⟩ ⟨9⟩.] — C̄ on satn. with HBr gas at a low temp., and allowed to warm only up to room temp., yields pure 3-bromopentane, b.p. 117.8–118.5° ⟨6⟩, in 82% yield ⟨7⟩. [Note that if C̄ is heated with HBr the product is a mixture ⟨6⟩ of 3-bromopentane and 2-bromopentane, b.p. 117–118°, e.g., in proportion of 29% to 71% ⟨8⟩.] — C̄ with excess HI (D = 1.70) *in cold* yields 3-iodopentane, b.p. 146°.

C̄ on oxidn. with $K_2Cr_2O_7$ + H_2SO_4 at 65° (cf. T 1.72) yields 73% ⟨10⟩ diethyl ketone (1:5420).

C̄ htd. at 100° with 9 N H_2SO_4 ⟨3⟩ or with conc. H_2SO_4 ⟨11⟩ gives 84% yield ⟨3⟩ of pentene-2, b.p. 36.2°. [Note that pentene-2 and pentanol-3 form a binary const. boilg. mixt., b.p. 31.4° ⟨3⟩.]

Ⓓ **Diethylcarbinyl 3,5-dinitrobenzoate:** m.p. 98.5–99.5° ⟨7⟩; 101° ⟨12⟩ [cf. T 1.82].

Ⓓ **Diethylcarbinyl *p*-toluenesulfonate:** m.p. 43–45° ⟨16⟩; 32–35° ⟨17⟩.

Ⓓ **Diethylcarbinyl *N*-phenylcarbamate:** m.p. 48–49° ⟨13⟩.

Ⓓ **Diethylcarbinyl *N*-(α-naphthyl)carbamate:** cryst. from lgr.; m.p. 95° ⟨14⟩ [cf. T 1.86]. [Other lower values in the literature are probably due to contamination with corresp. deriv. of pentanol-2 (1:6185).]

1:6175 ⟨1⟩ Timmermans, Hennaut-Roland, *J. chim. phys.* **29,** 543–544 (1932). ⟨2⟩ Norris, Cortese, *J. Am. Chem. Soc.* **49,** 2645 (1927). ⟨3⟩ Sherrill, Matlack, *J. Am. Chem. Soc.* **59,** 2138 (1937). ⟨4⟩ Ayres, *Ind. Eng. Chem.* **21,** 903–904 (1929). ⟨5⟩ Clark, Streight, *Trans. Roy. Soc. Can.* (3) **23,** III, 77–89 (1929). ⟨6⟩ Clark, Hallonquist, *Trans. Roy. Soc. Can.* (3) **24,** III, 117–118 (1930). ⟨7⟩ Lauer, Stodola, *J. Am. Chem. Soc.* **56,** 1216 (1934). ⟨8⟩ Shonle,

Keltch, Swanson, *J. Am. Chem. Soc.* **52,** 2442 (1930). ⟨9⟩ Hass, Weber, *Ind. Eng. Chem., Anal. Ed.* **7,** 233 (1935). ⟨10⟩ Allen, Spanagel, *J. Am. Chem. Soc.* **54,** 4346 (1932).

⟨11⟩ Hurd, Goodyear, Goldsby, *J. Am. Chem. Soc.* **58,** 236 (1936). ⟨12⟩ Conant, Blatt, *J. Am. Chem. Soc.* **51,** 1234 (1929). ⟨13⟩ Mannich, Zernick, *Arch. Pharm.* **246,** 182 (1908). ⟨14⟩ Brooks, *J. Am. Chem. Soc.* **56,** 2000 (1934). ⟨15⟩ Whitmore, Surmatis, *J. Am. Chem. Soc.* **62,** 995 (1940). ⟨16⟩ Shonle, *J. Am. Chem. Soc.* **56,** 2491 (1934). ⟨17⟩ Tabern, Volwiler, *J. Am. Chem. Soc.* **56,** 1141 (1934).

1:6180 ***n*-BUTYL ALCOHOL** $CH_3.CH_2.CH_2.CH_2.OH$ $C_4H_{10}O$ **Beil. I-367**

B.P. 118.0° ⟨1⟩ **M.P. −90.2°** ⟨1⟩ D_4^{20} = **0.80960** ⟨1⟩ n_D^{15} = **1.40118** ⟨1⟩
D_4^{25} = **0.8057** ⟨2⟩ n_D^{25} = **1.3974** ⟨2⟩

C̄ is sol. at 15° in abt. 11 vols. aq.; soly. in aq. passes through a minimum abt. 55° ⟨3⟩; C̄ is salted out from aq. solns. by K_2CO_3 or $CaCl_2$.

C̄ forms with aq. a binary heterogeneous const. boilg. mixt. (b.p. 92.25°) contg. 63% by wt. of C̄ ⟨4⟩ — C̄ forms with *n*-butyl acetate (1:3145) a binary const. boilg. mixt. (b.p. 116.5°) contg. 72.9 mole % of C̄ ⟨5⟩ [cf. ⟨6⟩] — C̄ forms with *n*-butyl acetate and aq. a ternary const. boilg. mixt. (b.p. 89.4°) contg. 27.4% by wt. of C̄, 35.3% by wt. of ester, and 37.3% by wt. of aq. ⟨6⟩ [cf. ⟨7⟩] — C̄ forms no const. boilg. mixt. with acetone ⟨5⟩.

For data on sp. gr. at 25° and on n_D^{25} for systems: C̄ + acetone and C̄ + *n*-butyl acetate see ⟨5⟩; for data on sp. gr. at 25° of ternary system: C̄ + *n*-butyl acetate + aq. see ⟨7⟩.

C̄ on oxidn. with CrO_3 + H_2SO_4 (T 1.72) yields *n*-butyraldehyde (1:0130) and *n*-butyric ac. (1:1035) [cf. ⟨8⟩ ⟨19⟩]. [Use in detn. of C̄ even in presence of EtOH ⟨9⟩ ⟨10⟩.] — C̄ on oxidn. with alk. $KMnO_4$ yields *n*-butyric ac. (1:1035).

For analysis of C̄, EtOH + acetone in aq. soln. see ⟨11⟩.

C̄, distd. with excess HBr (D = 1.48), yields *n*-butyl bromide, b.p. 101°; C̄, distd. with excess HI (D = 1.70), yields *n*-butyl iodide, b.p. 130°.

Ⓓ ***n*-Butyl *p*-nitrobenzoate:** m.p. 35–36° [cf. T 1.82]. [Use in identifn. of C̄ even in 0.25% aq. soln. ⟨12⟩.]

Ⓓ ***n*-Butyl 3,5-dinitrobenzoate:** m.p. 64° ⟨13⟩; 62.5° ⟨14⟩ [cf. T 1.82].

Ⓓ ***n*-Butyl hydrogen phthalate:** m.p. 73.1–73.5° cor.; Neut. Eq. 222 ⟨15⟩.

Ⓓ ***n*-Butyl hydrogen 3-nitrophthalate:** m.p. 146.8–147.0° cor.; Neut. Eq. 267.1 ⟨16⟩.

Ⓓ **Potassium *n*-butyl xanthate:** m.p. 223.9° cor. ⟨17⟩. [Note that corresp. deriv. of *n*-amyl alc. has m.p. 225°.]

Ⓓ ***n*-Butyl *N*-phenylcarbamate:** m.p. 61° ⟨18⟩ ⟨19⟩. [For optical data see ⟨24⟩.]

Ⓓ ***n*-Butyl *N*-(*p*-nitrophenyl)carbamate:** m.p. 95.5° ⟨20⟩; 96° ⟨21⟩.

Ⓓ ***n*-Butyl *N*-(α-naphthyl)carbamate:** m.p. 71–72° ⟨22⟩ [cf. T 1.86].

Ⓓ ***n*-Butyl *N*-(*p*-xenyl)carbamate:** m.p. 109° ⟨23⟩.

1:6180 ⟨1⟩ Timmermans, Martin, *J. chim. phys.* **25,** 427–428 (1928). ⟨2⟩ Brunel, Crenshaw, Tobin, *J. Am. Chem. Soc.* **43,** 575 (1921). ⟨3⟩ Führer, *Ber.* **57,** 512 (1924). ⟨4⟩ *Int. Crit. Tables,* III, 318. ⟨5⟩ Brunjes, Furnas, *Ind. Eng. Chem.* **27,** 396 (1935). ⟨6⟩ Hannotte, *Bull. soc. chim. Belg.* **35,** 101 (1926). ⟨7⟩ Brunjes, Furnas, *Ind. Eng. Chem.* **28,** 573–580 (1936). ⟨8⟩ Semichon, Flanzy, *Compt. rend.* **195,** 254 (1932). ⟨9⟩ Werkman, Osburn, *Ind. Eng. Chem., Anal. Ed.* **3,** 387–389 (1931). ⟨10⟩ Johnson, *Ind. Eng. Chem., Anal. Ed.* **4,** 20–22 (1932).

⟨11⟩ Christensen, Fulmer, *Ind. Eng. Chem., Anal. Ed.* **7,** 180–182 (1935). ⟨12⟩ Henstock, *J. Chem. Soc.* **1933,** 216. ⟨13⟩ Bryant, *J. Am. Chem. Soc.* **54,** 3760 (1932). ⟨14⟩ Malone, Reid, *J. Am. Chem. Soc.* **51,** 3426 (1929). ⟨15⟩ Goggans, Copenhaver, *J. Am. Chem. Soc.* **61,** 2909 (1939). ⟨16⟩ Dickinson, Crosson, Copenhaver, *J. Am. Chem. Soc.* **59,** 1095 (1937). ⟨17⟩ Whitmore, Lieber, *Ind. Eng. Chem., Anal. Ed.* **7,** 129 (1935). ⟨18⟩ Fournier, *Bull. soc. chim.* (4) **7,** 26 (1910). ⟨19⟩ Weizmann, Garrard, *J. Chem. Soc.* **117,** 328 (1920). ⟨20⟩ Shriner, Cox, *J. Am. Chem. Soc.* **53,** 1604, 3186 (1931).

⟨21⟩ Hoeke, *Rec. trav. chim.* **54,** 514 (1935). ⟨22⟩ Neuberg, Kansky, *Biochem. Z.* **20,** 447 (1909). ⟨23⟩ Morgan, Pettet, *J. Chem. Soc.* **1931,** 1125. ⟨24⟩ Dewey, Witt, *Ind. Eng. Chem., Anal. Ed.* **12,** 459 (1940).

1:6185 **d,l-PENTANOL-2** $C_5H_{12}O$ **Beil. I-384**

(*rac.*-Methyl-*n*-propyl-carbinol; *unsym. sec*-amyl alcohol)

$$CH_3—\overset{H}{\underset{OH}{C}}—CH_2.CH_2.CH_3$$

B.P. 119.85° ⟨1⟩ D_4^{20} = **0.80919** ⟨1⟩ n_D^{20} = **1.4060** ⟨3⟩

119.5° ⟨2⟩ D_4^{25} = **0.80528** ⟨2⟩ n_D^{25} = **1.4041** ⟨2⟩

$\bar{C}$ is sol. in 19 vols. aq. at 30°; in 24 vols. aq. at 70° ⟨4⟩. [For more precise data see ⟨5⟩.] $\bar{C}$ forms with aq. a binary const. boilg. mixt. (b.p. 92.3°) contg. 67.8% by wt. of $\bar{C}$ + 32.2% aq. ⟨4⟩.

$\bar{C}$ with $ZnCl_2$ + conc. HCl (T 1.85) rapidly clouds and yields 2-chloropentane, b.p. 96.6°. [For prepn. from $\bar{C}$ + conc. HCl see ⟨6⟩ ⟨7⟩.] — $\bar{C}$, on satn. with HBr gas at −10° and allowing to warm only to room temp. ⟨9⟩, gives pure 2-bromopentane, b.p. 117.0–118.0°, in 84% yield ⟨8⟩. [Note that if $\bar{C}$ is distd. with HBr (*D* = 1.48) the product is a mixture of 2-bromopentane and 3-bromopentane in varying proportions acc. to conditions but with sometimes as much as 19% of latter ⟨10⟩.]

$\bar{C}$ on oxidn. with $K_2Cr_2O_7$ + H_2SO_4 [cf. T 1.72] at 60° gives 70% yield ⟨11⟩ of methyl *n*-propyl ketone (1:5415) — $\bar{C}$ with I_2 + KI soln. + alk. (T 1.81) yields CHI_3.

$\bar{C}$ htd. on steam bath with 50–60% H_2SO_4 gives 65–80% yield ⟨12⟩ ⟨13⟩ pentene-2 (1:8215), b.p. 36.2°.

Ⓓ **Methyl-*n*-propyl-carbinyl 3,5-dinitrobenzoate:** m.p. 62.1° ⟨14⟩; 61.5–62° ⟨8⟩ [cf. T 1.82].

Ⓓ **Methyl-*n*-propyl-carbinyl hydrogen phthalate:** m.p. 60–61° ⟨15⟩ [m.p. of *d*- or *l*-isomer is 34° ⟨15⟩].

Ⓓ **Methyl-*n*-propyl-carbinyl hydrogen 3-nitrophthalate:** m.p. 102–103°; Neut. Eq. 281 [cf. T 1.83].

Ⓓ **Methyl-*n*-propyl-carbinyl *N*-(α-naphthyl)carbamate:** m.p. 74.5° ⟨16⟩; 72° ⟨17⟩.

Ⓓ **Methyl-*n*-propyl-carbinyl *N*-(*p*-xenyl)carbamate:** m.p. 94.5° ⟨18⟩.

1:6185 ⟨1⟩ Timmermans, Hennaut-Roland, *J. chim. phys.* **29,** 545–546 (1932). ⟨2⟩ Ellis, Reid, *J. Am. Chem. Soc.* **54,** 1678–1679 (1932). ⟨3⟩ Sherrill, Baldwin, Haas, *J. Am. Chem. Soc.* **51,** 3036 (1929). ⟨4⟩ Ayres, *Ind. Eng. Chem.* **21,** 904 (1929). ⟨5⟩ Ginnings, Baum, *J. Am. Chem. Soc.* **59,** 112 (1937). ⟨6⟩ Hass, Weber, *Ind. Eng. Chem., Anal. Ed.* **7,** 233 (1935). ⟨7⟩ Clark, Streight, *Trans. Roy. Soc. Can.* (3) **23,** III, 77–89 (1929). ⟨8⟩ Lauer, Stodola, *J. Am. Chem. Soc.* **56,** 1218 (1934). ⟨9⟩ Clark, Hallonquist, *Trans. Roy. Soc. Can.* (3) **24,** III, 117–118 (1930). ⟨10⟩ Shonle, Keltch, Swanson, *J. Am. Chem. Soc.* **52,** 2442–2443 (1930).

⟨11⟩ Allen, Spanagel, *J. Am. Chem. Soc.* **54,** 4346 (1932). ⟨12⟩ Norris, *Organic Syntheses, Coll. Vol.* I, 421–422 (1932). ⟨13⟩ Ref. 3, pages 3037–3038 (1929). ⟨14⟩ Malone, Reid, *J. Am. Chem. Soc.* **51,** 3426 (1929). ⟨15⟩ Pickard, Kenyon, *J. Chem. Soc.* **99,** 58, 63 (1911). ⟨16⟩ Adamson, Kenner, *J. Chem. Soc.* **1934,** 842. ⟨17⟩ Brooks, *J. Am. Chem. Soc.* **56,** 2000 (1934). ⟨18⟩ Morgan, Hardy, *Chemistry & Industry* **52,** 519 (1933).

1:6186 **2,2-DIMETHYLBUTANOL-3** $C_6H_{14}O$ **Beil. I-412**

(*ter*-Butyl-methyl-carbinol; pinacolyl alcohol)

$$CH_3—\overset{CH_3}{\underset{CH_3}{C}}—\overset{H}{\underset{OH}{C}}—CH_3$$

B.P. 120.4° ⟨1⟩ ⟨2⟩ **M.P. +5.3°** ⟨2⟩ D_4^{20} = **0.8185** n_D^{20} = **1.4148** ⟨2⟩

[For prepn. from *ter*-butyl MgCl + acetaldehyde in 52–80% yield see ⟨2⟩ ⟨3⟩.]

Ⓓ ***ter*-Butyl-methyl-carbinyl 3,5-dinitrobenzoate:** yel.-wh. ndls. from pet. ether; m.p. 107° ⟨4⟩ [cf. T 1.82].

Ⓓ ***ter*-Butyl-methyl-carbinyl hydrogen phthalate:** rods from lt. pet.; m.p. 85–86° ⟨5⟩.

Ⓓ ***ter*-Butyl-methyl-carbinyl *N*-phenylcarbamate:** from $\bar{C}$ + phenylisocyanate rapidly on mixing; cryst. from pet. eth., m.p. 77–78° ⟨6⟩; 77.5–78.5° ⟨7⟩.

1:6186 ⟨1⟩ Willcox, Brunel, *J. Am. Chem. Soc.* **38,** 1838 (1916). ⟨2⟩ Whitmore, Meunier, *J. Am. Chem. Soc.* **55,** 3722 (1933). ⟨3⟩ Conant, Blatt, *J. Am. Chem. Soc.* **51,** 1233 (1929). ⟨4⟩ Sutter, *Helv. Chim. Acta* **21,** 1271 (1938). ⟨5⟩ Pickard, Kenyon, *J. Chem. Soc.* **105,** 1120 (1914). ⟨6⟩ Rheinboldt, Roleff, *J. prakt. Chem.* (2) **109,** 189 (1925). ⟨7⟩ Whitmore, Rothrock, *J. Am. Chem. Soc.* **55,** 1107 (1933).

1:6187 2,3-DIMETHYLBUTANOL-2 (Dimethyl-isopropyl-carbinol) $C_6H_{14}O$ **Beil. I-413**

```
        CH3CH3
         |  |
   CH3—C—C—CH3
         |  |
         H  OH
```

B.P. 120-121° **M.P. −14°** D_0^{20} = **0.8208** n_D = **1.4140**

Ⓓ **Dimethyl-isopropyl-carbinyl 3,5-dinitrobenzoate:** yellowish lfts. from C_6H_6 + pet. eth.; m.p. 111° ⟨1⟩ [cf. T 1.82].

Ⓓ **Dimethyl-isopropyl-carbinyl *N*-phenylcarbamate:** from C̄ + phenylisocyanate slowly on stdg.; cryst. from pet. eth., m.p. 65–66° ⟨2⟩.

1:6187 ⟨1⟩ Sutter, *Helv. Chim. Acta* **21,** 1272 (1938). ⟨2⟩ Delacre, *Bull. soc. chim.* (4) **1,** 460 (1907).

1:6189 3-METHYLPENTANOL-3 (Diethyl-methyl-carbinol) $C_6H_{14}O$ **Beil. I-411**

```
              CH3
               |
   CH3.CH2—C—CH2.CH3
               |
              OH
```

B.P. 122.9° ⟨1⟩ ⟨2⟩ **M.P. −22°** D_4^{25} = **0.8233** ⟨1⟩ n_D^{25} = **1.4166** ⟨1⟩

C̄, on distn. with *p*-toluenesulfonyl chloride (93% yield) ⟨3⟩, or with equal wt. anhyd. $ZnCl_2$ ⟨4⟩, or with $KHSO_4$ ⟨5⟩, or with small amt. I_2 ⟨6⟩ ⟨7⟩, yields mixture of stereoisomeric forms of 3-methylpentene-2 (1:8260), b.p. 65–70°. [By most careful fractional distn. mixt. has been sepd. into two isomers of b.p. 65.1–65.7° and 70.2–70.5° ⟨8⟩.]

C̄, on oxidn. with $K_2Cr_2O_7$ + H_2SO_4 (cf. T 1.72), yields (only) acetic acid (1:1010) ⟨9⟩.

Ⓓ **Diethyl-methyl-carbinyl 3,5-dinitrobenzoate:** yellowish lfts. from pet. ether, m.p. 96.5° ⟨10⟩. [Cf. T 1.82.]

Ⓓ **Diethyl-methyl-carbinyl *N*-phenylcarbamate:** m.p. 43.5° ⟨11⟩.

Ⓓ **Diethyl-methyl-carbinyl *N*-α-naphthylcarbamate:** m.p. 83.5° ⟨11⟩. [Cf. T 1.86.]

Ⓓ **Diethyl-methyl-carbinyl allophanate:** m.p. 152° cor. ⟨12⟩.

1:6189 ⟨1⟩ Norris, Cortese, *J. Am. Chem. Soc.* **49,** 2644 (1927). ⟨2⟩ Willcox, Brunel, *J. Am. Chem. Soc.* **38,** 1838 (1916). ⟨3⟩ van Risseghem, *Bull. soc. chim. Belg.* **31,** 218 (1922). ⟨4⟩ Pariselle, Simon, *Compt. rend.* **173,** 86 (1921). ⟨5⟩ Glacet, *Bull. soc. chim.* (5) **5,** 900 (1938). ⟨6⟩ Church, Whitmore, McGrew, *J. Am. Chem. Soc.* **56,** 182 (1934). ⟨7⟩ Hickinbottom, *J. Chem. Soc.* **1935,** 1280. ⟨8⟩ van Risseghem, *Bull. soc. chim. Belg.* **47,** 47 (1938). ⟨9⟩ Reformatsky, *J. prakt. Chem.* (2) **36,** 345–346 (1887). ⟨10⟩ Sutter, *Helv. Chim. Acta* **21,** 1271 (1938).

⟨11⟩ Cottle, Powell, *J. Am. Chem. Soc.* **58,** 2270 (1936). ⟨12⟩ Grandière, *Bull. soc. chim.* (4) **35,** 189 (1934).

1:6190 2-METHYLPENTANOL-2 (Dimethyl-*n*-propyl-carbinol) $C_6H_{14}O$ **Beil. I-409**

```
         CH3
          |
   CH3—C—CH2.CH2.CH3
          |
         OH
```

B.P. 121.09° ⟨10⟩ **M.P. −103°** ⟨10⟩ D_4^{20} = **0.81341** ⟨10⟩ n_D^{20} = **1.4113** ⟨10⟩
B.P. 123° ⟨1⟩ **M.P. −108°** ⟨1⟩ D_4^{25} = **0.8051** ⟨2⟩ n_D^{25} = **1.4089** ⟨2⟩

C̄ htd. with excess HBr (D = 1.48) yields 2-bromo-2-methylpentane [Beil. I_1-(47)] ⟨1⟩. C̄ with 3 vols. conc. HCl yields 2-chloro-2-methylpentane, b.p. 111–113° ⟨3⟩ ⟨1⟩.

C̄, htd. with 25% H_2SO_4 ⟨4⟩, or with *p*-toluenesulfonic ac. (quant. yield) ⟨5⟩, or with anhyd. oxalic ac. ⟨6⟩ yields 2-methylpentene-2 (1:8275), b.p. 67.4° ⟨7⟩.

Ⓓ **Dimethyl-*n*-propyl-carbinyl benzoate:** from C̄ + BzCl in pyridine; cryst. from alc.; m.p. 182–183° ⟨1⟩ [cf. T 2.26-B].

Ⓓ **Dimethyl-*n*-propyl-carbinyl 3,5-dinitrobenzoate:** m.p. 72° ⟨8⟩ [cf. T 1.82].

Ⓓ **Dimethyl-*n*-propyl-carbinyl *N*-phenylcarbamate:** unknown. [The m.p. of 239° reported ⟨1⟩ for this compd. has been found ⟨3⟩ to represent the by-product *N,N'*-diphenylurea.]

Ⓓ **Dimethyl-*n*-propyl-carbinyl allophanate:** m.p. 128° ⟨9⟩.

1:6190 ⟨1⟩ Deschamps, *J. Am. Chem. Soc.* **42,** 2671–2672 (1920). ⟨2⟩ Norton, Hass, *J. Am. Chem. Soc.* **58,** 2149 (1936). ⟨3⟩ France, Maitland, Tucker, *J. Chem. Soc.* **1937,** 1743. ⟨4⟩ Montagne, *Ann. chim.* (10) **13,** 67–68 (1930). ⟨5⟩ van Risseghem, *Bull. soc. chim. Belg.* **32,** 145 (1923). ⟨6⟩ Read, Fletcher, *Trans. Am. Electrochem. Soc.* **47,** 96 (1925). ⟨7⟩ Schmitt, Boord, *J. Am. Chem. Soc.* **54,** 754 (1932). ⟨8⟩ Sutter, *Helv. Chim. Acta* **21,** 1271 (1938). ⟨9⟩ Béhal, *Bull. soc. chim.* (4) **25,** 475, 478 (1919). ⟨10⟩ Hovorka, Lankelma, Naujoks, *J. Am. Chem. Soc.* **55,** 4821 (1933).

1:6191 ETHYLENE GLYCOL METHYL *n*-PROPYL ETHER $C_6H_{14}O_2$ Beil. S.N. 30

(1-Methoxy-2-*n*-propoxyethane) $CH_3O.CH_2.CH_2.O.CH_2.CH_2.CH_3$

B.P. 124.5° ⟨1⟩ D_4^{20} = **0.8472** ⟨1⟩ n_D^{20} = **1.39467** ⟨1⟩

Misc. with aq.

1:6191 ⟨1⟩ Palomaa, Honkanen, *Ber.* **70,** 2204 (1937).

1:6194 2-METHYLPENTANOL-3 $C_6H_{14}O$ Beil. I-410

(Ethyl-isopropyl-carbinol)

$$CH_3.CH_2—\overset{\displaystyle H}{\underset{\displaystyle OH}{C}}—\overset{\displaystyle CH_3}{\underset{\displaystyle H}{C}}—CH_3$$

B.P. 126.68° ⟨5⟩ D_4^{20} = **0.82487** ⟨5⟩ n_D^{20} = **1.4168** ⟨5⟩

D_4^{25} = **0.8193** ⟨1⟩ n_D^{25} = **1.4151** ⟨1⟩

Ⓓ **Ethyl-isopropyl-carbinyl 3,5-dinitrobenzoate:** yel. lfts. from pet. ether; m.p. 85° ⟨2⟩ [cf. T 1.82].

Ⓓ **Ethyl-isopropyl-carbinyl hydrogen phthalate:** m.p. racemic form, 69–71° ⟨3⟩.

Ⓓ **Ethyl-isopropyl-carbinyl *N*-phenylcarbamate:** m.p. 50° (poor yield) ⟨4⟩.

1:6194 ⟨1⟩ Norton, Hass, *J. Am. Chem. Soc.* **58,** 2149 (1936). ⟨2⟩ Sutter, *Helv. Chim. Acta* **21,** 1270 (1938). ⟨3⟩ Pickard, Kenyon, *J. Chem. Soc.* **101,** 633 (1912). ⟨4⟩ Stas, *Bull. soc. chim. Belg.* **35,** 384 (1926). ⟨5⟩ Hovorka, Lankelma, Axelrod, *J. Am.Chem. Soc.* **62,** 188 (1940).

1:6195 *d-sec*-BUTYLCARBINOL $C_5H_{12}O$ Beil. I-385

(2-Methylbutanol-1; *act.*-amyl alcohol)

$$CH_3.CH_2.\underset{\displaystyle CH_3}{CH}.CH_2OH$$

B.P. 128.9° ⟨1⟩ $[\alpha]_D^{20.4}$ = **−5.756°** ⟨1⟩ D_4^{20} = **0.8193** ⟨1⟩ n_D^{20} = **1.4107** ⟨1⟩

Impt. component of " fusel oil " — [Note that C̄ is laevorotatory although designated " *d* " ⟨2⟩.] [For isolation of C̄ from fusel oil see ⟨1⟩.]

C̄ satd. at 0° with HCl gas and htd. in s.t. at 100° for 5 hrs. gives 20% yield ⟨1⟩ dextrorotatory 1-chloro-2-methylbutane, b.p. 100.5°, D_4^{20} = 0.8857; n_D^{20} = 1.4124; $[\alpha]_D^{20.1}$ = +1.644°. [For prepn. of corresp. *d,l*-deriv. from *d,l*-alcohol in 49% yield see ⟨3⟩.] — C̄, satd. with HBr gas at 0°, then htd. $2\frac{1}{2}$ hrs. at 95° in stream of HBr gives 70% yield dextrorotatory 1-bromo-2-methylbutane, b.p. 121.6°; D_4^{20} = 1.2234; n_D^{20} = 1.4451; $[\alpha]_D^{20.6}$ =

+4.043° ⟨1⟩ — C̄, satd. at 0° with HI, then htd. 1 hr. at 60–65° in stream of HI gives 65% yield of dextrorotatory 1-iodo-2-methylbutane (dec. on distn. at ord. press.), b.p. 66.5° at 50 mm., D_4^{20} = 1.5253; n_D^{20} = 1.4977; $[\alpha]_D^{19.8}$ = +5.685 ⟨1⟩.

C̄ on oxidn. with CrO_3 + H_2SO_4 (cf. T 1.72) yields ethyl-methyl-acetic ac. (1:1105) ⟨4⟩

Ⓓ ***d-sec*-Butylcarbinyl 3,5-dinitrobenzoate:** m.p. 70° ⟨5⟩ [cf. T 1.82].

Ⓓ ***act.*-Amyl hydrogen 3-nitrophthalate:** cryst. from aq.; m.p. 157–158° ⟨6⟩ [cf. T 1.83] [m.p. *d,l*-deriv. 152°].

Ⓓ ***act.*-Amyl *N*-(α-naphthyl)carbamate:** ndls. from lgr.; m.p. 82° ⟨7⟩ [cf. T 1.86].

1:6195 ⟨1⟩ Brauns, *J. Research Natl. Bur. Standards* **18**, 315–331 (1937). ⟨2⟩ Marckwald, *Ber.* **35**, 1599, Note 1 (1902). ⟨3⟩ Hass, Weber, *Ind Eng. Chem., Anal. Ed.* **7**, 233 (1935). ⟨4⟩ Marckwald, *Ber.* **37**, 1045 (1904). ⟨5⟩ Reichstein, *Helv. Chim. Acta* **9**, 802 (1926). ⟨6⟩ Nicolet, Sachs, *J. Am. Chem. Soc.* **47**, 2348 (1925). ⟨7⟩ Neuberg, Kansky, *Biochem. Z.* **20**, 448 (1909); *Cent.* **1909**, II, 1379; *Chem. Abs.* **4**, 1483 (1910).

1:6199 *d,l*-2-METHYLPENTANOL-4

$C_6H_{14}O$ **Beil. I-410**

(Isobutyl-methyl-carbinol; "methylamyl alcohol"; 4-methylpentanol-2)

$(CH_3)_2CH.CH_2.CH(OH)CH_3$

B.P. 131.85° ⟨1⟩; cf. ⟨10⟩

D_4^{20} = **0.80713** ⟨10⟩. n_D^{20} = **1.4011** ⟨10⟩
D_4^{25} = **0.80245** ⟨1⟩ n_D^{25} = **1.40895** ⟨1⟩

Action of 75% H_2SO_4 at 80° yields mixt. of two decenes, viz., 3,5,5-trimethylheptene-2 and 3,4,5,5-tetramethylhexene-2, inseparable by fractnl. distn. ⟨2⟩ — C̄ htd. with phthalic anhyd. 16 hrs. at 115° yields *d,l*-isobutyl-methyl-carbinyl hydrogen phthalate (use in resolution via brucine) ⟨8⟩, m.p. not given. C̄ on oxidn. with CrO_3 + AcOH yields 2-methylpentanone-4 (1:5430) ⟨9⟩.

Ⓓ **Isobutyl-methyl-carbinyl *p*-nitrobenzoate:** m.p. 24–26° ⟨3⟩.

Ⓓ **Isobutyl-methyl-carbinyl 3,5-dinitrobenzoate:** yellowish lfts. from pet. ether, m.p. 65° ⟨4⟩.

Ⓓ **Isobutyl-methyl-carbinyl *N*-phenylcarbamate:** cryst. from AcOEt, m.p. 143° ⟨5⟩.

Ⓓ **Isobutyl-methyl-carbinyl *N*-α-naphthylcarbamate:** cryst. from pet. ether, m.p. 87–88° ⟨6⟩.

Ⓓ **Isobutyl-methyl-carbinyl *N*-*p*-xenylcarbamate:** m.p. 95.5° ⟨7⟩.

1:6199 ⟨1⟩ Brunel, *J. Am. Chem. Soc.* **45**, 1337–1338 (1923). ⟨2⟩ Drake, Kline, Rose, *J. Am. Chem. Soc.* **56**, 2076–2079 (1934). ⟨3⟩ Banfield, Kenyon, *J. Chem. Soc.* **1926**, 1623. ⟨4⟩ Sutter, *Helv. Chim. Acta* **21**, 1266–1272 (1938). ⟨5⟩ Skita, *Ber.* **41**, 2939 (1908). ⟨6⟩ Brooks, *J. Am. Chem. Soc.* **56**, 2000 (1934). ⟨7⟩ Morgan, Hardy, *Chemistry & Industry* **52**, 519 (1933). ⟨8⟩ Levene, Mikesa, *J. Biol. Chem.* **65**, 509 (1925). ⟨9⟩ Fichter, Sutter, *Helv. Chim. Acta* **21**, 896 (1938). ⟨10⟩ Hovorka, Lankelma, Stanford, *J. Am. Chem. Soc.* **60**, 822–823 (1938).

1:6200 ISOAMYL ALCOHOL

$C_5H_{12}O$ **Beil. I-392**

(2-Methylbutanol-4; 3-methylbutanol-1; *prim.*-isoamyl alcohol)

```
        H
        |
CH3.C.CH2.CH2.OH
        |
       CH3
```

B.P. 132.0° ⟨1⟩ **M.P. −117°** D_4^{20} = **0.80918** ⟨1⟩ n_D^{15} = **1.40851** ⟨1⟩

Odor disagreeable, provoking coughing — 100 ml. aq. at room temp. dis. 3.3 ml. C̄. [For more precise data see ⟨2⟩.]

C̄ forms with aq. a binary const. boilg. mixt. (b.p. 95.15°) contg. 50.40% by wt. of C̄ + 49.60% by wt. of aq. ⟨3⟩ — C̄ forms no binary const. boilg. mixt. with C_6H_6, nor any ternary const. boilg. mixt. with C_6H_6 + aq. ⟨4⟩.

C̄ htd. 6 hrs. at 90° with 1/10 vol. conc. HCl in stream of HCl gas gives isoamyl chloride, b.p. 98.8° ⟨5⟩ — C̄ treated with HBr gas at 105–125° yields isoamyl bromide, b.p. 120.65°, D_4^{20} = 1.20299; n_D^{15} = 1.44352 ⟨1⟩. [Note: isoamyl bromide forms with C̄ a binary const. boilg. mixt., b.p. 118.3°, from which C̄ is removed with P_2O_5 ⟨1⟩.] — C̄ with excess HI (D = 1.70) yields isoamyl iodide, b.p. 147°.

Ⓓ **Isoamyl 3,5-dinitrobenzoate:** m.p. 61° ⟨6⟩ [cf. T 1.82].

Ⓓ **Isoamyl hydrogen 3-nitrophthalate:** cryst. from 30% alc., m.p. 163.2–163.4°; Neut. Eq. 281.1 ⟨7⟩; cryst. from aq., m.p. 165–166° ⟨8⟩ [cf. T 1.83].

Ⓓ **Isoamyl *N*-phenylcarbamate:** cryst. from lgr., m.p. 56–57° ⟨9⟩.

Ⓓ **Isoamyl *N*-(*p*-nitrophenyl)carbamate:** cryst. from CCl_4; m.p. 97.5° ⟨10⟩.

Ⓓ **Isoamyl *N*-(α-naphthyl)carbamate:** cryst. from dil. alc., m.p. 67–68° ⟨11⟩.

1:6200 ⟨1⟩ Timmermans, Hennaut-Roland, *Anales soc. españ. fís. quím.* **27**, 460–472 (1929), in French; *Chem. Abs.* **24**, 54 (1930). ⟨2⟩ Ginnings, Baum, *J. Am. Chem. Soc.* **59**, 1112 (1937). ⟨3⟩ Young, Fortey, *J. Chem. Soc.* **81**, 733–734 (1902). ⟨4⟩ Young, Fortey, *J. Chem. Soc.* **81**, 749–750 (1902). ⟨5⟩ Hass, Weber, *Ind. Eng. Chem., Anal. Ed.* **7**, 233 (1935). ⟨6⟩ Reichstein, *Helv. Chim. Acta* **9**, 802 (1926). ⟨7⟩ Dickinson, Crosson, Copenhaver, *J. Am. Chem. Soc.* **59**, 1095 (1937). ⟨8⟩ Nicolet, Sachs, *J. Am. Chem. Soc.* **47**, 2349 (1925). ⟨9⟩ Levene, Allen, *J. Biol. Chem.* **27**, 440 (1916). ⟨10⟩ Shriner, Cox, *J. Am. Chem. Soc.* **53**, 1604, 3186 (1931). ⟨11⟩ Neuberg, Kansky, *Biochem. Z.* **20**, 448 (1909).

1:6202 3-METHYLPENTANOL-2

(*sec*-Butyl-methyl-carbinol) $C_6H_{14}O$ **Beil. I-411**

$$CH_3.CH_2{-}\underset{H}{\overset{CH_3}{C}}{-}\underset{H}{\overset{OH}{C}}{-}CH_3$$

B.P. 134.2°/749 mm. ⟨1⟩

Ⓓ ***sec*-Butyl-methyl-carbinyl-3,5-dinitrobenzoate:** yellowish lfts. from pet. ether; m.p. 43.5° ⟨2⟩; 41° ⟨1⟩ [cf. T 1.82].

Ⓓ ***sec*-Butyl-methyl-carbinyl *N*-(α-naphthyl)carbamate:** m.p. 72° ⟨3⟩.

1:6202 ⟨1⟩ Norton, Hass, *J. Am. Chem. Soc.* **58**, 2149 (1936). ⟨2⟩ Sutter, *Helv. Chim. Acta* **21**, 1270 (1938). ⟨3⟩ Cottle, Powell, *J. Am. Chem. Soc.* **58**, 2270 (1936).

1:6203 HEXANOL-3

(Ethyl-*n*-propyl-carbinol) $C_6H_{14}O$ **Beil. I-408**

$$CH_3.CH_2.CH_2{-}\underset{OH}{\overset{H}{C}}{-}CH_2.CH_3$$

B.P. 135.52° ⟨3⟩

D_4^{20} = **0.81851** ⟨3⟩ n_D^{20} = **1.4159** ⟨3⟩
D_4^{25} = **0.81428** ⟨3⟩ n_D^{25} = **1.4139** ⟨3⟩

Ⓓ **Ethyl-*n*-propyl-carbinyl 3,5-dinitrobenzoate:** yel.-wh. lfts. from pet. ether; m.p. 77° ⟨1⟩ [cf. T 1.82].

Ⓓ **Ethyl-*n*-propyl-carbinyl hydrogen phthalate:** hard rhombs. from lt. pet., m.p. 76–77° ⟨2⟩.

1:6203 ⟨1⟩ Sutter, *Helv. Chim. Acta* **21**, 1270 (1938). ⟨2⟩ Pickard, Kenyon, *J. Chem. Soc.* **103**, 1942 (1913). ⟨3⟩ Hovorka, Lankelma, Stanford, *J. Am. Chem. Soc.* **60**, 822–823 (1938).

1:6204 2,2-DIMETHYLBUTANOL-1 (*ter*-Amylcarbinol) $CH_3.CH_2.C(CH_3)_2.CH_2.OH$ $C_6H_{14}O$ **Beil. I-412**

B.P. 136.69° ⟨5⟩ D^{20}_4 = **0.82834** ⟨5⟩ n^{20}_D = **1.4208** ⟨5⟩
D^{25}_4 = **0.82429** ⟨5⟩ n^{25}_D = **1.4188** ⟨5⟩

[For prepn. in 40–47% yield from *ter*-amyl MgCl + HCHO see ⟨2⟩.]

Ⓓ ***ter*-Amylcarbinyl 3,5-dinitrobenzoate:** yellowish lfts. from pet. ether; m.p. 51.0° ⟨1⟩. [Mixed m.p. with corresponding deriv. of 2,3-dimethylbutanol-1 (1:6221) shows no depression.] [Addn. prod. with α-naphthylamine; orange pdr. from pet. ether, m.p. 107.5° ⟨1⟩.] [Cf. T 1.82.]

Ⓓ ***ter*-Amylcarbinyl hydrogen phthalate:** from C̄ + phthalic anhyd. htd. 4–5 hrs. at 130–140° (85–90% yield); cryst. from lt. pet., m.p. 68–69°; Neut. Eq. 250 ⟨3⟩.

Ⓓ ***ter*-Amylcarbinyl hydrogen tetrachlorophthalate:** from C̄ + tetrachlorophthalic acid refluxed in C_6H_6 for 4–5 hrs. (60–70% yield); cryst. from C_6H_6, m.p. 149.5–150.5° ⟨3⟩.

Ⓓ ***ter*-Amylcarbinyl *N*-phenylcarbamate:** m.p. 65–66° ⟨4⟩.

Ⓓ ***ter*-Amylcarbinyl *N*-(α-naphthyl)carbamate:** from C̄ + α-naphthylisocyanate at 100° for 30 min. (80–85% yield); cryst. from lgr.; m.p. 80–81° ⟨3⟩.

1:6204 ⟨1⟩ Sutter, *Helv. Chim. Acta* **21,** 1268–1269 (1938). ⟨2⟩ Conant, Webb, Meldrum, *J. Am. Chem. Soc.* **51,** 1250 (1929). ⟨3⟩ Rice, Jenkins, Harden, *J. Am. Chem. Soc.* **59,** 2000 (1937). ⟨4⟩ Faworski, Ssakara, *Cent.* **1923,** III, 667. ⟨5⟩ Hovorka, Lankelma, Smith, *J. Am. Chem. Soc.* **62,** 2373 (1940).

1:6205 PENTANOL-1 $CH_3.CH_2.CH_2.CH_2.CH_2OH$ $C_5H_{12}O$ **Beil. I-383** (*n*-Amyl alcohol)

B.P. 138.0° cor. ⟨1⟩ **M.P. −78.5°** ⟨1⟩ D^{20}_4 = **0.81479** ⟨1⟩ n^{20}_D = **1.40994** ⟨1⟩
D^{25}_4 = **0.81159** ⟨5⟩ n^{25}_D = **1.4077** ⟨5⟩

C̄ is sol. in 5 vols. aq. at 30° ⟨2⟩; with aq. C̄ forms a const. boilg. mixt. (b.p. 95.8°) contg. 45.6% C̄ + 54.4% aq. ⟨3⟩. [For purifn. of comml. C̄ via formn., crystn. and hydrolysis of *n*-amyl *p*-hydroxybenzoate, m.p. 36° see ⟨4⟩.]

C̄ on distn. with HBr (D = 1.48) yields *n*-amyl bromide, b.p. 129.7° ⟨5⟩.

C̄ on oxidn. with $CrO_3 + H_2SO_4$ (cf. T 1.72) gives *n*-valeraldehyde ⟨6⟩ (1:0155); then *n*-valeric ac. (1:1060) [cf. ⟨7⟩].

n-Amyl *p*-nitrobenzoate is an oil, m.p. 8.5–10.5° ⟨8⟩. [The m.p. of 54° reported by ⟨9⟩ is certainly erroneous and probably due to recrystn. of his prod. from ethyl alcohol.]

Ⓓ ***n*-Amyl 3,5-dinitrobenzoate:** m.p. 46.4° ⟨10⟩ [cf. T 1.82].

Ⓓ ***n*-Amyl hydrogen phthalate:** m.p. 75.4–75.6°; Neut. Eq. 236 ⟨11⟩.

Ⓓ ***n*-Amyl hydrogen 3-nitrophthalate:** m.p. 136.2–136.4°; Neut. Eq. 281.1 ⟨12⟩ [T 1.83].

Ⓓ ***n*-Amyl hydrogen tetrachlorophthalate:** m.p. 105.5° ⟨13⟩.

Ⓓ **Potassium *n*-amyl xanthate:** m.p. 225° ⟨14⟩. [Does not distinguish from *n*-butyl alc. (1:6180).]

Ⓓ ***n*-Amyl *N*-phenylcarbamate:** m.p. 46° ⟨15⟩. [For optical data see ⟨20⟩.]

Ⓓ ***n*-Amyl *N*-(*p*-nitrophenyl)carbamate:** m.p. 86° ⟨16⟩; 91° ⟨17⟩.

Ⓓ ***n*-Amyl *N*-(α-naphthyl)carbamate:** m.p. 68° ⟨18⟩.

Ⓓ ***n*-Amyl *N*-(*p*-xenyl)carbamate:** m.p. 99° ⟨19⟩.

1:6205 ⟨1⟩ Simon, *Bull. soc. chim. Belg.* **38,** 56, 58 (1929). ⟨2⟩ Ayres, *Ind. Eng. Chem.* **21,** 904 (1929). ⟨3⟩ Hannotte, *Bull. soc. chim. Belg.* **35,** 94 (1926). ⟨4⟩ Olivier, *Rec. trav. chim.* **55,** 1027 (1936). ⟨5⟩ Ellis, Reid, *J. Am. Chem. Soc.* **54,** 1680–1683 (1932). ⟨6⟩ Kuhn, Grundmann, *Ber.* **70,** 1897–1898 (1937). ⟨7⟩ Semichon, Flanzy, *Compt. rend.* **195,** 254 (1932). ⟨8⟩ Adamson, Kenner, *J. Chem. Soc.* **1935,** 287. ⟨9⟩ Henstock, *J. Chem. Soc.* **1933,** 216. ⟨10⟩ Malone, Reid, *J. Am. Chem. Soc.* **51,** 3426 (1929).

⟨11⟩ Goggans, Copenhaver, *J. Am. Chem. Soc.* **61,** 2909 (1939). ⟨12⟩ Dickinson, Crosson, Copenhaver, *J. Am. Chem. Soc.* **59,** 1095 (1937). ⟨13⟩ Morgan, Hardy, Procter, *Chemistry & Industry,* **51T,** 7 (1932). ⟨14⟩ Whitmore, Lieber, *Ind. Eng. Chem., Anal. Ed.* **7,** 129 (1935). ⟨15⟩ Blaise, Piccard, *Ann. chim.* (8) **25,** 261 (1912). ⟨16⟩ Shriner, Cox, *J. Am. Chem. Soc.* **53,** 1604, 3186 (1931). ⟨17⟩ Hoeke, *Rec. trav. chim.* **54,** 514 (1935). ⟨18⟩ Bickel, French, *J. Am. Chem. Soc.* **48,** 749 (1926). ⟨19⟩ Morgan, Pettet, *J. Chem. Soc.* **1931,** 1125. ⟨20⟩ Dewey, Witt, *Ind. Eng. Chem., Anal. Ed.* **12,** 459 (1940).

1:6210 ***d,l*-HEXANOL-2** (*n*-Butyl-methyl-carbinol) $C_6H_{14}O$ **Beil. I-408**

$CH_3.CH_2.CH_2.CH_2—C(H)(OH)—CH_3$

B.P. 139.8° ⟨1⟩; cf. ⟨13⟩ D_4^{15} = **0.8171** ⟨2⟩ n_D^{15} = **1.4158** ⟨2⟩; cf. ⟨13⟩
D_4^{25} = **0.80977** ⟨1⟩ n_D^{25} = **1.4126** ⟨1⟩; cf. ⟨13⟩

C̄, htd. with HBr (D = 1.48) + conc. H_2SO_4 ⟨3⟩, or htd. with fumg. HBr (D = 1.78) + red P in s.t. at 100° ⟨4⟩ yields 2-bromohexane, b.p. 144°, D_4^{20} = 1.1658.

C̄ oxidized with ¾ theoret. amt. CrO_3 + H_2SO_4 at not above 50° gives 80% yield ⟨5⟩ of *n*-butyl methyl ketone (1:5435) — C̄ with I_2.KI soln. + alk. (T 1.81) yields CHI_3 ⟨6⟩.

C̄ htd. at 150° with *p*-toluenesulfonic ac. gives 80% yield ⟨2⟩ hexene-2 (1:8280), b.p. 68.1°.

Ⓓ ***n*-Butyl-methyl-carbinyl *p*-nitrobenzoate:** m.p. 40° [cf. T 1.82].

Ⓓ ***n*-Butyl-methyl-carbinyl 3,5-dinitrobenzoate:** m.p. 38° ⟨7⟩; 38.6° ⟨8⟩ [cf. T 1.82].

Ⓓ ***n*-Butyl-methyl-carbinyl hydrogen phthalate:** m.p. *d,l*-form unrecorded; m.p. *d*-form 29° ⟨9⟩.

Ⓓ ***n*-Butyl-methyl-carbinyl *N*-(α-naphthyl)carbamate:** m.p. 60.5° ⟨10⟩; 58–62° ⟨11⟩ [m.p. *d*-form, 81–82.5° ⟨12⟩] [cf. T 1.86].

1:6210 ⟨1⟩ Ellis, Reid, *J. Am. Chem. Soc.* **54,** 1678–1683 (1932). ⟨2⟩ van Risseghem, *Bull. soc. chim. Belg.* **35,** 330–334 (1926). ⟨3⟩ Green, *J. Am. Chem. Soc.* **56,** 1167 (1934). ⟨4⟩ Olivier, *Rec. trav. chim.* **55,** 1029 (1936). ⟨5⟩ Grignard, Fluchaire, *Ann. chim.* (10) **9,** 15 (1928). ⟨6⟩ Fichter, Leupin, *Helv. Chim. Acta* **21,** 616 (1938). ⟨7⟩ Sutter, *Helv. Chim. Acta* **21,** 1269 (1938). ⟨8⟩ Malone, Reid, *J. Am. Chem. Soc.* **51,** 3426 (1929). ⟨9⟩ Pickard, Kenyon, *J. Chem. Soc.* **99,** 58, 63 (1911). ⟨10⟩ Adamson, Kenner, *J. Chem. Soc.* **1934,** 842.

⟨11⟩ Brooks, *J. Am. Chem. Soc.* **56,** 2000 (1934). ⟨12⟩ Levene, Walti, *J. Biol. Chem.* **90,** 85–86 (1931). ⟨13⟩ Hovorka, Lankelma, Stanford, *J. Am. Chem. Soc.* **60,** 822–823 (1938).

1:6215 **2,4-DIMETHYLPENTANOL-3** (Diisopropylcarbinol) $C_7H_{16}O$ **Beil. I-417**

$CH_3—CH(CH_3)—CH(OH)—CH(CH_3)—CH_3$

B.P. 140° D_4^{20} = **0.8288** n_D^{20} = **1.42259**

Odor like mint and camphor.

C̄ on oxidn. with CrO_3 + H_2SO_4 ⟨1⟩ or $K_2Cr_2O_7$ + H_2SO_4 (85% yield) ⟨2⟩ gives diisopropyl ketone (1:5433).

C̄ htd. with ½ wt. of cryst. oxalic ac. yields 2,4-dimethylpentene-2, b.p. 82.9–83.4° ⟨3⟩.

Ⓓ **Diisopropylcarbinyl hydrogen succinate:** from C̄ htd. 4–6 hrs. with 20% excess succinic anhydride; cryst. from acetone, m.p. 61° ⟨4⟩; Neut. Eq. 216.

Ⓓ **Diisopropylcarbinyl hydrogen 3-nitrophthalate:** m.p. 150–151° ⟨5⟩; Neut. Eq. 309 [cf. T 1.83].

Ⓓ **Diisopropylcarbinyl *N*-phenylcarbamate:** long ndls. from ether + pet. ether; m.p. 95° ⟨6⟩.

1:6215 ⟨1⟩ Ssuknewitsch, Tschilingarjan, *Ber.* **69,** 1541 (1936). ⟨2⟩ Whitmore, Laughlin, *J. Am. Chem. Soc.* **54,** 4392 (1932). ⟨3⟩ Mulliken, Wakeman, Gerry, *J. Am. Chem. Soc.* **57,** 1607, Note 31 (1935). ⟨4⟩ Neunhoeffer, Schlüter, *Ann.* **526,** 71 (1936). ⟨5⟩ Graves, *Ind. Eng. Chem.* **23,** 1383 (1931). ⟨6⟩ Conant, Blatt, *J. Am. Chem. Soc.* **51,** 1235 (1929).

1:6218 3-ETHYLPENTANOL-3 (Triethylcarbinol) $C_7H_{16}O$ **Beil. I-417**

```
              OH
              |
CH3.CH2.C.CH2.CH3
              |
              CH2
              CH3
```

B.P. 142° D_4^{20} = **0.83889** n_D^{20} = **1.4305** ⟨1⟩
n_D^{25} = **1.4281** ⟨1⟩

Oil with camphoraceous odor. [For prepn. in 82–88% yield from diethyl ketone and $C_2H_5.MgBr$ see ⟨2⟩.]

$\bar{C}$, stirred at room temp. with 2 moles conc. HCl + 2 moles $ZnCl_2$, gives 94% yield 3-chloro-3-ethylpentane ⟨1⟩.

$\bar{C}$, refluxed with 1% conc. H_2SO_4 ⟨3⟩, or distd. with a trace of iodine ⟨4⟩, or htd. with equal wt. anhydrous oxalic ac. at 100° ⟨1⟩ yields 3-ethylpentene-2 (1:8330), b.p. 96°.

Ⓓ **Triethylcarbinyl allophanate:** m.p. 152° cor. ⟨5⟩; 182–183° ⟨6⟩.

1:6218 ⟨1⟩ Lucas, *J. Am. Chem. Soc.* **51,** 252 (1929). ⟨2⟩ Moyer, Marvel, *Organic Syntheses* **11,** 98–100 (1931). ⟨3⟩ Böeseken, Wildschut, *Rec. trav. chim.* **51,** 169 (1932). ⟨4⟩ Edgar, Calingaert, Marker, *J. Am. Chem. Soc.* **51,** 1485–1486 (1929). ⟨5⟩ Grandière, *Bull. soc. chim.* (4) **35,** 189 (1924). ⟨6⟩ Mavrodin, *Compt. rend.* **192,** 365 (1931).

1:6219 2,2-DIMETHYLBUTANOL-4 (Neopentylcarbinol; 3,3-dimethylbutanol-1) $C_6H_{14}O$ **Beil. I-412**

```
       CH3
       |
CH3—C—CH2.CH2OH
       |
       CH3
```

B.P. 142.6-143.6° ⟨1⟩
140-143° ⟨2⟩ ⟨3⟩

Ⓓ **Neopentylcarbinyl 3,5-dinitrobenzoate:** yel.-wh. ndls. from pet. ether; m.p. 83.5° ⟨2⟩ [cf. T 1.82].

1:6219 ⟨1⟩ Delacre, *Bull. acad. sci. Belg.* **1906,** 20. ⟨2⟩ Sutter, *Helv. Chim. Acta* **21,** 1269 (1938). ⟨3⟩ Strating, Backer, *Rec. trav. chim.* **55,** 911 (1936).

1:6221 2,3-DIMETHYLBUTANOL-1 $C_6H_{14}O$ **Beil. I_1-(204)**

```
       CH3 CH3
       |   |
CH3—C—C—CH2OH
       |   |
       H   H
```

B.P. 145° ⟨1⟩ ⟨2⟩ $D_4^{20.5}$ = **0.8297** ⟨1⟩ $n_D^{20.5}$ = **1.4195** ⟨1⟩

Ⓓ **2,3-Dimethylbutyl 3,5-dinitrobenzoate:** pale yel. lfts. from pet. eth.; m.p. 51.5° ⟨2⟩. [Mixed m.p. with corresponding deriv. of 2,2-dimethylbutanol-1 (1:6204) shows *no* depression.] [Addn. prod. with α-naphthylamine; red cryst. pdr. from pet. ether, m.p. 99° ⟨2⟩.] [Cf. T 1.82.]

Ⓓ **2,3-Dimethylbutyl *N*-phenylcarbamate:** m.p. 28–29° ⟨1⟩.

1:6221 ⟨1⟩ Gorski, *Cent.* **1913,** I, 2022. ⟨2⟩ Sutter, *Helv. Chim. Acta* **21,** 1268 (1938).

1:6222 ***d,l*-2-METHYLPENTANOL-1** $C_6H_{14}O$ **Beil. I-409**
(β-Methyl-*n*-amyl alcohol) $CH_3.CH_2.CH_2.CH(CH_3).CH_2OH$

B.P. 148.0° ⟨1⟩ ⟨2⟩ D_4^{20} = **0.8208** ⟨2⟩; cf. ⟨9⟩ n_D^{20} = **1.4190** ⟨9⟩
D_4^{25} = **0.8192** ⟨1⟩; cf. ⟨9⟩ n_D^{25} = **1.4180** ⟨1⟩

C̄ on oxidn. with $KMnO_4$ yields 2-methylpentanoic acid (1:1117) — C̄ with PBr_3 yields corresp. bromide. ⟨4⟩.

Ⓓ β-**Methylamyl 3,5-dinitrobenzoate:** yellowish lfts. from pet. ether, m.p. 50.5° ⟨5⟩; 49° ⟨8⟩ [cf. T 1.82].

Ⓓ β-**Methylamyl hydrogen 3-nitrophthalate:** m.p. 145°: Neut. Eq. 295 ⟨7⟩; pl. from C_6H_6; m.p. 141° ⟨8⟩ [cf. T 1.83].

Ⓓ β-**Methylamyl hydrogen tetrachlorophthalate:** m.p. 103° ⟨8⟩.

Ⓓ β-**Methylamyl *N*-(α-naphthyl)carbamate:** m.p. 75–76° ⟨3⟩ [cf. T 1.86].

Ⓓ β-**Methylamyl *N*-(*p*-xenyl)carbamate:** ndls. from C_6H_6 + pet., m.p. 98–99° ⟨6⟩ ⟨8⟩.

1:6222 ⟨1⟩ Norris, Cortese, *J. Am. Chem. Soc.* **49,** 2644 (1927). ⟨2⟩ Olivier, *Rec. trav. chim.* **55** 1027–1035 (1936). ⟨3⟩ Magnani, McElvain, *J. Am. Chem. Soc.* **60,** 818–819 (1938). ⟨4⟩ Shonle, Waldo, Keltch, Coles, *J. Am. Chem. Soc.* **58,** 586 (1936). ⟨5⟩ Sutter, *Helv. Chim. Acta* **21,** 1266–1272 (1938). ⟨6⟩ Morgan, Hardy, *Chemistry & Industry* **52,** 519 (1933). ⟨7⟩ Graves, *Ind. Eng. Chem.* **23,** 1381–1385 (1931). ⟨8⟩ Morgan, Hardy, Procter, *Chemistry & Industry* **51T,** 7 (1932). ⟨9⟩ Hovorka, Lankelma, Stanford, *J. Am. Chem. Soc.* **60,** 823 (1938).

1:6223 **2-ETHYLBUTANOL-1** $(CH_3.CH_2)_2.CH.CH_2OH$ $C_6H_{14}O$ **Beil. I-412**
(β,β-Diethylethyl alcohol; 3-methylolpentane)

B.P. 148.9° ⟨1⟩ D_4^{20} = **0.83345** ⟨6⟩ n_D^{20} = **1.4224** ⟨6⟩
147-147.6° ⟨2⟩ D_4^{25} = **0.82955** ⟨6⟩ n_D^{25} = **1.4205** ⟨6⟩
146.27° ⟨6⟩

C̄ boiled with HBr (48%) + conc. H_2SO_4 3 hrs. ⟨3⟩ or with dry HBr ⟨2⟩ yields 2-ethylbutyl bromide, b.p. 143–144° — C̄ on oxidn. with $KMnO_4$ yields diethylacetic acid (1:1115) ⟨4⟩.

Ⓓ **2-Ethylbutyl 3,5-dinitrobenzoate:** lfts. from pet. ether, m.p. 51.5° ⟨5⟩ [cf. T 1.82].

Ⓓ **2-Ethylbutyl hydrogen phthalate:** m.p. 54° ⟨4⟩.

1:6223 ⟨1⟩ *Synthetic Org. Chem., 10th Ed., Carbide and Carbon Chem. Corpn.* 1940. ⟨2⟩ Shonle, Waldo, Keltch, Coles, *J. Am. Chem. Soc.* **58,** 586 (1936). ⟨3⟩ Fourneau, Matti, *J. pharm. chim.* **14,** 513–522 (1931); *Cent.* **1932,** I, 2587. ⟨4⟩ Tiffeneau, Weill, *Compt. rend.* **204,** 592 (1937). ⟨5⟩ Sutter, *Helv. Chim. Acta,* **21,** 1266–1272 (1938). ⟨6⟩ Hovorka, Lankelma, Smith, *J. Am. Chem. Soc.* **62,** 2373 (1940).

1:6224 **2-METHYLPENTANOL-5** $C_6H_{14}O$ **Beil. I-411**
(4-Methylpentanol-1; isoamylcarbinol; isohexyl alcohol)

$$CH_3-\underset{CH_3}{\overset{H}{C}}-CH_2.CH_2.CH_2.OH$$

B.P. 151.8-152.8° ⟨1⟩ D_4^{20} = **0.8131** ⟨2⟩ n_D^{20} = **1.4153** ⟨7⟩
151.5-152.5° ⟨2⟩ ⟨3⟩; cf. ⟨7⟩. D_4^{25} = **0.8110** ⟨1⟩ n_D^{25} = **1.4134** ⟨1⟩

Ⓓ **Isoamylcarbinyl 3,5-dinitrobenzoate:** alm. colorless pdr. or lfts. from pet. ether; m.p. 72° ⟨3⟩; 69.8° cor. ⟨4⟩; 69° ⟨5⟩ [cf. T 1.82].

Ⓓ **Isoamylcarbinyl hydrogen 3-nitrophthalate:** pl. from C_6H_6 + pet. ether; m.p. 138.5–140° ⟨5⟩ [cf. T 1.83].

Ⓓ **Isoamylcarbinyl *N*-phenylcarbamate:** m.p. 48° cor. ⟨6⟩.

1:6224 ⟨1⟩ Norris, Cortese, *J. Am. Chem. Soc.* **49,** 2644 (1927). ⟨2⟩ Olivier, *Rec. trav. chim.* **5** 1033 (1936). ⟨3⟩ Sutter, *Helv. Chim. Acta* **21,** 1268 (1938). ⟨4⟩ Malone, Reid, *J. Am. Chem. Soc.* **51,** 3426 (1929). ⟨5⟩ Morgan, Hardy, Procter, *Chemistry & Industry* **51T,** 7 (1932 ⟨6⟩ Levene, Allen, *J. Biol. Chem.* **27,** 451 (1916). ⟨7⟩ Hovorka, Lankelma, Schneider, *J. Am. Chem. Soc.* **62,** 1097 (1940).

1:6226 3-METHYLPENTANOL-1 $C_6H_{14}O$ **Beil. S.N. 2**

$$\begin{array}{c} CH_3 \\ | \\ CH_3.CH_2—C—CH_2.CH_2OH \\ | \\ H \end{array}$$

B.P. 153.7-154.1° ⟨1⟩ D_4^{20} = **0.8242** ⟨2⟩ n_D^{20} = **1.4188** ⟨4
152.3-153.0° ⟨2⟩; cf. ⟨4⟩ D_4^{25} = **0.8205** ⟨1⟩ n_D^{25} = **1.4177** ⟨1

Ⓓ **3-Methylpentyl 3,5-dinitrobenzoate:** yellowish lfts. from pet. eth.; m.p. 38° ⟨3 [cf. T 1.82].

1:6226 ⟨1⟩ Norris, Cortese, *J. Am. Chem. Soc.* **49,** 2644 (1927). ⟨2⟩ Olivier, *Rec. trav. chim.* **5** 1033 (1936). ⟨3⟩ Sutter, *Helv. Chim. Acta* **21,** 1267–1268 (1938). ⟨4⟩ Hovorka, Lankelm Schneider, *J. Am. Chem. Soc.* **62,** 1097 (1940).

1:6228 *d,l*-HEPTANOL-4 (Di-*n*-propylcarbinol) $C_7H_{16}O$ **Beil. I-41**

$$\begin{array}{c} H \\ | \\ CH_3.CH_2.CH_2—C—CH_2.CH_2.CH_3 \\ | \\ OH \end{array}$$

B.P. 155.4°$_{755}$ ⟨1⟩ **M.P. −41.5°** ⟨1⟩ D_4^{20} = **0.8183** ⟨1⟩ n_D^{20} = **1.4205** ⟨
D_4^{25} = **0.8175** ⟨8⟩ n_D^{25} = **1.4173** ⟨

C̄ on oxidn. with $K_2Cr_2O_7 + H_2SO_4$ gives 85–90% yield ⟨2⟩ di-*n*-propyl ketone (1:544 — C̄, htd. not above 100° with conc. H_2SO_4 ⟨3⟩, or htd. with ½ wt. of cryst. oxalic ac. ⟨4 yields heptene-3 (1:8332), b.p. 96°.

C̄ treated with conc. HCl + $ZnCl_2$ in cold gives 60–64% of 4-chloroheptane ⟨5⟩; satd. at −10° with HBr gas gives 65–76% of 4-bromoheptane ⟨5⟩.

Ⓓ **Di-*n*-propylcarbinyl *p*-nitrobenzoate:** m.p. 35° [T 1.82].
Ⓓ **Di-*n*-propylcarbinyl 3,5-dinitrobenzoate:** m.p. 64° ⟨6⟩ [T 1.82].
Ⓓ **Di-*n*-propylcarbinyl hydrogen phthalate:** m.p. 60° ⟨7⟩; Neut. Eq. 264.
Ⓓ **Di-*n*-propylcarbinyl *N*-(α-naphthyl)carbamate:** m.p. 79–80° ⟨4⟩ [T 1.86].

1:6228 ⟨1⟩ Sherrill, *J. Am. Chem. Soc.* **52,** 1983–1984 (1930). ⟨2⟩ Ref. 1, pages 1990–19 ⟨3⟩ Mathus, Gibon, *Bull. soc. chim. Belg.* **34,** 303 (1926). ⟨4⟩ Mulliken, Wakeman, Ger *J. Am. Chem. Soc.* **57,** 1607, Note 31 (1935). ⟨5⟩ Ref. 1, pages 1985–1989. ⟨6⟩ Adki Connor, Cramer, *J. Am. Chem. Soc.* **52,** 5197 (1930). ⟨7⟩ Arcus, Kenyon, *J. Chem. Soc.* **19** 318. ⟨8⟩ Dillon, Lucas, *J. Am. Chem. Soc.* **50,** 1712 (1928).

1:6230 HEXANOL-1 $CH_3.CH_2.CH_2.CH_2.CH_2.CH_2.OH$ $C_6H_{14}O$ **Beil. I-4**
(*n*-Hexyl alcohol)

B.P. 157.5° ⟨1⟩ **M.P. −51.6°** ⟨3⟩ D_4^{20} = **0.81893** ⟨1⟩ n_D^{20} = **1.41778** ⟨
157.0-157.8° ⟨2⟩ **−46.1°** ⟨1⟩ D_4^{25} = **0.80528** ⟨4⟩ n_D^{25} = **1.4161** ⟨

[For purifn. of comml. C̄ via formn., crystn. and hydrolysis of *n*-hexyl *p*-hydroxybenzoa m.p. 52.2–52.8°, see ⟨2⟩.] — Soly. of C̄ in aq. at 25° is 0.624 wt. % ⟨5⟩. [For prepn. 60–62% yield from ethylene oxide + *n*-butyl MgBr see ⟨6⟩.] [For phys. constants see ⟨23

C̄ shaken 2 days in cold with 2 moles conc. HCl + 2 moles $ZnCl_2$ gives 45% yield *n*-hexyl chloride, b.p. 135–136°, D_{20}^{20} = 0.8759; n_D^{20} = 1.42364 ⟨7⟩ — C̄. htd. with fumi

HBr (D = 1.78) which has been satd. with HBr gas at 0°, yields *n*-hexyl bromide, b.p. 155.2–155.8°; D_4^{20} = 1.1739 ⟨2⟩ [cf. also ⟨21⟩].

C̄ on oxidn. with $K_2Cr_2O_7 + H_2SO_4$ (cf. T 1.72) yields *n*-caproic ac. (1:1130) ⟨8⟩.

Ⓓ ***n*-Hexyl 3,5-dinitrobenzoate:** m.p. 58.4° cor. ⟨9⟩; 58.2° ⟨10⟩; 60–61° ⟨11⟩; 60–61° ⟨12⟩; [cf. T 1.82].

Ⓓ ***n*-Hexyl hydrogen phthalate:** m.p. 24.6–25.4°; Neut. Eq. 250 ⟨13⟩.

Ⓓ ***n*-Hexyl hydrogen 3-nitrophthalate:** m.p. 123.9–124.4° ⟨14⟩; 123° ⟨15⟩; Neut. Eq. 295.1 [T 1.83].

Ⓓ ***n*-Hexyl *N*-phenylcarbamate:** m.p. 42° ⟨16⟩ ⟨17⟩. [For optical data see ⟨22⟩.]

Ⓓ ***n*-Hexyl *N*-(*p*-nitrophenyl)carbamate:** m.p. 103° ⟨18⟩; 104° ⟨19⟩.

Ⓓ ***n*-Hexyl *N*-(α-naphthyl)carbamate:** m.p. 59° ⟨20⟩ [cf. T 1.86].

Ⓓ ***n*-Hexyl *N*-(*p*-xenyl)carbamate:** m.p. 97–98° ⟨15⟩.

1:6230 ⟨1⟩ Bilterys, Gisseleire, *Bull. soc. chim. Belg.* **44,** 570 (1935). ⟨2⟩ Olivier, *Rec. trav. chim.* **55,** 1034–1035 (1936). ⟨3⟩ Timmermans, *Bull. soc. chim. Belg.* **31,** 390 (1922). ⟨4⟩ Ellis, Reid, *J. Am. Chem. Soc.* **54,** 1678 (1932). ⟨5⟩ Butler, Thomson, Maclennan, *J. Chem. Soc.* **1933,** 679–680. ⟨6⟩ Dreger, *Organic Syntheses, Coll. Vol.* I, 299–301 (1932). ⟨7⟩ Clark, Streight, *Trans. Roy. Soc. Can.* (3) **23,** III, 77–89 (1929). ⟨8⟩ Semichon, Flanzy, *Compt. rend.* **195,** 254 (1932). ⟨9⟩ Malone, Reid, *J. Am. Chem. Soc.* **51,** 3426 (1929). ⟨10⟩ Adamson, Kenner, *J. Chem. Soc.* **1935,** 287.

⟨11⟩ Reichstein, *Helv. Chim. Acta* **9,** 802 (1926). ⟨12⟩ Sutter, *Helv. Chim. Acta* **21,** 1267 (1938). ⟨13⟩ Goggans, Copenhaver, *J. Am. Chem. Soc.* **61,** 2909 (1939). ⟨14⟩ Dickinson, Crosson, Copenhaver, *J. Am. Chem. Soc.* **59,** 1095 (1937). ⟨15⟩ Morgan, Hardy, Procter, *Chemistry & Industry* **51T,** 7 (1932). ⟨16⟩ Bouveault, Blanc, *Compt. rend.* **138,** 149 (1904). ⟨17⟩ Fichter, Leupin, *Helv. Chim. Acta* **21,** 618 (1938). ⟨18⟩ Shriner, Cox, *J. Am. Chem. Soc.* **53,** 1604, 3186 (1931). ⟨19⟩ Hoeke, *Rec. trav. chim.* **54,** 514 (1935). ⟨20⟩ Adamson, Kenner, *J. Chem. Soc.* **1934,** 842.

⟨21⟩ Ref. 4, page 1686. ⟨22⟩ Dewey, Witt, *Ind. Eng. Chem., Anal. Ed.* **12,** 459 (1940). ⟨23⟩ Hovorka, Lankelma, Stanford, *J. Am. Chem. Soc.* **60,** 823 (1938).

1:6235 *d,l*-HEPTANOL-2 $C_7H_{16}O$ Beil. I-415

(*n*-Amyl-methyl-carbinol; *sec*-heptyl alcohol)

$$CH_3.(CH_2)_4—\underset{\displaystyle OH}{\overset{\displaystyle H}{\overset{|}{\underset{|}{C}}}}—CH_3$$

B.P. 158.7° ⟨1⟩ D_4^{20} = **0.8167** ⟨2⟩ n_D^{20} = **1.4210** ⟨2⟩

D_4^{25} = **0.8134** ⟨1⟩ n_D^{25} = **1.4190** ⟨1⟩

[For prepn. in 62–65% yield from *n*-amyl methyl ketone (1:5460) with NaOEt see ⟨3⟩.]

C̄ shaken with 2 moles conc. HCl + 2 moles $ZnCl_2$ in cold gives 60–64% yield ⟨4⟩ of 2-chloroheptane — C̄ satd. with HBr gas at −10° yields 2-bromoheptane ⟨4⟩ [cf. ⟨6⟩].

C̄ on oxidn. with $K_2Cr_2O_7 + H_2SO_4$ (cf. T. 1.72) gives 85–90% yield heptanone-2 (1:5460) ⟨5⟩.

Ⓓ ***n*-Amyl-methyl-carbinyl 3,5-dinitrobenzoate:** m.p. 49.4° ⟨7⟩ [cf. T 1.82].

Ⓓ ***n*-Amyl-methyl-carbinyl hydrogen phthalate:** m.p. 57–58° ⟨8⟩; 57.5° ⟨9⟩. [M.p. either *d*- or *l*-form, 76.5° ⟨8⟩.] [Does not distinguish from *d,l*-octanol-2 (1:6245), q.v.]

Ⓓ ***n*-Amyl-methyl-carbinyl *N*-(α-naphthyl)carbamate:** m.p. 54° ⟨10⟩ [cf. T 1.86].

1:6235 ⟨1⟩ Ellis, Reid, *J. Am. Chem. Soc.* **54,** 1678–1679 (1932). ⟨2⟩ Sherrill, *J. Am. Chem. Soc.* **52,** 1983–1984 (1930). ⟨3⟩ Whitmore, Otterbacher, *Organic Syntheses* **10,** 60–61 (1930). ⟨4⟩ Ref. 2, pages 1985–1989. ⟨5⟩ Ref. 2, page 1990. ⟨6⟩ Ref. 1, pages 1683–1686. ⟨7⟩ Malone, Reid, *J. Am. Chem. Soc.* **51,** 3426 (1929). ⟨8⟩ Pickard, Kenyon, *J. Chem. Soc.* **99,** 58, 63 (1911). ⟨9⟩ Arcus, Kenyon, *J. Chem. Soc.* **1938,** 699. ⟨10⟩ Adamson, Kenner, *J. Chem. Soc.* **1934,** 842.

1:6235-A ETHYLENE GLYCOL MONO-ISOBUTYL ETHER **Beil. S.N. 30**
(β-Hydroxyethyl isobutyl ether) $C_6H_{14}O_2$
$(CH_3)_2.CH.CH_2.O.CH_2.CH_2.OH$

B.P. 159.3°$_{746}$ ⟨1⟩ D_4^{20} = **0.8900 ⟨1⟩** n_D^{20} = **1.41428 ⟨1⟩**

For solvent characteristics see ⟨2⟩.

1:6235-A ⟨1⟩ Tallman, *J. Am. Chem. Soc.* **56,** 127 (1934). ⟨2⟩ Davidson, *Ind. Eng. Chem.* **18,** 669–675 (1926).

1:6235-B ETHYLENE GLYCOL MONO-*sec*-BUTYL ETHER **Beil. S.N. 30**
(*sec*-Butyl β-hydroxyethyl ether) $C_6H_{14}O_2$

$$CH_3.\overset{C_2H_5}{\underset{H}{C}}.O.CH_2.CH_2.OH$$

B.P. 159.3°$_{746}$ ⟨1⟩ D_4^{20} = **0.8966 ⟨1⟩** n_D^{20} = **1.41606 ⟨1⟩**

1:6235-B ⟨1⟩ Tallman, *J. Am. Chem. Soc.* **56,** 127 (1934).

1:6236 2,4-DIMETHYLPENTANOL-1 $C_7H_{16}O$ **Beil. S.N. 24**

$$CH_3—\overset{CH_3}{\underset{H}{C}}—CH_2—\overset{CH_3}{\underset{H}{C}}—CH_2OH$$

B.P. 159.8° ⟨1⟩ D_4^{20} = **0.793 ⟨2⟩** n_D^{20} = **1.427 ⟨2⟩**
D_4^{25} = **0.821 ⟨3⟩** n_D^{17} = **1.422 ⟨3⟩**

Ⓓ **2,4-Dimethylpentyl hydrogen 3-nitrophthalate:** pl. from C_6H_6 + pet. ether; m.p. 154–155° ⟨2⟩ ⟨4⟩; 149° ⟨3⟩; Neut. Eq. 309 [cf. T 1.83].

Ⓓ **2,4-Dimethylpentyl *N*-(*p*-xenyl)carbamate:** ndls. from pet.; m.p. 74–75° ⟨3⟩.

1:6236 ⟨1⟩ Shonle, Waldo, Keltch, Coles, *J. Am. Chem. Soc.* **58,** 586 (1936). ⟨2⟩ Chu, Marvel *J. Am. Chem. Soc.* **53,** 4449 (1931). ⟨3⟩ Morgan, Hardy, Procter, *Chemistry & Industry* **51T,** 7 (1932). ⟨4⟩ Graves, *Ind. Eng. Chem.* **23,** 1382 (1931).

1:6237 2-METHYLHEXANOL-1 $C_7H_{16}O$ **Beil. I-41**
(β-Methylhexanol)

$$CH_3.CH_2.CH_2.CH_2—\overset{H}{\underset{CH_3}{C}}—CH_2.OH$$

B.P. 164-165° ⟨1⟩ D_4^{20} = **0.8270** n_D^{20} = **1.4250**

Ⓓ **2-Methylhexyl hydrogen 3-nitrophthalate:** pearly pl. from pet., m.p. 131–132° Neut. Eq. 309 ⟨1⟩ [cf. T 1.83].

Ⓓ **2-Methylhexyl *N*-(*p*-xenyl)carbamate:** ndls. from pet.; m.p. 88–88.5° ⟨1⟩.

1:6237 ⟨1⟩ Morgan, Hardy, Procter, *Chemistry & Industry* **51T,** 7 (1932).

1:6238 3-METHYLHEXANOL-6 $C_7H_{16}O$ **Beil. S.N. 2**
(4-Methylhexanol-1)

$$CH_3.CH_2—\overset{H}{\underset{CH_3}{C}}—CH_2.CH_2.CH_2.OH$$

B.P. 165° D_4^{20} = **0.8239 ⟨2⟩** n_D^{20} = **1.4219 ⟨2⟩**
173° ⟨2⟩

Ⓓ **4-Methylhexyl hydrogen 3-nitrophthalate:** m.p. 144°; Neut. Eq. 309 ⟨1⟩ [cf. T 1.83]

Ⓓ **4-Methylhexyl *N*-(α-naphthyl)carbamate:** m.p. 50° ⟨2⟩.

1:6238 ⟨1⟩ Graves, *Ind. Eng. Chem.* **23,** 1382 (1931). ⟨2⟩ Dewael, Weckering, *Bull. soc. chim. Belg.* **33,** 503–504 (1924).

1:6239 2-ETHYLPENTANOL-1 $C_7H_{16}O$ **Beil. S.N. 24**
(β-Ethylamyl alcohol)

$$CH_3.CH_2.CH_2{-}\underset{\underset{CH_3}{CH_2}}{\overset{H}{C}}{-}CH_2.OH$$

B.P. 164–166° ⟨1⟩

Ⓓ **β-Ethylamyl hydrogen 3-nitrophthalate:** pl. from C_6H_6 + pet.; m.p. **127–128°** ⟨1⟩; Neut. Eq. 309 [cf. T 1.83].

Ⓓ **β-Ethylamyl *N*-(*p*-xenyl)carbamate:** ndls. from pet.; m.p. 77–77.5° ⟨1⟩.

1:6239 ⟨1⟩ Morgan, Hardy, Procter, *Chemistry & Industry* **51T,** 7 (1932).

1:6239-A 2,6-DIMETHYLHEPTANOL-4 $C_9H_{20}O$ **Beil. I-425**
(Diisobutylcarbinol)

$$CH_3.\underset{CH_3}{CH}.CH_2.\underset{OH}{\overset{H}{C}}.CH_2.\underset{CH_3}{CH}.CH_3$$

B.P. 171.4–173.4° ⟨1⟩ D_{20}^{20} = **0.8129** ⟨2⟩ n_D^{20} = **1.4242** ⟨2⟩

Oil with camphoraceous odor.

C̄ on oxidn. with $K_2Cr_2O_7 + H_2SO_4$ (cf. T 1.72) yields diisobutyl ketone (1:5472) ⟨3⟩.

Ⓓ **Diisobutylcarbinyl *N*-phenylcarbamate:** ndls. from lgr. + alc.; m.p. 61–62° ⟨3⟩.

Ⓓ **Diisobutylcarbinyl *N*-(*p*-xenyl)carbamate:** m.p. 118° ⟨4⟩.

1:6239-A ⟨1⟩ Willcox, Brunel, *J. Am. Chem. Soc.* **38,** 1838 (1916). ⟨2⟩ Tuot, *Compt. rend.* **202,** 1340 (1936). ⟨3⟩ Freylon, *Ann. chim.* (8) **19,** 572–574 (1910). ⟨4⟩ Morgan, Hardy, *Chemistry & Industry* **52,** 519 (1933).

1:6240 HEPTANOL-1 $CH_3.(CH_2)_5.CH_2OH$ $C_7H_{16}O$ **Beil. I-414**
(*n*-Heptyl alcohol)

B.P. 176.8° ⟨1⟩ ⟨2⟩ **M.P. −33.8°** ⟨1⟩ D_4^{20} = **0.82242** ⟨1⟩ n_D^{20} = **1.4245** ⟨5⟩
176.3° ⟨3⟩ ⟨4⟩ D_4^{25} = **0.81915** ⟨3⟩ n_D^{25} = **1.4222** ⟨3⟩

[For prepn. in 75–81% yield from *n*-heptaldehyde (1:0183) by reduction with Fe filings + acetic ac. see ⟨6⟩.] [For pruification via prepn., recrystn. and hydrolysis of *n*-heptyl *p*-hydroxybenzoate, m.p. 48.9–49.4° see ⟨2⟩.]

C̄ is sol. in aq. at 25° to extent of 0.180 wt. % ⟨7⟩.

C̄ shaken with 2 moles conc. HCl + 2 moles $ZnCl_2$ in cold yields abt. 60% ⟨8⟩ ⟨9⟩ *n*-heptyl chloride, b.p. 159°, D_{20}^{20} = 0.8741, n_D^{20} = 1.42844 ⟨9⟩ — C̄ htd. at 80° with conc. HBr ⟨2⟩ ⟨10⟩ or satd. with HBr gas at −10° ⟨8⟩ yields *n*-heptyl bromide, b.p. 179.5° ⟨2⟩; D_4^{25} = 1.13484, n_D^{25} = 1.4480 ⟨10⟩.

C̄ on oxidn. with $K_2Cr_2O_7 + H_2SO_4$ (cf. T 1.72) yields *n*-heptylic ac. (1:1140) ⟨11⟩.

C̄ htd. with 7% $NaHSO_4$ at 100° yields 80% di-*n*-heptyl ether, b.p. 260–262° and but little olefin; at 175°, however, only heptene-1 (1:8324), b.p. 96°, is formed.

Ⓓ ***n*-Heptyl 3,5-dinitrobenzoate:** m.p. 46° ⟨13⟩; 46.9° ⟨14⟩; 47–48.5° ⟨15⟩ [cf. T 1.82].

Ⓓ ***n*-Heptyl hydrogen phthalate:** m.p. 16.5–17.5°; Neut. Eq. 264 ⟨16⟩.

Ⓓ ***n*-Heptyl hydrogen 3-nitrophthalate:** m.p. 126.9–127.2°; Neut. Eq. 308.2 ⟨17⟩ [cf. T 1.83].

Ⓓ ***n*-Heptyl *N*-phenylcarbamate:** m.p. 60° ⟨18⟩; 65° ⟨23⟩. [For optical data see ⟨23⟩.

Ⓓ ***n*-Heptyl *N*-(*p*-nitrophenyl)carbamate:** m.p. 102° ⟨19⟩; 105° ⟨20⟩.

Ⓓ ***n*-Heptyl *N*-(α-naphthyl)carbamate:** m.p. 62° ⟨21⟩; 59.5° ⟨22⟩ [cf. T 1.86].

1:6240 ⟨1⟩ Bilterys, Gisseleire, *Bull. soc. chim. Belg.* **44,** 570 (1935). ⟨2⟩ Olivier, *Rec. trav. chim* **56,** 256 (1937). ⟨3⟩ Ellis, Reid, *J. Am. Chem. Soc.* **54,** 1678–1679 (1932). ⟨4⟩ Deffet, *Bull soc. chim. Belg.* **40,** 390 (1931). ⟨5⟩ Sherrill, *J. Am. Chem. Soc.* **52,** 1983–1984 (1930) ⟨6⟩ Clarke, Dreger, *Organic Syntheses, Coll. Vol.* I, 298–299 (1932). ⟨7⟩ Butler, Thomson Maclennan, *J. Chem. Soc.* **1933,** 680. ⟨8⟩ Ref. 5, pages 1985–1989. ⟨9⟩ Clark, Streight *Trans. Roy. Soc. Can.* (3) **23,** III, 81–85 (1929). ⟨10⟩ Ref. 3, pages 1683–1686.

⟨11⟩ Semichon, Flanzy, *Compt. rend.* **195,** 254 (1932). ⟨12⟩ Senderens, Aboulenc, *Compt rend.* **190,** 151 (1930). ⟨13⟩ Adamson, Kenner, *J. Chem. Soc.* **1935,** 287. ⟨14⟩ Malone, Reid *J. Am. Chem. Soc.* **51,** 3426 (1929). ⟨15⟩ Reichstein, *Helv. Chim. Acta* **9,** 802 (1926) ⟨16⟩ Goggans, Copenhaver, *J. Am. Chem. Soc.* **61,** 2909 (1939). ⟨17⟩ Dickinson, Crosson Copenhaver, *J. Am. Chem. Soc.* **59,** 1095 (1937). ⟨18⟩ Levene, Taylor, *J. Biol. Chem.* **35,** 28 (1918). ⟨19⟩ Shriner, Cox, *J. Am. Chem. Soc.* **53,** 1604, 3186 (1931). ⟨20⟩ Hoeke, *Rec. trav chim.* **54,** 514 (1935).

⟨21⟩ Neuberg, Kansky, *Biochem. Z.* **20,** 449 (1909). ⟨22⟩ Adamson, Kenner, *J. Chem. Soc* **1934,** 842. ⟨23⟩ Dewey, Witt, *Ind. Eng. Chem., Anal. Ed.* **12,** 459 (1940).

1:6245 ***d,l*-OCTANOL-2** (*n*-Hexyl-methyl-carbinol; *sec*-capryl alcohol) $C_8H_{18}O$ **Beil. I-41**

$$CH_3.(CH_2)_5.\overset{H}{\underset{OH}{C}}.CH_3$$

B.P. 179.0° ⟨1⟩ D_4^{20} = **0.8205** ⟨2⟩ n_D^{20} = **1.4265** ⟨2

D_4^{25} = **0.81678** ⟨1⟩ n_D^{25} = **1.4244** ⟨1

[For prepn. of C̄ from castor oil see ⟨3⟩ ⟨2⟩.]

C̄, htd. 2 hrs. with 5 pts. HBr (D = 1.48) ⟨4⟩, or htd. with more conc. HBr ⟨5⟩, or treate with PBr_3 ⟨6⟩ yields 2-bromooctane — C̄ satd. with dry HI at 0° and stood 15 hrs., give 65% yield ⟨7⟩ 2-iodooctane. [For identification of these halides see ⟨6⟩.]

C̄ on oxidn. with $K_2Cr_2O_7 + H_2SO_4$ under specified conditions gives 97% yield ⟨8⟩ c 85% yield ⟨2⟩ of octanone-2 (1:5490).

C̄ on htg. with H_3PO_4 (D = 1.7) at 225–235° yields a mixture of octene-2 (b.p. 125° and octene-1 (b.p. 120°) in ratio of abt. 4:1 ⟨9⟩. Approximately the same result is als obtd. by htg. C̄ with 4 pts. $ZnCl_2$ at 160° ⟨10⟩ or htg. C̄ with 1/10 pt. conc. H_2SO_4 unt temp. reaches 140° ⟨10⟩ — C̄ htd. at 140–145° with 10% $NaHSO_4$ gives octene-2 + 37% di-*sec*-octyl ether, b.p. 262° ⟨11⟩.

Ⓓ ***n*-Hexyl-methyl-carbinyl *p*-nitrobenzoate:** m.p. 28° [T 1.82].

Ⓓ ***n*-Hexyl-methyl-carbinyl 3,5-dinitrobenzoate:** m.p. 32° ⟨12⟩ [cf. T 1.82].

Ⓓ ***n*-Hexyl-methyl-carbinyl hydrogen phthalate:** *d,l*-form, m.p. 55° ⟨13⟩ ⟨14⟩. [Use fo resolution of C̄ via brucine salt ⟨14⟩; either *d*- or *l*-form, m.p. 75° ⟨13⟩. [This deriv does not distinguish C̄ from heptanol-2 (1:6235), q.v.]

Ⓓ ***n*-Hexyl-methyl-carbinyl *N*-phenylcarbamate:** oil ⟨15⟩. [Not recommended a deriv.]

Ⓓ ***n*-Hexyl-methyl-carbinyl *N*-(*p*-nitrophenyl)carbamate:** oil ⟨16⟩. [Not recommende as deriv.]

Ⓓ ***n*-Hexyl-methyl-carbinyl *N*-(α-naphthyl)carbamate:** m.p. 63–64° ⟨17⟩; 62.5° ⟨1 [cf. T 1.86].

1:6245 ⟨1⟩ Ellis, Reid, *J. Am. Chem. Soc.* **54,** 1678–1679 (1932). ⟨2⟩ Kao, Yen, *J. Chine Chem. Soc.* **2,** 27–29 (1934). ⟨3⟩ Adams, Marvel, *Organic Syntheses, Coll. Vol.* I, 358–36 (1932). ⟨4⟩ Norris, Watt, Thomas, *J. Am. Chem. Soc.* **38,** 1076 (1916). ⟨5⟩ Ref. pages 1683, 1686. ⟨6⟩ Schwartz, Johnson, *J. Am. Chem. Soc.* **53,** 1066–1068 (1931

⟨7⟩ Hughes, *J. Chem. Soc.* **1935,** 1528. ⟨8⟩ Verhulst, Glorieux, *Bull. soc. chim.* **41,** 501 (1932). ⟨9⟩ Whitmore, Herndon, *J. Am. Chem. Soc.* **55,** 3428–3430 (1933). ⟨10⟩ Kao, Chang, *Science Repts. Natl. Tsing Hua Univ.*, Ser. **A-4,** 35–37 (1937).
⟨11⟩ Senderens, Aboulenc, *Compt. rend.* **190,** 150–152 (1930). ⟨12⟩ Reichstein, *Helv. Chim. Acta* **9,** 802 (1926). ⟨13⟩ Pickard, Kenyon, *J. Chem. Soc.* **99,** 58, 63 (1911). ⟨14⟩ Kenyon, *Organic Syntheses, Coll. Vol.* I, 410–412 (1932). ⟨15⟩ Bloch, *Bull. soc. chim.* (3) **31,** 51 (1904). ⟨16⟩ Shriner, Cox, *J. Am. Chem. Soc.* **53,** 1602 (1931). ⟨17⟩ Bickel, French, *J. Am. Chem. Soc.* **48,** 749 (1926). ⟨18⟩ Adamson, Kenner, *J. Chem. Soc.* **1934,** 842.

1:6247 4-METHYLHEPTANOL-1 $C_8H_{18}O$ Beil. S.N. 24

$$CH_3.CH_2.CH_2—\overset{H}{\underset{CH_3}{C}}—CH_2.CH_2.CH_2OH$$

B.P. 182.7° ⟨1⟩ [cf. ⟨2⟩]

Ⓓ **4-Methylheptyl hydrogen 3-nitrophthalate:** m.p. 133° ⟨1⟩; Neut. Eq. 323 [cf. T 1.83].

1:6247 ⟨1⟩ Graves, *Ind. Eng. Chem.* **23,** 1382 (1931). ⟨2⟩ Shonle, Waldo, Keltch, Coles, *J. Am. Chem. Soc.* **58,** 586 (1936).

1:6248 2-ETHYLHEXANOL-1 $C_8H_{18}O$ Beil. S.N. 24

$$CH_3.CH_2.CH_2.CH_2—\overset{H}{\underset{CH_2.CH_3}{C}}—CH_2.OH$$

B.P. 184.6° ⟨1⟩ D_4^{20} = **0.8328** n_D^{20} = **1.4328**
D_4^{15} = **0.8435** ⟨2⟩ n_D^{16} = **1.4390** ⟨2⟩

C̄ on oxidn. with $KMnO_4$ ⟨3⟩ or CrO_3 ⟨4⟩ yields 2-ethylhexanoic ac. (1:1143), b.p. 228°.

Ⓓ **2-Ethyl-*n*-hexyl hydrogen 3-nitrophthalate:** pl. from pet., m.p. 107–108° ⟨5⟩ ⟨4⟩; Neut. Eq. 323 [cf. T 1.83].

Ⓓ **2-Ethyl-*n*-hexyl *N*-phenylcarbamate:** m.p. 33–34° ⟨4⟩.

Ⓓ **2-Ethyl-*n*-hexyl *N*-(α-naphthyl)carbamate:** m.p. 60–61° ⟨3⟩ [cf. T 1.86].

Ⓓ **2-Ethyl-*n*-hexyl *N*-(*p*-xenyl)carbamate:** ndls. from pet.; m.p. 80° ⟨5⟩; 79–79.5° ⟨6⟩.

1:6248 ⟨1⟩ Shonle, Waldo, Keltch, Coles, *J. Am. Chem. Soc.* **58,** 586 (1936). ⟨2⟩ Mastagli, *Compt. rend.* **204,** 1168 (1937). ⟨3⟩ Magnani, McElvain, *J. Am. Chem. Soc.* **60,** 819 (1938). ⟨4⟩ Weizmann, Bergmann, Haskelberg, *Chemistry & Industry* **56,** 587–591 (1937). ⟨5⟩ Morgan, Hardy, Procter, *Chemistry & Industry* **51T,** 7 (1932). ⟨6⟩ Morgan, Hardy, *Chemistry & Industry* **52,** 518–519 (1933).

1:6250 NONANOL-5 $C_9H_{20}O$ Beil. I-424

(Di-*n*-butylcarbinol)

$$CH_3.CH_2.CH_2.CH_2—\overset{H}{\underset{OH}{C}}—CH_2.CH_2.CH_2.CH_3$$

B.P. 194°_{743} D^{20} = **0.823** n_D^{18} = **1.4289** ⟨1⟩

[For prepn. in 83–85% yield from *n*-butyl MgBr + ethyl formate see ⟨2⟩.]

C̄ htd. with ½ its wt. of cryst. oxalic ac. yields nonene-4, b.p. 147.5–148.1° ⟨3⟩.

C̄ on oxidn. with $K_2Cr_2O_7 + H_2SO_4$ (cf. T 1.72) yields nonanone-5 (1:5493).

Ⓓ **Di-*n*-butylcarbinyl hydrogen phthalate:** m.p. 45° ⟨4⟩; Neut. Eq. 292.

Ⓓ **Di-*n*-butylcarbinyl allophanate:** m.p. 158° ⟨1⟩.

1:6250 ⟨1⟩ Vavon, Ivanoff, *Compt. rend.* **177,** 454 (1923). ⟨2⟩ Coleman, Craig, *Organic Syntheses* **15,** 11–13 (1935). ⟨3⟩ Mulliken, Wakeman, Gerry, *J. Am. Chem. Soc.* **57,** 1607, Note 31 (1935). ⟨4⟩ Vavon, Zaremba, *Bull. soc. chim.* (4) **49,** 1859–1860 (1931).

1:6255 OCTANOL-1 $CH_3.(CH_2)_6.CH_2OH$ $C_8H_{18}O$ **Beil. I-418**
(*n*-Octyl alcohol)

B.P. 194.7° ⟨1⟩ M.P. −16.7° D_4^{20} **= 0.8249 ⟨2⟩**
195.3°$_{764}$ ⟨2⟩ D_4^{25} **= 0.82137 ⟨1⟩** n_D^{25} **= 1.4274 ⟨1⟩**

[For purifn. via formn., recrystn. and hydrolysis of *n*-octyl *p*-hydroxybenzoate, m.p. 51.0–51.6°, see ⟨2⟩.] [For prepn. in 71% yield from *n*-hexyl Mg bromide + ethylene oxide see ⟨3⟩.]

Soly. of $\bar{C}$ in aq. at 25° is 0.0586 wt. % ⟨4⟩.

$\bar{C}$, htd. with conc. HCl + $ZnCl_2$ ⟨5⟩, or PCl_3 + $ZnCl_2$ (60% yield) ⟨5⟩, or PCl_5 + $ZnCl_2$ (69% yield) ⟨5⟩, or $SOCl_2$ (70% yield) ⟨5⟩, gives *n*-octyl chloride, b.p. 179–180°, D_{20}^{20} = 0.8745, n_D^{20} = 1.43424 ⟨5⟩ — $\bar{C}$ htd. at 80° with conc. HBr ⟨6⟩ ⟨2⟩ yields *n*-octyl bromide, b.p. 202.2° at 754.6 mm., D_4^{20} = 1.1129 ⟨2⟩, n_D^{25} = 1.4503 ⟨6⟩.

$\bar{C}$ with H_3PO_4 at 225° yields a mixt. of approx. 2 pts. octene-1 (1:8375) (b.p. 120°) and 1 pt. octene-2 (1:8380) (b.p. 125°) ⟨7⟩ ⟨8⟩. [Cf. octanol-2 (1:6245).]

Ⓓ ***n*-Octyl *p*-nitrobenzoate:** m.p. 12° [cf. T 1.82].

Ⓓ ***n*-Octyl 3,5-dinitrobenzoate:** m.p. 61–62° ⟨9⟩; 60.8° ⟨10⟩ [cf. T 1.82].

Ⓓ ***n*-Octyl hydrogen phthalate:** m.p. 21.5–22.5°; Neut. Eq. 278 ⟨11⟩. [The m.p. of the *p*-nitrobenzyl ester (T 1.39) of this acid phthalate is 41.0° ⟨12⟩.]

Ⓓ ***n*-Octyl hydrogen 3-nitrophthalate:** m.p. 127.8–128.2° cor.; Neut. Eq. 323.2 ⟨13⟩ [cf. T 1.83].

Ⓓ ***n*-Octyl *N*-phenylcarbamate:** m.p. 74–74.5° ⟨14⟩ ⟨18⟩; 73° ⟨15⟩. [For optical data see ⟨18⟩.]

Ⓓ ***n*-Octyl *N*-(*p*-nitrophenyl)carbamate:** m.p. 111° ⟨16⟩.

Ⓓ ***n*-Octyl *N*-(α-naphthyl)carbamate:** m.p. 66° ⟨17⟩.

1:6255 ⟨1⟩ Ellis, Reid, *J. Am. Chem. Soc.* **54,** 1678–1679 (1932). ⟨2⟩ Olivier, *Rec. trav. chim.* **56,** 256 (1937). ⟨3⟩ Vaughn, Spahr, Nieuwland, *J. Am. Chem. Soc.* **55,** 4208 (1933). ⟨4⟩ Butler, Thomson, Maclennan, *J. Chem. Soc.* **1933,** 680. ⟨5⟩ Clark, Streight, *Trans. Roy. Soc. Can.* (3) **23,** III, 77–89 (1929). ⟨6⟩ Ref. 1, pages 1680–1686. ⟨7⟩ Whitmore, Herndon, *J. Am. Chem. Soc.* **55,** 3428–3430 (1933). ⟨8⟩ Waterman, Te Nuyl, *Rec. trav. chim.* **51,** 534–535 (1932). ⟨9⟩ Reichstein, *Helv. Chim. Acta* **9,** 802 (1926). ⟨10⟩ Malone, Reid, *J. Am. Chem. Soc.* **51,** 3426 (1929).

⟨11⟩ Goggans, Copenhaver, *J. Am. Chem. Soc.* **61,** 2909 (1939). ⟨12⟩ Reid, *J. Am. Chem. Soc.* **39,** 1251 (1917). ⟨13⟩ Dickinson, Crosson, Copenhaver, *J. Am. Chem. Soc.* **59,** 1095 (1937). ⟨14⟩ Reichstein, Amman, Trivelli, *Helv. Chim. Acta* **15,** 267 (1932). ⟨15⟩ Nelson, Mottern, *Ind. Eng. Chem.* **26,** 635 (1934). ⟨16⟩ van Hoogstraten, *Rec. trav. chim.* **51,** 426 (1932). ⟨17⟩ Adamson, Kenner, *J. Chem. Soc.* **1934,** 842. ⟨18⟩ Dewey, Witt, *Ind. Eng. Chem., Anal. Ed.* **12,** 459 (1940).

1:6259 *d,l*-NONANOL-2 $C_9H_{20}O$ **Beil. I-423**
(Methyl-*n*-heptyl-carbinol)

$$CH_3—CH(OH)—CH_2(CH_2)_5.CH_3$$

B.P. 198.2° ⟨1⟩ D_4^{25} **= 0.81910 ⟨1⟩** n_D^{25} **= 1.4290 ⟨1⟩**

[For prepn. in 65% yield from *n*-heptyl MgBr + acetaldehyde see ⟨2⟩.]

Ⓓ **Methyl-*n*-heptyl-carbinyl 3,5-dinitrobenzoate:** m.p. 42.8° cor. ⟨3⟩ [cf. T 1.82].

Ⓓ **Methyl-*n*-heptyl-carbinyl hydrogen phthalate:** from $\bar{C}$ htd. with 1 mole phthalic anhyd. for 10 hrs. at 115°; m.p. 42–44° ⟨4⟩ [m.p. active form, 58–59°].

Ⓓ **Methyl-*n*-heptylcarbinyl *N*-(α-naphthyl)carbamate:** cryst. from lt. pet., m.p. 55.5° ⟨5⟩ [cf. T 1.86].

1:6259 ⟨1⟩ Ellis, Reid, *J. Am. Chem. Soc.* **54,** 1678–1679 (1932). ⟨2⟩ Ref. 1, page 1685. ⟨3⟩ Malone, Reid, *J. Am. Chem. Soc.* **51,** 3426 (1929). ⟨4⟩ Pickard, Kenyon, *J. Chem. Soc.* **95,** 58, 63 (1911). ⟨5⟩ Adamson, Kenner, *J. Chem. Soc.* **1934,** 842.

1:6260 ***l*-LINALOOL** (*l*-Linalyl alcohol) $C_{10}H_{18}O$ **Beil. I-460**

$$CH_3\text{—}\underset{\displaystyle CH_3}{\underset{|}{C}}\text{=}CH.CH_2.CH_2.\overset{\displaystyle OH}{\overset{|}{\underset{\displaystyle CH_3}{\underset{|}{C}}}}.CH\text{=}CH_2$$

B.P. 199° D^{20} = **0.8622** n_D^{20} = **1.46238**

C̄ has agreeable perfume odor — C̄ is laevorotatory: $[\alpha]_D$ = −3° to −17°. [The dextrorotary isomer is coriandrol [Beil. I-461].]

C̄ on oxidn. at 80–90° with $K_2Cr_2O_7$ + dil. H_2SO_4 ⟨1⟩ yields citral (1:0230); C̄, on oxidn. with $KMnO_4$, followed by CrO_3 + H_2SO_4 (cf. T 1.72), gives good yield ⟨2⟩ of acetone (1:5400) and levulinic ac. (1:0405).

C̄ on warming with Na yields sodium *l*-linalylate ⟨3⟩ [use in reactn. with phthalic anhydride ⟨3⟩] — C̄ adds 2 Br_2.

[For purifn. via formn. and hydrolysis of sodium linalyl phthalate see ⟨4⟩ ⟨3⟩.]

Ⓓ ***l*-Linalyl *p*-nitrobenzoate:** m.p. 70° [T 1.82].

Ⓓ ***l*-Linalyl *N*-phenylcarbamate:** m.p. 65–66° ⟨5⟩ ⟨6⟩.

Ⓓ ***l*-Linalyl *N*-(α-naphthyl)carbamate:** m.p. 53° [cf. T 1.86].

1:6260 ⟨1⟩ Bertram, Walbaum, *J. prakt. Chem.* (2) **45,** 599 (1892). ⟨2⟩ Tiemann, Semmler, *Ber.* **28,** 2130 (1895). ⟨3⟩ Tiemann, *Ber.* **31,** 838–840 (1898). ⟨4⟩ Charabot, *Ann. chim.* (7) **21,** 232–233 (1900). ⟨5⟩ Walbaum, Hüthig, *J. prakt. Chem.* (2) **67,** 323–325 (1903). ⟨6⟩ Ruzicka, Fornasir, *Helv. Chim. Acta* **2,** 187–188 (1919).

1:6263 ***d,l*-DECANOL-2** (Methyl-*n*-octyl-carbinol) $C_{10}H_{22}O$ **Beil. I₁-(213)**

$$CH_3\text{—}\overset{\displaystyle H}{\overset{|}{\underset{\displaystyle OH}{\underset{|}{C}}}}\text{—}CH_2.(CH_2)_5.CH_3$$

B.P. 210-211° ⟨1⟩ D_4^{20} = **0.8250** ⟨1⟩ (for *d*-isomer) n_D^{20} = **1.4344** ⟨1⟩ (for *d*-isomer)

Ⓓ **Methyl-*n*-octyl-carbinyl hydrogen phthalate:** from C̄ + phthalic anhyd. htd. 10 hrs. at 115°; m.p. 48–49° ⟨1⟩ [m.p. *d*-deriv. 38–39° ⟨1⟩].

Ⓓ **Methyl-*n*-octyl-carbinyl *N*-(α-naphthyl)carbamate:** cryst. from lt. pet.; m.p. 69° ⟨2⟩ [cf. T 1.86].

1:6263 ⟨1⟩ Pickard, Kenyon, *J. Chem. Soc.* **99,** 55, 58, 63 (1911). ⟨2⟩ Adamson, Kenner, *J. Chem. Soc.* **1934,** 842.

1:6265 **NONANOL-1** (*n*-Nonyl alcohol) $CH_3.(CH_2)_7.CH_2OH$ $C_9H_{20}O$ **Beil. I-423**

B.P. 213.5° ⟨1⟩ ⟨2⟩ D_4^{20} = **0.8271** ⟨2⟩ n_D^{20} = **1.43105** ⟨3⟩
D_4^{25} = **0.82303** ⟨1⟩ n_D^{25} = **1.4320** ⟨1⟩

[For purifn. of C̄ via formn., recrystn. and hydrolysis of *n*-nonyl *p*-hydroxybenzoate, m.p. 40.5–41.3° see ⟨2⟩.] [For prepn. in 55% yield from *n*-heptyl Mg bromide + ethylene oxide see ⟨13⟩.]

C̄, htd. with conc. HCl + $ZnCl_2$ ⟨4⟩, or PCl_3 + $ZnCl_2$ (53% yield) ⟨4⟩, or C̄ in C_6H_6 + PCl_5 + $ZnCl_2$ (58% yield) ⟨4⟩, or C̄ in C_6H_6 + $SOCl_2$ (62%yield) ⟨4⟩, gives *n*-nonyl chloride, b.p. 98–100° at 23 mm., D_{20}^{20} = 0.8679, n_D^{20} = 1.43962 ⟨4⟩ — C̄ htd. at 80° with conc. HBr ⟨5⟩ ⟨2⟩ yields *n*-nonyl bromide, b.p. 223.1–223.7° at 770.6 mm., D_4^{20} = 1.0899 ⟨2⟩, n_D^{25} = 1.4523 ⟨5⟩.

C̄ on oxidn. yields pelargonic ac. (1:0560).

Ⓓ ***n*-Nonyl 3,5-dinitrobenzoate:** m.p. 52.2° ⟨6⟩ [cf. T 1.82].

Ⓓ ***n*-Nonyl hydrogen phthalate:** m.p. 42.4–42.6°; Neut. Eq. 292 ⟨7⟩.

Ⓓ ***n*-Nonyl hydrogen 3-nitrophthalate:** m.p. 124.8–125.2°; Neut. Eq. 337 ⟨8⟩ [cf. T 1.83].

Ⓓ ***n*-Nonyl *N*-phenylcarbamate:** m.p. 69° ⟨3⟩; 62–64° ⟨9⟩; 59° ⟨10⟩; 60° ⟨14⟩. [For optical data see ⟨14⟩.]

Ⓓ ***n*-Nonyl *N*-(*p*-nitrophenyl)carbamate:** m.p. 104° ⟨11⟩.

Ⓓ ***n*-Nonyl *N*-(α-naphthyl)carbamate:** m.p. 65.5° ⟨12⟩ [cf. T 1.86].

1:6265 ⟨1⟩ Ellis, Reid, *J. Am. Chem. Soc.* **54,** 1678–1679 (1932). ⟨2⟩ Olivier, *Rec. trav. chim.* **56,** 256 (1937). ⟨3⟩ Béhal, *Bull. soc. chim.* (4) **25,** 480–481 (1919). ⟨4⟩ Clark, Streight, *Trans. Roy. Soc. Can.* (3) **23,** 77–89 (1929). ⟨5⟩ Ref. 1, pages 1683, 1686. ⟨6⟩ Malone, Reid, *J. Am. Chem. Soc.* **51,** 3426 (1929). ⟨7⟩ Goggans, Copenhaver, *J. Am. Chem. Soc.* **61,** 2909 (1939). ⟨8⟩ Dickinson, Crosson, Copenhaver, *J. Am. Chem. Soc.* **59,** 1095 (1937). ⟨9⟩ Stephan, *J. prakt. Chem.* (2) **62,** 532 (1900). ⟨10⟩ Bouveault, Blanc, *Bull. soc. chim.* (3), **31,** 674 (1904). ⟨11⟩ Hoppenbrouwers, *Rec. trav. chim.* **51,** 951 (1932). ⟨12⟩ Adamson, Kenner, *J. Chem. Soc.* **1934,** 842. ⟨13⟩ Vaughn, Spahr, Nieuwland, *J. Am. Chem. Soc.* **55,** 4208 (1933). ⟨14⟩ Dewey, Witt, *Ind. Eng. Chem., Anal. Ed.* **12,** 459 (1940).

1:6268 *d,l*-UNDECANOL-2 (Methyl-*n*-nonyl-carbinol)

$C_{11}H_{24}O$ **Beil. I-427**

$$CH_3.(CH_2)_8.\overset{\displaystyle H}{\underset{\displaystyle OH}{C}}.CH_3$$

B.P. 228-229° D^{18} **= 0.8263**

[For prepn. of C̄ from reduction of methyl *n*-nonyl ketone (1:5531) with Na + EtOH (70–80% yield) see ⟨1⟩ ⟨2⟩; with Na + moist ether (63% yield) see ⟨3⟩.]

C̄ on oxidn. with $CrO_3 + H_2SO_4$ (T 1.72) yields methyl *n*-nonyl ketone (1:5531) ⟨4⟩.

C̄ on boiling 8 hrs. with 5 pts. 60% H_2SO_4 yields 70–80% of a mixture of undecylenes, viz., 96% undecene-2 (b.p. 192–193°) and 4% undecene-1 (b.p. 192–195°) together with a little of di-*sec*-undecanol ether, $C_{22}H_{46}O$ ⟨2⟩.

Ⓓ **Methyl-*n*-nonyl-carbinyl hydrogen phthalate:** from C̄ on htg. with phthalic anhydride for 10 hrs. at 115°; m.p. 49–50° ⟨1⟩, Neut. Eq. 320. [Use in resolution of C̄; m.p. active form, 31–32° ⟨1⟩.]

1:6268 ⟨1⟩ Pickard, Kenyon, *J. Chem. Soc.* **99,** 58, 63 (1911). ⟨2⟩ Thoms, Mannich, *Ber.* **36,** 2547–2548 (1903). ⟨3⟩ Houben, Boedler, Fischer, *Ber.* **69,** 1782 (1936). ⟨4⟩ Weissgerber, *Ber.* **61,** 2115 (1928).

1:6270 GERANIOL

$$CH_2{=}\underset{\displaystyle CH_3}{C}.CH_2.CH_2.CH_2.\underset{\displaystyle CH_3}{C}{=}CH.CH_2OH$$

$C_{10}H_{18}O$ **Beil. I-457**

B.P. 230° D_4^{20} **= 0.8894** n_D^{20} **= 1.4766**

Odor like geranium and rose — Opt. inactive — Insol. aq., misc. alc., ether.

C̄ on oxidn. with $K_2Cr_2O_7 + H_2SO_4$ ⟨1⟩ yields mainly citral *a* (1:0230); on oxidn. with $KMnO_4$, followed by $CrO_3 + H_2SO_4$ ⟨2⟩, gives good yield of acetone (1:5400) and levulinic ac. (1:0405) — C̄ oxidized by long boiling with Al *ter*-butylate in a mixt. of acetone and benzene gives 70% yield pure pseudoionone [Beil. VII_1-(109)] whose 2,4-dinitrophenylhydrazone has m.p. 141° ⟨3⟩.

C̄, in $CHCl_3$ soln., adds 2 Br_2 yielding geraniol tetrabromide, m.p. 70–71° ⟨4⟩ but this prod. is dif. to crystallize ⟨5⟩ [dif. from nerol [Beil. I-459] which yields nerol tetrabromide, m.p. 118–119°, and easy to cryst. [Beil. I_1-(237)] ⟨5⟩].

For purifn. of C̄ via cpd. with $CaCl_2$ see ⟨6⟩. [Comml. C̄ sometimes conts. eugenol (1:1775) and bieugenol [Beil. VI-1178] ⟨13⟩.]

Ⓓ **Geranyl *p*-nitrobenzoate:** m.p. 35° [T 1.82].

Ⓓ **Geranyl 3,5-dinitrobenzoate:** m.p. 62–63° ⟨7⟩ [cf. T 1.82].

Ⓓ **Geranyl hydrogen phthalate:** from C̄ htd. at 100° with phthalic anhydride ⟨8⟩ or better boiled in C_6H_6 soln. with phthalic anhydride ⟨9⟩; tbls. from lgr., m.p. 47°. [The silver salt of this geranyl acid phthalate has m.p. 133° ⟨8⟩; 135–137° ⟨10⟩.]

Ⓓ **Geranyl hydrogen 3-nitrophthalate:** m.p. 117° [T 1.83].

Ⓓ **Geranyl *N*-(*α*-naphthyl)carbamate:** m.p. 47–48° [cf. T 1.86].

Ⓓ **Geranyl *N,N*-diphenylcarbamate:** from C̄ + *N,N*-diphenylcarbamyl chloride (cf. T 1.43) + pyridine htd. 4 hrs. at 100° ⟨4⟩ ⟨11⟩; easily crystd. from pet. ether in ndls., m.p. 82° ⟨11⟩ ⟨10⟩ [dif. and sepn. ⟨12⟩ from nerol whose corresp. deriv. melts 52° and is difficult to cryst. ⟨5⟩].

1:6270 ⟨1⟩ Semmler, *Ber.* **23,** 2966 (1890). ⟨2⟩ Bluman, Zeitschel, *Ber.* **44,** 2590–2593 (1911). ⟨3⟩ Batty, Burawoy, Harper, Heilbron, Jones, *J. Chem. Soc.* **1938,** 178. ⟨4⟩ von Soden, Treff, *Ber.* **39,** 913 (1906). ⟨5⟩ Ref. 2, page 2592, Note 1. ⟨6⟩ Bertram, Gildemeister, *J. prakt. Chem.* (2) **53,** 233 (1896); **56,** 507 (1897). ⟨7⟩ Reichstein, *Helv. Chim. Acta* **9,** 802 (1926). ⟨8⟩ Erdmann, Huth, *J. prakt. Chem.* (2) **56,** 15–21 (1897). ⟨9⟩ Flateau, Labbé, *Bull. soc. chim.* (3) **19,** 634 (1898). ⟨10⟩ Nelson, Mottern, *Ind. Eng. Chem.* **26,** 636 (1934).

⟨11⟩ Ref. 8, page 8. ⟨12⟩ Ref. 4, pages 907–909. ⟨13⟩ Jones, Haller, *J. Am. Chem. Soc.* **62,** 2558–2559 (1940).

1:6275 DECANOL-1 $CH_3.(CH_2)_8CH_2OH$ $C_{10}H_{22}O$ Beil. I-425

(*n*-Decyl alcohol)

B.P. 231° ⟨1⟩ **M.P. +5.99°** ⟨2⟩ **+6.4°** ⟨3⟩ D_4^{20} = **0.8292** ⟨1⟩ n_D^{20} = **1.43682** ⟨1⟩

Viscous oil — [For prepn. in 52% yield from *n*-octyl MgBr + ethylene oxide see ⟨13⟩.]

C̄ shaken with $KMnO_4$ + dil. H_2SO_4 yields *n*-capric ac. (1:0585) ⟨4⟩; C̄ htd. with calcd. amt. CrO_3 at 100° yields mainly *n*-decyl *n*-caprate ⟨5⟩.

Ⓓ ***n*-Decyl *p*-nitrobenzoate:** cryst. from alc., m.p. 30.2° ⟨6⟩ [cf. T 1.82].

Ⓓ ***n*-Decyl 3,5-dinitrobenzoate:** m.p. 56.7° ⟨7⟩ [cf. T 1.82].

Ⓓ ***n*-Decyl hydrogen phthalate:** m.p. 37.9° cor.; Neut. Eq. 306 ⟨12⟩.

Ⓓ ***n*-Decyl hydrogen 3-nitrophthalate:** m.p. 123.2°; Neut. Eq. 351.7 ⟨10⟩ [cf. T 1.83].

Ⓓ ***n*-Decyl *N*-phenylcarbamate:** ndls. from C_6H_6, then alc., m.p. 59.6° ⟨6⟩ ⟨8⟩, 61° ⟨14⟩.

Ⓓ ***n*-Decyl *N*-(*p*-nitrophenyl)carbamate:** m.p. 117° ⟨9⟩.

Ⓓ ***n*-Decyl *N*-(*α*-naphthyl)carbamate:** cryst. from C_6H_6, then alc.; m.p. 71.4° ⟨7⟩; 73° ⟨11⟩ [cf. T 1.86].

1:6275 ⟨1⟩ Kao, Ma, *Science Repts. Natl. Tsing Hua Univ.*, Ser. **A-1,** 182 (1932). ⟨2⟩ Meyer, Reid, *J. Am. Chem. Soc.* **55,** 1577 (1933). ⟨3⟩ Verkade, Coops, *Rec. trav. chim.* **46,** 908 (1927). ⟨4⟩ Schultz, *Ber.* **42,** 3611 (1909). ⟨5⟩ Bouveault, *Bull. soc. chim.* (3) **31,** 1311 (1904). ⟨6⟩ Komppa, Talvitie, *J. prakt. Chem.* (2) **135,** 201–202 (1932). ⟨7⟩ Reichstein, *Helv. Chim. Acta* **9,** 802 (1926). ⟨8⟩ Hoeke, *Rec. trav. chim.* **54,** 513 (1935). ⟨9⟩ van Hoogstraten, *Rec. trav. chim.* **51,** 426 (1932). ⟨10⟩ Dickinson, Crosson, Copenhaver, *J. Am. Chem. Soc.* **59,** 1095 (1937).

⟨11⟩ Adamson, Kenner, *J. Chem. Soc.* **1934,** 842. ⟨12⟩ Goggans, Copenhaver, *J. Chem. Soc.* **61,** 2909 (1939). ⟨13⟩ Vaughn, Spahr, Nieuwland, *J. Am. Chem. Soc.* **55,** 4208 (1933). ⟨14⟩ Dewey, Witt, *Ind. Eng. Chem., Anal. Ed.* **12,** 459 (1940).

1:6300 OLEYL ALCOHOL $C_{18}H_{36}O$ **Beil. I-45:**
(*cis*-Octadecenyl alcohol; $CH_3.(CH_2)_7.CH{=}CH.(CH_2)_7.CH_2OH$
cis-octadecen-9-ol-1)

B.P. 333-335° ⟨1⟩ D_4^{20} = **0.8489** ⟨1⟩ n_D^{20} = **1.4607** ⟨1

M.P. 0°

[For prepn. by reductn. of *n*-butyl oleate with Na + *n*-BuOH see ⟨2⟩.] C̄ adds Br_2 or I but not quant. (I_2 number always low) — With nitrous gases is very incompletely isomerize to elaidyl alcohol (1:5925).

C̄ on reductn. in AcOH with H_2 + Pt yields stearyl alc. (1:5953), m.p. 58.5° ⟨3⟩. C̄ in AcOH treated with O_3 gives 75% yield ω-hydroxy-*n*-nonylaldehyde, powd. from xylene m.p. 58° ⟨4⟩.

C̄ in AcOH treated with perhydrol at 95° for 2 hrs. gave 9,10-dihydroxystearyl alcohol lfts. from AcOEt, m.p. 82° [dif. from isomeric elaidyl alcohol (1:5925)] ⟨5⟩.

C̄ in dry pyridine stood 3 days with phthalic anhydride yields oleyl hydrogen phthalat as an oil; aq. NaOH soln. of prod. oxid. with $KMnO_4$ at 0° and subseq. hydrolyzed, yield 9,10-dihydroxystearyl alcohol, form of m.p. 81–82° ⟨5⟩. [Dif. from elaidyl alc.]

- Ⓓ **Oleyl *N*-phenylcarbamate:** oil whose purification is impossible ⟨6⟩ ⟨7⟩.
- Ⓓ **Oleyl *N*-(*p*-nitrophenyl)carbamate:** m.p. 85–91° ⟨8⟩.
- Ⓓ **Oleyl *N*-(β-naphthyl)carbamate:** cryst. from alc., m.p. 44–45° ⟨6⟩.
- Ⓓ **Oleyl allophanate:** separable by repeated crystn. from $CHCl_3$ into two isomers, m.p 135° and 129° ⟨6⟩.

1:6300 ⟨1⟩ Toyama, *Chem. Umschau Fette, Öle, Wachse, Harze,* **31,** 13–16 (1924). ⟨2⟩ Reid, et al. *Organic Syntheses* **15,** 51–54 (1935). ⟨3⟩ Sigmund, Haas, *Monatsh.* **50,** 363 (1928). ⟨4⟩ Helferich, Schäfer, *Ber.* **57,** 1913 (1924). ⟨5⟩ Collin, Hilditch, *J. Chem. Soc.* **1933,** 247–248 ⟨6⟩ André, Francois, *Compt. rend.* **185,** 281 (1927). ⟨7⟩ Bouveault, Blanc, *Bull. soc. chim.* (3, **31,** 1210 (1904). ⟨8⟩ van Hoogstraten, *Rec. trav. chim.* **51,** 426 (1932).

ORDER I: SUBORDER I: GENUS 8. ALCOHOLS

Division B; Liquid Alcohols

Section 2. Specific gravity greater than 0.90 at 20°/4°

1:6400 **1,4-DIOXANE** (Diethylene dioxide) $C_4H_8O_2$ **Beil. XIX-3**

```
     CH2CH2
    /      \
   O        O
    \      /
     CH2.CH2
```

B.P. 101.40° ⟨1⟩ **101.31** ⟨2⟩ ⟨3⟩ **M.P. +11.8°** ⟨1⟩ ⟨2⟩ D_4^{20} = **1.03361** ⟨1⟩ n_D^{15} = **1.42436** ⟨1⟩
n_D^{20} = **1.4232** ⟨4⟩
n_D^{25} = **1.4198** ⟨5⟩

Misc. with aq. and most org. solv. — C̄ with aq. forms a binary homogeneous const. boilg. mixt., b.p. 87.82° at 760 mm., contg. 48 mole % C̄ ⟨3⟩ [cf. ⟨4⟩]. C̄ forms with abs. EtOH a const. boilg. mixt. (b.p. 78.13°) contg. 9.3% C̄ ⟨15⟩. [For study of other azeotropes see ⟨6⟩.] [For data on D (10–80°) and n_D^{25} for system C̄ + H_2O see ⟨5⟩.]

Comml. C̄ is likely to contain as impurities ethylene acetal,

```
CH2—O     CH3
|     \   /
|       C
|     /   \
CH2—O      H
```

, acetaldehyde, water, and dioxane peroxide — The ethylene acetal, b.p. 82.5° ⟨7⟩, is best removed by refluxing 7 hrs. with 10% on 1 N HCl (in stream of air to remove acetaldehyde), followed by neutralization, drying over KOH, and distn. ⟨8⟩ ⟨2⟩. [For very impt. study of purifn. of C̄ see ⟨2⟩.] [For detn. of C̄ via oxidn. with $K_2Cr_2O_7$ see ⟨9⟩.]

C̄ readily forms somewhat unstable oxonium salts: e.g., with conc. H_2SO_4 C̄ yields ppt. of C̄.H_2SO_4, white ndls., m.p. 100–101° ⟨10⟩; C̄ with Br_2 yields C̄.Br_2, orange cryst., m.p. 65–66° ⟨11⟩; C̄ with I_2 either directly ⟨11⟩ or from evapn. of ether soln. ⟨12⟩ yields C̄.I_2, red violet solid, m.p. 84–85°.

C̄ in conc. aq. soln. on mixing with conc. aq. soln. of $HgCl_2$ ppts. white mol. cpd., C̄.$HgCl_2$ ⟨10⟩, so stable that it can be sublimed unchanged ⟨13⟩. [For data on mol. cpds. of C̄ with many other inorg. salts see ⟨14⟩.]

C̄ with PkOH yields mol. cpd., C̄.PkOH, pale yel. cryst., m.p. 66° ⟨12⟩.

1:6400 ⟨1⟩ Timmermans, Hennaut-Roland, *J. chim. phys.* **34,** 724–726 (1937). ⟨2⟩ Hess, Frahm, *Ber.* **71,** 2627–2636 (1938). ⟨3⟩ Smith, Wojciechowski, *J. Research Natl. Bur. Standards* **18,** 461–465 (1937). ⟨4⟩ Reid, Hofmann, *Ind. Eng. Chem.* **21,** 695 (1929). ⟨5⟩ Hovorka, Schaefer, Dreisbach, *J. Am. Chem. Soc.* **58,** 2264–2267 (1936). ⟨6⟩ De Mol, *Ing. chim.* **22,** 262-273 (1938). ⟨7⟩ Anschütz, Broeker, *Ber.* **59,** 2845 (1926). ⟨8⟩ Eigenberger, *J. prakt. Chem.* (2) **130,** 75–79 (1931). ⟨9⟩ Smeets, *Cent.* **1937,** I, 4102; *Chem. Abs.* **31,** 1815 (1937). ⟨10⟩ Paterno, Spallino, *Gazz. chim. ital.* **37,** I, 108–109 (1907).

⟨11⟩ Rheinboldt, Boy, *J. prakt. Chem.* (2) **129,** 275–276 (1931). ⟨12⟩ Favorski, *Cent.* **1907,** I, 15. ⟨13⟩ Clarke, *J. Chem. Soc.* **101,** 1803 (1912). ⟨14⟩ Rheinboldt, Luyken, Schmittmann, *J. prakt. Chem.* (2) **149,** 30–54 (1937). ⟨15⟩ Hopkins, Yerger, Lynch, *J. Am. Chem. Soc.* **61,** 2460–2461 (1939).

1:6405 ETHYLENE GLYCOL MONOMETHYL ETHER $C_3H_8O_2$ **Beil. I-467**
(β-Methoxyethanol; methyl-" cellosolve ") $CH_3O.CH_2.CH_2.OH$

B.P. 124.5° D_4^{20} **= 0.9647** n_D^{20} **= 1.40238**

Misc. with aq., ether, C_6H_6.

$\bar{C}$ on oxidn. with $Na_2Cr_2O_7 + H_2SO_4$ ⟨1⟩ or dehydrogenation over Cu at abt. 425° ⟨2⟩ yields methoxyacetaldehyde (1:0138) and probably methoxyacetic ac. (1:1065).

Many of the simple esters are liquids and are *not* recommended as derivs. for identification: acetate, b.p. 145°; benzoate, b.p. 255°; 3,5-dinitrobenzoate.

Ⓓ **β-Methoxyethyl *p*-nitrobenzoate:** from $\bar{C}$ + *p*-nitrobenzoyl chloride in pyridine; cryst. from dil. alc.; m.p. 50.5° ⟨3⟩ [cf. T 1.82].

Ⓓ **β-Methoxyethyl hydrogen 3-nitrophthalate:** from $\bar{C}$ on htg. with 3-nitrophthalic anhydride; cryst. from dil. alc., m.p. 128.4–129.0°; Neut. Eq. 269 ⟨4⟩ [cf. T 1.83].

Ⓓ **Potassium β-methoxyethyl xanthate:** from $\bar{C}$ + pdr. KOH + CS_2 in dry ether; purified by soln. in minimum quant. of alc. or acetone, cooling, and pptn. with dry ether; m.p. 202.5° cor. ⟨5⟩.

Ⓓ **β-Methoxyethyl triphenylmethyl ether:** from $\bar{C}$ on stdg. with triphenylchloromethane (3.6 pts.) in pyridine (8 pts.), 83% yield; large ndls. from alc., m.p. 104° ⟨6⟩ [cf. ⟨7⟩]. 105.5–106.0° u.c. ⟨8⟩.

Ⓓ **β-Methoxyethyl *N*-(*p*-nitrophenyl)carbamate:** from $\bar{C}$ + *p*-nitrophenylisocyanate (71% yield ⟨9⟩); m.p. 111–111.4° ⟨9⟩.

Ⓓ **β-Methoxyethyl *N*-(α-naphthyl)carbamate:** from $\bar{C}$ + α-naphthylisocyanate (88% yield ⟨9⟩); m.p. 112.5–113° ⟨9⟩. [Cf. T 1.86.]

Ⓓ **β-Methoxyethyl *N,N*-diphenylcarbamate:** from $\bar{C}$ + *N,N*-diphenylcarbamyl chloride in pyridine for 3 hrs. at 100° (74% yield ⟨9⟩); m.p. 50.3–50.8° ⟨9⟩. [Cf. T 1.43.]

1:6405 ⟨1⟩ Ghosh, *J. Indian Chem. Soc.* **13,** 326 (1936). ⟨2⟩ Drake, Duvall, Jacobs, Thompson, Sonnichsen, *J. Am. Chem. Soc.* **60,** 74–75 (1938). ⟨3⟩ Conn, Collett, Lazzell, *J. Am. Chem. Soc.* **54,** 4370–4372 (1932). ⟨4⟩ Veraguth, Diehl, *J. Am. Chem. Soc.* **62,** 233 (1940). ⟨5⟩ Whitmore, Lieber, *Ind. Eng. Chem. Anal. Ed.* **7,** 127–129 (1935). ⟨6⟩ Nierenstein, *Ber.* **60,** 1820–1821 (1927). ⟨7⟩ Helferich, Speidel, Toeldete, *Ber.* **56,** 767 (1923). ⟨8⟩ Seikel, Huntress, *J. Am. Chem. Soc.* **63,** 593–595 (1941). ⟨9⟩ Manning, Mason, *J. Am. Chem. Soc.* **62,** 3137 (1940).

1:6410 ETHYLENE GLYCOL MONOETHYL ETHER $C_4H_{10}O_2$ **Beil. I-467**
(β-Ethoxyethanol; " cellosolve "; ethyl β-hydroxyethyl ether) $CH_3.CH_2.O.CH_2.CH_2.OH$

B.P. 134.8° D_4^{20} **= 0.9297** n_D^{20} **= 1.40797**

Misc. with aq.; with aq. forms homogeneous binary const. boilg. mixt. (b.p. 98–99°) contg. abt. 40% $\bar{C}$ by vol. ⟨1⟩ [cf. ⟨2⟩]. [For data on n_D^{30} for binary systems $\bar{C} + H_2O$ and $\bar{C}$ + EtOH see ⟨2⟩; for data on ternary system $\bar{C} + H_2O$ + EtOH see ⟨9⟩.]

$\bar{C}$ on oxidn. with $Na_2Cr_2O_7 + H_2SO_4$ ⟨3⟩, or dehydrogenation over Cu at abt. 425° ⟨4⟩ yields ethoxyacetaldehyde (1:0159) and probably ethoxyacetic ac. (1:1070).

Many simpler esters are liquids and not recommended as derivs. for identification of $\bar{C}$: e.g., acetate (1:3323); benzoate (1:4146); *p*-nitrobenzoate ⟨5⟩ ⟨12⟩.

Ⓓ **β-Ethoxyethyl 3,5-dinitrobenzoate:** from $\bar{C}$ + 3,5-dinitrobenzoyl chloride in pyridine cryst. from alc., m.p. 75° [cf. T 1.82].

Ⓓ **β-Ethoxyethyl hydrogen 3-nitrophthalate:** from $\bar{C}$ on htg. with 3-nitrophthalic anhydride; cryst. from aq. alc. as monohydrate, m.p. 94.2–94.5° (Neut. Eq. 301); m.p. anhydrous material, 118.0–118.6° (Neut. Eq. 283) ⟨6⟩ [cf. T 1.83].

Ⓓ **Potassium β-ethoxyethyl xanthate:** from $\bar{C}$ + powd. KOH + CS_2 in dry ether; purified by soln. in minimum quant. alc. or acetone, cooling, and pptn. with dry ether; m.p. 185.7° ⟨7⟩.

Ⓓ **β-Ethoxyethyl triphenylmethyl ether:** from $\bar{C}$ (100% excess) + triphenylchloromethane in dry pyridine at 100° for 5 hrs. (92% yield); cryst. from alc., m.p. 77–78° ⟨8⟩; 79.0–79.5° u.c. ⟨13⟩. [With equal moles $\bar{C}$ + reagent yields 61–83% ⟨8⟩.]

Ⓓ **β-Ethoxyethyl *N*-(*p*-nitrophenyl)carbamate:** from $\bar{C}$ + *p*-nitrophenylisocyanate (80% yield ⟨11⟩); m.p. 79.4–80.1° ⟨11⟩.

Ⓓ **β-Ethoxyethyl *N*-(α-naphthyl)carbamate:** from $\bar{C}$ + α-naphthylisocyanate (81% yield ⟨11⟩); m.p. 67.3–67.5° ⟨11⟩. [Cf. T 1.86.]

Ⓓ **β-Ethoxyethyl *N,N*-diphenylcarbamate:** from $\bar{C}$ + *N,N*-diphenylcarbamyl chloride in pyridine for 3 hrs. at 100° (71% yield ⟨11⟩), m.p. 41.5–43° ⟨11⟩. [Cf. T 1.43.]

1:6410 ⟨1⟩ Davidson, *Ind. Eng. Chem.* **18**, 670 (1926). ⟨2⟩ Baker, Hubbard, Huguet, Michalowski, *Ind. Eng. Chem.* **31**, 1260 (1939). ⟨3⟩ Dunn, Redemann, Smith, *J. Biol. Chem.* **104**, 514 (1934). ⟨4⟩ Drake, Duvall, Jacobs, Thompson, Sonnichsen, *J. Am. Chem. Soc.* **60**, 74–75 (1938). ⟨5⟩ Conn, Collett, Lazzell, *J. Am. Chem. Soc.* **54**, 4370–4372 (1932). ⟨6⟩ Veraguth, Diehl, *J. Am. Chem. Soc.* **62**, 233 (1940). ⟨7⟩ Whitmore, Lieber, *Ind. Eng. Chem., Anal. Ed.* **7**, 127–129 (1935). ⟨8⟩ Hurd, Filachione, *J. Am. Chem. Soc.* **59**, 1950–1951 (1937). ⟨9⟩ Baker, Chaddock, Lindsay, Werner, *Ind. Eng. Chem.* **31**, 1263 (1939).

⟨11⟩ Manning, Mason, *J. Am. Chem. Soc.* **62**, 3137 (1940). ⟨12⟩ Mason, Manning, *J. Am. Chem. Soc.* **62**, 1638 (1940). ⟨13⟩ Seikel, Huntress, *J. Am. Chem. Soc.* **63**, 593–595 (1941).

1:6412 CYCLOPENTANOL

```
H2C——CH2
 |     |
H2C   CH2
   \  /
    C
   / \
  H   OH
```

$C_5H_{10}O$ **Beil. VI-5**

B.P. 140.85° ⟨1⟩

D_4^{20} = **0.94688** ⟨1⟩ n_D^{15} = **1.45512** ⟨1⟩
D_4^{20} = **0.9488** ⟨2⟩ n_D^{20} = **1.4530** ⟨2⟩

Colorless oil with odor reminis. of AmOH. Very spar. sol. aq., sol. alc. or ether.

[For prepn. from cyclopentanone (1:5446) by act. of Na on moist ether soln. see ⟨3⟩ or by cat. hydrogenation see ⟨2⟩ ⟨4⟩.]

$\bar{C}$ vig. oxidized by warm dil. HNO_3 yields mainly glutaric ac. (1:0440) accompanied by a little succinic ac. (1:0530) ⟨3⟩ — $\bar{C}$ with CrO_3 + H_2SO_4 (T 1.72) yields cyclopentanone (1:5446).

$\bar{C}$ treated with H_2SO_4 + HBr mixt. ⟨5⟩ or treated with PBr_3 at 0° ⟨2⟩ yields cyclopentyl bromide, b.p. 135–136°. [For careful study of many react. of latter see ⟨6⟩] — $\bar{C}$, htd. with $KHSO_4$, or P_2O_5 or *p*-toluenesulfonyl chloride yields cyclopentene (1:8037), b.p. 44°.

Ⓓ **Cyclopentyl *N*-phenylcarbamate:** ndls. from alc., m.p. 132.5° ⟨7⟩.

1:6412 ⟨1⟩ Timmermans, Hennaut-Roland, *J. chim. phys.* **34**, 715 (1937). ⟨2⟩ Noller, Adams, *J. Am. Chem. Soc.* **48**, 1084 (1926). ⟨3⟩ Wislicenus, Hentschel, *Ann.* **275**, 322–323 (1893). ⟨4⟩ Yohe, Adams, *J. Am. Chem. Soc.* **50**, 1505 (1928). ⟨5⟩ Grummitt, *Organic Syntheses* **19**, 88 (1939). ⟨6⟩ Loevenich, Utsch, Moldrickx, Schaefer, *Ber.* **62**, 3084–3096 (1929). ⟨7⟩ Meiser, *Ber.* **32**, 2049 (1899).

1:6413 ETHYLENE GLYCOL MONO-ISOPROPYL ETHER **Beil. S.N. 30**
(β-Hydroxyethyl isopropyl ether; isopropyl- "cellosolve") $(CH_3)_2CH.O.CH_2.CH_2.OH$ $C_5H_{12}O_2$

B.P. 141.5$^\circ_{736}$ ⟨1⟩ D_4^{20} **= 0.9030 ⟨1⟩** n_D^{20} **= 1.40954 ⟨1⟩**

For solvent characteristics see ⟨2⟩.

Ⓓ **β-Isopropoxyethyl triphenylmethyl ether:** from $\bar{C}$ (0.5 ml.) + triphenylchloromethane (0.5 equiv.) in pyridine (1 ml.) on htg. 5 min. at 100°; yield 50–60%; colorless ndls. from MeOH, m.p. 71.0–71.5° u.c. ⟨3⟩.

1:6413 ⟨1⟩ Tallman, *J. Am. Chem. Soc.* **56,** 127 (1934). ⟨2⟩ Davidson, *Ind. Eng. Chem.* **18,** 669–675 (1926). ⟨3⟩ Seikel, Huntress, *J. Am. Chem. Soc.* **63,** 593–595 (1941).

1:6414 ETHYLENE GLYCOL MONO-*n*-PROPYL ETHER **Beil. I$_1$-(244)**
(β-Hydroxyethyl *n*-propyl ether) $CH_3.CH_2.CH_2.O.CH_2.CH_2.OH$ $C_5H_{12}O_2$

B.P. 150.0$^\circ_{736}$ ⟨1⟩ D_4^{20} **= 0.9112 ⟨1⟩** n_D^{20} **= 1.41328 ⟨1⟩**

For solvent characteristics see ⟨2⟩.

1:6414 ⟨1⟩ Tallman, *J. Am. Chem. Soc.* **56,** 127 (1934). ⟨2⟩ Davidson, *Ind. Eng. Chem.* **18,** 669–675 (1926).

—— **ETHYLENE GLYCOL MONO-ISOBUTYL ETHER** $C_6H_{14}O_2$ **Beil. S.N. 30**
(β-Hydroxyethyl isobutyl ether) $(CH_3)_2.CH.CH_2.O.CH_2.CH_2.OH$

B.P. 159.3$^\circ_{746}$ D_4^{20} **= 0.8900** n_D^{20} **= 1.41428**

See 1:6235-A. Genus 8: Alcohols: Division B. Section 1.

—— **ETHYLENE GLYCOL MONO-*sec*-BUTYL ETHER** $C_6H_{14}O_2$ **Beil. S.N. 30**
(*sec*-Butyl β-hydroxyethyl ether)

$$CH_3-\underset{H}{\overset{C_2H_5}{C}}-O.CH_2.CH_2.OH$$

B.P. 159.3$^\circ_{746}$ D_4^{20} **= 0.8966** n_D^{20} **= 1.41606**

See 1:6235-B. Genus 8: Alcohols: Division B. Section 1.

1:6415 CYCLOHEXANOL $C_6H_{12}O$ **Beil. VI-5**
(Hexahydrophenol; hexalin)

$$CH_2\langle{}^{CH_2-CH_2}_{CH_2-CH_2}\rangle C\langle{}^{H}_{OH}$$

B.P. 161.1° ⟨1⟩ **M.P. +25.15° ⟨1⟩** D_4^{30} **= 0.94155 ⟨1⟩** n_D^{25} **= 1.46477 ⟨1⟩**
D_4^{45} **= 0.92994 ⟨1⟩**

Very hygroscopic ndls. of camphoraceous odor, sol. in 28 vols. aq. at 20° — Volatile with steam as const. boilg. mixt. (b.p. 97.9°) contg. 23% by wt. of $\bar{C}$ ⟨2⟩ — Comml. prod. usually liq.; purified by vac. distn. ⟨3⟩ — $\bar{C}$ with dry $CaCl_2$ gives solid [use in purifn. or removal from inert material ⟨4⟩].

$\bar{C}$ on oxidn. with conc. HNO_3 yields adipic ac. (1:0775) [use in prepn. of latter ⟨5⟩] — $\bar{C}$ does not reduce cold aq. $KMnO_4$ (T 1.34) — $\bar{C}$ oxidized with $CrO_3 + H_2SO_4$ (T 1.72) yields cyclohexanone (1:5465) — $\bar{C}$ does not react with Na in cold, but only on warming.

$\bar{C}$, dislvd. in 8 vols. conc. HCl at room temp., soon clouds and on htg. seps. 93% yield cyclohexyl chloride, b.p. 143° ⟨6⟩ [cf. T 1.85].

$\bar{C}$, htd. with a little conc. H_2SO_4 at 140–150° ⟨7⟩, or even better with 85% H_3PO_4 at 160–170° ⟨8⟩ ⟨9⟩ gives alm. quant. yield of cyclohexene, b.p. 83° (1:8070).

Cyclohexyl acetate (1:3412) and cyclohexyl benzoate are both liquids and *not* recommended as derivs. for identification.

Ⓓ **Cyclohexyl *p*-nitrobenzoate:** m.p. 50° [cf. T 1.82].

Ⓓ **Cyclohexyl 3,5-dinitrobenzoate:** from $\bar{C}$ + 3,5-dinitrobenzoyl chloride in pyridine, cryst. from alc., m.p. 112–113° ⟨10⟩ [cf. T 1.82].

Ⓓ **Cyclohexyl hydrogen phthalate:** m.p. 99° ⟨11⟩.

Ⓓ **Cyclohexyl hydrogen 3-nitrophthalate:** m.p. 160° [cf. T 1.83].

Ⓓ **Potassium cyclohexyl xanthate:** from $\bar{C}$ + powd. KOH + CS_2 in dry ether; purifn. by soln. in least possible alc. or acetone, cooling, and pptn. with dry ether; prod. darkens at 242° cor. ⟨12⟩.

Ⓓ **Cyclohexyl triphenylmethyl ether:** from $\bar{C}$ + triphenylchloromethane (3 pts.) in pyridine (7 pts.); pr. from alc., m.p. 103° ⟨13⟩.

Ⓓ **Cyclohexyl *N*-phenylcarbamate:** m.p. 82° ⟨14⟩.

Ⓓ **Cyclohexyl *N*-α-naphthylcarbamate:** m.p. 128–129° ⟨15⟩ [cf. T 1.86].

Ⓓ **Cyclohexyl *N*-(*p*-xenyl)carbamate:** m.p. 166° ⟨16⟩.

1:6415 ⟨1⟩ Timmermans, Hennaut-Roland, *J. chim. phys.* **34,** 718–720 (1937). ⟨2⟩ Lecat, *Z. anorg. allgem. Chem.* **186,** 138 (1930). ⟨3⟩ Lange, *Z. physik. Chem.* **A-160,** 80–82 (1932). ⟨4⟩ Wallach, *Ann.* **381,** 112, Note (1911). ⟨5⟩ Ellis, *Organic Syntheses, Coll. Vol.* I, 18–19 (1932). ⟨6⟩ Norris, Mulliken, *J. Am. Chem. Soc.* **42,** 2097 (1920). ⟨7⟩ Coleman, Johnston, *Organic Syntheses, Coll. Vol.* I, 177–178 (1932). ⟨8⟩ Dehn, Jackson, *J. Am. Chem. Soc.* **55,** 4285 (1933). ⟨9⟩ Hershberg, Ruhoff, *Organic Syntheses* **17,** 27 (1937). ⟨10⟩ Reichstein, *Helv. Chim. Acta* **9,** 802 (1926).

⟨11⟩ Brunel, *Bull. soc. chim.* (3) **33,** 274 (1905). ⟨12⟩ Whitmore, Lieber, *Ind. Eng. Chem., Anal. Ed.* **7,** 128–129 (1935). ⟨13⟩ Helferich, Speidel, Toeldte, *Ber.* **56,** 768 (1923). ⟨14⟩ Bouveault, *Bull. soc. chim.* (3) **29,** 1052 (1903). ⟨15⟩ Bickel, French, *J. Am. Chem. Soc.* **48,** 749 (1926). ⟨16⟩ Morgan, Pettet, *J. Chem. Soc.* **1931,** 1125.

1:6420 2-METHYLCYCLOHEXANOL-1 $C_7H_{14}O$ **Beil. VI-11**
(Hexahydro-*o*-cresol)

```
      H     OH
       \   /
         C      CH3
       /   \   /
   H2C       C——H
    |        |
   H2C       CH2
       \   /
         C
         H2
```

This product (from reductn. of *o*-cresol or 2-methylcyclohexanone) consists of a mixt. of two geom. isomers. *Each* of these isomers can be resolved into two opt. act. forms, although the data in this table will be only for the *d,l*-isomers. The serious confusion in the early literature has now been reconciled ⟨1⟩ ⟨2⟩ ⟨4⟩.

Both isomers on oxidn. with CrO_3—H_2SO_4 yield the same 2-methylcyclohexanone (1:5470), b.p. 165° ⟨1⟩ ⟨4⟩.

cis (β) ISOMER

B.P. 165.3° ⟨1⟩ **M.P. −9.3°** ⟨1⟩ D_4^{20} **= 0.9340** ⟨1⟩ ⟨2⟩ n_D^{20} **= 1.4640** ⟨2⟩

Ⓓ ***cis*-2-Methylcyclohexyl *p*-nitrobenzoate:** m.p. 51–52° ⟨1⟩; 55–56° ⟨4⟩. [With corresp. deriv. from *trans* isomer yields a non-separable mixt., m.p. 35–36° ⟨1⟩, orig. reported as the pure compd. ⟨3⟩.]

Ⓓ ***cis*-2-Methylcyclohexyl 3,5-dinitrobenzoate:** m.p. 98–99° ⟨2⟩ ⟨4⟩. [Mixed m.p. with corresp. deriv. of *trans* isomer melts 85–90°.]

Ⓓ ***cis*-2-Methylcyclohexyl hydrogen phthalate:** m.p. 103–104° ⟨1⟩; 104–105° ⟨4⟩. [Mixed m.p. with corresp. deriv. of *trans* isomer melts 95–96° ⟨1⟩.] [For m.p. composition curve of *cis* and *trans* acid phthalates see ⟨4⟩.] The value of 90° formerly reported was on impure material ⟨3⟩.

Ⓓ ***cis*-2-Methylcyclohexyl *N*-phenylcarbamate:** m.p. 90–91° ⟨2⟩; 93–94° ⟨4⟩. [This value obtd. on deriv. from pure *cis* alcohol; that of deriv. from crude alcohol rises through values formerly reported until it reaches that of *trans* isomer, m.p. 105°.]

trans (α) **ISOMER**

B.P. 167.4° ⟨1⟩ **M.P. = −21°** ⟨1⟩ D_4^{20} **= 0.9235** ⟨1⟩ ⟨2⟩ n_D^{20} **= 1.4611** ⟨2⟩

Ⓓ ***trans*-2-Methylcyclohexyl *p*-nitrobenzoate:** m.p. 65° ⟨1⟩ ⟨4⟩. [With corresp. deriv. from *cis* isomer yields a non-separable mixt., m.p. 35–36° ⟨1⟩, orig. reported as the pure compd. ⟨3⟩.]

Ⓓ ***trans*-2-Methylcyclohexyl 3,5-dinitrobenzoate:** m.p. 114–115° ⟨2⟩ ⟨4⟩. [Best deriv. for charact. of the isomers.] — [Mixed m.p. with corresp. deriv. of *cis* isomer melts 85–90° ⟨2⟩.]

Ⓓ ***trans*-2-Methylcyclohexyl hydrogen phthalate:** m.p. 124–125° ⟨1⟩ ⟨4⟩. [From tech. $\bar{C}$ + phthalic anhyd., htd. 4 hrs. at 140°; cryst. from AcOH; yield 74% — Hydrol. gives pure *trans* $\bar{C}$.]

Ⓓ ***trans*-2-Methylcyclohexyl *N*-phenylcarbamate:** m.p. 105° ⟨2⟩ ⟨4⟩. [Mixed m.p. with corresp. deriv. of *cis* isomer 75–80°.]

1:6420 ⟨1⟩ Hückel, Hagengurth, *Ber.* **64,** 2892–2895 (1931). ⟨2⟩ Skita, Faust, *Ber.* **64,** 2878–2892 (1931). ⟨3⟩ Gough, Hunter, Kenyon, *J. Chem. Soc.* **1926,** 2052–2071. ⟨4⟩ Vavon, Perlin, Horeau, *Bull. soc. chim.* (4) **51,** 644–650 (1932).

1:6423 DIACETONE ALCOHOL $CH_3.CO.CH_2.C(CH_3)_2$ (with OH on the C) $C_6H_{12}O_2$ **Beil. I-836**

B.P. 166° D^{25} **= 0.9306**

Misc. with aq., alc., ether — Fails in Generic Test 7 for ketones. [For prepn. from acetone + $Ba(OH)_2$ (71% yield) see ⟨1⟩.]

$\bar{C}$ is salted out from aq. solns. by KOH, NaOH or K_2CO_3 but on htg. with aq. alk. decomposes to acetone (1:5400) — $\bar{C}$ is sol. in conc. H_2SO_4 but decomposes to aq. + mesityl oxide (1:5445) — $\bar{C}$ reduces Fehling's soln. (T 1.22).

Ⓓ **Conversion to mesityl oxide:** Distn. of $\bar{C}$ with trace of I_2 gives mesityl oxide (1:5445) which is identified via its derivatives. ⟨2.⟩

Ⓓ **Diacetone alcohol oxime:** Aq. alc. soln. of $\bar{C}$ treated with $NaHCO_3$ and then NH_2OH.-HCl yields oxime on 24 hr. stdg. Extd. with ether, evapd., oxime distd. in vac. (b.p. 140° at 29 mm.), recrystd. from lgr. + ether; m.p. 57.5–58.5° with sintering at 54° ⟨3⟩.

Ⓓ **Mesityl oxide 2,4-dinitrophenylhydrazone:** from $\bar{C}$ by loss of water when treated with 2,4-dinitrophenylhydrazine reagt.; lt. red cryst. from alc., red from AcOH; m.p. 202–203° ⟨4⟩ ⟨5⟩ [cf. T 1.14].

1:6423 ⟨1⟩ Conant, Tuttle, *Organic Syntheses, Coll. Vol.* I, 193–195 (1932). ⟨2⟩ Conant, Tuttle, *Organic Syntheses, Coll. Vol.* I, 338–339 (1932). ⟨3⟩ Kohn, Lindauer, *Monatsh.* **23,** 755 (1902). ⟨4⟩ Allen, Richmond, *J. Org. Chem.* **2,** 225 (1937). ⟨5⟩ Campbell, *Analyst* **61,** 393 (1936).

1:6425 2-FURANCARBINOL (Furfuryl alcohol)

HC——CH ‖ ‖ HC C—CH_2OH \ / O

$C_5H_6O_2$ **Beil. XVII-112**

B.P. 170° D_{20}^{20} = **1.1351** n_D^{20} = **1.4868** ⟨13⟩

Misc. with aq.; easily volatile with steam as const. boilg. mixt. (b.p. 98.5°) contg. 20% by wt. of C̄ ⟨1⟩ — Eas. sol. alc., ether.

[For prepn. in 61–63% theory from furfural + NaOH see ⟨2⟩.] [For detn. of furfural in C̄ see ⟨12⟩.] [For study of system: C̄ + furfural (1:0185) see ⟨13⟩.]

Aq. soln. of C̄ decomposes on stdg. and seps. into layers — C̄ is very unstable toward mineral acids; with pine splinter soaked in conc. HCl gives blue-green color.

C̄ when free from furfural (1:0185) does not redden aniline acetate paper (T 1.23) ⟨3⟩ — C̄ instantly reduces $KMnO_4$ in cold, or NH_4OH + $AgNO_3$ on warming, yielding furoic ac. (1:0475) — C̄ deodorizes Br_2-aq.

Ⓓ **Furfuryl *p*-nitrobenzoate:** m.p. 76° [cf. T 1.82]; 75–77° ⟨14⟩.

Ⓓ **Furfuryl 3,5-dinitrobenzoate:** from C̄ + 3,5-dinitrobenzoyl chloride in pyridine, m.p. 80–81° ⟨4⟩ [cf. T 1.82].

Ⓓ **Furfuryl hydrogen phthalate:** from C̄, boiled with 1 Na in toluene, ppt. filtered, and then heated with 1 mole phthalic anhyd. in toluene, ppt. filtered, dislvd. in aq., acidified with HCl; m.p. 85° ⟨5⟩.

Ⓓ **Potassium furfuryl xanthate:** from C̄ + powd. KOH + CS_2 in dry ether; purified by soln. in least possible alc. or acetone, cooling, and pptn. with dry ether; m.p., 154.4° cor. ⟨6⟩.

Ⓓ **Furfuryl triphenylmethyl ether:** from C̄ + triphenylchloromethane in pyridine at 0°; cryst. from alc., m.p. 137–139° ⟨7⟩.

Ⓓ **Furfuryl *N*-phenylcarbamate:** m.p. 45° ⟨8⟩.

Ⓓ **Furfuryl *N*-(α-naphthyl)carbamate:** cryst. from lgr., m.p. 129–130° ⟨9⟩; 133° ⟨10⟩ [cf. T 1.86].

Ⓓ **Furfuryl *N,N*-diphenylcarbamate:** from C̄ + diphenylcarbamyl chloride in pyridine: yellowish ndls. from lgr. or alc., m.p. 97.5–98.0° ⟨11⟩ [cf. T 1.43].

1:6425 ⟨1⟩ Lecat, *Z. anorg. allgem. Chem.* **186,** 138 (1930). ⟨2⟩ Wilson, *Organic Syntheses, Coll. Vol.* I, 270–274 (1932). ⟨3⟩ Wienhaus, *Ber.* **53,** 1657, Note 4 (1920). ⟨4⟩ Reichstein, *Helv. Chim. Acta* **9,** 802 (1926). ⟨5⟩ Brown, Gilman, van Peursem, *Iowa State Coll. J. Sci.* **6,** 133–136 (1932); *Chem. Abs.* **26,** 3791 (1932). ⟨6⟩ Whitmore, Lieber, *Ind. Eng. Chem., Anal. Ed.* **7,** 128–129 (1935). ⟨7⟩ Hurd, Thomas, *J. Am. Chem. Soc.* **55,** 423 (1933). ⟨8⟩ Ref. 3, pages 1663–1664. ⟨9⟩ Bickel, French, *J. Am. Chem. Soc.* **48,** 749 (1926). ⟨10⟩ Neuberg, Hirschberg, *Biochem. Z.* **27,** 345 (1910).

⟨11⟩ Erdmann, *Ber.* **35,** 1851 (1902). ⟨12⟩ Dunlop, Trimble, *Ind. Eng. Chem., Anal. Ed.* **11,** 602–603 (1939). ⟨13⟩ Dunlop, Trimble, *Ind. Eng. Chem.* **32,** 1000–1002 (1940). ⟨14⟩ Kleene, Fried, *J. Am. Chem. Soc.* **62,** 3516 (1940).

1:6430 ETHYLENE GLYCOL MONO-*n*-BUTYL ETHER $C_6H_{14}O_2$ **Beil. S.N. 30**

(β-*n*-Butoxyethanol; *n*-butyl β-hydroxyethyl ether; butyl-" cellosolve ")

$C_4H_9OCH_2CH_2OH$

B.P. 170-176°/743 mm. ⟨1⟩ *D* = **0.9188** ⟨1⟩ n_D^{26} = **1.4177** ⟨1⟩

Colorless mobile odorless liq. — C̄ is sol. in aq. at 20° to extent of 5 g. C̄ in 100 g. aq. [for complete soly. curve with aq. at various temps. see ⟨2⟩].

C̄ reacts with Na forming a Na deriv. sol. in ether — C̄ with PCl_3 in pyridine gives (66.5% yield) *n*-butyl β-chloroethyl ether, b.p. 154.5° ⟨3⟩; C̄ with PBr_3 in pyridine gives (60% yield) *n*-butyl β-bromoethyl ether, b.p. 172° ⟨3⟩.

The *p*-nitrobenzoate ⟨4⟩ ⟨9⟩, 3,5-dinitrobenzoate ⟨5⟩, *N,N*-diphenylcarbamate ⟨8⟩, and *p*-toluenesulfonate ⟨5⟩ are oils and *not* recommended as derivs. for identification.

Ⓓ **β-*n*-Butoxyethyl hydrogen 3-nitrophthalate:** from C̄ htd. with 3-nitrophthalic anhydride; m.p. 120.0–120.6°; Neut. Eq. 311 ⟨6⟩ [cf. T 1.83].

Ⓓ **Potassium β-*n*-butoxyethyl xanthate:** from C̄ + powd. KOH + CS_2 in dry ether; purified by soln. in least possible alc. or acetone, cooling, and pptn. with dry ether; m.p. 167.9° cor. ⟨7⟩.

Ⓓ **β-*n*-Butoxyethyl *N*-(*p*-nitrophenyl)carbamate:** from C̄ + *p*-nitrophenylisocyanate (68% yield ⟨8⟩), cryst. from CCl_4, m.p. 58.7–59.1° ⟨8⟩. [Mixed m.p. of this prod. with *p*-nitrophenylisocyanate (m.p. 57–57.5°) is depressed, e.g., to 42–47° ⟨8⟩.]

1:6430 ⟨1⟩ Davidson, *Ind. Eng. Chem.* **18,** 670 (1926). ⟨2⟩ Cox, Cretcher, *J. Am. Chem. Soc.* **48,** 451–453 (1926). ⟨3⟩ Palomaa, Kenetti, *Ber.* **64,** 799 (1931). ⟨4⟩ Conn, Collett, Lazzell, *J. Am. Chem. Soc.* **54,** 4370–4372 (1932). ⟨5⟩ Butler, Renfrew, Cretcher, Souther, *J. Am. Chem. Soc.* **59,** 229 (1937). ⟨6⟩ Veraguth, Diehl, *J. Am. Chem. Soc.* **62,** 233 (1940). ⟨7⟩ Whitmore, Lieber, *Ind. Eng. Chem., Anal. Ed.* **7,** 128–129 (1935). ⟨8⟩ Manning, Mason, *J. Am. Chem. Soc.* **62,** 3137 (1940). ⟨9⟩ Mason, Manning, *J. Am. Chem. Soc.* **62,** 1638 (1940).

—— **PINACOL** $(CH_3)_2C(OH).C(OH)(CH_3)_2$ $C_6H_{14}O_2$ **Beil. I-487**

B.P. 173°

See 1:5805. Genus 8: Division A: Section 1. M.p. 35–38°.

1:6435 3-METHYLCYCLOHEXANOL-1 $C_7H_{14}O$ **Beil. VI-12**
(Hexahydro-*m*-cresol)

H OH
C
H_2C CH_2
H
H_2C C
C CH_3
H_2

This product (from reduction of *m*-cresol (1:1730) or 3-methylcyclohexanone) (1:5480) consists of a mixt. of two geom. isomers, contg. 80–86% α isomer ⟨2⟩. Each of these isomers can be resolved into two opt. act. forms, although the data in this table will be given only for the *d,l*-racemes.

cis (β) ISOMER

B.P. 173-174$^\circ_{760}$ ⟨1⟩ D_4^{20} = **0.919** ⟨1⟩ n_D^{20} = **1.4572** ⟨1⟩

Ⓓ ***cis*-3-Methylcyclohexyl *p*-nitrobenzoate:** m.p. 65° ⟨2⟩.

Ⓓ ***cis*-3-Methylcyclohexyl 3,5-dinitrobenzoate:** m.p. 91–92° ⟨1⟩. [Mixed m.p. with corresp. deriv. of *trans* isomer 80–85°.] Sapon. with aq. MeOH/NaOH yields pure *cis* alcohol.

Ⓓ ***cis*-3-Methylcyclohexyl hydrogen phthalate:** m.p. 82–83°. [Not suited to isolation of deriv. from crude alcohol ⟨2⟩.]

Ⓓ ***cis*-3-Methylcyclohexyl *N*-phenylcarbamate:** m.p. 87–88° ⟨1⟩. [Mixed m.p. with corresp. deriv. of *trans* isomer, 75–85°.]

trans (α) ISOMER

B.P. 174-175°$_{762}$ ⟨1⟩ D_4^{20} = **0.9145 ⟨1⟩** n_D^{20} = **1.4550 ⟨1⟩**

Ⓓ ***trans*-3-Methylcyclohexyl *p*-nitrobenzoate:** m.p. 58° ⟨2⟩.

Ⓓ ***trans*-3-Methylcyclohexyl 3,5-dinitrobenzoate:** m.p. 97–98° ⟨1⟩. [Mixed m.p. with corresp. deriv. of *cis* isomer, melts 80–85°.] Sapon. with aq. MeOH/NaOH yields pure *trans* alcohol.

Ⓓ ***trans*-3-Methylcyclohexyl hydrogen phthalate:** m.p. 93–94° [not suited to isolation of deriv. from crude alcohol ⟨2⟩].

Ⓓ ***trans*-3-Methylcyclohexyl *N*-phenylcarbamate:** m.p. 93–94° ⟨1⟩. [Mixed m.p. with corresp. deriv. of *cis* isomer melts 75–85° ⟨1⟩.]

1:6435 ⟨1⟩ Skita, Faust, *Ber.* **64,** 2889–2890 (1931). ⟨2⟩ Gough, Hunter, Kenyon, *J. Chem. Soc.* **1926,** 2062–2063.

1:6440 4-METHYLCYCLOHEXANOL-1 $C_7H_{14}O$ **Beil. VI-14**

(Hexahydro-*p*-cresol)

```
CH3        CH2—CH2       H
    \     /       \     /
     C               C
    /     \       /     \
H          CH2—CH2       OH
```

This product obtained by the reduction of *p*-cresol (1:1410) or of 4-methylcyclohexanone (1:5485) is a mixt. of two geom. isomers. All data prior to 1926 are on mixt. of uncertain compn. ⟨1⟩ ⟨2⟩. The two isomers are separated and identified by the derivatives indicated below.

cis (β) ISOMER

B.P. 173-174°$_{750}$ ⟨3⟩ D_4^{20} = **0.914 ⟨3⟩** n_D^{20} = **1.4549 ⟨3⟩**

Ⓓ ***cis*-4-Methylcyclohexyl *p*-nitrobenzoate:** m.p. 94° ⟨4⟩.

Ⓓ ***cis*-4-Methylcyclohexyl 3,5-dinitrobenzoate:** m.p. 134° ⟨3⟩. [Mixed m.p. with corresp. *trans* isomer is 125–130°.] — Sapon. with aq. MeOH/NaOH yields pure *cis* C̄.

Ⓓ **cis-4-Methylcyclohexyl hydrogen phthalate:** m.p. 72–73° ⟨5⟩. [Obtd. with difficulty from mother liq. of *trans* isomer.]

Ⓓ ***cis*-4-Methylcyclohexyl *N*-phenylcarbamate:** m.p. 118–119° ⟨3⟩. [Mixed m.p. with corresp. *trans* deriv. is 112–115°.]

trans (α) ISOMER

B.P. 173-174.5°$_{745}$ ⟨3⟩ D_4^{20} = **0.913 ⟨3⟩** n_D^{20} = **1.4534 ⟨3⟩**

Ⓓ ***trans*-4-Methylcyclohexyl *p*-nitrobenzoate:** m.p. 67° ⟨4⟩.

Ⓓ ***trans*-4-Methylcyclohexyl 3,5-dinitrobenzoate:** m.p. 139–140° ⟨3⟩. [Mixed m.p. with corresp. *cis* deriv. 125–130°.] — Sapon. with aq. MeOH/NaOH gives *trans* C̄ ⟨3⟩.

Ⓓ ***trans*-4-Methylcyclohexyl hydrogen phthalate:** from crude C̄ + phthalic anhyd. after five recrystns. from AcOH; m.p. 119–120°; Neut. Eq. 262 — Sapon. with alk. yields pure *trans* C̄ ⟨5⟩.

Ⓓ ***trans*-4-Methylcyclohexyl *N*-phenylcarbamate:** m.p. 124–125° ⟨3⟩. [Mixed m.p. with corresp. *cis* deriv. is 112–115°.]

1:6440 ⟨1⟩ Gough, Hunter, Kenyon, *J. Chem. Soc.* **1926,** 2052–2071. ⟨2⟩ Skita, Faust, *Ber.* **64,** 2878–2892 (1931). ⟨3⟩ Ref. 2, pages 2883, 2890–2892. ⟨4⟩ Ref. 1, page 2066. ⟨5⟩ Ref. 1, pages 2061–2062.

1:6445 TETRAHYDROFURANCARBINOL $C_5H_{10}O_2$ **Beil. S.N. 2380**
(Tetrahydrofurfuryl alcohol)

$$\begin{array}{l} CH_2\text{—}CH_2 \\ |\quad\quad\ \ |\ /H \\ CH_2\quad C\text{—}CH_2OH \\ \quad \diagdown\ \diagup \\ \quad\ \ O \end{array}$$

B.P. 177° ⟨1⟩ D_4^{20} = **1.0544** ⟨1⟩ n_D^{20} = **1.45167** ⟨1⟩

Misc. aq. but salted out by K_2CO_3 — $\bar{C}$, when pure, does not turn dark on exposure to light [dif. from furfuryl alc. (1:6425)].

Does not decolorize Br_2-aq. nor dil. $KMnO_4$ [dif. from furfuryl alc. (1:6425)] — Gives no color to pine splinter moistened with HCl [dif. from furfuryl alc.].

Ⓓ **Tetrahydrofurfuryl *p*-nitrobenzoate:** m.p. 46–48° ⟨5⟩ [cf. T 1.47].

Ⓓ **Tetrahydrofurfuryl 3,5-dinitrobenzoate:** m.p. 83–84° ⟨5⟩ [cf. T 1.47].

Ⓓ **Tetrahydrofurfuryl *p*-toluenesulfonate:** from $\bar{C}$ + *p*-toluenesulfonyl chloride in ether at −5° to −10° + powd. KOH; ndls. from C_6H_6 + pet. ether; m.p. 38.7–39.1° ⟨2⟩.

Ⓓ **Potassium tetrahydrofurfuryl xanthate:** from $\bar{C}$ + powd. KOH + CS_2 in dry ether; purified by soln. in least quant. abs. alc. or acetone, cooling, and pptn. with dry ether; m.p. 213.2° cor. ⟨3⟩.

Ⓓ **Tetrahydrofurancarbinyl *N*-phenylcarbamate:** cryst. from pet. ether, m.p. 61° ⟨1⟩; 60–61° ⟨4⟩.

Ⓓ **Tetrahydrofurancarbinyl *N,N*-diphenylcarbamate:** from $\bar{C}$ + diphenylcarbamyl chloride in pyridine; cryst. from MeOH, m.p. 81° ⟨1⟩ [cf. T 1.43].

1:6445 ⟨1⟩ Wienhaus, *Ber.* **53,** 1659–1664 (1920). ⟨2⟩ Barger, Robinson, Smith, *J. Chem. Soc.* **1937,** 720. ⟨3⟩ Whitmore, Lieber, *Ind. Eng. Chem., Anal. Ed.* **7,** 127–128 (1935). ⟨4⟩ Paul, *Compt. rend.* **193,** 1429 (1931).

1:6446 ISOBUTYLENE GLYCOL $C_4H_{10}O_2$ **Beil. I-480**
(Dimethylethylene glycol;
2-methylpropanediol-1,2)

$$(CH_3)_2C(OH)\text{—}CH_2OH$$

B.P. 178° D_4^{14} = **0.999** n_D^{17} = **1.4358**

Ⓓ **Isobutylene glycol bis-(*N*-phenylcarbamate):** from $\bar{C}$ + 4 pts. phenylisocyanate in 2.5 pts. ether htd. in s.t. at 100° for 40 hrs.; 60% yield; m.p. 140.5° ⟨1⟩.

1:6446 ⟨1⟩ Krasuskiĭ, Movsum-Zede, *Chem. Abs.* **31,** 1377 (1937).

1:6450 CYCLOHEXYLCARBINOL $C_6H_{11}.CH_2OH$ $C_7H_{14}O$ **Beil. VI-14**
(Hexahydrobenzyl alcohol)

B.P. 182° D_4^{20} = **0.9280** n_D^{20} = **1.4649**

Liq. with faintly camphoraceous odor — [For prepn. from cyclohexyl MgCl + paraformaldehyde see ⟨1⟩.]

$\bar{C}$ on oxidn. with CrO_3/H_2SO_4 (cf. T 1.72) gives hexahydrobenzaldehyde (1:0186) and hexahydrobenzoic ac. (1:0575) together with some cyclohexylcarbinyl hexahydrobenzoate ⟨2⟩. $\bar{C}$ on oxidn. with HNO_3 (D = 1.2) gives adipic ac. (1:0775).

1:6450 ⟨1⟩ Gilman, Catlin, *Organic Syntheses, Coll. Vol.* I, 182–185 (1932). ⟨2⟩ Bouveault, *Bull. soc. chim.* (3) **29,** 1049 (1903).

1:6452 ***d,l*-BUTYLENE GLYCOL-2,3** (2,3-Dihydroxybutane; butanediol-2,3)

$$CH_3-\underset{OH}{\overset{H}{C}}-\underset{OH}{\overset{H}{C}}-CH_3$$

$C_4H_{10}O_2$ **Beil. I-479**

B.P. 182.5° ⟨2⟩ **M.P. 24-27°** D_4^{20} = **1.0433 ⟨2⟩** n_D^{25} = **1.43637 ⟨2⟩**

This product, formerly obtd. mainly by fermentation processes, has, prior to 1936, been designated in the literature as the *d,l*-isomer. It is, however, probably mainly the *meso* form (obtd. from comml. C̄ by recrystn. from 4 pts. diisopropyl ether ⟨6⟩). By hydration of the *trans* and *cis* forms of 2,3-epoxybutane (1:6116), the true *meso* and *d,l*-forms of butanediol-2,3 have been prepared ⟨7⟩ with constants and derivs. as follows:

***d,l*-form:**

B.P. 176.7°_{742} dibenzoate: M.P. 53.0–54.0° di-*p*-bromobenzoate M.P. 205–209°
M.P. +7.6°

***meso*-form:**

B.P. 181.7°_{742} dibenzoate: M.P. 75.5–76.2° di-*p*-bromobenzoate M.P. 139.0–139.8°
M.P. +34.4°

[For m.p. + compn. diagram of *meso* and *d,l*-forms see ⟨7⟩.]

Hygroscopic solid showing strong supercooling — Misc. aq., alc.; sl. sol. ether — C̄ is not volatile with steam [dif. and sepn. from biacetyl (1:9500)]. [For prepn. of C̄ in 50% yield from 2,3-dibromobutane + PbO see ⟨2⟩.]

C̄, when pure, does not reduce Fehling's soln. (T 1.22) [dif. from its reductn. prod. acetoin (1:5448)] — C̄ treated with I_2/KI soln. + aq. NaOH (T 1.81) yields CHI_3 — C̄ on stdg. with Br_2-aq. in light gives biacetyl (1:9500) ⟨1⟩ [use in quant. detn. of C̄ ⟨3⟩] — C̄ on oxidn. with HIO_4 gives quant. yield acetaldehyde (1:0100) [use in detn. of C̄ ⟨4⟩].

Ⓓ ***d,l*-Butylene glycol bis-(*N*-phenylcarbamate):** from C̄ with 2 moles phenylisocyanate in dry ether, isomer dif. sol. alc.; m.p. 199.5° u.c. ⟨1⟩ ⟨5⟩; 201° ⟨8⟩. [Note that this prod. forms with *N,N'*-diphenylurea (from the reagent + adventitious water) a mol. cpd., m.p. 187.5° ⟨1⟩.] [From the orig. mother liquor a second alc. sol. bis-(*N*-phenylcarbamate), m.p. 157°, has also been obtd. ⟨1⟩.] [If insufficient phenylisocyanate has been used there may appear a mono *N*-phenylcarbamate, cryst. from alc., m.p. 100° which on further treatment yields the bis deriv., m.p. 199° ⟨1⟩.]

1:6452 ⟨1⟩ Walpole, *Proc. Roy. Soc.* **B-83,** 275–282 (1910). ⟨2⟩ Schierholtz, Staples, *J. Am. Chem. Soc.* **57,** 2710 (1935). ⟨3⟩ Matignon, Moureu, Dodé, *Bull. soc. chim.* (5) **1,** 411–419 (1934). ⟨4⟩ Brockmann, Werkman, *Ind. Eng. Chem., Anal. Ed.* **5,** 206–207 (1933). ⟨5⟩ Ciamician, Silber, *Ber.* **44,** 1285 (1911). ⟨6⟩ Winstein, Lucas, *J. Am. Chem. Soc.* **61,** 1579 (1939). ⟨7⟩ Wilson, Lucas, *J. Am. Chem. Soc.* **58,** 2401 (1936). ⟨8⟩ Fichter, Sutter, *Helv. Chim. Acta* **21,** 1406 (1938).

1:6455 ***d,l*-PROPYLENE GLYCOL** (1,2-Dihydroxypropane; propanediol-1,2; α-propylene glycol)

$$CH_3-\underset{OH}{\overset{H}{C}}-CH_2OH$$

$C_3H_8O_2$ **Beil. I-472**

B.P. 187.4° ⟨1⟩ D_4^{23} = **1.0354 ⟨1⟩** n_D^{25} = **1.43162 ⟨1⟩**
n_D^{17} = **1.4336 ⟨8⟩**

Visc. liq. with sweetish taste — Misc. with aq., alc.; sol. in 12–13 vols. ether. [Occurrence + identification in glycerol sweet-water ⟨2⟩.]

C̄ on oxidn. with CrO_3/H_2SO_4 (T 1.72) or with neut. $KMnO_4$ at 50–75° ⟨3⟩ gives acetic ac. (1:1010) and CO_2.

C̄ htd. at 100° with conc. HI (D = 1.70) yields I_2 (decolorized with alk.) and isopropyl iodide, b.p. 93° ⟨4⟩.

Ⓓ **Conversion to propionaldehyde** (by dehydration + enolization): Mix thoroughly 2 drops C̄ with 1 g. powd. anhyd. $ZnCl_2$ in a dry 6-in. tt. Arrange to distil through a glass delivery tube dipping into 2 ml. dist. aq. in a second tt. stdg. in ice water. Heat the $ZnCl_2$ mixt. strongly with a free flame. Test the distillate for propionaldehyde (1:0110) [cf. ⟨5⟩].

Ⓓ ***d,l*-Propylene glycol bis-(*N*-phenylcarbamate):** m.p. 153° ⟨6⟩; 143–144° ⟨7⟩.

1:6455 ⟨1⟩ Schierholtz, Staples, *J. Am. Chem. Soc.* **57,** 2710 (1935). ⟨2⟩ Schutt, *Oesterr. Chem. Ztg.* **30,** 170–171 (1927). ⟨3⟩ Evans, *J. Am. Chem. Soc.* **45,** 175 (1923). ⟨4⟩ Wurtz, *Ann. Supl.* **1,** 381 (1861). ⟨5⟩ Wurtz, *Ann. chim.* (3) **55,** 423 (1859). ⟨6⟩ Walpole, *Proc. Roy. Soc.* **B-83,** 285 (1910). ⟨7⟩ Ôeda, *Bull. Chem. Soc. Japan* **10,** 538, Note 15 (1935). ⟨8⟩ Moureu, Dodé, *Bull. soc. chim.* (5) **4,** 289 (1937).

1:6458 DIETHYLENE GLYCOL MONOMETHYL ETHER **Beil. S.N. 30**

(Methyl- " carbitol ") $CH_3O.CH_2.CH_2.O.CH_2.CH_2.OH$ $C_5H_{12}O_3$

B.P. 194° D_{20}^{20} = **1.035** n_D^{20} = **1.4244**

Misc. with aq.

Ⓓ **β-(β-Methoxyethoxy)ethyl hydrogen 3-nitrophthalate:** from C̄ on htg. with 3-nitrophthalic anhydride; cryst. from aq. alc. as monohydrate, m.p. 87–90°; anyhydrous form, m.p. 91.4–92.2°, Neut. Eq. 313 ⟨1⟩.

Ⓓ **β-(β-Methoxyethoxy)ethyl triphenylmethyl ether:** from C̄ (0.5 ml.) + triphenylchloromethane (0.5 equiv.) in pyridine (1 ml.) on htg. 5 min. at 100°; yield 55–60%; colorless tiny ndls. or lfts. from MeOH or EtOH, m.p. 58–59° u.c. ⟨2⟩. [For detection and removal of ethylene glycol from comml. samples of C̄ see ⟨3⟩.]

Ⓓ **β-(β-Methoxyethoxy)ethyl *N*-(*p*-nitrophenyl)carbamate:** from C̄ + *p*-nitrophenylisocyanate (68% yield ⟨4⟩), m.p. 73.4–73.7° ⟨4⟩. [This prod. depresses m.p. (80°) of corresp. deriv. of ethylene glycol monoethyl ether (1:6410) ⟨4⟩.]

1:6458 ⟨1⟩ Veraguth, Diehl, *J. Am. Chem. Soc.* **62,** 233 (1940). ⟨2⟩ Seikel, Huntress, *J. Am. Chem. Soc.* **63,** 593–595 (1941). ⟨3⟩ Seikel, *Ind. Eng. Chem., Anal. Ed.* **13,** in press (1941).

1:6460 2-METHYLPENTANEDIOL-2,4 $C_6H_{14}O_2$ **Beil. I-486**

```
       CH3           H
       |             |
CH3—C—CH2—C—CH3
       |             |
       OH           OH
```

B.P. 196° D_4^{17} = **0.9240** $n_D^{16.7}$ = **1.42976**

Visc. liq. with odor like pinacol — Sol. aq., alc., ether.

C̄, htd. with 2% by vol. of HBr (D = 1.48) and pumice gives 30% ⟨1⟩, or htd. with 2% aniline hydrobromide gives 50% ⟨2⟩ of a diene, b.p. 75.5–76° [structure disputed ⟨1⟩ ⟨3⟩], which adds quant. to maleic anhyd. in C_6H_6 to yield deriv., m.p. 56–57° ⟨4⟩.

1:6460 ⟨1⟩ Whitby, Gallay, *Can. J. Research* **6,** 285 (1932). ⟨2⟩ Kyriakides, *J. Am. Chem. Soc.* **36,** 994–995 (1914). ⟨3⟩ Farmer, Lawrence, Scott, *J. Chem. Soc.* **1930,** 511, 517. ⟨4⟩ Diels, Alder, *Ann.* **470,** 98 (1929).

1:6465 ETHYLENE GLYCOL $HO.CH_2.CH_2.OH$ $C_2H_6O_2$ **Beil. I-465**

B.P. 197.85° ⟨1⟩ **M.P. −12.6°** ⟨1⟩ D_4^{15} = **1.11710** ⟨1⟩ n_D^{15} = **1.43312** ⟨1⟩
D_4^{20} = **1.11361** ⟨1⟩ n_D^{20} = **1.43192** ⟨2⟩
D_4^{30} = **1.10664** ⟨1⟩ n_D^{25} = **1.43072** ⟨2⟩

Colorless, odorless, very hygros. liq.; more visc. than aq.; less visc. than glycerol — Misc. with aq. and not salted out by KOH or K_2CO_3 but sepd. by fractnl. distn. — Immiscible with ether, C_6H_6, chlorobenzene, $CHCl_3$, CCl_4, CS_2 — [For $n_D^{15.6}$ of mixts. of $\bar{C}$ with aq., or $\bar{C}$ with diethylene glycol (1:6525) see ⟨3⟩.] [For solubility of inorg. salts in mixts. of $\bar{C}$ + aq. see ⟨4⟩; for ternary systems of $\bar{C}$ with org. liquids see ⟨5⟩.]

$\bar{C}$ does not react with excess hot 6 *N* HCl; $\bar{C}$ refluxed 2 hrs. with 3 moles HBr (D = 1.48) gives 36% yield ethylene dibromide ⟨6⟩.

For study of detection of $\bar{C}$ in presence of glycerol see ⟨7⟩ ⟨21⟩; for detn. of $\bar{C}$ see ⟨8⟩ ⟨9⟩ ⟨20⟩.

$\bar{C}$ htd. with powd. $KHSO_4$ as directed for propylene glycol (1:6455) gives acetaldehyde (1:0100) [dif. from propylene glycol or glycerol (1:6540)].

Ⓓ **Ethylene glycol dibenzoate:** from $\bar{C}$ in dil. aq. alk., shaken in cold with 2 moles BzCl (cf. T 2.26-B); cryst. from ether; m.p. 73° ⟨10⟩. [Note that glyceryl tribenzoate has m.p. 72°.]

Ⓓ **Ethylene glycol di-(*p*-nitrobenzoate):** m.p. 140° ⟨11⟩; 141° [cf. T 1.82].

Ⓓ **Ethylene glycol di-(3,5-dinitrobenzoate):** m.p. 169° [cf. T 1.82].

Ⓓ **Ethylene glycol bis-(*p*-toluenesulfonate):** from $\bar{C}$ + *p*-toluenesulfonyl chloride in pyridine; white pl. from alc., m.p. 126° ⟨12⟩. [Attempts to prepare a mono-*p*-toluenesulfonate invariably led to the bis deriv. ⟨12⟩.]

Ⓓ **Ethylene glycol bis-(triphenylmethyl ether):** from $\bar{C}$ (0.1 ml.) + triphenylchloromethane (*exactly two equivs.*) in dry pyridine (1–2 ml.) htd. 15 min. at 100°; yield 60–70%; colorless hexagonal tablets from acetone, m.p. 187–188° u.c. ⟨19⟩, 185–186° ⟨13⟩. [The corresponding monoether (β-hydroxyethyl triphenylmethyl ether) forms rect. pr. or cubes from MeOH or EtOH, m.p. 105–105.5° u.c. ⟨19⟩; cryst. from pet. ether, m.p. 102–103° ⟨14⟩, 98–100° ⟨13⟩.]

Ⓓ **Ethylene glycol bis-(*N*-phenylcarbamate):** m.p. 157° ⟨15⟩.

Ⓓ **Ethylene glycol bis-[*N*-(*p*-nitrophenyl)carbamate]:** m.p. 135.5° ⟨16⟩; 236° ⟨17⟩ [one of these probably a misprint].

Ⓓ **Ethylene glycol bis-[*N*-(α-naphthyl)carbamate]:** m.p. 176° ⟨18⟩ [cf. T 1.86].

Ⓓ **Ethylene glycol bis-(*N,N*-diphenylcarbamate):** pr. from alc., m.p. 157.5° s.t. ⟨15⟩ [cf. T 1.43].

1:6465 ⟨1⟩ Timmermans, Hennaut-Roland, *J. chim. phys.* **32**, 507–508 (1935). ⟨2⟩ Schierholtz, Staples, *J. Am. Chem. Soc.* **57**, 2710 (1935). ⟨3⟩ Matignon, Moureu, Dodé, *Bull. soc. chim.* (5) **1**, 1313 (1934). ⟨4⟩ Trimble, *Ind. Eng. Chem.* **23**, 165–167 (1931). ⟨5⟩ Trimble, Frazer, *Ind. Eng. Chem.* **21**, 1063–1065 (1929). ⟨6⟩ Norris, Watt, Thomas, *J. Am. Chem. Soc.* **38**, 1079 (1916). ⟨7⟩ Middleton, *Analyst* **59**, 522–524 (1934). ⟨8⟩ Müller, *Chem. Ztg.* **44**, 513–515 (1920). ⟨9⟩ Cuthill, *Analyst* **63**, 259–261 (1938). ⟨10⟩ Gabriel, Heymann, *Ber.* **23**, 2498 (1890).

⟨11⟩ Cretcher, Pittenger, *J. Am. Chem. Soc.* **47**, 2562 (1925). ⟨12⟩ Butler, Nelson, Renfrew, Cretcher, *J. Am. Chem. Soc.* **57**, 577 (1935). ⟨13⟩ Helferich, Speidel, Toeldte, *Ber.* **56**, 769 (1923). ⟨14⟩ Hurd, Filachione, *J. Am. Chem. Soc.* **59**, 1950 (1937). ⟨15⟩ Snape, *Ber.* **18**, 2430 (1885). ⟨16⟩ Shriner, Cox, *J. Am. Chem. Soc.* **53**, 1604, 3186 (1931). ⟨17⟩ van Hoogstraten, *Rec. trav. chim.* **51**, 427 (1932). ⟨18⟩ Bickel, French, *J. Am. Chem. Soc.* **48**, 749 (1926). ⟨19⟩ Seikel, Huntress, *J. Am. Chem. Soc.* **63**, 593–595 (1941). ⟨20⟩ Lamprey, Sommer, Kiffer, *Ind. Eng. Chem., Anal. Ed.* **12**, 526–527 (1940).

⟨21⟩ Allen, Charbonnier, Coleman, *Ind. Eng. Chem., Anal. Ed.* **12**, 384–387 (1940).

1:6470 DIETHYLENE GLYCOL MONOETHYL ETHER $C_6H_{14}O_3$ Beil. S.N. 30

(" Carbitol ") $C_2H_5.O.CH_2.CH_2.O.CH_2.CH_2.OH$

B.P. 196°$_{763}$ ⟨1⟩ (198°) D_{20}^{20} = **1.023** ⟨1⟩ n_D^{20} = **1.4298** ⟨3⟩

D_{15}^{15} = **0.9996** ⟨2⟩

Misc. with aq.

The *p*-nitrobenzoate ⟨4⟩ ⟨7⟩, 3-5-dinitrobenzoate, and acid 3-nitrophthalate ⟨5⟩ are all oils and not recommended as derivs. for identif. of $\bar{C}$.

Ⓓ *β*-(*β*-**Ethoxyethoxy)ethyl** *N*-(*p*-**nitrophenyl)carbamate:** from C̄ + *p*-nitrophenylisocyanate (53% yield ⟨6⟩), m.p. 65.8–66.3° ⟨6⟩. [This prod. depresses m.p. of corresp. deriv. of diethylene glycol monomethyl ether (1:6458) ⟨6⟩.]

1:6470 ⟨1⟩ Gardner, Brewer, *Ind. Eng. Chem.* **29,** 179 (1937). ⟨2⟩ Davidson, *Ind. Eng. Chem.* **18,** 670 (1926). ⟨3⟩ Hofmann, Reid, *Ind. Eng. Chem.* **21,** 957 (1928). ⟨4⟩ Conn, Collett, Lazzell, *J. Am. Chem. Soc.* **54,** 4370–4372 (1932). ⟨5⟩ Veraguth, Diehl, *J. Am. Chem. Soc.* **62,** 233 (1940). ⟨6⟩ Manning, Mason, *J. Am. Chem. Soc.* **62,** 3137 (1940). ⟨7⟩ Mason, Manning, *J. Am. Chem. Soc.* **62,** 1638 (1940).

1:6475 *d,l*-METHYL-PHENYL-CARBINOL $C_8H_{10}O$ Beil. VI-475

(α-Phenylethyl alcohol)

CH_3—CH(OH)—C_6H_5

B.P. abt. 202° **F.P. 20.1° ⟨1⟩** D_4^{20} = **1.0129 ⟨1⟩** n_D^{20} = **1.5275 ⟨1⟩**
D_4^{15} = **1.008** n_D^{15} = **1.526**

Insol. aq.; misc. with alk. or ether.

C̄ shaken 10 min. at room temp. with **7.5** pts. 6 *N* HCl gives 75% yield α-chloroethylbenzene [Beil. V-354] ⟨2⟩ — C̄ distd. with 4 pts. HBr (*D* = 1.48) gives 95% yield α-bromoethyl benzene [Beil. V–355] ⟨2⟩.

C̄ with CrO_3 + H_2SO_4 (T 1.72) yields acetophenone (1:5515).

C̄ slowly distd. with 5% $NaHSO_4$ gives 75% yield styrene (1:7435) ⟨3⟩ — C̄ htd. at 110° with 2% by vol. of $H_2SO_4.3H_2O$ yields styrene; with ⅓ its vol. of $H_2SO_4.3H_2O$ for 20 hrs. at room temp. gives layer contg. 84% corresp. ether; b.p. 280–282° ⟨4⟩.

Ⓓ ***d,l*-Methyl-phenyl-carbinyl *p*-nitrobenzoate:** ndls. from alc., m.p. 42.5–43.5° cor. ⟨11⟩; 47–48° ⟨12⟩.

Ⓓ ***d,l*-Methyl-phenyl-carbinyl 3,5-dinitrobenzoate:** m.p. 93° [cf. T 1.82], m.p. 95° ⟨5⟩.

Ⓓ ***d,l*-Methyl-phenyl-carbinyl hydrogen phthalate:** from C̄ and phthalic anhyd. in dry pyridine at 100° in 85% yield; cryst. from AcOH or C_6H_6, m.p. 108° ⟨9⟩ [cf. ⟨10⟩].

Ⓓ ***d,l*-Methyl-phenyl-carbinyl *N*-phenylcarbamate:** ndls. from lgr.; m.p. 91–92° ⟨6⟩ ⟨7⟩.

Ⓓ ***d,l*-Methyl-phenyl-carbinyl *N*-α-naphthylcarbamate:** m.p. 106° ⟨8⟩ [cf. T 1.86].

1:6475 ⟨1⟩ Deschamps, *Bull. soc. chim. Belg.* **33,** 270 (1924). ⟨2⟩ Norris, Watt, Thomas, *J. Am. Chem. Soc.* **38,** 1078 (1916). ⟨3⟩ D. Gauthier, P. Gauthier, *Bull. soc. chim.* (4) **53,** 323–326 (1933). ⟨4⟩ Senderens, *Compt. rend.* **182,** 613–614 (1926). ⟨5⟩ Ashworth, Burkhardt, *J. Chem. Soc.* **1928,** 1798. ⟨6⟩ Stobbé, *Ann.* **308,** 115 (1899). ⟨7⟩ Straus, Grindel, *Ann.* **439,** 299 (1924). ⟨8⟩ Bickel, French, *J. Am. Chem. Soc.* **48,** 749 (1926). ⟨9⟩ Houssa, Kenyon, *J. Chem. Soc.* **1930,** 2261. ⟨10⟩ Levene, Mikesa, *J. Biol. Chem.* **70,** 357 (1926).
⟨11⟩ King, *J. Am. Chem. Soc.* **61,** 2386 (1939). ⟨12⟩ Ward, *J. Chem. Soc.* **1927,** 453.

1:6480 BENZYL ALCOHOL C_6H_5—$CH_2.OH$ C_7H_8O Beil. VI-428

B.P. 205.45° ⟨1⟩ **M.P. −15.3° ⟨1⟩** D_4^{20} = **1.04540 ⟨1⟩** n_D^{20} = **1.53955**
n_D^{15} = **1.54259 ⟨1⟩**

Odor faintly arom. — Sol. in 25 pts. aq. at 17°; misc. with most org. solv. except. pet. ether — Slowly volat. with steam — After distn. at ord. press. always conts. notable traces of BzH and dibenzyl ether ⟨2⟩ — Slowly oxid. in air to BzH (1:0195).

C̄ on shak. pet. ether soln. with anhyd. $CaCl_2$ yields mol. cpd. 3C̄.$CaCl_2$; dissociated by aq. [Use in detn. of C̄ ⟨3⟩.]

C̄ on oxidn. with CrO_3/H_2SO_4 (cf. T 1.72) or $KMnO_4$ [use in quant. detn. of small amts. C̄ ⟨4⟩] yields BzOH (1:0715) — C̄ warmed with conc. HCl gives benzyl chloride, b.p. 179°; with HBr (*D* = 1.48) yields benzyl bromide, b.p. 198°; with HI (*D* = 1.7) yields benzyl iodide, m.p. 24°.

Ⓓ **Benzyl *p*-nitrobenzoate:** m.p. 85° [cf. T 1.82]. [Use in detn. of C̄ in presence of ethyl-phenyl-carbinol (1:6504) ⟨5⟩.]

Ⓓ **Benzyl 3,5-dinitrobenzoate:** m.p. 113° [cf. T 1.82].

Ⓓ **Benzyl hydrogen phthalate:** m.p. 104° ⟨6⟩; 106° ⟨7⟩. [The *p*-nitrobenzyl ester (cf. T 1.39) of this acid phthalate has m.p. 83° ⟨8⟩.]

Ⓓ **Benzyl hydrogen 3-nitrophthalate:** m.p. 176°; Neut. Eq. 301 [cf. T 1.83].

Ⓓ **Benzyl *p*-toluenesulfonate:** from C̄ + *p*-toluenesulfonyl chloride in dry ether + powdered KOH at 0° ⟨9⟩; pptd. from C_6H_6 soln. by addn. of pet. ether ⟨10⟩; m.p. 55° ⟨9⟩; 58° ⟨10⟩. [Stable for a week over $CaCl_2$ but decomposes in 15 min. over H_2SO_4 ⟨10⟩.]

Ⓓ **Benzyl *N*-phenylcarbamate:** from C̄ + equiv. phenylisocyanate on stdg. overnight; ndls. from pet. ether, m.p. 75.5–76° ⟨11⟩; 77° ⟨12⟩ ⟨16⟩. [For optical data see ⟨16⟩.] [This prod. depresses m.p. of corresp. deriv. of β-phenylethyl alc. (1:6505).]

Ⓓ **Benzyl *N*-(*p*-nitrophenyl)carbamate:** m.p. 157° ⟨13⟩.

Ⓓ **Benzyl *N*-(α-naphthyl)carbamate:** m.p. 134° ⟨14⟩ [cf. T 1.86].

Ⓓ **Benzyl *N*,*N*-diphenylcarbamate:** m.p. 109.8–110.4° ⟨7⟩.

Ⓓ **Benzyl *N*-(*p*-xenyl)carbamate:** m.p. 156° ⟨15⟩.

1:6480 ⟨1⟩ Timmermans, Hennaut-Roland, *J. chim. phys.* **32,** 519–521 (1935). ⟨2⟩ Lachman, *J. Am. Chem. Soc.* **45,** 2359 (1923). ⟨3⟩ Leonhardt, Wasicky, *Arch. Pharm.* **270,** 249–252 (1932). ⟨4⟩ Callaway, Reznek, *J. Assoc. Official Agr. Chem.* **16,** 285–289 (1933). ⟨5⟩ Meisenheimer, *Ann.* **442,** 193–194 (1925); *Ann.* **446,** 81 (1926). ⟨6⟩ Bischoff, von Hedenström, *Ber.* **35,** 4093 (1902). ⟨7⟩ Hoejenbos, Coppens, *Rec. trav. chim.* **50,** 1046 (1931). ⟨8⟩ Reid, *J. Am. Chem. Soc.* **39,** 1251 (1917). ⟨9⟩ Gilman, Beaber, *J. Am. Chem. Soc.* **47,** 522–523 (1925). ⟨10⟩ Medwedew, Alexejewa, *Ber.* **65,** 132–133 (1932).

⟨11⟩ Straus, Grindel, *Ann.* **439,** 311–312 (1924). ⟨12⟩ Karrer, Gränacher, Schlosser, *Helv. Chim. Acta* **6,** 1111–1112 (1923). ⟨13⟩ van Hoogstraten, *Rec. trav. chim.* **51,** 426 (1932). ⟨14⟩ Bickel, French, *J. Am. Chem. Soc.* **48,** 749 (1926). ⟨15⟩ Morgan, Pettet, *J. Chem. Soc.* **1931,** 1125. ⟨16⟩ Dewey, Witt, *Ind. Eng. Chem., Anal. Ed.* **12,** 459 (1940).

1:6482 *d,l*-BUTYLENE GLYCOL-1,3 $C_4H_{10}O_2$ Beil. I-477

(1,3-Dihydroxybutane; butanediol-1,3)

$CH_3—CH(OH)—CH_2.CH_2OH$

P.B. 207.5° ⟨1⟩ D_4^{20} = **1.0053** ⟨1⟩ $n_D^{19.5}$ = **1.44252** ⟨1⟩

n_D^{25} = **1.44098** ⟨1⟩

Sol. aq., alc.; insol. ether.

[For prepn. in 75% yield by Al/Hg reduction of acetaldol (1:0270) see ⟨1⟩.]

Ⓓ **Butylene glycol-1,3-bis-(*N*-phenylcarbamate):** m.p. 122–123° ⟨2⟩.

1:6482 ⟨1⟩ Schierholtz, Staples, *J. Am. Chem. Soc.* **57,** 2710 (1935). ⟨2⟩ Walpole, *Proc. Roy. Soc.* **B-83,** 285 (1911); *Cent.* **1911,** I, 1309.

—— BENZYL-DIMETHYL-CARBINOL $C_{10}H_{14}O$ Beil. VI-523

$C_6H_5—CH_2.C(CH_3)_2OH$

B.P. 214–216°

See 1:5910. Genus 8: Division A: Section 2. M.P. 24°.

1:6490 TRIMETHYLENE GLYCOL $HO.CH_2.CH_2.CH_2.OH$ $C_3H_8O_2$ **Beil. I-475**
(Propanediol-1,3)

B.P. 214.7° ⟨12⟩ **M.P. = −30°** D_4^{20} = **1.0538** ⟨12⟩ n_D^{20} = **1.43983**
n_D^{25} = **1.43940** ⟨12⟩

Visc. liq. with sweetish taste — Misc. with aq., alc. [For prepn. from " glycerol sweet-water " see ⟨1⟩ ⟨2⟩.]

$\bar{C}$ htd. with dry HCl at 150–170° gives 60% trimethylene chlorohydrin, b.p. 160.5° ⟨3⟩; $\bar{C}$ distd. with 10 vols. conc. HCl gives 28% same ⟨4⟩ — $\bar{C}$ htd. with HBr (D = 1.48) + H_2SO_4 gives 90% yield trimethylene dibromide, b.p. 165° ⟨5⟩.

$\bar{C}$ htd. with $KHSO_4$ as described under propylene glycol (1:6455) gives dist. which does *not* color fuchsin-ald. reagt. [dif. from ethylene glycol or glycerol].

[For detn. of $\bar{C}$ see ⟨7⟩ ⟨2⟩. [For resin formn. with phthalic anhyd. see ⟨6⟩.]

Ⓓ **Trimethylene glycol dibenzoate:** from $\bar{C}$ + BzCl via Schotten-Baumann method (cf. T 2.26-B); m.p. 59° ⟨8⟩. [The monobenzoate is an oil.]

Ⓓ **Trimethylene glycol di-(*p*-nitrobenzoate):** m.p. 119° ⟨8⟩ ⟨9⟩ [cf. T 1.82]. [The mono-*p*-nitrobenzoate melts at 49° ⟨8⟩.]

Ⓓ **Trimethylene glycol di-(3,5-dinitrobenzoate):** m.p. 178° [cf. T 1.82].

Ⓓ **Trimethylene glycol di-*p*-toluenesulfonate:** from $\bar{C}$ + *p*-toluenesulfonyl chloride in pyridine at 0°; cryst. from MeOH, m.p. 93–94° ⟨13⟩.

Ⓓ **Trimethylene glycol di-(*N*-phenylcarbamate):** m.p. 137° ⟨10⟩.

Ⓓ **Trimethylene glycol di-(*N*-α-naphthylcarbamate):** m.p. 164° ⟨11⟩ [cf. T 1.86].

1:6490 ⟨1⟩ Rojahn, *Ber.* **54,** 3115 (1921). ⟨2⟩ Rayner, *J. Soc. Chem. Ind.* **45T,** 265–266; 287–288 (1926). ⟨3⟩ Marvel, Calvery, *Organic Syntheses, Coll. Vol.* I, 519–521 (1932). ⟨4⟩ Norris, Mulliken, *J. Am. Chem. Soc.* **42,** 2096 (1920). ⟨5⟩ Kamm, Marvel, *Organic Syntheses, Coll. Vol.* I, 28–29 (1932). ⟨6⟩ Carothers, Arvin, *J. Am. Chem. Soc.* **51,** 2569 (1929). ⟨7⟩ Cocks, Salway, *J. Soc. Chem. Ind.* **41T,** 17–20, 32 (1922). ⟨8⟩ Fischer, *Ber.* **53,** 1642–1644 (1920). ⟨9⟩ Fischer, Ahlström, Richter, *Ber.* **64,** 614 (1931). ⟨10⟩ Bennett, Heathcoat, *J. Chem. Soc.* **1929,** 269.
⟨11⟩ Bickel, French, *J. Am. Chem. Soc.* **48,** 749 (1926). ⟨12⟩ Schierholtz, Staples, *J. Am. Chem. Soc.* **57,** 2710 (1935). ⟨13⟩ Gough, King, *J. Chem. Soc.* **1928,** 2446.

1:6495 *m*-TOLYLCARBINOL $C_8H_{10}O$ **Beil. VI-494**
(*m*-Xylyl alcohol)

CH_3 / CH_2OH

B.P. 217° D^{17} = **0.9157**

$\bar{C}$ on oxidn. with calcd. amt. $K_2Cr_2O_7 + H_2SO_4$ (cf. T 1.72) yields *m*-tolualdehyde (1:0208) ⟨1⟩; with $KMnO_4$ yields *m*-toluic ac. (1:0705).

Ⓓ ***m*-Xylyl *N*-(α-naphthyl)carbamate:** m.p. 116° ⟨2⟩ [cf. T 1.86].

1:6495 ⟨1⟩ Sommer, *Ber.* **33** 1078 (1990). ⟨2⟩ Bickel, French, *J. Am. Chem. Soc.* **48** 749 (1926).

1:6502 METHYL-*p*-TOLYL-CARBINOL $C_9H_{12}O$ **Beil. VI-508**

H / CH_3—C— / —CH_3 / OH

B.P. 219° $D_4^{15.5}$ = **0.9668**

$\bar{C}$ on oxidn. with $CrO_3 + H_2SO_4$ (T 1.72) yields *p*-methylacetophenone (1:5530).

Ⓓ **Methyl-*p*-tolyl-carbinyl *N*-phenylcarbamate:** from $\bar{C}$ + equiv. phenylisocyanate in lgr. on gentle warming: ndls. from pet. ether, m.p. 96° ⟨1⟩ ⟨2⟩.

1:6502 ⟨1⟩ Klages, *Ber.* **35,** 2247 (1902). ⟨2⟩ Dieterle, Kaiser, *Arch. Pharm.* **271,** 341 (1933).

1:6504 ***d,l*-ETHYL-PHENYL-CARBINOL** $C_9H_{12}O$ **Beil. VI-502**
(α-Phenyl-*n*-propyl alcohol) C_2H_5—CH(OH)—⟨benzene ring⟩

B.P. abt. 219° D_{20}^{20} = **1.0056** ⟨1⟩ n_D^{20} = **1.5257** ⟨1⟩

C̄ slowly distd. with 5% of $NaHSO_4$ gives 85% yield 1-phenylpropene-1, b.p. 177° [Beil. V-481] ⟨2⟩ which with Br_2 yields α,β-dibromo-*n*-propylbenzene, m.p. 66°.
C̄ on oxidn. with $CrO_3 + H_2SO_4$ (cf. T 1.72) gives ethyl phenyl ketone (1:5525) ⟨3⟩.

Ⓓ ***d,l*-Ethyl-phenyl-carbinyl *p*-nitrobenzoate:** m.p. 59–60° ⟨4⟩, 56.5–57.5° ⟨6⟩ [cf. T 1.82]. [Poor yield because of much formn. of α-chloroethylbenzene.] [Mixed m.p. with 10% of corresponding deriv. of benzyl alc. (1:6480) only lowered to 57–60°; with 20%, m.p. 57–65°.]
Ⓓ ***d,l*-Ethyl-phenyl-carbinyl *N*-α-naphthylcarbamate:** m.p. 102° ⟨5⟩ [cf. T 1.86].

1:6504 ⟨1⟩ Vernimmen, *Bull. soc. chim. Belg.* **33,** 98 (1924). ⟨2⟩ D. Gauthier, P. Gauthier, *Bull. soc. chim.* (4) **53,** 323–326 (1933). ⟨3⟩ Schorigin, *Ber.* **57,** 1636 (1924). ⟨4⟩ Meisenheimer, *Ann.* **446,** 81 (1926); **442,** 193 (1925). ⟨5⟩ Bickel, French, *J. Am. Chem. Soc.* **48,** 749 (1926). ⟨6⟩ King, *J. Am. Chem. Soc.* **61,** 2386 (1939).

1:6505 **β-PHENYLETHYL ALCOHOL** $C_6H_5.CH_2.CH_2OH$ $C_8H_{10}O$ **Beil. VI-478**
(Benzylcarbinol)

B.P. 219.8° **M.P. = −25.8°** D_4^{25} = **1.0235** n_D^{20} = **1.5240**

[For important survey of synthesis see ⟨1⟩.]
Faint rose-like odor — Sol. in abt. 45 vols. aq. — Volat. with steam — Forms compd. with solid anhyd. $CaCl_2$, insol. and unaffected by pet. ether, dissoc. by aq. [Use in sepn. and purifn. of C̄ ⟨2⟩.]
C̄ refluxed 2 hrs. with 7.5 pts. 6 *N* HCl gave only small yield β-phenylethyl chloride ⟨3⟩ — C̄ slowly distd. with 6 pts. HBr (*D* = 1.48) gave 86% β-phenylethyl bromide, b.p. 218° sl. dec. [Beil. V-356] ⟨3⟩.
C̄ on distn. over small amt. solid KOH is catalytically dehydrated to styrene, b.p. 146° (1:7435) ⟨4⟩.
C̄ on oxidn. with 2 pts. $KMnO_4$ in abt. 60 pts. aq. yields BzOH, m.p. 121° (1:0715) ⟨5⟩; with $CrO_3 + H_2SO_4$ (T 1.72) gives phenylacetaldehyde (1:0200) and phenylacetic ac., m.p. 76–77° (1:0665) ⟨5⟩.
C̄ (5 drops?), htd. with 0.1 g. anhydrous oxalic ac. 1–2 min. over free flame, 1 ml. aq. added, then 2 ml. alc., warmed to dis., then allowed to cryst. gives good yield di-(β-phenylethyl) oxalate, m.p. 51–51.5° ⟨4⟩.

Ⓓ **β-Phenylethyl *p*-nitrobenzoate:** from C̄ + *p*-nitrobenzoyl chloride in pyridine; cryst. from 95% alc.; m.p. 62–63° ⟨6⟩, 61.5–62.0° cor. ⟨13⟩. [cf. T 1.82].
Ⓓ **β-Phenylethyl 3,5-dinitrobenzoate:** m.p. 108° ⟨7⟩ [cf. T 1.82].
Ⓓ **β-Phenylethyl hydrogen phthalate:** m.p. 188–189° ⟨8⟩; Neut. Eq. 270. [The *p*-nitrobenzyl ester (T 1.39) of this acid phthalate forms cryst. from 76% alc.; m.p. 84.3° ⟨9⟩.]
Ⓓ **β-Phenylethyl hydrogen 3-nitrophthalate:** m.p. 123°; Neut. Eq. 315 [cf. T 1.83].
Ⓓ **β-Phenylethyl *N*-phenylcarbamate:** cryst. from alc.; m.p. 79–80° ⟨5⟩, 78° ⟨14⟩. [This prod. depresses m.p. of corr. deriv. of benzyl alc. (1:6480).] [For optical data see ⟨14⟩.]
Ⓓ **β-Phenylethyl *N*-(*p*-nitrophenyl)carbamate:** ndls. from alc., m.p. 135° ⟨10⟩.
Ⓓ **β-Phenylethyl *N*-(α-naphthyl)carbamate:** m.p. 119° ⟨11⟩ [cf. T 1.86].
Ⓓ **β-Phenylethyl *N,N*-diphenylcarbamate:** m.p. 98.5–99.5° ⟨12⟩ [cf. T 1.43].

1:6505 ⟨1⟩ Leonard, *J. Am. Chem. Soc.* **47,** 1774–1779 (1925). ⟨2⟩ Hesse, Zeitschel, *J. prakt. Chem.* (2) **66,** 489 (1902). ⟨3⟩ Norris, Watt, Thomas, *J. Am. Chem. Soc.* **38,** 1078 (1916). ⟨4⟩ Palfray, Sabetay, Sontag, *Compt. rend.* **193,** 941–944 (1931); **195,** 1392–1394 (1932). ⟨5⟩ Walbaum, *Ber.* **33,** 2300 (1900). ⟨6⟩ Kirner, *J. Am. Chem. Soc.* **48,** 1112 (1926). ⟨7⟩ Ashworth, Burkhardt, *J. Chem. Soc.* **1928,** 1798. ⟨8⟩ von Soden, Rojahn, *Ber.* **33,** 1723 (1900). ⟨9⟩ Reid, *J. Am. Chem. Soc.* **39,** 1252 (1917). ⟨10⟩ Hoeke, *Rec. trav. chim.* **54,** 513 (1935). ⟨11⟩ Bickel, French, *J. Am. Chem. Soc.* **48,** 749 (1926). ⟨12⟩ Hoejenbos, Coppens, *Rec. trav. chim.* **50,** 1047 (1931). ⟨13⟩ King, *J. Am. Chem. Soc.* **61,** 2386 (1939). ⟨14⟩ Dewey, Witt, *Ind. Eng. Chem., Anal. Ed.* **12,** 459 (1940).

1:6507 *d,l-α*-TERPINEOL $C_{10}H_{18}O$ Beil. VI-56

$CH_3—C$ ring: $CH_2—CH_2$ / $CH—CH_2$ (double bond C=CH) — $C(H)—C(OH)(CH_3)_2$

B.P. 221.1°$_{763}$ ⟨1⟩ **M.P. 35°** **D_4^{20} = 0.9337** **n_D^{20} = 1.4834**
n_D^{25} = 1.4788 ⟨1⟩

Comml. prod. is always liq. but from ether soln. yields cryst., m.p. 35° [m.p. of either *d*- or *l*-isomer, 37–38°] — Lilac odor when suff. dil. — Insol. aq.; very sol. alc., ether, $CHCl_3$, AcOH — Volat. with steam.

C̄, treated with dry HCl gas, evolves ht., turns purple, ultimately cryst. to mass of dipentene bis-hydrochloride [Beil. V-50], tbls. from alc., m.p. 50° ⟨2⟩ — C̄ shaken a few moments with conc. aq. HI yields a heavy oil which soon solidifies to dipentene bis-hydroiodide [Beil. V-55], m.p. 77° ⟨3⟩.

Soln. of C̄ in 5 pts. 80% H_3PO_4 at 30°, stood for a short time, then diluted with 6 vols. cold aq. gives bulky ppt. of terpin hydrate (1:5965), m.p. 120° rap. htg. ⟨4⟩, 116–117° dec. ⟨5⟩.

Similar results also obtd. by use of other acids, e.g., 40% H_2SO_4 at 0° for 5 hrs. ⟨6⟩.

Soln. of C̄ in alc. + ether allowed to stand with excess Br_2 deposits cryst. of dipentene tetrabromide, m.p. 124° ⟨3⟩. [Use of bromide-bromate method for quant. detn. ⟨7⟩.]

Ⓓ ***d,l-α*-Terpinyl *p*-nitrobenzoate:** cryst. from MeOH, m.p. 139° ⟨8⟩.

Ⓓ ***d,l-α*-Terpinyl 3,5-dinitrobenzoate:** cryst. from lgr.; m.p. 78–79° ⟨9⟩ [cf. T 1.82].

Ⓓ ***d,l-α*-Terpinyl hydrogen phthalate:** from C̄ + metallic K (not Na) in C_6H_6 on treatment with phthalic anhyd. (80% yield); cryst. from AcOH, m.p. 117–118°; Neut. Eq. 302 ⟨10⟩. [Use in resolution of racemic cpd. ⟨10⟩.]

Ⓓ ***d,l-α*-Terpinyl *N*-phenylcarbamate:** ndls. from MeOH; m.p. 112–113° ⟨4⟩.

Ⓓ ***d,l-α*-Terpinyl *N*-(*α*-naphthyl)carbamate:** m.p. 151–152° ⟨11⟩ [cf. T 1.86].

1:6507 ⟨1⟩ Gardner, Brewer, *Ind. Eng. Chem.* **29,** 179 (1937). ⟨2⟩ Tilden, *J. Chem. Soc.* **33,** 249 (1878). ⟨3⟩ Wallach, *Ann.* **230,** 265–266 (1885). ⟨4⟩ Perkin, *J. Chem. Soc.* **85,** 667–668 (1904). ⟨5⟩ Prins, *Chem. Weekblad* **14,** 630–631 (1917); *Chem. Abs.* **11,** 2773 (1917). ⟨6⟩ Aschan, *Cent.* **1919,** I, 284. ⟨7⟩ Klimont, *Arch. Pharm.* **250,** 579 (1912). ⟨8⟩ Hückel, Nerdel, *Ann.* **528,** 69 (1937). ⟨9⟩ Reichstein, *Helv. Chim. Acta* **9,** 802 (1926). ⟨10⟩ Fuller, Kenyon, *J. Chem. Soc.* **125,** 2309–2310 (1924).
⟨11⟩ Neuberg, Hirschberg, *Biochem. Z.* **27,** 344 (1910).

1:6515 *d,l*-ISOPROPYL-PHENYL-CARBINOL $C_{10}H_{14}O$ Beil. VI-523

$(CH_3)_2CH—C(H)(OH)—C_6H_5$

B.P. 222-224° **D_{20}^{20} = 0.9790** **$n_D^{18.7}$ = 1.51932**

C̄ oxidized with CrO_3 + H_2SO_4 (cf. T 1.72) yields isopropyl phenyl ketone (1:5528).

Ⓓ **Isopropyl-phenyl-carbinyl hydrogen phthalate:** from C̄, htd. with equal wt. phthalic anhyd. for 4 hrs.; m.p. not stated ⟨1⟩.

Ⓓ **Isopropyl-phenyl-carbinyl *N*-(α-naphthyl)carbamate:** m.p. 116–117° ⟨2⟩ [cf. T 1.86].

1:6515 ⟨1⟩ Levene, Mikesa, *J. Biol. Chem.* **70,** 359 (1926). ⟨2⟩ Magnani, McElvain, *J. Am. Chem. Soc.* **60,** 819 (1938).

1:6516 TETRAMETHYLENE GLYCOL $C_4H_{10}O_2$ Beil. I-478

(Butanediol-1,4) $HO.CH_2.CH_2.CH_2.CH_2.OH$

B.P. 230° (235°) **M.P. +19-19.5°** ⟨1⟩ D_4^{20} = **1.0171** ⟨1⟩ n_D^{20} = **1.4467** ⟨1⟩

Misc. aq., alc.; spar. sol. ether — C̄ is salted out from aq. solns. by K_2CO_3. [For prepn. in 54% yield by reductn. of diethyl succinate (1:3756) with Na + alc. see ⟨2⟩; cf. ⟨1⟩.]

C̄ on oxidn. with HNO_3 yields succinic ac. (1:0530) — C̄ refluxed 2 hrs. with 50 pts. 7.5 *N* H_2SO_4 gives 76% yield ⟨3⟩ tetrahydrofuran [Beil. XVII-10], b.p. 64–65°, n_D^{21} = 1.4043.

Ⓓ **Tetramethylene glycol dibenzoate:** from C̄ + BzCl + aq. alk.; cryst. from ether, m.p. 81–82° ⟨4⟩.

Ⓓ **Tetramethylene glycol di-*p*-nitrobenzoate:** cryst. from boilg. AcOH; m.p. 175° ⟨5⟩.

Ⓓ **Tetramethylene glycol bis-(*N*-phenylcarbamate):** cryst. from $CHCl_3$ or lgr. + alc. (10:1), m.p. 183–183.5° cor. ⟨2⟩; 180° ⟨6⟩; 179.5° ⟨1⟩. [After fusion and resolidification remelts 163–164° ⟨2⟩.]

Ⓓ **Tetramethylene glycol bis-(*N*-α-naphthylcarbamate):** ndls. from butanol or xylene; m.p. 198.5–199° ⟨1⟩; 198° ⟨6⟩ [cf. T 1.86].

1:6516 ⟨1⟩ Kirner, Richter, *J. Am. Chem. Soc.* **51,** 2505 (1929). ⟨2⟩ Müller, *Monatsh.* **49,** 28–29 (1928). ⟨3⟩ Hurd, Isenhour, *J. Am. Chem. Soc.* **54,** 328 (1932). ⟨4⟩ Dekkers, *Rec. trav. chim.* **9,** 101 (1890). ⟨5⟩ Carothers, Van Natta, *J. Am. Chem. Soc.* **52,** 323 (1930). ⟨6⟩ Bennett, Heathcoat, *J. Chem. Soc.* **1929,** 269.

1:6517 DIETHYLENE GLYCOL MONO-*n*-BUTYL ETHER Beil. S.N. 30

(Butyl " carbitol ") $n\text{-}C_4H_9.O.CH_2.CH_2.O.CH_2.CH_2.OH$ $C_8H_{18}O_3$

B.P. 232.1°$_{766}$ ⟨1⟩ D_{20}^{20} = **0.957** ⟨1⟩ n_D^{20} = **1.4341**
n_D^{27} = **1.4258** ⟨1⟩

Misc. aq.

The *p*-nitrobenzoate ⟨2⟩ ⟨4⟩, 3,5-dinitrobenzoate and hydrogen 3-nitrophthalate ⟨3⟩ are oils and *not* recommended as derivatives for identification of C̄.

C̄ refluxed with conc. HI (*D* = 1.7) yields *n*-butyl iodide, sepd. by steam distn. and converted (by means of silver 3,5-dinitrobenzoate) (T 5.2) to *n*-butyl 3,5-dinitrobenzoate, m.p. 64°.

Ⓓ **β-(β-*n*-Butoxyethoxy)ethyl *N*-(*p*-nitrophenyl)carbamate:** from C̄ + *p*-nitrophenylisocyanate (65% yield ⟨5⟩), m.p. 54.5–55.3° ⟨5⟩. [This prod. depresses m.p. (59°) of corresp. deriv. of ethylene glycol mono-*n*-butyl ether (1:6430) only very slightly ⟨5⟩.]

1:6517 ⟨1⟩ Gardner, Brewer, *Ind. Eng. Chem.* **29,** 179 (1937). ⟨2⟩ Conn, Collett, Lazzell, *J. Am. Chem. Soc.* **54,** 4370–4372 (1932). ⟨3⟩ Veraguth, Diehl, *J. Am. Chem. Soc.* **62,** 233 (1940). ⟨4⟩ Mason, Manning, *J. Am. Chem. Soc.* **62,** 1638 (1940). ⟨5⟩ Manning, Mason, *J. Am. Chem. Soc.* **62,** 3137 (1940).

1:6518 ETHYLENE GLYCOL MONOPHENYL ETHER $C_8H_{10}O_2$ **Beil. VI-146**
(β-Hydroxyethyl phenyl ether; $C_6H_5O.CH_2.CH_2.OH$
(β-Phenoxyethyl alcohol;
phenyl " cellosolve ")

B.P. 237° (245°) D^{22} = **1.102** ⟨1⟩ n_D^{20} = **1.534** ⟨1⟩

Dif. sol. aq., misc. alc., eas. sol. ether. [For prepn. from Na phenoxide + ethylene chlorohydrin (84% yield) see ⟨2⟩.]

C̄ with $SOCl_2$ and pyridine yields (88%) β-phenoxyethyl chloride (b.p. 122° at 26 mm.) — C̄ htd. 5 hrs. with $ZnCl_2$ at 190–225° gives small yield (25%) coumaran (b.p. 88–90° at 18 mm.) ⟨1⟩.

Ⓓ **β-Phenoxyethyl benzoate:** m.p. 64° ⟨3⟩.

Ⓓ **β-Phenoxyethyl *p*-toluenesulfonate:** from C̄ + *p*-toluenesulfonyl chloride + aq. NaOH (yield 90%); pr. from alc., m.p. 80° ⟨4⟩ ⟨6⟩.

Ⓓ **β-Phenoxyethyl hydrogen 3-nitrophthalate:** m.p. 112.0–113.0° ⟨5⟩; Neut. Eq. 331 [cf. T 1.83].

Ⓓ **β-Phenoxyethyl triphenylmethyl ether:** from C̄ (0.5 ml.) + triphenylchloromethane (0.5 equiv.) in pyridine (1 ml.) on htg. 5 min. at 100°; yield 75–85%; colorless 1 cm. ndls. from MeOH, EtOH, or acetone, m.p. 123.5–124.0° u.c. ⟨7⟩.

1:6518 ⟨1⟩ Rindfusz, *J. Am. Chem. Soc.* **41,** 669 (1919). ⟨2⟩ Kirner, *J. Am. Chem. Soc.* **48,** 2748 (1926). ⟨3⟩ Bollmann, *U. S.* 1,841,430; *Chem. Abs.* **26,** 1617 (1932). ⟨4⟩ Peacock, Tha, *J. Chem. Soc.* **1928,** 2305. ⟨5⟩ Veraguth, Diehl, *J. Am. Chem. Soc.* **62,** 233 (1940). ⟨6⟩ Butler, Renfrew, Cretcher, Souther, *J. Am. Chem. Soc.* **59,** 229 (1937). ⟨7⟩ Seikel, Huntress, *J. Am. Chem. Soc.* **63,** 593–595 (1941).

1:6519 PENTAMETHYLENE GLYCOL $C_5H_{12}O_2$ **Beil. I-481**
(Pentanediol-1,5) $HOCH_2.CH_2.CH_2.CH_2.CH_2.OH$

B.P. 238-239° D_{20}^{20} = **0.9939** n_D^{20} = **1.4499**

Viscous liq.; misc. aq., alc.; spar. sol. ether.

[For prepn. in 46% yield by reduction of diethyl glutarate (1:3967) with Na + alc. see ⟨1⟩.]

Ⓓ **Pentamethylene glycol di-*p*-nitrobenzoate:** cryst. from C_6H_6 + alc., m.p. 104–105° ⟨2⟩.

Ⓓ **Pentamethylene glycol bis-(*N*-phenylcarbamate):** ndls. from abs. alc. or alc. + $CHCl_3$; m.p. 174–175° cor. ⟨1⟩; 176° ⟨3⟩ ⟨4⟩. [After fusion and resolidification shows m.p. 142–143° cor. ⟨1⟩.]

Ⓓ **Pentamethylene glycol bis-(*N*-α-naphthylurethane):** m.p. 147° ⟨4⟩ [cf. T 1.86].

1:6519 ⟨1⟩ Müller, Rölz, *Monatsh.* **50,** 107–108 (1928). ⟨2⟩ Carothers, Van Natta, *J. Am. Chem. Soc.* **52,** 324 (1930). ⟨3⟩ Paul, *Bull. soc. chim.* (5) **1,** 978 (1934). ⟨4⟩ Bennett, Heathcoat, *J. Chem. Soc.* **1929,** 269.

1:6520 γ-PHENYL-*n*-PROPYL ALCOHOL $C_9H_{12}O$ **Beil. VI-503**
(Hydrocinnamyl alcohol) C_6H_5—$CH_2.CH_2.CH_2.OH$

B.P. 237.4° D_4^{20} = **1.0079** n_D^{20} = **1.53565**

Viscous oil — Spar. sol. aq.; misc. alc., ether, AcOH.

C̄ cautiously oxidized with CrO_3 in AcOH yields hydrocinnamic ac. (1:0615) ⟨1⟩ — C̄ htd. with 2.2 pts. HBr (*D* = 1.48) for 2 hrs. gives 63% yield γ-phenyl-*n*-propyl bromide ⟨2⟩.

Ⓓ **Hydrocinnamyl *p*-nitrobenzoate:** m.p. 45–46° ⟨3⟩, 46.5–47.5° ⟨6⟩ [cf. T 1.82].

Ⓓ **Hydrocinnamyl *p*-nitrobenzoate:** m.p. 45–46° ⟨3⟩ [cf. T 1.82].

Ⓓ **Hydrocinnamyl 3,5-dinitrobenzoate:** m.p. 92° [cf. T 1.82].

Ⓓ **Hydrocinnamyl hydrogen 3-nitrophthalate:** m.p. 117°; Neut. Eq. 329 [cf. T 1.83].

Ⓓ **Hydrocinnamyl *N*-phenylcarbamate:** from $\bar{C}$ + phenylisocyanate at 130° for 2 hrs.; cryst. from alc.; m.p. 47–48° ⟨3⟩; 56° ⟨4⟩; 45° ⟨7⟩. [For optical data see ⟨7⟩.]

Ⓓ **Hydrocinnamyl *N*-(*p*-nitrophenyl)carbamate:** cryst. from pet. ether; m.p. 104° ⟨5⟩.

1:6520 ⟨1⟩ Rugheimer, *Ann.* **172,** 123 (1874). ⟨2⟩ Norris, Watt, Thomas, *J. Am. Chem. Soc.* **38,** 1078 (1916). ⟨3⟩ Kirner, *J. Am. Chem. Soc.* **48,** 1111–1112 (1926). ⟨4⟩ Ôeda, *Bull. Chem. Soc. Japan* **10,** 537 (1935). ⟨5⟩ Hoeke, *Rec. trav. chim.* **54,** 513 (1935). ⟨6⟩ King, *J. Am. Chem. Soc.* **61,** 2386 (1939). ⟨7⟩ Dewey, Witt, *Ind. Eng. Chem., Anal. Ed.* **12,** 459 (1940).

1:6525 DIETHYLENE GLYCOL $C_4H_{10}O_3$ **Beil. I-468**

(β,β'-Dihydroxydiethyl ether) $HO.CH_2.CH_2.O.CH_2.CH_2.OH$

B.P. 244.5° ⟨1⟩ F.P. = −10.45° ⟨1⟩ D_{15}^{15} = 1.1212 ⟨1⟩ n_D^{20} = 1.4475 ⟨1⟩

Colorless, odorless, rather visc. liq. with slightly sweet, somewhat burning taste — Very hygros.; misc. with aq., MeOH, alc., AcOH, acetone, $CHCl_3$, pyridine, aniline, etc. — Immiscible with ether, C_6H_6, toluene, CS_2, CCl_4.

[For refractive indices of mixtures of $\bar{C}$ with ethylene glycol (1:6465) or triethylene glycol (1:6538) see ⟨2⟩ — For solvent power of $\bar{C}$ on cellulose esters, gums, etc., see ⟨3⟩.]

$\bar{C}$ htd. for several days at 100° with conc. HI yields ppt. of α,β-diiodoethane [Beil. I-99], ndls. from hot alc., m.p. 81° ⟨4⟩.

The diacetate ⟨5⟩ and dibenzoate ⟨5⟩ of $\bar{C}$ are liquids and not recommended as derivs. for identification.

Ⓓ **Diethylene glycol bis-(3,5-dinitrobenzoate):** cryst. from AcOH, m.p. 149° [cf. T 1.82].

Ⓓ **Diethylene glycol bis-(triphenylmethyl ether):** from $\bar{C}$ (0.25 ml.) + triphenylchloromethane (*exactly two equivs.*) in dry pyridine (1–2 ml.) htd. for 1 hr. at 100°; yield 60–70%; colorless stocky ndls. from acetone, m.p. 157.5–158.0° u.c. ⟨6⟩. [The corresp. monotriphenylmethyl ether forms opaque or transparent granules from MeOH or EtOH, m.p. 112.5–113.5° u.c. ⟨6⟩.]

1:6525 ⟨1⟩ Rinkenbach, *Ind. Eng. Chem.* **19,** 474–476 (1927). ⟨2⟩ Matignon, Moureu, Dodé, *Bull. soc. chim.* (5) **1,** 1314 (1934). ⟨3⟩ Davidson, *Ind. Eng. Chem.* **18,** 671 (1926). ⟨4⟩ Wurtz, *Ann. chim.* (3) **69,** 332 (1863). ⟨5⟩ Cretcher, Pittenger, *J. Am. Chem. Soc.* **47,** 165 (1925). ⟨6⟩ Seikel, Huntress, *J. Am. Chem. Soc.* **63,** 593–595 (1941).

1:6530 *o*-METHOXYBENZYL ALCOHOL $C_8H_{10}O_2$ **Beil. VI-893**

(Saligenin methyl ether; *o*-anisyl alcohol)

—CH_2OH

OCH_3

B.P. 247° D_{15}^{15} = 1.0495 n_D^{17} = 1.549

[For prepn. from *o*-methoxybenzaldehyde (1:0235) + formaldehyde + MeOH/NaOH see ⟨4⟩ ⟨5⟩.]

Ⓓ ***o*-Methoxybenzyl benzoate:** by Schotten-Baumann method, cryst. from lgr., m.p. 59° ⟨1⟩.

Ⓓ ***o*-Methoxybenzyl *N*-(α-naphthyl)carbamate:** m.p. 135–136° ⟨2⟩ [cf. T 1.86].

Ⓓ ***o*-Methoxybenzyl allophanate:** m.p. 180° ⟨3⟩.

1:6530 ⟨1⟩ Vavon, *Ann. chim.* (9) **1,** 154 (1914). ⟨2⟩ Bickel, French, *J. Am. Chem. Soc.* **48,** 749 (1926). ⟨3⟩ Béhal, *Bull. soc. chim.* (4) **25,** 473–479 (1919). ⟨4⟩ Lauer, Hansen, *J. Am. Chem. Soc.* **61,** 3040 (1939). ⟨5⟩ Davidson, Bogert, *J. Am. Chem. Soc.* **57,** 905 (1935).

—— **CINNAMYL ALCOHOL** $C_6H_5.CH{=}CH.CH_2OH$ $C_9H_{10}O$ **Beil. VI-570**

B.P. 257°

See 1:5920. Genus 8: Division A: Section 2. M.P. 33°.

—— ***p*-ANISYL ALCOHOL** $CH_3O.C_6H_4.CH_2OH$ $C_8H_{10}O_2$ **Beil. VI-897**

B.P. 258°

See 1:5915. Genus 8: Division A: Section 2. M.P. 25°.

—— **LAURYL ALCOHOL** $CH_3.(CH_2)_{10}.CH_2OH$ $C_{12}H_{26}O$ **Beil. I-428**

B.P. 259°

See 1:5900. Genus 8: Division A: Section 2. M.P. 23.8°.

1:6533 ETHYLENE GLYCOL MONOBENZYL ETHER **Beil. S.N. 30**

(Benzyl β-hydroxyethyl ether; benzyl-" cellosolve ") C_6H_5—$CH_2.O.CH_2.CH_2OH$ $C_9H_{12}O_2$

B.P. 265.0° D^{20}_{20} = **1.0700** n^{20}_D = **1.5225**

Spar. sol. aq.; sol. alc. or ether.

C̄ with $SOCl_2$ in $CHCl_3$ + dimethylaniline below 30° ⟨1⟩ or with $SOCl_2$ in pyridine ⟨2⟩ yields benzyl β-chloroethyl ether.

Ⓓ **β-Benzyloxyethyl triphenylmethyl ether:** from C̄ (0.5 ml.) + triphenylchloromethane (0.5 equiv.) in pyridine (1 ml.) on htg. 5 min. at 100°; yield 50–70%; colorless stocky ndls. from MeOH or EtOH, m.p. 76–77° ⟨3⟩.

1:6533 ⟨1⟩ Bennett, *J. Chem. Soc.* **127,** 1280. ⟨2⟩ Kirner, Richter, *J. Am. Chem. Soc.* **51,** 2504 (1929). ⟨3⟩ Seikel, Huntress, *J. Am. Chem. Soc.* **63,** 593–595 (1941).

1:6535 *n*-HEXYL-PHENYL-CARBINOL $C_{13}H_{20}O$ **Beil. VI₁-(272)**

$C_6H_{13}.CH(OH).C_6H_5$

B.P. 275° *D* = **0.946** n_D = **1.501**

C̄ on oxidn. with $CrO_3 + H_2SO_4$, yields *n*-hexyl phenyl ketone (1:5590).

Ⓓ ***n*-Hexyl-phenyl-carbinyl *N*-phenylcarbamate:** m.p. 77°.

1:6538 TRIETHYLENE GLYCOL $C_6H_{14}O_4$ **Beil. I-468**

(Ethylene glycol di-(β-hydroxyethyl) ether) $HO.CH_2.CH_2.O.CH_2.CH_2.O.CH_2.CH_2.OH$

B.P. 285° ⟨1⟩ **M.P. −9.4° ⟨2⟩** D^{15}_4 = **1.1274 ⟨1⟩** n^{15}_D = **1.4578 ⟨1⟩**

Misc. with aq. or alc.; spar. sol. ether. [For refractive indices of mixts. with diethylene glycol (1:6525) see ⟨1⟩.] The bis-*N*-phenylcarbamate (prepd. indirectly) melts 108° ⟨3⟩.

Ⓓ **Triethylene glycol bis-(triphenylmethyl ether):** from C̄ (0.1 ml.) + triphenylchloromethane (*exactly two equivs.*) in dry pyridine (1–2 ml.) htd. 15 min. at 100°; yield 45-

60%; colorless granules from acetone, m.p. 142–142.5° u.c. ⟨4⟩. [This ditrityl ether exists in two forms, the stable form described above, and also a labile form, m.p. 130.5–131.5° u.c. The latter can be converted to the former by htg. at 125° and rubbing the gummy residue with acetone ⟨4⟩.]

1:6538 ⟨1⟩ Matignon, Moureu, Dodé, *Bull. soc. chim.* (5) **1,** 1314 (1934). ⟨2⟩ Gallaugher, Hibbert, *J. Am. Chem. Soc.* **58,** 815 (1936). ⟨3⟩ Jacobson, *J. Am. Chem. Soc.* **60,** 1744 (1938). ⟨4⟩ Seikel, Huntress, *J. Am. Chem. Soc.* **63,** 593–595 (1941).

1:6540 GLYCEROL $CH_2(OH).CH(OH)CH_2.OH$ $C_3H_8O_3$ **Beil. I-502**

B.P. 290° cor. **M.P. +17.9°** D_4^{20} = **1.26134** ⟨1⟩ n_D^{20} = **1.4729**
n_D^{15} = **1.47547** ⟨1⟩

Viscous hygroscopic odorless liq. with sweetish taste — Misc. aq., alc.; sol. in 500 pts. ether, 11 pts. AcOEt; insol. pet. ether, C_6H_6, $CHCl_3$, CS_2.

Comml. $\bar{C}$ usually contains much water but b.p. rises on distn. [For b.p. of glycerol-aq. mixtures see ⟨2⟩; for density see ⟨3⟩.] [For phys. const. of system: $\bar{C}$ + ethyl alc. + aq. see ⟨4⟩.]

[For detn. of $\bar{C}$ in presence of *d*-glucose see ⟨15⟩; for detection and/or detn. of $\bar{C}$ in presence of ethylene glycol (1:6465) or diethylene glycol (1:6525) or both see ⟨16⟩.]

$\bar{C}$ (1 mole) added to NaOEt (1 mole) in excess abs. alc. gives white ppt. of α-mono-sodium glyceroxide as cpd. with 1 C_2H_5OH, lost in vac. at 100° ⟨5⟩ — $\bar{C}$ in pyridine htd. 5 hrs. with 3 moles triphenylchloromethane gave 12% yield glycerol tris-(triphenylmethyl ether); pptd. from C_6H_6 by addn. of alc., m.p. 196–197° ⟨6⟩.

Ⓟ **Acrolein formation:** $\bar{C}$ htd. with $KHSO_4$ by method described under propylene glycol (1:6455) yields distillate contg. acrolein (1:0115) ⟨7⟩.

Ⓟ **Pyrogallol-H_2SO_4 color reaction:** To soln. of 1 drop $\bar{C}$ in 2 ml. cold aq., add 5 drops 1% aq. pyrogallol and 2 ml. conc. H_2SO_4. Shake, boil 20–25 sec., cool immed. in running aq. Diln. to 20 ml. with alc. gives purplish-red (VR-T_1–VR-T_2) soln., fading after some minutes — Applicable to weak aq. solns. without further diln.; presence of other polyhydric alcs. or sugars may obscure test ⟨8⟩. [This test also given by ethylene glycol (1:6465) ⟨9⟩; for detection of $\bar{C}$ in presence of ethylene glycol see ⟨9⟩.]

Ⓓ **Glyceryl tribenzoate:** Shake together 1 drop $\bar{C}$, 0.4 ml. BzCl, and 5.0 ml. 10% NaOH for 5–8 min. with cooling until a solid separates. Add 10 ml. cold aq., shake, filter and wash first with 20 ml. aq., then with 10 ml. dil. AcOH (20%). Cryst. from 15 ml. hot dil. alc. (33%), filtering hot, then cooling and shaking. Filter ppt. and wash with dil. alc. Dry on porous tile in air; m.p. 71–72° u.c. [This test may be applied to dil. aq. solns. in absence of other polyhydric alcs. ⟨8⟩.] [The glycerol tribenzoate has also been obtd. in a form of m.p. 76°; on slow resolidification of fused material or on recrystn. from lgr. m.p. changed to 72° ⟨10⟩.]

Ⓓ **Glyceryl tri-(*p*-nitrobenzoate):** from $\bar{C}$ + *p*-nitrobenzoyl chloride in pyridine, m.p. 188° [cf. T 1.82]. [Note: glycerol *α-mono-p*-nitrobenzoate (from mono-sodium glyceroxide + *p*-nitrobenzoyl chloride in ether) has m.p. 107° ⟨11⟩; glycerol *β*-mono-*p*-nitrobenzoate has m.p. 120–121° ⟨12⟩.]

Ⓓ **Glyceryl tri-(benzenesulfonate):** from disodium glyceroxide + benzenesulfonyl Cl in ether or C_6H_6; ndls. from alc., m.p. 80° ⟨10⟩.

Ⓓ **Glyceryl tri-(*p*-toluenesulfonate):** from either mono-or disodium glyceroxide + *p*-toluenesulfonyl chloride in dry ether or C_6H_6; ndls. from alc., m.p. 103° ⟨10⟩.

Ⓓ **Glyceryl tri-[*N*-(*p*-nitrophenyl)carbamate]:** cryst. from alc., m.p. 216° ⟨13⟩.

Ⓓ **Glyceryl tri-[*N*-(α-naphthyl)carbamate]:** cryst. from alc., m.p. 191–192° ⟨14⟩ [cf. T 1.86].

1:6540 ⟨1⟩ Timmermans, Hennaut-Roland, *J. chim. phys.* **32,** 509 (1935). ⟨2⟩ Grün, Wirth, *Z. angew. Chem.* **32,** 60 (1919). ⟨3⟩ Bosart, Snoddy, *Ind. Eng. Chem.* **19,** 506–510 (1927). ⟨4⟩ Ernst, Watkins, Ruwe, *J. Phys. Chem.* **40,** 627–635 (1936). ⟨5⟩ Fairbourne, Toms, *J. Chem. Soc.* **119,** 1037 (1921). ⟨6⟩ Hurd, Mack, Filachione, Sowden, *J. Am. Chem. Soc.* **59,** 1953 (1937). ⟨7⟩ Fresenius, Grünhut, *Z. anal. Chem.* **38,** 41 (1899). ⟨8⟩ Mulliken, " Method " I, 169–170 (1904). ⟨9⟩ Hovey, Hodgkins, *Ind. Eng. Chem., Anal. Ed.* **9,** 509–511 (1937). ⟨10⟩ Fairbourne, Foster, *J. Chem. Soc.* **127,** 2762–2763 (1925).

⟨11⟩ Fairbourne, Foster, *J. Chem. Soc.* **1926,** 2763. ⟨12⟩ Fairbourne, Stephens, *J. Chem. Soc.* **1932,** 1975. ⟨13⟩ van Hoogstraten, *Rec. trav. chim.* **51,** 427 (1932). ⟨14⟩ Bickel, French, *J. Am. Chem. Soc.* **48,** 749 (1926). ⟨15⟩ Fulmer, Hickey, Underkofler, *Ind. Eng. Chem., Anal. Ed.* **12,** 729–730 (1940). ⟨16⟩ Allen, Charbonnier, Coleman, *Ind. Eng. Chem., Anal. Ed.* **12,** 384–387 (1940).

1:6550 ***p*-ANISYL-METHYL-CARBINOL** (*p*-Methoxyphenyl-methyl-carbinol) $C_9H_{12}O_2$ **Beil. VI-903**

$CH_3O—C_6H_4—C(H)(OH)—CH_3$

B.P. abt. 310° cor./760 mm. ⟨1⟩ D_4^{16} = **1.086** ⟨2⟩ n_D = **1.537** ⟨2⟩

Oil with odor of anise — On distn. dec. with loss of water and polymerization ⟨3⟩ but when pure can be distd. under reduced pressure.

C̄ on oxidn. with CrO_3 + H_2SO_4 (T 1.72) yields *p*-methoxyacetophenone (1:5140).

Ⓓ ***p*-Anisyl-methyl-carbinyl *N*-phenylcarbamate:** from C̄ + phenylisocyanate on stdg. at room temp.; ndls. from alc., m.p. 82–83° ⟨2⟩.

1:6550 ⟨1⟩ Zeichmeister, Rom, *Ann.* **468,** 125 (1929). ⟨2⟩ Klages, *Ber.* **36,** 3592 (1903). ⟨3⟩ Edgar Stedman, Ellen Stedman, *J. Chem. Soc.* **1929,** 613–614.

Alcohols for Which Data Are Available Only under Reduced Pressure

1:6700 ***d,l*-PHENYL-*n*-PROPYL-CARBINOL** $C_{10}H_{14}O$ **Beil. VI-522**

$C_6H_5—C(H)(OH)—CH_2.CH_2.CH_3$

M.P. 16° ⟨1⟩ $D_4^{16.2}$ = **0.9822** ⟨1⟩ n_D^{22} = **1.5166** ⟨1⟩
$D_4^{26.3}$ = **0.9739** ⟨1⟩ n_D^{25} = **1.5191** ⟨2⟩

C̄ dist. only under reduced press., b.p. 78.0–78.2°/0.5 mm. ⟨2⟩; 94–96°/6 mm. ⟨3⟩; 117–118°/18 mm. ⟨1⟩.

C̄ htd. with $KHSO_4$ yields 1-phenylbutene-2, b.p. 184–186° ⟨4⟩.

C̄ on oxidn. with CrO_3 + H_2SO_4 (T 1.72) yields phenyl *n*-propyl ketone (1:5535).

Ⓓ ***d,l*-Phenyl-*n*-propyl-carbinyl *p*-nitrobenzoate:** m.p. 58° ⟨5⟩.

Ⓓ ***d,l*-Phenyl *n*-propyl-carbinyl hydrogen phthalate:** ndls. from CS_2 + lt. pet., m.p. 90–91°; Neut. Eq. 298 ⟨1⟩. [Use in resolution of C̄ ⟨1⟩.]

Ⓓ ***d,l*-Phenyl-*n*-propyl-carbinyl *N*-(α-naphthyl)carbamate:** m.p. 98–99° ⟨6⟩.

1:6700 ⟨1⟩ Kenyon, Partridge, *J. Chem. Soc.* **1936,** 128–129. ⟨2⟩ Norris, Cortese, *J. Am. Chem. Soc.* **49,** 2645 (1927). ⟨3⟩ Huston, Strickler, *J. Am. Chem. Soc.* **55,** 4317 (1933). ⟨4⟩ Glacet, *Bull. soc. chim.* (5) **5,** 898 (1938). ⟨5⟩ Abragam, Deux, *Compt. rend.* **205,** 285–286 (1937). ⟨6⟩ Magnani, McElvain, *J. Am. Chem. Soc.* **60,** 819 (1938).

1:6710 ***n*-BUTYL-PHENYL-CARBINOL** $C_{11}H_{16}O$ **Beil. S.N. 533**

$n\text{-}C_4H_9\text{—}CH(OH)\text{—}C_6H_5$

B.P. 123-124°/12 mm. ⟨1⟩ D_{20}^{20} = **0.9672** ⟨1⟩ n_D^{20} = **1.5112** ⟨1⟩
137°/21 mm. ⟨2⟩

C̄ on oxidn. with $CrO_3 + H_2SO_4$ (T 1.72) yields *n*-butyl phenyl ketone (1:5555).

1:6710 ⟨1⟩ Vernimmen, *Bull. soc. chim. Belg.* **33,** 100 (1924). ⟨2⟩ Roblin, Davidson, Bogart, *J. Am. Chem. Soc.* **57,** 155 (1935).

1:6720 ***n*-AMYL-PHENYL-CARBINOL** $C_{12}H_{18}O$ **Beil. S.N. 533**

$n\text{-}C_5H_{11}\text{—}CH(OH)\text{—}C_6H_5$

B.P. 170°/50 mm. ⟨1⟩ D_4^{25} = **0.9477** ⟨1⟩ n_D^{25} = **1.5042** ⟨1⟩

C̄ on oxidn. with $K_2Cr_2O_7 + H_2SO_4$ (cf. T 1.72) yields *n*-amyl phenyl ketone ⟨1⟩ (1:5111).

1:6720 ⟨1⟩ Davies, Dixon, Jones, *J. Chem. Soc.* **1930,** 470.

CHAPTER XI

GENUS 9. ETHERS, HYDROCARBONS, ETC.

1. Alphabetical Name Index*

*For complete alphabetical name index covering all listed names of all numbered compounds in this book se the main alphabetical index.

2. Chemical Type Index

(Names used here are not necessarily same as subject index names)

I. Ethers

α. Monoethers

A. *Purely aliphatic ethers*

A_1 Symmetrical saturated ethers

Diethyl ether............ **1:6110**
Di-*n*-propyl ether........ **1:7885**
Diisopropyl ether......... **1:6125**
Di-*n*-butyl ether.......... **1:7950**
Diisobutyl ether.......... **1:7945**
Di-*sec*-butyl ether........ **1:7935**
Di-*n*-amyl ether.......... **1:7970**
Diisoamyl ether.......... **1:7960**
Di-*n*-hexyl ether......... **1:7980**
Di-*n*-heptyl ether......... **1:7990**

A_2 Symmetrical unsaturated ethers

Divinyl ether............ **1:7800**
Diallyl ether............. **1:7900**

A_3 Unsymmetrical saturated ethers

(*a*) *Those with a methyl group*

Methyl ethyl ether....... **1:6100**
Methyl *n*-propyl ether.... **1:7815**
Methyl isopropyl ether.... **1:7805**
Methyl *n*-butyl ether..... **1:7855**
Methyl isobutyl ether..... **1:7835**
Methyl *sec*-butyl ether.... **1:7840**
Methyl *ter*-butyl ether.... **1:7830**
Methyl *n*-amyl ether...... **1:7905**
Methyl isoamyl ether..... **1:7890**
Methyl *ter*-amyl ether..... **1:7880**

(*b*) *Those with an ethyl group*

Ethyl methyl ether....... **1:6100**
Ethyl *n*-propyl ether...... **1:7845**
Ethyl isopropyl ether..... **1:7825**
Ethyl *n*-butyl ether....... **1:7895**
Ethyl isobutyl ether...... **1:7865**
Ethyl *sec*-butyl ether...... **1:7870**
Ethyl *ter*-butyl ether...... **1:7860**
Ethyl isoamyl ether...... **1:7920**
Ethyl *ter*-amyl ether...... **1:7910**

(*c*) *Those with a n-propyl group*

n-Propyl methyl ether..... **1:7815**
n-Propyl ethyl ether...... **1:7845**
n-Propyl isopropyl ether... **1:7875**
n-Propyl *n*-butyl ether.... **1:7925**

(*d*) *Those with an isopropyl group*

Isopropyl methyl ether.... **1:7805**
Isopropyl ethyl ether..... **1:7825**
Isopropyl *n*-propyl ether... **1:7875**
Isopropyl *n*-butyl ether.... **1:7915**

(*e*) *Those with a n-butyl group*

n-Butyl methyl ether..... **1:7855**
n-Butyl ethyl ether....... **1:7895**
n-Butyl *n*-propyl ether.... **1:7925**
n-Butyl isopropyl ether.... **1:7915**

(*f*) *Those with an isobutyl group*

Isobutyl methyl ether..... **1:7835**
Isobutyl ethyl ether...... **1:7865**

(*g*) *Those with a sec-butyl group*

sec-Butyl methyl ether.... **1:7840**
sec-Butyl ethyl ether...... **1:7870**

(*h*) *Those with a ter-butyl group*

ter-Butyl methyl ether.... **1:7830**
ter-Butyl ethyl ether...... **1:7860**

(*i*) *Those with amyl groups*

n-Amyl methyl ether...... **1:7905**
Isoamyl methyl ether..... **1:7890**
Isoamyl ethyl ether....... **1:7920**
ter-Amyl methyl ether..... **1:7880**
ter-Amyl ethyl ether...... **1:7910**

A_4 Unsymmetrical unsaturated ethers

Vinyl ethyl ether......... **1:7810**
Allyl methyl ether........ **1:7820**
Allyl ethyl ether......... **1:7850**

B. *Alkyl aryl ethers*

B_1 Methyl aryl ethers

Methyl phenyl ether...... **1:7445**

Methyl *o*-tolyl ether...... **1:7480**
Methyl *m*-tolyl ether...... **1:7510**
Methyl *p*-tolyl ether...... **1:7495**

Methyl α-naphthyl ether.. **1:7630**
Methyl β-naphthyl ether.. **1:7180**

Methyl *o*-xenyl ether...... **1:7130**
Methyl *p*-xenyl ether..... **1:7215**

Methyl *p*-propenylphenyl ether (anethole) **1:7115**

B_2 Ethyl aryl ethers

Ethyl phenyl ether....... **1:7485**

Ethyl *o*-tolyl ether........ **1:7525**
Ethyl *m*-tolyl ether....... **1:7545**
Ethyl *p*-tolyl ether........ **1:7535**

Ethyl α-naphthyl ether.... **1:7635**
Ethyl β-naphthyl ether.... **1:7135**

B_3 Propyl aryl ethers

n-Propyl phenyl ether..... **1:7533**
Isopropyl phenyl ether.... **1:7512**

B_4 Butyl aryl ethers

n-Butyl phenyl ether...... **1:7555**
n-Butyl *o*-tolyl ether...... **1:7575**

B_5 Amyl aryl ethers

n-Amyl α-naphthyl ether.. **1:7132**
n-Amyl β-naphthyl ether.. **1:7117**
Isoamyl α-naphthyl ether.. **1:7645**
Isoamyl β-naphthyl ether.. **1:7128**

B_6 Phenol alkyl ethers

Phenyl methyl ether...... **1:7445**
Phenyl ethyl ether........ **1:7485**
Phenyl *n*-propyl ether..... **1:7533**
Phenyl isopropyl ether.... **1:7512**
Phenyl *n*-butyl ether...... **1:7555**

o-Tolyl methyl ether...... **1:7480**
o-Tolyl ethyl ether........ **1:7525**
o-Tolyl *n*-butyl ether...... **1:7575**

m-Tolyl methyl ether..... **1:7510**
m-Tolyl ethyl ether....... **1:7545**

p-Tolyl methyl ether...... **1:7495**
p-Tolyl ethyl ether....... **1:7535**

α-Naphthyl methyl ether.. **1:7630**
α-Naphthyl ethyl ether.... **1:7635**
α-Naphthyl *n*-amyl ether.. **1:7132**
α-Naphthyl isoamyl ether. **1:7645**

β-Naphthyl methyl ether.. **1:7180**
β-Naphthyl ethyl ether.... **1:7135**
β-Naphthyl *n*-amyl ether.. **1:7117**
β-Naphthyl isoamyl ether.. **1:7128**

o-Xenyl methyl ether..... **1:7130**
p-Xenyl methyl ether..... **1:7215**

C. *Alkaryl alkyl ethers*

Benzyl methyl ether...... **1:7475**
Benzyl ethyl ether........ **1:7530**
Benzyl *n*-butyl ether...... **1:7565**
Benzyl isobutyl ether..... **1:7562**

D. *Alkaryl aryl ethers*

Benzyl α-naphthyl ether... **1:7190**
Benzyl β-naphthyl ether... **1:7241**

E. *Dialkaryl ethers*

Dibenzyl ether........... **1:7640**

F. *Diaryl ethers*

Diphenyl ether........... **1:7125**

G. *Ethers with 1 hetero O atom*

Furan................... **1:8015**
2,5-Dimethylfuran........ **1:8080**
Dibenzofuran............ **1:7205**
Xanthone............... **1:7275**
Cineole................. **1:7500**

β. Diethers (2 ether linkages)

A. *Purely aliphatic*

Ethylene glycol dimethyl ether................. **1:6141**
Ethylene glycol methyl ethyl ether............ **1:6159**
Ethylene glycol methyl *n*-propyl ether........... **1:6191**

B. *Partly aromatic*

Ethylene glycol diphenyl ether................. **1:7235**
Trimethylene glycol diphenyl ether................ **1:7170**

Pyrocatechol dimethyl ether **1:7560**
Pyrocatechol diethyl ether. **1:7140**
Pyrocatechol dibenzyl ether **1:7172**

Resorcinol dimethyl ether.. **1:7570**
Resorcinol diethyl ether.... **1:7585**

Hydroquinone dimethyl ether.................. **1:7160**
Hydroquinone diethyl ether................. **1:7185**
Hydroquinone dibenzyl ether................ **1:7255**

4-Allylpyrocatechol dimethyl ether................. **1:7606**
4-Propenylpyrocatechol dimethyl ether........... **1:7625**
4-Allyl-1,2-methylenedioxybenzene (safrole) **1:7580**
4-Propenyl-1,2-methylenedioxybenzene (isosafrole).. **1:7610**

γ. Triethers (three ether linkages)

Pyrogallol trimethyl ether. **1:7145**
Hydroxyhydroquinone trimethyl ether........... **1:7607**
Phloroglucinol trimethyl ether................. **1:7148**

II. Hydrocarbons

α. Purely Acyclic Hydrocarbons

A. *Alkanes*

C_5H_{12} *n*-Pentane........ **1:8505**
2-Methylbutane... **1:8500**
2,2-Dimethylpropane........... **1:8499**

C_6H_{14} *n*-Hexane **1:8530**
2-Methylpentane.. **1:8520**
3-Methylpentane.. **1:8525**

2,2-Dimethylbutane **1:8510**
2,3-Dimethylbutane **1:8515**

C_7H_{16} *n*-Heptane........ **1:8575**

	2-Methylhexane...	**1:8559**
	3-Methylhexane...	**1:8564**
	2,2-Dimethylpentane........	**1:8534**
	2,3-Dimethylpentane........	**1:8554**
	2,4-Dimethylpentane........	**1:8539**
	3,3-Dimethylpentane........	**1:8549**
	3-Ethylpentane....	**1:8569**
	2,2,3-Trimethylbutane.........	**1:8544**
C_8H_{18}	*n*-Octane.........	**1:8655**
	2-Methylheptane..	**1:8615**
	3-Methylheptane..	**1:8640**
	4-Methylheptane..	**1:8625**
	2,2-Dimethylhexane	**1:8585**
	2,3-Dimethylhexane	**1:8610**
	2,5-Dimethylhexane	**1:8590**
	3,3-Dimethylhexane	**1:8595**
	3,4-Dimethylhexane	**1:8620**
	3-Ethylhexane.....	**1:8635**
	2,2,4-Trimethylpentane........	**1:8580**
	2,2,3-Trimethylpentane........	**1:8593**
	2,3,3-Trimethylpentane........	**1:8605**
	2,3,4-Trimethylpentane........	**1:8600**
	3-Ethyl-3-methylpentane........	**1:8630**
	2,2,3,3-Tetramethylbutane (hexamethylethane) ..	**1:7090**
C_9H_{20}	*n*-Nonane........	**1:8710**
	2-Methyloctane....	**1:8700**
	3-Methyloctane....	**1:8705**
	4-Methyloctane....	**1:8690**
	2,3-Dimethylheptane........	**1:8685**
	2,4-Dimethylheptane........	**1:8660**
	2,5-Dimethylheptane........	**1:8670**
	2,6-Dimethylheptane........	**1:8665**
	3,3-Dimethylheptane........	**1:8675**
	3-Ethylheptane....	**1:8695**
	2,2,5-Trimethylhexane.........	**1:8650**
	3,3-Diethylpentane	**1:8680**
	2,2,4,4-Tetramethylpentane........	**1:8645**
$C_{10}H_{22}$	*n*-Decane.........	**1:8800**
	2,7-Dimethyloctane	**1:8720**
$C_{11}H_{24}$	*n*-Undecane.......	**1:8820**
$C_{12}H_{26}$	*n*-Dodecane.......	**1:8840**
$C_{14}H_{30}$	*n*-Tetradecane.....	**1:8860**
$C_{15}H_{32}$	*n*-Pentadecane.....	**1:8880**
$C_{16}H_{34}$	*n*-Hexadecane.....	**1:8900**
$C_{17}H_{36}$	*n*-Heptadecane....	**1:7035**
$C_{18}H_{38}$	*n*-Octadecane......	**1:7040**
$C_{20}H_{42}$	*n*-Eicosane........	**1:7045**
$C_{22}H_{46}$	*n*-Docosane.......	**1:7050**
$C_{24}H_{50}$	*n*-Tetracosane.....	**1:7065**
$C_{26}H_{54}$	*n*-Hexacosane.....	**1:7070**
$C_{32}H_{66}$	*n*-Dotriacontane (bicetyl)	**1:7080**

B. *Alkenes*

C_5H_{10}	Pentene-1........	**1:8205**
	Pentene-2........	**1:8215**
	2-Methylbutene-1..	**1:8210**
	3-Methylbutene-1	**1:8200**
	2-Methylbutene-2..	**1:8220**
C_6H_{12}	Hexene-1.........	**1:8255**
	Hexene-2.........	**1:8280**
	Hexene-3.........	**1:8270**
	2-Methylpentene-1	**1:8250**
	3-Methylpentene-1	**1:8235**
	4-Methylpentene-1	**1:8230**
	2-Methylpentene-2	**1:8275**
	3-Methylpentene-2	**1:8260**
	4-Methylpentene-2	**1:8240**
	2,3-Dimethylbutene-1.......	**1:8245**
	3,3-Dimethylbutene-1........	**1:8225**
	2,3-Dimethylbutene-2........	**1:8290**
	2-Ethylbutene-1...	**1:8265**

C_7H_{14} Heptene-1 . . . . **1:8324**
Heptene-2 . . . . **1:8334**
Heptene-3 . . . . **1:8332**

2-Methylhexene-1 . . **1:8320**
3-Methylhexene-1 . . **1:8298**
4-Methylhexene-1 . . **1:8316**
5-Methylhexene-1 . . **1:8302**
2-Methylhexene-2 . . **1:8328**
3-Methylhexene-2 . . **1:8322**
4-Methylhexene-2 . . **1:8306**
5-Methylhexene-2 . . **1:8308**
2-Methylhexene-3 . . **1:8314**

2,3-Dimethylpentene-1 . . . . **1:8300**
2,4-Dimethylpentene-1 . . . . **1:8296**
3,3-Dimethylpentene-1 . . . . **1:8294**
4,4-Dimethylpentene-1 . . . . **1:8285**
3,4-Dimethylpentene-2 . . . . **1:8310**
4,4-Dimethylpentene-2 . . . . **1:8292**

2-Ethylpentene-1 . . **1:8326**
3-Ethylpentene-2 . . **1:8330**

2-Ethyl-3-methylbutene-1 . . . . **1:8318**

C_8H_{16} Octene-1 . . . . **1:8375**
Octene-2 . . . . **1:8380**

4-Methylheptene-1 **1:8360**
2-Ethylhexene-1 . . . **1:8370**

2,4,4-Trimethylpentene-1 . . . . **1:8340**
2,4,4-Trimethylpentene-2 . . . . **1:8345**

C_9H_{18} Nonene-1 . . . . **1:8385**

$C_{16}H_{32}$ Hexadecene-1 . . . . . **1:7000**

$C_{17}H_{34}$ Heptadecene-1 . . . . **1:7020**

$C_{18}H_{36}$ Octadecene-1 . . . . . . **1:7030**

C. *Alkynes*

C_4H_6 Butyne-1 . . . . **1:8000**
Butyne-2 . . . . **1:8005**

C_5H_8 Pentyne-1 . . . . **1:8025**
Pentyne-2 . . . . **1:8040**
3-Methylbutyne-1 . **1:8010**

C_6H_{10} Hexyne-1 . . . . **1:8055**
Hexyne-2 . . . . **1:8075**
Hexyne-3 . . . . **1:8065**

C_7H_{12} Heptyne-1 . . . . **1:8085**
Heptyne-2 . . . . **1:8100**
Heptyne-3 . . . . **1:8095**

C_8H_{14} Octyne-1 . . . . **1:8105**
Octyne-2 . . . . **1:8120**
Octyne-3 . . . . **1:8115**
Octyne-4 . . . . **1:8110**

C_9H_{16} Nonyne-1 . . . . **1:8125**
Nonyne-2 . . . . **1:8155**
Nonyne-3 . . . . **1:8135**

$C_{16}H_{30}$ Hexadecyne-1 . . . . . **1:7025**

D. *Alkadienes*

C_5H_8 Pentadiene-1,3 . . . . **1:8035**
2-Methylbutadiene-1,3 . . . . **1:8020**

C_6H_{10} Hexadiene-1,5 . . . . . **1:8045**
Hexadiene-2,4 . . . . . **1:8060**
2,3-Dimethylbutadiene-1,3 . . . . . **1:8050**

β. Cyclic Hydrocarbons

A. *Cyclanes*

C_5H_{10} Cyclopentane **1:8400**

C_6H_{12} Cyclohexane **1:8405**
Methylcyclopentane **1:8403**

C_7H_{14} Methylcyclohexane **1:8410**
Ethylcyclopentane . **1:8415**

C_8H_{16} Ethylcyclohexane . . **1:8460**
cis-1,2-Dimethylcyclohexane **1:8450**
trans-1,2-Dimethylcyclohexane **1:8430**
cis-1,3-Dimethylcyclohexane **1:8435**
trans-1,3-Dimethylcyclohexane **1:8425**
cis-1,4-Dimethylcyclohexane **1:8440**
trans-1,4-Dimethylcyclohexane **1:8420**

n-Propylcyclopentane **1:8455**
Isopropylcyclopentane **1:8445**

C_9H_{18} *n*-Propylcyclohexane **1:8468**
Isopropylcyclohexane **1:8464**

$C_{10}H_{20}$ *n*-Butylcyclohexane **1:8472**
p-Menthane **1:7465**

$C_{11}H_{22}$ *n*-Amylcyclohexane **1:8488**
Isoamylcyclohexane **1:8484**

$C_{10}H_{18}$ *cis*-Decahydronaphthalene.......... **1:8480**
trans-Decahydronaphthalene..... **1:8476**

$C_{12}H_{22}$ Dicyclohexyl...... **1:8490**

B. *Cyclenes*

C_5H_8 Cyclopentene..... **1:8037**

C_6H_{10} Cyclohexene...... **1:8070**

C. *Cycladienes*

C_5H_6 Cyclopentadiene-1,3............ **1:8030**

C_6H_8 Cyclohexadiene-1,3 **1:8057**

D. *Aromatic hydrocarbons*

D_1 Mononuclear

C_6H_6 Benzene.......... **1:7400**
C_7H_8 Toluene.......... **1:7405**
o-Xylene......... **1:7430**
m-Xylene......... **1:7420**
p-Xylene......... **1:7415**
Ethylbenzene...... **1:7410**

C_9H_{12} Mesitylene........ **1:7455**
Pseudocumene..... **1:7470**
n-Propylbenzene... **1:7450**
Isopropylbenzene.. **1:7440**

$C_{10}H_{14}$ *p*-Cymene........ **1:7505**
m-Diethylbenzene.. **1:7520**
Prehnitene (1,2,3,4-tetramethylbenzene)........... **1:7548**
Durene (1,2,4,5-tetramethylbenzene).......... **1:7195**
n-Butylbenzene.... **1:7515**
sec-Butylbenzene... **1:7490**
ter-Butylbenzene... **1:7460**

$C_{11}H_{16}$ Pentamethylbenzene........... **1:7150**
n-Amylbenzene.... **1:7549**
ter-Amylbenzene... **1:7540**

$C_{12}H_{18}$ Hexamethylbenzene **1:7265**

$C_{18}H_{30}$ Hexaethylbenzene.. **1:7260**

D_2 Binuclear

C_9H_8 Indene........... **1:7522**
$C_{10}H_8$ Naphthalene...... **1:7200**
$C_{11}H_{10}$ α-Methylnaphthalene........... **1:7600**
β-Methylnaphthalene............ **1:7605**

$C_{12}H_{10}$ Biphenyl......... **1:7175**

$C_{13}H_{12}$ Diphenylmethane.. **1:7120**
$C_{14}H_{14}$ Dibenzyl......... **1:7149**

$C_{18}H_{14}$ *o*-Diphenylbenzene **1:7165**
m-Diphenylbenzene **1:7210**
p-Diphenylbenzene **1:7280**

$C_{19}H_{16}$ Triphenylmethane **1:7220**
1,3,5-Triphenylbenzene........... **1:7270**

D_3 Polynuclear

$C_{12}H_{10}$ Acenaphthene..... **1:7225**
$C_{13}H_{10}$ Fluorene.......... **1:7245**
$C_{14}H_{10}$ Anthracene....... **1:7285**
Phenanthrene..... **1:7240**

$C_{16}H_{10}$ Fluoranthene...... **1:7243**
$C_{18}H_{18}$ Retene........... **1:7237**

E. *Aromatic hydrocarbons* (*with unsaturated side chain*)

C_8H_6 Phenylacetylene... **1:7425**
C_8H_8 Styrene.......... **1:7435**
$C_{14}H_{12}$ Stilbene.......... **1:7250**

F. *Hydrogenated aromatic hydrocarbons*

C_6H_{12} Hexahydrobenzene **1:8405**
C_7H_{14} Hexahydrotoluene **1:8410**

C_8H_{16} Hexahydroethylbenzene........ **1:8460**
cis-Hexahydro-*o* xylene.......... **1:8450**
trans-Hexahydro-*o*-xylene.......... **1:8430**
cis-Hexahydro-*m*-xylene.......... **1:8435**
trans-Hexahydro-*m*-xylene.......... **1:8425**
cis-Hexahydro-*p*-xylene.......... **1:8440**
trans-Hexahydro-*p*-xylene.......... **1:8420**

C_9H_{10} Hydrindene (indane).......... **1:7511**
C_9H_{18} Hexahydro-*n*-propylbenzene......... **1:8468**
Hexahydro-isopropylbenzene........ **1:8464**

$C_{10}H_{18}$ *cis*-Decahydronaphthalene..... **1:8480**
trans-Decahydronaphthalene..... **1:8476**
$C_{10}H_{20}$ Hexahydro-*n*-butylcyclohexane..... **1:8472**
Hexahydro-*p*-cymene......... **1:7465**

$C_{11}H_{22}$	Hexahydro-*n*-amylbenzene	**1:8488**
	Hexahydro-isoamylbenzene	**1:8484**
$C_{12}H_{12}$	1,2,3,4-Tetrahydronaphthalene	**1:7550**
$C_{12}H_{16}$	Phenylcyclohexane	**1:7595**
$C_{12}H_{22}$	Dodecahydrobiphenyl	**1:8490**

G. *Terpene hydrocarbons*

$C_{10}H_{16}$	Dipentene	**1:8165**
	d-Limonene	**1:8175**
	α-Pinene	**1:8150**

III. Unreactive Ketones Falling in Genus 9

d-Fenchone....... **1:7547**

ORDER I: SUBORDER I: GENUS 9: HYDROCARBONS, etc.

Division A, Solids

Section 1. " Non-aromatics "

—— **DICYCLOHEXYL** $C_{12}H_{22}$ **Beil. V-108**
(Cyclohexylcyclohexane;
dodecahydrobiphenyl)

```
        CH2—CH2           CH2—CH2
       /       \H   H/   /       \
    H2C          C—C              CH2
       \       /     \   \       /
        CH2—CH2           CH2—CH2
```

M.P. 3.5-4.0° D_4^{20} **= 0.8848** n_D^{20} **= 1.4795**

See 1:8490. Genus 9: Division B: Section 5.

1:7000 HEXADECENE-1 $CH_3.(CH_2)_{13}.CH{=}CH_2$ $C_{16}H_{32}$ **Beil. I-226**
(Cetene)

M.P. **+4.0°** ⟨1⟩ **B.P. 154.5-155**$^{\circ}_{15}$ ⟨1⟩ D_4^{20} **= 0.7825** ⟨2⟩ n_D^{20} **= 1.4418** ⟨3⟩
n_D^{25} **= 1.4396** ⟨3⟩

$\bar{C}$ adds Br_2 (T 1.91) [yielding cetene dibromide (1,2-dibromohexadecane) [Beil. I-172]], cryst. from alc., m.p. 13.5° ⟨4⟩ ⟨5⟩. B.B. No. = 71 (T 1.925).

[For conversion of $\bar{C}$ to hexadecyne-1 (1:7025) via actn. of alc. KOH on cetene dibromide (86% yield) see ⟨1⟩.]

$\bar{C}$ on oxidn. with hot 1% aq. $KMnO_4$ gives *n*-pentadecylic acid (1:0620) ⟨6⟩.

1:7000 ⟨1⟩ Langedijk, Stedehouder, *Rec. trav. chim.* **56,** 526–528 (1937). ⟨2⟩ Waterman, Van't Spijker, Van Westen, *Rec. trav. chim.* **48,** 1108 (1929). ⟨3⟩ Evans, *J. Inst. Petroleum Tech.* **24,** 334 (1938). ⟨4⟩ Krafft, *Ber.* **17,** 1373 (1884). ⟨5⟩ Krafft, Grosjean, *Ber.* **23,** 2352–2353 (1890). ⟨6⟩ Landa, *Bull. soc. chim.* (4) **43,** 1087 (1928).

—— ***n*-TETRADECANE** $CH_3.(CH_2)_{12}.CH_3$ $C_{14}H_{30}$ **Beil. I-171**

M.P. +5.5° **B.P. 252.5°** D_4^{20} **= 0.7636**

See 1:8860. Genus 9: Division B: Section 6.

—— **CYCLOHEXANE** C_6H_{12} **Beil. V-20**
(Hexahydrobenzene)

```
        CH2—CH2
       /       \
    H2C         CH2
       \       /
        CH2—CH2
```

M.P. +6.47° **B.P. 80.8°** D_4^{20} **= 0.7784** n_D^{20} **= 1.42635**

See 1:8405. Genus 9: Division B: Section 5.

—— **PHENYLCYCLOHEXANE** $C_{12}H_{16}$ **Beil. V-503**
(Cyclohexylbenzene; hexahydrobiphenyl)

$$C_6H_5-\overset{H}{C}H<\begin{matrix}CH_2-CH_2\\CH_2-CH_2\end{matrix}>CH_2$$

M.P. +7.0° **B.P. 238.7°** D_4^{20} = **0.9441** n_D^{20} = **1.5254**
See 1:7595. Genus 9: Division B: Section 1.

—— *n*-**PENTADECANE** $CH_3.(CH_2)_{13}.CH_3$ $C_{15}H_{32}$ **Beil. I-172**
M.P. +10° **B.P. 270.5°** D_4^{20} = **0.7689** n_D^{25} = **1.431**
See 1:8880. Genus 9: Division B: Section 6.

1:7020 HEPTADECENE-1 $CH_3.(CH_2)_{14}.CH{=}CH_2$ $C_{17}H_{34}$ **Beil. S.N. 11**
M.P. 11.2° ⟨1⟩ **B.P. 155.4-156.4$^\circ_{10}$ ⟨1⟩** D_4^{20} = **0.7892 ⟨1⟩**
D_4^{25} = **0.7859 ⟨1⟩** n_D^{25} = **1.4417 ⟨1⟩**

1:7020 ⟨1⟩ Kozaick, Reid, *J. Am. Chem. Soc.* **60,** 2436 (1938).

1:7025 HEXADECYNE-1 $CH_3.(CH_2)_{13}.C{\equiv}CH$ $C_{16}H_{30}$ **Beil. I-262**
(Cetyne)

M.P. +15° ⟨1⟩ **B.P. 156-157$^\circ_{15}$ ⟨1⟩** D_{20}^{20} = **0.7965 ⟨2⟩**
$\bar{C}$ adds Br_2 (T 1.91); B.B. No. (T 1.925) = 31.
$\bar{C}$ treated with $NH_4OH/CuCl$ reagt. (T 1.96) gives yellowish green ppt. of cuprous deriv. — $\bar{C}$ treated with alk. K_2HgI_4 (T 1.96-B) yields a mercury salt, m.p. 95–96°.

1:7025 ⟨1⟩ Mulliken, Wakeman, Gerry, *J. Am. Chem. Soc.* **57,** 1607 (1935). ⟨2⟩ Krafft, Reuter, *Ber.* **25,** 2247 (1892).

1:7030 OCTADECENE-1 $CH_3.(CH_2)_{15}.CH{=}CH_2$ $C_{18}H_{36}$ **Beil. I-226**
M.P. +18° ⟨1⟩; cf. ⟨4⟩ **B.P. 179-180$^\circ_{18}$ ⟨1⟩** D_{22}^{22} = **0.7884 ⟨2⟩** n^{22} = **1.4443 ⟨2⟩**
$\bar{C}$ adds Br_2 (T 1.91). [$\bar{C}$ in CS_2 treated with Br_2 yields octadecene dibromide (1,2-dibromo-octadecane) [Beil. I-173], lfts. from alc., m.p. 24° ⟨3⟩, 22° ⟨1⟩.]

1:7030 ⟨1⟩ Meyer, Streuli, *Helv. Chim. Acta* **20,** 1180 (1937). ⟨2⟩ Dover, Hensley, *Ind. Eng. Chem.* **27,** 338 (1935). ⟨3⟩ Krafft, *Ber.* **17,** 1373 (1884). ⟨4⟩ Deatherage, Olcott, *J. Am. Chem. Soc.* **61,** 630–631 (1939).

—— *n*-**HEXADECANE** $CH_3.(CH_2)_{14}.CH_3$ $C_{16}H_{34}$ **Beil. I-172**
(Cetane)

M.P. +18.1° **B.P. 288.6$^\circ_{765}$** D_4^{20} = **0.7751** n_D^{20} = **1.4352**
See 1:8900. Genus 9: Division B: Section 6.

1:7035 *n*-**HEPTADECANE** $CH_3.(CH_2)_{15}.CH_3$ $C_{17}H_{36}$ **Beil. I-173**
M.P. 21.97° ⟨1⟩ **B.P. 290-292$^\circ_{738}$ ⟨3⟩** $D_{22.5}^{22.5}$ = **0.7767 ⟨2⟩** n_D^{25} = **1.4360 ⟨3⟩**
$\bar{C}$ cryst. from *n*-propyl alc. + acetone, or from acetone in transparent pl. becoming opaque at abt. 10° — Spar. sol. MeOH, EtOH, or AcOH; mod. eas. sol. *n*-propyl alc., acetone, ether; eas. sol. C_6H_6, lgr. — M.p. in cap. tube 23° ⟨1⟩.

[For f.p.-compn. diagram of system: C̄ + *n*-hexadecane (1:8900) see ⟨1⟩; for system: C̄ + *n*-octadecane (1:7040) see ⟨1⟩.]

1:7035 ⟨1⟩ Carey, Smith, *J. Chem. Soc.* **1933,** 1350–1351. ⟨2⟩ Mai, *Ber.* **22,** 2134 (1889). ⟨3⟩ Wojick, Adkins, *J. Am. Chem. Soc.* **55,** 1293 (1933).

1:7040 ***n*-OCTADECANE** $CH_3.(CH_2)_{16}.CH_3$ $C_{18}H_{38}$ **Beil. I-173**

M.P. 28.02° (β-form) ⟨1⟩
27.6° (α-form) ⟨1⟩

All specimens of C̄ after repeated crystallization show m.p. 27.9–28.0°, but may be supercooled as low as 27.4°. Transparent (α) cryst. then suddenly appear; on htg. cryst. become opaque (conv. to β-form) ⟨1⟩.

[For prepn. in 97% yield by reduction of *n*-octadecyl iodide with Zn + AcOH see ⟨2⟩.]
[For f.p.-compn. data on system: C̄ + *n*-heptadecane (1:7035) see ⟨1⟩.]

1:7040 ⟨1⟩ Carey, Smith, *J. Chem. Soc.* **1933,** 1351. ⟨2⟩ Carey, Smith, *J. Chem. Soc.* **1933,** 346–347.

1:7045 ***n*-EICOSANE** $CH_3.(CH_2)_{18}.CH_3$ $C_{20}H_{42}$ **Beil. I-174**

M.P. 36.4° ⟨1⟩; cf. ⟨2⟩ ⟨3⟩

1:7045 ⟨1⟩ Parks, Huffman, Thomas, *J. Am. Chem. Soc.* **52,** 1034 (1930). ⟨2⟩ Carothers, Hill, Kirby, Jacobson, *J. Am. Chem. Soc.* **52,** 5282 (1930). ⟨3⟩ Hildebrand, Wachter, *J. Am. Chem. Soc.* **51,** 2487–2488 (1929).

1:7050 ***n*-DOCOSANE** $CH_3.(CH_2)_{20}.CH_3$ $C_{22}H_{46}$ **Beil. I-174**

M.P. 44.5° ⟨1⟩ ⟨2⟩

Pl. from toluene — Sol. in abt. 25 pts. boilg. alc.
[For prepn. from *n*-undecyl iodide + Na in toluene see ⟨1⟩.]

1:7050 ⟨1⟩ Robinson, *J. Chem. Soc.* **125,** 229 (1924). ⟨2⟩ Hildebrand, Wachter, *J. Am. Chem. Soc.* **51,** 2487–2488 (1929).

1:7065 ***n*-TETRACOSANE** $CH_3.(CH_2)_{22}.CH_3$ $C_{24}H_{50}$ **Beil. I-175**

M.P. 51° ⟨1⟩ ⟨2⟩

[For prepn. by Zn.Hg + HCl reduction of *n*-hexyl *n*-heptadecyl ketone see ⟨1⟩.]

1:7065 ⟨1⟩ Müller, Saville, *J. Chem. Soc.* **127,** 599–600 (1925). ⟨2⟩ Hildebrand, Wachter, *J. Am. Chem. Soc.* **51,** 2487–2488 (1929).

1:7070 ***n*-HEXACOSANE** $CH_3.(CH_2)_{24}.CH_3$ $C_{26}H_{54}$ **Beil. I-175**

M.P. 56-57° ⟨1⟩ ⟨2⟩

1:7070 ⟨1⟩ Schenck, Kintzinger, *Rec. trav. chim.* **42,** 762 (1923). ⟨2⟩ Hildebrand, Wachter, *J. Am. Chem. Soc.* **51,** 2487–2488 (1929).

1:7080 ***n*-DOTRIACONTANE** $CH_3.(CH_2)_{30}.CH_3$ $C_{32}H_{66}$ **Beil. I-177**
(Dicetyl; bicetyl)

M.P. 70° ⟨1⟩ ⟨2⟩

Alm. insol. cold alc. or lgr.; sol. boilg. ether; eas. sol. hot AcOH.
[For detn. of optical properties see ⟨3⟩.]

1:7080 ⟨1⟩ Hildebrand, Wachter, *J. Am. Chem. Soc.* **51,** 2487–2488 (1929). ⟨2⟩ Seyer, Fordyce, *J. Am. Chem. Soc.* **58,** 2029 (1936). ⟨3⟩ West, *J. Am. Chem. Soc.* **59,** 742–743 (1937).

1:7090 **2,2,3,3-TETRAMETHYLBUTANE** (Hexamethylethane; di-*ter*-butyl) C_8H_{18} **Beil. I-165**

$$CH_3-\underset{\underset{CH_3}{|}}{\overset{\overset{CH_3}{|}}{C}}-\underset{\underset{CH_3}{|}}{\overset{\overset{CH_3}{|}}{C}}-CH_3$$

M.P. 101.2° ⟨1⟩ **B.P. 106.5°**
101° ⟨2⟩

[For study of 11 methods of prepn. of C̄ see ⟨2⟩.]

1:7090 ⟨1⟩ Smittenberg, Hoog, Henkes, *J. Am. Chem. Soc.* **60,** 18 (1938). ⟨2⟩ Whitmore, Stehman, Herndon, *J. Am. Chem. Soc.* **55,** 3807–3809 (1933).

ORDER I: SUBORDER I: GENUS 9: HYDROCARBONS, etc.

Division A, Solids

Section 2. " Chiefly Aromatics "

—— **CINEOLE** (" Eucalyptol ") $C_{10}H_{18}O$ **Beil. XVII-24**

M.P. +1 **B.P. 172.5°** $D^{20} = 0.9267$ $n_D = 1.4596$

See 1:7500. Genus 9: Division B: Section 1.

—— **BENZENE** C_6H_6 **Beil. V-179**

M.P. +5.5° **B.P. 80°** $D_4^{20} = 0.8774$ $n_D^{20} = 1.50149$

See 1:7400. Genus 9: Division B: Section 1.

—— ***d*-FENCHONE** $C_{10}H_{16}O$ **Beil. VII-96**

M.P. +6° **B.P. 195°** $D^{19} = 0.947$ $n_D^{18} = 1.46355$

See 1:7547. Genus 9: Division B: Section 1.

—— **ISOSAFROLE** $C_{10}H_{10}O_2$ **Beil. XIX-35**

M.P. +6.8° **B.P. 248°** $D_4^{20} = 1.122$ $n_D^{20} = 1.5782$

See 1:7610. Genus 9: Division B: Section 1.

— **PHENYLCYCLOHEXANE** (Cyclohexylbenzene; hexahydrobiphenyl) $C_{12}H_{16}$ **Beil. V-503**

H, CH₂—CH₂, C, CH₂, CH₂—CH₂

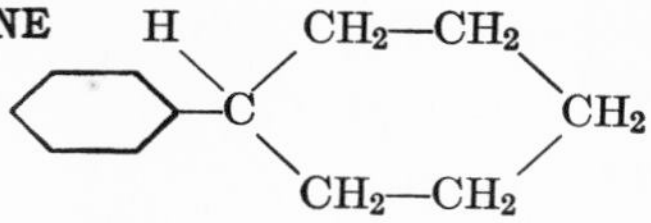

M.P. +7.0° **B.P. 238.7°** D_4^{20} = **0.9441** n_D^{20} = **1.5254**

See 1:7595. Genus 9: Division B: Section 1.

— **SAFROLE** (4-Allyl-1,2-methylene-dioxybenzene) $C_{10}H_{10}O_2$ **Beil. XIX-39**

O—CH₂, O, CH₂—CH=CH₂

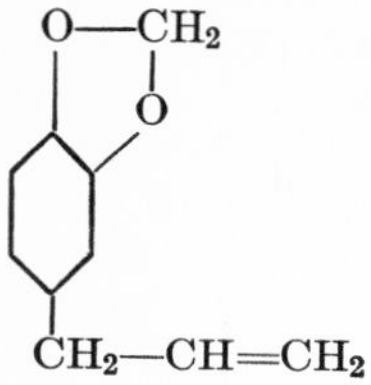

M.P. +11° **B.P. 233°**

See 1:7580. Genus 9: Division B: Section 1.

— **RESORCINOL DIETHYL ETHER** $C_{10}H_{14}O_2$ **Beil. VI-814**

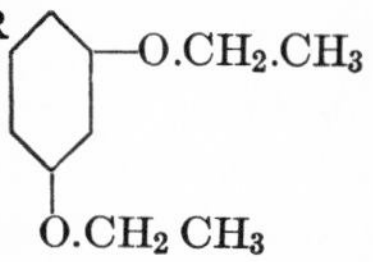

O.CH₂.CH₃, O.CH₂ CH₃

M.P. +12.4° **B.P. 235°**

See 1:7585. Genus 9: Division B: Section 1.

— ***p*-XYLENE** (*p*-Dimethylbenzene) C_8H_{10} **Beil. V-382**

CH₃—C₆H₄—CH₃

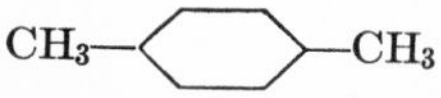

M.P. +13° **B.P. 138°** cor. D_4^{20} = **0.8611** n_D^{20} = **1.4956**

See 1:7415. Genus 9: Division B: Section 1.

— **ISOEUGENOL METHYL ETHER** ("Methylisoeugenol"; 1,2-dimethoxy-4-propenylbenzene) $C_{11}H_{14}O_2$ **Beil. VI-956**

OCH₃, CH₃.CH=CH—, OCH₃

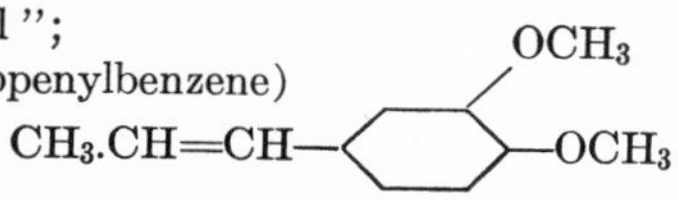

M.P. +16-17° **B.P. 264°** D_4^{20} = **1.055** n_D^{20} = **1.5692**

See 1:7625. Genus 9: Division B: Section 1.

— **HYDROXYHYDROQUINONE TRIMETHYL ETHER** (1,2,4-Trimethoxybenzene) $C_9H_{12}O_3$ **Beil. VI-1088**

OCH₃, OCH₃, OCH₃

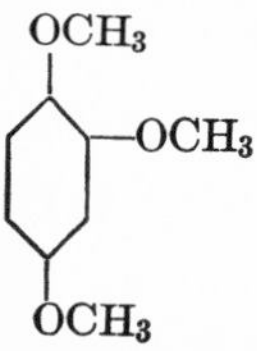

M.P. 19-20° **B.P. 247°** (251°)

See 1:7607. Genus 9: Division B: Section 1.

1:7115 ANETHOLE (*p*-Propenylanisole) $CH_3—C—H$ ‖ $H—C—C_6H_4—OCH_3$ $C_{10}H_{12}O$ **Beil. VI-566**

M.P. 22° **B.P. 235° cor.**

Odor and taste of oil of anise — Lfts. from alc. — Alm. insol. aq.; misc. in all proportions with abs. alc., ether, AcOEt, acetone, $CHCl_3$, C_6H_6, CS_2, pet. ether.

C̄ decomposes on exposure to light ⟨1⟩ yielding (amongst other products) 4,4′-dimethoxystilbene (" photoanethole ") [Beil. VI-1023] — Under influence of acid reagents C̄ yields various polymers; C̄ htd. with $ZnCl_2$ ⟨2⟩ or treated with $FeCl_3$ in ether ⟨3⟩ yields a dimeric " metanethole " or dianethole, m.p. 133°; C̄ on shaking with small amts. conc. H_2SO_4 or H_3PO_4, or in C_6H_6 soln. with $SnCl_4$ yields a hemicolloid polyanethole (" anisoin ") [for study see ⟨4⟩ ⟨5⟩]; C̄ on boiling with MeOH + HCl yields a liquid dimer (" isoanethole ") [for structure see ⟨6⟩]. [For study of structure of dianethole see ⟨16⟩.]

C̄ on oxidation with $KMnO_4$ gives (92% yield ⟨7⟩) *p*-methoxybenzoic ac. (anisic acid) (1:0805) [with alk. $KMnO_4$ both anisic ac. (1:0805) and anisaldehyde (1:0240) result ⟨7⟩]. C̄ on oxidation with 3.5 pts. dil. HNO_3 in 2 pts. AcOH for ½ hr. gives (70% yield ⟨8⟩) anisaldehyde (1:0240) [cf. ⟨9⟩].

C̄ adds Br_2 (T 1.91) — C̄ in 5 vols. ether treated with 1 mole Br_2 in cold gives anethole dibromide [Beil. VI-500], ndls. from pet. ether, m.p. 67° ⟨10⟩, 65° ⟨11⟩; 62–64° ⟨12⟩ ⟨14⟩. [C̄ with 2 moles Br_2 gives 2-bromoanethole dibromide: see below.]

C̄ in $CHCl_3$ treated with PkOH in $CHCl_3$ yields anethole picrate, C̄.PkOH; long or.-red ndls., m.p. 69–70° u.c. ⟨13⟩, 70° ⟨14⟩. [This cpd. loses C̄ on exposure to air ⟨14⟩.]

Ⓓ **2-Bromoanethole dibromide** [Beil. VI-501]: to 0.37 g. C̄ dislvd. in 4 ml. abs. ether and cooled in ice is added, dropwise, during 8 min. 0.84 g. Br_2 dislvd. in 3 ml. abs. ether. The solid left after evapn. of ether is ground up in a mortar with 1 ml. alc., then recrystd. from 18 ml. pet. ether, yielding 0.68 g. ndls., m.p. 108° ⟨15⟩ [cf. ⟨14⟩].

1:7115 ⟨1⟩ Hoering, Grälert, *Ber.* **42,** 1204–1207 (1909). ⟨2⟩ Orndorff, Terasse, Morton, *Am. Chem. J.* **19,** 858–860 (1897). ⟨3⟩ Puxxeda, *Gazz. chim. ital.* **50,** I, 149–154 (1920). ⟨4⟩ Staudinger, Brunner, *Helv. Chim. Acta* **12,** 972–984 (1929). ⟨5⟩ Staudinger, Dreher, *Ann.* **317,** 99–102 (1935). ⟨6⟩ Goodall, Haworth, *J. Chem. Soc.* **1930,** 2482–2487. ⟨7⟩ King, Murch, *J. Chem. Soc.* **127,** 2640–2641 (1925). ⟨8⟩ Labbé, *Bull. soc. chim.* (3) **21,** 1076–1077 (1889). ⟨9⟩ Shoesmith, *J. Chem. Soc.* **123,** 2702 (1923). ⟨10⟩ Hell, Günthert, *J. prakt. Chem.* (2) **52,** 198 (1895).

⟨11⟩ Mannich, Jacobsohn, *Ber.* **43,** 191 (1910). ⟨12⟩ Pond, Erb, Ford, *J. Am. Chem. Soc.* **24,** 331 (1902). ⟨13⟩ Baril, Megrdichian, *J. Am. Chem. Soc.* **58,** 1415 (1936). ⟨14⟩ Orndorff, Morton, *Am. Chem. J.* **23,** 184–186 (1900). ⟨15⟩ Underwood, Baril, Toone, *J. Am. Chem. Soc.* **52,** 4090–4091 (1930). ⟨16⟩ Baker, Enderby, *J. Chem. Soc.* **1940,** 1094–1098.

—— **VERATROLE** (Pyrocatechol dimethyl ether; *o*-dimethoxybenzene) $C_6H_4(O.CH_3)_2$ $C_8H_{10}O_2$ **Beil. VI-771**

M.P. +22.5° **B.P. 207°** D_4^{20} = **1.080**

See 1:7560. Genus 9: Division B: Section 1.

1:7117 *n*-AMYL β-NAPHTHYL ETHER $C_{15}H_{18}O$ **Beil. S.N. 538**

$CH_3.CH_2.CH_2.CH_2.CH_2—O—C_{10}H_7$

M.P. 24.5° ⟨1⟩ ⟨2⟩ **B.P. 327.5° cor.** ⟨1⟩ n_D^{30} = **1.5587** ⟨3⟩

[For prepn. (75% yield ⟨2⟩) from sodium β-naphtholate + *n*-amyl halide in alc. see ⟨1⟩ ⟨2⟩.]

C̄ in hot alc. soln. treated with equiv. amt. PkOH in hot alc. gives on cooling a picrate, C̄.PkOH, orange ndls., m.p. 66.5–67° ⟨1⟩; 64° ⟨2⟩; Neut. Eq. 443.

1:7117 ⟨1⟩ V. H. Dermer, O. C. Dermer, *J. Org. Chem.* **3,** 289–293 (1938). ⟨2⟩ Wang, *J. Chinese Chem. Soc.* **1,** 59–63 (1933). ⟨3⟩ Wilson, Ma, T'ien, *J. Chinese Chem. Soc.* **1,** 11–16 (1933).

1:7120 DIPHENYLMETHANE (Benzylbenzene) C_6H_5—CH_2—C_6H_5 $C_{13}H_{12}$ **Beil. V-588**

M.P. 25.09° ⟨7⟩ **B.P. 261°**
264.7° cor.

Long prism. ndls. with orange-like odor — Insol. aq.; eas. sol. alc., ether, $CHCl_3$. [For purification of C̄ and change of m.p. on stdg. see ⟨7⟩.]

[For prepn. (50–53% yield) from benzyl chloride + C_6H_6 + Al/Hg see ⟨1⟩.]

C̄ on oxidation with CrO_3 + H_2SO_4 (cf. T 1.72) yields benzophenone (1:5150).

C̄, treated slowly below 50° with mixt. of HNO_3 (*D* 1.52) + conc. H_2SO_4, followed by further addn. at 70° of mixt. of fumg. HNO_3 + fumg. H_2SO_4 according to specific directions ⟨2⟩ (100% yield ⟨2⟩), or C̄, melted and added dropwise below 25° to a soln. of KNO_3 in conc. H_2SO_4, followed by more solid KNO_3 (70% yield ⟨3⟩; 77 % yield ⟨4⟩) gives 2,4,2′,4′-tetranitrodiphenylmethane [Beil. V-596] pale yel. pr. from AcOH, m.p. 172–173°.

C̄ with sublimed $AlCl_3$ (T 1.94) gives YO color — C̄ with soln. of $SbCl_5$ in CCl_4 yields green addn. prod. ⟨5⟩.

C̄ forms no cpds. with PkOH, 1,3,5-trinitrobenzene, or 2,4,6-trinitrotoluene ⟨6⟩.

1:7120 ⟨1⟩ Hartman, Phillips, *Organic Syntheses* **14,** 34–35 (1934). ⟨2⟩ Parkes, Morley, *J. Chem. Soc.* **1936,** 1478–1479. ⟨3⟩ Gulland, Robinson, *J. Chem. Soc.* **127,** 1499 (1925). ⟨4⟩ Matsumara, *J. Am. Chem. Soc.* **51,** 817–818 (1929). ⟨5⟩ Hilpert, Wolf, *Ber.* **46,** 2217 (1913). ⟨6⟩ Kremann, Müller, *Monatsh.* **42,** 182 (1921). ⟨7⟩ DeVries, Strow, *J. Am. Chem. Soc.* **61,** 1797 (1939).

1:7125 DIPHENYL ETHER (Diphenyl oxide; " phenyl ether ") C_6H_5—O—C_6H_5 $C_{12}H_{10}O$ **Beil. VI-145**

M.P. 28° **B.P. 259°**

Geranium odor. Alm. insol. aq.; eas. sol. alc., ether, AcOH, C_6H_6.

Sol. in $CH_3.NO_2$ (T 1.922) at 20°; in aniline (T 1.922) at 20°. [The eutectic mixt. of C̄ with biphenyl (1:7175) has m.p. +12° and contains 73.5% by wt. of C̄ + 26.5% by wt. biphenyl (used as comml. heat transfer liq.) ⟨10⟩; the eutectic mixt. of C̄ with naphthalene (1:7200) has m.p. +16° and conts. abt. 85% C̄ + 15% naphthalene by wt. ⟨11⟩.]

C̄ is unaffected by CrO_3/AcOH, Zn dust ignition, or HI at 200°. [C̄ with soln. of Na in liquid NH_3, however, undergoes quant. cleavage to phenol (1:1420) ⟨1⟩.] [For mercuration of C̄ see ⟨2⟩.]

C̄ with fumg. HNO_3 yields (amongst other products) 4,4′-dinitrodiphenyl ether, almost colorless ndls. from alc., m.p. 144.4° ⟨3⟩; 144.0–144.3° cor. ⟨4⟩. [For prepn. of mononitrodiphenyl ether see ⟨5⟩.] — C̄ nitrated with KNO_3 + conc. H_2SO_4 gives (80% yield ⟨6⟩) 2,4,2′,4′-tetranitrodiphenyl ether, pale yel. pr. from AcOH, m.p. 195–197° ⟨6⟩; 198° ⟨7⟩.

Ⓓ **4,4′-Dibromodiphenyl ether** [Beil. VI-200]: 0.43 g. C̄ dislvd. in 2 ml. alc., treated dropwise during 10 min. with 0.8 g. Br_2, and stood overnight yielded solid cryst. from 6 ml. alc.; 0.94 g. lfts., m.p. 54–55° ⟨8⟩.

Ⓓ **Diphenyl ether 4,4′-disulfonamide:** cryst. from alc., m.p. 159° u.c. ⟨9⟩ [from C̄ on treatment with excess chlorosulfonic acid and conversion of resultant disulfonyl chloride to disulfonamide with $(NH_4)_2CO_3$; 86% yield ⟨9⟩].

1:7125 ⟨1⟩ Sartoretto, Sowa, *J. Am. Chem. Soc.* **59,** 603–605 (1937). ⟨2⟩ Schroeder, Brewster, *J. Am. Chem. Soc.* **60,** 751 (1938). ⟨3⟩ Smyth, Walls, *J. Am. Chem. Soc.* **54,** 3230 (1932). ⟨4⟩ Hampson, Farmer, Sutton, *Proc. Roy. Soc. (London)* **A-143,** 150 (1933). ⟨5⟩ Suter, *J. Am. Chem. Soc.* **51,** 2581–2583 (1929). ⟨6⟩ Matsumura, *J. Am. Chem. Soc.* **52,** 3201 (1930). ⟨7⟩ van Alphen, *Rec. trav. chim.* **51,** 458 (1932). ⟨8⟩ Underwood, Baril, Toone, *J. Am. Chem. Soc.* **52,** 4090–4091 (1930). ⟨9⟩ Huntress, Carten, *J. Am. Chem. Soc.* **62,** 603 (1940). ⟨10⟩ Ullock, Gaffert, Konz, Brown, *Trans. Am. Inst. Chem. Engrs.* **32,** 73–86 (1936).
⟨11⟩ Heindel, *Trans. Am. Inst. Chem. Engrs.* **30,** 379–380 (1934).

1:7128 ISOAMYL β-NAPHTHYL ETHER $C_{15}H_{18}O$ Beil. VI-642

$(CH_3)_2CH.CH_2.CH_2.O$—

M.P. 28.0-28.5° ⟨1⟩ **B.P. 321.0°** cor. ⟨1⟩

[For prepn. (75% yield ⟨2⟩) from sodium β-naphtholate + isoamyl halide in alc. see ⟨1⟩ ⟨2⟩.]

C̄ in hot alc. soln. treated with equiv. amt. PkOH in hot alc. and cooled gives picrate, C̄.PkOH; m.p. 93.5–94.0° cor. ⟨1⟩; 90.5–91.0° ⟨2⟩; Neut. Eq. 443.

1:7128 ⟨1⟩ V. H. Dermer, O. C. Dermer, *J. Org. Chem.* **3,** 289–293 (1938). ⟨2⟩ Wang, *J. Chinese Chem. Soc.* **1,** 59–63 (1933).

1:7130 2-METHOXYBIPHENYL $C_{13}H_{12}O$ Beil. VI-672

(*o*-Phenylphenol methyl ether;
methyl *o*-xenyl ether, *o*-phenylanisole)

OCH_3

M.P. 29° **B.P. 274°**

Pr. from pet. ether. [For prepn. from *o*-phenylphenol + $(CH_3)_2SO_4$ + 10% NaOH see ⟨1⟩.]

C̄ dislvd. in 10 pts. AcOH and warmed at 100° with 2.5 pts. conc. HNO_3 (D = 1.39) for ½ hr., first turns almost black, then pales and on cooling (or on dilution) deposits 5-nitro-2-methoxybiphenyl, pale yel. ndls. from MeOH, m.p. 95–96° ⟨1⟩.

1:7130 ⟨1⟩ Borsche, Scholten, *Ber.* **50,** 601 (1917).

1:7132 *n*-AMYL α-NAPHTHYL ETHEP $C_{15}H_{18}O$ Beil. S.N. 537

$CH_3.CH_2.CH_2.CH_2.CH_2.O$—

M.P. 30° ⟨1⟩ **B.P. 322°** cor. ⟨1⟩

C̄ in hot alc. soln. treated with equiv. amt. PkOH in hot alc. gives on cooling a picrate, C̄.PkOH, m.p. 75–75.5° cor. ⟨1⟩; Neut. Eq. 443.

1:7132 ⟨1⟩ V. H. Dermer, O. C. Dermer, *J. Org. Chem.* **3,** 289–293 (1938).

—— β-METHYLNAPHTHALENE $C_{11}H_{10}$ Beil. V-567

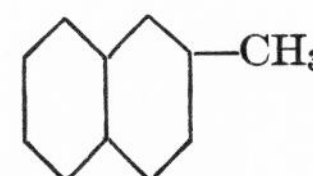

M.P. 32-33° **B.P. 241°**

See 1:7605. Genus 9: Division B: Section 1.

1:7135 ETHYL β-NAPHTHYL ETHER $C_{12}H_{12}O$ **Beil. VI-641**
(" Neonerolin ";
2-ethoxynaphthalene)

$CH_3.CH_2.O$—

M.P. 37° **B.P. 282°** cor. ⟨1⟩
274° u.c.

Tbls.; insol. aq.; sol. alc., ether, pet. ether, CS_2, toluene.

C̄ refluxed with const. boilg. HBr (D = 1.48) is said to yield β-naphthol (1:1540) and ethyl bromide (b.p. 39°).

C̄ htd. with Na (preferably in atmosphere of H_2 ⟨2⟩) begins to react at 200°, and on warming 100 min. at 220–235° ⟨3⟩ gives naphthalene (1:7200), β-naphthol (1:1540), ethyl alcohol (1:6130), together with gaseous products (ethane, ethylene, etc.).

C̄ (2 g.) dislvd. in mixt. of AcOH (1 mole) + abs. HNO_3 (14 ml.) at 0° and poured onto ice yields 1.2 g. of 1,6,8-trinitro-2-ethoxynaphthalene, golden ndls. from AcOH, m.p. 186° ⟨11⟩.

Mol. cpds.: C̄.PkOH, fine or.-yel. ndl. clusters, from 95% alc. ⟨1⟩, or $CHCl_3$ ⟨4⟩; m.p. 101.0–101.5° cor. ⟨1⟩; 99–100.5° ⟨4⟩, 104.5° ⟨5⟩ — C̄.1,3,5-trinitrobenzene: yel. ndls., m.p. 95° ⟨6⟩; C̄.2 moles 1,3,5-trinitrobenzene, yel. tbls. m.p. 128° ⟨6⟩ — C̄.2,4,6-trinitrotoluene: pale yel. ndls., m.p. 72° ⟨6⟩.

Ⓓ **1-Bromo-2-ethoxynaphthalene:** 0.43 g. C̄ dislvd. in 1 ml. AcOH, treated during 3 min. with 0.42 g. Br_2, then cooled 10 min., gives solid, recryst. from pet. ether, m.p. 66° ⟨7⟩ ⟨8⟩. [C̄ with 2 moles Br_2 at 100° yields 1,6-dibromo-2-ethoxynaphthalene, ndls. from pet. ether, m.p. 94° ⟨9⟩.]

Ⓓ **7-Ethoxynaphthalenesulfonamide-1:** cryst. from alc., m.p. 161–163° u.c. ⟨10⟩ [from C̄ with chlorosulfonic acid followed by conversion of resultant sulfonyl chloride to sulfonamide by treatment with $(NH_4)_2CO_3$ (58% yield) ⟨10⟩].

1:7135 ⟨1⟩ V. H. Dermer, O. C. Dermer, *J. Org. Chem.* **3,** 290–291 (1939). ⟨2⟩ Schorigin, *Ber.* **57,** 1632–1633 (1924). ⟨3⟩ Schorigin, *Ber.* **56,** 184 (1923). ⟨4⟩ Baril, Megrdichian, *J. Am. Chem. Soc.* **58,** 1415 (1936). ⟨5⟩ Wang, *J. Chinese Chem. Soc.* **1,** 61–62 (1933). ⟨6⟩ Sudborough, Beard, *J. Chem. Soc.* **99,** 215 (1911). ⟨7⟩ Underwood, Baril, Toone, *J. Am. Chem. Soc.* **52,** 4090–4091 (1930). ⟨8⟩ Davis, *J. Chem. Soc.* **77,** 38 (1900). ⟨9⟩ Ref. 8, page 40. ⟨10⟩ Huntress, Carten, *J. Am. Chem. Soc.* **62,** 603 (1940).
⟨11⟩ van der Kam, *Rec. trav. chim.* **45,** 571 (1926).

1:7140 PYROCATECHOL DIETHYL ETHER $C_{10}H_{14}O_2$ **Beil. VI-771**
(*o*-Diethoxybenzene)

—$O.CH_2.CH_3$
—$O.CH_2.CH_3$

M.P. 43°

Cryst. from dil. alc.

C̄ with $CHCl_3$ soln. of picric acid yields a mol. cpd., C̄.PkOH; red-brown rhombic cryst., m.p. 69–71°; unstable in air ⟨1⟩.

Ⓓ **3,4-Diethoxybenzenesulfonamide:** cryst. from alc., m.p. 162–163° u.c. ⟨2⟩ [from C̄ + chlorosulfonic acid, followed by conversion of resultant sulfonyl chloride to sulfonamide with $(NH_4)_2CO_3$ (81% yield) ⟨2⟩].

1:7140 ⟨1⟩ Baril, Megrdichian, *J. Am. Chem. Soc.* **58,** 1415 (1936). ⟨2⟩ Huntress, Carten, *J. Am. Chem. Soc.* **62,** 603 (1940).

1:7145 PYROGALLOL TRIMETHYL ETHER $C_9H_{12}O_3$ **Beil. VI-1081**
(1,2,3-Trimethoxybenzene)

OCH_3 / OCH_3 / OCH_3

M.P. 47° **B.P. 241°**

Ndls. from dil. alc. — Eas. sol. alc., ether, C_6H_6.

[For prepn. in 70–80% yield from pyrogallol (1:1555) with alk. and $(CH_3)_2SO_4$ see ⟨1⟩ ⟨2⟩ ⟨3⟩ ⟨4⟩.]

C̄ on treatment with conc. HNO_3 (preferably in alc. with caution) ⟨5⟩ ⟨6⟩ ⟨7⟩ yields mixt. of 2,6-dimethoxybenzoquinone-1,4 [Beil. VIII-385] (sol. in dil. alk. and repptd. by acids), golden-yel. pr. from AcOH, m.p. 255° cor. ⟨5⟩ and 5-nitro-1,2,3-trimethoxybenzene [Beil. VI-1086] (insol. alk.), pr. from AcOH, m.p. 100° ⟨7⟩.

C̄ with excess Br_2 ⟨8⟩ yields 4,5,6-tribromo-1,2,3-trimethoxybenzene [Beil. VI-1085], m.p. 73–74° ⟨3⟩. [The mono- and dibromopyrogallol trimethyl ethers are liquids.]

Molecular cpds.: picrate, C̄.PkOH, yel. thin rhomb. pl., m.p. 78.5–80° ⟨9⟩; C̄ + 1 mole 1,3,5-trinitrobenzene, pale yel. pr., m.p. 81° ⟨10⟩; C̄ + 1 mole 2,4,6-trinitrotoluene, thick dark yel. ndls., m.p. 56.5° ⟨10⟩.

Ⓓ **2,3,4-Trimethoxybenzenesulfonamide:** m.p. 123–124° u.c. (29% yield) ⟨11⟩.

1:7145 ⟨1⟩ Price, Bogert, *J. Am. Chem. Soc.* **56,** 2444 (1934). ⟨2⟩ Slotta, Szyszka, *J. prakt. Chem.* (2) **137,** 346–347 (1933). ⟨3⟩ Kohn, Grün, *Monatsh.* **46,** 79–80 (1925). ⟨4⟩ Ullmann, *Ann.* **327,** 116 (1903). ⟨5⟩ Graebe, Hess, *Ann.* **340,** 238–239 (1905). ⟨6⟩ Chapman, Perkin, Robinson, *J. Chem. Soc.* **1927,** 3028. ⟨7⟩ Will, *Ber.* **21,** 608, 612 (1888). ⟨8⟩ Ref. 7, page 607. ⟨9⟩ Baril, Megrdichian, *J. Am. Chem. Soc.* **58,** 1415 (1936). ⟨10⟩ Sudborough, Beard, *J. Chem. Soc.* **99,** 214–215 (1911).
⟨11⟩ Huntress, Carten, *J. Am. Chem. Soc.* **62,** 603 (1940).

1:7148 PHLOROGLUCINOL TRIMETHYL ETHER $C_9H_{12}O_3$ **Beil. VI-1101**
(1,3,5-Trimethoxybenzene)

CH_3O / OCH_3 / OCH_3

M.P. 52-53° **B.P. 255.5°** cor.

Pr. from alc.; sol. alc., ether, C_6H_6; insol. aq. and volatile with steam — Sublimes.

[For prepn. in 80–85% yield from phloroglucinol triacetate in MeOH + 50% KOH + $(CH_3)_2SO_4$ see ⟨1⟩; in 80% yield from phloroglucinol (1:1620) see ⟨2⟩.]

C̄ with excess Br_2 yields 2,4,6-tribromo-1,3,5-trimethoxybenzene [Beil. VI-1105], long colorless ndls. from alc., m.p. 145° ⟨3⟩ [2,4-dibromo-1,3,5-trimethoxybenzene [Beil. VI-1104], forms lfts. and pr. from alc., m.p. 129–130° ⟨4⟩ ⟨5⟩; 2-bromo-1,3,5-trimethoxybenzene [Beil. VI-1104] forms ndls. from dil. alc., m.p. 96–97° ⟨5⟩].

1:7148 ⟨1⟩ Freudenberg, *Ann.* **433,** 237 (1923). ⟨2⟩ Freudenberg, *Ber.* **53,** 1425 (1920). ⟨3⟩ Will, *Ber.* **21,** 603 (1888). ⟨4⟩ Freudenberg, Orthner, Fikentscher, *Ann.* **436,** 296 (1924). ⟨5⟩ Leuchs, *Ann.* **460,** 15–16 (1928).

1:7149 BIBENZYL C_6H_5—$CH_2.CH_2$—C_6H_5 $C_{14}H_{14}$ **Beil. V-598**
(Dibenzyl;
1,2-diphenylethane)

M.P. 52° **B.P. 284°**

Monoclin. pr. from alc. — Fairly sol. cold alc., eas. sol. ether, CS_2 — [For optical data on crystals see ⟨1⟩.] [For m.p. compn. diagrams of systems: C̄ + biphenyl (1:7175) with eutectic, m.p. 29.6° and C̄ + naphthalene (1:7200); eutectic, m.p. 32.6° see ⟨6⟩.]

C̄ on oxidn. with CrO_3 + AcOH, or $K_2Cr_2O_7$ + H_2SO_4, or alk. $KMnO_4$ yields BzOH (1:0715).

C̄ treated with 3 pts. conc. HNO_3 (D = 1.42) at 70–80° for 6 hrs. gives (95% yield ⟨2⟩) 4,4′-dinitrobibenzyl [Beil. V-604], light yel. ndls. from alc., m.p. 180.5° cor. ⟨2⟩ — C̄ dislvd. in 10 pts. fumg. HNO_3 (D = 1.53) at −15°, stood 1 hr. at room temp., poured into aq., solid extracted with hot alc. to remove lower nitration products, gives (70% yield ⟨3⟩) 2,4,2′,4′-tetranitrobibenzyl, m.p. 168–169° ⟨3⟩, 170.9° cor. ⟨2⟩. [By using higher temperature and longer time yield can be raised to 90–95% ⟨2⟩.]

C̄ forms no true picrate ⟨4⟩; but with 1,3,5-trinitrobenzene gives a mol. cpd., C̄.2T.N.B., canary-yel. cryst., m.p. 102° ⟨5⟩.

1:7149 ⟨1⟩ Hendricks, Jefferson, *J. Optical Soc. Am.* **23,** 302 (1933). ⟨2⟩ Rinkenbach, Aaronson, *J. Am. Chem. Soc.* **52,** 5041 (1930). ⟨3⟩ von Braun, Rawicz, *Ber.* **49,** 802 (1916). ⟨4⟩ Jefremow, *Cent.* **1923,** III, 379–380. ⟨5⟩ Sudborough, *J. Chem. Soc.* **109,** 1344 (1916). ⟨6⟩ Lee, Warner, *J. Am. Chem. Soc.* **57,** 319 (1935).

1:7150 PENTAMETHYLBENZENE

(Structure: benzene ring with CH_3 groups at five positions: CH_3, CH_3, CH_3, CH_3, CH_3)

$C_{11}H_{16}$ **Beil. V-443**

M.P. 54.0° ± 0.1° ⟨1⟩ B.P. 231°

Pr. from 95% alc. or C_6H_6.

[For prepn. from xylene + $AlCl_3$ + CH_3Cl see ⟨2⟩ ⟨3⟩; from xylene by repeated interaction with HCl + H_2CO, followed by reduction of resultant poly(chloromethyl)benzenes see ⟨4⟩.] [For optical crystallographic data see ⟨5⟩.]

C̄ treated with conc. H_2SO_4 yields under specified conditions ⟨6⟩ prehnitenesulfonic acid + hexamethylbenzene (1:7265). [Use as best method of prepn. of prehnitene (1,2,3,4-tetramethylbenzene) (1:7548) by hydrolysis of the sulfonic acid ⟨6⟩.]

C̄ added to $CHCl_3$ floating on mixt. of fumg. HNO_3 + conc. H_2SO_4 at 0° under specified conditions ⟨7⟩ gives (65–75% yield) dinitroprehnitene (5,6-dinitro-1,2,3,4-tetramethylbenzene), white ndls. from alc., m.p. 176–177°.

C̄ in $CHCl_3$ treated with Br_2 + trace of I_2 in cold ⟨14⟩ or C̄ + Br_2 in sunlight yields 6-bromo-1,2,3,4,5-pentamethylbenzene, m.p. 160.5° ⟨15⟩. [This halide will not form an R.MgBr compd. directly but only by " entrainment " method in presence of C_2H_5Br ⟨16⟩.]

C̄ (1 mole) + Ac_2O (12 moles) + $AlCl_3$ (2.2 moles) in CS_2 gives 80% yield ⟨8⟩ ⟨9⟩ acetopentamethylbenzene (methyl pentamethylphenyl ketone); cryst. from MeOH, m.p. 84°.

C̄ (1 mole) in 5 vols. MeOH treated with $Hg(OAc)_2$ (or 1 mole HgO + 2 moles AcOH), refluxed 5–7 days ppts. acetoxymercuripentamethylbenzene (80% yield), cryst. from $CHCl_3$, m.p. 180° ⟨10⟩. [This, in 5 pts. $CHCl_3$, treated with ethyl nitrite + HCl + AcOH gives 80% yield nitrosopentamethylbenzene, ndls. from $CHCl_3$, m.p. 160° dec. (varies with rate of htg.) ⟨11⟩.]

C̄.PkOH, gold.-yel. pr., m.p. 131° ⟨12⟩ [can be recrystd. from boilg. alc. ⟨13⟩].

1:7150 ⟨1⟩ Smith, MacDougall, *J. Am. Chem. Soc.* **51,** 3002, 3006 (1929). ⟨2⟩ Smith, *Organic Syntheses* **10,** 34–35 (1930). ⟨3⟩ Smith, Dobrovolny, *J. Am. Chem. Soc.* **48,** 1417 (1926). ⟨4⟩ von Braun, Nelles, *Ber.* **67,** 1094–1099 (1934). ⟨5⟩ Hendricks, Jefferson, *J. Optical Soc. Am.* **23,** 302 (1933). ⟨6⟩ Smith, Lux, *J. Am. Chem. Soc.* **51,** 2994–3000 (1929). ⟨7⟩ Smith, Harris, *J. Am. Chem. Soc.* **57,** 1291 (1935). ⟨8⟩ Smith, Guss, *J. Am. Chem. Soc.* **59,** 805 (1937). ⟨9⟩ Smith, Webster, Guss, *J. Am. Chem. Soc.* **59,** 1080 (1937). ⟨10⟩ Smith, Taylor, *J. Am. Chem. Soc.* **57,** 2370–2371 (1935).

⟨11⟩ Smith, Taylor, *J. Am. Chem. Soc.* **57,** 2461 (1935). ⟨12⟩ Baril, Hauber, *J. Am. Chem. Soc.* **53,** 1089 (1931). ⟨13⟩ Jacobson, *Ber.* **20,** 898 (1887). ⟨14⟩ Friedel, Crafts, *Ann. chim.* (6) **1,** 473 (1884). ⟨15⟩ Korczynski, *Ber.* **35,** 871 (1902). ⟨16⟩ Ref. 9, page 1081.

1:7160 HYDROQUINONE DIMETHYL ETHER $C_8H_{10}O_2$ **Beil. VI-843**

(*p*-Dimethoxybenzene; *p*-methoxyanisole)

CH_3O—⟨ ⟩—OCH_3

M.P. 56° **B.P. 213°** cor.

Lustrous flakes from 75% alc.

[For prepn. in 88.5% yield from hydroquinone (1:1590) in 15% aq. NaOH + $(CH_3)_2SO_4$ see ⟨1⟩ ⟨2⟩.] [Note that hydroquinone monomethyl ether (1:1435) also has m.p. 56° but unlike C̄ is sol. in alk.]

C̄ is sol. in conc. H_2SO_4 with yel. color — C̄ on boilg. with conc. HBr (D = 1.49) is said to yield hydroquinone (1:1590) and CH_3Br (B.P. +4°) — C̄ with $AlBr_3$ in lgr. yields two diff. mol. cpds. acc. to conditions: C̄.$AlBr_3$ seps. on mixing sep. filtered solns. of C̄ (0.7 g.) in 30–35 ml. lgr. with $AlBr_3$ (1.2 g.) in 30–35 ml. lgr.; C̄.2$AlBr_3$ seps. on adding to filtered soln. of C̄ (0.75 g.) in 30–40 ml. lgr. a soln. of $AlBr_3$ (3.64 g.) in dry C_6H_6; the latter cpd. on boiling with C_6H_6 evolves HBr, after 2 hrs. ppts. $Br_2Al.O$—⟨ ⟩—$OAlBr_2$ which with aq. yields hydroquinone (1:1590) ⟨3⟩.

C̄ in 4 pts. AcOH at 30° treated with 4 pts. conc. HNO_3 gives (100% yield ⟨2⟩; 90% yield ⟨4⟩) 2-nitro-1,4-dimethoxybenzene [Beil. VI-857], gold.-yel. ndls. from dil. AcOH or from 50% alc., m.p. 72°. [2,3-Dinitro-1,4-dimethoxybenzene has m.p. 177°; 2,5-dinitro-1,4-dimethoxybenzene has m.p. 202°.]

Mol. cpds.: C̄.PkOH, from $CHCl_3$ solns. of C̄ + PkOH; long or.-red blades, m.p. 47–48°, unstable on exposure to air ⟨5⟩; C̄.2 moles 1,3,5-trinitrobenzene, long bright red pr., m.p. 86.5° ⟨6⟩; C̄.1 mole of 2,4,6-trinitrotoluene, gold.-br. prism. ndls., m.p. 45° ⟨6⟩.

Ⓓ ***x,x*-Dibromohydroquinone dimethyl ether:** 0.35 g. C̄ dislvd. in 1 ml. AcOH, treated during 5 min. with 0.84 g. Br_2 in 1 ml. AcOH, gave immed. ppt., washed with 3 ml. 80% AcOH, recrystd. from 15 ml. AcOH, gave 0.7 g. prod., m.p. 142° ⟨7⟩ ⟨8⟩.

Ⓓ **2,5-Dimethoxybenzenesulfonamide:** cryst. from alc., m.p. 148° u.c. ⟨9⟩ [from C̄ by treatment with excess chlorosulfonic acid and conversion of resulting sulfonyl chloride with $(NH_4)_2CO_3$ to sulfonamide (53% yield) ⟨9⟩].

1:7160 ⟨1⟩ Bogert, Howells, *J. Am. Chem. Soc.* **52,** 840–841 (1930). ⟨2⟩ Vermeulen, *Rec. trav. chim.* **25,** 27–28 (1906). ⟨3⟩ Pfeiffer, Haack, *Ann.* **460,** 169–170 (1928). ⟨4⟩ Robinson, Smith, *J. Chem. Soc.* **1926,** 392. ⟨5⟩ Baril, Megrdichian, *J. Am. Chem. Soc.* **58,** 1415 (1936). ⟨6⟩ Sudborough, Beard, *J. Chem. Soc.* **99,** 214–215 (1911). ⟨7⟩ Underwood, Baril, Toone, *J. Am. Chem. Soc.* **52,** 4090–4091 (1930). ⟨8⟩ Habermann, *Ber.* **11,** 1036 (1878). ⟨9⟩ Huntress, Carten, *J. Am. Chem. Soc.* **62,** 603 (1940).

1:7165 *o*-DIPHENYLBENZENE $C_{18}H_{14}$ **Beil. S.N. 487**

(*o*-Terphenyl)

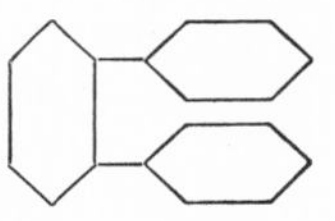

M.P. 56-57° ⟨1⟩ **B.P. 332°** cor. ⟨1⟩.

Colorless monoclinic pr. from MeOH; readily sol. acetone, $CHCl_3$.

C̄ (5 g.) on oxidn. with CrO_3 in AcOH (cf. T 1.72) yields ⟨1⟩ 0.1 g. *o*-phenylbenzoic acid [Beil. IX-670], m.p. 110°. [C̄ reduced by htg. 24 hrs. at 220° with Ni catalyst and H_2 at 100 kg./sq. cm. gives quant. yield 1,2-dicyclohexylcyclohexane, cryst. from acetone, m.p. 44.5–46° ⟨2⟩.]

1:7165 ⟨1⟩ Bachmann, Clarke, *J. Am. Chem. Soc.* **49,** 2093 (1927). ⟨2⟩ Corson, Ipatieff, *J. Am. Chem. Soc.* **60,** 749 (1938).

1:7170 1,3-DIPHENOXYPROPANE $C_{15}H_{16}O_2$ **Beil. VI-147**
(Trimethylene glycol diphenyl ether)

CH_2—O—C_6H_5
|
CH_2
|
CH_2—O—C_6H_5

M.P. 61° **B.P. 338-340° cor.**

Lfts. from alc. — Insol. aq.; sol. alc., ether.

Ⓓ ***α,γ*-Diphenoxypropane-4,4′-disulfonamide:** cryst. from alc., m.p. 245–255° u.c. ⟨1⟩ [from C̄ by treatment with excess chlorosulfonic ac. and conversion of resultant disulfonyl chloride to disulfonamide with $(NH_4)_2CO_3$ (44% yield) ⟨1⟩].

1:7170 ⟨1⟩ Huntress, Carten, *J. Am. Chem. Soc.* **62,** 603 (1940).

1:7172 PYROCATECHOL DIBENZYL ETHER $C_{20}H_{18}O_2$ **Beil. VI-772**

$C_6H_4(O.CH_2—C_6H_5)_2$

M.P. 63-64° ⟨1⟩

Pr. from alc.; white ndls. from MeOH or pet. ether ⟨2⟩ — Not volatile with steam.
[For prepn. from pyrocatechol (1:1520) + benzyl chloride + K_2CO_3 in acetone see ⟨1⟩.]

Ⓓ **4-Nitropyrocatechol dibenzyl ether:** from C̄ in 5 pts. AcOH treated with soln. of 1 pt. conc. HNO_3 in 5 pts. AcOH; after 1 hr. prod. is pptd. by aq. and recrystd. from alc.; yield 83%; pale yel. ndls., m.p. 98° ⟨1⟩.

1:7172 ⟨1⟩ Baker, Kirby, Montgomery, *J. Chem. Soc.* **1932,** 2878–2879. ⟨2⟩ Druey, *Bull. soc. chim.* (5) **2,** 1738 (1935).

1:7175 BIPHENYL $C_{12}H_{10}$ **Beil. V-576**
(Diphenyl)

$C_6H_5—C_6H_5$

M.P. 70° **B.P. 255°**

Monoclin. pr. from alc. — Insol. aq.; sol. MeOH, EtOH, ether — Sol. in $CH_3.NO_2$ (T 1.922) at +31°. [For optical properties of C̄ see ⟨10⟩.]

[For m.p.-compn. diagrams of C̄ + bibenzyl (1:7149) (eutectic m.p. 29.6°); and of C̄ + naphthalene (1:7200) (eutectic m.p. 39.5°) see ⟨1⟩.]

C̄ in 10 pts. AcOH refluxed with 2 moles Br_2 for 3 hrs. gives on cooling (70.6% yield ⟨2⟩) 4,4′-dibromobiphenyl, m.p. 164°.

C̄ in 1 pt. hot AcOH treated with 0.65 pt. fumg. HNO_3 (D = 1.5) at 75–95° for 1 hr., cooled ⟨3⟩ ⟨4⟩, gives ppt. (55% yield ⟨3⟩) of 4-nitrobiphenyl; ndls. from alc., m.p. 114° — [C̄ dislvd. in fumg. HNO_3 and briefly boiled gives only poor yield (18% ⟨5⟩; 21% ⟨6⟩ ⟨7⟩) of 4,4′-dinitrobiphenyl, ndls. from alc., C_6H_6, or AcOH, m.p. 234°.] [C̄ dislvd. in 6 pts. fumg. HNO_3 (D = 1.5) with cooling and treated with fumg. H_2SO_4 until red liq. becomes yellow and shows two layers, poured onto ice yields 2,4,2′,4′-tetranitrobiphenyl; crystals from acetone + alc., dimorphous forms: lower melting, m.p. 150–151°; higher melting, m.p. 166° ⟨8⟩ ⟨9⟩.]

C̄ with $AlCl_3$ (T 1.94) gives intense and quite permanent blue color (B) — C̄ with $SbCl_5$ in CCl_4 gives yel.-red color, then ppt. (dif. from anthracene) — C̄ forms no true picrate ⟨11⟩.

Ⓓ **4′-Phenylbenzophenone-carboxylic acid-2:** ndls. from boilg. alc.; m.p. 224–225° u.c. ⟨12⟩, 225–226° ⟨13⟩; Neut. Eq. 302 [from C̄ + phthalic anhydride + $AlCl_3$ in CS_2 ⟨12⟩; 92% yield ⟨13⟩].

1:7175 ⟨1⟩ Lee, Warner, *J. Am. Chem. Soc.* **57,** 319 (1935). ⟨2⟩ Scholl, Neovius, *Ber.* **44,** 1087, Note 1 (1911). ⟨3⟩ Kimura, Nihayashi, *Ber.* **68,** 2030 (1935). ⟨4⟩ Morgan, Walls, *J. Soc. Chem. Ind.* **49,** 15T (1930). ⟨5⟩ Willstätter, Kalb, *Ber.* **39,** 3478 (1906). ⟨6⟩ Bell, Kenyon, *J. Chem. Soc.* **1926,** 2707. ⟨7⟩ Gull, Turner, *J. Chem. Soc.* **1929,** 494–495. ⟨8⟩ Ullmann, Bielecki, *Ber.* **34,** 2178–2179 (1901). ⟨9⟩ van Alphen, *Rec. trav. chim.* **51,** 456–457 (1932). ⟨10⟩ Hendricks, Jefferson, *J. Optical Soc. Am.* **23,** 302 (1933).

⟨11⟩ Jefremow, *Cent.* **1923,** II, 379–380. ⟨12⟩ Underwood, Walsh, *J. Am. Chem. Soc.* **57,** 940–942 (1935). ⟨13⟩ Scholl, Neovius, *Ber.* **44,** 1078 (1911).

1:7180 **METHYL β-NAPHTHYL ETHER** $C_{11}H_{10}O$ **Beil. VI-640**
(" Nerolin ";
2-methoxynaphthalene)

—O.CH_3

M.P. 72.5-73° cor. ⟨1⟩ **B.P. 273°** ⟨1⟩

Pl. from ether — Sol. ether, C_6H_6, $CHCl_3$; less sol. CS_2; spar. sol. MeOH, EtOH — Volatile with steam — C̄ has odor of orange blossoms — C̄ is sol. in $CH_3.NO_2$ (T 1.922) at +18°.

[For prepn. in 65–73% yield from β-naphthol (1:1540) + aq. NaOH + $(CH_3)_2SO_4$ see ⟨2⟩.]

C̄ (0.9 g.) + $AlBr_3$ (1 g.) in lgr. gives mol. cpd. C̄.$AlBr_3$ which on boilg. with C_6H_6 separates a brown oil ($C_{10}H_7O.AlBr_2$); this oil on treatment with aq. gives β-naphthol (1:1540).

C̄ (2.5 g.) in AcOH (30 ml.) treated with conc. HNO_3 (2 ml.) at not above +15° yields mainly 1-nitro-2-methoxynaphthalene, yel. pr. from AcOH, m.p. 128°, accompanied by small amts. of 6-nitro-2-methoxynaphthalene, m.p. 134° and 8-nitro-2-methoxynaphthalene, m.p. 69° ⟨4⟩ ⟨5⟩ — C̄ (2 g.) dislvd. in mixt. of AcOH (1 ml.) at 0° and poured onto ice yields 1 g. of 1,6,8-trinitro-2-methoxynaphthalene, cryst. from AcOH, or ndls. from acetone, m.p. 215° dec. ⟨6⟩.

C̄ in alc. treated with alc. PkOH yields picrate, C̄.PkOH; deep yel. ndls., m.p. 116.5–117.0° cor. ⟨1⟩, 118° ⟨7⟩, 113.0–113.5° ⟨8⟩; Neut. Eq. 389 — C̄ yields mol. cpd. with 1,3,5-trinitrobenzene, C̄.$C_6H_3O_6N_3$, yel. ndls., m.p. 93.5° ⟨9⟩.

Ⓓ ***x*-Bromo-2-methoxynaphthalene:** from C̄ (0.4 g.) dislvd. in AcOH (2 ml.), treated with Br_2 (0.42 g.) during 3 minutes gives ppt. (0.63 g.) within 5 minutes; pl. from pet. ether (18 ml.), m.p. 62–63° ⟨10⟩ [m.p. challenged by ⟨7⟩]. [1-Bromo-2-methoxynaphthalene has m.p. 83–84° ⟨12⟩, 84–85° ⟨15⟩; 3-bromo-2-methoxynaphthalene has m.p. 77–78° ⟨13⟩, 76° ⟨14⟩; 6-bromo-2-methoxynaphthalene has m.p. 108° ⟨15⟩.]

Ⓓ **7-Methoxynaphthalenesulfonamide-1:** cryst. from alc., m.p. 150–151° ⟨11⟩ [from C̄ by treatment with chlorosulfonic acid, followed by conversion of resultant sulfonyl chloride to sulfonamide with $(NH_4)_2CO_3$ (65% yield) ⟨11⟩].

1:7180 ⟨1⟩ V. H. Dermer, O. C. Dermer, *J. Org. Chem.* **3,** 290–291 (1939). ⟨2⟩ Hiers, Hager, *Organic Syntheses, Coll. Vol.* I, 51 (1932). ⟨3⟩ Pfeiffer, Haack, *Ann.* **460,** 170–171 (1928). ⟨4⟩ Mundici, *Gazz. chim. ital.* **39,** II, 127 (1909). ⟨5⟩ Davis, *Chem. News* **74,** 302 (1896). ⟨6⟩ van der Kam, *Rec. trav. chim.* **45,** 571 (1926). ⟨7⟩ Wang, *J. Chinese Chem. Soc.* **1,** 61–62 (1933). ⟨8⟩ Baril, Megrdichian, *J. Am. Chem. Soc.* **58,** 1415 (1936). ⟨9⟩ Sudborough, Beard, *J. Chem. Soc.* **99,** 215 (1911). ⟨10⟩ Underwood, Baril, Toone, *J. Am. Chem. Soc.* **52,** 4090–4091 (1930).

⟨11⟩ Huntress, Carten, *J. Am. Chem. Soc.* **62,** 603 (1940). ⟨12⟩ Knapp, *Monatsh.* **67,** 339 (1936). ⟨13⟩ Fries, Schimmelschmidt, *Ann.* **484,** 268 (1930). ⟨14⟩ Clemo, Spence, *J. Chem. Soc.* **1928,** 2819. ⟨15⟩ Franzen, Stäuble, *J. prakt. Chem.* (2) **103,** 368–370 (1922).

1:7185 HYDROQUINONE DIETHYL ETHER $C_{10}H_{14}O_2$ Beil. VI-844

(*p*-Diethoxybenzene)

$CH_3.CH_2.O—\langle\ \ \rangle—O.CH_2.CH_3$

M.P. 72°

Lfts. with odor like anise — Very sol. alc., ether, $CHCl_3$, C_6H_6 — Volatile with steam. [For prepn. in 84% yield from hydroquinone (1:1590) + ethyl *p*-toluenesulfonate + 10% NaOH see ⟨1⟩.]

C̄ dislvd. in 4–5 pts. AcOH, cooled, and grad. treated with equal vol. HNO_3 (D = 1.3) with stirring, yields nitrohydroquinone diethyl ether [Beil. VI-857], gold.-yel. ndls. from 60% alc., m.p. 49° ⟨2⟩. [In the above procedure use of fumg. HNO_3 (D = 1.48) in place of that directed yields a mixt. of 2,3-dinitrohydroquinone diethyl ether [Beil. VI-858], yel. ndls., m.p. 130°, and 2,5-dinitrohydroquinone diethyl ether [Beil. VI-858], yel. ndls., m.p. 176°, separable by tedious fract. crystn. from alc. ⟨3⟩.]

Ⓓ **2,5-Diethoxybenzenesulfonamide:** cryst. from alc., m.p. 154–155° u.c. ⟨4⟩ [from C̄ + chlorosulfonic acid, followed by reactn. of intermediate sulfonyl chloride with $(NH_4)_2CO_3$; 47% yield ⟨4⟩]. [This deriv. depresses m.p. of corresp. deriv. (m.p. 148°) from hydroquinone dimethyl ether (1:7160) ⟨4⟩.]

1:7185 ⟨1⟩ Finzi, *Ann. chim. applicata* **15,** 41–50 (1925); *Chem. Abs.* **19,** 2648 (1925). ⟨2⟩ Nietzki, *Ann.* **215,** 145–146 (1882). ⟨3⟩ Ref. 2, pages 149–150. ⟨4⟩ Huntress, Carten, *J. Am. Chem. Sc.* **62,** 603 (1940).

1:7190 BENZYL α-NAPHTHYL ETHER $C_{17}H_{14}O$ Beil. S.N. 537

$O.CH_2—\langle\ \ \rangle$

M.P. 77° cor. ⟨1⟩ **B.P. dec.** (see text)

C̄ htd. 20 hrs. at 240° gives α-naphthol (1:1500) + 4-benzylnaphthol-1 (22.5% yield), ndls. from 85% formic ac., m.p. 120° ⟨2⟩.

C̄ in alc. treated with alc. PkOH yields a picrate, C̄.PkOH, Neut. Eq. 463 but this dec. 85–100° cor. ⟨1⟩.

1:7190 ⟨1⟩ V. H. Dermer, O. C. Dermer, *J. Org. Chem.* **3,** 290–291 (1939). ⟨2⟩ Behagel, Freiensehner, *Ber.* **67,** 1375 (1934).

1:7195 DURENE $C_{10}H_{14}$ Beil. V-431

(1,2,4,5-Tetramethylbenzene)

CH_3—, —CH_3, CH_3—, —CH_3

M.P. 79.3° ⟨1⟩ **B.P. 193°**

Colorless lfts. with odor like camphor — Sol. alc., ether, C_6H_6 — Sublimes; volatile with steam — Sol. in $CH_3.NO_2$ (T 1.922) at 100°.

[For prepn. (25–35% yield) from xylene + CH_3Cl + $AlCl_3$ see ⟨2⟩ ⟨3⟩.] [For purification see 1⟩; for freezing point compn. diagram of system C̄ + isodurene see ⟨1⟩.]

C̄ in 2 pts. CCl_4 treated with 5% more than 1 mole Br_2 in CCl_4 out of direct sunlight for $1\frac{1}{2}$ hrs. gives (79% yield ⟨4⟩) bromodurene (3-bromo-1,2,4,5-tetramethylbenzene) [Beil. V-432], white cryst. from 95% alc., m.p. 60.5° ⟨4⟩ — C̄ in 3 vols. AcOH + trace I_2 treated with 2 moles Br_2 in AcOH gives (87–100% yield ⟨4⟩) dibromodurene (3,6-dibromo-1,2,4,5-

tetramethylbenzene) [Beil. V-432], cryst. from $CHCl_3$ on addn. of alc., m.p. 200° ⟨4⟩. [The m.p. of mixts. of this dibromodurene with the corresp. deriv. of isodurene or prehnitene (1:7548) is not much depressed ⟨4⟩.]

C̄ shaken with mixt. of conc. + fumg. H_2SO_4 at room temp. gives (94% yield) crude durenesulfonic acid; purified by soln. in least possible 20% HCl at 80° and cooling to 0° (70% yield), m.p. 113° ⟨5⟩. [The corresponding deriv. of isodurene has m.p. 79° ⟨5⟩.] [For conversion of C̄ to prehnitene (1,2,3,4-tetramethylbenzene) (1:7548) by actn. of H_2SO_4 (Jacobsen reaction) see ⟨6⟩.]

C̄ in $CHCl_3$ floated on conc. H_2SO_4, rapidly stirred at 10° and treated with fumg. HNO_3 (D = 1.5) gives (92–94% yield ⟨7⟩) dinitrodurene (3,6-dinitro-1,2,4,5-tetramethylbenzene) [Beil. V-433], snow white pr. from alc., m.p. 207–208° ⟨8⟩. [The m.p. of mixtures of this dinitrodurene with the corresp. derivs. of isodurene and prehnitene is (in contrast to dibromo derivs.) sharply depressed ⟨4⟩.]

C̄ with equiv. PkOH forms an unstable picrate, C̄.PkOH; gold.-yel. pr., m.p. 92–95° ⟨10⟩.

Ⓓ **1′,2′,4′,5′-Tetramethylbenzophenone-2-carboxylic acid** [Beil. X-772]: cryst. from 40% alc., m.p. 263–265° u.c.; Neut. Eq. 282 ⟨9⟩ [from C̄ + phthalic anhydride + $AlCl_3$ in CS_2 ⟨9⟩].

1:7195 ⟨1⟩ Smith, MacDougall, *J. Am. Chem. Soc.* **51**, 3001, 3005–3007 (1929). ⟨2⟩ Smith, *Organic Syntheses* **10**, 32–39 (1930). ⟨3⟩ Smith, Dobrovolny, *J. Am. Chem. Soc.* **48**, 1413–1419 (1926). ⟨4⟩ Smith, Moyle, *J. Am. Chem. Soc.* **55**, 1680–1681 (1933). ⟨5⟩ Smith, Cass, *J. Am. Chem. Soc.* **54**, 1612 (1932). ⟨6⟩ Smith, Cass, *J. Am. Chem. Soc.* **54**, 1620–1621 (1932). ⟨7⟩ Smith, *Organic Syntheses* **10**, 40–42 (1930). ⟨8⟩ Smith, Dobrovolny, *J. Am. Chem. Soc.* **48**, 1420–1421 (1926). ⟨9⟩ Underwood, Walsh, *J. Am. Chem. Soc.* **57**, 940–942 (1935). ⟨10⟩ Baril, Hauber, *J. Am. Chem. Soc.* **53**, 1089 (1931).

1:7200 NAPHTHALENE

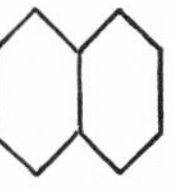

$C_{10}H_8$ **Beil. V-531**

M.P. 80.1° ⟨1⟩ B.P. 217.96° ⟨1⟩ ⟨2⟩

Colorless tbls. from alc. — Characteristic odor — Sublimes readily above m.p. — Easily volatile with steam — Insol. aq.; spar. sol. cold pet. ether, mod. sol. MeOH, cold EtOH; eas. sol. most other org. solv. [for quant. data on 11 solvents see ⟨3⟩] — Sol. in $CH_3.NO_2$ (T 1.922) at +46°. [For optical props. of C̄ see ⟨4⟩.]

[C̄ + diphenyl ether (1:7125) gives a eutectic, m.p. abt. 16°, contg. 15% C̄, and commercially used as a heat transfer medium ⟨5⟩.]

C̄ with sublimed $AlCl_3$ (T 1.94) gives green-blue color.

C̄ forms mol. cpds. with many nitro cpds. [Use in identification of nitro cpds. ⟨6⟩; e.g., C̄.PkOH (see below); C̄ + 1,3,5-trinitrobenzene gives cpd., C̄.T.N.B., m.p. 152° ⟨7⟩ ⟨8⟩ ⟨9⟩ ⟨13⟩; C̄ with 2,4,6-trinitrotoluene gives cpd., C̄.T.N.T., m.p. 97–98° ⟨7⟩; 96.5° ⟨10⟩.]

Ⓓ **Naphthalene picrate,** C̄.PkOH: Dis. 0.05 C̄ and 0.10 g. PkOH in 2 ml. boilg. alc. and allow to cool gradually. Collect the long hair-like yellow (Y-YT₁) ndls. on a small filter and wash with 1 ml. alc. Drain, transfer to porous tile, press out remaining mother liquor. Form cryst. into small mound on a dry part of the tile, rinse with 5–10 drops alc. Repeat this washing twice more in same way. Spread cryst. on fresh dry tile for 20 min. at 50° (long continued drying at higher temp. is inadvisable because of gradual loss of naphthalene); m.p. 150.5° u.c. ⟨11⟩; 149° ⟨12⟩ ⟨13⟩ [yel. pr. and pl. from EtOAc; yel. cryst. from ether ⟨12⟩]. [Use in quant. detn. of C̄.] [For m.p. + compn. diagram of mixts. of picrates of C̄ and of β-methylnaphthalene (1:7605) see ⟨17⟩.]

Ⓓ **2-(α-Naphthoyl)benzoic acid** [Beil. X-782]: pr. from dil. alc., m.p. 172–173° u.c. ⟨14⟩; 173.5° ⟨15⟩ (97% yield ⟨16⟩); Neut. Eq. 276 [from C̄ + phthalic anhydride + $AlCl_3$ in CS_2 ⟨14⟩].

1:7200 ⟨1⟩ Marti, *Bull. soc. chim. Belg.* **39,** 591, 615–618 (1930). ⟨2⟩ Eppley, *J. Franklin Inst.* **205,** 392 (1928). ⟨3⟩ Ward, *J. Phys. Chem.* **30,** 1327 (1926). ⟨4⟩ Hendricks, Jefferson, *J. Optical Soc. Am.* **23,** 302 (1933). ⟨5⟩ Heindel, *Trans. Am. Inst. Chem. Engrs.* **30,** 379–380 (1934). ⟨6⟩ Dermer, Smith, *J. Am. Chem. Soc.* **61,** 748–750 (1939). ⟨7⟩ Hepp, *Ann.* **215,** 377–378 (1882). ⟨8⟩ Kremann, *Monatsh.* **25,** 1279–1281 (1904). ⟨9⟩ Sudborough, *J. Chem. Soc.* **109,** 1344 (1916). ⟨10⟩ Kremann, *Monatsh.* **25,** 1246–1248 (1904).

⟨11⟩ Mulliken, " Method " I, 201 (1904). ⟨12⟩ Baril, Hauber, *J. Am. Chem. Soc.* **53,** 1090 (1931). ⟨13⟩ Hertel, *Ann.* **451,** 191 (1926). ⟨14⟩ Underwood, Walsh, *J. Am. Chem. Soc.* **57,** 940–942 (1935). ⟨15⟩ Graebe, *Ann.* **340,** 249–252 (1905). ⟨16⟩ Heller, Schülke, *Ber.* **41,** 3633 (1908). ⟨17⟩ Meyer, Meyer, *Ber.* **52,** 1251–1254 (1919).

1:7205 BIPHENYLENE OXIDE (Diphenylene oxide; dibenzofuran) $C_{12}H_8O$ Beil. XVII-70

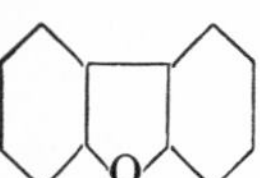

M.P. 86° **B.P. 288°** cor.

Small white lfts. from alc. — Insol. aq., fairly eas. sol. alc., very eas. sol. ether, C_6H_6, AcOH — Volatile with steam.

[For prepn. (20% yield) by distn. of phenol (1:1420) with litharge (PbO) see ⟨1⟩ ⟨2⟩.]

C̄ is unaffected by distn. over hot Zn dust or by HI at 250° — C̄ with 2 moles PCl_5 gives (80% yield ⟨3⟩) of *x*-chlorodiphenylene oxide, m.p. 94–96° — C̄, htd. with equal wt. $AlCl_3$ for 2½ hrs. at 140°, dark violet liq. poured into aq., extracted with ether and the ether soln. extracted with alk. gives on acidification phenol (1:1420) ⟨4⟩.

C̄ (1 mole) in AcOH (500 ml.) at 60–65° treated with fumg. HNO_3 (152 ml.) gives heavy ppt. (75.8% yield ⟨5⟩) of 3-nitrodibenzofuran, m.p. 181–182° ⟨5⟩. [The mother liquors contain a mixt. of the 2-nitro and 3-nitro compd.] — C̄ (5 g.) in 20 ml. AcOH or CCl_4 treated with 5 ml. fumg. HNO_3, htd. 5 min. at 100° gives alm. quant. yield ⟨6⟩ of a dinitrodiphenylene oxide, cryst. from acetone, m.p. 245° — [For sulfonation of C̄ see ⟨7⟩; for mercuration ⟨8⟩.]

C̄ forms with PkOH a picrate, C̄.PkOH, m.p. 94° ⟨9⟩; with 1,3,5-trinitrobenzene a cpd., C̄.T.N.B., citron-yel. ndls., m.p. 96° ⟨10⟩.

1:7205 ⟨1⟩ Cullinane, *J. Chem. Soc.* **1930,** 2268. ⟨2⟩ Cullinane, Davey, Padfield, *J. Chem. Soc.* **1934,** 716. ⟨3⟩ Whitmore, Langlois, *J. Am. Chem. Soc.* **55,** 1520 (1933). ⟨4⟩ Kraemer, Weissgerber, *Ber.* **34,** 1664–1665 (1901). ⟨5⟩ Gilman, Bywater, Parke, *J. Am. Chem. Soc.* **57,** 886 (1935). ⟨6⟩ Ryan, Cullinane, *Sci. Proc. Roy. Dublin Soc.* **17,** 321–326 (1924); *Chem. Abs.* **18,** 1655 (1924). ⟨7⟩ Gilman, Smith, Oatfield, *J. Am. Chem. Soc.* **56,** 1412–1414 (1934). ⟨8⟩ Gilman, Young, *J. Am. Chem. Soc.* **56,** 1415–1416 (1934). ⟨9⟩ Goldschmiedt, von Schmidt, *Monatsh.* **2,** 14 (1881). ⟨10⟩ Sudborough, Beard, *J. Chem. Soc.* **99,** 215 (1911).

1:7210 *m*-DIPHENYLBENZENE (*m*-Terphenyl) $C_{18}H_{14}$ Beil. V-695

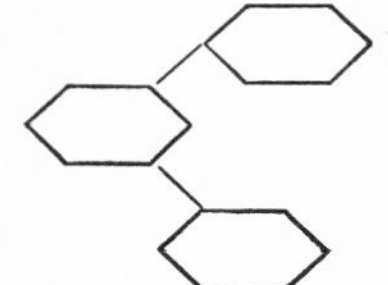

M.P. 87° ⟨1⟩ **B.P. 365°** cor. ⟨1⟩

Ndls. from dil. alc. — Eas. sol. alc., ether, C_6H_6, AcOH.

C̄ on oxidn. with CrO_3 + AcOH (cf. T 1.72) yields benzoic ac. (1:0715) and biphenylcarboxylic acid-3 [Beil. IX-671], m.p. 161° — C̄ forms no picrate.

[For study of nitration of C̄ see ⟨2⟩; chlorination and bromination of C̄ see ⟨3⟩; for study of reactn. with AcCl + $AlCl_3$ in nitrobenzene see ⟨4⟩.]

[C̄ on reduction by htg. 24 hrs. with Ni catalyst at 200° under initial hydrogen press. of 100 kg./sq. cm. yields 1,3-dicyclohexylcyclohexane, cryst. from acetone, m.p. 62.5–63.5° ⟨5⟩.]

1:7210 ⟨1⟩ Bachmann, Clarke, *J. Am. Chem. Soc.* **49,** 2093 (1927). ⟨2⟩ Wardner, Lowy, *J. Am. Chem. Soc.* **54,** 2511–2514 (1932). ⟨3⟩ W. A. Cook, K. H. Cook, *J. Am. Chem. Soc.* **55,** 1212–1217 (1933). ⟨4⟩ Goodman, Lowy, *J. Am. Chem. Soc.* **60,** 2155–2157 (1938). ⟨5⟩ Corson, Ipatieff, *J. Am. Chem. Soc.* **60,** 749 (1938).

1:7215 4-METHOXYBIPHENYL $C_{13}H_{12}O$ **Beil. VI-674**

(*p*-Phenylphenol methyl ether; methyl *p*-xenyl ether; *p*-phenylanisole)

—OCH_3

M.P. 89°

C̄ (7.4 g.) in Ac_2O (40 ml.) treated with a soln. of 2 ml. HNO_3 (D = 1.5) in Ac_2O (8 ml.) evolves heat and after 1 hr. is poured into aq.; repeated recrystn. of the pptd. mixt. of nitro cpds. from alc. yields 4.2 g. (45% yield) of 3-nitro-4-methoxybiphenyl, ndls. from alc., m.p. 91–92° ⟨1⟩. [The mother liquor contains a mixt. inseparable by crystn.] [The dinitro derivs. of C̄ have following values: 3,5-dinitro-4-methoxybiphenyl, silky yel. ndls. from alc., m.p. 137–138°; 3,4′-dinitro-4-methoxybiphenyl (in 50% yield from further nitration of 3-nitro-4-methoxybiphenyl with conc. HNO_3) has m.p. 171° ⟨1⟩.]

C̄ (8 g.) in $CHCl_3$ (25 ml.) treated with Br_2 (7 g.) in $CHCl_3$ (10 ml.), evapd. and residue fractionally recrystd. from pet. yields 4′-bromo-4-methoxybiphenyl, pl. from pet., m.p. 144°, and the more sol. 3-bromo-4-methoxybiphenyl, large prismatic ndls., m.p. 79° ⟨2⟩. [The dibromo derivs. of C̄ have following values: 3,4′-dibromo-4-methoxybiphenyl (from further bromination of either 144° or 79° monobromo cpds. in $CHCl_3$), m.p. 134°; 3,5-dibromo-4-methoxybiphenyl (indirectly), ndls. from pet., m.p. 87° ⟨2⟩.]

C̄ (1.5 g.) + $AlBr_3$ (0.9 g.) dry lgr. yields a mol. cpd. which seps. in lfts.; on addn. of C_6H_6 this yields a prod., C̄.$2AlBr_3.C_6H_6$, which on 10 hr. refluxing with C_6H_6 splits yielding 4-hydroxybiphenyl (1:1585) ⟨3⟩.

[For reaction of C̄ with AcCl + $AlCl_3$ yielding 4′-aceto-4-methoxybiphenyl, cryst. from MeOH, m.p. 153–154° see ⟨4⟩; for reactn. of C̄ with BzCl + $AlCl_3$ yielding 39% of 4′-benzoyl-4-methoxybiphenyl, m.p. 165–167°, see ⟨5⟩ ⟨6⟩.]

1:7215 ⟨1⟩ Bell, Kenyon, *J. Chem. Soc.* **1926,** 3047–3048. ⟨2⟩ Bell, *J. Chem. Soc.* **1930,** 1075. ⟨3⟩ Pfeiffer, Haack, *Ann.* **460,** 169–170 (1928). ⟨4⟩ Fieser, Bradsher, *J. Am. Chem. Soc.* **58,** 1741 (1936). ⟨5⟩ Fieser, Bradsher, *J. Am. Chem. Soc.* **58,** 2337–2338 (1936). ⟨6⟩ Blicke, Weinkauff, *J. Am. Chem. Soc.* **54,** 332 (1932).

1:7220 TRIPHENYLMETHANE $C_{19}H_{16}$ **Beil. V-698**

(" Tritan ")

CH

M.P. 92° **B.P. 358°**

Lfts. from alc.; spar. sol. cold alc. or AcOH; eas. sol. hot alc., ether, $CHCl_3$; very spar. sol. lgr. — Two cryst. forms are known: the stable, m.p. 92° and the labile, m.p. 81°; the former (stable) form does not combine with C_6H_6 and gives yel. color to conc. H_2SO_4 only after 24 hrs.; the latter (labile) form cryst. from C_6H_6 as a mol. cpd., $\bar{C}.C_6H_6$, m.p. 78° ⟨1⟩ an with conc. H_2SO_4 gives yel. color immediately ⟨2⟩ ⟨3⟩. The lower melting (labile) form i converted to the higher melting (stable) form on slight warming ⟨2⟩.

[For prepn. of $\bar{C}$ from $CCl_4 + C_6H_6 + AlCl_3$ (68–84% yield) see ⟨4⟩ ⟨5⟩; for prepn. fro triphenylcarbinol (1:5985) by treatment with alc. + conc. H_2SO_4 see (1:5985).]

$\bar{C}$ with sublimed $AlCl_3$ (T 1.94) gives YO color, soon darkening — $\bar{C}$ with $SbCl_5$ in CC gives a green addn. prod. ⟨6⟩ — $\bar{C}$ forms no picrate ⟨7⟩.

Ⓟ **Fuchsin formation:** Nitrate 0.1 g. $\bar{C}$ by dissolving in 2 ml. fumg. HNO_3 without ht Ppt. yel. trinitro compd. by diln. with aq. Dis. ppt. in 10 ml. hot AcOH and reduce b successive addns. of Zn dust until strong red color that first appears is nearly discharge Decant, add few cg. PbO_2 to soln., producing intense fuchsin-red at once ⟨8⟩ ⟨9⟩; c ⟨10⟩.

Ⓓ **Tris-(4-nitrophenyl)methane** [Beil. V-707]: cryst. from C_6H_6, or from $CHCl_3$ b pptn. with ether, m.p. 212.5° cor. ⟨11⟩ ⟨12⟩; 206–207° u.c. ⟨13⟩ ⟨14⟩ [from $\bar{C}$ gra added to well cooled HNO_3 (D = 1.5) ⟨13⟩, or finely pdrd. $\bar{C}$ (1 pt.) gradually adde to a mixt. of 7.8 pts. conc. HNO_3 (D = 1.42) + 12 pts. conc. H_2SO_4 (D = 1.84) (55 yield ⟨14⟩; 65% yield ⟨12⟩)].

Ⓓ **Triphenylcarbinol** (1:5985): from $\bar{C}$ in 100% yield on boiling for a few min. wit HNO_3 (D = 1.33) ⟨15⟩; m.p. 162°.

1:7220 ⟨1⟩ Hartley, Thomas, *J. Chem. Soc.* **89,** 1018–1021 (1906). ⟨2⟩ Zelinsky, Gawerdowskaj *Ber.* **61,** 1050 (1928). ⟨3⟩ Gawerdowskaja-Juschkewitsch, *Cent.* **1937,** II, 1796. ⟨4⟩ Norri *Organic Syntheses, Coll. Vol.* I, 532–534 (1932). ⟨5⟩ Norris, Young, *J. Am. Chem. Soc.* **4** 2580–2583 (1924). ⟨6⟩ Hilpert, Wolf, *Ber.* **46,** 2217 (1913). ⟨7⟩ Jefremow, *Cent.* **1923,** II 378–380. ⟨8⟩ Mulliken, "Method" I, 177 (1904). ⟨9⟩ E. Fischer, O. Fischer, *Ann.* **19** 274 (1878). ⟨10⟩ Meyer, Tögel, *Ann.* **347,** 69 (1906).

⟨11⟩ Montagne, *Rec. trav. chim.* **24,** 126 (1905). ⟨12⟩ Shoesmith, Sosson, Hetheringto *J. Chem. Soc.* **1927,** 2227. ⟨13⟩ Ref. 9, page 255. ⟨14⟩ Hantzsch, Hein, *Ber.* **52,** 495 (1919 ⟨15⟩ Schmidlin, Garcia-Banus, *Ber.* **45,** 3191 (1912).

1:7225 ACENAPHTHENE

$H_2C—CH_2$ $C_{12}H_{10}$ **Beil. V-58**

M.P. 95° **B.P. 278°** cor.

Long ndls. from alc.; eas. sol. hot alc., but spar. sol. cold.

$\bar{C}$ oxidized under specified conditions ⟨1⟩ with $Na_2Cr_2O_7$ in AcOH gives naphthalic aci (1:0890) and acenaphthenequinone (1:9090).

$\bar{C}$ with sublimed $AlCl_3$ (T 1.94) gives greenish-blue (GB) color.

$\bar{C}$ with 1,3,5-trinitrobenzene gives mol. cpd., $\bar{C}$.T.N.B., gold.-yel. ndls. from alc., m. 168° ⟨2⟩ ⟨3⟩; 161° ⟨4⟩; $\bar{C}$ with 2,4,6-trinitrotoluene gives a mol. cpd., yel. ndls. from alc 109.7° ⟨5⟩; 109° ⟨6⟩; 112° ⟨4⟩. [For picrate see below.]

Ⓓ **Acenaphthene picrate** ($\bar{C}$.PkOH): Dis. 0.05 g. $\bar{C}$ and 0.10 g. PkOH in 2.5 ml. boil alc. in dry tt., and allow to cool slowly to room temp. Collect the beautifully cryst orange colored product on small filter, wash with 3 ml. cold alc. Dry 15 min. on porou tile at 100°, m.p. 161–162° u.c. ⟨7⟩; 160.5° ⟨8⟩; 160° ⟨3⟩.

Ⓓ **2-(Acenaphthoyl)benzoic acid** [Beil. X-786]: from $\bar{C}$ + phthalic anhydride + AlC in CS_2; cryst. from 50% alc., m.p. 198–200° u.c. ⟨9⟩; 200° ⟨10⟩; Neut. Eq. 302.

1:7225 ⟨1⟩ Graebe, Gfeller, *Ann.* **276,** 3–5 (1893). ⟨2⟩ Sudborough, *J. Chem. Soc.* **109,** 1344 (1916). ⟨3⟩ Hertel, *Ann.* **451,** 191 (1926). ⟨4⟩ Kremann, Strzelba, *Monatsh.* **42,** 177–180 (1921). ⟨5⟩ Giua, *Gazz. chim. ital.* **45,** II, 359 (1915). ⟨6⟩ Ref. 3, page 206. ⟨7⟩ Mulliken, "Method" I, 200 (1904). ⟨8⟩ Baril, Hauber, *J. Am. Chem. Soc.* **53,** 1090 (1931). ⟨9⟩ Underwood, Walsh, *J. Am. Chem. Soc.* **57,** 940–942 (1935). ⟨10⟩ Graebe, Perutz, *Ann.* **327,** 99–100 (1903).

1:7235 1,2-DIPHENOXYETHANE $C_{14}H_{14}O_2$ Beil. VI-146

(Ethylene glycol diphenyl ether)

CH_2—O—C_6H_5
|
CH_2—O—C_6H_5

M.P. 98°

Lfts. from alc. — Insol. aq.; spar. sol. cold alc., eas. sol. hot alc.; eas. sol. $CHCl_3$, ether. [For crystallographic data see ⟨4⟩.]

C̄ in satd. AcOH soln. at room temp. treated with slight excess of Br_2 in AcOH immed. separates 50–70% yield of 1,2-di-(*p*-bromophenoxy)ethane; cryst. from alc., m.p. 134–135° u.c. ⟨1⟩.

C̄, gradually added at −10° to 8 pts. fumg. HNO_3, then poured into aq. gives (62% yield) 1,2-di-(2′,4′-dinitrophenoxy)ethane, pale yel. pdr. from acetone or phenol, m.p. 215.2° cor. ⟨2⟩.

Ⓓ **α,β-Diphenoxyethane-4,4′-disulfonamide:** cryst. from alc., m.p. 228–229° u.c. ⟨3⟩ [from C̄ by treatment with excess chlorosulfonic ac. and conversion of resultant disulfonyl chloride to disulfonamide with $(NH_4)_2CO_3$; 74% yield ⟨3⟩].

1:7235 ⟨1⟩ Cope, *J. Am. Chem. Soc.* **57,** 573–574 (1935). ⟨2⟩ Dosios, Tsatsas, *Compt. rend.* **180,** 1275–1277 (1925); *Chem. Abs.* **19,** 2194 (1925); *Cent.* **1925,** II, 167. ⟨3⟩ Huntress, Carten, *J. Am. Chem. Soc.* **62,** 603 (1940). ⟨4⟩ Gilta, *Bull. soc. chim. Belg.* **31,** 251–252 (1922).

1:7237 RETENE $C_{18}H_{18}$ Beil. V-683

(7-Isopropyl-1-methylphenanthrene)

$(CH_3)_2CH$— (phenanthrene ring) —CH_3

M.P. 98.5-99° B.P. 390°

Micaceous lfts. from alc. — Spar. sol. cold alc., eas. sol. hot alc. or boilg. ether, CS_2, lgr., C_6H_6 or AcOH — Sublimes far below b.p.; somewhat volatile with steam. [For extensive review of chemistry of C̄ see ⟨1⟩.]

C̄ with sublimed $AlCl_3$ (T 1.94) gives deep brownish *red* changing quickly to black.

C̄ with PkOH in boilg. alc. yields on concn. a picrate, C̄.PkOH, or.-red. ndls., m.p. 123–124° ⟨2⟩; 127° ⟨6⟩ — [*Not* pptd. by mixing cold satd. alc. solns. of C̄ + PkOH]; C̄ with 1,3,5-trinitrobenzene gives cpd., C̄.T.N.B., yel. ndls., m.p. 139–140° ⟨3⟩.

C̄ (1 g.) in AcOH (3.5 ml.) slowly treated with CrO_3 (1.9 g.) in AcOH (10 ml.), refluxed gently 1–2 hrs., cooled, gives ⟨4⟩ ppt. of retenequinone (1:9082). [After washing with 80% alc. and drying, product is purified by soln. in $CHCl_3$ and repptn. with alc. ⟨4⟩ [cf. ⟨5⟩ ⟨6⟩].]

1:7237 ⟨1⟩ Adelson, Bogert, *Chem. Rev.* **24,** 135–176 (1939). ⟨2⟩ Ekstrand, *Ann.* **185,** 80–81 (1877). ⟨3⟩ Sudborough, *J. Chem. Soc.* **109,** 1344 (1916). ⟨4⟩ Bamberger, Hooker, *Ann.* **229,** 117–119 (1885). ⟨5⟩ Fieser, Young, *J. Am. Chem. Soc.* **53,** 4127 (1931). ⟨6⟩ Vesterberg, *Ber.* **36,** 4201–4202 (1903).

1:7240 PHENANTHRENE $C_{14}H_{10}$ Beil. V-667

M.P. 100° **B.P. 340°** cor.

Colorless pl. — Soly. at 25° in 100 g. solvent: alc. 4.9 g.; hexane 9.2; CCl_4 26.3; ether 42.9; C_6H_6 59.5; CS_2 80.3 ⟨1⟩; cf. ⟨2⟩ — Sublimes readily.

$\bar{C}$ with sublimed $AlCl_3$ (T 1.94) gives greenish-blue to blue (GB-B) color.

$\bar{C}$, dislvd. in 5 pts. AcOH and treated with 2.2 pts. CrO_3 in 5 pts. AcOH, refluxed, poured into aq., ppts. crude phenanthraquinone. For purification this is warmed at 50–60° with 40% $NaHSO_3$ soln., filtered from solid; cooled to 0° and acidified with dil. H_2SO_4 yielding phenanthraquinone (1:9086); m.p. 202° ⟨3⟩ ⟨4⟩. [The same result may also be obtd. using $K_2Cr_2O_7 + H_2SO_4$ ⟨5⟩ ⟨6⟩.] [For quant. detn. of $\bar{C}$ by oxidn. to phenanthraquinone with iodic ac. see ⟨7⟩.]

$\bar{C}$ dislvd. in 5 pts. pure CCl_4, cooled in ice and treated with Br_2 at 0° in sunlight gives (65% yield ⟨8⟩) phenanthrene dibromide-9,10 [Beil. V-642], purified by soln. in minimum amt. C_6H_6 at 40–45°, adding equal vol. pet. ether and cooling to −15°; colorless pl. with greenish tinge, m.p. 98–99° dec. ⟨8⟩. [Use in prepn. of pure $\bar{C}$ by reduction with Zn dust + alc. (90% yield) ⟨8⟩.] [For purification of $\bar{C}$ by treatment with HNO_3 see ⟨9⟩.]

Mol. cpds.: with 1,3,5-trinitrobenzene, $\bar{C}$.T.N.B. pale or.-yel., m.p. 158° ⟨17⟩ ⟨14⟩; with 2,4,6-trinitrotoluene, $\bar{C}$.T.N.T., m.p. 158° ⟨18⟩.

Ⓓ **Phenanthrene picrate** ($\bar{C}$.PkOH): Dis. 0.10 $\bar{C}$ and 0.20 g. PkOH in 5.0 ml. boilg. alc. and allow to cool slowly. Collect prod., $\bar{C}$.PkOH, on filter, suck dry, redissolve in 1 ml. boilg. alc. and cool as before. Dry on porous tile, washing with 5 drops alc. Dry 15 min. at 100° and detn. m.p.; orange-yel. ndls. (OY), m.p. 143° u.c. ⟨10⟩ ⟨11⟩ ⟨12⟩; 145° ⟨13⟩ ⟨14⟩; 132.8° ⟨15⟩ ⟨16⟩.

1:7240 ⟨1⟩ Hildebrand, Ellefson, Beebe, *J. Am. Chem. Soc.* **39,** 2302 (1917). ⟨2⟩ Clark, *J. Ind. Eng. Chem.* **11,** 204–208 (1919). ⟨3⟩ Graebe, *Ann.* **167,** 140 (1873). ⟨4⟩ Courtot, *Ann. chim.* (10) **14,** 69–70 (1930). ⟨5⟩ Oyster, Adkins, *J. Am. Chem. Soc.* **43,** 208–209 (1921). ⟨6⟩ Moore, Huntress, *J. Am. Chem. Soc.* **49,** 1328 (1927). ⟨7⟩ Williams, *J. Am. Chem. Soc.* **43,** 1911–1919 (1921). ⟨8⟩ Price, Arntzen, Weaver, *J. Am. Chem. Soc.* **60,** 2837–2839 (1938). ⟨9⟩ Cohen, Cormier, *J. Am. Chem. Soc.* **52,** 4363–4364 (1930). ⟨10⟩ Mulliken, " Method " I, 201 (1904). ⟨11⟩ Fittig, Ostermayer, *Ann.* **166,** 363 (1873). ⟨12⟩ Hayduck, *Ann.* **167,** 180 (1873). ⟨13⟩ Ref. 3, pages 137–139. ⟨14⟩ Hertel, *Ann.* **451,** 191 (1926). ⟨15⟩ Jefremow, *Cent.* **1923,** III, 379. ⟨16⟩ Baril, Hauber, *J. Am. Chem. Soc.* **53,** 1090 (1931). ⟨17⟩ Sudborough, *J. Chem. Soc.* **109,** 1344 (1916). ⟨18⟩ Ref. 14, page 206.

1:7241 BENZYL β-NAPHTHYL ETHER $C_{17}H_{14}O$ Beil. VI-642

$-CH_2.O-$

M.P. 101.5° cor. ⟨1⟩

Lfts. from alc.; eas. sol. alc., ether, $CHCl_3$, C_6H_6.

$\bar{C}$ htd. 48 hrs. at 240–250° gives β-naphthol (1:1540) + 1-benzylnaphthol-2 (10%), ndls. from 85% formic ac., m.p. 110° ⟨2⟩ — $\bar{C}$, htd. with Na under H_2 for 3 hrs. at 180–270° yields toluene, + β-naphthol (1:1540) + phenyl-β-naphthyl-carbinol [Beil. VI-710] ⟨3⟩ ⟨4⟩.

$\bar{C}$ in alc. treated with alc. PkOH yields picrate, $\bar{C}$.PkOH, or. ndls.; m.p. 123.0° cor. ⟨1⟩; 122° ⟨5⟩; Neut. Eq. 463.

1:7241 ⟨1⟩ V. H. Dermer, O. C. Dermer, *J. Org. Chem.* **3,** 290–291 (1939). ⟨2⟩ Behagel, Freienhner, *Ber.* **67,** 1375 (1934). ⟨3⟩ Schorigin, *Ber.* **57,** 1632 (1924). ⟨4⟩ Schorigin, *Ber.* **57,** 1636 (1924). ⟨5⟩ Wang, *J. Chinese Chem. Soc.* **1,** 62 (1933).

1:7243 FLUORANTHENE $C_{16}H_{10}$ **Beil. V-685**
(1,2-Benzacenaphthene; idryl)

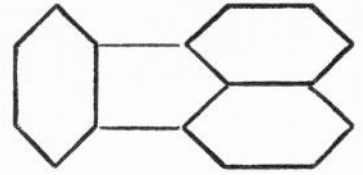

M.P. 109-110° **B.P. 393°**

Ndls. from conc. alc.; tbls. from dil. alc.; sol. alc., ether, $CHCl_3$, CS_2, C_6H_6, AcOH — $\bar{C}$ can be distd. unchanged with Hg vapor ⟨1⟩. [For isolation of $\bar{C}$ from C black see ⟨11⟩.]

$\bar{C}$ with warm conc. H_2SO_4 dissolves with greenish-blue color ⟨2⟩ ⟨3⟩.

$\bar{C}$ on oxidn. with CrO_3 in AcOH gives (48% yield ⟨4⟩) fluorenone-1-carboxylic acid [Beil. X-773], orange-red ndls. from dil. alc., m.p. 191–192°, together with fluoranthenequinone [Beil. VII-822], red ndls. from alc., m.p. 188° ⟨5⟩. [Note: fluoranthene forms with fluoranthenequinone a mol. cpd. of compn. $2\bar{C}.C_{16}H_8O_2$, red ndls., m.p. 102°, eas. dissociated by alc. ⟨5⟩.]

For bromination of $\bar{C}$ see ⟨6⟩; for nitration see ⟨7⟩.

Mol. cpds.: $\bar{C}$.PkOH, reddish-yel. ndls., spar. sol. cold alc., more easily hot alc., can be recrystd. from alc. without decomposition; m.p. 182–183° ⟨8⟩ ⟨9⟩, 183.5° ⟨10⟩, 184–185° ⟨2⟩ ⟨3⟩ — $\bar{C}$.1,3,5-trinitrobenzene, pale citron-yel., m.p. 200.5° ⟨10⟩.

1:7243 ⟨1⟩ Decker, *Ber.* **67,** 1640 (1934). ⟨2⟩ Goldschmiedt, *Ber.* **10,** 2029 (1877). ⟨3⟩ von Braun, Anton, *Ber.* **62,** 151 (1929). ⟨4⟩ Fieser, Seligman, *J. Am. Chem. Soc.* **57,** 2175 (1935). ⟨5⟩ Fittig, Liepmann, *Ann.* **200,** 3–5 (1879). ⟨6⟩ von Braun, Manz, *Ann.* **488,** 115–116 (1931). ⟨7⟩ Ref. 6, pages 122–123. ⟨8⟩ Fittig, Gebhardt, *Ann.* **193,** 146 (1878). ⟨9⟩ Mayer, Taeger, *Ber.* **53,** 1264 (1920). ⟨10⟩ Hertel, *Ann.* **451,** 191 (1926).
⟨11⟩ Rehner, *J. Am. Chem. Soc.* **62,** 2243 (1940).

1:7245 FLUORENE $C_{13}H_{10}$ **Beil. V-625**
(Diphenylenemethane)

H_2
C

M.P. 114° **B.P. 294° cor.**

White lfts. from AcOH or alc., with faint violet fluorescence (very strong in filtered ultraviolet light) — Insol. aq.; spar. sol. cold alc.; eas. sol. hot alc., ether, C_6H_6, CS_2 — Sublimes readily — Volatile with steam. [For review of chemistry of fluorene see ⟨1⟩.]

$\bar{C}$ is unaffected by cold conc. H_2SO_4 but on warming dis. with blue color ⟨2⟩ — $\bar{C}$ with $SbCl_5$ in CCl_4 gives green coloration ⟨3⟩ — $\bar{C}$ on fusion with 1 mole KOH at 280° yields mono-potassiumfluorene (non-volatile) [use in removal of $\bar{C}$ from anthracene, phenanthrene, etc.], which with aq. regenerates $\bar{C}$ ⟨4⟩ ⟨5⟩.

$\bar{C}$ dislvd. in 8–9 pts. warm AcOH and treated with 1.2 pts. conc. HNO_3 ($D = 1.42$) at 60–80° gives (90% yield ⟨6⟩; 79% yield ⟨7⟩) 2-nitrofluorene, ndls. from AcOH or 50% acetic ac., m.p. 156° cor. ⟨8⟩ — $\bar{C}$, added gradually to 10 pts. mixt. of equal vols. AcOH + fumg. HNO_3 ($D = 1.5$), stood 12 hrs., filtered, gives ppt. of mixt. of dinitrofluorenes; extraction with boilg. AcOH dissolves the more sol. 2,5-dinitrofluorene (23% yield ⟨9⟩), which seps. on cooling in long straw colored ndls., m.p. 207° ⟨9⟩ ⟨10⟩; the residual material (very spar. sol. in hot AcOH) (60% yield ⟨9⟩) gives on recrystn. from AcOH, acetone, or AcOEt 2,7-dinitrofluorene, m.p. 334° ⟨9⟩ [cf. ⟨11⟩ ⟨12⟩].

$\bar{C}$ on oxidation with $Na_2Cr_2O_7$ in AcOH gives (60–70% yield ⟨13⟩) fluorenone (1:9014).

Molecular compds.: $\bar{C}$ with equiv. amt. PkOH in ether or $CHCl_3$ soln. yields an unstable red brown picrate, $\bar{C}$.PkOH, m.p. 80–82° ⟨14⟩, 84° ⟨15⟩, 79–80° ⟨16⟩, 77° ⟨17⟩; $\bar{C}$ with 1,3,5-trinitrobenzene gives a cpd., $2\bar{C}$.3T.N.B., gold.-yel. tbls., m.p. 105° ⟨15⟩; $\bar{C}$ with 2,4,6-trinitrotoluene gives a cpd., $\bar{C}$.T.N.T., m.p. 85° ⟨15⟩.

Ⓓ **2-(o-Carboxybenzoyl)fluorene** [Beil. X-788]: from C̄ + phthalic anhydride + $AlCl_3$ in CS_2; cryst. from 50% alc., m.p. 227–229° ⟨18⟩, 227–230° ⟨19⟩; Neut. Eq. 314.

1:7245 ⟨1⟩ Rieveschl, Ray, *Chem. Rev.* **23,** 287–389 (1938). ⟨2⟩ Goldschmiedt, Lipschitz, *Ber.* **36,** 4036 (1903). ⟨3⟩ Hilpert, Wolf, *Ber.* **46,** 2217 (1913). ⟨4⟩ Weissgerber, *Ber.* **34,** 1659–1661 (1901). ⟨5⟩ Weger, Döring, *Ber.* **36,** 878–881 (1903). ⟨6⟩ Courtot, *Ann. chim.* (10) **14,** 49 (1930). ⟨7⟩ Kuhn, *Organic Syntheses* **13,** 74–75 (1933). ⟨8⟩ Diels, *Ber.* **34,** 1759 (1901). ⟨9⟩ Ref. 6, page 83. ⟨10⟩ Morgan, Thomason, *J. Chem. Soc.* **1926,** 2693.

⟨11⟩ Ref. 1, page 350. ⟨12⟩ Anantakrishnan, Hughes, *J. Chem. Soc.* **1935,** 1607–1608. ⟨13⟩ Huntress, Hershberg, Cliff, *J. Am. Chem. Soc.* **53,** 2721–2723 (1931). ⟨14⟩ Barbier, *Ann. chim.* (5) **7,** 487 (1876). ⟨15⟩ Kremann, *Monatsh.* **32,** 614–616 (1911). ⟨16⟩ Fittig, Schmitz, *Ann.* **193,** 136–137 (1878). ⟨17⟩ Baril, Hauber, *J. Am. Chem. Soc.* **53,** 1090 (1931). ⟨18⟩ Underwood, Walsh, *J. Am. Chem. Soc.* **57,** 940–942 (1935). ⟨19⟩ Ref. 2, page 4035.

1:7250 STILBENE $C_{14}H_{12}$ Beil. V-630

(*trans*-1,2-Diphenylethylene)

M.P. 124° **B.P. 306° cor.**

Cryst. from alc. — Insol. aq., spar. sol. cold alc.; eas. sol. ether, C_6H_6 — Sublimes; volatile with steam.

[For prepn. (50% yield) from benzoin (1:5210) by reduction with Zn dust + $HgCl_2$ in dil. alc. see ⟨1⟩; from benzyl MgCl + BzH in ether (25–35% yield) see ⟨2⟩; from benzyl-phenyl-carbinol (1:5958) on htg. 3–4 hrs. at 220–230° (64 %yield) see ⟨3⟩.] [For m.p.-compn. data on C̄ + isostilbene (the *cis* isomer) see ⟨4⟩.]

C̄ on oxidn. with $K_2Cr_2O_7$ + H_2SO_4 followed by steam distn. yields BzH (1:0195) and BzOH (1:0715) ⟨5⟩ — C̄ with Na + alc. reduces smoothly to bibenzyl (1:7149) ⟨6⟩.

C̄ decolorizes Br_2-aq. only on warming — C̄ + Br_2 in CS_2 or ether ppts. mixture of two stereoisomeric stilbene dibromides; washing with hot abs. alc. leaves insol. α-stilbene dibromide [Beil. V-602], m.p. 237°; mother liquor conts. β-stilbenedibromide [Beil. V-603], cryst. from alc., m.p. 110° ⟨7⟩ ⟨8⟩.

C̄ fused with equiv. amt. PkOH gives unstable red-brown picrate, C̄.PkOH, m.p. 94° ⟨9⟩, 90–91° ⟨10⟩, decomposing on fusion or treatment with solvents. With 1,3,5-trinitrobenzene C̄ yields a cpd., C̄.2T.N.B.; gold.-yel. ndls., m.p. abt. 107–110° ⟨11⟩; 115–120° ⟨12⟩; 120° ⟨13⟩.

1:7250 ⟨1⟩ Ballard, Dehn, *J. Am. Chem. Soc.* **54,** 3969–3970 (1932). ⟨2⟩ Adkins, Zartman, *Organic Syntheses* **17,** 89–90 (1937). ⟨3⟩ Ruggli, Lang, *Helv. Chim. Acta* **21,** 47 (1938). ⟨4⟩ Taylor, Murray, *J. Chem. Soc.* **1938,** 2079. ⟨5⟩ Zincke, *Ber.* **4,** 839 (1871). ⟨6⟩ Klages, *Ber.* **35,** 2647 (1902). ⟨7⟩ Wislicenus, Seeler, *Ber.* **28,** 2694 (1895). ⟨8⟩ Young, Pressman, Coryell, *J. Am. Chem. Soc.* **61,** 1644 (1939). ⟨9⟩ Reddelien, *J. prakt. Chem.* (2) **91,** 244 (1915). ⟨10⟩ Baril, Hauber, *J. Am. Chem. Soc.* **53,** 1090 (1931).

⟨11⟩ Pfeiffer, *Ann.* **421,** 298–299 (1916). ⟨12⟩ Ley, *Ber.* **50,** 249 (1917). ⟨13⟩ Sudborough, *J. Chem. Soc.* **109,** 1344 (1916).

1:7255 HYDROQUINONE DIBENZYL ETHER $C_{20}H_{18}O_2$ Beil. S.N. 555

M.P. 128-129° ⟨1⟩

Cryst. from 50 pts. alc. [The mono-benzyl ether (1:1539) may be separated from C̄ by its soly. in alc.]

1:7255 ⟨1⟩ Druey, *Bull. soc. chim.* (5) **2,** 1741 (1935).

1:7260 HEXAETHYLBENZENE $C_{18}H_{30}$ **Beil. V-471**

C_2H_5 (×6 on benzene ring)

M.P. 129° **B.P. 298°** cor.

White ndls. from alc.; can also be recrystd. unchanged from hot conc. H_2SO_4 ⟨1⟩ or even fumg. H_2SO_4 ⟨5⟩. Eas. sol. hot alc., ether, or AcOH.

[For prepn. in 43% yield from C_6H_6 + excess C_2H_5Cl + $AlCl_3$ see ⟨2⟩.] [For optical data on cryst. see ⟨3⟩.]

$\bar{C}$ is not attacked by alk. $KMnO_4$ alone, and on treatment with HNO_3 followed by alk. $KMnO_4$ gives only CO_2, no mellitic acid ⟨4⟩ — $\bar{C}$ (5 g.) + 2 moles $AlCl_3$ (5.6 g.) htd. together at 90° yield a mol. cpd., $\bar{C}.2AlCl_3$ ⟨5⟩ ⟨6⟩ ⟨1⟩; this is a viscous dark yel. liq. (crystg. on cooling) which does not wet glass and is much more stable to aq. than $AlCl_3$. At higher temp. it decomposes with evoln. of HCl.

$\bar{C}$ (2 g.) added at 10° in small portions to a vigorously stirred mixt. of conc. H_2SO_4 (50 ml.) + fumg. HNO_3 (D = 1.52) (15 ml.) + $CHCl_3$ (50 ml.) gave 0.3 g. (13% yield) of 1,4-dinitro-2,3,5,6-tetraethylbenzene [Beil. V-456]; white ndls. from alc., m.p. 143–145° ⟨7⟩, 144° ⟨8⟩, 145–147° ⟨9⟩.

1:7260 ⟨1⟩ Gustavson, *J. prakt. Chem.* (2) **68**, 227 (1903). ⟨2⟩ Wertypoch, Firla, *Ann.* **500**, 293–294 (1933). ⟨3⟩ Hendricks, Jefferson, *J. Optical Soc. Am.* **23**, 302 (1933). ⟨4⟩ Juettner, *J. Am. Chem. Soc.* **59**, 1474 (1937). ⟨5⟩ Schleicher, *J. prakt. Chem.* (2) **105**, 359 (1923). ⟨6⟩ Ipatieff, Komarewsky, Grosse, *J. Am. Chem. Soc.* **57**, 1723 (1935). ⟨7⟩ Smith, Harris, *J. Am. Chem. Soc.* **57**, 1292 (1935). ⟨8⟩ Jannasch, Bartels, *Ber.* **31**, 1716 (1898). ⟨9⟩ Smith, Guss, *J. Am. Chem. Soc.* **62**, 2637 (1940).

1:7265 HEXAMETHYLBENZENE $C_{12}H_{18}$ **Beil. V-450**

CH_3 (×6 on benzene ring)

M.P. 164-165° **B.P. 264°**

Pr. from C_6H_6, tbls. from alc. — $\bar{C}$ sublimes in lfts. — Sol. at 0° in 500 pts. 95% alc.; much more eas. sol. hot alc., very eas. sol. C_6H_6 — $\bar{C}$ best crystd. from boilg. $CHCl_3$ by addn. of hot 95% alc. + cooling, followed by recrystn. from its own wt. C_6H_6 ⟨1⟩ — [Note, however, that pentamethylbenzene (1:7150) is not removed by recrystn. but only by fractional distn. ⟨10⟩.]

[For prepn. (as by-product) from xylene + CH_3Cl + $AlCl_3$ see ⟨2⟩ ⟨3⟩.] [For optical data see ⟨4⟩ ⟨5⟩.]

$\bar{C}$ (2 g.) added at 0–5° in small portions to a vigorously stirred mixt. of conc. H_2SO_4 (50 ml.) + fumg. HNO_3 (D = 1.52) (15 ml.) + $CHCl_3$ (50 ml.), waiting between additions for red color to fade to yellow, prod. poured onto ice, gave 0.6 g. (22% yield) dinitroprehnitene (5,6-dinitro-1,2,3,4-tetramethylbenzene) [Beil. V-430], pr. from alc., m.p. 176° ⟨6⟩.

Molecular cpds.: $\bar{C}$.PkOH, or.-yel. pl., m.p. 170° ⟨7⟩ ⟨8⟩ ⟨9⟩ [loses $\bar{C}$ at 100–110°; alc. removes PkOH ⟨9⟩]; $\bar{C}$.1,3,5-trinitrobenzene, yel. ndls. from AcOH, m.p. 174–175° ⟨10⟩ ⟨8⟩.

1:7265 ⟨1⟩ Smith, MacDougall, *J. Am. Chem. Soc.* **51,** 3002 (1929). ⟨2⟩ Smith, *Organic Syntheses* **10,** 35–39 (1930). ⟨3⟩ Smith, Dobrovolny, *J. Am. Chem. Soc.* **48,** 1418–1419 (1926). ⟨4⟩ Hendricks, Jefferson, *J. Optical Soc. Am.* **23,** 302 (1933). ⟨5⟩ Brockway, Robinson, *J. Chem. Soc.* **1939,** 1326. ⟨6⟩ Smith, Harris, *J. Am. Chem. Soc.* **57,** 1292 (1935). ⟨7⟩ Friedel, Crafts, *Ann. chim.* (6) **10,** 417–418 (1887). ⟨8⟩ Hertel, *Ann.* **451,** 191 (1926). ⟨9⟩ Baril, Hauber, *J. Am. Chem. Soc.* **53,** 1089 (1931). ⟨10⟩ Pfeiffer, *Ann.* **412,** 298 (1916).

1:7270 1,3,5-TRIPHENYLBENZENE $C_{24}H_{18}$ **Beil. V-737**

M.P. 174.3-174.5° cor. ⟨1⟩

White ndls. from AcOH or lgr.; tbls. from ether — Insol. aq., spar. sol. aq. alc., more easily in abs. alc., ether, CS_2; eas. sol. C_6H_6.

[For prepn. in 65–85% yield from acetophenone (1:5515) by htg. with K pyrosulfate + conc. H_2SO_4 for 30 hrs. at 45° see ⟨2⟩ (70% yield ⟨3⟩) and nature of yellow by-product ⟨3⟩; prepn. in alm. quant. yield from phenylacetylene (1:7425) by htg. with 5 moles 33% aq. CH_3NH_2 (or $C_2H_5.NH_2$) in s.t. for 5 hrs. at 260° see ⟨4⟩.] [For crystallographic data see ⟨5⟩.]

$\bar{C}$ is unattacked by aq. $K_2Cr_2O_7 + H_2SO_4$; with CrO_3 in AcOH for $\frac{1}{2}$ hr. at 70° gives good yield BzOH (1:0715) ⟨6⟩.

$\bar{C}$ in 10 pts. boilg. AcOH treated with $2\frac{1}{2}$ pts. fumg. HNO_3 (D = 1.52) during 15 minutes at not over 120° gives on cooling 1-(*p*-nitrophenyl)-3,5-diphenylbenzene (70% yield), white ndls. from AcOH, m.p. 142–143° cor. ⟨7⟩.

1:7270 ⟨1⟩ Baxter, Hale, *J. Am. Chem. Soc.* **59,** 507–508 (1937). ⟨2⟩ Odell, Hines, *J. Am. Chem. Soc.* **35,** 82 (1913). ⟨3⟩ Le Fevre, *J. Chem. Soc.* **1938,** 1467. ⟨4⟩ Krassuski, Kiprianow, *Cent.* **1926,** I, 895. ⟨5⟩ Orelkin, Lonsdale, *Proc. Roy. Soc. London* **A-144,** 630–636 (1934). ⟨6⟩ Mellin, *Ber.* **23,** 2533–2534 (1890). ⟨7⟩ Vorländer, Fischer, Wille, *Ber.* **62,** 2837 (1929).

1:7275 XANTHONE $C_{13}H_8O_2$ **Beil. XVII-354**
(Dibenzo-γ-pyrone;
" benzophenone-*o*-oxide ")

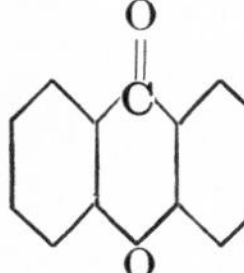

M.P. 174° u.c. **B.P. 351°**

Long colorless ndls. from alc., or by repeated crystn. from AcOH or nitrobenzene ⟨1⟩ — Insol. cold aq., alk. or dil. acids; sol. hot alc.; sol. $CHCl_3$, C_6H_6; spar. sol. ether — Easily sublimable but spar. volatile with steam.

$\bar{C}$ is sol. in conc. H_2SO_4 with yel. color and intense light-blue fluores.

[For prepn. in 61–63% yield by htg. phenyl salicylate (1:1415) see ⟨2⟩ ⟨3⟩.]

$\bar{C}$, on boilg. with 40 pts. 10% EtOH/NaOH with gradual addn. of excess Zn dust and pptn. by finally pouring into aq., or on reduction with alc. + 3% Na/Hg (91–95% yield ⟨4⟩), or Al isopropylate in isopropyl alc. (90% yield ⟨5⟩), gives xanthydrol (1:5205), q.v.

$\bar{C}$ does not react readily with either phenylhydrazine, hydroxylamine, or semicarbazide salts (although the sulfur analog, xanthione [Beil. XVII-357], yields the corresponding xanthone derivatives).

C̄ dislvd. in minimum amt. nitrobenzene, treated with trace of I_2 + exactly 1 mole Br_2, heated in oil bath at 80–100° until evoln. of HBr ceases, then refluxed, cooled, alc. added, pptd. solid filtered, washed with alc., recrystd. from C_6H_6, gives 3-bromoxanthone, m.p. 133° ⟨1⟩ ⟨6⟩ [2,7-dibromoxanthone: ndls. from alc., m.p. 213°].

C̄ + $HgCl_2$ in either AcOH or alc. yields mol. cpd., C̄.$HgCl_2$, colorless ndls., m.p. 229–230° to lt. brown liq. ⟨7⟩.

1:7275 ⟨1⟩ Dhar, *J. Chem. Soc.* **109,** 745 (1916). ⟨2⟩ Holleman, *Organic Syntheses, Coll. Vol.* I, 539–540 (1932). ⟨3⟩ Kny-Jones, Ward, *Analyst* **54,** 574–575 (1929). ⟨4⟩ Holleman, *Organic Syntheses, Coll. Vol.* I, 537–538 (1932). ⟨5⟩ Lund, *Ber.* **70,** 1524 (1937). ⟨6⟩ Dhar, *J. Chem. Soc.* **117,** 1060 (1920). ⟨7⟩ Anderson, Gooding, *J. Am. Chem. Soc.* **57,** 1006 (1935).

—— **d-CAMPHOR** $C_{10}H_{16}O$ **Beil. VII-101**

M.P. 179° **B.P. 209°**

See 1:5215. Genus 7: Ketones.

1:7280 ***p*-DIPHENYLBENZENE** $C_{18}H_{14}$ **Beil. V-695**
(*p*-Terphenyl)

M.P. 213° cor. **B.P. 376°** cor. ⟨1⟩
(**209°**) ⟨2⟩

White lfts. from alc., from $CHCl_3$ + acetone, from C_6H_6 + alc. (2:1), or from C_6H_6 — C̄ is very spar. sol. hot alc. or AcOH; moderately sol. ether, CS_2; eas. sol. C_6H_6; eas. sol. warm AmOAc, or nitrobenzene.

Sublimes, but is not volatile with steam — Forms no picrate — C̄ does *not* fluoresce in C_6H_6 soln. ⟨2⟩ ⟨3⟩ — C̄ gives no color with conc. H_2SO_4 ⟨2⟩.

C̄ (2 g.) in boilg. AcOH (300 ml.) oxidized with CrO_3 (6 g.) ⟨2⟩ yields *p*-phenylbenzoic acid (0.6 g.) [Beil. IX-671], ndls. from ether, m.p. 218°.

[For extensive study of preparation see ⟨4⟩; of nitration see ⟨4⟩; of bromination see ⟨4⟩ ⟨5⟩; of hydrogenation see ⟨7⟩.]

C̄ (3 g.) + BzCl (10 g.) + $AlCl_3$ (8 g.) htd. 2 hrs. at 100° gives 70% yield ⟨6⟩ *p,p'*-dibenzoyl-*p*-terphenyl [4′,4″-dibenzoylterphenyl], cryst. from nitrobenzene, then from dioxane, m.p. 294° ⟨6⟩.

1:7280 ⟨1⟩ Bachmann, Clarke, *J. Am. Chem. Soc.* **49,** 2093 (1927). ⟨2⟩ Kühn, Winterstein, *Ber.* **60,** 434 (1927). ⟨3⟩ Gerngross, Dunkel, *Ber.* **57,** 744 (1924). ⟨4⟩ France, Heilbron, Hey, *J. Chem. Soc.* **1938,** 1364–1375. ⟨5⟩ von Braun, Irmisch, Nelles, *Ber.* **66,** 1481 (1933). ⟨6⟩ Müller, Sok, *Ber.* **70,** 1992 (1937). ⟨7⟩ Corson, Ipatieff, *J. Am. Chem. Soc.* **60,** 749 (1938).

1:7285 **ANTHRACENE** $C_{14}H_{10}$ **Beil. V-656**

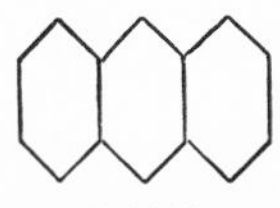

M.P. 216.4–216.7° cor. ⟨1⟩ **B.P. 339.9°** ⟨11⟩

Lfts. or tbls., usually yellowish, but when perfectly pure, colorless with beautiful violet fluorescence. [For purification see ⟨1⟩.] — Solid C̄ on long exposure to light (even in glass bottles), or in C_6H_6 or toluene soln. on exposure to ultraviolet light gives "dianthracene," $C_{28}H_{20}$ [Beil. V-663] ⟨2⟩.

C̄ is insol. aq., spar. sol. alc., AcOH, lgr.; sol. $CHCl_3$, ether; eas. sol. C_6H_6 — C̄ is sol. in $CH_3.NO_2$ (T 1.922) at 100°.

C̄ treated with Br_2 substitutes very rapidly (good source of HBr gas); C̄ suspended in CCl_4 and treated dropwise with Br_2, followed by refluxing to expel HBr, gives ppt. (83–85%

yield) of 9,10-dibromoanthracene [Beil. V-665], bright yel. ndls. from xylene, m.p. 226° u.c. ⟨3⟩.

C̄ with sublimed $AlCl_3$ (T 1.94) gives OY-S_2—Y-S_2 color — C̄ with soln. of $SbCl_5$ in CCl_4 gives green color ⟨4⟩ (also shown by carbazole). [Use in detection of C̄ in anthraquinone (1:9095) ⟨4⟩.]

Molecular cpds.: C̄ with PkOH in boilg. alc., C_6H_6, or on fusion, yields picrate, C̄.PkOH, ruby-red ndls., m.p. 138° ⟨5⟩ ⟨6⟩ [another picrate, C̄.2PkOH, red ndls., m.p. abt. 175°, is also known ⟨7⟩] — With 1,3,5-trinitrobenzene C̄ yields a cpd., C̄.T.N.B., yel.-or., m.p. 164° ⟨5⟩; scarlet, m.p. 164° ⟨8⟩ [cf. ⟨9⟩].

Ⓓ **Anthraquinone** (1:9095): In 6-in. test-tube place 0.05 g. C̄, 1.5 g. CrO_3, 4 ml. AcOH, and 1 ml. aq. Support the test-tube by a clamp so that it rests in a circular hole in a piece of asbestos board, and reflux gently for 10 min. — Pour into 20 ml. cold aq., collect ppt. on suction filter, wash with much aq., and finally with 5 ml. cold alc. Transfer ppt. to dry test-tube, boil with 10 ml. alc., cool, collect nearly white ppt. on small filter, wash with 5 ml. cold alc. Repeat in same way. Dry 15 min. at 100° ⟨10⟩; m.p. 275° u.c.; 285° cor.

1:7285 ⟨1⟩ Baxter, Hale, *J. Am. Chem. Soc.* **58,** 511 (1936); **59,** 508 (1937). ⟨2⟩ Orndorff, Cameron, *Am. Chem. J.* **17,** 658–681 (1895). ⟨3⟩ Heilbron, Heaton, *Organic Syntheses, Coll. Vol.* I, 201–203 (1932). ⟨4⟩ Hilpert, Wolf, *Ber.* **46,** 2216–2217 (1913). ⟨5⟩ Hertel, *Ann.* **451,** 191 (1926). ⟨6⟩ Baril, Hauber, *J. Am. Chem. Soc.* **53,** 1090 (1931). ⟨7⟩ Sandqvist, Hagelin, *Ber.* **51,** 1517, Note 1 (1918). ⟨8⟩ Sudborough, *J. Chem. Soc.* **109,** 1344 (1916). ⟨9⟩ Kremann, Müller, *Monatsh.* **42,** 190 (1921). ⟨10⟩ Mulliken, " Method " I, 200 (1904).
⟨11⟩ Marti, *Bull. soc. chim. Belg.* **39,** 591, 623–624 (1930).

ORDER I: SUBORDER I: GENUS 9: HYDROCARBONS

Division B, Liquids

Section 1. Aromatics

1:7400 BENZENE C_6H_6 **Beil. V-179**

B.P. 80.094° ⟨1⟩ **M.P. +5.51°** ⟨1⟩ D_4^{20} = **0.87895** ⟨2⟩ n_D^{20} = **1.50124** ⟨2⟩
D_4^{25} = **0.87366** ⟨1⟩ n_D^{25} = **1.49807** ⟨1⟩

Colorless liq. with characteristic odor — Insol. aq.; sol. org. solvents; sol. in $CH_3.NO_2$ (T 1.922) even at −20°; in aniline (T 1.922) at +20°.

$\bar{C}$ with abs. EtOH forms a binary const. boilg. mixt. (b.p. 68.25°) contg. 67.6% $\bar{C}$ + 32.4% alc. ⟨3⟩; $\bar{C}$ forms with EtOH + aq. a ternary const. boilg. mixt. (b.p. 64.85°) contg. 74.1% $\bar{C}$, 18.5% alc. + 7.4% aq. ⟨3⟩.

$\bar{C}$ htd. with Br_2 + iron catalyst yields mainly *p*-dibromobenzene, cryst. from alc., m.p. 89° — $\bar{C}$ forms with PkOH a picrate, colorless ndls., m.p. 83.9° ⟨4⟩ rapidly losing $\bar{C}$ in air.

[For microcolorimetric method for detn. of $\bar{C}$, based on the reddish-purple color produced by its nitration products in presence of ethyl methyl ketone + KOH, and with an accuracy of 5% in range 0.01–0.06 mg. $\bar{C}$ in either liq. or gas phase see ⟨5⟩.] [For use of this principle in detection of $\bar{C}$ in alc. see ⟨8⟩; for detn. of $\bar{C}$ in solvent mixtures by rapid method involving oxidn. of $\bar{C}$ by ferric salts + H_2O_2 see ⟨9⟩.]

Ⓓ ***m*-Dinitrobenzene:** In a dry tt. mix 3 drops $\bar{C}$, 1 ml. conc. HNO_3 (D = 1.42) and 1 ml. conc. H_2SO_4 (D = 1.84). Heat the mixt. until it begins to boil, and maintain this temp. for half a minute. Pour slowly into 10 ml. cold aq., cool, shake and filter the bulky flocculent ppt. on a small filter with suction, washing with aq. until filtrate is colorless. Recryst. from 8 ml. boilg. 50% alc., allowing to stand until soln. is at room temp. Collect the long pearly-white ndls. on a small filter, wash with 5 ml. cold 50% alc., dry at 50°; m.p. 89–89.5° u.c. ⟨6⟩.

Ⓓ ***o*-Benzoylbenzoic acid** (1:0720): from $\bar{C}$ + phthalic anhydride + $AlCl_3$ in CS_2; cryst. from 30% alc., m.p. 127–128° ⟨7⟩; Neut. Eq. 226. [Note that this product forms with aq. a monohydrate (1:0670), m.p. 93–94°, Neut. Eq. 244, readily losing aq. above 100° or on distn. with xylene and yielding anhydrous form (1:0720).] [For conversion to anthraquinone see (1:0720).]

1:7400 ⟨1⟩ Wojciechowski, *J. Research Natl. Bureau Standards* **19,** 347–352 (1937). ⟨2⟩ Timmermans, Martin, *J. chim. phys.* **23,** 750–753 (1926). ⟨3⟩ Young, *J. Chem. Soc.* **81,** 710 (1902). ⟨4⟩ Baril, Hauber, *J. Am. Chem. Soc.* **53,** 1089 (1931). ⟨5⟩ Schrenk, Pearce, Yant, *U. S. Bur. Mines, Rept. of Investigations,* No. 3287, Oct. 1935. ⟨6⟩ Mulliken, " Method " I, 200 (1904). ⟨7⟩ Underwood, Walsh, *J. Am. Chem. Soc.* **57,** 940–942 (1935). ⟨8⟩ Lansing, *Ind. Eng. Chem., Anal. Ed.* **7,** 184–185 (1935). ⟨9⟩ Cook, Ficklen, *Ind. Eng. Chem., Anal. Ed.* **4,** 406–408 (1932).

1:7405 TOLUENE (Methylbenzene) CH_3—⬡ C_7H_8 **Beil. V-280**

B.P. 110.80° ⟨1⟩ **M.P. −95.0° ⟨1⟩** D_4^{20} = **0.86697 ⟨1⟩** n_D^{20} = **1.49685 ⟨1⟩**
D_4^{25} = **0.86233 ⟨1⟩** n_D^{25} = **1.49385 ⟨1⟩**

Colorless liq. with characteristic odor — Insol. aq.; misc. with organic solvents; sol. in $CH_3.NO_2$ (T 1.922) even at −20°; in aniline (T 1.922) at +20°. [For soly. and refractive index data on ternary system, C̄ + EtOH + aq., see ⟨6⟩.]

C̄ oxidized with dil. aq. $KMnO_4$ (abt. 4.5%) for 8 hrs. at 95° gives (90% yield ⟨2⟩) benzoic acid (1:0715).

C̄ on dinitration (by shaking 0.5–1.0 ml. C̄ with 5 ml. of mixt. of 2 vols. conc. H_2SO_4 + 1 vol. conc. HNO_3 for 3–5 min., then pouring onto ice), reduction of crude prod. with Sn + HCl, and subsequent acetylation (all under specified conditions ⟨3⟩) yields 2,4-di-(acetylamino)toluene [Beil. XIII-133], small ndls. from hot aq. or alc., m.p. 221° u.c. ⟨3⟩. [This prod. depresses the m.p. (223°) of the corresp. deriv. from ethylbenzene (1:7410), e.g., to 190–195° ⟨3⟩.]

[For microcolorimetric method for detn. of C̄, based on reddish-blue color produced by its nitration products in presence of ethyl methyl ketone + KOH, and with an accuracy of abt. 10% in range 0.05–0.25 mg. C̄ in either liq. or vapor phase see ⟨4⟩.]

C̄ with PkOH forms a picrate, light yel. pl., m.p. 88.2° ⟨9⟩, rapidly losing C̄ in air.

Ⓓ **2,4-Dinitrotoluene:** Dis. 3 drops C̄ in 1.5 ml. fumg. HNO_3 (D = 1.5) and add immediately without cooling, 1.5 ml. fuming H_2SO_4 (10% SO_3). After half a min. pour the mixt. into 10 ml. cold aq., cool, shake until the nitration product seps. in yel.-white flocks, and then filter, washing with cold aq. Recryst. by dislvg. in 8 ml. boilg. 50% alc., cool, shake vigorously, filter, wash ppt. with 5 ml. cold 50% alc. Recryst. a second time in same way. M.p. 70–71° u.c. ⟨5⟩.

Ⓓ ***o*-(*p*-Toluyl)benzoic acid** (1:0750): from C̄ + phthalic anhydride + $AlCl_3$ in CS_2; cryst. from 30% alc. as hydrate, water being lost above 100°; m.p. 137–138° ⟨7⟩, 138–139° ⟨8⟩; Neut. Eq. 240. [This prod. can readily be ring closed yielding 2-methylanthraquinone (1:9075); for details see (1:0750).]

1:7405 ⟨1⟩ Timmermans, Martin, *J. chim. phys.* **23,** 754–755 (1926). ⟨2⟩ Ullmann, Uzbachian, *Ber.* **36,** 1798 (1903). ⟨3⟩ Ipatieff, Schmerling, *J. Am. Chem. Soc.* **59,** 1056–1059 (1937). ⟨4⟩ Yant, Pearce, Schrenk, *U. S. Bur. Mines Rept. of Investigations,* No. 3323 (1936). ⟨5⟩ Mulliken, " Method ", I, 202 (1904). ⟨6⟩ Washburn, Beguin, Beckford, *J. Am. Chem. Soc.* **61,** 1694–1695 (1939). ⟨7⟩ Underwood, Walsh, *J. Am. Chem. Soc.* **57,** 940–942 (1935). ⟨8⟩ Fieser, *Organic Syntheses, Coll. Vol.* I, 504 (1932). ⟨9⟩ Baril, Hauber, *J. Am. Chem. Soc.* **53,** 1089 (1931).

1:7410 ETHYLBENZENE $CH_3.CH_2$—⬡ C_8H_{10} **Beil. V-351**

B.P. 136.15° ⟨1⟩ **M.P. −94.4° ⟨1⟩** D_4^{20} = **0.86690 ⟨1⟩** n_D^{20} = **1.49587 ⟨1⟩**
D_4^{25} = **0.86250 ⟨1⟩** n_D^{25} = **1.49317 ⟨1⟩**

Colorless mobile liq.; insol. aq.; sol. in $CH_3.NO_2$ (T 1.922) at +20°.

C̄ on oxidn. with CrO_3 + H_2SO_4 ⟨2⟩, or by dil. HNO_3 (1 vol. conc. HNO_3 to 2 vols. aq.) ⟨3⟩, or by $KMnO_4$ yields benzoic acid (1:0715) — C̄ on oxidn. with CrO_3 in AcOH yields benzoic acid (1:0715) and acetophenone (1:5515) ⟨4⟩. [For oxidn. of C̄ by O_2 at 115–130° in liq. phase in presence of MnO_2 yielding acetophenone (1:5515), methyl-phenyl-carbinol (1:6475) and sometimes benzoic acid (1:0715) see ⟨5⟩.]

C̄ on dinitration (by shaking 0.5–1.0 ml. C̄ with 5 ml. of mixt. of 2 vols. conc. H_2SO_4 and 1 vol. conc. HNO_3 for 3–5 min. then pouring onto ice), reduction of crude prod. with Sn + HCl, and subsequent acetylation (all under specified conditions ⟨6⟩) yields 2,4-di-(acetylamino)-1-ethylbenzene [Beil. XIII-177], small ndls. from hot aq. or alc., m.p. 223° u.c. ⟨6⟩; 224° ⟨7⟩. [This prod. depresses the m.p. (221°) of the corresp. deriv. from toluene (1:7405), e.g., to 190–195° ⟨6⟩.] [C̄ (1 pt.) treated with mixt. of fumg. HNO_3 (D = 1.52) (4 pts.) + fumg. H_2SO_4 (25% SO_3) (4 pts.) ⟨8⟩ ⟨9⟩ gives (72% yield ⟨9⟩) 2,4,6-trinitro-1-ethylbenzene, ndls. from alc., m.p. 37°.] [For data on other isomeric trinitroethylbenzenes see ⟨10⟩; on dinitroethylbenzenes see ⟨11⟩; on mononitroethylbenzenes see ⟨12⟩.]

C̄ with PkOH forms a picrate, light yel. pl., m.p. 96.6° ⟨16⟩.

Ⓓ ***p*-Ethylbenzenesulfonamide** [Beil. XI-120]: Shake 0.25 ml. C̄ in tt. with 1 ml. of conc. H_2SO_4; then heat 15 min. in boilg. aq. until soln. is complete. Cool, pour into 10 ml. satd. NaCl soln., cool, shake. Filter white pasty mass and wash with 10 ml. satd. NaCl soln. Press on porous tile and dry in hot closet 25 min. Mix thoroughly with equal vol. PCl_5, and heat 10 min. at 100°. Cool, pour slowly into 5 ml. ice-water, shake and allow to settle. Decant through a wet filter, wash by decantation with 5 ml. cold aq., returning any ppt. from filter to tt. Add 2 ml. conc. NH_4OH (D = 0.90) and boil until NH_3 is expelled. Dilute with 10 ml. aq., boil, and filter hot. Cool with ice-water, shake, and collect the sulfonamide on small filter. Wash with 5 ml. cold aq. Recryst. from 5 ml. boiling aq. and dry; m.p. 109°; cf. ⟨13⟩.

Ⓓ ***o*-(4-Ethylbenzoyl)benzoic acid:** from C̄ + phthalic anhydride + $AlCl_3$ + CS_2; cryst. from dil. alc. or xylene, m.p. 122° ⟨14⟩ ⟨15⟩; Neut. Eq. 254.

Ⓓ ***o*-(4-Ethylbenzoyl)tetrachlorobenzoic acid:** from C̄ + tetrachlorophthalic anhydride + $AlCl_3$ + CS_2; cryst. from 70% alc., m.p. 172–173° ⟨15⟩; Neut. Eq. 392.

1:7410 ⟨1⟩ Timmermans, Martin, *J. chim. phys.* **23,** 758–759 (1926). ⟨2⟩ Fittig, *Ann.* **133,** 223 (1865). ⟨3⟩ Fittig, König, *Ann.* **144,** 280–281 (1867). ⟨4⟩ Friedel, Balsohn, *Bull. soc. chim.* (2) **32,** 616–617 (1879). ⟨5⟩ Senseman, Stubbs, *Ind. Eng. Chem.* **25,** 1286–1287 (1933). ⟨6⟩ Ipatieff, Schmerling, *J. Am. Chem. Soc.* **59,** 1056–1059 (1937). ⟨7⟩ O'Connor, Sowa, *J. Am. Chem. Soc.* **60,** 127 (1938). ⟨8⟩ Schultz, *Ber.* **42,** 2634 (1909). ⟨9⟩ Weisweiller, *Monatsh.* **21,** 44 (1900). ⟨10⟩ Day, *J. Chem. Soc.* **1930,** 252–256.

⟨11⟩ Brady, Day, Allam, *J. Chem. Soc.* **1928,** 978–982. ⟨12⟩ Cline, Reid, *J. Am. Chem. Soc.* **49,** 3150–3156 (1927). ⟨13⟩ Fricke, Spilker, *Ber.* **58,** 1595–1596 (1925). ⟨14⟩ Scholl, Potschiwauscheg, Lenko, *Monatsh.* **32,** 691 (1911). ⟨15⟩ Underwood, Walsh, *J. Am. Chem. Soc.* **57,** 940–942 (1935). ⟨16⟩ Baril, Hauber, *J. Am. Chem. Soc.* **53,** 1089 (1931).

1:7415 ***p*-XYLENE** (*p*-Dimethylbenzene) C_8H_{10} **Beil. V-382**

CH_3 — benzene ring — CH_3

B.P. 138.40° ⟨1⟩ **M.P. +13.35°** ⟨1⟩ D_4^{20} = **0.86100** ⟨1⟩ n_D^{20} = **1.49615** ⟨1⟩; cf. ⟨13⟩

D_4^{25} = **0.85665** ⟨1⟩ n_D^{25} = **1.49370** ⟨1⟩; cf. ⟨13⟩

C̄ is sol. in $CH_3.NO_2$ (T 1.922) even at −20°; in aniline (T 1.922) at +20°.

C̄ on oxidn. with dil. HNO_3 (e.g., 2 hrs. at 100°) gives *p*-toluic acid (1:0795) (together with some terephthalic acid (1:0910)) ⟨2⟩ ⟨3⟩ — C̄ on oxidn. with CrO_3 + H_2SO_4 or $K_2Cr_2O_7$ + H_2SO_4 yields mainly terephthalic acid (1:0910) — C̄ on oxidn. with 5% $KMnO_4$ yields terephthalic acid (1:0910). [Use in quant. detn. of C̄ alone or in mixts. with *o*-xylene (1:7430) or *m*-xylene (1:7420) ⟨4⟩.]

[For detn. of C̄ in presence of *o*-xylene and *m*-xylene by method based on f.p. lowering see ⟨4⟩.] [For sepn. of C̄ from *m*-xylene (1:7420) by high vac. distn. see ⟨12⟩.]

C̄ with PkOH gives a picrate, C̄.PkOH, lemon-yel. ndls., m.p. 90.5° ⟨11⟩. [Does not distinguish from the other xylenes.]

Ⓓ **2,3,5-Trinitro-*p*-xylene:** Add two drops $\bar{C}$ to a mixt. of 1 ml. fumg. HNO_3 (D = 1.5) with 2 ml. conc. H_2SO_4 (D = 1.84) in a dry tt.; shake, then boil gently for one min. over a small flame. Break up with a stirring rod any hard lumps which may form and pour into 10–12 ml. cold aq. Collect the solid on a very small filter and wash well with cold aq., followed by 5 ml. cold alc. Transfer to a tt. and redis. in 5 ml. alc.* (The compd. dis. quite slowly.) Cool, shake vigorously, collect the cryst. ppt. in the point of a small filter, and wash with 5 ml. cold alc. (**). Drain on a piece of porous tile, dry 15 min. at 100°; m.p. 138.5–139° u.c. ⟨5⟩, 139° ⟨6⟩. [This prod. is more sol. in acetone than corresp. deriv. of *m*-xylene (1:7420), viz., 2,4,6-trinitro-*m*-xylene, and can thus be sepd. in quant. detn. of latter as trinitro-cpd. ⟨7⟩.]

Ⓓ ***o*-(2′,5′-Dimethylbenzoyl)benzoic acid** [Beil. X-767]: from $\bar{C}$ + phthalic anhydride + $AlCl_3$ in CS_2 ⟨8⟩ or in acetylene tetrachloride ⟨9⟩ or without solvent ⟨10⟩; cryst. from C_6H_6, m.p. 149° ⟨10⟩, 132° ⟨8⟩.

Ⓓ ***o*-(2′,5′-Dimethylbenzoyl)tetrachlorobenzoic acid:** cryst. from 40% alc., m.p. 244–246° u.c., Neut. Eq. 392 ⟨8⟩ [from $\bar{C}$ + tetrachlorophthalic anhydride + $AlCl_3$ + CS_2 ⟨8⟩].

1:7415 ⟨1⟩ Timmermans, Martin, *J. chim. phys.* **23,** 756–757 (1926). ⟨2⟩ Yssel de Schepper, Beilstein, *Ann.* **137,** 302–303 (1866). ⟨3⟩ Dittmar, Kekulé, *Ann.* **162,** 340, Note (1872). ⟨4⟩ Norris, Vaala, *J. Am. Chem. Soc.* **61,** 2133–2134 (1939). ⟨5⟩ Mulliken, "Method" I, 202 (1904). ⟨6⟩ Giua, *Gazz. chim. ital.* **49,** II, 149, Note (1919). ⟨7⟩ Reichel, *Chem. Ztg.* **55,** 744 (1931). ⟨8⟩ Underwood, Walsh, *J. Am. Chem. Soc.* **57,** 940–942 (1935). ⟨9⟩ Scholl, Böttger, *Ber.* **63,** 2135 (1930). ⟨10⟩ Barnett, Low, *Ber.* **64,** 52 (1931).

⟨11⟩ Baril, Hauber, *J. Am. Chem. Soc.* **53,** 1089 (1931). ⟨12⟩ von Elbe, Scott, *Ind. Eng. Chem., Anal. Ed.* **10,** 284–286 (1938). ⟨13⟩ White, Rose, *Bur. Standards J. Research* **9,** 718 (1932).

1:7420 *m*-XYLENE (*m*-Dimethylbenzene) — C_8H_{10} — Beil. V-370

CH_3

CH_3

B.P. 139.30° ⟨1⟩ **M.P. −47.4°** ⟨1⟩ D_4^{20} = **0.86407** ⟨1⟩ n_D^{20} = **1.49749** ⟨1⟩; cf. ⟨2⟩
D_4^{25} = **0.85979** ⟨1⟩ n_D^{25} = **1.49509** ⟨1⟩; cf. ⟨2⟩

$\bar{C}$ is sol. in $CH_3.NO_2$ (T 1.922) even at −20°; in aniline (T 1.922) at +20°.

$\bar{C}$ on boiling with dil. HNO_3 (1 conc. HNO_3:2 aq.) is unattacked ⟨3⟩ but with stronger acid (2 vols. conc. HNO_3:3 vols. aq.) ⟨4⟩ yields *m*-toluic acid (1:0705) — $\bar{C}$ on oxidn. with CrO_3 + H_2SO_4 or with $KMnO_4$ (95% yield ⟨18⟩) yields isophthalic acid (1:0900). [Use in detn. of $\bar{C}$ by $KMnO_4$ oxidn. under specified conditions ⟨5⟩.]

[For sepn. of pure $\bar{C}$ from tech. xylene via selective sulfonation, fractional crystn. of *m*-xylenesulfonic acid (or its salts) and subsequent selective hydrolysis, regenerating $\bar{C}$ see ⟨6⟩ ⟨7⟩ ⟨8⟩.] [For m.p.-compn. diagrams of system, $\bar{C}$ + *o*-xylene (1:7430), see ⟨9⟩.]

$\bar{C}$ with PkOH forms a picrate, $\bar{C}$.PkOH, lemon-yel. ndls., m.p. 90–91.5° ⟨10⟩ [does not distinguish from *o*-xylene (1:7430) or *p*-xylene (1:7415)].

Ⓓ **2,4,6-Trinitro-*m*-xylene** [Beil. V-381]: Nitrate 2 drops $\bar{C}$ exactly as for *p*-xylene following directions literally except that the ppt. at the point marked (**) should again be recrystd. from 10 ml. 95% alc.; m.p. 181–182° u.c. ⟨11⟩ ⟨12⟩. [Use in quant. detn. of $\bar{C}$ ⟨13⟩ ⟨14⟩.]

Ⓓ ***o*-(2′,4′-Dimethylbenzoyl)tetrachlorobenzoic acid:** cryst. from 80% alc., m.p. 222–224° u.c. ⟨15⟩; Neut. Eq. 392 [from $\bar{C}$ + tetrachlorophthalic anhydride + $AlCl_3$ +

CS_2 ⟨15⟩]. [The corresponding prod. from C̄ + phthalic anhydride + $AlCl_3$ in CS_2, viz., *o*-(2′,4′-dimethylbenzoyl)benzoic acid, is reported with very divergent values for m.p., viz., 126° ⟨15⟩, 130–133° ⟨16⟩, and 143° ⟨17⟩ and is unsatisfactory as a deriv. for identification of C̄.]

1:7420 ⟨1⟩ Timmermans, Hennaut-Roland, *J. chim. phys.* **27,** 402–403 (1930). ⟨2⟩ White, Rose, *Bur. Standards J. Research* **9,** 717 (1932). ⟨3⟩ Fittig, Bieber, *Ann.* **156,** 237 (1870). ⟨4⟩ Reuter, *Ber.* **17,** 2028–2029 (1884). ⟨5⟩ Norris, Vaala, *J. Am. Chem. Soc.* **61,** 2133–2134 (1939). ⟨6⟩ Clarke, Taylor, *J. Am. Chem. Soc.* **45,** 830–833 (1923). ⟨7⟩ Patterson, McMillan, Somerville, *J. Chem. Soc.* **125,** 2488–2490 (1924). ⟨8⟩ Nakatsuchi, *J. Soc. Chem. Ind., Japan* **32,** Suppl. binding 335–336 (1929); *Chem. Abs.* **24,** 4768 (1930). ⟨9⟩ Nakatsuchi, *J. Soc. Chem. Ind., Japan* **32,** Suppl. binding, 333–335 (1929); *Chem. Abs.* **24,** 4768 (1930). ⟨10⟩ Baril, Hauber, *J. Am. Chem. Soc.* **53,** 1089 (1931).

⟨11⟩ Mulliken, "Method" I, 202 (1904). ⟨12⟩ Vorio, Spoerri, *J. Am. Chem. Soc.* **60,** 935 (1938). ⟨13⟩ Reichel, *Chem. Ztg.* **55,** 744 (1931). ⟨14⟩ Sharapova, Proschin, *Cent.* **1936,** I, 4770–4771; *Chem. Abs.* **29,** 7872 (1935). ⟨15⟩ Underwood, Walsh, *J. Am. Chem. Soc.* **57,** 940–942 (1935). ⟨16⟩ Fieser, Martin, *J. Am. Chem. Soc.* **58,** 1445 (1936). ⟨17⟩ Dougherty, Gleason, *J. Am. Chem. Soc.* **52,** 1027 (1930). ⟨18⟩ Ullmann, Uzbachian, *Ber.* **36,** 1798 (1903).

1:7425 PHENYLACETYLENE (Phenylethyne) C_6H_5—C≡C.H C_8H_6 **Beil. V-511**

B.P. 141.7° ⟨1⟩ **M.P. −48 to −40°** ⟨2⟩ D^{25}_{25} = **0.9246** ⟨1⟩ n^{25}_D = **1.5517** ⟨1⟩

[For prepn. of C̄ from β-bromostyrene via distn. with molten KOH (67–70% yield) see ⟨3⟩ ⟨4⟩; via Na in liq. NH_3 (96% yield crude) ⟨1⟩; via $NaNH_2$ in liq. NH_3 (64% yield) see ⟨5⟩.]

C̄ adds Br_2 (T 1.91). [C̄ in $CHCl_3$ at 0° treated with Br_2 in $CHCl_3$ yields phenylacetylene dibromide (α,β-dibromostyrene) [Beil. V-478], b.p. 136–138° at 17 mm. ⟨6⟩ ⟨7⟩; the prod. which would corresp. to addn. of 2 Br_2 is unknown.] [For detn. of C̄ via $KBr/KBrO_3$ titration (results 11% low) see ⟨8⟩] — C̄ treated with 1 mole I_2 in alc. ⟨1⟩ or KI soln. ⟨9⟩ gives excellent yield phenylacetylene diiodide (α,β-diiodostyrene) [Beil. V-478], m.p. 75.4–75.8° ⟨1⟩, 76° ⟨9⟩.

C̄ treated with $NH_4OH/CuCl$ (T 1.96-A) yields pale yel. floc. ppt. ⟨10⟩ of $C_6H_5.C{\equiv}C.Cu$, which when dry explodes on htg. [For use in either gravimetric or volumetric detn. of C̄ see ⟨11⟩.] [This cuprous phenylacetylide on warming with aq. $CuCl_2$ (88% yield ⟨12⟩) or aq. $K_3Fe(CN)_6$ (65% yield ⟨13⟩) gives diphenyldiacetylene $C_6H_5.C{\equiv}C.C{\equiv}C.C_6H_5$ [Beil. V-693], cryst. from AcOH or alc., m.p. 87–88° — C̄ with alc. $AgNO_3$ (T 1.96-A) yields gelatinous white ppt. — C̄ on treatment with alk. K_2HgI_4 (T 1.96-B) or alk. $Hg(CN)_2$ ⟨14⟩ gives (90% yield) of bis-(phenylethynyl)mercury, $(C_6H_5.C{\equiv}C)_2Hg$, white lfts. from 95% alc., m.p. 124.5–125° ⟨15⟩, 124.2–124.6° ⟨1⟩ — C̄ in dry ether evolves H_2 on treatment with Na yielding $C_6H_5.C{\equiv}C.Na$.

C̄ is resinified by conc. HNO_3 or conc. H_2SO_4 — C̄ on shaking with aq. H_2SO_4 (3 vols. H_2SO_4:1 vol. aq.) slowly dissolves to brown soln. which on dilution with aq. separates methyl phenyl ketone (acetophenone) (1:5515) ⟨16⟩.

C̄ on ozonolysis ⟨17⟩ ⟨18⟩ yields benzoic acid (1:0715) and formic acid (1:1005).

1:7425 ⟨1⟩ Vaughn, *J. Am. Chem. Soc.* **56,** 2064–2065 (1934). ⟨2⟩ Manchot, Haas, *Ann.* **399,** 150, Note 2 (1918). ⟨3⟩ Hessler, *Organic Syntheses, Coll. Vol.* I, 428–430 (1932); *J. Am. Chem. Soc.* **44,** 425–426 (1922). ⟨4⟩ Rupe, Rinderknecht, *Ann.* **442,** 66 (1925). ⟨5⟩ Vaughn, Vogt, Nieuwland, *J. Am. Chem. Soc.* **56,** 2120–2122 (1934). ⟨6⟩ Taylor, *J. Chem. Soc.* **1937,** 305. ⟨7⟩ Nef, *Ann.* **308,** 273 (1899). ⟨8⟩ Lucas, Pressman, *Ind. Eng. Chem., Anal. Ed.* **10,** 140–142 (1938). ⟨9⟩ Peratoner, *Gazz. chim. ital.* **22,** II, 69 (1892). ⟨10⟩ Glaser, *Ann.* **154,** 158 (1870).

⟨11⟩ Hein, Meyer, *Z. anal. Chem.* **72,** 30–31 (1927). ⟨12⟩ Straus, Kollek, *Ber.* **59,** 1680–1681 (1926). ⟨13⟩ Straus, *Ann.* **342,** 223–224 (1905). ⟨14⟩ Vaughn, *J. Am. Chem. Soc.* **55,** 3456 (1933). ⟨15⟩ Johnson, McEwen, *J. Am. Chem. Soc.* **48,** 474 (1926). ⟨16⟩ Friedel, Balsohn, *Bull. soc. chim.* (2) **35,** 55–56 (1881). ⟨17⟩ Hurd, Christ, *J. Org. Chem.* **1,** 144–145 (1937). ⟨18⟩ Paillard, Wieland, *Helv. Chim. Acta* **21,** 1361–1362 (1938).

1:7430 **o-XYLENE** (o-Dimethylbenzene) [structure: benzene ring with two adjacent $-CH_3$ groups] C_8H_{10} **Beil. V-362**

B.P. 144.05° ⟨1⟩ **M.P. −25.0°** ⟨1⟩
D_4^{20} = **0.88011** ⟨1⟩; cf. ⟨5⟩ n_D^{20} = **1.50547** ⟨1⟩; cf. ⟨5⟩

C̄ is sol. in $CH_3.NO_2$ (T 1.922) even at −20°; in aniline (T 1.922) at +20°.

C̄ on long boiling with dil. HNO_3 (1 pt. conc. HNO_3 + 2 pts. aq.) ⟨2⟩ yields *o*-toluic acid (1:0690) but by $CrO_3 + H_2SO_4$ is completely oxidized to $CO_2 + H_2O$ — C̄ with $KMnO_4$ gives phthalic acid (1:0820) [use under specified conditions for quant. detn. of C̄ ⟨3⟩]; but some *o*-toluic acid (1:0690) may also be formed as well as benzoic acid (1:0715) ⟨4⟩. [The rate of oxidation of *o*-toluic acid to phthalic acid is same as rate of oxidn. of C̄ to *o*-toluic ⟨4⟩.]

[For isolation of C̄ from the isomeric *m*- and *p*-xylenes via differential hydrolysis of their sulfonic acids, or isolation, purification and hydrolysis of Na or Ca salts see ⟨6⟩ ⟨13⟩.] [For m.p.-compn. diagrams of systems: C̄ + *m*-xylene (1:7420) or C̄ + *p*-xylene (1:7415) see ⟨7⟩.]

C̄ with PkOH forms a picrate, C̄.PkOH, lemon-yel. ndls., m.p. 88.5° ⟨8⟩ [does not distinguish C̄ from *m*-xylene (1:7420) or *p*-xylene (1:7415)].

Ⓓ **1,2-Dimethylbenzene-4-sulfonamide** [Beil. XI-121]: from C̄ (0.25 ml.) treated exactly as described under ethylbenzene (1:7410); m.p. 143.5–144.0° u.c. ⟨9⟩ ⟨10⟩ ⟨11⟩. [1,2-dimethylbenzene-3-sufonamide has m.p. 165° ⟨11⟩.]

Ⓓ ***o*-(2′,3′-Dimethylbenzoyl)tetrachlorobenzoic acid**: cryst. from 70% alc., m.p. 177.5–178.5° u.c. ⟨12⟩; Neut. Eq. 392 [from C̄ + tetrachlorophthalic anhydride + $AlCl_3$ + CS_2 ⟨12⟩].

1:7430 ⟨1⟩ Miller, *Bull. soc. chim. Belg.* **41,** 217–219 (1932). ⟨2⟩ Fittig, Bieber, *Ann.* **156,** 240–242 (1870). ⟨3⟩ Norris, Vaala, *J. Am. Chem. Soc.* **61,** 2133–2134 (1939). ⟨4⟩ Nemzow, Schenderowitsch, *Cent.* **1936,** II, 4242. ⟨5⟩ White, Rose, *Bur. Standards J. Research* **9,** 717 (1932). ⟨6⟩ Nakatsuchi, *J. Soc. Chem. Ind., Japan* **33,** Suppl. binding 65–66B (1930); *Chem. Abs.* **24,** 2733 (1930). ⟨7⟩ Nakatsuchi, *J. Soc. Chem. Ind., Japan* **32,** Suppl. binding 333–335B (1929); *Chem. Abs.* **24,** 4768 (1930). ⟨8⟩ Baril, Hauber, *J. Am. Chem. Soc.* **53,** 1089 (1931). ⟨9⟩ Mulliken, " Method " I, 202 (1904). ⟨10⟩ Patterson, McMillan, Somerville, *J. Chem. Soc.* **125,** 2489 (1924).

⟨11⟩ Lauer, *J. prakt. Chem.* (2) **138,** 89 (1933). ⟨12⟩ Underwood, Walsh, *J. Am. Chem. Soc.* **57,** 940–942 (1935). ⟨13⟩ Clarke, Taylor, *J. Am. Chem. Soc.* **45,** 830–833 (1923).

1:7435 **STYRENE** (Phenylethylene; vinylbenzene) [structure: benzene ring —CH=CH₂] C_8H_8 **Beil. V-474**

B.P. 145-145.8° ⟨1⟩ **M.P. −33°** ⟨1⟩ D_4^{20} = **0.9090** ⟨1⟩ $n_D^{20.05}$ = **1.54633** ⟨1⟩

[For prepn. (38–41% yield) by distn. of cinnamic acid (1:0735) see ⟨2⟩; for prepn. from α,β-dibromoethyl ethyl ether + C_6H_5MgBr (89% yield) and for review of all previous prepns. see ⟨1⟩.]

Strongly refractive liq. with odor simultaneously reminiscent of benzene and of naphthalene — Very spar. sol. aq.; misc. with alc., ether; sol. MeOH, CS_2, acetone; sol. in $CH_3.NO_2$ (T 1.922) even at −10°.

C̄ can be retained in monomolecular form only with difficulty, e.g., by stabilization with small traces of antioxidants such as hydroquinone, etc. [The polymerization of C̄ in presence of O_2 is inhibited by hydroquinone even at 100° but the latter is without effect on the thermal polymerization in absence of O_2; see ⟨3⟩.]

C̄ polymerizes to glassy mass of " metastyrene " on stdg.; this change is greatly accelerated by light, heat, or drop of H_2SO_4. No attempt will be made here to distinguish between the many styrene polymers.

C̄ adds Br_2 (T 1.91). [C̄ in ether treated at 0° with 1 mole Br_2 in ether in direct sunlight gives (98% yield ⟨4⟩) styrene dibromide (α,β-dibromoethylbenzene) [Beil. V-356], lfts. or ndls. from 80% alc., m.p. 73–74°.] [For detn. of C̄ by titration of CCl_4 soln. with standard Br_2/AcOH soln. see ⟨5⟩.]

C̄ added to AcOH susp. of NaSCN + anhydrous $CuSO_4$ yields styrene dithiocyanate, white cryst. from alc., m.p. 102.5–103.0° ⟨6⟩.

C̄ on oxidn. with $K_2Cr_2O_7$ + H_2SO_4 (T 1.72) yields benzoic acid (1:0715); C̄ on reduction with Na + boilg. EtOH ⟨7⟩ or on hydrogenation using 10% palladium black as catalyst ⟨1⟩ yields ethylbenzene (1:7410). [Hydrogenation with 10% platinum black as catalyst ⟨1⟩ yields ethylcyclohexane (1:8460) ⟨1⟩.]

1:7435 ⟨1⟩ Waterman, de Kok, *Rec. trav. chim.* **53,** 1133–1138 (1934). ⟨2⟩ Abbott, Johnson, *Organic Syntheses, Coll. Vol.* I, 430–432 (1932). ⟨3⟩ Breitenbach, Springer, Horeischy, *Ber.* **71,** 1438–1441 (1938). ⟨4⟩ Evans, Morgan, *J. Am. Chem. Soc.* **35,** 57 (1913). ⟨5⟩ Williams, *J. Chem. Soc.* **1938,** 247. ⟨6⟩ Dermer, Dysinger, *J. Am. Chem. Soc.* **61,** 750 (1939). ⟨7⟩ Klages, Keil, *Ber.* **36,** 1632 (1903).

1:7440 CUMENE (Isopropylbenzene) C_9H_{12} **Beil. V-393**

$(CH_3)_2CH-C_6H_5$

B.P. 152.5° ⟨1⟩; cf. ⟨2⟩ **M.P. −96.2°** ⟨2⟩ ⟨3⟩
D_4^{20} = **0.8633** ⟨2⟩ n_D^{20} = **1.49157** ⟨2⟩; cf. ⟨3⟩

C̄ on oxidn. with dil. HNO_3 ⟨4⟩ or CrO_3 + H_2SO_4 ⟨5⟩ yields benzoic acid (1:0715).

C̄, shaken with 2 vols. conc. H_2SO_4 until complete soln. occurs, poured into satd. NaCl soln. and pptd. Na salt converted with PCl_5 to corresponding sulfonyl chloride and thence with NH_4OH to sulfonamide ⟨7⟩ gives 1-isopropylbenzene sulfonamide-4, m.p. 98° ⟨7⟩, 106° ⟨8⟩, 106.5–107° ⟨9⟩, 107–108° ⟨10⟩. [This product depresses the m.p. of corresp. deriv. of *n*-propylbenzene (1:7450), the eutectic mixt. (57% iso- to 43% *n*-) being claimed at 73° ⟨7⟩.]

C̄ on mononitration (by shaking 0.5–1.0 ml. C̄ with 5 ml. mixt. of equal vols. conc. H_2SO_4 + conc. HNO_3 for 3–5 min., then pouring onto ice), reduction of crude prod. with Sn + HCl, with subsequent acetylation (all under specified conditions ⟨11⟩) yields 4-acetylamino-1-isopropylbenzene, glistening flakes from hot aq. or alc., m.p. 106° ⟨11⟩, 102–102.5° ⟨12⟩. [The m.p. of a mixt. of this prod. with corresp. deriv. (m.p. 96°) from *n*-propylbenzene (1:7450) is depressed, e.g., to 90–92° for 50/50 mixt. ⟨11⟩; with corresp. prod. (m.p. 105°) from *n*-butylbenzene (1:7515) to 83–87° ⟨11⟩.] [For study of mono-, di- and trinitration of C̄ see ⟨6⟩.]

C̄ on dinitration (by shaking 0.5–1.0 ml. C̄ with 5 ml. of mixt. of 2 vols. conc. H_2SO_4 + 1 vol. conc. HNO_3 for 3–5 min., then pouring onto ice), reduction of crude with Sn + HCl, and subsequent acetylation (all under specified conditions ⟨11⟩) yields 2,4-di-(acetylamino)-1-isopropylbenzene, six-sided pr., m.p. 216° ⟨11⟩. [The m.p. of a mixt. of this prod. with corresp. deriv. (m.p. 208°) of *n*-propylbenzene (1:7450) is depressed, e.g., to 197–200° ⟨11⟩; that of a mixt. with corresp. deriv. (m.p. 214°) of *n*-butylbenzene (1:7515) is depressed, e.g., to 187–190° ⟨11⟩.] [For use of optical characteristics of the diacetylamino derivs. in identification of mixtures of isopropylbenzene (C̄) and *n*-propylbenzene (1:7450) see ⟨11⟩.]

Ⓓ **o-(4′-Isopropylbenzoyl)benzoic acid** [Beil. X₁-(336)]: cryst. from 30% alc., m.p. 133–134° ⟨13⟩ ⟨14⟩; Neut. Eq. 268 [from C̄ + phthalic anhydride + $AlCl_3$ in CS_2 ⟨13⟩ ⟨14⟩].

1:7440 ⟨1⟩ Timmermans, *Bull. soc. chim. Belg.* **36,** 503 (1927). ⟨2⟩ White, Rose, *J. Research Natl. Bureau Standards* **21,** 164 (1938). ⟨3⟩ Smittenberg, Hoog, Henkes, *J. Am. Chem. Soc.* **60,** 18 (1938). ⟨4⟩ Abel, *Ann.* **63,** 308 (1847). ⟨5⟩ Fittig, Schaeffer, König, *Ann.* **149,** 324–325 (1869). ⟨6⟩ Brady, Cunningham, *J. Chem. Soc.* **1934,** 121–124. ⟨7⟩ Simons, Arder, Adams, *J. Am. Chem. Soc.* **60,** 2955 (1938). ⟨8⟩ Bogert, Fourman, *J. Am. Chem. Soc.* **55,** 4676 (1933). ⟨9⟩ Spica, *Gazz. chim. ital.* **9,** 440 (1879). ⟨10⟩ Meyer, Baur, *Ann.* **219,** 300 (1883).

⟨11⟩ Ipatieff, Schmerling, *J. Am. Chem. Soc.* **59,** 1056–1059 (1937). ⟨12⟩ Constam, Goldschmidt, *Ber.* **21,** 1159 (1888). ⟨13⟩ Underwood, Walsh, *J. Am. Chem. Soc.* **57,** 940–942 (1935). ⟨14⟩ Scholl, Potschiwauscheg, Lenko, *Monatsh.* **32,** 705 (1911).

1:7445 ANISOLE (Methyl phenyl ether) $CH_3.O—C_6H_5$ C_7H_8O **Beil. VI-138**

B.P. 153.80° ⟨1⟩ M.P. −37.5° ⟨1⟩ D_4^{20} = 0.99393 ⟨1⟩ n_D^{20} = 1.52211 ⟨1⟩

[For prepn. from phenol (1:1420) + $(CH_3)_2SO_4$ + aq. NaOH (72–75% yield) see ⟨2⟩.]

Liq. with agreeable aromatic odor; insol. aq.; sol. alc., ether; sol. in $CH_3.NO_2$ (T 1.922) at +20°.

C̄, on htg. with conc. HCl at 130°, or with conc. HI at 130–140° ⟨3⟩, or on boiling with 48% HBr in 4 vols. AcOH (85% yield ⟨4⟩), or on htg. with 1½ pts. $AlCl_3$ at 120° for three hours ⟨5⟩ yields phenol (1:1420).

C̄ (1 vol.) warmed with equal vol. conc. H_2SO_4 until sample gives clear soln. in aq., then cooled and treated with mixt. of 1 vol. fumg. HNO_3 + 1 vol. conc. H_2SO_4 while kept at room temp., then poured into aq. ⟨6⟩ ⟨7⟩, seps. ppt. of 2,4-dinitroanisole [Beil. VI-254], colorless ndls. from alc. or hot aq., m.p. 86.9°. [Note, however, that this product is known in two cryst. forms, the second m.p. 94.55° ⟨8⟩.]

C̄ with 2 moles Br_2 yields 2,4-dibromoanisole [Beil. VI-202], scales from alc., m.p. 61°.

Ⓓ **4′-Nitro-4-methoxybenzophenone** [Beil. VIII-163]: C̄ (1 ml.), *p*-nitrobenzoyl chloride (0.8 g.), dry CS_2 (1 ml.), and gran. anhyd. $AlCl_3$ (0.1 g.) are placed in a dry tt., warmed over free flame to start reaction, then refluxed *gently* under small aq. condenser for half an hour. Contents of the tube are then rinsed into a small beaker with 15 ml. aq., cooled, extd. with a 15 ml. and 5 ml. portion of ether. Combd. ether layers are shaken with 15 ml. 10% NaOH, then dried over Na_2SO_4. Evapn. of ether yields solid, recrystd. 2–3 times from 5 ml. alc. or AcOH; m.p. 120.5–121° ⟨9⟩, 121° ⟨10⟩.

Ⓓ **Anisole picrate** (C̄.PkOH): from C̄ + PkOH in $CHCl_3$; bright yel. tbls., m.p. 79–81° u.c. ⟨11⟩. [This prod. is unstable in air.]

Ⓓ ***p*-Methoxybenzenesulfonamide:** cryst. from alc., m.p. 110–111° u.c. ⟨12⟩. [From C̄ by treatment with excess chlorosulfonic acid and conversion of resultant sulfonyl chloride to sulfonamide by treatment with $(NH_4)_2CO_3$ (53% yield) ⟨12⟩.] [The m.p. of a mixt. of this prod. with the corresp. deriv. (m.p. 110–111°) from ethyl *m*-tolyl ether (1:7545) is depressed, e.g., to 99–103° ⟨12⟩.]

1:7445 ⟨1⟩ Timmermans, Hennaut-Roland, *J. chim. phys.* **32,** 521–523 (1935). ⟨2⟩ Hiers, Hager, *Organic Syntheses, Coll. Vol.* I, 50–52 (1932). ⟨3⟩ Graebe, *Ann.* **139,** 149–150 (1866). ⟨4⟩ Stoermer, *Ber.* **41,** 321–323 (1908). ⟨5⟩ Hartmann, Gattermann, *Ber.* **25,** 3531 (1892). ⟨6⟩ Meldola, Woolcott, Wray, *J. Chem. Soc.* **69,** 1330 (1896). ⟨7⟩ Griffiths, Walkey, Watson, *J. Chem. Soc.* **1934,** 631–633. ⟨8⟩ van Alphen, *Ber.* **63,** 94–95 (1930). ⟨9⟩ Underwood, Baril, Toone, *J. Am. Chem. Soc.* **52,** 4089 (1930). ⟨10⟩ von Auwers, *Ber.* **36,** 3898–3899 (1903).

⟨11⟩ Baril, Megrdichian, *J. Am. Chem. Soc.* **58,** 1415–1416 (1936). ⟨12⟩ Huntress, Carten, *J. Am. Chem. Soc.* **62,** 603 (1940).

1:7450 ***n*-PROPYLBENZENE** [benzene ring]—$CH_2.CH_2.CH_3$ C_9H_{12} **Beil. V-390**

B.P. 159.45° ⟨1⟩ **M.P. −99.2°** ⟨1⟩ D_4^{20} = **0.86214** ⟨1⟩ n_D^{20} = **1.49198** ⟨1⟩

[For prepn. (70–75% yield) from $C_6H_5.CH_2.Cl$ + diethyl sulfate see ⟨2⟩.]

C̄ on oxidn. with $K_2Cr_2O_7$ + dil. H_2SO_4 ⟨3⟩ yields benzoic acid (1:0715).

C̄ shaken with 2 vols. conc. H_2SO_4 until complete soln. occurs, poured into satd. NaCl soln. and pptd. Na salt converted with PCl_5 to the corresp. sulfonyl chloride and thence with NH_4OH to amide ⟨4⟩ gives 1-*n*-propylbenzenesulfonamide-4, m.p. 110° ⟨5⟩, 109–110° ⟨6⟩, 102.5° ⟨4⟩. [This product depresses the m.p. of the corresp. deriv. of isopropylbenzene (1:7440), the eutectic mixture (43% *n*- to 57% iso-) being claimed at 73% ⟨4⟩.]

C̄ on mononitration (by shaking 0.5–1.0 ml. with 5 ml. of mixt. of equal vols. conc. H_2SO_4 + conc. HNO_3 for 3–5 min., then pouring onto ice), reduction of crude prod. with Sn + HCl, and subsequent acetylation (all under specified conditions ⟨7⟩) yields 4-acetylamino-1-*n*-propylbenzene, pearly flakes from hot aq. or alc., m.p. 96° ⟨7⟩ ⟨8⟩. [The m.p. of a mixt. of this product with the corresp. deriv. (m.p. 106°) of isopropylbenzene is depressed, e.g., to 90–92° for a 50:50 mixt. ⟨7⟩.]

C̄ on dinitration (by shaking 0.5–1.0 ml. C̄ with 5 ml. of mixt. of 2 vols. conc. H_2SO_4 + 1 vol. conc. HNO_3 for 3–5 min., then pouring onto ice), reduction with Sn + HCl, and subsequent acetylation (all under specified conditions ⟨7⟩) yields 2,4-di-(acetylamino)-1-*n*-propylbenzene, small feathery ndls. from hot aq. or alc., m.p. 208° ⟨7⟩. [The m.p. of a mixt. of this product with corresp. deriv. (m.p. 216°) from isopropylbenzene (1:7440) is depressed, e.g., to 197–200° ⟨7⟩; that of a mixt. with corresp. deriv. (m.p. 210°) of *ter*-butylbenzene (1:7460) is depressed, e.g., to 180–185° ⟨7⟩.] [For use of optical characteristics of the diacetylamino derivs. in identification of mixts. of *n*-propylbenzene (C̄) and isopropylbenzene (1:7440) see ⟨7⟩.]

Ⓓ ***o*-(4′-*n*-Propylbenzoyl)benzoic acid** [Beil. X_1-(366)]: ndls. from 30% alc. or dil. HCl, m.p. 125–126° ⟨9⟩ ⟨10⟩; Neut. Eq. 268 [from C̄ + phthalic anhydride + $AlCl_3$ in CS_2 ⟨9⟩ ⟨10⟩].

Ⓓ ***n*-Propylbenzene picrate:** C̄.PkOH, yel. plates, m.p. 103.5° ⟨11⟩.

1:7450 ⟨1⟩ Timmermans, Hennaut-Roland, *J. chim. phys.* **27**, 404–405 (1930). ⟨2⟩ Gilman, Catlin, *Organic Syntheses, Coll. Vol.* I, 458–460 (1932). ⟨3⟩ Fittig, Schaeffer, König, *Ann.* **149**, 325–326 (1869). ⟨4⟩ Simons, Archer, Adams, *J. Am. Chem. Soc.* **60,** 2955 (1938). ⟨5⟩ Meyer, Baur, *Ann.* **219,** 298 (1883). ⟨6⟩ Moody, *Chem. News* **79,** 81 (1899). ⟨7⟩ Ipatieff, Schmerling, *J. Am. Chem. Soc.* **59,** 1056–1059 (1937). ⟨8⟩ Baddely, Kenner, *J. Chem. Soc.* **1935**, 308. ⟨9⟩ Underwood, Walsh, *J. Am. Chem. Soc.* **57,** 940–942 (1935). ⟨10⟩ Scholl, Potschiwauscheg, Lenko, *Monatsh.* **32,** 698 (1911).

⟨11⟩ Baril, Hauber, *J. Am. Chem. Soc.* **53,** 1089 (1931).

1:7455 **MESITYLENE** (1,3,5-Trimethylbenzene) C_9H_{12} **Beil. V-406**

[benzene ring with CH_3 at positions 1, 3, 5]

B.P. 164.64° ⟨1⟩ **M.P.** ***α*-form −44.78°** ⟨1⟩ D_4^{20} = **0.8653** ⟨1⟩ n_D^{20} = **1.4991** ⟨1⟩
***β*-form −51.74°** ⟨1⟩ n_D^{25} = **1.4967** ⟨1⟩

[For prepn. of C̄ from acetone + conc. H_2SO_4 (13–15% yield) see ⟨2⟩; from tech. *m*-xylene + CH_3Cl + $AlCl_3$ at 100° (63% yield based on CH_3Cl) see ⟨3⟩; from toluene + CH_3OH + $AlCl_3$ see ⟨4⟩.]

C̄ (1 vol.) shaken with 2 vols. conc. H_2SO_4 completely dissolves in 5–10 min.; while still warm the clear yellowish liq. is poured into 4 vols. conc. HCl at 10° or lower, or onto 3 pts.

ice with vigorous stirring, pptg. (90% yield ⟨5⟩) 1,3,5-trimethylbenzenesulfonic acid (mesitylenesulfonic acid) dihydrate, snow white cryst. from 4 pts. $CHCl_3$, m.p. 78° ⟨5⟩. [This dihydrate loses its aq. over conc. H_2SO_4 at room temp. and regains it quickly in air; the m.p. of the anhydrous acid is indefinite, highest value being 98.5–100° ⟨5⟩.] [Mesitylenesulfonic acid is completely hydrolyzed to mesitylene + H_2SO_4 on htg. at 80° for 1 hr. with either conc. or 20% HCl ⟨5⟩ (dif. from pseudocumenesulfonic acid (see 1:7470), which is unaffected under these conditions); use in sepn. of C̄ from pseudocumene (1:7470) ⟨5⟩ ⟨6⟩.] [Note that refractive index of mixts. of C̄ and pseudocumene is linear function of composition (use in analysis of mixt.) ⟨5⟩; note use of refractive index of C̄ in microscopic detn. of *n* ⟨7⟩.]

C̄ treated in cold with excess Br_2 ⟨8⟩ or C̄ htd. with Br_2 + a little fumg. HNO_3 ⟨9⟩ ⟨10⟩ yields 2,4,6-tribromo-1,3,5-trimethylbenzene, ndls. from alc., pr. from C_6H_6, m.p. 224° ⟨8⟩ ⟨11⟩, 222° ⟨9⟩ ⟨10⟩. [C̄ in CCl_4 treated with 1 mole Br_2 gives (79–82% yield ⟨12⟩) of 2-bromo-1,3,5-trimethylbenzene (bromomesitylene), b.p. 105–107° at 16–17 mm.] [2,4-Dibromo-1,3,5-trimethylbenzene (from C̄ in AcOH + Br_2), forms ndls. from CCl_4, m.p. 62° ⟨10⟩, 64° ⟨13⟩.]

C̄ on oxidn. at 95° for 25–26 hrs. with aq. $KMnO_4$ gives (64% yield ⟨19⟩) trimesic acid (1:0559) ⟨19⟩.

Ⓓ **2,4,6-Trinitro-1,3,5-trimethylbenzene** (trinitromesitylene): Nitrate *one* drop of C̄ by the procedure given for *p*-xylene (1:7415), following the quantities and direction literally, except that the quantity of alc. used for recrystn. at the point marked (*) should be 15 ml.; m.p. 235° u.c. ⟨14⟩ ⟨15⟩. [For prepn. of 2-nitro-1,3,5-trimethylbenzene (nitromesitylene) by nitration of C̄ in AcOH + Ac_2O + fumg. HNO_3 (76% yield) see ⟨16⟩. It forms pale yel. cryst. from MeOH, m.p. 43–44° ⟨16⟩.]

Ⓓ ***o*-(2,4,6-Trimethylbenzoyl)·benzoic acid** [Beil. X-771]: ndls. from 80% alc., m.p. 211–212° u.c. ⟨17⟩, 212–212.5° ⟨18⟩; Neut. Eq. 268 [from C̄ + phthalic anhydride + $AlCl_3$ in CS_2 ⟨17⟩].

1:7455 ⟨1⟩ Mair, Schicktanz, *Bur. Standards J. Research* **11,** 673–674 (1933). ⟨2⟩ Adams, Hufferd, *Organic Syntheses, Coll. Vol.* I, 334–338 (1932). ⟨3⟩ Norris, Rubinstein, *J. Am. Chem. Soc.* **61,** 1169 (1939). ⟨4⟩ Norris, Ingraham, *J. Am. Chem. Soc.* **60,** 1422 (1938). ⟨5⟩ Smith, Cass, *J. Am. Chem. Soc.* **54,** 1606–1608 (1932). ⟨6⟩ Ref. 1, page 671. ⟨7⟩ Kunz, Spulnik, *Ind. Eng. Chem., Anal. Ed.* **8,** 485 (1936). ⟨8⟩ Fittig, Storer, *Ann.* **147,** 11 (1868). ⟨9⟩ Datta, Chatterjee, *J. Am. Chem. Soc.* **38,** 2552 (1916). ⟨10⟩ Varma, Subrahmanian, *J. Indian Chem. Soc.* **13,** 192–193 (1936).

⟨11⟩ Smith, Moyle, *J. Am. Chem. Soc.* **58,** 6 (1936). ⟨12⟩ Smith, *Organic Syntheses* **11,** 24–25 (1931). ⟨13⟩ Süssenguth, *Ann.* **215,** 248 (1882). ⟨14⟩ Mulliken, " Method " I, 201 (1904). ⟨15⟩ Hinkel, Ayling, Morgan, *J. Chem. Soc.* **1931,** 1172. ⟨16⟩ Powell, Johnson, *Organic Syntheses* **14,** 68–70 (1934). ⟨17⟩ Underwood, Walsh, *J. Am. Chem. Soc.* **57,** 940–942 (1935). ⟨18⟩ Gresly, Meyer, *Ber.* **15,** 639 (1882). ⟨19⟩ Ullmann, Uzbachian, *Ber.* **36,** 1799 (1903).

1:7460 *ter*-BUTYLBENZENE $C_{10}H_{14}$ **Beil. V-415**

$$(CH_3)_3C-C_6H_5$$

CH₃ / CH₃—C—⟨benzene ring⟩ / CH₃

B.P. 168.8° ⟨1⟩ **M.P. −58°** ⟨1⟩ D_4^{20} = **0.8671** ⟨2⟩ n_D^{20} = **1.4925** ⟨2⟩
D_{25}^{25} = **0.8623** ⟨3⟩ n_D^{25} = **1.4905** ⟨3⟩

C̄, on mononitration (by shaking 0.5–1.0 ml. C̄ with 5 ml. of mixt. of equal vols. conc. H_2SO_4 and conc. HNO_3 for 3–5 min. and then pouring onto ice), reduction of crude prod. with Sn + HCl, and subsequent acetylation (all under specified conditions ⟨4⟩) yields 4-acetylamino-1-*ter*-butylbenzene, pearly flakes from hot aq. or dil. alc., m.p. 170° u.c. ⟨4⟩; 168–170° ⟨5⟩; 169–170° ⟨6⟩. [For detailed study of mononitration of C̄ see ⟨6⟩.]

C̄, on dinitration (by shaking 0.5–1.0 ml. C̄ with 5 ml. of mixt. of 2 vols. conc. H_2SO_4 and 1 vol. conc. HNO_3 for 3–5 min. and then pouring onto ice), reduction of crude prod. with Sn + HCl, and subsequent acetylation (all under specified conditions ⟨4⟩) yields 2,4-di-(acetylamino)-1-*ter*-butylbenzene, rect. pr., m.p. 210° u.c. ⟨4⟩ ⟨7⟩. [The m.p. of a mixt. of this product (m.p. 210°) with the corresp. deriv. (m.p. 214°) from *n*-butylbenzene (1:7515) is sharply depressed, e.g., to 180–185° ⟨4⟩; that of a mixt. with corresp. deriv. (m.p. 208°) from *n*-propylbenzene (1:7450) is depressed to 185–189° ⟨4⟩.]

C̄ (1 pt.) stirred for 5 hrs. at 60° with mixt. of 2 pts. by wt. of HNO_3 (D = 1.51) and 3 pts. by wt. conc. H_2SO_4 then poured onto ice, gives 2,4-dinitro-*ter*-butylbenzene, white pr. from alc., m.p. 61–62° ⟨8⟩.

1:7460 ⟨1⟩ Huffman, Parks, Daniels, *J. Am. Chem. Soc.* **52,** 1548 (1930). ⟨2⟩ Grosse, Ipatieff, *J. Am. Chem. Soc.* **57,** 2418 (1935). ⟨3⟩ McKenna, Sowa, *J. Am. Chem. Soc.* **59,** 471 (1937). ⟨4⟩ Ipatieff, Schmerling, *J. Am. Chem. Soc.* **59,** 1056–1059 (1937). ⟨5⟩ Potts, Carpenter, *J. Am. Chem. Soc.* **61,** 664 (1939). ⟨6⟩ Craig, *J. Am. Chem. Soc.* **57,** 195–197 (1935). ⟨7⟩ Bowden, *J. Am. Chem. Soc.* **60,** 646 (1938). ⟨8⟩ Shoesmith, Mackie, *J. Chem. Soc.* **1928,** 2336–2337.

1:7465 *p*-MENTHANE

(Hexahydro-*p*-cymene;
4-Isopropyl-1-methylcyclohexane)

$C_{10}H_{20}$ **Beil. V-47**

CH₃–CH(cyclohexane ring: H₂C, H₂C, CH₂, CH₂)–CH–CH(CH₃)₂

Ordinary	**B.P. 167-168°** cor. ⟨1⟩	D_4^{20} = **0.8038** ⟨2⟩	n_D^{20} = **1.4395** ⟨2⟩
		D_4^{25} = **0.8061** ⟨3⟩	n_D^{25} = **1.4370** ⟨3⟩
trans	**B.P. 168.5°** ⟨4⟩	D_4^{20} = **0.816** ⟨4⟩	n_D^{20} = **1.45149** ⟨4⟩
cis	**B.P. 161.0°** ⟨4⟩	D_4^{20} = **0.792** ⟨4⟩	n_D^{20} = **1.43931** ⟨4⟩

Liquid with faint peppermint odor — Ordinary C̄ is mixt. of *cis* and *trans* stereoisomers in proportions varying according to method of preparation [cf. ⟨5⟩].

C̄ on htg. in s.t. with HNO_3 (D = 1.1) at 115–120° is said to yield 1,8-dinitro-*p*-menthane, m.p. 107.5–108.5° ⟨6⟩.

1:7465 ⟨1⟩ Sabatier, Murat, *Ann. chim.* (9) **4,** 277 (1915). ⟨2⟩ Brown, Durand, Marvel, *J. Am. Chem. Soc.* **58,** 1596 (1936). ⟨3⟩ Adams, Marshall, *J. Am. Chem. Soc.* **50,** 1972 (1928). ⟨4⟩ Skita, Schneck, *Ber.* **55,** 149 (1922). ⟨5⟩ Keats, *J. Chem. Soc.* **1937,** 2003–2007. ⟨6⟩ Konowalow, *Cent.* **1906,** II, 343.

1:7470 PSEUDOCUMENE

(1,2,4-Trimethylbenzene)

C_9H_{12} **Beil. V-400**

(benzene ring with CH₃ at 1, 2, 4)

B.P. 169.18° ⟨1⟩; cf. ⟨2⟩ **M.P. −45.0°** ⟨1⟩ D_4^{20} = **0.8762** ⟨2⟩ n_D^{20} = **1.5048** ⟨3⟩
n_D^{25} = **1.5025** ⟨2⟩

Ordinary C̄ from coal tar is always contaminated with mesitylene (1,3,5-trimethylbenzene) (1:7455).

C̄ shaken with 2 vols. conc. H_2SO_4 completely dissolves in 5–10 min.; after cooling and pouring onto ice or into conc. HCl ppts. (85% yield ⟨3⟩) pseudocumene-5-sulfonic acid

(1,2,4-trimethylbenzene-5-sulfonic acid) [Beil. XI-131], tiny white glistening pl. from 20% HCl, m.p. 111–112° (with usual 1½ H_2O); hydrate water lost on htg. at 105° for 1 hr., m.p. anhydrous cpd., 128–131° ⟨3⟩. [Of the three possible monosulfonic acids only the 5-isomer is obtd. by direct sulfonation ⟨3⟩.] [On distn. of this sulfonic acid with steam from 50% H_2SO_4 at 140°, hydrolysis occurs and C̄ is regenerated ⟨3⟩; for use of this property in separation of C̄ and mesitylene (whose sulfonic acid forms easily under same conditions but is hydrolyzed by steam at 80–90°) see ⟨3⟩ ⟨2⟩.] [Note that refractive index of mixt. of C̄ and mesitylene (1:7455) is linear function of composition of mixt. ⟨3⟩.]

C̄ treated with 3 moles Br_2 gives 3,5,6-tribromo-1,2,4-trimethylbenzene [Beil. V-403], m.p. 232° ⟨4⟩, 229–230° ⟨5⟩, 233° cor. ⟨6⟩ (lower values may be due to presence of mesitylene). [C̄ in $CHCl_3$ at 0° treated with 1 mole Br_2 gives (68% yield ⟨7⟩) 5-bromopseudocumene, cryst. from alc., m.p. 71–72°; also obtd. from pseudocumene-5-sulfonic acid (above) in aq. on treatment with Br_2 in alc. (77% yield ⟨7⟩).]

C̄ on oxidn. with CrO_3 in AcOH gives trimellitic acid (1:0551) ⟨8⟩ ⟨9⟩.

Ⓓ **3,5,6-Trinitropseudocumene** [Beil. V-405]: Nitrate two drops of C̄ by directions given for *p*-xylene (1:7415). Follow directions literally, except that more than usual care must be taken to avoid overheating during nitration. The tt. should be held some distance above the flame, and the heating interrupted before the expiration of one minute if the mixture shows signs of darkening, or if a sublimate should begin to appear on the sides of the tube; spar. sol. boilg. alc., eas. sol. C_6H_6; m.p. 184–185° ⟨10⟩ ⟨11⟩. [C̄ on nitration under specified conditions ⟨12⟩ yields 5-nitropseudocumene, cryst. from MeOH, m.p. 67–68° ⟨13⟩; 3,5-dinitropseudocumene has m.p. 171–172° ⟨11⟩.]

Ⓓ **Pseudocumene picrate** (C̄.PkOH): yel. ndls., m.p. 96–97° ⟨14⟩. [Note that this value is pract. identical with corresp. deriv. of mesitylene ⟨14⟩.]

1:7470 ⟨1⟩ Smith, Lund, *J. Am. Chem. Soc.* **52,** 4144–4150 (1930). ⟨2⟩ Mair, Schicktanz, *Bur. Standards J. Research* **11,** 671–673 (1933). ⟨3⟩ Smith, Cass, *J. Am. Chem. Soc.* **54,** 1606–1608 (1932). ⟨4⟩ Smith, Moyle, *J. Am. Chem. Soc.* **58,** 6 (1936). ⟨5⟩ R. Meyer, W. Meyer, *Ber.* **51,** 1579 (1918). ⟨6⟩ Jacobsen, *Ber.* **19,** 1222 (1886). ⟨7⟩ Ref. 4, page 8. ⟨8⟩ Schultz, *Ber.* **42,** 3604 (1909). ⟨9⟩ Morgan, Coulson, *J. Chem. Soc.* **1929,** 2554. ⟨10⟩ Mulliken, "Method" I, 201 (1904).

⟨11⟩ Ref. 8, page 3608. ⟨12⟩ Ref. 8, page 3606. ⟨13⟩ Fisher, Walling, *J. Am. Chem. Soc.* **57,** 1701 (1935). ⟨14⟩ Baril, Hauber, *J. Am. Chem. Soc.* **53,** 1089 (1931).

1:7475 BENZYL METHYL ETHER $C_8H_{10}O$ Beil. VI-431

(C₆H₅)—$CH_2.O.CH_3$

B.P. 170–171° cor. ⟨1⟩ D_4^{20} = **0.9649** ⟨1⟩ n_D^{20} = **1.5008** ⟨1⟩
167–168° u.c. ⟨1⟩ D_4^{25} = **0.9594** ⟨1⟩ n_D^{25} = **1.4983** ⟨1⟩

Sol. in $CH_3.NO_2$ (T 1.922) even at −17°. [For ease of formn. of peroxides in air see ⟨2⟩.]

Ⓓ **Benzyl methyl ether picrate** (C̄.PkOH): from $CHCl_3$ solns. of C̄ and of PkOH; sq. cream-colored pl.; m.p. 115–116° u.c. ⟨3⟩.

1:7475 ⟨1⟩ Sah, Lei, *Science Repts. Natl. Tsing Hua Univ.*, Ser. **A-1,** 195 (1932). ⟨2⟩ Clover, *J. Am. Chem. Soc.* **46,** 425–427 (1924). ⟨3⟩ Baril, Megrdichian, *J. Am. Chem. Soc.* **58,** 1415 (1936).

1:7480 METHYL *o*-TOLYL ETHER $C_8H_{10}O$ Beil. VI-352

("*o*-Cresyl" methyl ether)

$CH_3.O$—, CH_3— (on benzene ring, ortho)

B.P. 171° D_4^{20} = **0.9853** n_D^{20} = **1.505**

Liq. with arom. odor suggesting oil of wintergreen — Insol. aq., eas. sol. alc., ether — Sol. in $CH_3.NO_2$ (T 1.922) even at −18°.

C̄ on boilg. with HBr (D = 1.49) is said to yield *o*-cresol (1:1400) and CH_3Br (b.p. +4°). C̄ on oxidn. with aq. $KMnO_4$ ⟨1⟩ gives *o*-methoxybenzoic ac. (1:0685).

C̄, added dropwise to 10 pts. fumg. HNO_3 (D = 1.5) at 5–10°, poured onto ice yields ⟨2⟩ 3,5-dinitro-*o*-cresol methyl ether (3,5-dinitro-2-methoxytoluene [Beil. VI_1-(180)], lt. yel. ndls. from MeOH, m.p. 69° ⟨2⟩; m.p. 72° ⟨3⟩ ⟨4⟩; 71–72° ⟨5⟩.

Ⓓ **5-Bromo-2-methoxytoluene:** 0.31 g. C̄ in 2 ml. alc. treated dropwise during 5 min. with 0.42 g. Br_2, yields solid after 10 min., recrystd. from 8 ml. alc. giving 0.46 g. plates, m.p. 63–64° ⟨6⟩; m.p. 68° ⟨7⟩; 74–75° ⟨8⟩.

Ⓓ **Methyl *o*-tolyl ether picrate:** from $CHCl_3$ solns. of C̄ + PkOH; short lt. yel. pr., m.p. 113–114° u.c. ⟨9⟩.

Ⓓ **3-Methyl-4-methoxybenzenesulfonamide:** cryst. from alc., m.p. 137° u.c. ⟨10⟩ [from C̄ on treatment with excess chlorosulfonic ac. and conversion of resultant sulfonyl chloride to sulfonamide with $(NH_4)_2CO_3$; 84% yield ⟨10⟩]. [This deriv. depresses m.p. of corresponding deriv. (m.p. 138°) from ethyl *p*-tolyl ether (1:7535) ⟨10⟩.]

1:7480 ⟨1⟩ Bromwell, *Am. Chem. J.* **19**, 577 (1897). ⟨2⟩ Brady, Day, *J. Chem. Soc.* **123**, 2263 (1923). ⟨3⟩ Gibson, *J. Chem. Soc.* **127**, 48 (1925). ⟨4⟩ Borsche, *Ber.* **56**, 1489 (1923). ⟨5⟩ Robinson, *J. Chem. Soc.* **109**, 1086 (1916). ⟨6⟩ Underwood, Baril, Toone, *J. Am. Chem. Soc.* **52**, 4090–4091 (1930). ⟨7⟩ Bogert, Hamann, *Am. Perfumer* **25**, 19–20, 75–76 (1930); *Cent.* **1930**, II, 287. ⟨8⟩ Meldrum, Shah, *J. Chem. Soc.* **123**, 1985 (1923). ⟨9⟩ Baril, Megrdichian, *J. Am. Chem. Soc.* **58**, 1415 (1936). ⟨10⟩ Huntress, Carten, *J. Am. Chem. Soc.* **62**, 603 (1940).

1:7485 PHENETOLE $CH_3.CH_2.O$—⟨benzene ring⟩ $C_8H_{10}O$ **Beil. VI-140**
(Ethyl phenyl ether)

B.P. 172° **M.P. −33°** D_4^{20} **= 0.9666** n_D^{20} **= 1.5080**

Liq. with agreeable arom. odor; insol. aq.; sol. alc., ether; sol. in $CH_3.NO_2$ (T 1.922) at +20°; in aniline at +20°.

C̄ (10 g.) mixed with $AlCl_3$ (15 g.) evolves ht. and gives solid addn. cpd., which on htg. in open flask 3 hrs. at 120° evolves C_2H_5Cl; the residue upon acidification yields phenol (1:1420) ⟨1⟩.

Ⓓ **4′-Nitro-4-ethoxybenzophenone** [Beil. VIII-163]: from C̄ (1 ml.) + *p*-nitrobenzoyl chloride (0.8 g.) + $AlCl_3$ (0.1 g.) in CS_2 (1 ml.) by procedure given under anisole (1:7445); cryst. from alc., m.p. 110.5–111° ⟨2⟩, 112° ⟨3⟩.

Ⓓ **Phenetole picrate** (C̄.PkOH): from C̄ + PkOH in $CHCl_3$ as very light yel. sq. pl., m.p. 91–92° ⟨4⟩. [This prod. is unstable in air ⟨4⟩.]

Ⓓ ***p*-Ethoxybenzenesulfonamide:** cryst. from alc., m.p. 149–150° u.c. ⟨5⟩ [from C̄ on treatment with excess chlorosulfonic acid and conversion of resultant sulfonyl chloride to sulfonamide by treatment with $(NH_4)_2CO_3$ (78% yield) ⟨5⟩].

1:7485 ⟨1⟩ Hartmann, Gattermann, *Ber.* **25**, 3531 (1892). ⟨2⟩ Underwood, Baril, Toone, *J. Am. Chem. Soc.* **52**, 4089 (1930). ⟨3⟩ von Auwers, *Ber.* **36**, 3897 (1903). ⟨4⟩ Baril, Megrdichian, *J. Am. Chem. Soc.* **58**, 1415–1416 (1936). ⟨5⟩ Huntress, Carten, *J. Am. Chem. Soc.* **62**, 603 (1940).

1:7490 *sec*-BUTYLBENZENE ⟨benzene ring⟩—C(CH₃)(H)—$CH_2.CH_3$ $C_{10}H_{14}$ **Beil. V-414**

B.P. 172.5° ⟨1⟩ **M.P. −82.7° ⟨1⟩** n_D^{20} **= 1.4902 ⟨3⟩**
D_{25}^{25} **= 0.8577 ⟨4⟩** n_D^{25} **= 1.4880 ⟨4⟩**

C̄ on mononitration (by shaking 0.5–1.0 ml. C̄ with 5 ml. of mixt. of equal vols. conc. H_2SO_4 and conc. HNO_3 for 3–5 min., then pouring onto ice), reduction of crude prod. with

Sn + HCl, and subsequent acetylation (all under specified conditions ⟨5⟩) yields 4-acetylamino-1-*sec*-butylbenzene, pearly flakes from alc. or hot aq., m.p. 125–126° ⟨5⟩ ⟨3⟩ ⟨6⟩, 124–125° ⟨7⟩. [This prod. depresses m.p. of corresp. deriv. from cyclohexylbenzene (1:7595) ⟨5⟩.]

C̄ on dinitration (by shaking 0.5–1.0 ml. C̄ with 5 ml. of mixt. of 2 vols. conc. H_2SO_4 + 1 vol. conc. HNO_3, then pouring onto ice), reduction of crude prod. with Sn + HCl, and subsequent acetylation (all under specified conditions ⟨5⟩) yields 2,4-di-(acetylamino)-1-*sec*-butylbenzene, stout ndls. from alc. or hot aq., m.p. 192° ⟨5⟩.

C̄ on oxidn. with CrO_3 gives (70% yield ⟨8⟩) acetophenone (1:5515).

1:7490 ⟨1⟩ Timmermans, *Bull. soc. chim. Belg.* **36,** 503 (1927). ⟨3⟩ Ipatieff, Corson, Pines, *J. Am. Chem. Soc.* **58,** 921–922 (1936). ⟨4⟩ McKenna, Sowa, *J. Am. Chem. Soc.* **59,** 471 (1937). ⟨5⟩ Ipatieff, Schmerling, *J. Am. Chem. Soc.* **59,** 1056–1059 (1937). ⟨6⟩ Reilly, Hickinbottom, *J. Chem. Soc.* **117,** 120 (1920). ⟨7⟩ Barkenbus, Hopkins, Allen, *J. Am. Chem. Soc.* **61,** 2453 (1939). ⟨8⟩ Meyer, Bernhauer, *Monatsh.* **53/54,** 728 (1929).

1:7495 METHYL *p*-TOLYL ETHER $C_8H_{10}O$ **Beil. VI-392**

("*p*-Cresyl" methyl ether)

$CH_3.O-\langle\ \rangle-CH_3$

B.P. 176° D_4^{20} = **0.970** n_D^{20} = **1.512**

Sol. in $CH_3.NO_2$ (T 1.922) even at −19° — C̄ on boiling with HBr (*D* = 1.49) is said to yield *p*-cresol (1:1410) and CH_3Br (b.p. +4°).

Ⓓ ***p*-Anisic acid** (*p*-methoxybenzoic acid) (1:0805): 0.5 g. C̄, 2.5 g. conc. H_2SO_4, 37 ml. aq., and 1.75 g. powd. $K_2Cr_2O_7$ are refluxed 4 hrs., cooled, diluted with 50 ml. aq., transf. to sep. funnel, extd. with 30, 10, and 10 ml. ether. Combined ether layers shaken with 25 ml. 10% Na_2CO_3 soln., and latter acid. with 20 ml. 6 *N* HCl. Ppt. filtered, washed with 5 ml. aq., recrystd. from 50 ml. hot aq. gave 0.2 g. anisic ac., m.p. 184° ⟨1⟩.

Ⓓ **Methyl *p*-tolyl ether picrate** (C̄.PkOH): from $CHCl_3$ solns. of C̄ + PkOH; long yel.-or. pr., m.p. 88–89° u.c. ⟨2⟩.

Ⓓ **5-Methyl-2-methoxybenzenesulfonamide:** cryst. from alc.; m.p. 182° u.c. ⟨3⟩ [from C̄ on treatment with excess chlorosulfonic acid and conversion of resultant sulfonyl chloride to sulfonamide with $(NH_4)_2CO_3$; 86% yield ⟨3⟩].

1:7495 ⟨1⟩ Underwood, Baril, Toone, *J. Am. Chem. Soc.* **52,** 4092 (1930). ⟨2⟩ Baril, Megrdichian, *J. Am. Chem. Soc.* **58,** 1415 (1936). ⟨3⟩ Huntress, Carten, *J. Am. Chem. Soc.* **62,** 603 (1940).

1:7500 CINEOLE-1,8 $C_{10}H_{18}O$ **Beil. XVII-24**

("Eucalyptol")

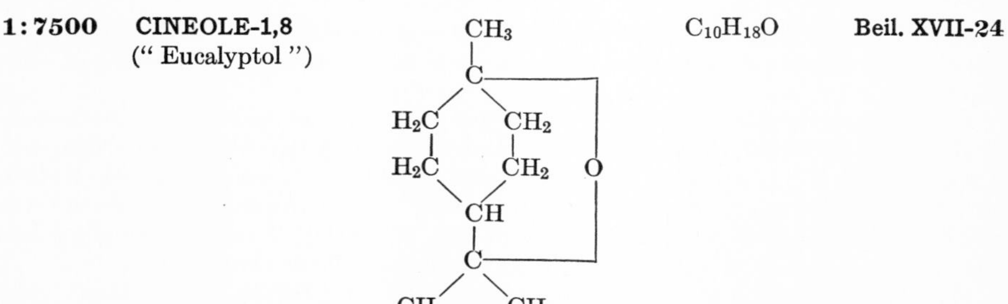

B.P. 176° **M.P. +1.3° ⟨2⟩** D_{20}^{20} = **0.9267 ⟨1⟩** n_D^{20} = **1.45839 ⟨1⟩**

Colorless liq. with characteristic camphoraceous odor — Opt. inactive (dif. from oil of eucalyptus) — C̄, though hygroscopic ⟨2⟩, is only very spar. sol. aq., aq. acids or aq. alk.

$\bar{C}$ does not react with cold PCl_3 or BzCl, gives no color with $FeCl_3$, and is inert toward phenylhydrazine or hydroxylamine hydrochloride.

$\bar{C}$ adds Br_2 (T 1.91) [yielding an unstable addn. product ⟨3⟩ ⟨4⟩]. [$\bar{C}$ in ether treated with $1\frac{1}{2}$ moles Br_2 and then with HBr gives long or.-red ndls. of an addn. prod., $\bar{C}.Br_2.HBr$ ⟨5⟩] — $\bar{C}$ treated with acidified I_2.KI soln. yields dark green cryst. of a cpd., $2\bar{C}.HI.I_2$ ⟨6⟩ — [For actn. of $\bar{C}$ with Cl_2 see ⟨7⟩.]

$\bar{C}$ in equal vol. AcOH treated at 0° with dry HCl gas yields *cis*-(dipentene dihydrochloride) [Beil. V-50], m.p. 25° ⟨8⟩; $\bar{C}$ at 40–50° treated with dry HCl gas gives mainly *trans*-(dipentene dihydrochloride) [Beil. V-50], m.p. 50–51° ⟨9⟩; while boiling $\bar{C}$ treated with HCl gas yields ⟨10⟩ dipentene (1:8165) — $\bar{C}$ in AcOH treated in cold with HBr in AcOH yields first an addn. prod., $\bar{C}$.HBr; then as main prod. *cis*-(dipentene dihydrobromide) [Beil. V-52], m.p. 39° (if solution is not cooled prod. is *trans*-(dipentene dihydrobromide), m.p. 64° ⟨8⟩). $\bar{C}$ in pet. ether treated in cold with HBr gas yields spar. sol. addn. prod., $\bar{C}$.HBr, m.p. 56–57° ⟨11⟩, 55–56° ⟨12⟩ (well suited for detection of $\bar{C}$ ⟨11⟩).

$\bar{C}$ on oxidn. with hot aq. $KMnO_4$ gives (50% yield ⟨13⟩) *d,l*-cineolic acid [Beil. XVIII-322], m.p. 204–206° ⟨14⟩.

$\bar{C}$ forms mol. cpds. with many phenols; e.g., that with 1 mole $\bar{C}$ + 1 mole *o*-cresol (1:1400) has m.p. 56.3° ⟨15⟩. [Use in detn. of *o*-cresol ⟨16⟩.] [For detn. of $\bar{C}$ via cpd. with resorcinol (1:1530) see ⟨18⟩.]

[For survey of macro-, micro- and histo-chemical methods for detection of $\bar{C}$ see ⟨17⟩.]

1:7500 ⟨1⟩ Wallach, *Ann.* **245**, 195 (1888). ⟨2⟩ Berry, Swanson, *Perfumery Essent. Oil Record* **23**, 371–373 (1932); *Chem. Abs.* **27**, 561 (1933). ⟨3⟩ Wallach, Brass, *Ann.* **225**, 302–305 (1884). ⟨4⟩ Wallach, *Ann.* **230**, 227–228 (1885). ⟨5⟩ Kehrmann, Falke, *Helv. Chim. Acta* **7**, 995 (1924). ⟨6⟩ Fromm, Fluck, *Ann.* **405**, 177–178 (1914). ⟨7⟩ Gandini, *Gazz. chim. ital.* **64**, 118–135; 302–314 (1934). ⟨8⟩ Baeyer, *Ber.* **26**, 2863 (1893). ⟨9⟩ Hall, Ritter, *Ber.* **17**, 1978 (1884). ⟨10⟩ Ref. 3, page 299.

⟨11⟩ Wallach, Gildemeister, *Ann.* **246**, 280–281 (1888). ⟨12⟩ Power, Lees, *J. Chem. Soc.* **81**, 1590 (1902). ⟨13⟩ Rupe, Hirschmann, *Helv. Chim. Acta* **16**, 509–510 (1933). ⟨14⟩ Rupe, Ronus, *Ber.* **33**, 3544, Note 1 (1900). ⟨15⟩ Berry, Swanson, *Chem. Abs.* **27**, 4975 (1933). ⟨16⟩ Sage, Fleck, *Analyst* **57**, 567–569 (1932). ⟨17⟩ Wasicky, Gmach, *Chem. Abs.* **29**, 1577–1578 (1935). ⟨18⟩ Kleber, von Rechenberg, *J. prakt. Chem.* (2) **101**, 171–176 (1920).

1:7505 *p*-CYMENE (4-Isopropyl-1-methylbenzene) $C_{10}H_{14}$ Beil. V-420

$(CH_3)_2CH—C_6H_4—CH_3$

B.P. 177.3-177.4° ⟨1⟩ M.P. −72.3° ⟨1⟩ D_4^{20} = 0.8570 ⟨1⟩ n_D^{20} = 1.4904 ⟨1⟩

Important constituent of "sulfite turpentine" — [For careful study of purifn. of $\bar{C}$ see ⟨1⟩ ⟨2⟩.] [$\bar{C}$ should not be confused with *m*-cymene or *o*-cymene which have almost same b.p.]

$\bar{C}$ on oxidn. with boilg. dil. HNO_3 (1:3) for 8 hrs. yields *p*-toluic acid (1:0795) and terephthalic acid (1:0910) ⟨3⟩, the former being separated by extn. with ether — $\bar{C}$ on oxidn. with $CrO_3 + H_2SO_4$ (T 1.72) yields terephthalic acid (1:0910) — $\bar{C}$ on oxidn. with $KMnO_4$ gives 4-(α-hydroxyisopropyl)benzoic acid (see below) — [$\bar{C}$ treated with stream of O_2 in bright daylight for 10 days yields on treatment with 35% NaOH the sodium salt of a peroxide; this prod. on boiling with aq. yields *p*-isopropylbenzaldehyde (1:0234) ⟨4⟩.]

$\bar{C}$ on careful nitration at −15 to −10° with mixt. of fumg. HNO_3 + conc. H_2SO_4 gives (50% yield ⟨5⟩) 2,6-dinitro-*p*-cymene (2,6-dinitro-4-isopropyl-1-methylbenzene), cryst. from MeOH, m.p. 54° ⟨6⟩, 38–40° ⟨5⟩. [For extensive study of mononitration of $\bar{C}$ yielding 82% 2-nitro-*p*-cymene + 8% *p*-nitrotoluene see ⟨7⟩; for its reduction to 2-amino-*p*-cymene see ⟨8⟩.]

C̄ + acetyl chloride + $AlCl_3$ in CS_2 at not above 5° gives (50–55% yield ⟨9⟩) 2-acetyl-*p*-cymene (5-isopropyl-2-methylacetophenone) (1:5550).

Ⓓ **Pentabromotoluene:** To 7 ml. Br_2 to which has been added 0.2 g. Al is dropped in, with ice cooling, 1 g. C̄. After stdg. some time, mixt. is poured into small evapg. dish and excess Br_2 expelled in water bath. The prod. is extd. with hot C_6H_6, filtered from Al, cooled. After recrystn. from C_6H_6, prod. forms colorless fine ndls., m.p. 280° ⟨10⟩. [Dif. from *p*-diethylbenzene which gives tetrabromo-*p*-diethylbenzene, m.p. 112° ⟨10⟩.]

Ⓓ **4-(α-Hydroxyisopropyl)benzoic acid** [Beil. X-272]: 2 g. C̄ is refluxed for 6 hrs. with a soln. of 6.5 g. $KMnO_4$ in 300 ml. aq., the mixt. being vigorously shaken at frequent intervals. The MnO_2 is filtered off (excess $KMnO_4$ being reduced if necessary), the soln. evapd. to dryness, and extd. with boiling alc. Addn. of dil. H_2SO_4 to the alc. soln. ppts. prod., cryst. from alc., m.p. 156–157° ⟨10⟩ ⟨11⟩.

Ⓓ ***o*-(2-Methyl-5-isopropylbenzoyl)benzoic acid:** colorless pr. from C_6H_6 or dil. alc., m.p. 123–124° ⟨12⟩, 124° cor. ⟨13⟩; Neut. Eq. 282 [from C̄ + phthalic anhydride + $AlCl_3$ ⟨13⟩ in CS_2 ⟨12⟩ (84% yield ⟨13⟩)]. [This prod. on htg. 2 hrs. at 100° with fumg. H_2SO_4 (15% SO_3), pouring into aq. gives (43% yield) 4-isopropyl-2-methylanthraquinone, yel. ndls. from alc., m.p. 113.8° cor. ⟨13⟩.]

1:7505 ⟨1⟩ Richter, Wolff, *Ber.* **63,** 1722–1724 (1930). ⟨2⟩ Mann, Montonna, Larian, *Ind. Eng. Chem.* **28,** 598–600 (1936). ⟨3⟩ Ipatieff, Corson, Pines, *J. Am. Chem. Soc.* **58,** 921 (1936). ⟨4⟩ Helberger, von Rebay, Fettback, *Ber.* **72,** 1644–1645 (1939). ⟨5⟩ Kyker, Bost, *J. Am. Chem. Soc.* **61,** 2469–2470 (1939). ⟨6⟩ Aschan, *Cent.* **1919,** I, 227. ⟨7⟩ Kobe, Doumani, *Ind. Eng. Chem.* **31,** 257–263 (1939). ⟨8⟩ Doumani, Kobe, *Ind. Eng. Chem.* **31,** 264–265 (1939). ⟨9⟩ Allen, *Organic Syntheses* **14,** 1–3 (1934). ⟨10⟩ von Auwers, *Ber.* **38,** 1707–1708 (1905).
⟨11⟩ Wallach, *Ann.* **264,** 10–11 (1891). ⟨12⟩ Underwood, Walsh, *J. Am. Chem. Soc.* **57,** 940–941 (1935). ⟨13⟩ Phillips, *J. Am. Chem. Soc.* **46,** 2534–2535 (1924).

1:7510 METHYL *m*-TOLYL ETHER ("*m*-Cresyl" methyl ether)

CH_3O–(benzene ring)–CH_3 (meta) $C_8H_{10}O$ **Beil. VI-376**

B.P. 177° cor. D_4^{20} = **0.972** n_D^{20} = **1.513**

[For prepn. from *m*-cresol (1:1730) + 30% aq. NaOH + $(CH_3)_2SO_4$ (97% yield) see ⟨1⟩.]

Sol. in $CH_3.NO_2$ (T 1.922) even at −18° — Volatile with steam.

C̄ on boilg. with HBr (D = 1.48) is said to yield *m*-cresol (1:1730) + CH_3Br (b.p. +4°).

C̄ on oxidn. with boilg. aq. $KMnO_4$ yields ⟨1⟩ *m*-methoxybenzoic ac. (1:0703).

C̄ added dropwise to HNO_3 (D = 1.52) dissolves with violent reaction; after htg. few minutes cooling and pouring into aq. gives ⟨2⟩ 2,4,6-trinitro-3-methoxytoluene [Beil. VI-388] (61% yield ⟨3⟩); colorless cryst. from alc., m.p. 92°. [C̄ on nitration in AcOH at 5–10° with HNO_3 (D = 1.5) gives 48% yield 2-nitro-5-methoxytoluene [Beil. VI-386], colorless ndls. from pet. ether, m.p. 54–55° ⟨4⟩.]

Ⓓ **Methyl *m*-tolyl ether picrate:** from $CHCl_3$ solns. of C̄ + PkOH; or. yel. pr.; m.p. 113–114° u.c. ⟨5⟩.

Ⓓ **2-Methyl-4-methoxybenzenesulfonamide:** cryst. from alc., m.p. 129–130° u.c. ⟨6⟩ [from C̄ on treatment with excess chlorosulfonic acid and conversion of resultant sulfonyl chloride to sulfonamide with $(NH_4)_2CO_3$, 69% yield ⟨6⟩].

1:7510 ⟨1⟩ Ullmann, Uzbachian, *Ber.* **36,** 1804–1805 (1903). ⟨2⟩ Blanksma, *Rec. trav. chim.* **21,** 331–332 (1902). ⟨3⟩ Holleman, *Rec. trav. chim.* **49,** 501 (1930). ⟨4⟩ Wieland, Konz, Mittasch, *Ann.* **513,** 20 (1934). ⟨5⟩ Baril, Megrdichian, *J. Am. Chem. Soc.* **58,** 1415 (1936). ⟨6⟩ Huntress, Carten, *J. Am. Chem. Soc.* **62,** 603 (1940).

1:7511 HYDRINDENE C_9H_{10} **Beil. V-486**
(Indane;
2,3-dihydroindene)

B.P. 177° D^{20}_4 = **0.9645** n^{20}_D = **1.5381**

Liquid, volatile with steam — C̄ oxidizes on long stdg. in air, espec. if exposed to light ⟨1⟩. [For study of ozonization of C̄ see ⟨7⟩.]

[For prepn. from indene (1:7522) by hydrogenation with Na + EtOH see ⟨2⟩; by reduction in MeOH soln. with H_2 + $PdCl_2$ at ord. press. (80% yield) see ⟨3⟩.]

C̄ shaken with cold conc. H_2SO_4 becomes yellowish ⟨1⟩ but does not dissolve nor resinify ⟨5⟩ (dif. from indene (1:7522)). [C̄ with equal vol. conc. H_2SO_4 at 150° gives hydrindene-2-sulfonic acid ⟨4⟩.] — C̄ is stable to cold aq. $KMnO_4$.

C̄ dislvd. in boilg. $CHCl_3$ and treated with somewhat more than 3 Br_2 (in $CHCl_3$) yields on evapn. of solvent 1,2,3-tribromoindane, cryst. from alc., m.p. 134° ⟨6⟩ — C̄ + trace solid I_2 treated with Br_2 at ord. temp. yields 4,5,6,7-tetrabromoindane, ndls. from hot alc. or pl. from toluene, m.p. 200° ⟨6⟩.

1:7511 ⟨1⟩ Weger, *Ber.* **36,** 311 (1903). ⟨2⟩ Jacobi, *J. prakt. Chem.* (2) **129,** 66 (1931). ⟨3⟩ von Braun, Arkuszewski, Köhler, *Ber.* **51,** 291 (1919). ⟨4⟩ Borsche, Pommer, *Ber.* **54,** 104–106 (1921). ⟨5⟩ Krämer, Spilker, *Ber.* **23,** 3281 (1890). ⟨6⟩ R. Meyer, W. Meyer, *Ber.* **51,** 1581–1583 (1918). ⟨7⟩ Long, Fieser, *J. Am. Chem. Soc.* **62,** 2670-2673 (1940).

1:7512 ISOPROPYL PHENYL ETHER $C_9H_{12}O$ **Beil. VI-143**
(2-Phenoxypropane)

$(CH_3)_2CH.O-C_6H_5$

B.P. 178° D^{20}_4 = **0.975** ⟨1⟩ n^{20}_D = **1.4992** ⟨1⟩
D^{20}_{20} = **0.978** ⟨2⟩ n^{25}_D = **1.4944** ⟨3⟩

Colorless oil with anise odor.

[For prepn. from phenol (1:1420) + propylene + BF_3 (54% yield) see ⟨4⟩.]

C̄, treated with soln. of conc. H_2SO_4 in AcOH ⟨5⟩, or with BF_3 (65% yield ⟨1⟩) gives o-isopropylphenol, b.p. 213–214°, sol. in alk. (dif. from C̄), and characterized (T 1.46) as o-isopropylphenoxyacetic acid, m.p. 130° ⟨5⟩.

1:7512 ⟨1⟩ Sowa, Hinton, Nieuwland, *J. Am. Chem. Soc.* **54,** 2019–2021 (1932). ⟨2⟩ Smith, *J. Am. Chem. Soc.* **56,** 718 (1934). ⟨3⟩ Sowa, Hinton, Nieuwland, *J. Am. Chem. Soc.* **55,** 3406 (1933). ⟨4⟩ Sowa, Hinton, Nieuwland, *J. Am. Chem. Soc.* **54,** 3696 (1932). ⟨5⟩ Niederl, Natelson, *J. Am. Chem. Soc.* **53,** 1932–1933 (1931).

1:7515 *n*-BUTYLBENZENE $C_{10}H_{14}$ **Beil. V-413**

$CH_3.CH_2.CH_2.CH_2-C_6H_5$

B.P. 183.10° ⟨1⟩ **M.P. −81.2°** ⟨1⟩ D^{20}_4 = **0.86065** ⟨1⟩ n^{20}_D = **1.4899** ⟨2⟩

[For prepn. of C̄ from *n*-butyl bromide + bromobenzene see ⟨3⟩.]

C̄, on mononitration (by shaking 0.5–1.0 ml. C̄ with 5 ml. of mixt. of equal vols. conc. H_2SO_4 and conc. HNO_3 for 3–5 min., then pouring onto ice), reduction of the crude prod. with Sn + HCl, and subsequent acetylation (all under specified conditions ⟨4⟩) yields 4-acetylamino-1-*n*-butylbenzene, pearly flakes from hot aq. or alc., m.p. 105° u.c. ⟨4⟩ ⟨5⟩. [The m.p. of mixts. of this deriv. (105°) with the corresp. prod. (m.p. 106°) from isopropylbenzene (1:7440) are sharply depressed; e.g., to 83–87° ⟨4⟩.]

C̄, on dinitration (by shaking 0.5–1.0 ml. C̄ with 5 ml. of mixt. of 2 vols. conc. H_2SO_4 + 1 vol. conc. HNO_3 for 3–5 min., then pouring onto ice), reduction of crude prod. with Sn +

HCl, and subsequent acetylation (all under specified conditions ⟨4⟩) yields 2,4-di-(acetyl amino)-1-*n*-butylbenzene, soft white ndls., m.p. 214° u.c. ⟨4⟩. [The m.p. of mixts. of thi deriv. (m.p. 214°) with the corresp. prod. (m.p. 216°) from isopropylbenzene (1:7440) ar sharply depressed; e.g., to 187–190° ⟨4⟩.]

Ⓓ **4′-*n*-Butylbenzophenonecarboxylic acid-2:** cryst. from 50% acetic ac. or from 30% alc., m.p. 99° ⟨6⟩, 97–98° u.c. ⟨7⟩; Neut. Eq. 282 [from C̄ + phthalic anhydride + $AlCl_3$ in CS_2 ⟨7⟩].

1:7515 ⟨1⟩ Timmermans, Martin, *J. chim. phys.* **25,** 415–416 (1928). ⟨2⟩ Schmidt, Hopp Schoeller, *Ber.* **72,** 1895 (1939). ⟨3⟩ Read, Foster, *J. Am. Chem. Soc.* **48,** 1606–1607 (1926) ⟨4⟩ Ipatieff, Schmerling, *J. Am. Chem. Soc.* **59,** 1056–1059 (1937). ⟨5⟩ Reilly, Hickinbottom *J. Chem. Soc.* **117,** 111 (1920). ⟨6⟩ Harris, Marriott, Smith, *J. Chem. Soc.* **1936,** 1840 ⟨7⟩ Underwood, Walsh, *J. Am. Chem. Soc.* **57,** 940–942 (1935).

1:7520 ***m*-DIETHYLBENZENE** $C_{10}H_{14}$ **Beil. V-42**

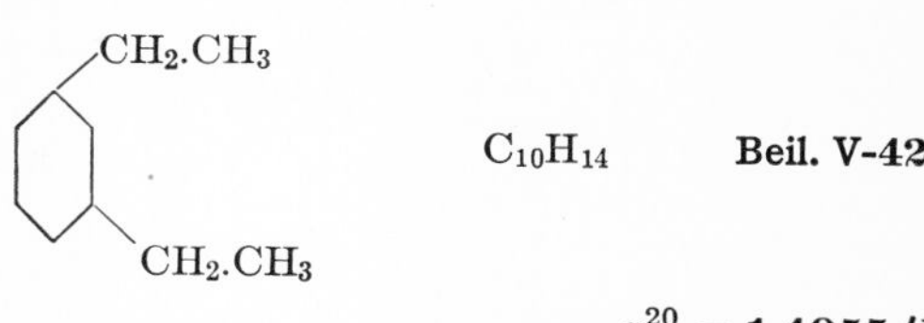

B.P. 180.55° cor. ⟨1⟩ n_D^{20} = **1.4955** ⟨1

D_{25}^{25} = **0.8579** ⟨1⟩ n_D^{25} = **1.4926** ⟨1

C̄ with Br_2 yields 2,4,5,6-tetrabromo-1,3-diethylbenzene, pr. from alc., m.p. 74° ⟨2⟩, 72 ⟨3⟩.

C̄ on appropriate nitration yields 2,4,6-trinitro-1,3-diethylbenzene, pr. from pet. ether lfts. from alc., m.p. 62° ⟨2⟩.

Ⓓ **2′,4′-Diethylbenzophenonecarboxylic acid-2:** cryst. from 30% alc., m.p. 114–116 u.c. ⟨4⟩; Neut. Eq. 282. [From C̄ + phthalic anhydride + $AlCl_3$ + CS_2 ⟨4⟩.] [Thi product htd. with 10 pts. conc. H_2SO_4 yields 1,3-diethylanthraquinone, m.p. 83–85° ⟨5⟩.

1:7520 ⟨1⟩ Copenhaver, Reid, *J. Am. Chem. Soc.* **49,** 3160 (1927). ⟨2⟩ Voswinkel, *Ber.* **21,** 283 (1888). ⟨3⟩ Ipatieff, Pines, Komarewsky, *Ind. Eng. Chem.* **28,** 223 (1936). ⟨4⟩ Underwood Walsh, *J. Am. Chem. Soc.* **57,** 940–942 (1935). ⟨5⟩ Quayle, Reid, *J. Am. Chem. Soc.* **47,** 236 (1925).

1:7522 **INDENE** C_9H_8 **Beil. V-515**

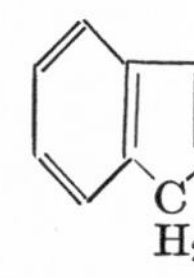

B.P. 182.4° **M.P. −2°** D_4^{20} = **0.9915** n_D^{20} = **1.5764**

D_4^{25} = **0.9813** n_D^{25} = **1.5755**

C̄ when pure is clear water white liq., but on stdg. turns yellow — C̄ even at ord. temps. in the dark begins to polymerize; polymerization occurs rapidly on htg. or in presence of catalysts. A dimer (di-indene) [Beil. V_1-(342)], cryst. from AcOH, m.p. 56–57° ⟨1⟩ can be obtd. from C̄ in 63–73% yield from C̄ by boiling 10–15 hrs. with equal vol. 23% HCl and a little pumice stone ⟨1⟩ ⟨2⟩ ⟨7⟩ ⟨8⟩ — A so-called " tri-indene," really a mixt. of lower polymers, is also known ⟨2⟩. [For studies of polyindenes see ⟨3⟩ ⟨4⟩ ⟨5⟩ ⟨6⟩ ⟨7⟩.]

C̄ adds Br_2 (T 1.91). [C̄ in 3 vols. ether treated with 1 Br_2 at 0° ⟨9⟩, or better C̄ in $CHCl_3$ treated with 1 Br_2 ⟨10⟩, gives indene dibromide (1,2-dibromoindane) [Beil. V-487], white cryst. from lgr., m.p. 31.5–32.5° ⟨10⟩ ⟨11⟩. This product with conc. H_2SO_4 gives a characteristic fuchsin-red color ⟨11⟩.] [Note that C̄ treated with Br_2-aq. in excess ⟨12⟩, or better C̄ treated with Br_2 in KBr soln. (85% yield ⟨13⟩), gives HOBr addn. prod., indene bromohydrin (2-bromo-1-hydroxyindane) [Beil. VI-574], colorless ndls. from aq. alc., m.p. 128–129° ⟨12⟩, 126–128° ⟨14⟩, also obtd. from indene dibromide (above) on boilg. with dil. acetone susp. of $MgCO_3$ ⟨15⟩.] [C̄ gives somewhat low results in $KBr/KBrO_3$ titration ⟨16⟩; but can be detd. by titration in CCl_4 with standard Br_2/CCl_4 soln. ⟨17⟩.]

C̄, treated with dry HCl gas in cold gives 1-chloroindane [Beil. V_1-(234)], which on oxidn. with CrO_3 in AcOH gives (50–60% yield on C̄) α-hydrindone (indanone-1) (1:5144) ⟨18⟩.

C̄ forms with PkOH a mol. cpd., C̄.PkOH, golden-yel. cryst., m.p. 98° ⟨9⟩ ⟨19⟩; with 1,3,5-trinitrobenzene a cpd., C̄.T.N.B., citron-yel. cryst., m.p. 101–102° ⟨20⟩ ⟨19⟩.

1:7522 ⟨1⟩ Whitby, Katz, *Can. J. Research* **4,** 358 (1931). ⟨2⟩ Risi, Gauvin, *Can. J. Research* **13-B,** 231–232 (1935). ⟨3⟩ Risi, Gauvin, *Can. J. Research* **13-B,** 228–255 (1935). ⟨4⟩ Staudinger, Ashdown, Brunner, Bruson, Wehrli, *Helv. Chim. Acta* **12,** 934–957 (1929). ⟨5⟩ Staudinger, Johner, Wiedersheim, *Helv. Chim. Acta* **12,** 958–961 (1929). ⟨6⟩ Staudinger, Johner, Schiemann, Wiedersheim, *Helv. Chim. Acta* **12,** 962–972 (1929). ⟨7⟩ Stobbé, Färber, *Ber.* **57,** 1838– 1851 (1924). ⟨8⟩ Bergmann, Taubadel, *Ber.* **65,** 463–467 (1932). ⟨9⟩ Krämer, Spilker, *Ber.* **23,** 3277–3279 (1890). ⟨10⟩ Jacobi, *J. prakt. Chem.* (2) **129,** 81 (1931).

⟨11⟩ Spilker, Dombrowsky, *Ber.* **42,** 573 (1909). ⟨12⟩ Pope, Read, *J. Chem. Soc.* **99,** 2072–2073 (1911). ⟨13⟩ Pope, Read, *J. Chem. Soc.* **101,** 760 (1912). ⟨14⟩ Porter, Suter, *J. Am. Chem. Soc.* **57,** 2024 (1935). ⟨15⟩ Ishiwara, *J. prakt. Chem.* (2) **108,** 194–195 (1924). ⟨16⟩ Cortese, *Rec. trav. chim.* **48,** 564–567 (1929). ⟨17⟩ Hammick, Langrish, *J. Chem. Soc.* **1937,** 797–801. ⟨18⟩ Pacaud, Allen, *Organic Syntheses* **18,** 47–49 (1938). ⟨19⟩ Hertel, *Ann.* **451,** 191 (1926). ⟨20⟩ Bruni, Tornani, *Gazz. chim. ital.* **35,** II, 305 (1905).

1:7525 ETHYL *o*-TOLYL ETHER $C_9H_{12}O$ Beil. VI-352

("*o*-Cresyl" ethyl ether)

$CH_3.CH_2.O$— (benzene ring) —CH_3

B.P. 184° D_4^{20} = **0.953** n_D^{20} = **1.505**

Sol. in $CH_3.NO_2$ even at −18°.

Ⓓ ***o*-Ethoxybenzoic acid** (1:0571): C̄ (0.5 g.) + conc. H_2SO_4 (2.5 g.) + aq. (37 ml.) + powd. $K_2Cr_2O_7$ (1.75 g.) are refluxed 2 hrs., cooled, diluted with 50 ml. aq., extracted with 30, 10, and 10 ml. portions of ether. The combined ether layers are then shaken with 10% Na_2CO_3 soln. (25 ml.) and the latter acidified with 6 *N* HCl (20 ml.). The product ppts. as an oil, which on drying over anhydrous Na_2SO_4 gives on evapn. of solvent 0.1 g. product; m.p. 19–19.5° ⟨1⟩.

Ⓓ **Ethyl *o*-tolyl ether picrate** (C̄.PkOH): from $CHCl_3$ solns. of C̄ and of PkOH; short lt. yel. pr.; m.p. 117.5–118.5° u.c. ⟨2⟩.

Ⓓ **3-Methyl-4-ethoxybenzenesulfonamide:** cryst. from alc.; m.p. 148–149° u.c. ⟨3⟩ [from C̄ on treatment with excess chlorosulfonic acid and conversion of resultant sulfonyl chloride to sulfonamide with $(NH_4)_2CO_3$; 71% yield ⟨3⟩]. [This derivative depresses the m.p. of the corresponding product (m.p. 148°) from hydroquinone dimethyl ether (1:7160).]

1:7525 ⟨1⟩ Underwood, Baril, Toone, *J. Am. Chem. Soc.* **52,** 4092 (1930). ⟨2⟩ Baril, Megrdichian, *J. Am. Chem. Soc.* **58,** 1415 (1936). ⟨3⟩ Huntress, Carten, *J. Am. Chem. Soc.* **62,** 603 (1940).

1:7530 BENZYL ETHYL ETHER $C_9H_{12}O$ Beil. VI-431

(Homophenetole)

(benzene ring)—$CH_2.O.CH_2.CH_3$

B.P. 184-186° cor. ⟨1⟩ D_4^{20} = **0.9478** ⟨1⟩ n_D^{20} = **1.4958** ⟨1⟩

181-183° u.c. ⟨1⟩ D_4^{25} = **0.9446** ⟨1⟩ n_D^{25} = **1.4934** ⟨1⟩

Oil, with aromatic odor — Volatile with steam.

C̄ refluxed with C_6H_6 + $1\frac{1}{2}$ pts. P_2O_5 evolves ethylene and leaves residue which on fractnl. distn. gives diphenylmethane (1:7120) ⟨2⟩.

1:7530 ⟨1⟩ Sah, Lei, *Science Repts. Natl. Tsing Hua Univ.*, Ser. **A-1**, 195 (1932). ⟨2⟩ Nef, *Ann.* **298**, 255 (1897).

1:7533 PHENYL *n*-PROPYL ETHER $C_9H_{12}O$ **Beil. VI-142**
(1-Phenoxypropane)

C_6H_5—$O.CH_2.CH_2.CH_3$

B.P. 189.3° cor. ⟨1⟩ ⟨2⟩ D^{15}_{15} = **0.9530** ⟨3⟩ n^{14}_D = **1.503** ⟨4⟩
D^{20}_{20} = **0.9494** ⟨3⟩ n^{20}_D = **1.5011** ⟨5⟩

[For prepn. in 88% yield from phenol (1:1420) + alc. KOH + *n*-propyl *p*-toluenesulfonate see ⟨2⟩.]

Ⓓ ***p*-(*n*-Propoxy)benzenesulfonamide:** cryst. from alc., m.p. 116–117° u.c. ⟨6⟩ [from C̄ on treatment with excess chlorosulfonic acid and conversion of resultant sulfonyl chloride to sulfonamide by treatment with $(NH_4)_2CO_3$ (68% yield) ⟨6⟩].

1:7533 ⟨1⟩ Perkin, *J. Chem. Soc.* **69**, 1250 (1896). ⟨2⟩ Slotta, Franke, *Ber.* **63**, 684–685 (1930). ⟨3⟩ Perkin, *J. Chem. Soc.* **69**, 1186 (1896). ⟨4⟩ Levaillant, *Compt. rend.* **188**, 263 (1929). ⟨5⟩ Ipatieff, Orloff, Petroff, *Ber.* **60**, 1007 (1927). ⟨6⟩ Huntress, Carten, *J. Am. Chem. Soc.* **62**, 603 (1940).

1:7535 ETHYL *p*-TOLYL ETHER $C_9H_{12}O$ **Beil. VI-393**
("*p*-Cresyl" ethyl ether)

$CH_3.CH_2.O$—C_6H_4—CH_3

B.P. 190.5° D^{20}_4 = **0.949** n^{20}_D = **1.505**

Ⓓ ***p*-Ethoxybenzoic acid** (1:0817): from oxidation of C̄ (0.5 g.) for 3 hrs. by process described for methyl *p*-tolyl ether (1:7495), except that final prod. is recrystd. from alc. (10 ml.) instead of aq.; yield 0.5 g., m.p. 195–195.5° ⟨1⟩.

Ⓓ **Ethyl *p*-tolyl ether picrate** (C̄.PkOH): from $CHCl_3$ solns. of C̄ and of PkOH; long yel.-or. pr., m.p. 110–111° u.c. ⟨2⟩.

Ⓓ **5-Methyl-2-ethoxybenzenesulfonamide:** cryst. from alc., m.p. 138–138.5° u.c. ⟨3⟩ [from C̄ on treatment with excess chlorosulfonic acid and conversion of resultant sulfonyl chloride to sulfonamide with $(NH_4)_2CO_3$; yield 77% ⟨3⟩]. [This deriv. depresses m.p. of corresponding product (m.p. 137°) from *o*-tolyl methyl ether (1:7480).]

1:7535 ⟨1⟩ Underwood, Baril, Toone, *J. Am. Chem. Soc.* **52**, 4092 (1930). ⟨2⟩ Baril, Megrdichian, *J. Am. Chem. Soc.* **58**, 1415 (1936). ⟨3⟩ Huntress, Carten, *J. Am. Chem. Soc.* **62**, 603 (1940).

1:7540 *ter*-AMYLBENZENE $C_{11}H_{16}$ **Beil. V-436**
(2-Methyl-2-phenylbutane)

$CH_3.CH_2$—$C(CH_3)_2$—C_6H_5

B.P. 190-191° ⟨1⟩ D^{20}_4 = **0.8737** ⟨1⟩ n^{20}_D = **1.4934** ⟨1⟩
D^{25}_{25} = **0.8550** ⟨2⟩ n^{25}_D = **1.4860** ⟨2⟩

C̄, on mononitration (by shaking 0.5–1.0 ml. C̄ with 5 ml. of mixt. of equal vols. conc. H_2SO_4 and conc. HNO_3 for 3–5 min., then pouring onto ice), reduction of crude prod. with Sn + HCl, and subsequent acetylation (all under specified conditions ⟨3⟩ ⟨1⟩) yields 4-acetylamino-1-*ter*-amylbenzene, pearly flakes from hot aq. or dil. alc., m.p. 141–142° u.c. ⟨1⟩, 142° u.c. ⟨3⟩. [Benzoylation of the reduction product yields 4-benzamino-1-*ter*-amylbenzene, m.p. 112–113° u.c. ⟨1⟩.]

C̄, on dinitration (by shaking 0.5–1.0 ml. C̄ with 5 ml. of mixt. of 2 vols. conc. H_2SO_4 + 1 vol. conc. HNO_3, then pouring onto ice), reduction of crude dinitro-cpd. with Sn + HCl, and subsequent acetylation (all under specified conditions ⟨3⟩ ⟨1⟩) yields 2,4-di-(acetylamino)-1-

ter-amylbenzene, m.p. 180–181° ⟨3⟩ ⟨1⟩. [This deriv. forms a hemihydrate, m.p. 169–170°, losing aq. on fusion, and afterward melting at 180–181° ⟨1⟩.] [M.p.'s of mixts. of this deriv. (m.p. 180–181°) with corresp. prod. (m.p. 181–182°) from 2-phenylpentane are sharply depressed ⟨1⟩.]

1:7540 ⟨1⟩ Ipatieff, Schmerling, *J. Am. Chem. Soc.* **60**, 1478–1479 (1938). ⟨2⟩ O'Connor, Sowa, *J. Am. Chem. Soc.* **60**, 127 (1938). ⟨3⟩ Ipatieff, Schmerling, *J. Am. Chem. Soc.* **59**, 1056–1059 (1937).

1:7545 ETHYL *m*-TOLYL ETHER ("*m*-Cresyl" ethyl ether) $CH_3.CH_2.O$–C_6H_4–CH_3 $C_9H_{12}O$ **Beil. VI-376**

B.P. 190.5° D_4^{20} **= 0.949** n_D^{20} **= 1.506**

Sol. in $CH_3.NO_2$ (T 1.922) even at −19°.

Ⓓ **Ethyl *m*-tolyl ether picrate** (C̄.PkOH): from $CHCl_3$ solns. of C̄ and of PkOH; or.-yel. pr., m.p. 114–115° ⟨1⟩.

Ⓓ **2-Methyl-4-ethoxybenzenesulfonamide:** cryst. from alc., m.p. 110–111° u.c. ⟨2⟩ [from C̄ on treatment with excess chlorosulfonic ac. and conversion of resultant sulfonyl chloride to sulfonamide with $(NH_4)_2CO_3$; yield 61% ⟨2⟩. [This depresses the m.p. of the corresponding product (m.p. 110–111°) from anisole (1:7445).]

1:7545 ⟨1⟩ Baril, Megrdichian, *J. Am. Chem. Soc.* **58**, 1415 (1936). ⟨2⟩ Huntress, Carten, *J. Am. Chem. Soc.* **62**, 603 (1940).

1:7547 *d*-FENCHONE $C_{10}H_{16}O$ **Beil. VII-96**

(Structural formula: CH_3–C; H_2C, C=O; CH_2, CH_3; H_2C, C; C–H, CH_3)

B.P. 193° ⟨1⟩ **M.P. +6° ⟨1⟩** D_{19}^{19} **= 0.9465 ⟨1⟩** n_D^{19} **= 1.46306 ⟨1⟩**

Oil with pleasant camphoraceous odor; volatile with steam — Opt. active; $[\alpha]_D^{20}$ = +63.0° (undiluted).

C̄ is sol. in cold conc. H_2SO_4 and repptd. unchanged on dilution ⟨1⟩. [C̄ on warming with 5 vols. conc. H_2SO_4 at 80° evolves SO_2 and gives (70% yield ⟨2⟩) 3,4-dimethylacetophenone [Beil. VII-323], b.p. 250°.] — C̄ is fairly sol. in conc. HCl *in cold* but separates on warming ⟨1⟩ — C̄ is sol. in conc. or fumg. HNO_3 and separates on dilution [C̄ is unattacked by fumg. or conc. HNO_3 even on protracted boiling; e.g., even after boiling 6 days 50% C̄ recovered unchanged ⟨3⟩]. C̄ may be purified by boiling with 3 pts. conc. HNO_3 until action ceases, pouring into aq., washing with dil. alk., steam distg. and drying ⟨1⟩. [This method, however, does not remove *d*-camphor (1:5215) which is best separated by formation of its semicarbazone, the relatively unreactive C̄ then being distd. over with steam ⟨4⟩.]

C̄ does not react with phenylhydrazine ⟨1⟩ and therefore fails to respond to Generic Test 7 for ketones — C̄ does not react with satd. aq. $NaHSO_3$ soln. (T 1.12).

C̄ on htg. at 115–130° with 3 pts. P_2O_5 ⟨5⟩ ⟨6⟩ ⟨7⟩ gives (77% yield ⟨7⟩) *m*-cymene [Beil. V-419] (*m*-isopropyltoluene), b.p. 175.6–175.8°, D_4^{20} = 0.8606, n_D^{20} = 1.4920 ⟨6⟩.

Ⓓ ***d*-Fenchone α-oxime:** m.p. 164–165° rap. htg. ⟨1⟩, 164–165° ⟨8⟩, 167° ⟨9⟩. [For prepn. from C̄ + alk. $NH_2OH.HCl$ see ⟨10⟩ ⟨11⟩.] [From the mother liquors *d*-fenchone-β-oxime, m.p. 123° has been isolated ⟨9⟩.] [*d,l*-Fenchone oxime has m.p. 158–159° ⟨12⟩.] [For characterization of C̄ via oxime in presence of *d*-camphor (1:5215) see ⟨16⟩.]

Ⓓ ***d*-Fenchone-2,4-dinitrophenylhydrazone:** or.-yel. ndls. from alc.; m.p. 140° after sintering at 125° ⟨13⟩ [cf. T 1.14].

Ⓓ ***d*-Fenchone semicarbazone:** cryst. from alc., m.p. 182–183° ⟨14⟩, 184° ⟨15⟩, after sintering at 174° ⟨14⟩ [forms slowly and in low yield (40–50%) ⟨14⟩].

1:7547 ⟨1⟩ Wallach, *Ann.* **263,** 130–136 (1891). ⟨2⟩ Marsh, *J. Chem. Soc.* **75,** 1058–1060 (1899). ⟨3⟩ Gardner, Cockburn, *J. Chem. Soc.* **73,** 708–709 (1898). ⟨4⟩ Wallach, *Ann.* **353,** 214–215 (1907). ⟨5⟩ Wallach, *Ann.* **275,** 157–159 (1893); *Ann.* **284,** 324 (1895). ⟨6⟩ Richter, Wolff, *Ber.* **63,** 1724 (1930). ⟨7⟩ Lacourt, *Bull. soc. chim. Belg.* **39,** 134–135 (1930). ⟨8⟩ Zeitschel, Todenhöfer, *J. prakt. Chem.* (2) **133,** 376 (1932). ⟨9⟩ Hückel, Sachs, *Ann.* **498,** 180 (1932). ⟨10⟩ Wallach, *Ann.* **271,** 104–105 (1892).
⟨11⟩ Wallach, *Ann.* **315,** 278, Note 1 (1901). ⟨12⟩ Ruzicka, *Ber.* **50,** 1374 (1917). ⟨13⟩ Brady, *J. Chem. Soc.* **1931,** 758. ⟨14⟩ Ref. 4, pages 210–212. ⟨15⟩ G. G. Henderson, J. A. R. Henderson, Heilbron, *Ber.* **47,** 887 (1914). ⟨16⟩ Délépine, *Bull. soc. chim.* (4) **35,** 1330–1335 (1924).

1:7548 PREHNITENE (1,2,3,4-Tetramethylbenzene) $C_{10}H_{14}$ **Beil. V-430**

[Structure: benzene ring with CH_3 groups at positions 1,2,3,4]

B.P. 204.6° cor. ⟨1⟩ n_D^{20} = **1.5202**
F.P. −6.4° ⟨2⟩

[For prepn. from pentamethylbenzene (1:7150) by Jacobsen rearr. with conc. H_2SO_4 and " flash hydrolysis " of resultant prehnitenesulfonic ac. see ⟨3⟩.]

C̄ in AcOH treated with Br_2 in AcOH ⟨4⟩ yields 5,6-dibromo-1,2,3,4-tetramethylbenzene, ndls. from alc. + $CHCl_3$, m.p. 208° ⟨4⟩, 209–211° ⟨5⟩. [Mixed m.p.'s with corresponding dibromo-derivatives of durene (1:7195) and isodurene are only very slightly depressed [cf. ⟨6⟩]. [5-Monobromoprehnitene, cryst. from pet. ether, has m.p. 26.3° ⟨2⟩.] [C̄ + Br_2 in direct sunlight at 140° yields 41% 2,3,6-trimethylbenzyl bromide, b.p. 146°_{23} ⟨3⟩.]

C̄ (10 g.) shaken with conc. H_2SO_4 (20 ml.), poured onto ice, filtered, gives 91% yield crude prehnitenesulfonic acid, purified by soln. in cold aq. and pptn. with HCl gas (70% yield); m.p. 104° ⟨8⟩.

C̄, dislvd. in $CHCl_3$ and the soln. floated on conc. H_2SO_4, rapidly stirred at 0° during dropwise addn. of fumg. HNO_3 (D = 1.5) according to ⟨9⟩, gives 80% yield ⟨10⟩ dinitroprehnitene (5,6-dinitro-1,2,3,4-tetramethylbenzene) [Beil. V-430], almost white pr. from alc., m.p. 176°. [Mixed m.p.'s with corresp. derivs. of durene (1:7195) and isodurene *are* sharply depressed ⟨6⟩.]

C̄ on oxidn. with $KMnO_4$ yields ⟨11⟩ benzene-1,2,3,4-tetracarboxylic ac. (1:0553).

C̄ + 1 mole PkOH, htd. at 100°, then recrystd. from 95% alc. yields picrate, C̄.PkOH; stout bright yellow ndls., m.p. 89.5–90.5° ⟨2⟩; 88–89° ⟨12⟩. [This picrate, on exposure to air, slowly loses C̄ with result that color fades and m.p. rises to that of PkOH ⟨12⟩.]

1:7548 ⟨1⟩ MacDougall, Smith, *J. Am. Chem. Soc.* **52,** 1999 (1930). ⟨2⟩ Smith, MacDougall, *J. Am. Chem. Soc.* **51,** 3004–3006 (1929). ⟨3⟩ Smith, Lux, *J. Am. Chem. Soc.* **51,** 2997–2999 (1929). ⟨4⟩ Smith, Moyle, *J. Am. Chem. Soc.* **55,** 1681 (1933). ⟨5⟩ Noller, *J. Am. Chem. Soc.* **56,** 1582 (1934). ⟨6⟩ Ref. 4, page 1680. ⟨7⟩ Smith, Agre, *J. Am. Chem. Soc.* **60,** 653 (1938). ⟨8⟩ Smith, Cass, *J. Am. Chem. Soc.* **54,** 1612 (1932). ⟨9⟩ Smith, Dobrovolny, *J. Am. Chem. Soc.* **48,** 1421 (1926). ⟨10⟩ Smith, Hac, *J. Am. Chem. Soc.* **56,** 477 (1934).
⟨11⟩ Ruzicka, Schillenberg, Goldberg, *Helv. Chim. Acta* **20,** 796 (1937). ⟨12⟩ Ruzicka, et al., *Helv. Chim. Acta* **15,** 1501–1502 (1932).

1:7549 ***n*-AMYLBENZENE** $C_{11}H_{16}$ **Beil. V-434**
(1-Phenylpentane)

C_6H_5—$CH_2.CH_2.CH_2.CH_2.CH_3$

B.P. 205.3° cor. ⟨1⟩ **M.P. −78.25°** ⟨1⟩ D_4^{20} = **0.85874** ⟨1⟩ n_D^{20} = **1.48847** ⟨2⟩
D_4^{25} = **0.85487** ⟨1⟩ n_D^{25} = **1.48633** ⟨2⟩

[For prepn. in 50–60% yield from benzyl MgCl + *n*-butyl *p*-toluenesulfonate see ⟨3⟩ ⟨4⟩ ⟨5⟩; from *n*-butyl phenyl ketone (1:5555) by reduction with Zn + dil. HCl (50% yield) ⟨6⟩; from *n*-amyl iodide + bromobenzene + Na (66% yield) ⟨7⟩.]

C̄ + Br_2 yields 1′,2′-dibromo-*n*-amylbenzene, lfts. from dil. alc., m.p. 64–64.5° ⟨6⟩.

1:7549 ⟨1⟩ Simon, *Bull. soc. chim. Belg.* **38,** 56 (1929). ⟨2⟩ Ref. 1, page 58. ⟨3⟩ Gilman, Robinson, *Organic Syntheses* **10,** 4–5 (1930). ⟨4⟩ Gilman, Beaber, *J. Am. Chem. Soc.* **47,** 523 (1925). ⟨5⟩ Rossander, Marvel, *J. Am. Chem. Soc.* **50,** 1495 (1928). ⟨6⟩ Stenzl, Fichter, *Helv. Chim. Acta* **17,** 679 (1934). ⟨7⟩ Ref. 1, page 49.

1:7550 **1,2,3,4-TETRAHYDRONAPHTHALENE** $C_{10}H_{12}$ **Beil. V-491**
(" Tetralin ")

B.P. 207° **F.P. −31°** D_4^{18} = **0.9732** n_D^{20} = **1.5402**

Oil, water white when freshly distd. but turning yellow and darkening with time on stdg. — C.S.T. in $CH_3.NO_2$ is −16°; sol. in aniline (T 1.922) at 20°.

C̄ on long stdg. in air or when treated at 75° for 45–50 hrs. with a stream of air forms a solid peroxide. This may be isolated by distg. off unoxidized C̄ at 1–2 mm., chilling residue, and recrystg. ppt. from mixt. of EtOAc + pet. ether (22:70) ⟨1⟩, or by shaking the oxidized C̄ with conc. aq. NaOH, filtering off thick cream of resultant sodium salt, washing with acetone, dislvg. in aq. and acidifying with dil. acetic acid ⟨2⟩. The tetralin peroxide forms white cryst., m.p. 56° ⟨1⟩ ⟨3⟩; it is insol. aq., sol. in aq. alk. from which it is repptd. by acids, even CO_2; with KI and dil. acetic ac. it liberates iodine.

C̄ (1 pt.) susp. in 480 pts. boilg. aq. and slowly treated with powd. $KMnO_4$ (8 pts.) under specified conditions ⟨4⟩ ⟨5⟩ ⟨6⟩ gives phthalonic ac. [Beil. X-857], crystg. from aq. as dihydrate, but losing aq. above 100° and when anhydrous, m.p. 145° — C̄ suspended in dil. H_2SO_4 and treated dropwise at 10–15° with 3% $KMnO_4$ soln. in amt. insufficient to oxidize all of C̄ yields ⟨7⟩ ⟨8⟩ *o*-carboxyhydrocinnamic acid [Beil. IX-872], m.p. 165.5° cor. — C̄ with dil. HNO_3 oxidizes to phthalic acid (1:0820) ⟨9⟩.

C̄ does not react with Br_2 in cold ⟨10⟩ ⟨11⟩.

[For distinction between C̄ and decahydronaphthalene (1:8476) in presence of each other, by means of color reaction with formaldehyde or furfural see ⟨12⟩.]

Ⓓ **2-(Tetrahydronaphthoyl)benzoic acid:** cryst. from 30% alc., m.p. 153–155° u.c.; Neut. Eq. 280 ⟨13⟩ [from C̄ + phthalic anhydride + $AlCl_3$ in CS_2 ⟨13⟩].

1:7550 ⟨1⟩ Nussle, Perkins, Toennies, *Am. J. Pharm.* **107,** 29–32 (1935). ⟨2⟩ Hartmann Seiberth, *Helv. Chim. Acta* **15,** 1390–1392 (1932). ⟨3⟩ Hock, Susemihl, *Ber.* **66,** 65 (1933) ⟨4⟩ Davies, Poole, *J. Chem. Soc.* **1928,** 1617–1618. ⟨5⟩ von Braun, *Ber.* **56,** 2333–2334 (1923) ⟨6⟩ Cornillot, *Ann. chim.* (10) **7,** 278–282 (1927). ⟨7⟩ Bamberger, Kitschelt, *Ber.* **23,** 156 (1890). ⟨8⟩ Green, Rowe, *J. Chem. Soc.* **113,** 970 (1918). ⟨9⟩ Does, *Cent.* **1902,** II, 111 ⟨10⟩ von Braun, Deutsch, *Ber.* **45,** 1271 (1912).

⟨11⟩ Willstätter, King, *Ber.* **46,** 533 (1913). ⟨12⟩ Castiglioni, *Z. anal. Chem.* **101,** 414–41 (1935); *Chem. Abs.* **30,** 1696 (1936). ⟨13⟩ Underwood, Walsh, *J. Am. Chem. Soc.* **57,** 940–94 (1935).

1:7555 ***n*-BUTYL PHENYL ETHER** $C_{10}H_{14}O$ **Beil. VI-14**
(1-Phenoxybutane)

$CH_3.CH_2.CH_2.CH_2.O—C_6H_5$

B.P. 206° ⟨1⟩ ⟨2⟩ D_4^{20} = **0.9515** ⟨2⟩ n_D^{20} = **1.5049** ⟨2
D^{26} = **0.9547** ⟨3⟩ n_D^{26} = **1.5019** ⟨3

[For prepn. from phenol (1:1420) + aq. 10% NaOH + *n*-butyl *p*-toluenesulfonat (80% yield ⟨1⟩; 73% yield ⟨2⟩) see ⟨1⟩ ⟨2⟩ — Sol. in $CH_3.NO_2$ (T 1.922) even at −17°.]

$\bar{C}$ treated in small portions with 1 mole $AlCl_3$, with cooling, stood 36 hrs. at room temp and treated with ice + HCl, product dissolved in 10% NaOH, repptd. with HCl, washe dried and distd. gives *p-n*-butylphenol (1:1771), b.p. 278° and *o*-butylphenol, b.p. 238 D^{22} = 0.973, n_D^{22} = 1.5205 ⟨3⟩.

Ⓓ ***n*-Butyl phenyl ether picrate** ($\bar{C}$.PkOH): light yel. hexag. pl. from $CHCl_3$, m.p. 110–11 u.c. ⟨4⟩ [from $\bar{C}$ + sl. excess of PkOH in $CHCl_3$ ⟨4⟩; this picrate is unstable in air

Ⓓ ***p*-(*n*-Butoxy)benezenesulfonamide:** cryst. from alc., m.p. 103–104° u.c. ⟨5⟩ [from by treatment with excess chlorosulfonic acid and conversion of resultant sulfon chloride to sulfonamide with $(NH_4)_2CO_3$; 35% yield ⟨5⟩].

1:7555 ⟨1⟩ Slotta, Franke, *Ber.* **63,** 684–685 (1930). ⟨2⟩ Sekera, Marvel, *J. Am. Chem. Soc.* **5** 348 (1933). ⟨3⟩ Smith, *J. Am. Chem. Soc.* **56,** 1419 (1934). ⟨4⟩ Baril, Megrdichian, *J. Am Chem. Soc.* **58,** 1415 (1936). ⟨5⟩ Huntress, Carten, *J. Am. Chem. Soc.* **62,** 603 (1940).

1:7560 **VERATROLE** $C_8H_{10}O_2$ **Beil. VI-77**
(Pyrocatechol dimethyl ether;
o-dimethoxybenzene)

$C_6H_4(OCH_3)_2$

B.P. 207° **M.P. +22.5°** D_4^{20} = **1.080**

[For prepn. in 95% yield from pyrocatechol (1:1520) + aq. MeOH + KOH + (CH_3) SO_4 see ⟨1⟩; from guaiacol (1:1405) similarly in 95% yield see ⟨2⟩.]

$\bar{C}$ (1 pt.) in equal vol. AcOH treated dropwise with ice cold soln. of conc. HNO_3 (1¼ pt.) i aq. (2½ pts.), stirred 2 hrs., first at 0°, then at room temp. gives (81.5% yield ⟨3⟩), 4-nitr veratrole (4-nitro-1,2-dimethoxybenzene) [Beil. VI-789], yel. ndls. from MeOH on addn. aq., m.p. 95–96° ⟨3⟩; 96° ⟨4⟩. [This 4-nitroveratrole on further nitration with fumg. HN (6 pts.) yields ⟨5⟩ ⟨6⟩ 4,5-dinitroveratrole (4,5-dinitro-1,2-dimethoxybenzene) [Beil. VI-792 citron-yel. ndls. from alc., m.p. 131° ⟨6⟩; and this nitrated again with mixt. of fumg. HN (2.5 pts.) + conc. H_2SO_4 (2.5 pts.) at 0° gives ⟨5⟩ 3,4,5-trinitroveratrole (3,4,5-trinitro-1, dimethoxybenzene) [Beil. VI-792], pr. from dil. alc., m.p. 145° ⟨5⟩.

Ⓓ **4,5-Dibromoveratrole** (4,5-dibromo-1,2-dimethoxybenzene) [Beil. VI-785]: $\bar{C}$ (0.35 g dislvd. in 5 ml. alc., treated during 5 min. with 0.84 g. Br_2 in 3 ml. alc., was diluted wit 40 ml. aq., stirred, stood 2 hrs., filtered. The residue, recrystd. from 2 ml. alc., ga 0.25 g. prod., m.p. 92–93° ⟨7⟩.

Ⓓ **Veratrole picrate** ($\bar{C}$.PkOH): from $\bar{C}$ in 2 pts. alc. treated with excess 10% alc. PkOH soln., and poured into 40 pts. aq. at 40°, yielding on cooling red tbls., m.p. 56–57° ⟨8⟩. [Also from $CHCl_3$ soln., red-or. six-sided pr., m.p. 56–57.5° ⟨9⟩.]

Ⓓ **3,4-Dimethoxybenzenesulfonamide:** cryst. from alc., m.p. 135–136° u.c. ⟨10⟩ [from $\bar{C}$ on treatment with excess chlorosulfonic acid and conversion of resultant sulfonyl chloride to sulfonamide with $(NH_4)_2CO_3$ (89% yield) ⟨10⟩].

1:7560 ⟨1⟩ Perkin, Weizmann, *J. Chem. Soc.* **89,** 1649 (1906). ⟨2⟩ Barger, Silberschmidt, *J. Chem. Soc.* **1928,** 2924. ⟨3⟩ Clark, *J. Am. Chem. Soc.* **53,** 3434 (1931). ⟨4⟩ Vermeulen, *Rec. trav. chim.* **25,** 24–25 (1906). ⟨5⟩ Kohn, Löff, *Monatsh.* **45,** 612 (1924). ⟨6⟩ Vermeulen, *Rec. trav. chim.* **48,** 969 (1929). ⟨7⟩ Underwood, Baril, Toone, *J. Am. Chem. Soc.* **52,** 4090–4091 (1930). ⟨8⟩ Pschorr, Silberbach, *Ber.* **37,** 2151 (1904). ⟨9⟩ Baril, Megrdichian, *J. Am. Chem. Soc.* **52,** 1415 (1936). ⟨10⟩ Huntress, Carten, *J. Am. Chem. Soc.* **62,** 603 (1940).

1:7562 BENZYL ISOBUTYL ETHER $C_{11}H_{16}O$ Beil. VI-431

C_6H_5—$CH_2.O.CH_2.CH(CH_3)_2$

B.P. 210-212° cor. ⟨1⟩ D_4^{20} = **0.9233** ⟨1⟩ n_D^{20} = **1.4826** ⟨1⟩
D_4^{25} = **0.9174** ⟨1⟩ n_D^{25} = **1.4803** ⟨1⟩

Colorless liq. with fragrant odor. Insol. aq. but sol. org. solvents.

1:7562 ⟨1⟩ Sah, Lei, *Science Repts. Natl. Tsing Hua Univ.*, Ser. **A-1,** 193–195 (1932).

1:7565 BENZYL *n*-BUTYL ETHER $C_{11}H_{16}O$ Beil. S.N. 528

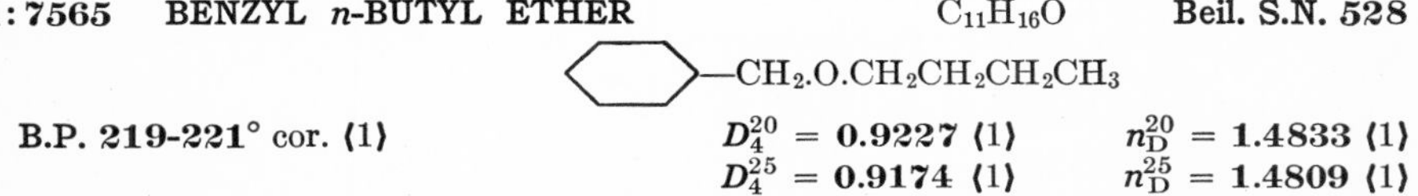

B.P. 219-221° cor. ⟨1⟩ D_4^{20} = **0.9227** ⟨1⟩ n_D^{20} = **1.4833** ⟨1⟩
D_4^{25} = **0.9174** ⟨1⟩ n_D^{25} = **1.4809** ⟨1⟩

Colorless liq. with fragrant odor. Insol. aq. but sol. org. solvents. [For reaction with PCl_5 see ⟨2⟩.]

1:7565 ⟨1⟩ Sah, Lei, *Science Repts. Natl. Tsing Hua Univ.*, Ser. **A-1,** 193–195 (1932). ⟨2⟩ Whitmore, Langlois, *J. Am. Chem. Soc.* **55,** 1519 (1933).

1:7570 RESORCINOL DIMETHYL ETHER $C_8H_{10}O_2$ Beil. VI-813

(*m*-Dimethoxybenzene; *m*-methoxyanisole)

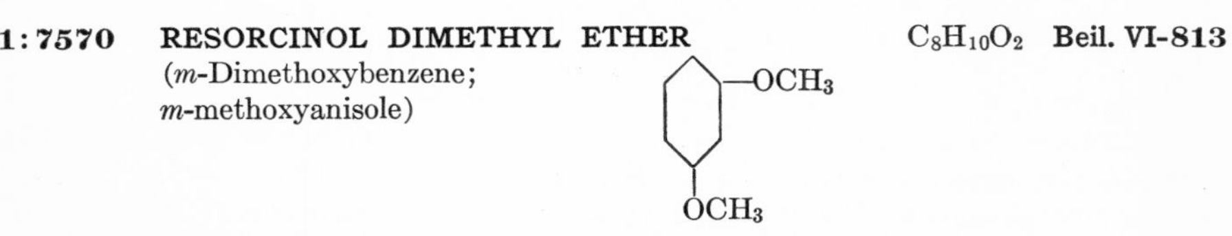

B.P. 217° cor. **M.P. −52°** D_{25}^{25} = **1.0552**

Oil, spar. sol. aq.; eas. sol. alc., ether, C_6H_6 — Sol. in conc. H_2SO_4 with yellow color. [For prepn. from resorcinol (1:1530) with 5 *N* aq. NaOH + $(CH_3)_2SO_4$ see ⟨1⟩; with MeOH/NaOMe + $(CH_3)_2SO_4$ see ⟨2⟩.] [$\bar{C}$ is insol. in aq. alk. (dif. from resorcinol monomethyl ether (1:1765)).]

$\bar{C}$ (1 pt.) dislvd. in 6 vols. conc. H_2SO_4 and well cooled soln. grad. added to mixt. of 6 pts. by vol. of fuming HNO_3 + 6 pts. by vol. conc. H_2SO_4 at 0°, another 2 pts. fuming HNO_3 finally being added, the whole stood ½ hr. ⟨3⟩, then poured onto ice gives (50% yield ⟨3⟩) dimethyl styphnate (2,4,6-trinitro-1,3-dimethoxybenzene) [Beil. VI-832]; very pale yel. ndls. from alc., m.p. 123–124° ⟨4⟩, 124–125° ⟨5⟩, 125° ⟨6⟩. [The reaction of $\bar{C}$ with fuming HNO_3 or conc. HNO_3 + conc. H_2SO_4 direct is very violent!] [Of the several dinitro derivs.

the 4,6-isomer (4,6-dinitro-1,3-dimethoxybenzene) [Beil. VI-828] forms white ndls. from alc., m.p. 157°; the 2,4-isomer (2,4-dinitro-1,3-dimethoxybenzene) [Beil. VI-827] forms pale yel. ndls. from alc. or CCl_4, m.p. 72°.]

Ⓓ **4,6-Dibromoresorcinol dimethyl ether** (4,6-dibromo-1,3-dimethoxybenzene): 0.35 g. C̄ dislvd. in 3 ml. alc., treated during 5 min. with 0.88 g. Br_2, gave immed. ppt. of solid; filtered, washed with 1 ml. alc., twice recrystd. from 8 ml. alc., gave 0.55 g. product; ndls., m.p. 140° ⟨7⟩.

Ⓓ **Resorcinol dimethyl ether picrate** (C̄.PkOH): from C̄ + PkOH in $CHCl_3$; tetragonal yel.-or. ndls., m.p. 56–58° u.c. ⟨8⟩ [unstable on exposure to air ⟨8⟩].

Ⓓ **2,4-Dimethoxybenzenesulfonamide:** cryst. from alc., m.p. 166–167° u.c. ⟨9⟩ ⟨10⟩ [from C̄ on treatment with excess chlorosulfonic acid and conversion of resultant sulfonyl chloride to sulfonamide by treatment with $(NH_4)_2CO_3$ (53% yield) ⟨9⟩].

1:7570 ⟨1⟩ Vermeulen, *Rec. trav. chim.* **25,** 28 (1906). ⟨2⟩ Flood, Nieuwland, *J. Am. Chem. Soc.* **50,** 2570–2571 (1928). ⟨3⟩ Kohn, Löff, *Monatsh.* **45,** 608–609 (1924). ⟨4⟩ Hönig, *Ber.* **11,** 1042 (1878). ⟨5⟩ Kaufmann, Franck, *Ber.* **40,** 4003 (1907). ⟨6⟩ Blanksma, *Rec. trav. chim.* **21,** 324 (1902). ⟨7⟩ Underwood, Baril, Toone, *J. Am. Chem. Soc.* **52,** 4090–4091 (1930). ⟨8⟩ Baril, Megrdichian, *J. Am. Chem. Soc.* **58,** 1415 (1936). ⟨9⟩ Huntress, Carten, *J. Am. Chem. Soc.* **62,** 603 (1940). ⟨10⟩ Suter, Hansen, *J. Am. Chem. Soc.* **55,** 2082 (1933).

1:7575 *n*-BUTYL *o*-TOLYL ETHER — $C_{11}H_{16}O$ — Beil. VI-353

(*n*-Butyl "*o*-cresyl" ether)

$CH_3.CH_2.CH_2.CH_2.O$—(benzene ring with CH_3 ortho)

B.P. 223° ⟨1⟩ D^0_0 = **0.9437 ⟨1⟩**

Ⓓ **4-(*n*-Butoxy)-5-methylbenzenesulfonamide:** cryst. from alc., m.p. 95–96° u.c. ⟨2⟩ [from C̄ by treatment with excess chlorosulfonic acid and conversion of resultant sulfonyl chloride to sulfonamide with $(NH_4)_2CO_3$ (44% yield) ⟨2⟩].

1:7575 ⟨1⟩ Pinette, *Ann.* **243,** 39 (1888). ⟨2⟩ Huntress, Carten, *J. Am. Chem. Soc.* **62,** 603 (1940).

1:7580 SAFROLE — $C_{10}H_{10}O_2$ — Beil. XIX-39

(4-Allyl-1,2-methylene-dioxybenzene)

H—C—H ‖ H—C—CH_2—(benzene ring)—O—CH_2—O

B.P. 233° **M.P. +11° ⟨1⟩** D^{20}_4 = **1.100 ⟨1⟩** n^{20}_D = **1.5383 ⟨1⟩**

Oil with strong sassafras odor! — Insol. aq.; sol. alc., ether — Sol. in $CH_3.NO_2$ (T 1.922) even at +20° — Volatile with steam. [For sepn. from isosafrole (1:7610) see ⟨9⟩.]

C̄ in acetone oxidized in cold with aq. $KMnO_4$ gives ⟨2⟩ piperonylic acid (1:0865) together with a small amt. of piperonylacetic acid [Beil. XIX-275], m.p. 87–88° [cf. ⟨3⟩] — C̄ on oxidn. with $K_2Cr_2O_7$ + dil. H_2SO_4 yields piperonal (1:0010) ⟨4⟩.

C̄ dis. in conc. H_2SO_4 with intense red color ⟨5⟩ [like isosafrole (1:7610)].

C̄ with 1,3,5-trinitrobenzene gives a mol. cpd., C̄.T.N.B., gold.-yel. tbls., m.p. 51° ⟨6⟩.

Ⓓ **Tribromosafrole dibromide** ("pentabromosafrole") [Beil. XIX-29]: 0.41 g. C̄ dislvd. in 3 ml. alc., treated with 2.0 g. Br_2 during 8 min., then heated 15 min. on aq. bath, gave solid on cooling; recrystd. from 7 ml. C_6H_6 gave 1.14 g. ndls., m.p. 169–170° ⟨7.⟩

Ⓓ **Safrole picrate** (C̄.PkOH): from C̄ + PkOH in $CHCl_3$ soln.; long or.-red blades, m.p. 104–105.5° u.c. ⟨8⟩.

1:7580 ⟨1⟩ Waterman, Priester, *Rec. trav. chim.* **47**, 849–851 (1928). ⟨2⟩ Luff, Perkin, Robinson, *J. Chem. Soc.* **97**, 1139 (1910). ⟨3⟩ Decker, *Ann.* **395**, 295 (1913). ⟨4⟩ Power, Lees, *J. Chem. Soc.* **85**, 638 (1904). ⟨5⟩ Ciamician, Silber, *Ber.* **23**, 1160 (1890). ⟨6⟩ Sudborough, Beard, *J. Chem. Soc.* **99**, 214 (1911). ⟨7⟩ Underwood, Baril, Toone, *J. Am. Chem. Soc.* **52**, 4090–4091 (1930). ⟨8⟩ Baril, Megrdichian, *J. Am. Chem. Soc.* **58**, 1415 (1936). ⟨9⟩ Balbiano, *Ber.* **42**, 1505 (1909).

1:7585 RESORCINOL DIETHYL ETHER $C_{10}H_{14}O_2$ **Beil. VI-814**
(m-Diethoxybenzene)

O.CH_2.CH_3

O.CH_2.CH_3

B.P. 235° **M.P. +12.4°**

Very eas. volatile with steam. [For prepn. from resorcinol (1:1530) with ethyl p-toluenesulfonate + 10% NaOH in 82% yield see ⟨1⟩; with $(C_2H_5)_2SO_4$ (1 mole) see ⟨2⟩.]

C̄ in 20 pts. AcOH treated with Br_2 until yel. color appears in soln. yields predominantly 4,6-dibromoresorcinol diethyl ether [Beil. VI-821], pr. from alc., m.p. 100–101° ⟨3⟩ ⟨4⟩, accompanied by some isomeric x,x-dibromoresorcinol diethyl ether (m.p. 75–77°), more easily sol. in alc. or AcOH. [The above 4,6-dibromoresorcinol diethyl ether, on direct treatment with excess Br_2, yields 2,4,6-tribromoresorcinol diethyl ether [Beil. VI-822] fibers from alc., m.p. 68–69° ⟨5⟩.]

C̄ with $CHCl_3$ soln. of picric ac. yields mol. cpd., C̄.PkOH, brown-yel. long slender rods, m.p. 108–109° ⟨6⟩.

Ⓓ **2,4-Diethoxybenzenesulfonamide:** cryst. from alc., m.p. 184–185° u.c. ⟨7⟩ [from C̄ + chlorosulfonic acid, followed by conversion of resultant sulfonyl chloride to sulfonamide with $(NH_4)_2CO_3$ (59% yield) ⟨7⟩.

1:7585 ⟨1⟩ Finzi, *Ann. chim. applicata* **15**, 41–50 (1925); *Chem. Abs.* **19**, 2648 (1925). ⟨2⟩ Hodgson, Clay, *J. Chem. Soc.* **1930**, 1873–1874. ⟨3⟩ Jackson, Dunlap, *Am. Chem. J.* **18**, 120–121 (1896). ⟨4⟩ Herzog, Zeisel, *Monatsh.* **11**, 302–303 (1890). ⟨5⟩ Ref. 3, page 121. ⟨6⟩ Baril, Megrdichian, *J. Am. Chem. Soc.* **58**, 1415 (1936). ⟨7⟩ Huntress, Carten, *J. Am. Chem. Soc.* **62**, 603 (1940).

— ANETHOLE $C_{10}H_{12}O$ **Beil. VI-566**
(p-Propenylanisole)

CH_3—C—H
‖
H—C—⟨ ⟩—OCH_3

B.P. 235° cor. **M.P. 22°**

See 1:7115. Genus 9: Division A: Section 2.

1:7595 PHENYLCYCLOHEXANE $C_{12}H_{16}$ **Beil. V-503**
(Cyclohexylbenzene;
hexahydrobiphenyl)

CH_2—CH_2 H
H_2C C—⟨ ⟩
CH_2—CH_2

B.P. 238.7°$_{756}$ ⟨1⟩ **M.P. +7.0°** ⟨2⟩ ⟨3⟩ ⟨1⟩ D_4^{20} = **0.9441** ⟨2⟩ n_D^{20} = **1.5254** ⟨1⟩
D_{25}^{25} = **0.9338** ⟨4⟩ n_D^{25} = **1.5190** ⟨4⟩

Oil, insol. aq. but volatile with steam — C.S.T. in $CH_3.NO_2$ (T 1.922) is +23.5°.

[For prepn. from cyclohexene (1:8070) + C_6H_6 + H_2SO_4 (65–68% yield) see ⟨5⟩ ⟨1⟩; from cyclohexene (1:8070) + C_6H_6 + $AlCl_3$ see ⟨1⟩; from cyclohexyl chloride + C_6H_6 + $AlCl_3$ (60–78% yield) see ⟨6⟩ ⟨7⟩.]

C̄ is stable to cold aq. $KMnO_4$, but refluxing 40 hrs. ⟨2⟩ with alk. $KMnO_4$ gives BzOH (1:0715).

C̄ at 165° treated with 3 wts. Br_2 over 2 hrs. evolves HBr, and after distn. (b.p. 253–273°) distillate solidifies to (97% yield ⟨1⟩) biphenyl (1:7175). [C̄ treated with large excess Br_2 in presence of a trace of Al gives hexabromobenzene [Beil. V-215], cryst. from xylene, m.p. 315–316° ⟨8⟩.]

C̄ on treatment with 4–6 pts. fumg. HNO_3 with stirring and cooling, poured onto ice, washed, dried, distd. in vac. ⟨9⟩ ⟨10⟩ gives (62% yield ⟨9⟩) 4-nitrophenylcyclohexane, pale yel. pl. from alc., m.p. 58.5° ⟨9⟩, 56–58° ⟨10⟩, 57.5–58.5° ⟨11⟩, 57° ⟨6⟩; accompanied by 2-nitrophenylcyclohexane, m.p. 45° ⟨6⟩. [For f.p.-compn. data for mixts. of 4- and 2-nitrophenylcyclohexane see ⟨9⟩.] [4-Nitrophenylcyclohexane on oxidn. with dichromate gives 98.7% yield *p*-nitrobenzoic acid, but the 2-nitrophenylcyclohexane is completely destroyed ⟨9⟩.] [Under certain conditions nitration of C̄ may also yield 2,4-dinitrophenylcyclohexane, pale yel. pl. from alc., m.p. 57° ⟨9⟩, which on dichromate oxidn. yields 2,4-dinitrobenzoic ac. ⟨9⟩.]

C̄ on mononitration, reduction, and subsequent acetylation (all under specified conditions ⟨12⟩) gives 4-acetylaminophenylcyclohexane, m.p. 130–131° u.c. ⟨12⟩ ⟨10⟩; 128–129.5° ⟨11⟩.

C̄ on dinitration, reduction, and subsequent acetylation (all under specified conditions ⟨12⟩) gives 2,4-(diacetylamino)phenylcyclohexane, m.p. 261–262° u.c. ⟨12⟩.

1:7595 ⟨1⟩ Corson, Ipatieff, *J. Am. Chem. Soc.* **59,** 645–647 (1937). ⟨2⟩ Kursanoff, *Ann.* **318,** 312–313 (1901). ⟨3⟩ Gelissen, Hermans, *Ber.* **59,** 665 (1926). ⟨4⟩ McKenna, Sowa, *J. Am. Chem. Soc.* **59,** 471 (1937). ⟨5⟩ Corson, Ipatieff, *Organic Syntheses* **19,** 36–37 (1939). ⟨6⟩ Neunhoeffer, *J. prakt. Chem.* (2) **133,** 105–107 (1932). ⟨7⟩ Mayes, Turner, *J. Chem. Soc.* **1929,** 502. ⟨8⟩ Bodroux, *Ann. chim.* (10) **11,** 546–547 (1929). ⟨9⟩ Ref. 7, pages 503–504. ⟨10⟩ Hickinbottom, *J. Chem. Soc.* **1932,** 2649–2650.

⟨11⟩ Ref. 2, pages 321–324. ⟨12⟩ Ipatieff, Schmerling, *J. Am. Chem. Soc.* **59,** 1056–1059 (1937).

1:7600 α-METHYLNAPHTHALENE $C_{11}H_{10}$ **Beil. VI-566**

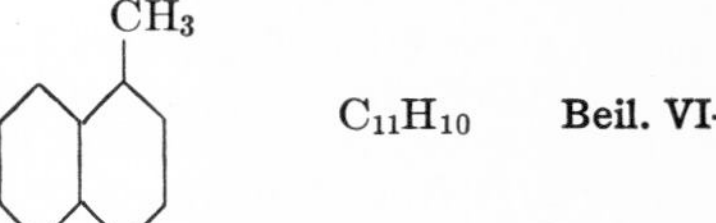

B.P. 241° **M.P. −31 to −33°** ⟨1⟩ $D_4^{19.8}$ = **1.0192** ⟨2⟩ $n_{He}^{19.8}$ = **1.61757** ⟨2⟩

Oil, insol. aq. but volatile with steam. Eas. sol. alc., ether — Sol. in $CH_3.NO_2$ (T 1.922) even at −17°. [Comml. samples of coal tar origin may contain nitrogen cpds.] [For f.p.-compn. curve of system: C̄ + β-methylnaphthalene (1:7605) see ⟨1⟩; for sepn. of α + β-methylnaphthalenes via sulfonation of mixture, pptn. of α-naphthalenesulfonic acids and subsequent desulfonation with superheated steam see ⟨1⟩.]

C̄ treated dropwise with shaking and cooling with 3.2 pts. conc. HNO_3 (D = 1.42) gives (70% yield ⟨3⟩) 4-nitro-1-methylnaphthalene [Beil. V_1-(266)], pale yel. ndls. from alc., m.p. 71–72° ⟨4⟩, 68–69° ⟨5⟩, together with some 5-nitro-1-methylnaphthalene, m.p. 82–83° ⟨6⟩ and less 2-nitro-1-methylnaphthalene, m.p. 58–59° ⟨7⟩. [For di- and trinitro-α-methylnaphthalenes see ⟨8⟩ ⟨9⟩ ⟨14⟩.]

C̄ with PkOH in conc. alc. soln. or in $CHCl_3$ soln. gives a picrate, C̄.PkOH, lemon-yel. ndls., m.p. 141–142° ⟨10⟩ ⟨11⟩, 140–141° ⟨12⟩, 139–140° ⟨1⟩. [For m.p.-compn. diagram for mixtures of the picrates of α- and of β-methylnaphthalene see ⟨13⟩; note that when m.p. is detd. in usual capillary m.p. tube the presence of up to 66.7% β-methylnaphthalene picrate causes lowering of m.p. but more gives only m.p. identical with pure α-methylnaphthalene picrate (115°); a 50–50 mixt. has cap. m.p. 121–122° ⟨13⟩; cf. ⟨1⟩.]

1:7600 ⟨1⟩ Morgan, Coulson, *J. Soc. Chem. Ind.* **53T,** 73–74 (1934). ⟨2⟩ von Auwers, Wunderling, *Ber.* **64,** 2751 (1931). ⟨3⟩ Thompson, *J. Chem. Soc.* **1932,** 2311. ⟨4⟩ Lesser, *Ann.* **402,** 12 (1914). ⟨5⟩ Veselý, Štursa, Olejniček, Rein, *Collection Czechoslov. Chem. Commun.* **1,** 498 (1929). ⟨6⟩ Ref. 5, page 505. ⟨7⟩ Ref. 5, page 500. ⟨8⟩ Veselý, et al., *Collection Czechoslov. Chem. Commun.* **2,** 145–157 (1930). ⟨9⟩ Ref. 3, pages 2310, 2313. ⟨10⟩ Ref. 4, page 10.
⟨11⟩ Meyer, Fricke, *Ber.* **47,** 2770 (1914). ⟨12⟩ Baril, Hauber, *J. Am. Chem. Soc.* **53,** 1090 (1931). ⟨13⟩ R. Meyer, W. Meyer, *Ber.* **52,** 1251–1254 (1919). ⟨14⟩ Madinaveita, Saenz de Buruaga, *Cent.* **1930,** I, 684.

1:7605 β-METHYLNAPHTHALENE —CH_3 $C_{11}H_{10}$ Beil. V-567

B.P. 241° **M.P. 34.5°** ⟨1⟩
32–33° ⟨2⟩ ⟨16⟩

Sol. in $CH_3.NO_2$ (T 1.922) even at −17°. [Comml. samples of coal tar origin may cont. nitrogen compounds.] [For f.p.-compn. curve of system: C̄ + α-methylnaphthalene (1:7600) see ⟨2⟩; for sepn. of α- and β-methylnaphthalenes see ⟨2⟩.]

C̄ added in portions with cooling to 5 pts. HNO_3 (D = 1.38) gives (58% yield ⟨3⟩; 60% yield ⟨8⟩) 1-nitro-2-methylnaphthalene [Beil. V-568], ndls. from alc., m.p. 81° ⟨4⟩ ⟨8⟩, 80° ⟨5⟩.

[C̄ (7 g.) treated grad. with conc. HNO_3 (10 ml.) and after first reaction has subsided with equal vol. conc. H_2SO_4, warmed and poured into aq. gives ppt. of dinitro-β-methylnaphthalene; after extraction with alc. (to remove mono nitro cpds.) and recrystn. from C_6H_6; m.p. 206° ⟨6⟩; cf. ⟨7⟩.] [C̄ dissolved in least possible AcOH and treated dropwise with 10 pts. fumg. HNO_3, poured into aq. and ppt. recrystd. from acetone, then C_6H_6, gives trinitro-β-methylnaphthalene, m.p. 182° ⟨6⟩.]

C̄ dislvd. in AcOH or Ac_2O ⟨15⟩ and oxidized with CrO_3 in AcOH gives (29% yield ⟨9⟩; 25–40% yield ⟨10⟩) 2-methylnaphthoquinone-1,4 (1:9021).

C̄ with PkOH in alc. or $CHCl_3$ soln. gives a picrate, C̄.PkOH, lemon-yel. ndls., m.p. 115–116° ⟨11⟩; 115° ⟨12⟩ ⟨13⟩; 117–117.3° ⟨1⟩. [For m.p.-compn. diagram for mixtures of the picrates of α- and of β-methylnaphthalenes see ⟨13⟩; note that when m.p. is taken in usual cap. m.p. tube as much as 33.3% of α-compd. can be present without affecting the m.p. (115°) of the pure β-derivative; a 50–50 mixt. of picrates of α- and of β-methylnaphthalene has m.p. 121–122° ⟨13⟩; cf. ⟨2⟩.] [For m.p.-compn. diagram of mixts. of picrates of C̄ and of naphthalene (1:7200) see ⟨13⟩; note that as much as 33.3% of naphthalene picrate has no effect on m.p. (115°) of pure β-methylnaphthalene picrate, m.p. 150° ⟨13⟩.]

C̄ forms with 1,3,5-trinitrobenzene a mol. cpd., C̄.T.N.B., canary-yel. ndls., m.p. 123° ⟨14⟩.

1:7605 ⟨1⟩ Olivier, Wit, *Rec. trav. chim.* **57,** 92 (1938). ⟨2⟩ Morgan, Coulson, *J. Soc. Chem. Ind.* **53T,** 73–75 (1934). ⟨3⟩ Veselý, Kapp, *Rec. trav. chim.* **44,** 364 (1925). ⟨4⟩ Lesser, *Ann.* **402,** 32 (1914). ⟨5⟩ Bodroux, *Bull. soc. chim.* (3) **25,** 494 (1901). ⟨6⟩ Madinaveita, Saenz de Buruaga, *Cent.* **1930,** I, 684. ⟨7⟩ Giral, *Cent.* **1934,** II, 939–940. ⟨8⟩ Fierz-David, Mannhart, *Helv. Chim. Acta* **20,** 1027–1028 (1937). ⟨9⟩ Fieser, Campbell, Fry, Gates, *J. Am. Chem. Soc.* **61,** 3218 (1939). ⟨10⟩ Smith, Webster, *J. Am. Chem. Soc.* **59,** 666 (1937).
⟨11⟩ Baril, Hauber, *J. Am. Chem. Soc.* **53,** 1090 (1931). ⟨12⟩ Meyer, Fricke, *Ber.* **47,** 2770 (1914). ⟨13⟩ R. Meyer, W. Meyer, *Ber.* **52,** 1251–1254 (1919). ⟨14⟩ Sudborough, *J. Chem. Soc.* **109,** 1344 (1916). ⟨15⟩ Ref. 3, page 370. ⟨16⟩ Lesser, *Ann.* **402,** 30–31 (1914).

1:7606 EUGENOL METHYL ETHER $C_{11}H_{14}O_2$ **Beil. VI-963**

(" Methyleugenol "; 1,2-dimethoxy-4-allylbenzene)

CH_2=CH.CH_2—⟨ring⟩—OCH_3, OCH_3

B.P. 244° **D_4^{15} = 1.0386** **n_D^{20} = 1.5360**

Oil with faint odor suggesting eugenol — Sol. in $CH_3.NO_2$ (T 1.922) even at −17°.

C̄ on oxidn. with $K_2Cr_2O_7$ in AcOH ⟨1⟩, or C̄ in acetone oxidized with satd. aq. $KMnO_4$ ⟨2⟩ gives mainly veratric acid (3,4-dimethoxybenzoic acid) [Beil. X-393], cryst. from aq., m.p. 179°. [A little 3,4-dimethoxyphenylacetic acid (homoveratric acid) [Beil. X-409], m.p. monohydrate (from aq.), 82°, anhydrous m.p. 98° is also formed but easily separated ⟨2⟩.]

Ⓓ ***x*-Bromoeugenol methyl ether dibromide** [Beil. VI-922]: C̄ (0.45 g.) dislvd. in 5 ml. dry ether is treated during 10 min. with 0.8 g. Br_2. During this bromination, mixt. is cooled in ice, subsequently stood ½ hr. at room temp., then cooled in ice-HCl bath. After inducing crystn. by scratching, solid is filtered, washed with 3 ml. cold alc., recrystd. from 8 ml. abs. alc. at 60°, yielding 0.88 g. ndls., m.p. 78° ⟨3⟩.

Ⓓ **Eugenol methyl ether picrate:** C̄.PkOH; red-brown rhombic cryst. from $CHCl_3$, m.p. 114–115° u.c. ⟨4⟩ [from C̄ + PkOH in $CHCl_3$ ⟨4⟩].

1:7606 ⟨1⟩ Graebe, Borgmann, *Ann.* **158,** 282 (1871). ⟨2⟩ Luff, Perkin, Robinson, *J. Chem. Soc.* **97,** 1138–1139 (1910). ⟨3⟩ Underwood, Baril, Toone, *J. Am. Chem. Soc.* **52,** 4090–4091 (1930). ⟨4⟩ Baril, Megrdichian, *J. Am. Chem. Soc.* **58,** 1415 (1936).

1:7607 HYDROXYHYDROQUINONE TRIMETHYL ETHER **Beil. VI-1088**

(1,2,4-Trimethoxybenzene) $C_9H_{12}O_3$

OCH_3, OCH_3, OCH_3 (ring)

B.P. 247° **M.P. 19-20° ⟨1⟩**
251-252° ⟨1⟩; 250-255° ⟨2⟩

[For prepn. from hydroxyhydroquinone (1:1570) in MeOH soln. + NaOH + $(CH_3)_2SO_4$ see ⟨3⟩.]

C̄ treated with Br_2 in AcOH yields ⟨4⟩ ⟨5⟩ 5-bromo-1,2,4-trimethoxybenzene [Beil. VI_1-(542)], rhomb. pr. from lt. pet. ether, or rods + pr. from alc.; m.p. 54–55° ⟨4⟩ ⟨5⟩ ⟨6⟩ ⟨7⟩.

1:7607 ⟨1⟩ Baker, Jukes, Subrahmanyam, *J. Chem. Soc.* **1934,** 1682. ⟨2⟩ Rodinow, Fedorova, *Bull. soc. chim.* (5) **4,** 1706 (1937). ⟨3⟩ Bargellini, Martogiani, *Gazz. chim. ital.* **41,** II, 448–449 (1911). ⟨4⟩ Baker, Evans, *J. Chem. Soc.* **1938,** 375. ⟨5⟩ Fabinyi, Szeki, *Ber.* **43,** 2681 (1910). ⟨6⟩ Bargellini, Madesani, *Gazz. chim. ital.* **61,** 687 (1931). ⟨7⟩ Clark, *J. Am. Chem. Soc.* **53,** 3433 (1931).

1:7610 ISOSAFROLE $C_{10}H_{10}O_2$ **Beil. XIX-35**

(1,2-Methylenedioxy-4-propenylbenzene)

CH_3—C—H ‖ H—C—⟨ring⟩ with O—CH_2—O

B.P. 248° **M.P. +6.8° ⟨1⟩** **D_4^{20} = 1.122 ⟨2⟩** **n_D^{20} = 1.5782 ⟨2⟩**

[Although two geometrical isomers would be expected, only the *trans* (or β) isomer is known with certainty. The *cis* or α-isosafrole reported in the literature ⟨3⟩ is a mixt. of safrole + *trans*-isosafrole ⟨4⟩.]

Oil with anise-like odor — Misc. with alc., ether, C_6H_6 — Volatile with steam.

C̄ dislvd. in 3 pts. AcOH and htd. 3 hrs. at 100° with a very little conc. H_2SO_4 ⟨5⟩, or C̄ htd. with alc. HCl in a s.t. at 160° ⟨6⟩ yields a dimer (di-isosafrole) [Beil. XIX-440], m.p. 145°, which is probably a dihydroanthracene deriv. ⟨7⟩. [An isomeric di-isosafrole of m.p. 91° is also known.]

C̄ (5 g.) oxidized in acid soln. with $K_2Cr_2O_7$ (25 g.) + H_2SO_4 (8 g.) in aq. (80 ml.) gives piperonal (1:0010) [yield 4 g. as $NaHSO_3$ cpd. ⟨8⟩] — C̄ on oxidn. with $KMnO_4$ gives piperonylic acid (1:0865); e.g., C̄ (15 g.) in 135 ml. aq. stirred vigorously and treated at 80–90° with a 4% aq. soln. of $KMnO_4$ (69 g.) dropwise during an hour, yields 11.9 g. (80% yield) piperonylic ac. ⟨9⟩.

C̄ with 1,3,5-trinitrobenzene gives a mol. cpd. C̄.T.N.B.; bright scarlet ndls., m.p. 85–86° ⟨15⟩.

Ⓓ **Bromo-isosafrole dibromide** [Beil. XIX-28]: C̄ (0.41 g.) in CS_2 (2 ml.) treated dropwise during 15 min. with 2.0 g. Br_2, stood 24 hrs. yields solid, ground in mortar with 3 ml. cold alc., recrystd. from 5 ml. pet. ether, gives 0.55 g. ndls., m.p. 109° ⟨10⟩; 109–110° ⟨11⟩; 110–111° ⟨12⟩. [Isosafrole dibromide [Beil. XIX-28], from C̄ + 1 mole Br_2 in CS_2, ether, or pet. ether, after crystallization by seeding has m.p. 52–53° ⟨13⟩.]

Ⓓ **Isosafrole picrate:** dark red thick ndl. clusters from $CHCl_3$ or alc., m.p. 74–75° u.c. ⟨14⟩.

1:7610 ⟨1⟩ Waterman, Priester, *Rec. trav. chim.* **48,** 1272 (1929). ⟨2⟩ Waterman, Priester, *Rec. trav. chim.* **47,** 851 (1928). ⟨3⟩ Hoering, Baum, *Ber.* **42,** 3076–3088 (1909). ⟨4⟩ Waterman, Priester, *Rec. trav. chim.* **47,** 1036 (1928). ⟨5⟩ Robinson, *J. Chem. Soc.* **107,** 275 (1915). ⟨6⟩ Angeli, Mole, *Gazz. chim. ital.* **24,** II, 128 (1894). ⟨7⟩ Haworth, Mavin, *J. Chem. Soc.* **1931,** 1364. ⟨8⟩ Ciamician, Silber, *Ber.* **23,** 1160 (1890). ⟨9⟩ Imoto, *Cent.* **1934,** I, 1973. ⟨10⟩ Underwood, Baril, Toone, *J. Am. Chem. Soc.* **52,** 4090–4091 (1930).
⟨11⟩ Ref. 8, page 1163–1164. ⟨12⟩ Pond, Erb, Ford, *J. Am. Chem. Soc.* **24,** 341 (1902). ⟨13⟩ Waterman, Priester, *Rec. trav. chim.* **48,** 941–943 (1929). ⟨14⟩ Baril, Megrdichian, *J. Am. Chem. Soc.* **58,** 1415 (1936). ⟨15⟩ Sudborough, Beard, *J. Chem. Soc.* **99,** 214 (1911).

1:7625 ISOEUGENOL METHYL ETHER $C_{11}H_{14}O_2$ Beil. VI-956

(" Methylisoeugenol ";
1,2-dimethoxy-4-propenylbenzene)

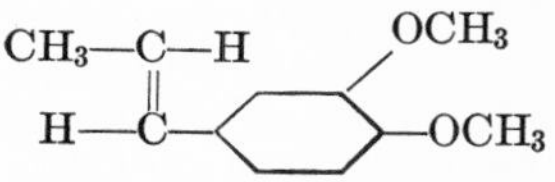

CH_3—C—H ‖ H—C—C_6H_3(OCH_3)(OCH_3)

B.P. 264° **M.P. 16-17°** ⟨1⟩ D_4^{20} = **1.0528** ⟨1⟩ n_D^{20} = **1.5692** ⟨1⟩

Colorless liq. with almost no odor — C̄ is known in both *cis* and *trans* forms and ordinary C̄ is undoubtedly mixt. of both; the *cis* form, prepd. from liq. stereoisomer of isoeugenol (1:1785), is an oil, D_4^{20} = 1.0521; n_D^{20} = 1.5616 ⟨1⟩; the *trans* form, prepd. from the cryst. stereoisomer of isoeugenol (1:1785), has constants shown above ⟨1⟩ (cf. ⟨2⟩) — C̄ is sol. in $CH_3.NO_2$ (T 1.922) even at −17°.

C̄ in ether treated with dry HCl ⟨3⟩, or refluxed with 20 pts. 5 *N* MeOH + HCl ⟨4⟩, gives a dimer (bis-isoeugenol methyl ether) [Beil. VI-957], colorless ndls. from dil. alc. or dil. acetic ac., m.p. 106° ⟨3⟩ ⟨4⟩.

C̄ + PkOH in $CHCl_3$ gives a picrate, C̄.PkOH; very dark red rods from $CHCl_3$, m.p. 42–45° u.c. ⟨5⟩; 40–45° ⟨6⟩ — C̄ with 1,3,5-trinitrobenzene gives a cpd., C̄.T.N.B., bright scarlet pl., m.p. 69–70° ⟨7⟩.

Ⓓ **Isoeugenol methyl ether dibromide** [Beil. VI-921]: To C̄ (0.45 g.) in dry ether (5 ml.) is added during 8 min., Br_2 (0.4 g.). During treatment mixt. is cooled in ice, subsequently allowed to stand half an hr. at room temp., then cooled in ice-HCl mixt. After crystn. is induced by scratching, solid recrystd. from 8 ml. dry ether, giving 0.61 g. plates, m.p. 101–101.5° ⟨8⟩.

1:7625 ⟨1⟩ Boedecker, Volk, *Ber.* **64,** 64 (1931). ⟨2⟩ von Auwers, *Ber.* **68,** 1347 (1935). ⟨3⟩ Szeki, *Ber.* **39,** 2422–2423 (1906). ⟨4⟩ Haworth, Mavin, *J. Chem. Soc.* **1931,** 1365. ⟨5⟩ Baril, Megrdichian, *J. Am. Chem. Soc.* **58,** 1415 (1936). ⟨6⟩ Bruni, Tornani, *Gazz. chim. ital.* **34,** II, 477 (1905). ⟨7⟩ Sudborough, Beard, *J. Chem. Soc.* **99,** 214 (1911). ⟨8⟩ Underwood, Baril, Toone, *J. Am. Chem. Soc.* **52,** 4090–4091 (1930).

—— DIPHENYLMETHANE (Benzylbenzene)

C_6H_5—CH_2—C_6H_5 $C_{13}H_{12}$ **Beil. V-588**

B.P. 264.7° cor. **M.P. 25.09°**

See 1:7120. Genus 9: Division A: Section 2.

1:7630 METHYL α-NAPHTHYL ETHER (1-Methoxynaphthalene)

$CH_3.O$—$C_{10}H_7$ $C_{11}H_{10}O$ **Beil. VI-606**

B.P. 271° cor. ⟨1⟩ **M.P. <−10°** ⟨1⟩ D_4^{20} = **1.09159** n_D^{25} = **1.6940** ⟨2⟩

Colorless oil — Insol. aq., eas. sol. alc., ether, C_6H_6, $CHCl_3$, CS_2 — Volatile with steam.

C̄ (0.4 g.) dislvd. in $CHCl_3$ (3 ml.), treated dropwise during 8 min. with Br_2 (0.42 g.) with ice cooling, stood overnight at room temp. gives 0.6 g. *x*-bromo-1-methoxynaphthalene, ndls. from alc. (8 ml.); m.p. 46° ⟨3⟩ [5-bromo-1-methoxynaphthalene (prepd. indirectly ⟨4⟩) has m.p. 67.5–68°; 4-bromo-1-methoxynaphthalene has been reported only as an oil, b.p. 181° ⟨5⟩, b.p. 182° ⟨6⟩].

C̄ (5 g.) in CCl_4 (10 g.) treated dropwise with Br_2 (6.2 g.) in CCl_4 (10 g.), solvent distd., gives (80% yield) 2,4-dibromo-1-methoxynaphthalene, ndls. from alc., m.p. 54–55° ⟨7⟩.

C̄ (10 g.) dislvd. in Ac_2O (20 ml.) treated grad. during 3 hrs. at 3–5° with a soln. of diacetylorthonitric ac. (15 ml.) in Ac_2O (10 ml.), kept overnight, diluted with aq. (10 ml.) gives ppt. (97% yield) of 4-nitro-1-methoxynaphthalene, long yel. ndls. from alc., m.p. 85° ⟨8⟩. [The 2-nitro isomer (not formed here) has m.p. 80° and depresses m.p. of this 4-nitro product ⟨8⟩.]

C̄ with 1,3,5-trinitrobenzene forms a mol. cpd. C̄.T.N.B., yel. ndls., m.p. 137–138° ⟨11⟩.

Ⓓ **Methyl α-naphthyl ether picrate,** C̄.PkOH: yel.-or. silky ndl. clusters from $CHCl_3$, m.p. 129.5–130.5° cor. ⟨1⟩, 127–127.5° u.c. ⟨9⟩; Neut. Eq. 389. [From C̄ + equiv. PkOH in hot alc. ⟨1⟩ or $CHCl_3$ ⟨9⟩.]

Ⓓ **4-Methoxynaphthalenesulfonamide-1:** cryst. from alc., m.p. 156–157° u.c. ⟨10⟩ [from C̄ by treatment with excess chlorosulfonic acid followed by conversion of the resultant sulfonyl chloride to sulfonamide with $(NH_4)_2CO_3$ (55% yield) ⟨10⟩]. [This deriv. depresses m.p. of corresp. product from methyl β-naphthyl ether (1:7180) ⟨10⟩.]

1:7630 ⟨1⟩ V. H. Dermer, O. C. Dermer, *J. Org. Chem.* **3,** 290–291 (1938). ⟨2⟩ Musser, Adkins, *J. Am. Chem. Soc.* **60,** 667 (1938). ⟨3⟩ Underwood, Baril, Toone, *J. Am. Chem. Soc.* **52,** 4090–4091 (1930). ⟨4⟩ Hill, Short, Stromberg, *J. Chem. Soc.* **1937,** 1621. ⟨5⟩ Shoesmith, Rubli, *J. Chem. Soc.* **1927,** 3102. ⟨6⟩ Fieser, Desreux, *J. Am. Chem. Soc.* **60,** 2260 (1938).

⟨7⟩ Kohn, Schwarz, *Monatsh.* **46,** 350 (1925). ⟨8⟩ Hodgson, Smith, *J. Chem. Soc.* **1935,** 672. ⟨9⟩ Baril, Megrdichian, *J. Am. Chem. Soc.* **58,** 1415 (1936). ⟨10⟩ Huntress, Carten, *J. Am. Chem. Soc.* **62,** 603 (1940).
⟨11⟩ Sudborough, Beard, *J. Chem. Soc.* **99,** 214 (1911).

1:7635 ETHYL α-NAPHTHYL ETHER $C_{12}H_{12}O$ **Beil. VI-606**
(1-Ethoxynaphthalene)

$CH_3.CH_2.O$—

B.P. 280.5° cor. ⟨1⟩ **M.P. < −10°** ⟨1⟩ D^{20}_{20} = **1.0605** n^{25}_D = **1.5953** ⟨2⟩
+5.5° ⟨3⟩

[For prepn. (85% yield) from sodium α-naphtholate + diethyl sulfate see ⟨4⟩; for prepn. (80% yield) from α-naphthol (1:1500) + aq. alk. + ethyl *p*-toluenesulfonate see ⟨5⟩.]

C̄ (10 g.) treated with 1½ pts. HNO_3 (D = 1.24) at 60–70° for ½ hr. and poured into aq. gives (71% yield ⟨6⟩) 4-nitro-1-ethoxynaphthalene [Beil. VI-616] cryst. from alc.; m.p. 116–117° ⟨6⟩. [2-Nitro-1-ethoxynaphthalene [Beil. VI-615] has m.p. 84° ⟨7⟩.]

C̄ with 1,3,5-trinitrobenzene forms mol. cpd., C̄.T.N.B., yel. ndls., m.p. 125.5° ⟨8⟩.

Ⓓ **4-Bromo-1-ethoxynaphthalene** [Beil. VI-613]: 0.43 g. C̄ in 3 ml. $CHCl_3$ (cooled with ice during Br_2 addn. and 15 min. afterward) was treated during 5 min. with 0.42 g. Br_2 and stood overnight. Solid recrystd. from 10 ml. alc. yielded 0.55 g. prod., m.p. 48° u.c. ⟨9⟩ ⟨10⟩.

Ⓓ **Ethyl α-naphthyl ether picrate:** m.p. 118.5–119.0° cor. ⟨1⟩; 107–108° u.c. ⟨11⟩; Neut. Eq. 401 [from C̄ + PkOH in alc. ⟨1⟩ or $CHCl_3$ ⟨11⟩].

Ⓓ **4-Ethoxynaphthalenesulfonamide:** cryst. from alc., m.p. 164–165° u.c. ⟨12⟩ [from C̄ on treatment with excess chlorosulfonic acid and conversion of resultant sulfonyl chloride to sulfonamide with $(NH_4)_2CO_3$ (64% yield) ⟨12⟩].

1:7635 ⟨1⟩ V. H. Dermer, O. C. Dermer, *J. Org. Chem.* **3,** 289–293 (1938). ⟨2⟩ Musser, Adkins, *J. Am. Chem. Soc.* **60,** 67 (1938). ⟨3⟩ Witt, Schneider, *Ber.* **34,** 3175 (1901). ⟨4⟩ Kamm, McClugage, Landstrom, *J. Am. Chem. Soc.* **39,** 1245 (1917). ⟨5⟩ Finzi, *Cent.* **1925,** I, 2491. ⟨6⟩ Heermann, *Ann.* **429,** 173 (1922). ⟨7⟩ Heermann, *J. prakt. Chem.* (2) **44,** 240 (1891). ⟨8⟩ Sudborough, Beard, *J. Chem. Soc.* **99,** 214 (1911). ⟨9⟩ Underwood, Baril, Toone, *J. Am. Chem. Soc.* **52,** 4090–4091 (1930). ⟨10⟩ Marchetti, *Gazz. chim. ital.* **9,** 544 (1879).
⟨11⟩ Baril, Megrdichian, *J. Am. Chem. Soc.* **58,** 1415 (1936). ⟨12⟩ Huntress, Carten, *J. Am. Chem. Soc.* **62,** 603 (1940).

1:7640 DIBENZYL ETHER $C_{14}H_{14}O$ **Beil. VI-434**
(Benzyl ether)

—$CH_2.O.CH_2$—

B.P. 290-300° dec. **M.P. +3.6°** ⟨1⟩ D^{20}_4 = **1.0428** ⟨1⟩

Oil; on cooling to −15° and stirring vigorously, crystallizes ⟨1⟩ — On stdg. in air grad. decomposes with formn. of BzH, odor of which is not eliminated even on vac. distn. ⟨1⟩ — C̄ autoxidizes even more readily than ord. diethyl ether ⟨2⟩.

Ⓓ ***x,x*-Dibromodibenzyl ether:** from C̄ (0.5 g.), dislvd. in alc. (1 ml.), treated during 5 min. with Br_2 (0.8 g.), stood overnight, gives solid; recrystd. from alc. (10 ml.) gives 0.47 g. plates, m.p. 107–108° u.c. ⟨3⟩; cf. ⟨4⟩.

Ⓓ **Dibenzyl ether picrate,** C̄.PkOH: or.-yel. pr. clusters from $CHCl_3$; m.p. 77–78° u.c. ⟨5⟩ [from C̄ + PkOH in $CHCl_3$ ⟨5⟩].

1:7640 ⟨1⟩ Bennett, Willis, *J. Chem. Soc.* **1928,** 2305–2307. ⟨2⟩ Rieche, Meister, *Angew. Chem.* **49,** 102 (1936). ⟨3⟩ Underwood, Baril, Toone, *J. Am. Chem. Soc.* **52,** 4090–4091 (1930). ⟨4⟩ Lachmann, *J. Am. Chem. Soc.* **45,** 2359–2360 (1923). ⟨5⟩ Baril, Megrdichian, *J. Am. Chem. Soc.* **58,** 1415 (1936).

1:7645 ISOAMYL α-NAPHTHYL ETHER $C_{15}H_{18}O$ **Beil. VI-607**

$(CH_3)_2.CH.CH_2.CH_2.O$—

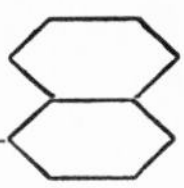

B.P. 317.5° cor. ⟨1⟩ **M.P. <−10°** $D_4^{14.2}$ = **1.00689** ⟨2⟩ $n_D^{14.2}$ = **1.57049** ⟨2⟩

$\bar{C}$ in hot alc. soln. treated with equiv. amt. PkOH in hot alc. gives on cooling a picrate, $\bar{C}$.PkOH, m.p. 96.0–97.0° cor. ⟨1⟩; Neut. Eq. 443.

1:7645 ⟨1⟩ V. H. Dermer, O. C. Dermer, *J. Org. Chem.* **3,** 289–293 (1938). ⟨2⟩ Costa, *Gazz. chim. ital.* **19,** 491 (1889).

—— **ISOAMYL β-NAPHTHYL ETHER** $C_{15}H_{18}O$ **Beil. VI-642**

$(CH_3)_2.CH.CH_2.CH_2.O$—

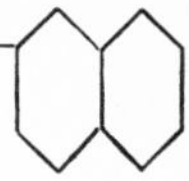

B.P. 321.0° cor. **M.P. 28°**

See 1:7128. Genus 9: Division A: Section 2.

—— ***n*-AMYL α-NAPHTHYL ETHER** $C_{15}H_{18}O$ **Beil. S.N. 537**

$CH_3.CH_2.CH_2.CH_2.CH_2.O$—

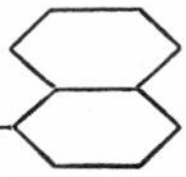

B.P. 322° cor. **M.P. 30°**

See 1:7132. Genus 9: Division A: Section 2.

—— ***n*-AMYL β-NAPHTHYL ETHER** $C_{15}H_{18}O$ **Beil. S.N. 538**

$CH_3.CH_2.CH_2.CH_2.CH_2.O$—

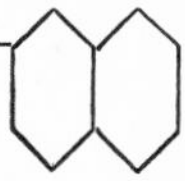

B.P. 327.5° cor. **M.P. 24.5°** n_D^{30} = **1.5587**

See 1:7117. Genus 9: Division A: Section 2.

ORDER I: SUBORDER I: GENUS 9: HYDROCARBONS

Division B, Liquids

Section 2. Acyclic Ethers

—— **ETHYL METHYL ETHER** $CH_3.CH_2.O.CH_3$ C_3H_8O **Beil. I-314**

B.P. 10.8° **D_0^0 = 0.7260**

See 1:6100. Genus 8: Division B: Section 1.

1:7800 DIVINYL ETHER $CH_2{=}CH.O.CH{=}CH_2$ C_4H_6O **Beil. I-433**

B.P. 28.3° ⟨1⟩ **M.P. −101.1° ⟨6⟩** **D_4^{20} = 0.773 ⟨1⟩** **n_D^{20} = 1.3989 ⟨1⟩ ⟨6⟩**

[For study of prepn. of C̄ from β,β'-dichlorodiethyl ether + KOH see ⟨1⟩ ⟨2⟩.] [For study of explosion hazards see ⟨3⟩.] [For study of vapor pressure see ⟨4⟩.]

C̄ reacts violently with conc. H_2SO_4 yielding a black tarry resin and some free acetaldehyde (1:0100) — C̄ with conc. HCl gives yellow color and acetaldehyde odor — C̄ with dil. HCl is rapidly hydrolyzed to acetaldehyde (1:0100). C̄ gradually gives fuchsin-aldehyde test (Generic Test 1) owing to hydrolysis ⟨1⟩.

C̄ reduces aq. $KMnO_4$ but not cold Tollens' reagent (T 1.11) — C̄ rapidly adds Br_2 (T 1.91). [C̄ in $CHCl_3$ at −15° slowly treated with 2 moles Br_2, solvent evapd. and resultant oil mixed with pet. ether gives 78–80% yield of a mixt. of two distinct cryst. diastereomers of $\alpha,\alpha',\beta,\beta'$-tetrabromodiethyl ether; prisms, m.p. 65–66°; ndls. (much more difficult to obtain), m.p. 62–63°. The m.p. of a mixt. of the two crystn. forms is depressed, e.g., to 45–57° ⟨5⟩.]

C̄ on treatment with I_2.KI soln. + aq. alk. (T 1.81) gives immediate ppt. of CHI_3 ⟨1⟩.

1:7800 ⟨1⟩ Ruigh, Major, *J. Am. Chem. Soc.* **53,** 2662–2671 (1931). ⟨2⟩ Lott, Smith, Christiansen, *J. Am. Pharm. Assoc.* **26,** 203–208 (1937). ⟨3⟩ Jones, Beattie, *Ind. Eng. Chem.* **26,** 557–560 (1934). ⟨4⟩ Miles, Menzies, *J. Phys. Chem.* **37,** 425–430 (1933). ⟨5⟩ Ruigh, Major, *J. Am. Chem. Soc.* **53,** 3133–3135 (1931). ⟨6⟩ Dolliver, Gresham, Kistiakowsky, Smith, Vaughan, *J. Am. Chem. Soc.* **60,** 442 (1938).

1:7805 ISOPROPYL METHYL ETHER $(CH_3)_2CH.O.CH_3$ $C_4H_{10}O$ **Beil. I-362**

B.P. 32.5° ⟨1⟩ **D_4^{15} = 0.7237 ⟨2⟩** **n_D^{20} = 1.35756 ⟨3⟩**

Soly. of C̄ in aq. at 25° is 6.5 wt. % ⟨2⟩. C̄ does not react with K/Na alloy ⟨4⟩.

1:7805 ⟨1⟩ Clusius, *J. Chem. Soc.* **1930,** 2611. ⟨2⟩ Bennett, Philip, *J. Chem. Soc.* **1928,** 1931, 1934. ⟨3⟩ Henry, *Rec. trav. chim.* **23,** 326 (1904). ⟨4⟩ Henstock, *J. Chem. Soc.* **1931,** 371–372.

—— **DIETHYL ETHER** $CH_3.CH_2.O.CH_2.CH_3$ $C_4H_{10}O$ **Beil. I-315**

B.P. 34.60° **M.P. stable form −116.3°** **D_4^{20} = 0.71352** **n_D^{20} = 1.3526**
metastable form −123.3°

See 1:6110. Genus 8: Division B: Section 1.

1:7810 ETHYL VINYL ETHER $CH_3.CH_2.O.CH{=}CH_2$ C_4H_8O **Beil. I-433**

B.P. 35.72° ⟨1⟩ **M.P. −115.8°** ⟨1⟩ D_4^{20} = **0.7589** ⟨2⟩ n_D^{20} = **1.3768** ⟨1⟩

C̄ is only sparingly sol. aq. [For occurrence in ord. diethyl ether see ⟨3⟩.]

C̄ in presence of dil. acids is rapidly hydrolyzed to acetaldehyde (1:0100) and ethyl alc. (1:6130). [For rate measurements see ⟨4⟩.]

C̄ on stdg. with I (2% soln. in $CHCl_3$) is rapidly polymerized. [For study of products see ⟨2⟩ ⟨5⟩.]

1:7810 ⟨1⟩ Dolliver, Gresham, Kistiakowsky, Smith, Vaughan, *J. Am. Chem. Soc.* **60,** 441 (1938). ⟨2⟩ Chalmers, *Can. J. Research* **7,** 464–471 (1932); *Chem. Abs.* **27,** 701 (1933). ⟨3⟩ King, *Nature* **120,** 843 (1927). ⟨4⟩ Zahorka, Weimann, *Monatsh.* **71,** 229–240 (1938). ⟨5⟩ Chalmers, *Can. J. Research* **7,** 472–480 (1932); *Chem. Abs.* **27,** 701 (1933).

1:7815 METHYL *n*-PROPYL ETHER $CH_3.O.CH_2.CH_2.CH_3$ $C_4H_{10}O$ **Beil. I-354**

B.P. 39° $D_4^{13.0}$ = **0.7356** ⟨1⟩

Soly. of C̄ in aq. at 25° is 3.05% by wt. ⟨1⟩ — C̄ is not attacked by K/Na alloy ⟨2⟩.

1:7815 ⟨1⟩ Bennett, Philip, *J. Chem. Soc.* **1928,** 1931, 1934. ⟨2⟩ Henstock, *J. Chem. Soc.* **1931,** 371–372.

1:7820 ALLYL METHYL ETHER $CH_2{=}CH.CH_2.O.CH_3$ C_4H_8O **Beil. I-437**

B.P. 46°

C̄ adds Br_2 (T 1.91) yielding methyl β,γ-dibromo-*n*-propyl ether [Beil. I-357], b.p. 185°, D_4^{20} = 1.8329 ⟨1⟩ ⟨2⟩.

1:7820 ⟨1⟩ Henry, *Ber.* **5,** 455 (1872). ⟨2⟩ Irvine, Macdonald, Soutar, *J. Chem. Soc.* **107,** 351 (1915).

1:7825 ETHYL ISOPROPYL ETHER $C_5H_{12}O$ **Beil. I-362**

$CH_3.CH_2.O.CH(CH_3)_2$

B.P. 53-54° ⟨1⟩ D_4^{20} = **0.7211** ⟨2⟩
D_4^{25} = **0.720** ⟨1⟩

C̄ is only slightly sol. aq. [At 25° soly. of C̄ in aq. is 2.40 wt. %; soly. of aq. in C̄ is 0.52 wt. % ⟨3⟩.]

C̄ does not react with K/Na alloy ⟨2⟩ — C̄ on htg. with 1% H_2SO_4 in s.t. at 150° yields ethyl alcohol (1:6130) and isopropyl alcohol (1:6135) ⟨4⟩.

1:7825 ⟨1⟩ Norris, Rigby, *J. Am. Chem. Soc.* **54,** 2097 (1932). ⟨2⟩ Henstock, *J. Chem. Soc.* **1931,** 371–372. ⟨3⟩ Bennett, Philip, *J. Chem. Soc.* **1928,** 1934. ⟨4⟩ Eltekow, *Ber.* **10,** 1902 (1877).

1:7830 *ter*-BUTYL METHYL ETHER $(CH_3)_3C.O.CH_3$ $C_5H_{12}O$ **Beil. I-381**

B.P. 55.2° ⟨1⟩ ⟨2⟩ D_4^{20} = **0.7405** ⟨2⟩ n_D^{20} = **1.3689** ⟨2⟩
D_4^{25} = **0.7354** ⟨1⟩ n_D^{25} = **1.3667** ⟨1⟩

Liq. with camphoraceous odor — C̄ is only slightly sol. aq. [At 20° soly. of C̄ in aq. is 4.8 g. per 100 g. soln.; soly. of aq. in C̄ is 1.5 g. per 100 g. soln. ⟨2⟩.]

[For prepn. of C̄ from *ter*-butyl alc. (1:6140) by distn. with dil. H_2SO_4 see ⟨1⟩.]

C̄ forms with aq. a const. boilg. mixt., b.p. 52.6°, contg. 96% by wt. of C̄; C̄ forms with methyl alc. a const. boilg. mixt., b.p. 51.6°, contg. 85% by wt. of C̄ ⟨2⟩.

1:7830 ⟨1⟩ Norris, Rigby, *J. Am. Chem. Soc.* **54,** 2095–2098 (1932). ⟨2⟩ Evans, Edlund, *Ind. Eng. Chem.* **28,** 1188 (1936). ⟨3⟩ Evans, *Ind. Eng. Chem., Anal. Ed.* **8,** 208 (1936).

1:7835 ISOBUTYL METHYL ETHER $C_5H_{12}O$ **Beil. I-376**

$(CH_3)_2.CH.CH_2.O.CH_3$

B.P. 58° ⟨1⟩ D_4^{20} = **0.7311 ⟨1⟩**

$\bar{C}$ is only slightly sol. in aq. [At 25° soly. of $\bar{C}$ in aq. is 1.10 wt. %; soly. of aq. in $\bar{C}$ is 2.02 wt. % ⟨1⟩.]

$\bar{C}$ is not attacked by K/Na alloy ⟨2⟩.

1:7835 ⟨1⟩ Bennett, Philip, *J. Chem. Soc.* **1928,** 1931, 1934. ⟨2⟩ Henstock, *J. Chem. Soc.* **1931,** 371–372.

1:7840 *sec*-BUTYL METHYL ETHER $C_5H_{12}O$ **Beil. S.N. 24**

$CH_3.CH_2.CH(CH_3).O.CH_3$

B.P. 59° ⟨1⟩ D_4^{20} = **0.7415 ⟨1⟩**

$\bar{C}$ is only slightly sol. in aq. [At 25° soly. of $\bar{C}$ in aq. is 1.60 wt. %; soly. of aq. in $\bar{C}$ is 1.95 wt. % ⟨1⟩.]

1:7840 ⟨1⟩ Bennett, Philip, *J. Chem. Soc.* **1928,** 1931, 1934.

1:7845 ETHYL *n*-PROPYL ETHER $C_5H_{12}O$ **Beil. I-354**

$CH_3.CH_2.O.CH_2.CH_2.CH_3$

B.P. 63.6° ⟨1⟩ **M.P. < −79°** D_4^{20} = **0.7386 ⟨2⟩** n_D^{20} = **1.36948 ⟨2⟩**

$\bar{C}$ is only slightly sol. aq. [At 25° soly. of $\bar{C}$ in aq. is 1.87 wt. %; soly. of aq. in $\bar{C}$ is 1.13 wt. % ⟨3⟩.]

$\bar{C}$ forms with EtOH a const. boilg. mixt., b.p. 61.2° contg. 75% $\bar{C}$ ⟨4⟩.

$\bar{C}$ does not react with K/Na alloy ⟨5⟩.

1:7845 ⟨1⟩ Staveley, Hinshelwood, *Proc. Roy. Soc. (London)* **A-159,** 199 (1937). ⟨2⟩ Brühl, *Ann.* **200,** 177 (1879). ⟨3⟩ Bennett, Philip, *J. Chem. Soc.* **1928,** 1934. ⟨4⟩ Lecat, *Rec. trav. chim.* **46,** 243 (1927). ⟨5⟩ Henstock, *J. Chem. Soc.* **1931,** 371–372.

—— **DIISOPROPYL ETHER** $(CH_3)_2CH.O.CH(CH_3)_2$ $C_6H_{14}O$ **Beil. I-362**

B.P. 67.5° **M.P. −60°** D_{20}^{20} = **0.7247** n_D^{23} = **1.3678**

See 1:6125. Genus 8: Division B: Section 1.

1:7850 ALLYL ETHYL ETHER $C_5H_{10}O$ **Beil. I-438**

$CH_2{=}CH.CH_2.O.CH_2.CH_3$

B.P. 66-67°$_{742}$ ⟨1⟩ D_4^{20} = **0.7651 ⟨1⟩** n_D^{20} = **1.3881 ⟨1⟩**

$\bar{C}$ adds Br_2 (T 1.91) yielding ethyl β,γ-dibromo-*n*-propyl ether [Beil. I-357], b.p. 193–195°.

$\bar{C}$ on htg. with 2% H_2SO_4 is largely decomposed into ethyl alcohol (1:6130) and allyl alcohol (1:6145) ⟨2⟩.

1:7850 ⟨1⟩ Brühl, *Ann.* **200,** 178 (1879). ⟨2⟩ Eltekow, *Ber.* **10,** 1903 (1877).

1:7855 *n*-BUTYL METHYL ETHER $C_5H_{12}O$ **Beil. I-369**

$CH_3.CH_2.CH_2.CH_2.O.CH_3$

B.P. 70.5-71.0° ⟨1⟩ **M.P. −115.5° ⟨2⟩** D_4^{20} = **0.7455 ⟨1⟩** n_D^{20} = **1.3728 ⟨1⟩**

$\bar{C}$ is only slightly sol. aq. [At 25° soly. of $\bar{C}$ in aq. is 0.89 wt. %; soly. of aq. in $\bar{C}$ is 0.91 wt. % ⟨3⟩.]

C̄ is not attacked by K/Na alloy ⟨4⟩.

C̄ on oxidn. with alk. $KMnO_4$ at 35–40° gives acetic acid (1:1010) and methoxyacetic acid (1:1065) ⟨1⟩.

1:7855 ⟨1⟩ Jacobson, Dykstra, Carothers, *J. Am. Chem. Soc.* **56,** 1170 (1934). ⟨2⟩ Timmermans *Bull. soc. chim. Belg.* **36,** 505 (1927). ⟨3⟩ Bennett, Philip, *J. Chem. Soc.* **1928,** 1931, 1934. ⟨4⟩ Henstock, *J. Chem. Soc.* **1931,** 371–372.

1:7860 *ter*-BUTYL ETHYL ETHER $C_6H_{14}O$ Beil. I-381

$(CH_3)_3C.O.CH_2.CH_3$

B.P. 73.1° cor. ⟨1⟩ D_4^{20} = **0.7404** ⟨2⟩ n_D^{20} = **1.3760** ⟨2⟩
D_4^{25} = **0.7364** ⟨1⟩ n_D^{25} = **1.3728** ⟨1⟩

C̄ is only slightly sol. aq. [At 20° soly. of C̄ in aq. is 1.2 g. per 100 g. soln.; soly. of aq. in C̄ is 0.5 g. per 100 g. soln. ⟨2⟩.]

[For prepn. of C̄ in 95% yield by distn. of *ter*-butyl alcohol (1:6140) with dil. H_2SO_4 see ⟨1⟩.]

C̄ forms with aq. a const. boilg. mixt., b.p. 65.2°, contg. 94% C̄ by wt.; C̄ forms with ethyl alc. (1:6130) a const. boilg. mixt., b.p. 66.6°, contg. 79% C̄ by wt. ⟨2⟩.

C̄ with Denigès' reagt. gives opalescence in 2 min., yel. coloration in 3 min. at room temp.; on htg. gives dark yel. curdy ppt. ⟨3⟩ [dif. from ethyl isobutyl ether (1:7865) ⟨3⟩].

1:7860 ⟨1⟩ Norris, Rigby, *J. Am. Chem. Soc.* **54,** 2095–2098 (1932). ⟨2⟩ Evans, Edlund, *Ind. Eng. Chem.* **28,** 1188 (1936). ⟨3⟩ Marks, Lipkin, *J. Org. Chem.* **3,** 598–602 (1939).

1:7865 ETHYL ISOBUTYL ETHER $C_6H_{14}O$ Beil. I-376

$CH_3.CH_2.O.CH_2.CH(CH_3)_2$

B.P. 81.1° cor. ⟨1⟩ D_4^{25} = **0.7323** ⟨1⟩ n_D^{25} = **1.3739** ⟨1⟩

C̄ forms with aq. a mixt. of minimum b.p. 69° ⟨1⟩.

[For prepn. of C̄ in 70% yield from isobutyl alc. (1:6165) + Na + $(C_2H_5)_2SO_4$ see ⟨2⟩.]

C̄ does not react with K/Na alloy ⟨3⟩.

C̄ gives no reaction with Denigès' reagt. ⟨4⟩ [dif. from *ter*-butyl ethyl ether (1:7860)].

1:7865 ⟨1⟩ Norris, Rigby, *J. Am. Chem. Soc.* **54,** 2098 (1932). ⟨2⟩ Marks, Lipkin, Bettman, *J. Am. Chem. Soc.* **59,** 946–947 (1937). ⟨3⟩ Henstock, *J. Chem. Soc.* **1931,** 371–372. ⟨4⟩ Marks, Lipkin, *J. Org. Chem.* **3,** 598–602 (1939).

1:7870 *sec*-BUTYL ETHYL ETHER $C_6H_{14}O$ Beil. S.N. 24

$CH_3.CH_2.CH(CH_3).O.CH_2.CH_3$

B.P. 81.2° cor. ⟨1⟩ D_4^{20} = **0.7503** ⟨2⟩ n_D^{20} = **1.3802** ⟨2⟩
D_4^{25} = **0.7377** ⟨1⟩ n_D^{25} = **1.3753** ⟨1⟩

C̄ with aq. shows minimum b.p. of 71° ⟨1⟩.

1:7870 ⟨1⟩ Norris, Rigby, *J. Am. Chem. Soc.* **54,** 2097–2098 (1932). ⟨2⟩ Waterman, de Kok, Leendertse, Schoenmaker, *Rec. trav. chim.* **56,** 440 (1937).

1:7875 ISOPROPYL *n*-PROPYL ETHER $C_6H_{14}O$ Beil. I-362

$(CH_3)_2CH.O.CH_2.CH_2.CH_3$

B.P. 83° ⟨1⟩ D_4^{20} = **0.7370** ⟨2⟩ n_D^{21} = **1.376** ⟨3⟩

[For prepn. from *n*-propyl benzenesulfonate + sodium isopropylate (55% yield) see ⟨3⟩.]

C̄ is only slightly sol. aq. [At 25° soly. of C̄ in aq. is 0.47 wt. % ⟨1⟩.]

C̄ is not attacked by K/Na alloy ⟨4⟩.

1:7875 ⟨1⟩ Bennett, Philip, *J. Chem. Soc.* **1928,** 1931, 1934. ⟨2⟩ Wuyts, Lacourt, *Bull. soc. chim. Belg.* **39,** 165 (1930). ⟨3⟩ Truchet, Graves, *Bull. soc. chim.* (4) **51,** 688 (1932). ⟨4⟩ Henstock, *J. Chem. Soc.* **1931,** 371–372.

—— ETHYLENE GLYCOL DIMETHYL ETHER $C_4H_{10}O_2$ Beil. I-467

$CH_3.O.CH_2.CH_2.O.CH_3$

B.P. 84.7° D_4^{20} = **0.8665** n_D^{20} = **1.37965**

See 1:6141. Genus 8: Division B: Section 1.

1:7880 *ter*-AMYL METHYL ETHER $C_6H_{14}O$ Beil. I-389

$CH_3.CH_2.C(CH_3)_2.O.CH_3$

B.P. 86.3° ⟨1⟩ D_4^{20} = **0.7703 ⟨1⟩** n_D^{20} = **1.3885 ⟨1⟩**
D_4^{25} = **0.7656 ⟨1⟩**

C̄ is only slightly sol. aq. [At 20° soly. of C̄ in aq. is 1.15 g. per 100 g. soln.; soly. of aq. in C̄ is 0.6 g. per 100 g. soln. ⟨1⟩ ⟨2⟩.]

C̄ forms with aq. a const. boilg. mixt., b.p. 73.8°, contg. 91% C̄ by wt.; C̄ forms with methyl alc. (1:6120) a const. boilg. mixt., b.p. 62.3°, contg. 50% C̄ by wt. ⟨1⟩.

C̄ with Denigès' reagt. gives opalescence and yel. color within 4 min. at room temp.; white ndls. after htg. ⟨3⟩ [dif. from di-*n*-propyl ether (1:7885)].

1:7880 ⟨1⟩ Evans, Edlund, *Ind. Eng. Chem.* **28,** 1188 (1936). ⟨2⟩ Evans, *Ind. Eng. Chem., Anal. Ed.* **8,** 208 (1936). ⟨3⟩ Marks, Lipkin, *J. Org. Chem.* **3,** 598–602 (1939).

1:7885 DI-*n*-PROPYL ETHER $C_6H_{14}O$ Beil. I-354

$CH_3.CH_2.CH_2.O.CH_2.CH_2.CH_3$

B.P. 90.1° ⟨1⟩ **M.P. −122° ⟨1⟩** D_4^{20} = **0.74698 ⟨1⟩** n_D^{20} = **1.3829 ⟨2⟩**

C̄ is only slightly sol. in aq. [At 25° soly. of C̄ in aq. is 0.49% by wt.; soly. of aq. in C̄ is 0.45% ⟨3⟩.]

C̄ forms with aq. a binary const. boilg. mixt., b.p. 75.4°; C̄ forms with *n*-propyl alc. (1:6150) a binary const. boilg. mixt., b.p. 85.8°, contg. 67.8% C̄; C̄ forms with both *n*-propyl alc. and aq. a ternary const. boilg. mixt., b.p. 74.8°, contg. 68.1% C̄, 20.2% *n*-propyl alc., and 11.7% aq. ⟨4⟩.

C̄ htd. with 3,5-dinitrobenzoyl chloride + $ZnCl_2$ (T 1.98) yields *n*-propyl 3,5-dinitrobenzoate, m.p. 73.5–74° ⟨5⟩.

1:7885 ⟨1⟩ Timmermans, Hennaut-Roland, *J. chim. phys.* **27,** 416 (1930). ⟨2⟩ Ipatieff, Orloff, Petroff, *Ber.* **60,** 1007 (1927). ⟨3⟩ Bennett, Philip, *J. Chem. Soc.* **1928,** 1934. ⟨4⟩ Popelier, *Bull. soc. chim. Belg.* **32,** 193 (1923). ⟨5⟩ Underwood, Baril, Toone, *J. Am. Chem. Soc.* **52,** 4088 (1930).

1:7890 ISOAMYL METHYL ETHER $C_6H_{14}O$ Beil. I-400

$(CH_3)_2.CH.CH_2.CH_2.O.CH_3$

B.P. 91° D_4^{11} = **0.6871**

1:7895 *n*-**BUTYL ETHYL ETHER** $C_6H_{14}O$ **Beil. I-369**

$CH_3.CH_2.CH_2.CH_2.O.CH_2.CH_3$

B.P. 92.3° cor. ⟨1⟩ **M.P. −124°** ⟨2⟩ D_4^{20} = **0.7505** ⟨3⟩ n_D^{20} = **1.3820** ⟨3⟩
D_4^{25} = **0.7447** ⟨1⟩ n_D^{25} = **1.3798** ⟨1⟩

C̄ with aq. gives mixt. of minimum b.p. 75° ⟨1⟩ — C̄ is unattacked by K/Na alloy ⟨4⟩.

1:7895 ⟨1⟩ Norris, Rigby, *J. Am. Chem. Soc.* **54,** 2098 (1932). ⟨2⟩ Timmermans, Metaar, *Bull. soc. chim. Belg.* **30,** 214 (1921). ⟨3⟩ Jacobson, Dykstra, Carothers, *J. Am. Chem. Soc.* **56,** 1170 (1934). ⟨4⟩ Henstock, *J. Chem. Soc.* **1931,** 371–372.

1:7900 DIALLYL ETHER $C_6H_{10}O$ **Beil. I-438**

$CH_2{=}CH.CH_2.O.CH_2.CH{=}CH_2$

B.P. 94.3° cor. D_0^{18} = **0.8046**

C̄ is only sparingly sol. aq. [At 25° soly. of C̄ in aq. is 8.86 wt. %; soly. of aq. in C̄ is 1.51 wt. % ⟨1⟩.]

C̄ adds Br_2 (T 1.91).

1:7900 ⟨1⟩ Bennett, Philip, *J. Chem. Soc.* **1928,** 1934.

1:7905 *n*-**AMYL METHYL ETHER** $C_6H_{14}O$ **Beil. I₁-(193)**

$CH_3.CH_2.CH_2.CH_2.CH_2.O.CH_3$

B.P. 99-100° ⟨1⟩ D_4^{22} = **0.759** ⟨1⟩ n_D^{22} = **1.3862** ⟨1⟩

[For prepn. in 67% yield from *n*-butyl MgBr + chloromethyl methyl ether see ⟨1⟩.]

1:7905 ⟨1⟩ Gredy, *Bull. soc. chim.* (5) **3,** 1094 (1936).

1:7910 *ter*-**AMYL ETHYL ETHER** $C_7H_{16}O$ **Beil. I-389**

$CH_3.CH_2.C(CH_3)_2.O.CH_2.CH_3$

B.P. 101° ⟨1⟩ D_4^{20} = **0.7657** ⟨1⟩ n_D^{20} = **1.3912** ⟨1⟩
D_4^{25} = **0.7609** ⟨1⟩

C̄ is only slightly sol. in aq. [At 20° soly. of C̄ in aq. is 0.4 g. per 100 g. soln.; soly. of aq. in C̄ is 0.2 g. per 100 g. soln. ⟨1⟩.]

C̄ forms with aq. a const. boilg. mixt., b.p. 81.2°, contg. 87% C̄ by wt.; C̄ forms with ethyl alc. (1:6130) a const. boilg. mixt. b.p. 66.6°, contg. 79% C̄ by wt. ⟨1⟩.

C̄ with Deniges' reagt. gives opalescence within 6 min. at room temp., white ndls. on warming ⟨2⟩ [dif. from *n*-amyl methyl ether (1:7905)].

1:7910 ⟨1⟩ Evans, Edlund, *Ind. Eng. Chem.* **28,** 1188 (1936). ⟨2⟩ Marks, Lipkin, *J. Org. Chem.* **3,** 598–602 (1939).

—— **ETHYLENE GLYCOL ETHYL METHYL ETHER** $C_5H_{12}O_2$ **Beil. S.N. 30**

$C_2H_5.O.CH_2.CH_2.O.CH_3$

B.P. 102° D_4^{20} = **0.8529** n_D^{20} = **1.38677**

See 1:6159. Genus 8: Division B: Section 1.

1:7915 ***n*-BUTYL ISOPROPYL ETHER** $C_7H_{16}O$ **Beil. S.N. 24**

$CH_3.CH_2.CH_2.CH_2.O.CH(CH_3)_2$

B.P. 108$^\circ_{738}$ (1) D^{15} = **0.7594** (1) $n^{24.9}_{5461}$ = **1.3889** (1)

$\bar{C}$ boiled with conc. HI gives *n*-butyl iodide + a very little isopropyl iodide (1). $\bar{C}$ is unattacked by K/Na alloy (1).

For solubility in conc. H_2SO_4 see (2).

1:7915 (1) Henstock, *J. Chem. Soc.* **1931,** 371–372. (2) Kirrmann, Graves, *Bull. soc. chim.* (5) **1,** 1497–1498 (1934).

1:7920 **ETHYL ISOAMYL ETHER** $C_7H_{16}O$ **Beil. I-401**

$CH_3.CH_2.O.CH_2.CH_2.CH(CH_3)_2$

B.P. 112° D^{18} = **0.764**

1:7925 ***n*-BUTYL *n*-PROPYL ETHER** $C_7H_{16}O$ **Beil. I-369**

$CH_3.CH_2.CH_2.CH_2.O.CH_2.CH_2.CH_3$

B.P. 117° D^0_0 = **0.7773**

1:7935 **DI-*sec*-BUTYL ETHER** $C_8H_{18}O$ **Beil. I-372**

$$CH_3.CH_2.\overset{\overset{H}{|}}{\underset{\underset{CH_3}{|}}{C}}—O—\overset{\overset{H}{|}}{\underset{\underset{CH_3}{|}}{C}}.CH_3.CH_3$$

B.P. 121° (1) D^{25} = **0.759** (1) n^{25}_D = **1.3928** (1)

$\bar{C}$ satd. with HBr gas and refluxed 3 hrs. gives 81% yield *sec*-butyl bromide, b.p. 90–91°, D^{25} = 1.250, n^{25}_D = 1.250 (1).

$\bar{C}$ htd. with 3,5-dinitrobenzoyl chloride + $ZnCl_2$ (T 1.98) yields *sec*-butyl 3,5-dinitrobenzoate, m.p. 75.5° (1).

1:7935 (1) Drake, Veitch, *J. Am. Chem. Soc.* **57,** 2624–2625 (1935).

1:7945 **DIISOBUTYL ETHER** $C_8H_{18}O$ **Beil. I-376**

$(CH_3)_2CH.CH_2.O.CH_2.CH(CH_3)_2$

B.P. 123° D^{15}_{15} = **0.7616**

$\bar{C}$ forms with isobutyl alc. (1:6165) and aq. a ternary const. boilg. mixt., b.p. 85.4° (1).

$\bar{C}$ htd. with 3,5-dinitrobenzoyl chloride + $ZnCl_2$ (T 1.98) yields isobutyl 3,5-dinitrobenzoate, m.p. 84.5–85.5° (2).

1:7945 (1) Popelier, *Bull. soc. chim. Belg.* **32,** 193 (1923). (2) Underwood, Baril, Toone, *J. Am. Chem. Soc.* **52,** 4088 (1930).

—— **ETHYLENE GLYCOL METHYL *n*-PROPYL ETHER** **Beil. S.N. 30**

$CH_3.O.CH_2.CH_2.O.CH_2.CH_2.CH_3$ $C_6H_{14}O_2$

B.P. 124.5° D^{20}_4 = **0.8472** n^{20}_D = **1.39467**

See 1:6191. Genus 8: Division B: Section 1.

1:7950 **DI-*n*-BUTYL ETHER** $C_8H_{18}O$ **Beil. I-369**

$CH_3.CH_2.CH_2.CH_2.O.CH_2.CH_2.CH_2.CH_3$

B.P. 142.4° (1) **M.P. −95.3°** (2) D^{20}_4 = **0.76829** (1) n^{15}_D = **1.4010** (3)
−98° (1)

$\bar{C}$ is practically insol. aq. [soly. at 17° is less than 0.01% (4)].

$\bar{C}$ forms with aq. a binary const. boilg. mixt., b.p. 93.5°; $\bar{C}$ forms with *n*-butyl alc. (1:6180) a binary const. boilg. mixt., b.p. 117.25° contg. 12% $\bar{C}$; $\bar{C}$ forms with both *n*-butyl alc.

and aq. a ternary const. boilg. mixt., b.p. 91°, contg. 27.7% C̄, 42.9% *n*-butyl alc. and 29.3% aq. ⟨5⟩.

[For prepn. from *n*-butyl alc. (1:6180) see ⟨6⟩.] [For study of peroxide formation see ⟨7⟩.]

C̄ htd. with $ZnCl_2$ + 3,5-dinitrobenzoyl chloride (T 1.98) yields *n*-butyl 3,5-dinitrobenzoate, m.p. 62–63° ⟨8⟩.

1:7950 ⟨1⟩ Timmermans, Hennaut-Roland, *J. chim. phys.* **27,** 417 (1930). ⟨2⟩ Archibald, *J. Am. Chem. Soc.* **53,** 4452 (1931). ⟨3⟩ Popelier, *Bull. soc. chim. Belg.* **32,** 186 (1923). ⟨4⟩ Bennett, Philip, *J. Chem. Soc.* **1928,** 1934. ⟨5⟩ Ref. 3, page 193. ⟨6⟩ Hillman, Davis, Clarke, *J. Am. Chem. Soc.* **43,** 368 (1921). ⟨7⟩ Clover, *J. Am. Chem. Soc.* **46,** 422–424 (1924). ⟨8⟩ Underwood, Baril, Toone, *J. Am. Chem. Soc.* **52,** 4088 (1930).

1:7960 DIISOAMYL ETHER $C_{10}H_{22}O$ Beil. I-401

$(CH_3)_2.CH.CH_2.CH_2.O.CH_2.CH_2.CH(CH_3)_2$

B.P. 172.5° ⟨1⟩ D^{25}_{25} = **0.77408 ⟨1⟩**

C̄ forms with aq. a const. boilg. mixt., b.p. 97.2°; C̄ forms with isoamyl alc. (1:6200) + aq. a ternary const. boilg. mixt., b.p. 94.4° ⟨2⟩.

[For prepn. of pure C̄ see ⟨3⟩.] [For autoxidation see ⟨4⟩.]

C̄ htd. with 3,5-dinitrobenzoyl chloride + $ZnCl_2$ (T 1.98) gives isoamyl 3,5-dinitrobenzoate, m.p. 60–61° ⟨5⟩.

1:7960 ⟨1⟩ Perkin, *J. prakt. Chem.* (2) **31,** 513 (1885). ⟨2⟩ Popelier, *Bull. soc. chim. Belg.* **32,** 193 (1923). ⟨3⟩ Schorigin, Makaroff-Semljanski, *Ber.* **65,** 1293–1295 (1932). ⟨4⟩ Clover, *J. Am. Chem. Soc.* **46,** 424–425 (1924). ⟨5⟩ Underwood, Baril, Toone, *J. Am. Chem. Soc.* **52,** 4088 (1930).

1:7970 DI-*n*-AMYL ETHER $C_{10}H_{22}O$ Beil. S.N. 24

$CH_3(CH_2)_3.CH_2.O.CH_2.(CH_2)_3.CH_3$

B.P. 187.5° ⟨1⟩ **M.P. −69.3° ⟨1⟩** D^{20}_4 = **0.78298 ⟨1⟩** n^{15}_D = **1.41392 ⟨1⟩**

C̄ htd. with 3,5-dinitrobenzoyl chloride + $ZnCl_2$ (T 1.98) yields *n*-amyl 3,5-dinitrobenzoate, m.p. 42–43° ⟨2⟩.

1:7970 ⟨1⟩ Timmermans, Martin, *J. chim. phys.* **25,** 437 (1928). ⟨2⟩ Underwood, Baril, Toone, *J. Am. Chem. Soc.* **52,** 4088 (1930).

1:7980 DI-*n*-HEXYL ETHER $C_{12}H_{26}O$ Beil. S.N. 24

$CH_3.(CH_2)_4CH_2.O.CH_2.(CH_2)_4.CH_3$

B.P. 228–229°$_{761}$ ⟨1⟩ D^{20}_4 = **0.7936 ⟨1⟩**

C̄ htd. with 3,5-dinitrobenzoyl chloride + $ZnCl_2$ (T 1.98) yields *n*-hexyl 3,5-dinitrobenzoate, m.p. 54.5–55.5° ⟨2⟩ [cf. somewhat higher values given under *n*-hexyl alc. (1:6230)].

1:7980 ⟨1⟩ Olivier, *Rec. trav. chim.* **55,** 1034 (1936). ⟨2⟩ Underwood, Baril, Toone, *J. Am. Chem. Soc.* **52,** 4088 (1930).

1:7990 DI-*n*-HEPTYL ETHER $C_{14}H_{30}O$ [Beil. I-415

$CH_3(CH_2)_5.CH_2.O.CH_2(CH_2)_5.CH_3$

B.P. 261.5°$_{745}$ ⟨1⟩ D^{20}_{20} = **0.8056 ⟨1⟩**

1:7990 ⟨1⟩ Schroeter, *Ann.* **418,** 201 (1919).

ORDER I: SUBORDER I: GENUS 9: HYDROCARBONS

Division B, Liquids

Section 3: Dienes, alkynes, cyclenes, terpenes, etc.

1:8000 **BUTYNE-1** $CH_3.CH_2.C{\equiv}C.H$ C_4H_6 **Beil. I-248**
(Ethylacetylene)

B.P. +8.6° ⟨1⟩ ⟨2⟩ **M.P. −122.5°** ⟨1⟩ D^0 = **0.6784** ⟨1⟩
+7.9° ⟨3⟩

[For prepn. from $H.C{\equiv}C.Na$ in liq. NH_3 with $C_2H_5.I$ (78% yield) see ⟨4⟩; with $(C_2H_5)_2$-SO_4 (100% yield ⟨5⟩; 60% yield ⟨6⟩) see ⟨5⟩ ⟨6⟩.]

$\bar{C}$ with $NH_4OH/CuCl$ (T 1.96-A) gives a yel. ppt.; $\bar{C}$ with alk. K_2HgI_4 (T 1.96-B) gives white ppt. of dibutynylmercury, long white ndls. or glistening flakes from alc., m.p. 162–163° ⟨7⟩.

1:8000 ⟨1⟩ Morehouse, Maass, *Can. J. Research* **5,** 311 (1931). ⟨2⟩ Morehouse, Maass, *Can. J. Research* **11,** 637–641 (1934). ⟨3⟩ Krieger, Wenzke, *J. Am. Chem. Soc.* **60,** 2118 (1938). ⟨4⟩ Lai, *Bull. soc. chim.* (4) **53,** 687–692 (1933). ⟨5⟩ Vaughn, Hennison, Vogt, Nieuwland, *J. Org. Chem.* **2,** 9 (1938). ⟨6⟩ Hurd, Meinert, *J. Am. Chem. Soc.* **53,** 296 (1931). ⟨7⟩ Johnson, McEwen, *J. Am. Chem. Soc.* **48,** 472 (1926).

1:8005 **BUTYNE-2** $CH_3.C{\equiv}C.CH_3$ C_4H_6 **Beil. I-249**
(Dimethylacetylene)

B.P. 27.2° ⟨1⟩ ⟨2⟩ D^{25} = **0.688** ⟨1⟩ n_D^{25} = **1.3893** ⟨1⟩
26.69° ⟨3⟩

[For prepn. from $CH_3.C{\equiv}C.Na + CH_3I$ see ⟨1⟩ ⟨4⟩; from $Na.C{\equiv}C.Na + (CH_3)_2SO_4$ in liq. NH_3 (80% yield) see ⟨3⟩; from 2,3-dibromobutane + alc. KOH see ⟨2⟩.]

$\bar{C}$ does not react with $NH_4OH/CuCl$, $NH_4OH/AgNO_3$ (dif. from ethylacetylene (1:8000)).

$\bar{C}$ adds Br_2 (T 1.91); $\bar{C}$ in CS_2 treated with 1 mole Br_2 in 4 vols. CS_2 in cold and dark yields *cis*-2,3-dibromobutene-2 [Beil. I-206], b.p. 146–146.5° ⟨5⟩; $\bar{C}$ similarly treated with at least 2 moles Br_2 yields 2,2,3,3-tetrabromobutane [Beil. I-122], cryst. from ether or lgr., m.p. 243° ⟨5⟩ ⟨6⟩.

$\bar{C}$ treated with 3 vols. of HBr (satd. at 0°) yields ⟨7⟩ *trans*-2-bromobutene-2, b.p. 84–85° ⟨8⟩. [The *cis* isomer (apparently not formed here) has b.p. 94.9° ⟨8⟩.]

1:8005 ⟨1⟩ Heisig, Davis, *J. Am. Chem. Soc.* **57,** 339 (1935). ⟨2⟩ Pauling, Springall, Palmer, *J. Am. Chem. Soc.* **61,** 928 (1939). ⟨3⟩ Conn, Kistiakowsky, Smith, *J. Am. Chem. Soc.* **61,** 1868 (1939). ⟨4⟩ Heisig, *J. Am. Chem. Soc.* **53,** 3256 (1931). ⟨5⟩ Wislicenus, Schmidt, *Ann.* **313,** 225 (1900). ⟨6⟩ Durio, *Gazz. chim. ital.* **66,** 490 (1936). ⟨7⟩ Ref. 5, page 222. ⟨8⟩ Lebrun, *Bull. soc. chim. Belg.* **39,** 426 (1930).

1:8010 3-METHYLBUTYNE-1 (Isopropylacetylene) C_5H_8 **Beil. I-251**

```
      CH3
      |
CH3.C.C≡C.H
      |
      H
```

B.P. 27.5-28.5° ⟨1⟩ D_4^{19} = **0.666 ⟨1⟩** n_D^{19} = **1.3785 ⟨1⟩**

[For prepn. from H.C≡C.Na + isopropyl sulfate in liq. NH_3 see ⟨2⟩.]

C̄ adds Br_2 (T 1.91) [allegedly yielding with 1 mole Br_2 1,2-dibromo-3-methylbutene-1 [Beil. I-214], b.p. 175° dec.; with 2 moles Br_2 1,1,2,2-tetrabromo-3-methylbutane [Beil. I-138], b.p. 275° ⟨3⟩].

C̄ htd. with $ZnCl_2$ in s.t. at 150° (quant. yield ⟨4⟩), or C̄ treated with H_2SO_4 (D = 1.65) ⟨5⟩ gives methyl isopropyl ketone (1:5410).

C̄ treated with NH_4OH/CuCl (T 1.96-A) gives a yellow ppt.; with alc. $AgNO_3$ a white ppt. ⟨1⟩.

1:8010 ⟨1⟩ Gredy, *Bull. soc. chim.* (5) **2,** 1953 (1935). ⟨2⟩ Kranzfelder, Sowa, *J. Am. Chem. Soc.* **59,** 1491 (1937). ⟨3⟩ Bruylants, *Ber.* **8,** 407 (1875). ⟨4⟩ Kutscheroff, *Ber.* **42,** 2761 (1909). ⟨5⟩ Flavitzky, Kriloff, *Ber.* **10,** 2240 (1877); *Ber.* **11,** 1940 (1878).

1:8015 FURAN 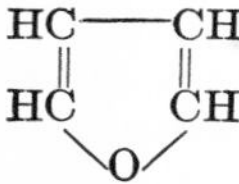 C_4H_4O **Beil. XVII-27**

B.P. 31.27° ⟨1⟩ **F.P. −85.6° ⟨1⟩** D_4^{20} = **0.9366 ⟨2⟩** n_D^{20} = **1.42157 ⟨2⟩**

Peculiar odor! Insol. aq., eas. sol. alc., ether — C̄ is quant. absorbed by 82.5% H_2SO_4 (dif. from ethylene ⟨3⟩).

[For prepn. of C̄ (72–78% yield ⟨4⟩) by decarboxylation of furoic acid (1:0475) by htg. see ⟨4⟩; reaction is much facilitated by use of catalysts such as $CuSO_4$, CuO, or quinoline ⟨5⟩ ⟨6⟩.]

C̄ is unaffected by Na or K, or by alkalies, but is very sensitive to and resinified by conc. minl. acids.

C̄ decolorizes Br_2 (T 1.91) [for detn. of C̄ via KBr/$KBrO_3$ titration see ⟨7⟩].

C̄ in contact with pine splinter moistened with HCl gives emerald-green color [dif. from 2,5-dimethylfuran (1:8080) which gives red; but green color is also given by 2-methylfuran (sylvan) ⟨8⟩].

C̄ (1.4 g.) + maleic anhydride (2 g.) in abs. ether, stood some hrs. in cold, seps. white ppt. of 3,6-endoxo-Δ^4-tetrahydrophthalic anhydride, m.p. 125° ⟨9⟩, 118° ⟨10⟩ with decompn. into its components.

[For extensive reviews of furan series see ⟨11⟩ ⟨12⟩.]

1:8015 ⟨1⟩ Dolliver, Gresham, Kistiakowsky, Smith, Vaughan, *J. Am. Chem. Soc.* **60,** 442 (1938). ⟨2⟩ von Auwers, *Ann.* **408,** 270 (1915). ⟨3⟩ Hurd, Goldsby, *J. Am. Chem. Soc.* **54,** 2558 (1932). ⟨4⟩ Wilson, *Organic Syntheses, Coll. Vol.* I, 269–270 (1932). ⟨5⟩ Gilman, Louisinian, *Rec. trav. chim.* **52,** 156–159 (1933). ⟨6⟩ Wagner, Simons, *J. Chem. Education* **13,** 270 (1936). ⟨7⟩ Cortese, *Rec. trav. chim.* **48,** 566 (1929). ⟨8⟩ Reichstein, *Helv. Chim. Acta* **15,** 1111 (1932). ⟨9⟩ Diels, Alder, *Ber.* **62,** 557 (1929). ⟨10⟩ von Bruchhausen, Bersch, *Arch. Pharm.* **266,** 700 (1928).

⟨11⟩ Gilman, Wright, *Chem. Rev.* **11,** 323–367 (1932). ⟨12⟩ Peters, *Ind. Eng. Chem.* **28,** 755–759 (1936).

1:8020 ISOPRENE CH_3 C_5H_8 **Beil. I-252**
(2-Methylbutadiene-1,3)

$$H_2C{=}\overset{\displaystyle CH_3}{\overset{|}{C}}.CH{=}CH_2$$

B.P. 34.076° ⟨1⟩ **M.P. −146.8°** ⟨1⟩ D_4^{20} = **0.6805** ⟨1⟩ n_D^{20} = **1.42160** ⟨1⟩

[For prepn. by " cracking " of dipentene (*d,l*-limonene) (1:8165) via " isoprene lamp " see ⟨1⟩ ⟨2⟩ ⟨3⟩; by distn. of crude rubber see ⟨4⟩.] [For purification of $\bar{C}$ via formn. of " isoprene sulfone " with liq. SO_2, recrystn. from aq., and subsequent regeneration of $\bar{C}$ by htg. at 120–135° see ⟨5⟩; via addn. of Br_2 to form " isoprene tetrabromide," b.p. 155–160° and treatment of latter with Zn dust see ⟨2⟩.]

$\bar{C}$ is very reactive and unstable; it oxidizes and polymerizes on stdg. in air.

$\bar{C}$ adds Br_2 (T 1.91). [$\bar{C}$ in $CHCl_3$ at −25° with 1 mole Br_2 in $CHCl_3$ yields 1,4-dibromo-2-methylbutene-2 (isoprene dibromide), b.p. 90–96° at 12 mm., in 60–80% yield ⟨6⟩ ⟨7⟩; $\bar{C}$ in $CHCl_3$ at −10° (75–80% yield ⟨2⟩), or in CS_2 (alm. quant. yield ⟨7⟩) treated with 2 moles Br_2 gives 1,2,3,4-tetrabromo-2-methylbutane, b.p. 155–160° at 12 mm.] [Use in purification of $\bar{C}$, see above.] [$\bar{C}$ does *not* give good results in $KBr/KBrO_3$ titration (T 1.925); B.B. No. found 410, 415, calcd. 471.]

$\bar{C}$ in AcOH + NaSCN in AcOH treated at 5° with Br_2 in AcOH gives (abt. 22% yield ⟨8⟩) a cpd. $\bar{C}.(SCN)_2$, cryst. from C_6H_6 + lgr., m.p. 76–77° cor.

$\bar{C}$ treated with diazotized 2,4-dinitroaniline couples yielding 2,4-dinitrobenzeneazo-isoprene, or.-yel. cryst., m.p. 98° with explosion ⟨9⟩.

$\bar{C}$ in C_6H_6 treated with 1 mole maleic anhydride in C_6H_6, stood at 0° for a few hours, gives 100% yield of addn. prod., 1,2,5,6-tetrahydro-4-methylphthalic anhydride, cryst. from lgr., m.p. 63–64° ⟨10⟩ ⟨11⟩ ⟨12⟩ ⟨13⟩. [This prod. on boilg. for a few minutes with aq. yields corresp. acid, 1,2,5,6-tetrahydro-4-methylphthalic ac., m.p. 147–148° ⟨11⟩.] [Note that the m.p. of the anhydride (63–64°) is very close to the corresp. prod. (61–62°) from pentadiene-1,3 (1:8035), and that the m.p. of the corresp. acid (147–148°) is also very close to that (155°) from pentadiene-1,3 (1:8035).]

1:8020 ⟨1⟩ Bekkedahl, Wood, Wojciechowski, *J. Research Natl. Bur. Standards* **17**, 883–894 (1936). ⟨2⟩ Whitby, Crozier, *Can. J. Research* **6**, 210–212 (1932). ⟨3⟩ Harries, Gottlob, *Ann.* **283**, 228–229 (1911). ⟨4⟩ Bassett, Williams, *J. Chem. Soc.* **1932**, 2324–2328. ⟨5⟩ Jones, Williams, *J. Chem. Soc.* **1934**, 832. ⟨6⟩ Shepard, Johnson, *J. Am. Chem. Soc.* **54**, 4388 (1932). ⟨7⟩ Staudinger, Muntwyler, Kupfer, *Helv. Chim. Acta* **5**, 765–766 (1922). ⟨8⟩ Bruson, Calvert, *J. Am. Chem. Soc.* **50**, 1736 (1928). ⟨9⟩ Meyer, *Ber.* **52**, 1473 (1919). ⟨10⟩ Diels, Alder, *Ann.* **470**, 101–102 (1929).

⟨11⟩ Böeseken, van der Gracht, *Rec. trav. chim.* **56**, 1207 (1937). ⟨12⟩ Farmer, Warren, *J. Chem. Soc.* **1931**, 3234–3235. ⟨13⟩ Ref. 4, pages 2327–2328.

1:8025 PENTYNE-1 $CH_3.CH_2.CH_2.C{\equiv}C.H$ C_5H_8 **Beil. I-250**
(*n*-Propylacetylene)

B.P. 39.7° ⟨1⟩ **M.P. −98.0°** ⟨1⟩ D_4^{20} = **0.6945** ⟨1⟩ n_D^{20} = **1.3847** ⟨2⟩
39.3° ⟨3⟩ D^{25} = **0.6909** ⟨3⟩ n_D^{25} = **1.38270** ⟨3⟩

$\bar{C}$ adds Br_2 (T 1.91) [yielding 1,1,2,2-tetrabromopentane, b.p. 275° ⟨4⟩ ⟨9⟩]. [For detn. of $\bar{C}$ via $KBr/KBrO_3$ titration see ⟨5⟩.]

$\bar{C}$ treated with $NH_4OH/CuCl$ (T 1.96-A) gives ppt. [dif. from pentyne-2 (1:8040)].

$\bar{C}$ treated with alk. K_2HgI_4 (T 1.96-B) gives di-(*n*-pentyn-1-yl)mercury, m.p., 118.4–118.8° ⟨6⟩; 117.9–118.3° ⟨2⟩.

$\bar{C}$ htd. with dil. H_2SO_4 (1:5) in s.t. at 110° ⟨7⟩ cf. ⟨8⟩ yields pentanone-2 (1:5415).

1:8025 ⟨1⟩ Morehouse, Maass, *Can. J. Research* **11**, 637 (1934). ⟨2⟩ Hall, Bachmann, *Ind. Eng. Chem.* **28**, 59 (1936). ⟨3⟩ Krieger, Wenzke, *J. Am. Chem. Soc.* **60**, 2118 (1938). ⟨4⟩ Bruylants, *Ber.* **8**, 412 (1875). ⟨5⟩ Lucas, Pressman, *Ind. Eng. Chem., Anal. Ed.* **10**, 142 (1938). ⟨6⟩ Vaughn, *J. Am. Chem. Soc.* **55**, 3454 (1933). ⟨7⟩ Faworsky, *J. prakt. Chem.* (2) **37**, 388 (1888). ⟨8⟩ Thomas, Campbell, Hennion, *J. Am. Chem. Soc.* **60**, 718 (1938). ⟨9⟩ Durio, *Gazz. chim. ital.* **66**, 490 (1936).

1:8030 CYCLOPENTADIENE-1,3 HC—CH ‖ ‖ HC CH \CH₂/ C_5H_6 **Beil. V-112**

B.P. 40.83°$_{772}$ ⟨1⟩ M.P. −85° ⟨2⟩ $D_4^{19.5}$ = 0.7983 ⟨3⟩ $n_D^{19.5}$ = 1.4398 ⟨3⟩

C̄ is insol. aq. but misc. with alc., ether, or C_6H_6 — C̄ on stdg. or on htg. or sometimes spontaneously, polymerizes to a dimer, dicyclopentadiene [Beil. V-495], m.p. 32°, b.p. 170° with partial depolymerization to C̄. [Owing to this behavior samples of C̄ are usually produced by distn. of dicyclopentadiene; cf. ⟨1⟩.] [Higher polymers, e.g., the trimer, m.p. 60°, the tetramer, m.p. 190°, the pentamer, m.p. 270°, and a polymer $(C_5H_6)_x$, m.p. 373° are also known ⟨2⟩ ⟨19⟩.] [For extensive review of thermal polymerization of C̄ see ⟨4⟩.]

C̄ (and also its dimer) absorbs O_2 on stdg. in air yielding peroxides ⟨5⟩ — C̄ reduces $NH_4OH/AgNO_3$ — C̄ reacts explosively with conc. H_2SO_4 or fumg. HNO_3.

C̄ adds Br_2 (T 1.91). [C̄ in pet. ether ⟨6⟩ or in $CHCl_3$ ⟨7⟩ with 1 mole Br_2 in corresp. solvent at −10 to −15° yields a mixt. of two stereoisomeric dibromides [Beil. V-62]; the solid one (*trans*) separates from pet. ether ⟨6⟩ ⟨20⟩ as colorless cryst., m.p. 45–46°, the liquid (*cis*) isomer remaining in soln.; both forms are soluble in $CHCl_3$ and do not ppt.; on treatment of either of these with a 2nd mole Br_2 both yield a liquid 1,2,3,4-tetrabromocyclopentane [Beil. V-19].] [For detn. of C̄ via titration in CCl_4 with standard Br_2 soln. see ⟨8⟩.]

C̄ (1 drop) dislvd. in $CHCl_3$ (1 ml.) + AcOH (1 ml.) and treated with conc. H_2SO_4 (2–3 drops) gives distinct purple coloration ⟨9⟩ [this test not specific since 2,3-dimethylbutadiene-1,3 (1:8030) gives a red-violet ring; butadiene-1,3 and 2-methylbutadiene-1,3 (1:8020) give red-brown rings ⟨10⟩] — C̄ passed through aq. soln. of $Hg(NO_3)_2$ slightly acidified with HNO_3 gives white cloudiness (not shown by butadiene-1,3) ⟨10⟩ — C̄ + quinone (0.35% soln. in alc.) gives deep blue color (not interfered with by either butene or ethylene) ⟨10⟩.

C̄ + 1 mole benzoquinone in alc. ⟨11⟩, hexane ⟨12⟩, C_6H_6 ⟨12⟩, CCl_4 ⟨12⟩, or CS_2 ⟨12⟩ gives alm. quant. yields of an addition product, cyclopentadienebenzoquinone, m.p. 75–76° ⟨13⟩, 76–77° ⟨14⟩, 77–78° ⟨11⟩. [This product serves for quant. sepn. of C̄ from other inert hydrocarbons ⟨15⟩.] [The dimer of C̄, dicyclopentadiene, gives with benzoquinone a quant. yield of a corresp. addn. prod., dicyclopentadienequinone, white ndls., m.p. 157–158° ⟨16⟩.]

C̄ (1 mole) grad. added to a susp. of maleic anhydride (1 mole) in 5 pts. C_6H_6 with cooling, evolves ht. and soon ppts. alm. quant. yield of addn. prod., *cis*-3,6-endomethylene-Δ^4-tetrahydrophthalic anhydride, cryst. from boilg. lgr., m.p. 164–165° ⟨17⟩, 163–164° ⟨18⟩. [This anhydride dissolves on boiling with aq., and on cooling yields *cis*-3,6-endomethylene-Δ^4-tetrahydrophthalic acid, cryst. from aq., m.p. 177–179° ⟨17⟩, 173–174° ⟨18⟩.]

1:8030 ⟨1⟩ Kistiakowsky, Ruhoff, Smith, Vaughan, *J. Am. Chem. Soc.* **58,** 148 (1936). ⟨2⟩ Staudinger, *Ber.* **59,** 3026 (1926). ⟨3⟩ Zelinsky, Lewina, *Ber.* **66,** 477 (1933). ⟨4⟩ Alder, Stein, *Angew. Chem.* **47,** 837–842 (1934). ⟨5⟩ Stobbé, Dünnhaupt, *Ber.* **52,** 1436–1439 (1919). ⟨6⟩ Kraemer, Spilker, *Ber.* **29,** 555–556 (1896). ⟨7⟩ Thiele, *Ann.* **314,** 300–303 (1901). ⟨8⟩ Hammiah, Langrish, *J. Chem. Soc.* **1937,** 797–799. ⟨9⟩ Afanasiev, *Ind. Eng. Chem., Anal. Ed.* **8,** 15 (1936). ⟨10⟩ Terent'ev, Ivanova, *Cent.* **1938,** I, 2414; *Chem. Abs.* **32,** 84 (1938). ⟨11⟩ Albrecht, *Ann.* **348,** 34 (1906). ⟨12⟩ Wasserman, *J. Chem. Soc.* **1935,** 835–839; 1511–1514. ⟨13⟩ Ref. 12, page 1514. ⟨14⟩ Ref. 12, page 837. ⟨15⟩ Potolowski, Vimberg, *Cent.* **1936,** II, 2833; *Chem. Abs.* **31,** 2797 (1937). ⟨16⟩ Ref. 11, page 47. ⟨17⟩ Diels, Alder, *Ann.* **460,** 111–112 (1928). ⟨18⟩ Dedussenko, *Chem. Abs.* **31,** 1992 (1937); *Cent.* **1937,** I, 2717. ⟨19⟩ Staudinger, Rheiner, *Helv. Chim. Acta* **7,** 23–31 (1924). ⟨20⟩ Farmer, Scott, *J. Chem. Soc.* **1929,** 177.

1:8035 PENTADIENE-1,3 $CH_2.CH{=}CH.CH{=}CH_2$ C_5H_8 **Beil. I-251**
(Piperylene)

B.P. 41.91-41.93° ⟨1⟩ M.P. −88.9° ⟨1⟩ D_4^{20} = 0.6803 ⟨2⟩ n_D^{20} = 1.4309 ⟨2⟩
D_4^{25} = 0.6794 ⟨3⟩ n_D^{25} = 1.4206 ⟨3⟩

C̄ is mixt. of geom. isomers, sol. in $CH_3.NO_2$ (T 1.922) even at −20°; in aniline (T 1.922) even at −20°.

C̄ adds Br_2 (T 1.91) [with 2 moles Br_2 without solvent ⟨4⟩ or in CCl_4 ⟨1⟩ gives 1,2,3,4-tetrabromopentane, cryst. from hot alc., m.p. 114–114.5° ⟨1⟩, 116° ⟨4⟩]. [This product apparently results only from some of the isomers but not from all ⟨5⟩.] [B.B. No. (T 1.925) found 470, calcd. 471.]

C̄ reduces $KMnO_4$ (T 1.34) yielding formic acid (1:1005) and acetic acid (1:1010) ⟨6⟩, but does not react with $NH_4OH/CuCl$ (T 1.96-A).

C̄ shaken with cold soln. of diazotized *p*-nitroaniline yields *p*-nitrobenzeneazopiperylene [Beil. XVI_1-(225)], yel. ndls. from acetone, m.p. 137° ⟨7⟩ [corresp. product from isoprene (1:8020) has m.p. 145° ⟨8⟩].

C̄ in C_6H_6 at 0° treated with 1 mole maleic anhydride and stood 5 days gives (95% yield ⟨9⟩) 3-methyl-1,2,3,6-tetrahydrophthalic anhydride, ndls. from pet., m.p. 61° ⟨9⟩, 62° ⟨10⟩, 61–62° ⟨11⟩. [This anhydride when boiled with aq. yields 3-methyl-1,2,3,6-tetrahydrophthalic acid, m.p. 155° ⟨9⟩, or when dehydrogenated by htg. with 1 mole sulfur for 2 hrs. at 250–260° gives (54% yield) 3-methylphthalic anhydride, m.p. 115–116° ⟨11⟩.] [Note that the m.p. of the maleic anhydride addn. prod. is very close to that of the corresponding product (m.p. 63–64°) from isoprene (1:8020).]

1:8035 ⟨1⟩ Dolliver, Gresham, Kistiakowsky, Vaughan, *J. Am. Chem. Soc.* **59,** 833 (1937). ⟨2⟩ Farmer, Warren, *J. Chem. Soc.* **1931,** 3228. ⟨3⟩ Reif, *Ber.* **41,** 2744 (1908). ⟨4⟩ Demjanow, Dojarenko, *Ber.* **55,** 2726 (1922). ⟨5⟩ Prévost, *Ann. chim.* (10) **10,** 172–175 (1928). ⟨6⟩ Thiele, *Ann.* **319,** 226–227 (1901). ⟨7⟩ Meyer, *Ber.* **52,** 1473 (1919). ⟨8⟩ Meyer, Irschick, Schlösser, *Ber.* **47,** 1754 (1914). ⟨9⟩ Ref. 2, page 3234. ⟨10⟩ Diels, Alder, *Ann.* **470,** 102 (1929).
⟨11⟩ Newman, *J. Am. Chem. Soc.* **59,** 1004–1005 (1937).

1:8037 CYCLOPENTENE

```
HC═════CH
 |      |
H2C    CH2
  \CH2/
```

C_5H_8 **Beil. V-61**

B.P. 44.17° ⟨1⟩ M.P. −134.6° ⟨1⟩ D_4^{20} = 0.7736 ⟨2⟩ n_D^{20} = 1.42246 ⟨2⟩

[For prepn. from cyclopentanol (1:6412) by distn. with P_2O_5 see ⟨2⟩; with anhydrous oxalic acid (83–84% yield) see ⟨1⟩ ⟨3⟩.]

C̄ adds Br_2 (T 1.91) [yielding 1,2-dibromocyclopentane [Beil. V-19], b.p. 71.5° at 12 mm., D_4^{19} = 1.8713, n_D^{19} = 1.5510 ⟨3⟩]. [C̄ in hexane soln. may readily be detd. by titration with standard Br_2/CCl_4 soln., the absorption being more rapid and end pt. sharper than with cyclohexene (1:8070) ⟨4⟩.]

C̄ in $CHCl_3$ treated with perbenzoic acid gives (77% yield) cyclopentene oxide (1,2-epoxycyclopentane) [Beil. XVII-21], b.p. 102–103°, insol. aq. and yielding on hydrolysis with 0.01 *N* H_2SO_4 75% *trans*-cyclopentanediol-1,2 ⟨5⟩.

C̄ in dry ether at 0° treated with N_2O_3 gas ppts. (20–30% yield) cyclopentenepseudonitrosite, filtered off and washed with dry ether, m.p. 69–70° ⟨6⟩. [This prod. is very unstable and decomposes within a few hrs. ⟨6⟩.]

1:8037 ⟨1⟩ Dolliver, Gresham, Kistiakowsky, Vaughan, *J. Am. Chem. Soc.* **59,** 832 (1937). ⟨2⟩ Vogel, *J. Chem. Soc.* **1938,** 1330. ⟨3⟩ Zelinsky, Lewina, *Ber.* **66,** 477 (1933). ⟨4⟩ Menzies, Robinson, *J. Chem. Soc.* **125,** 2166 (1924). ⟨5⟩ Verkade, Coops, Mean, Verkade-Sandbergen, *Ann.* **467,** 222 (1928). ⟨6⟩ Treibs, *Ann.* **524,** 290 (1936).

1:8040 PENTYNE-2 $CH_3.CH_2.C{\equiv}C.CH_3$ C_5H_8 **Beil. I-250**
(Ethyl-methyl-acetylene)

B.P. 55.9° ⟨1⟩ D_4^{20} **= 0.7115 ⟨1⟩** n_D^{20} **= 1.4040 ⟨1⟩**

C̄ adds Br_2 (T 1.91) but does not react with $NH_4OH/CuCl$ (T 1.96-A) or alk. K_2HgI_4 (T 1.96-B).

C̄ on oxidn. with 2% aq. $KMnO_4$ ⟨2⟩ or CrO_3 ⟨2⟩ yields acetic acid (1:1010) and propionic acid (1:1025).

C̄ treated at 0° with 4 vols. 80% H_2SO_4 gives mixt. of pentanone-2 (1:5415) and pentanone-3 (1:5420) ⟨4⟩.

1:8040 ⟨1⟩ Sherrill, Launspach, *J. Am. Chem. Soc.* **60,** 2563 (1938). ⟨2⟩ Krestinsky, Kelbowskaja, *Ber.* **68,** 517–518 (1935). ⟨3⟩ Faworsky, *J. prakt. Chem.* (2) **37,** 388 (1888). ⟨4⟩ Mowat, Smith, *J. Chem. Soc.* **1938,** 21.

1:8045 HEXADIENE-1,5 $CH_2{=}CH.CH_2.CH_2.CH{=}CH_2$ C_6H_{10} **Beil. I-253**
(Biallyl; diallyl)

B.P. 59.57° ⟨1⟩ cf. ⟨2⟩ **M.P. −140.8° ⟨2⟩** D_4^{20} **= 0.6912 ⟨1⟩** n_D^{20} **= 1.4044 ⟨1⟩**
D_4^{25} **= 0.6863 ⟨1⟩** n_D^{25} **= 1.4012 ⟨1⟩**

[For prepn. (68% yield) from allyl bromide + Mg and survey of previous prepns. see ⟨1⟩.]

C̄ does not have sharp odor, but does have penetrating nauseating odor readily inducing anesthesia. Ord. samples develop sharp odor and deposit yel. oil on stdg.; pure C̄ in sealed tubes keeps indefinitely ⟨1⟩.

C̄ adds Br_2 (T 1.91). [C̄ + 2 Br_2 gives mixt. of stereoisomeric 1,2,5,6-tetrabromohexanes (diallyl tetrabromides) [Beil. I–145]; higher melting, m.p. 64–65°, 63° ⟨5⟩; lower melting, m.p. 53–54°; the mixt. has m.p. 52° ⟨3⟩, 53–55° ⟨4⟩ (dif. from pentadiene-1,3 (1:8035)).] [For detn. of C̄ via $KBr.KBrO_3$ titration (T 1.925) see ⟨6⟩.]

C̄ on shaking with 5 vols. conc. HCl for 120 hrs. yields mixt. of 5-chlorohexene-1 and 2,5-dichlorohexane ⟨7⟩ — C̄ in 4 vols. AcOH treated with conc. HBr (1 mole) gives mixt. of monohydrobromide (47%) and dihydrobromide (53%) ⟨8⟩.

C̄ on oxidn. with $K_2Cr_2O_7 + H_2SO_4$ ⟨9⟩ gives CO_2 and acetic acid (1:1010); with dil. HNO_3 (D = 1.18) yields ⟨10⟩ succinic acid (1:0530); with large excess $KMnO_4$ yields ⟨11⟩ CO_2, succinic acid, oxalic acid, and acetic acid — C̄ on ozonolysis ⟨8⟩ yields acetaldehyde (1:0100) and formaldehyde (1:0145).

C̄ does not react with diazotized *p*-nitroaniline or diazotized 2,4-dinitroaniline ⟨12⟩ [dif. from hexadiene-2,4 (1:8060) which couples with both] — C̄ does not react with maleic anhydride [dif. from hexadiene-2,4 (1:8060)].

C̄ with 65% H_2SO_4 at room temp. is converted to oxide and polymers but C̄ with equal vol. 100% H_2SO_4 at −15 to +4° gives (small yield) of neutral crystn. cyclic monosulfuric acid ester of hexanediol-2,5, cryst. from acetone, m.p. 90° ⟨13⟩ (recommended for identif. of C̄ ⟨1⟩).

1:8045 ⟨1⟩ Cortese, *J. Am. Chem. Soc.* **51,** 2266–2268 (1929). ⟨2⟩ Kistiakowsky, Ruhoff, Smith, Vaughan, *J. Am. Chem. Soc.* **58,** 147 (1936). ⟨3⟩ Staudinger, Kreis, Schilt, *Helv. Chim. Acta* **5,** 755 (1922). ⟨4⟩ Hurd, Yarnall, *J. Am. Chem. Soc.* **59,** 1689 (1937). ⟨5⟩ Ciamician, Anderlini, *Ber.* **22,** 2497–2498 (1889). ⟨6⟩ Cortese, *Rec. trav. chim.* **48,** 564–567 (1929). ⟨7⟩ Cortese, *J. Am. Chem. Soc.* **52,** 1519–1521 (1930). ⟨8⟩ Baker, Burton, *J. Chem. Soc.* **1933,** 815, 817. ⟨9⟩ Sorokin, *J. prakt. Chem.* (2) **23,** 6–9 (1881). ⟨10⟩ Merling, *Ann.* **324,** 344–345 (1891).
⟨11⟩ Ref. 9, pages 10–13. ⟨12⟩ Terent'ev, Demidova, *Chem. Abs.* **32,** 2094 (1938); *Cent.* **1939,** I, 640. ⟨13⟩ Cortese, *Ber.* **62,** 504–508 (1929).

1:8050 2,3-DIMETHYLBUTADIENE-1,3 $H_2C{=}C(CH_3){-}C(CH_3){=}CH_2$ C_6H_{10} **Beil. I-256**
(" Methylisoprene "; diisopropenyl)

B.P. 68.70°$_{765}$ ⟨1⟩ M.P. −76.0° ⟨1⟩ D_4^{20} = 0.7263 ⟨2⟩ n_D^{20} = 1.4390 ⟨1⟩

[For prepn. from pinacol (1:5805) by distn. with trace of const. boilg. HBr (D = 1.48) (70% yield) see ⟨3⟩ ⟨4⟩ ⟨5⟩; by vapor phase dehydration over activated Al_2O_3 (71.5% yield) see ⟨1⟩; by simple distn. with 10% of its wt. of alum ⟨6⟩ ⟨8⟩.]

C̄ polymerizes on stdg. in light to a white fluffy solid; C̄ on treatment with acids gives various dimerides and polymerides [for study see ⟨7⟩].

C̄ adds Br_2 (T 1.91). [C̄ in pet. ether, AcOH or $CHCl_3$ at −10° treated with 1 mole Br_2 yields 80% of *trans*-1,4-dibromo-2,3-dimethylbutene-2, pale yel. ndls. from lgr., m.p. 47° ⟨9⟩ ⟨10⟩, accompanied in the mother liquor by a small amt. of the *cis* isomer, m.p. +4.0–4.1° ⟨9⟩; C̄ in AcOH treated with 2 moles Br_2 gives 1,2,3,4-tetrabromo-2,3-dimethylbutane [Beil. I-153], colorless pr. from C_6H_6, AcOH, ether, or CCl_4, m.p. 138° ⟨11⟩.] [C̄ does *not* give good results in $KBr.KBrO_3$ titration according to ⟨12⟩.]

C̄ treated with HBr gas at 0° gives 95% yield of 1-bromo-2,3-dimethylbutene-2, b.p. 49–52° at 15 mm. ⟨5⟩ ⟨13⟩ ⟨14⟩.

C̄ + diazotized *p*-nitroaniline couples to give *p*-nitrobenzeneazo-2,3-dimethylbutadiene-1,3 [Beil. XVI_1-(225)], yel. ndls. from AcOEt, m.p. 177° ⟨15⟩. [Use of this reaction in detn. of C̄ ⟨16⟩.]

C̄ treated with 1 mole maleic anhydride in dry C_6H_6, stood 24 hrs. at room temp. gives quant. yield of 1,2,5,6-tetrahydro-3,4-dimethylphthalic anhydride, long colorless ndls. from pet., m.p. 78–79° ⟨17⟩, 78° ⟨18⟩. [On htg. for a few minutes with 10 pts. aq. this anhydride yields *cis*-1,2,5,6-tetrahydro-3,4-dimethylphthalic acid, colorless pr. from alc., m.p. 180–192° with partial reconversion to anhydride ⟨18⟩.]

1:8050 ⟨1⟩ Dolliver, Gresham, Kistiakowsky, Vaughan, *J. Am. Chem. Soc.* **59,** 833 (1937). ⟨2⟩ Whitby, Gallay, *Can. J. Research.* **6,** 284 (1932). ⟨3⟩ Kyriakides, *J. Am. Chem. Soc.* **36,** 987–993 (1914). ⟨4⟩ Whitby, Crozier, *Can. J. Research* **6,** 213–214 (1932). ⟨5⟩ Kilby, Kipping, *J. Chem. Soc.* **1939,** 437. ⟨6⟩ Backer, Bottema, *Rec. trav. chim.* **51,** 295 (1932). ⟨7⟩ Farmer, Pitkethly, *J. Chem. Soc.* **1938,** 11–19, 287–291. ⟨8⟩ Macallum, Whitby, *Trans. Roy. Soc. Can.* **22,** III, 33–38 (1928); *Chem. Abs.* **22,** 2079 (1928). ⟨9⟩ Kogerman, *Chem. Abs.* **29,** 3297 (1935); *Cent.* **1935,** I, 2965. ⟨10⟩ Farmer, Lawrence, Scott, *J. Chem. Soc.* **1930,** 519–520.

⟨11⟩ Pope, Kipping, *J. Chem. Soc.* **1930,** 2592. ⟨12⟩ Lucas, Pressman, *Ind. Eng. Chem., Anal. Ed.* **10,** 140–142 (1938). ⟨13⟩ Farmer, Marshall, *J. Chem. Soc.* **1931,** 132–133. ⟨14⟩ Claisen, *J. prakt. Chem.* (2) **105,** 86–87 (1923). ⟨15⟩ Meyer, *Ber.* **52,** 1473–1474 (1919). ⟨16⟩ Terent'ev, Vinogradova, Galpern, *Cent.* **1937,** II, 1628–1629. ⟨17⟩ Diels, Alder, *Ann.* **470,** 102 (1929). ⟨18⟩ Farmer, Warren, *J. Chem. Soc.* **1929,** 902.

1:8055 HEXYNE-1 $CH_3.CH_2.CH_2.CH_2.C{\equiv}C.H$ C_6H_{10} **Beil. I-253**
(*n*-Butyacetylene)

B.P. 71.35-71.40° ⟨1⟩ F.P. −124° ⟨1⟩

D_4^{25} = 0.7193 ⟨1⟩ $n_{He\ (yellow)}^{15}$ = 1.40195 ⟨1⟩
D_4^{20} = 0.7170 ⟨2⟩ n_D^{20} = 1.3988 ⟨2⟩

[For prepn. from H.C≡C.Na + *n*-butyl bromide (64% yield ⟨3⟩) see ⟨3⟩ ⟨4⟩.] [For purification via $AgNO_3$ treatment (see below) see ⟨3⟩ ⟨5⟩.] [For detn. via Ag salt (see below) see ⟨3⟩ ⟨6⟩; via $KBr/KBrO_3$ titration see ⟨7⟩.]

C̄ adds Br_2 (T 1.91). [For study of additions of Cl_2 see ⟨8⟩.] — C̄ adds HBr (as gas) [for study see ⟨9⟩].

C̄ readily forms peroxidic cpds. on stdg. ⟨5⟩ — C̄ on ozonolysis yields equiv. amts. formic acid (1:1005) and *n*-valeric acid (1:1060) ⟨3⟩.

C̄ in 70% MeOH, or 70% acetone, or 60% acetic acid treated with very small amt HgSO$_4$ + conc. H$_2$SO$_4$ gives (63–79% yield) hexanone-2 (1:5435) ⟨10⟩.

C̄ in 95% alc. treated with conc. aq. soln. of AgNO$_3$ (4 N) gives white ppt. of C$_4$H$_9$.C≡C.Ag.AgNO$_3$. This ppt. can be recrystd. from 95% alc.; on refluxing with aq. NaCN the orig. C̄ is regenerated. [Use in purification of C̄ ⟨5⟩ ⟨3⟩; use in detn. ⟨3⟩.]

C̄ treated with NH$_4$OH/CuCl (T 1.96-A) gives ppt.; C̄ treated with alk. K$_2$HgI (T 1.96-B) gives (C$_4$H$_9$.C≡C)$_2$Hg, cryst. from MeOH, m.p. 96.2–96.4° ⟨11⟩, 96.0–96.4° ⟨2⟩

1:8055 ⟨1⟩ van Risseghem, *Bull. soc. chim. Belg.* **35,** 356–357 (1926). ⟨2⟩ Hall, Bachmann, *Ind. Eng. Chem.* **28,** 59 (1936). ⟨3⟩ Hurd, Christ, *J. Org. Chem.* **1,** 143–145 (1937) ⟨4⟩ Vaughn, Hennion, Vogt, Nieuwland, *J. Org. Chem.* **2,** 5–6, 9 (1938). ⟨5⟩ Young, Vogt, Nieuwland, *J. Am. Chem. Soc.* **58,** 56 (1936). ⟨6⟩ Hill, Tyson, *J. Am. Chem. Soc.* **50,** 17[illegible] (1928). ⟨7⟩ Lucas, Pressman, *Ind. Eng. Chem., Anal. Ed.* **10,** 142 (1938). ⟨8⟩ Hennion, Welsh, *J. Am. Chem. Soc.* **62,** 1367–1368 (1940). ⟨9⟩ Young, Vogt, Nieuwland, *J. Am. Chem. Soc.* **58,** 1806–1808 (1936). ⟨10⟩ Thomas, Campbell, Hennion, *J. Am. Chem. Soc.* **60,** 718–72[illegible] (1938).
⟨11⟩ Vaughn, *J. Am. Chem. Soc.* **55,** 3454 (1933).

1:8057 CYCLOHEXADIENE-1,3 C$_6$H$_8$ Beil. V-11[illegible]

(1,2-Dihydrobenzene)

```
        H
        C
     //   \
 H.C        CH2
    |        |
 H.C        CH2
     \\   /
        C
        H
```

B.P. 80.31°$_{757}$ ⟨1⟩ M.P. −104.8° ⟨1⟩ D_4^{20} = 0.8413 ⟨2⟩ n_D^{20} = 1.4740 ⟨1⟩; cf. ⟨2⟩

[For prepn. from cyclohexene (1:8070) see ⟨1⟩ ⟨3⟩.] [C̄ forms with MeOH a const. boilg mixt., b.p. 56.65° at 762 mm. ⟨1⟩.]

C̄ adds Br$_2$ (T 1.91). [C̄ in n-hexane or CHCl$_3$ treated with 1 mole Br$_2$, solvent evapd., and pet. ether added, yields (if worked up immediately) 1,2-dibromocyclohexene-3, prisms, m.p. 68°; but if allowed to stand this product isomerizes (rapidly in soln.) to the isomeric 1,4-dibromocyclohexene-2, colorless pr. from pet., m.p. 108° ⟨4⟩. This 108° m.p. product does *not* add more Br$_2$ ⟨5⟩ (contradicting ⟨6⟩) but its progenitors (above) with further Br$_2$ yield 1,2,3,4-tetrabromocyclohexane [Beil. V$_1$-(10)], known in two forms, one m.p. 87–89°, the other m.p. 155–156° ⟨7⟩.]

C̄ couples with diazotized p-nitroaniline yielding red br.-ndls. ⟨8⟩. [Use in detn. of C̄ in heptane, cyclohexane, etc. ⟨8⟩.]

C̄ (5 pts.) + quinone (1 pt.) in alc. (2 pts.) htd. in s.t. for 5 hrs. at 100° yields bis-cyclohexadienequinone, colorless cryst. from alc., m.p. 196–197° ⟨9⟩ — C̄ (1 g.) dislvd. in pure dry C$_6$H$_6$ (3 ml.) and treated with maleic anhydride (1.2 g.) evolves ht. and on stdg. seps. cryst. (obtd. in quant. yield on evapn. of solvent) of 3,6-endoethylene-1,2,3,6-tetrahydrophthalic anhydride, recrystd. from lgr., m.p. 147° ⟨10⟩.

[For study of addn. prod. of C̄ + liq. SO$_2$ see ⟨11⟩.]

1:8057 ⟨1⟩ Kistiakowsky, Ruhoff, Smith, Vaughan, *J. Am. Chem. Soc.* **58,** 147–148 (1936). ⟨2⟩ Carr, Stücklen, *J. Chem. Phys.* **6,** 55 (1938). ⟨3⟩ Hofmann, Damm, *Chem. Abs.* **22,** 1249 (1928). ⟨4⟩ Farmer, Scott, *J. Chem. Soc.* **1929,** 175–176. ⟨5⟩ Bedos, Ruyer, *Compt. rend.* **204,** 1350–1352 (1937). ⟨6⟩ Harries, *Ber.* **45,** 2586 (1912). ⟨7⟩ Harries, *Ber.* **45,** 814 (1912). ⟨8⟩ Terent'ev, Galpern, Vinogradova, *Cent.* **1937,** II, 1628–1629. ⟨9⟩ Diels, Alder, *Ber.* **62,** 2359–2360 (1929). ⟨10⟩ Diels, Alder, *Ann.* **460,** 115–116 (1928).
⟨11⟩ Seyer, King, *J. Am. Chem. Soc.* **55,** 3143–3145 (1933).

1:8060 **HEXADIENE-2,4** $CH_3.CH{=}CH.CH{=}CH.CH_3$ C_6H_{10} **Beil. I-254**
(Bipropenyl; dipropenyl)

B.P. 79.4-81.6$^{\circ}_{765}$ ⟨1⟩ D_4^{20} = **0.7152** ⟨1⟩; cf. ⟨2⟩ n_D^{20} = **1.4493** ⟨1⟩; cf. ⟨2⟩
80-82° ⟨2⟩

[For prepn. (65–67% yield) by distn. of hexene-2-ol-4 (from crotonaldehyde + C_2H_5.-MgBr) with a little 48% HBr see ⟨3⟩ ⟨2⟩] — C̄ is mixt. of geom. stereoisomers.

C̄ adds Br_2 (T 1.91). [C̄ in dilute hexane or $CHCl_3$ soln. treated with 1 mole Br_2 yields exclusively ⟨4⟩ 2,5-dibromohexene-3, b.p. 85° at 11 mm., D_4^{19} = 1.622, n_D^{19} = 1.534; C̄ in $CHCl_3$ treated with 2 moles Br_2 at −10° yields 2,3,4,5-tetrabromohexane (dipropenyl tetrabromide) [Beil. I-146], cryst. from alc., ether, or $CHCl_3$, m.p. 180° u.c. ⟨5⟩, 185° ⟨6⟩.] [Other tetrabromides, e.g., m.p. 162°, m.p. 108° and a liquid isomer, supposed to arise from the other geom. isomers of C̄ have been reported ⟨6⟩.] [For detn. of C̄ via $KBr/KBrO_3$ titration see ⟨9⟩.]

C̄ shaken with 5 pts. conc. HCl for 20 hrs. gives a mixt. of monochlorohexenes, dichlorohexanes and polymers ⟨7⟩ — C̄ adds HBr but gives an inseparable mixt. ⟨8⟩.

C̄ with SO_2 in ether in s.t. at 100° yields an addition prod., 1,1-dioxo-2,5-dimethylthiacyclopentene-3, cryst. from ether, m.p. 43–43.5° ⟨10⟩.

C̄ couples with diazotized *p*-nitroaniline (using excess $NaNO_2$ and destroying excess HNO_2 by addn. of urea) giving (37% yield) *p*-nitrobenzeneazohexadiene-2,4, m.p. 172–173° ⟨11⟩ [using 70% AcOH as solvent gives pract. quant. yield ⟨12⟩] — C̄ couples with diazotized 2,4-dinitroaniline yielding 2,4-dinitrobenzeneazohexadiene-2,4, purified by pptn. from acetone soln. with aq., m.p. 127–129° dec. ⟨12⟩. [Neither of these couplings is shown by hexadiene-1,5 (1:8045).]

C̄ in pure dry C_6H_6 treated with 1 mole maleic anhydride, stood 24 hrs. and solvent evapd., gives quant. yield of 2,5-dimethyl-1,2,5,6-tetrahydrophthalic anhydride, long cryst. ndls. from lgr., m.p. 95–96° ⟨13⟩, 92° ⟨4⟩. [This anhydride is so stable toward aq. that any excess maleic anhydride may be extracted with hot aq. before recrystg. prod. ⟨13⟩.] [For detn. of C̄ by reactn. in toluene with excess maleic anhydride, followed by titration of excess latter see ⟨14⟩.]

1:8060 ⟨1⟩ Farmer, Warren, *J. Chem. Soc.* **1931,** 3228. ⟨2⟩ Whitby, Gallay, *Can. J. Research,* **6,** 285 (1932). ⟨3⟩ Adams, Geissman, *J. Am. Chem. Soc.* **61,** 2086 (1939). ⟨4⟩ Farmer, Lawrence, Scott, *J. Chem. Soc.* **1930,** 515. ⟨5⟩ Reif, *Ber.* **41,** 2744 (1908). ⟨6⟩ Prévost, *Ann. chim.* (10) **10,** 359–364 (1928). ⟨7⟩ Cortese, *J. Am. Chem. Soc.* **52,** 1520–1521 (1930). ⟨8⟩ Farmer, Marshall, *J. Chem. Soc.* **1929,** 134–135. ⟨9⟩ Cortese, *Rec. trav. chim.* **48,** 564–567 (1929). ⟨10⟩ Backer, Strating, Kool, *Rec. trav. chim.* **58,** 778–784 (1939).
⟨11⟩ Arbuzov, Rafikov, *Chem. Abs.* **32,** 515 (1938); *Cent.* **1938,** I, 3033–3034. ⟨12⟩ Terent'ev, Demidova, *Cent.* **1939,** I, 640; *Chem. Abs.* **32,** 2094 (1938). ⟨13⟩ Diels, Alder, *Ann.* **470,** 102 (1929). ⟨14⟩ D'yachkov, Ermolova, *Chem. Abs.* **31,** 6138; *Cent.* **1937,** II, 2565.

1:8065 **HEXYNE-3** $CH_3.CH_2.C{\equiv}C.CH_2.CH_3$ C_6H_{10} **Beil. S.N. 12**
(Diethylacetylene)

B.P. 81.5$^{\circ}_{744}$ ⟨1⟩ **M.P. −51°** ⟨2⟩ D^{25} = **0.7263** ⟨1⟩ n_D^{25} = **1.4112** ⟨1⟩

C̄ adds Br_2 (T 1.91), but does not react with $NH_4OH/CuCl$ (T 1.96-A) nor alk. K_2HgI_4 (T 1.96-B).

1:8065 ⟨1⟩ Bried, Hennion, *J. Am. Chem. Soc.* **59,** 1310 (1937). ⟨2⟩ Lespieau, Wiemann, *Bull. soc. chim.* (4) **45,** 634 (1929).

1:8070 CYCLOHEXENE (Tetrahydrobenzene) C_6H_{10} **Beil. V-63**

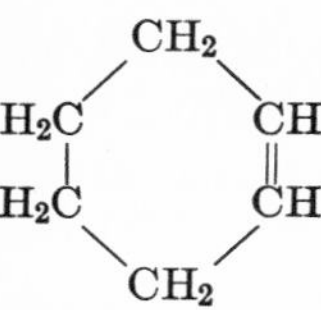

B.P. 83.63°$_{767}$ ⟨1⟩ M.P. −103.4° ⟨1⟩ D_4^{20} = 0.8088 ⟨2⟩ n_D^{20} = 1.44646 ⟨2⟩

[For prepn. from cyclohexanol (1:6415) by dehydration with conc. H_2SO_4 (79–87% yield) see ⟨3⟩ ⟨1⟩; with 85% H_3PO_4 (96% yield) see ⟨4⟩; by passing over silica gel at 280–300° (73% yield) see ⟨5⟩; or by passing over saturated Al_2O_3 at 380–450° (89% yield) see ⟨6⟩.]

C̄ adds Br_2 (T 1.91). [C̄ in CCl_4 in sunlight at 0° treated with 1 mole Br_2 gives (73–86% yield ⟨7⟩) 1,2-dibromocyclohexane [Beil. V-24], b.p. 101–103°$_{13}$, $D_4^{19.5}$ = 1.7759, n_D^{19} = 1.5445 ⟨8⟩.] [This product is apparently exclusively the *cis* isomer ⟨8⟩ ⟨9⟩, and by conversion with AgOAc to the corresp. diacetate and thence by alc. KOH to the glycol yields *cis*-cyclohexanediol-1,2, m.p. 98° ⟨8⟩.] [For detn. of C̄ via $KBr/KBrO_3$ titration see ⟨10⟩.] [Note that C̄, treated with Br_2 in aq. KBr yields not only 1,2-dibromocyclohexane (above) but substantial amts. of 2-bromocyclohexanol (by addn. of HOBr) ⟨11⟩.]

C̄ dislvd. in inert solvent (best heptane or xylene ⟨12⟩) adds HBr giving cyclohexyl bromide [Beil. V-24], b.p. 165° or HCl giving cyclohexyl chloride [Beil. V-21], b.p. 142°. [For study of influence of solvent on rate of reaction see ⟨12⟩.]

C̄ in AcOH treated at 0° with ethyl nitrite + conc. HCl gives (23% yield ⟨13⟩) of "cyclohexene nitrosochloride," white cryst. from ether, m.p. 152–153° dec. ⟨14⟩ ⟨15⟩, 149° ⟨17⟩, entirely stable at ord. temp. — C̄ added to susp. of NaSCN + $CuSO_4$ in AcOH, stood overnight at 0°, yields $(SCN)_2$ addn. prod., cyclohexene 1,2-dithiocyanate, white cryst., m.p. 58.0–58.5° ⟨18⟩ — C̄ adds liq. SO_2 (but only in presence of oxidizing catalysts) yielding a polymeric sulfone ⟨16⟩ ⟨19⟩.

[For study of polymerization of C̄ by conc. H_2SO_4 see ⟨20⟩, by P_2O_5 to cyclohexylcyclohexene-1 see ⟨21⟩.]

1:8070 ⟨1⟩ Kistiakowsky, Ruhoff, Smith, Vaughan, *J. Am. Chem. Soc.* **58**, 140–141 (1936). ⟨2⟩ Vogel, *J. Chem. Soc.* **1938**, 1332. ⟨3⟩ Coleman, Johnstone, *Organic Syntheses, Coll. Vol.* I, 177–178 (1932). ⟨4⟩ Dehn, Jackson, *J. Am. Chem. Soc.* **55**, 4285–4286 (1933). ⟨5⟩ Bartlett, Berry, *J. Am. Chem. Soc.* **56**, 2684 (1934). ⟨6⟩ Hershberg, Ruhoff, *Organic Syntheses* **17**, 27, Note 1 (1937). ⟨7⟩ Greengard, *Organic Syntheses* **12**, 26–27 (1932). ⟨8⟩ Rothstein, *Ann. chim.* (10) **14**, 542–544 (1930). ⟨9⟩ Kohlrausch, Pongratz, Seka, *Monatsh.* **70**, 225 (1937). ⟨10⟩ Lucas, Pressman, *Ind. Eng. Chem., Anal. Ed.* **10**, 140–142 (1938).

⟨11⟩ Swarts, *Bull. soc. chim. Belg.* **46**, 13–19 (1937); *Chem. Abs.* **31**, 5771 (1937). ⟨12⟩ O'Connor, Baldinger, Vogt, Hennion, *J. Am. Chem. Soc.* **61**, 1454–1456 (1939). ⟨13⟩ Wallach, *Ann.* **353**, 49–50 (1905). ⟨14⟩ Baeyer, *Ann.* **278**, 108–109 (1893). ⟨15⟩ Kenner, Wain, *Ber.* **72**, 458 (1939). ⟨16⟩ Frederick, Cogan, Marvel, *J. Am. Chem. Soc.* **56**, 1815–1819 (1934). ⟨17⟩ Ref. 16, page 1818. ⟨18⟩ Dermer, Dysinger, *J. Am. Chem. Soc.* **61**, 750 (1939). ⟨19⟩ Seyer, King, *J. Am. Chem. Soc.* **55**, 3140–3149 (1933). ⟨20⟩ Nametkin, Abakumovskaia, *Ber.* **66**, 358–360 (1933).

⟨21⟩ Truffault, *Bull. soc. chim.* (5) **3**, 442–459 (1936).

1:8075 HEXYNE-2 $CH_3.C{\equiv}C.CH_2.CH_2.CH_3$ C_6H_{10} **Beil. I-253**
(Methyl-*n*-propylacetylene)

B.P. 83.7-84.0° ⟨1⟩ M.P. −92° ⟨1⟩ D_4^{15} = 0.7352 ⟨1⟩ $n_{He\,(yellow)}^{15}$ = 1.4166 ⟨1⟩

C̄ adds Br_2 (T 1.91), but does not react with $NH_4OH/CuCl$ (T 1.96-A) or alk. K_2HgI_4 (T 1.96-B).

C̄ on oxidn. with CrO_3 or $K_2Cr_2O_7 + H_2SO_4$ ⟨2⟩ yields CO_2, acetic acid (1:1010) and *n*-butyric acid (1:1035).

C̄ shaken with 5 parts H_2SO_4 (5 H_2SO_4:1 aq.) yields mixt. of abt. 56% hexanone-2 (1:5435) and abt. 44% of hexanone-3 [Beil. I-690] ⟨3⟩.

1:8075 ⟨1⟩ van Risseghem, *Bull. soc. chim. Belg.* **35,** 354 (1926). ⟨2⟩ Hecht, *Ber.* **11,** 1052–1053 (1878). ⟨3⟩ Michael, *Ber.* **39,** 2147–2148 (1906).

1:8080 2,5-DIMETHYLFURAN HC——CH / ‖ ‖ / CH₃—C C—CH₃ / \ / / O C_6H_8O **Beil. XVII-41**

B.P. 94° $D_4^{20.1}$ = **0.888** ⟨1⟩ $n_D^{21.6}$ = **1.4363** ⟨1⟩

C̄ is insol. aq. or aq. alk.; resinifies with conc. minl. acids.

C̄ boiled with equal vol. of 50% acetic acid contg. small amt. of 10% H_2SO_4 gives (86–90% yield ⟨2⟩) of acetonylacetone (hexanedione-2,4) (1:5495).

C̄ in contact with pine splinter moistened with HCl slowly gives red color (dif. from furan (1:8015) which gives green) ⟨3⟩.

C̄ + conc. HBr at −15° treated with Br_2 yields a pentabromo-deriv. $C_6H_3OBr_5$, ndls. from $CHCl_3$, m.p. 180° ⟨4⟩.

C̄ + maleic anhydride (1 mole) in abs. ether gives deep yellow color ⟨5⟩ (not shown by furan (1:8015) ⟨5⟩) and on stdg. in refrigerator at 6–8° begins to sep. addn. product in 6 hrs. ⟨5⟩; product is 3,6-endoxo-3,6-dimethyl-Δ^4-tetrahydrophthalic anhydride, cryst. from ether, m.p. 78° ⟨6⟩. [If ether soln. is evapd. prod. can be obtd. in quant. yield ⟨6⟩.]

1:8080 ⟨1⟩ von Auwers, *Ann.* **408,** 271 (1915). ⟨2⟩ Johnson, Stevenson, Benson, *Organic Syntheses* **16,** 26 (1936). ⟨3⟩ Reichstein, *Helv. Chim. Acta* **15,** 1111 (1932). ⟨4⟩ Trefil'ev, Goroshko, *Chem. Abs.* **24,** 4782 (1930). ⟨5⟩ Butz, *J. Am. Chem. Soc.* **57,** 1315 (1935). ⟨6⟩ Diels, Alder, *Ber.* **62,** 560–561 (1929).

1:8085 HEPTYNE-1 $CH_3.CH_2.CH_2.CH_2.CH_2.C{\equiv}C.H$ C_7H_{12} **Beil. I-256**
(*n*-Amylacetylene)

B.P. 98.0° ⟨1⟩ **M.P. −81 to −80°** ⟨2⟩ D^{20} = **0.7338** ⟨2⟩ n_D^{20} = **1.4086** ⟨2⟩
D_4^{25} = **0.7297** ⟨1⟩ n_D^{25} = **1.40553** ⟨1⟩

[For prepn. of C̄ from various metal acetylides + *n*-AmCl and/or *n*-AmBr in liq. NH_3 see ⟨3⟩ ⟨4⟩; from 1,1-dichloroheptane (76% yield) and other halogen cpds. see ⟨5⟩.]

C̄ adds Br_2 (T 1.91). [For detn. of C̄ via KBr/$KBrO_3$ titration see ⟨6⟩.]

C̄ on ozonolysis yields formic acid (1:1005) and *n*-caproic acid (1:1130) ⟨4⟩ ⟨7⟩.

C̄ dislvd. in 60% acetic acid contg. a very little H_2SO_4 + $HgSO_4$ and stirred at 70° for 3 hrs. gives 87% yield heptanone-2 (1:5460) ⟨8⟩.

C̄ treated with 5% alc. soln. of $AgNO_3$ gives white ppt. of $C_5H_{11}.C{\equiv}C.Ag.AgNO_3$; on sepn. and distn. with NH_4SCN this regenerates original C̄ [use in purification of C̄ ⟨4⟩]. [Use in quant. detn. of C̄ ⟨4⟩ ⟨9⟩ ⟨10⟩.]

C̄ treated with NH_4OH/CuCl (T 1.96-A) yields yel. ppt. of $C_5H_{11}.C{\equiv}C.Cu$ [use in detn. of C̄ ⟨10⟩] — C̄ treated with alk. K_2HgI_4 (T 1.96-B) yields $(C_5H_{11}.C{\equiv}C)_2Hg$ (80% yield ⟨11⟩), white ndls. from MeOH, m.p. 61° ⟨11⟩ ⟨12⟩.

1:8085 ⟨1⟩ Krieger, Wenzke, *J. Am. Chem. Soc.* **60,** 2118 (1938). ⟨2⟩ Landrieu, Baylocq, *Bull. soc. chim.* (4) **45,** 219 (1929). ⟨3⟩ Vaughn, Hennion, Vogt, Nieuwland, *J. Org. Chem.* **2,** 6–9 (1937). ⟨4⟩ Hurd, Christ, *J. Org. Chem.* **1,** 143–145 (1937). ⟨5⟩ Bachmann, Hill, *J. Am. Chem. Soc.* **56,** 2730–2732 (1934). ⟨6⟩ Lucas, Pressman, *Ind. Eng. Chem., Anal. Ed.* **10,** 140–142 (1938). ⟨7⟩ Paillard, Wieland, *Helv. Chim. Acta* **21,** 1356–1361 (1938). ⟨8⟩ Thomas, Campbell, Hennion, *J. Am. Chem. Soc.* **60,** 718–720 (1938). ⟨9⟩ Hurd, Christ, *J. Am. Chem. Soc.* **59,** 2163 (1937). ⟨10⟩ Hill, Tyson, *J. Am. Chem. Soc.* **50,** 176–177 (1928).
⟨11⟩ Johnson, McEwen, *J. Am. Chem. Soc.* **48,** 473 (1926). ⟨12⟩ Bachmann, *J. Am. Chem. Soc.* **57,** 1089 (1935).

1:8095 HEPTYNE-3 $CH_3.CH_2.C{\equiv}C.CH_2.CH_2.CH_3$ C_7H_{12} **Beil. I-257**
(Ethyl-*n*-propyl-acetylene)

B.P. 105-106° ⟨1⟩ ⟨2⟩ D^{25} = **0.7337 ⟨1⟩** n_D^{25} = **1.415 ⟨1⟩**

C̄ adds Br_2 (T 1.91) but does not react with $NH_4OH/CuCl$ (T 1.96-A).

C̄ added dropwise to 2 pts. ord. conc. H_2SO_4 at 0°, diluted, neutralized with Na_2CO_3 and distd. gives di-*n*-propyl ketone (heptanone-4) (1:5447) ⟨2⟩.

1:8095 ⟨1⟩ Lespieau, Wiemann, *Bull. soc. chim.* (4) **45,** 635 (1929). ⟨2⟩ Béhal, *Ann. chim.* (6) **15,** 415–416 (1888).

1:8100 HEPTYNE-2 $CH_3.CH_2.CH_2.CH_2.C{\equiv}C.CH_3$ C_7H_{12} **Beil. I-257**
(*n*-Butyl-methyl-acetylene)

B.P. 111.5-112.5° ⟨1⟩ D_4^{20} = **0.748 ⟨2⟩** n_D^{20} = **1.4230 ⟨2⟩**
110-111°$_{747}$ ⟨2⟩ D^{25} = **0.745 ⟨3⟩** n_D^{25} = **1.4220 ⟨3⟩**

[For prepn. from *n*-$C_4H_9.C{\equiv}C.Na$ converted to *n*-$C_4H_9.C{\equiv}C.MgBr$ and treated with $(CH_3)_2SO_4$ see ⟨2⟩.]

C̄ adds Br_2. [For detn. of C̄ via $KBr/KBrO_3$ titration see ⟨4⟩.]

C̄ htd. with 5 pts. aq. in s.t. at 325° yields mixt. of equal pts. heptanone-2 (1:5460) and heptanone-3 [Beil. I-699] ⟨5⟩.

C̄ does not react with $NH_4OH/CuCl$ nor alc. $AgNO_3$ (T 1.96-A).

1:8100 ⟨1⟩ Gredy, *Compt. rend.* **197,** 328 (1933). ⟨2⟩ Thorn, Hennion, Nieuwland, *J. Am. Chem. Soc.* **58,** 796–797 (1936). ⟨3⟩ Vaughn, Hennion, Vogt, Nieuwland, *J. Org. Chem.* **2,** 20 (1937). ⟨4⟩ Lucas, Pressman, *Ind. Eng. Chem., Anal. Ed.* **10,** 140–142 (1938). ⟨5⟩ Desgrez, *Ann. chim.* (7) **3,** 234–236 (1894).

1:8105 OCTYNE-1 $CH_3.(CH_2)_5.C{\equiv}C.H$ C_8H_{14} **Beil. I-258**

B.P. 126° ⟨1⟩ **M.P. −80 to −79° ⟨2⟩** D^{20} = **0.7470 ⟨2⟩** n_D^{20} = **1.4172 ⟨2⟩**
D_4^{25} = **0.7414 ⟨3⟩**

C̄ dislvd. in 65% acetic acid contg. a little conc. H_2SO_4 + $HgSO_4$ stirred 3 hrs. at 80° gives (91% yield) octanone-2 (1:5490) ⟨4⟩.

C̄ with $NH_4OH/CuCl$ (T 1.96-A) or with alc. $AgNO_3$ gives ppt. — C̄ treated with alk. K_2HgI_4 (T 1.96-B) gives ppt. of $(C_6H_{13}.C{\equiv}C)_2Hg$, cryst. from MeOH, m.p. 80.4–80.7° ⟨5⟩, 80.5° ⟨6⟩.

1:8105 ⟨1⟩ Bourgeul, *Ann. chim.* (10) **3,** 211, 358 (1925). ⟨2⟩ Landrieu, Baylocq, *Bull. soc. chim.* (4) **45,** 219 (1929). ⟨3⟩ Moureu, Muller, Varin, *Ann. chim.* (9) **2,** 275 (1914). ⟨4⟩ Thomas, Campbell, Hennion, *J. Am. Chem. Soc.* **60,** 718–720 (1938). ⟨5⟩ Vaughn, *J. Am. Chem. Soc.* **55,** 3454 (1933). ⟨6⟩ Bachmann, *J. Am. Chem. Soc.* **57,** 1090 (1935).

1:8110 OCTYNE-4 $CH_3.CH_2.CH_2.C{\equiv}C.CH_2.CH_2.CH_3$ C_8H_{14} **Beil. S.N. 12**
(Di-*n*-propylacetylene)

B.P. 130.4-130.6°$_{745}$ ⟨1⟩ D^{25} = **0.7484 ⟨1⟩** n_D^{25} = **1.4226 ⟨1⟩**

C̄ adds Br_2 (T 1.91) but does not react with $NH_4OH/CuCl$ (T 1.96-A).

1:8110 ⟨1⟩ Vaughn, Hennion, Vogt, Nieuwland, *J. Org. Chem.* **2,** 18 (1937).

1:8115 OCTYNE-3 $CH_3.CH_2.C{\equiv}C.CH_2.CH_2.CH_2.CH_3$ C_8H_{14} **Beil. S.N. 12**

B.P. 131.0-131.5° ⟨1⟩ D_4^{20} = **0.748 ⟨2⟩** n_D^{20} = **1.4261 ⟨2⟩**
D^{25} = **0.7501 ⟨3⟩** n_D^{25} = **1.4230 ⟨3⟩**

C̄ adds Br_2 (T 1.91) but does not react with $NH_4OH/CuCl$ (T 1.96-A).

1:8115 ⟨1⟩ Bourgeul, *Ann. chim.* (10) **3,** 212 (1925). ⟨2⟩ Thorn, Hennion, Nieuwland, *J. Am. Chem. Soc.* **58,** 797 (1936). ⟨3⟩ Bried, Hennion, *J. Am. Chem. Soc.* **59,** 1310 (1937).

1:8120 OCTYNE-2 $CH_3(CH_2)_4.C{\equiv}C.CH_3$ C_8H_{14} **Beil. I-258**

B.P. 138.0-138.4° ⟨1⟩ D^{25} = **0.761** n_D^{25} = **1.4285**
135.5-137° ⟨2⟩

C̄ adds Br_2 (T 1.91) but does not react with $NH_4OH/CuCl$ (T 1.96-A).

1:8120 ⟨1⟩ Mulliken, Wakeman, Gerry, *J. Am. Chem. Soc.* **57,** 1607 (1935). ⟨2⟩ Bourgeul, *Ann. chim.* (10) **3,** 212 (1925).

1:8125 NONYNE-1 $CH_3.(CH_2)_6.C{\equiv}C.H$ C_9H_{16} **Beil. I₁-(122)**

B.P. 151° cor. ⟨1⟩ D^{20} = **0.760** ⟨1⟩ n_D^{20} = **1.423** ⟨1⟩

C̄ treated with alk. K_2HgI_4 yields $(C_7H_{15}.C{\equiv}C)_2Hg$, cryst. from MeOH, m.p. 67.8–68.5° ⟨2⟩.

1:8125 ⟨1⟩ Bourgeul, *Ann. chim.* (10) **3,** 211, 359 (1925). ⟨2⟩ Vaughn, *J. Am. Chem. Soc.* **55,** 3454 (1933).

1:8135 NONYNE-3 $CH_3(CH_2)_4.C{\equiv}C.CH_2.CH_3$ C_9H_{16} **Beil. S.N. 12**

B.P. 153-155°₁₄₅ ⟨1⟩ D_4^{20} = **0.765** ⟨1⟩ n_D^{20} = **1.4299** ⟨1⟩
D^{25} = **0.762** ⟨2⟩ n_D^{25} = **1.4300** ⟨2⟩

C̄ adds Br_2 (T 1.91) but does not react with $NH_4OH/CuCl$ (T 1.96-A).

1:8135 ⟨1⟩ Thorn, Hennion, Nieuwland, *J. Am. Chem. Soc.* **58,** 797 (1936). ⟨2⟩ Vaughn, Hennion, Vogt, Nieuwland, *J. Org. Chem.* **2,** 20 (1937).

1:8150 α-PINENE $C_{10}H_{16}$ **Beil. V-144**

CH_3
C
HC CH_3 CH
CCH_3
H_2C CH_2
C
H

B.P. 156.0-156.3° ⟨1⟩; cf. ⟨2⟩ D_4^{20} = **0.8600** ⟨1⟩; cf. ⟨2⟩ n_D^{20} = **1.4560** ⟨1⟩; cf. ⟨2⟩

C̄ is chief constituent of oil of turpentine, odor penetrating and characteristic! — C̄ occurs naturally in both *d*- and *l*-forms; that of American or English origin (" Australene ") is usually dextrorotatory; that of French origin (" Terebenthene ") is laevorotatory. However, C̄ from Douglas fir balsam is the *l*-form. An optically inactive (*d,l*) form can also be prepd. Optical rotation varies somewhat but may be as high as $[\alpha]_D^{20}$ = +51.14° or $[\alpha]_D^{20}$ = −51.28° in 4% alc. soln. ⟨2⟩. C̄ on htg. in s.t. at 200° for 50–100 hrs. loses its optical activity, not because of racemization, but by conversion to dipentene (1:8165) ⟨1⟩. C̄ and dipentene, however, cannot be separated by fract. distn. ⟨1⟩.

C̄ adds Br_2 (T 1.91) — C̄ at 0° or below treated with a stream of *dry* Br_2 (2 moles) in CO_2 (by bubbling dry CO_2 through weighed amt. Br_2) gives (15% yield ⟨3⟩) pinene dibromide (2,6-dibromocamphane) [Beil. V-99] which separates as crystals, recrystd. from alc.,

AcOEt, or $CHCl_3$, m.p. 169° ⟨3⟩, 169–170° ⟨4⟩. [C̄ in dry CCl_4 treated with 2 moles Br_2 ⟨4 gives only 7% yield.] [Because of its very large molar f.p. lowering (80.9°) this pinen dibromide is suggested ⟨5⟩ instead of *d*-camphor (1:5215) (40.0°) in the Rast method ⟨6 for detn. of mol. wt. [C̄ does *not* give satisfactory results in $KBr/KBrO_3$ titration (T 1.925)

C̄ as such, or in dry ether, satd. with dry HCl gas at 10–15°, then stood at −5° for an hou ⟨2⟩ first gives the true pinene hydrochloride which immediately rearranges ⟨7⟩ ⟨8⟩ to borny chloride [Beil. V-94], purified by recrystn. from dry MeOH, or by sublimation, m.p. 132.5 133.5° cor. ⟨9⟩, 132° cor. ⟨2⟩, $[\alpha]_D^{20}$ in 1% alc. soln. = ±33.4° ⟨2⟩ — C̄ in $CHCl_3$ treated wit dry HBr similarly yields bornyl bromide [Beil. V-98], m.p. 89° ⟨5⟩ [also used in Rast mol. wt method because of its large molar f.p. lowering, viz. 66.9° ⟨5⟩].

C̄ (1 pt.) in 90% MeOH (1 pt.) treated with ethyl nitrite (1 pt.) and then at −20° wit MeOH—HCl (5 *N*) during 2½ hrs., stood, ppts. the inactive pinene nitrosochloride; fror the filtrate after cooling to −20° further addn. of 90% MeOH ppts. the active form; th yields vary but are always low; m.p. *d*- or *l*-pinene nitrosochloride is 89.5–90.0°; m.p. c *d,l* product 115° ⟨2⟩. [The yield of nitrosochloride varies widely from pinenes of differen origins and is the smaller the higher the optical rotation of C̄ ⟨10⟩.] [This pinene nitrosc chloride on warming with excess piperidine alone or in alc. soln. gives on pptn. with aq. ⟨11 crystn. ppt. of pinenenitrolpiperidine [Beil. XX-42]; that from either *d*- or *l*-nitrosochlorid has m.p. 84° ⟨12⟩; that from *d,l*-nitrosochloride has m.p. 118–119° ⟨11⟩.]

1:8150 ⟨1⟩ Conant, Carlson, *J. Am. Chem. Soc.* **51**, 3464–3469 (1929). ⟨2⟩ Thurber, Thielk *J. Am. Chem. Soc.* **53**, 1030–1032 (1931). ⟨3⟩ Aschan, *Ber.* **61**, 42–43 (1928). ⟨4⟩ Wallac *Ann.* **264**, 4–8 (1891). ⟨5⟩ Pirsch, *Ber.* **65**, 863, 1839 (1932). ⟨6⟩ Rast, *Ber.* **55**, 1051–105 3727–3728 (1922). ⟨7⟩ Meerwein, van Emster, *Ber.* **55**, 2521–2522 (1922). ⟨8⟩ Meerwei Vorster, *J. prakt. Chem.* (2) **147**, 83–92 (1936). ⟨9⟩ Uchida, *J. Am. Chem. Soc.* **38**, 700–70 (1916). ⟨10⟩ Lynn, *J. Am. Chem. Soc.* **41**, 362 (1919).
⟨11⟩ Wallach, *Ann.* **245**, 253 (1888). ⟨12⟩ Ref. 10, page 365.

1:8155 NONYNE-2 $CH_3.(CH_2)_5.C{\equiv}C.CH_3$ C_9H_{16} **Beil. S.N. 1**

B.P. 161° cor. ⟨1⟩ D_4^{20} = **0.769** ⟨2⟩ n_D^{20} = **1.4331** ⟨2

C̄ adds Br_2 (T 1.91) but does not react with $NH_4OH/CuCl$ (T 1.96-A).

1:8155 ⟨1⟩ Bourgeul, *Ann. chim.* (10) **3**, 212, 358 (1925). ⟨2⟩ Thorn, Hennion, Nieuwland *J. An Chem. Soc.* **58**, 797 (1936).

1:8165 DIPENTENE (*d,l*-Limonene) $C_{10}H_{16}$ **Beil. V-13**

CH₃–C ring structure: CH_3 | C(=CH)–H_2C / H_2C–CH_2 / C—H | C(CH_3)=CH_2

B.P. 177.6–178° $D_4^{20.8}$ = **0.8402** $n_D^{19.6}$ = **1.472**

Agreeable oil of lemon odor.

C̄ adds Br_2 (T 1.91) — C̄ (1 mole) dislvd. in cold mixt. of alc. (4 vols.) + ether (4 vols treated with Br_2 (0.7 vol.) yields on evapn. of solvent ⟨1⟩ dipentene tetrabromide (*d,l*-1,2,8,9 tetrabromo-*p*-menthane) [Beil. V-54], pr. from ether, AcOEt, or $CHCl_3$ + pet. ether, m.p 125° ⟨2⟩ ⟨3⟩; 124–125° ⟨4⟩. [C̄ in 10 vols. AcOH treated with Br_2 ppts. tetrabromid directly ⟨5⟩.]

C̄ dislvd. in ½ vol. AcOH and treated over surface (not in the liquid) with stream of HCl gas soon crystallizes yielding *trans*-(dipentene dihydrochloride) (1,8-dichloro-*p*-menthane) [Beil. V-49], purified by soln. in alc. and pptn. with aq., tbls. from alc., m.p. 50–51° ⟨6⟩.

1:8165 ⟨1⟩ Wallach, *Ann.* **227,** 280 (1885). ⟨2⟩ Wallach, Brass, *Ann.* **225,** 311 (1884). ⟨3⟩ Power, Kleber, *Arch. Pharm.* **232,** 646 (1894). ⟨4⟩ Stephan, Hammerich, *J. prakt. Chem.* (2) **129,** 301 (1931). ⟨5⟩ Wallach, *Ann.* **239,** 3 (1887). ⟨6⟩ Wallach, *Ann.* **245,** 267 (1888).

1:8175 *d*-LIMONENE $C_{10}H_{16}$ Beil. V-133

```
            CH3
             |
             C
          //   \\
       H2C      CH
        |        |
       H2C      CH2
          \    /
           C—H
           |
           C
         /   \\
      CH3     CH2
```

B.P. 178° D_4^{20} = **0.8411 ⟨1⟩** n_D^{21} = **1.4743**

176-176.4° ⟨1⟩

Oil with characteristic oil of lemon odor! — Optically active; $[\alpha]_D^{20}$ = +126° (as pure C̄) ⟨1⟩.

C̄ adds Br_2 (T 1.91) — C̄ (3 g.) dislvd. in 1 pt. AmOH (or AcOEt) + 2 pts. ether and treated with Br_2 (2.2 ml.) in ether (10 ml.) gives (54% yield ⟨2⟩) *d*-limonene tetrabromide (*d*-1,2,8,9-tetrabromo-*p*-menthane) [Beil. I-53], m.p. 104° ⟨1⟩ ⟨2⟩ ⟨3⟩. [The corresp. tetrabromide from *l*-limonene also has m.p. 104°, but mixt. of exactly equal pts. of the *d*- and the *l*-tetrabromides gives the *d,l*-limonene (dipentene) tetrabromide, m.p. 124° ⟨1⟩; cf. (1:8165).] [*d*- or *l*-Limonene tetrabromide dislvd. in 5 vols. ether and treated with Mg (3 atoms) + trace of I_2 regenerates (80% yield ⟨1⟩) *d*- (or *l*-) limonene ⟨1⟩ ⟨3⟩; used in purification of C̄.]

C̄ in ether treated with HCl gas yields *trans*-(dipentene dihydrochloride), m.p. 50° identical with that from dipentene (1:8165)

C̄ (5 ml.) + amyl nitrite (7 ml.) + AcOH (12 ml.) treated gradually in cold with mixt. of conc. HCl (6 ml.) in AcOH (6 ml.) and finally alc. (5 ml.) added, yields ⟨4⟩ a mixt. of *d*-limonene α- and β-nitrosochlorides in 45–50% yield, the α isomer always comprising 75–80% of the mixt. ⟨5⟩. From the mixt. the more sol. α isomer can be obtd. by digestion with cold $CHCl_3$, filtration (to remove β) and pptn. of α from the filtrate by addn. of MeOH; m.p. α form 103–104°. This product on warming with equal wt. piperidine in 3 pts. alc. yields in turn mixt. of two *d*-limonene nitrolpiperidides [Beil. XX-41] separable with pet. ether; the more sol. α form cryst. from alc. has m.p. 93–94°; the less sol. β form has m.p. 110–111° ⟨6⟩. [Note that a mixt. of the *d*- and the *l*-limonenenitrolpiperidides, each m.p. 93–94°, mixed in pet. ether and solv. evapd. yield a compd., dipentene α-nitrolpiperidide, m.p. 154°; similar treatment of the pair of active β-nitrolpiperidides of m.p. 110–111° yields the corresp. dipentene-β-nitrolpiperidide, cryst. from alc., m.p. 152° ⟨7⟩.]

1:8175 ⟨1⟩ von Braun, Lemke, *Ber.* **56,** 1562–1563 (1923). ⟨2⟩ Gaponenkov, *Cent.* **1937,** II, 1377; *Chem. Abs.* **31,** 5340 (1937). ⟨3⟩ Rule, Chambers, *J. Chem. Soc.* **1937,** 152. ⟨4⟩ Wallach, *Ann.* **252,** 109–111 (1889). ⟨5⟩ Wallach, *Ann.* **270,** 174 (1892). ⟨6⟩ Ref. 4, pages 113–117. ⟨7⟩ Ref. 4, pages 125–126.

ORDER I: SUBORDER I: GENUS 9: HYDROCARBONS

Division B, Liquids

Section 4. Alkenes

1:8200 **3-METHYLBUTENE-1** $CH_2{=}CH.C.CH_3$ (with CH_3 on C) C_5H_{10} **Beil. I-213**
(2-Methylbutene-3;
isopropylethylene)

B.P. 20.1° ⟨1⟩ D_4^{15} = **0.63197 ⟨1⟩** n_D^{15} = **1.3675 ⟨1⟩**
20.18-20.21° ⟨2⟩

$\bar{C}$ (10 moles) shaken with conc. H_2SO_4 (1 mole) polymerizes in a few minutes ⟨3⟩ yielding no dimer but a mixt. of products b.p. mainly 150–325° ⟨4⟩. [Under same conditions trimethylethylene (1:8220) yields mostly a dimer ⟨3⟩.] — $\bar{C}$ (10 moles) stood for 7 days with 2:1 H_2SO_4 (1 mole) gave almost entirely dimer, b.p. 153–158° ⟨3⟩.

$\bar{C}$ does not dissolve in 75% H_2SO_4 [dif. and sepn. from trimethylethylene (1:8220) ⟨5⟩ ⟨6⟩].

$\bar{C}$ adds Br_2 (T 1.91) yielding 3,4-dibromo-2-methylbutane [Beil. I-137], b.p. 61–62° at 12 mm., D_4^{20} = 1.6776, n_D^{20} = 1.50932.

1:8200 ⟨1⟩ Norris, Reuter, *J. Am. Chem. Soc.* **49,** 2633 (1927). ⟨2⟩ Dolliver, Gresham, Kistiakowsky, Vaughan, *J. Am. Chem. Soc.* **59,** 832 (1937). ⟨3⟩ Norris, Joubert, *J. Am. Chem. Soc.* **49,** 879 (1927). ⟨4⟩ Ipatieff, Pines, *J. Org. Chem.* **1,** 480 (1937). ⟨5⟩ Ref. 4, page 474. ⟨6⟩ Ipatieff, Pines, Schmerling, *J. Am. Chem. Soc.* **60,** 354 (1938).

1:8205 **PENTENE-1** $CH_2{=}CH.CH_2.CH_2.CH_3$ C_5H_{10} **Beil. I-210**
(*n*-Propylethylene)

B.P. 30.1-30.2° ⟨1⟩ ⟨5⟩ D_4^{20} = **0.6410 ⟨1⟩ ⟨5⟩** n_D^{20} = **1.3710 ⟨1⟩ ⟨5⟩**

$\bar{C}$ forms with MeOH a const. boilg. mixt., b.p. 25.8–26.0°$_{754}$ contg. 92% $\bar{C}$ ⟨1⟩.

$\bar{C}$ adds Br_2 yielding 1,2-dibromopentane, b.p. 68° at 12 mm., D^{19} = 1.592, n_D^{19} = 1.5012 ⟨2⟩.

[For behavior with H_2SO_4 see ⟨3⟩ ⟨4⟩.] [$\bar{C}$ in AcOH treated with HBr at 0–5° gives exclusively 1-bromopentane; $\bar{C}$ with aq. HBr gives exclusively 2-bromopentane ⟨1⟩.]

1:8205 ⟨1⟩ Sherrill, Mayer, Walter, *J. Am. Chem. Soc.* **56,** 926–930 (1934). ⟨2⟩ Kirrmann, *Bull. soc. chim.* (4) **39,** 990 (1926). ⟨3⟩ Norris, Joubert, *J. Am. Chem. Soc.* **49,** 875–877 (1927). ⟨4⟩ Brooks, *J. Am. Chem. Soc.* **56,** 1998–2000 (1934). ⟨5⟩ Sherrill, Walter, *J. Am. Chem. Soc.* **58,** 744 (1936).

1:8210 **2-METHYLBUTENE-1** $CH_2{=}C.CH_2.CH_3$ (with CH_3 on C) C_5H_{10} **Beil. 1-210**
(*unsym.*-Ethyl-methyl-
ethylene)

B.P. 31.05° ⟨1⟩ D_4^{20} = **0.6504 ⟨1⟩** n_D^{20} = **1.3777 ⟨1⟩**

$\bar{C}$ forms with MeOH a const. boilg. mixt., b.p. 27.5° ⟨1⟩.

$\bar{C}$ adds Br_2 yielding 1,2-dibromo-2-methylbutane, b.p. 47.4–48.0° at 8.5–9.0 mm., D_4^{20} = 1.6711, n_D^{20} = 1.5088 ⟨1⟩.

[For behavior with H_2SO_4 see ⟨2⟩ ⟨3⟩.]

1:8210 ⟨1⟩ Sherrill, Walter, *J. Am. Chem. Soc.* **58,** 744 (1936). ⟨2⟩ Norris, Joubert, *J. Am. Chem. Soc.* **49,** 875–880 (1927). ⟨3⟩ Brooks, Humphrey, *J. Am. Chem. Soc.* **40,** 830–831 (1918).

1:8215 PENTENE-2 C_5H_{10} **Beil. I-210**

(*sym.*-Ethyl-methyl-ethylene)

$CH_3.C.H$ and $CH_3.C.H$ (double bond) $CH_3.CH_2.C.H$ and $H.C.CH_2.CH_3$

cis **B.P. 37.0°** ⟨1⟩; cf. ⟨2⟩ **F.P. −180 to 178°** ⟨3⟩
D_4^{20} = **0.6562** ⟨1⟩ n_D^{20} = **1.3822** ⟨1⟩; cf. ⟨2⟩

trans **B.P. 36.25°** ⟨4⟩; cf. ⟨3⟩ **F.P. −135 to −136°** ⟨3⟩
D_4^{20} = **0.6486** ⟨4⟩ n_D^{20} = **1.3790** ⟨4⟩; cf. ⟨2⟩

[This pair of geometrical stereoisomers are so nearly alike as to be distinguishable only by the most careful work. The controversy over their reactions with HBr and HCl is so extended as to preclude summarization here. For further details see ⟨2⟩ and references there given.]

[For prepn. of ordinary sample of $\bar{C}$ from pentanol-2 (1:6185) by htg. with H_2SO_4 (65–80% yield) see ⟨5⟩.]

$\bar{C}$ forms with MeOH a const. boilg. mixt., b.p. 30.85° ⟨6⟩; $\bar{C}$ forms with EtOH a const. boilg. mixt., b.p. 33.7° ⟨6⟩.

Both forms of $\bar{C}$ add Br_2 yielding diastereomeric *d,l*-2,3-dibromopentanes: that from *cis*-pentene-2 has b.p. 92.4° at 50.1 mm., D_4^{20} = 1.6817, n_D^{20} = 1.5096; f.p. −44 to −41°; that from *trans*-pentene-2 has b.p. 91.0° at 50.1 mm., D_4^{20} = 1.6809, n_D^{20} = 1.5096 and f.p. −55 to −53° ⟨3⟩.

[For estn. of $\bar{C}$ via KBr/$KBrO_3$ titration (T 1.925); B.B. No. = 229 ⟨7⟩.]

1:8215 ⟨1⟩ Sherrill, Launspach, *J. Am. Chem. Soc.* **60,** 2562–2563 (1938). ⟨2⟩ Kharasch, Walling, Mayo, *J. Am. Chem. Soc.* **61,** 1559–1564 (1939). ⟨3⟩ Lucas, Prater, *J. Am. Chem. Soc.* **59,** 1682–1686 (1937). ⟨4⟩ Sherrill, Matlack, *J. Am. Chem. Soc.* **59,** 2134–2138 (1937). ⟨5⟩ Norris, *Organic Syntheses, Coll. Vol.* I, 421–422 (1932). ⟨6⟩ Sherrill, Baldwin, Haas, *J. Am. Chem. Soc.* **51,** 3038 (1929). ⟨7⟩ Cortese, *Rec. trav. chim.* **48,** 564–567 (1929).

1:8220 2-METHYLBUTENE-2 $CH_3.CH{=}C(CH_3).CH_3$ C_5H_{10} **Beil. I-211**

(Trimethylethylene)

B.P. 38.4° ⟨1⟩ **M.P. −123 ± 2°** ⟨1⟩ D_4^{20} = **0.66201** ⟨1⟩ n_D^{20} = **1.3878** ⟨1⟩
D_4^{25} = **0.65694** ⟨1⟩ n_D^{25} = **1.3846** ⟨1⟩

[For prepn. from *ter*-amyl alcohol (1:6160) see latter; note that reaction yields about 78% $\bar{C}$ accompanied by 22% of 2-methylbutene-1 (1:8210) ⟨2⟩.]

$\bar{C}$ adds Br_2 but reaction is accompanied by substitution and does not yield a homogeneous product ⟨3⟩.

$\bar{C}$ + amyl nitrite treated with conc. HCl yields trimethylethylene nitrosochloride, white pr., m.p. 74–75° ⟨4⟩; 71–72° ⟨5⟩.

[For reaction of $\bar{C}$ with H_2SO_4 see ⟨6⟩ ⟨7⟩.] [For estn. of $\bar{C}$ via KBr/$KBrO_3$ titration (T 1.925) see ⟨8⟩; B.B. No. 229.]

1:8220 ⟨1⟩ Norris, Reuter, *J. Am. Chem. Soc.* **49,** 2633 (1927). ⟨2⟩ Church, Whitmore, McGrew, *J. Am. Chem. Soc.* **56,** 183 (1934). ⟨3⟩ Vaughan, Rust, *J. Am. Chem. Soc.* **61,** 216 (1939). ⟨4⟩ Schmidt, *Ber.* **35,** 3730–3733 (1902). ⟨5⟩ Nasarow, *Ber.* **70,** 612 (1937). ⟨6⟩ Norris, Joubert, *J. Am. Chem. Soc.* **49,** 876–881 (1927). ⟨7⟩ Ipatieff, Pines, *J. Org. Chem.* **1,** 464–465 (1937). ⟨8⟩ Cortese, *Rec. trav. chim.* **48,** 564–567 (1929).

1:8225 3,3-DIMETHYLBUTENE-1 (2,2-Dimethylbutene-3) $H_2C{=}CH.C(CH_3)_2.CH_3$ C_6H_{12} **Beil. I-217**

B.P. 41.18° ⟨1⟩
41.0-41.2° ⟨2⟩
D_4^{20} = **0.6510 ⟨2⟩** n_D^{20} = **1.3765 ⟨1⟩**

C̄ adds Br_2 yielding 1,2-dibromo-3,3-dimethylpentane (3,4-dibromo-2,2-dimethylpentane), b.p. 95.3–95.6° at 10 mm., D_4^{20} = 1.5615, n_D^{20} = 1.5109 ⟨2⟩.

1:8225 ⟨1⟩ Dolliver, Gresham, Kistiakowsky, Vaughan, *J. Am. Chem. Soc.* **59,** 833 (1937). ⟨2⟩ Schurman, Boord, *J. Am. Chem. Soc.* **55,** 4932–4933 (1933).

1:8230 4-METHYLPENTENE-1 (2-Methylpentene-4) $CH_2{=}CH.CH_2.CH(CH_3).CH_3$ C_6H_{12} **Beil. I-217**

B.P. 53.6-53.9° ⟨1⟩
53.8-54.0° ⟨2⟩
D_4^{20} = **0.6646 ⟨1⟩** n_D^{20} = **1.3825 ⟨1⟩**

C̄ adds Br_2 yielding 1,2-dibromo-4-methylpentane, b.p. 87° at 21 mm., D_4^{20} = 1.5689, n_D^{20} = 1.4980 ⟨1⟩; cf. ⟨2⟩.

1:8230 ⟨1⟩ Schmitt, Boord, *J. Am. Chem. Soc.* **54,** 754, 760 (1932). ⟨2⟩ van Risseghem, *Bull. soc. chim. Belg.* **42,** 229–237 (1933).

1:8235 3-METHYLPENTENE-1 $CH_2{=}CH.CH(CH_3).CH_2.CH_3$ C_6H_{12} **Beil. S.N. 11**

B.P. 53.6-54.°0 ⟨1⟩ D_4^{20} = **0.6700 ⟨1⟩** n_D^{20} = **1.3835 ⟨1⟩**

C̄ adds Br_2 yielding 1,2-dibromo-3-methylpentane, b.p. 99° at 30 mm., D_4^{20} = 1.6016, n_D^{20} = 1.5060 ⟨1⟩.

1:8235 ⟨1⟩ Schmitt, Boord, *J. Am. Chem. Soc.* **54,** 754, 760 (1932).

1:8240 4-METHYLPENTENE-2 (2-Methylpentene-3) $CH_3.CH{=}CH.CH(CH_3).CH_3$ C_6H_{12} **Beil. I-217**

trans **B.P. 57.7-58.5° ⟨1⟩** D_4^{20} = **0.6709 ⟨1⟩** n_D^{20} = **1.3885 ⟨1⟩**
58.2-58.6° ⟨2⟩
cis **B.P. 54.2-55.2° ⟨1⟩** D_4^{20} = **0.6702 ⟨1⟩** n_D^{20} = **1.3881 ⟨1⟩**
55.5° ⟨2⟩

C̄ (*trans*) adds Br_2 yielding a 2,3-dibromo-4-methylpentane, b.p. 78° at 22 mm., D_4^{20} = 1.5996, n_D^{20} = 1.5070; C̄ (*cis*) adds Br_2 yielding a 2,3-dibromo-4-methylpentane, b.p. 72–73° at 18 mm., D_4^{20} = 1.5983, n_D^{20} = 1.5060 ⟨1⟩.

1:8240 ⟨1⟩ Schmitt, Boord, *J. Am. Chem. Soc.* **54,** 754, 760 (1932). ⟨2⟩ van Risseghem, *Bull. soc. chim. Belg.* **47,** 57 (1938).

1:8245 2,3-DIMETHYLBUTENE-1 $H_2C{=}C(CH_3)—CH(CH_3).CH_3$ C_6H_{12} **Beil. I-218**

B.P. 56.0-56.5° ⟨1⟩; cf. ⟨2⟩ **M.P. −120 to −125° ⟨2⟩**
D_4^{20} = **0.6803 ⟨1⟩**; cf. ⟨2⟩ n_D^{20} = **1.3995 ⟨1⟩**; cf. ⟨2⟩

C̄ is formed only in small amt. (20%) by dehydration of dimethyl-isopropyl-carbinol (1:6187) with anhydrous oxalic acid, the main product (80%) being tetramethylethylene (1:8290) ⟨2⟩.

C̄ forms with MeOH a const. boilg. mixt., b.p. 44.22°_{762} ⟨3⟩.

C̄ adds Br_2 yielding 1,2-dibromo-2,3-dimethylbutane, b.p. 80° at 17 mm., D_4^{20} = 1.6033, n_D^{20} = 1.5105 ⟨1⟩.

1:8245 ⟨1⟩ Schmitt, Boord, *J. Am. Chem. Soc.* **54,** 754, 760 (1932). ⟨2⟩ Schurman, Boord, *J. Am. Chem. Soc.* **55,** 4932–4934 (1933). ⟨3⟩ Kistiakowsky, Ruhoff, Smith, Vaughan, *J. Am. Chem. Soc.* **58,** 140 (1936).

1:8250 2-METHYLPENTENE-1 $CH_2{=}\overset{H}{\underset{CH_3}{C}}.CH_2.CH_2.CH_3$ C_6H_{12} **Beil. S.N. 11**

B.P. 61.5-62.0° ⟨1⟩ D_4^{20} = **0.6817 ⟨1⟩** n_D^{20} = **1.3921 ⟨1⟩**

C̄ adds Br_2 yielding 1,2-dibromo-2-methylpentane, b.p. 87–88° at 20 mm., D_4^{20} = 1.5581, n_D^{20} = 1.5015 ⟨1⟩.

1:8250 ⟨1⟩ Schmitt, Boord, *J. Am. Chem. Soc.* **54,** 754, 760 (1932).

1:8255 HEXENE-1 $CH_2{=}CH.CH_2.CH_2.CH_2.CH_3$ C_6H_{12} **Beil. I-215**

B.P. 63.4-63.7° ⟨1⟩ M.P. −138° ⟨2⟩
$63.8\text{-}64.0^\circ_{778}$ ⟨2⟩

D_4^{20} = **0.6750 ⟨2⟩**; cf. ⟨1⟩ n_D^{20} = **1.38767 ⟨2⟩**; cf. ⟨1⟩

C̄ adds Br_2 yielding 1,2-dibromohexane, b.p. 89–90° at 18 mm., D_4^{20} = 1.5774, n_D^{20} = 1.5024 ⟨1⟩.

[For analysis of C̄ via $KBr/KBrO_3$ titration see ⟨3⟩.]

1:8255 ⟨1⟩ Schmitt, Boord, *J. Am. Chem. Soc.* **54,** 754, 760 (1932). ⟨2⟩ Waterman, de Kok, *Rec. trav. chim.* **52,** 251–256 (1933). ⟨3⟩ Lucas, Pressman, *Ind. Eng. Chem., Anal. Ed.* **10,** 140–142 (1938).

1:8260 3-METHYLPENTENE-2 $CH_3.CH{=}\underset{CH_3}{C}.CH_2.CH_3$ C_6H_{12} **Beil. I-217**

cis **B.P. 65.1-65.7° ⟨1⟩** D_4^{20} = **0.6940 ⟨2⟩** n_D^{20} = **1.3994 ⟨2⟩**
65.7-66.2° ⟨2⟩

trans **B.P. 70.2-70.5° ⟨1⟩** D_4^{20} = **0.6956 ⟨2⟩** n_D^{20} = **1.4002 ⟨2⟩**
67.6-68.2° ⟨2⟩

C̄ is main product from dehydration of diethyl-methyl-carbinol (1:6189) by htg. with I_2, the isomeric 2-ethylbutene-1 (1:8265) being present only in traces ⟨3⟩.

1:8260 ⟨1⟩ van Risseghem, *Bull. soc. chim. Belg.* **47,** 47–51 (1938). ⟨2⟩ Schmitt, Boord, *J. Am. Chem. Soc.* **54,** 754 (1932). ⟨3⟩ Church, Whitmore, McGrew, *J. Am. Chem. Soc.* **56,** 183 (1934).

1:8265 2-ETHYLBUTENE-1 $CH_2{=}\underset{CH_2.CH_3}{CH}.CH_2.CH_3$ C_6H_{12} **Beil. S.N. 11**

B.P. 66.2-66.7° ⟨1⟩ D_4^{20} = **0.6914 ⟨1⟩** n_D^{20} = **1.3990 ⟨1⟩**

[Only a trace of C̄ is formed by dehydration of diethyl-methyl-carbinol (1:6189) with I_2, the reaction yielding mainly 3-methylpentene-2 (1:8260) ⟨2⟩.]

C̄ adds Br_2 yielding 1,2-dibromo-2-ethylbutane, b.p. 87° at 21 mm., D_4^{20} = 1.6045, n_D^{20} = 1.5112 ⟨1⟩.

1:8265 ⟨1⟩ Schmitt, Boord, *J. Am. Chem. Soc.* **54,** 754, 760 (1932). ⟨2⟩ Church, Whitmore, McGrew, *J. Am. Chem. Soc.* **56,** 183 (1934).

1:8270 HEXENE-3 $CH_3.CH_2.CH{=}CH.CH_2.CH_3$ C_6H_{12} **Beil. I-215**

trans **B.P. 67.28-67.35°** ⟨1⟩ D_4^{20} = **0.6779** ⟨1⟩ n_D^{20} = **1.39377** ⟨6⟩
cis **B.P. 66.58-66.72°** ⟨1⟩ D_4^{20} = **0.6792** ⟨1⟩ n_D^{20} = **1.39338** ⟨6⟩
mixt. **B.P. 66.6-67.0°** ⟨2⟩ D_4^{20} = **0.6816** ⟨2⟩ n_D^{20} = **1.3942** ⟨2⟩

C̄ (mixture) adds Br_2 yielding 3,4-dibromohexane, b.p. 80–81° at 13 mm., D_4^{20} = 1.6027, n_D^{20} = 1.5045 ⟨2⟩.

[For reactions of C̄ (mixture) with conc. H_2SO_4, SO_2Cl_2, PCl_5, HCl, HBr see ⟨3⟩ ⟨4⟩.]

[For extensive study of *cis-trans* isomers see ⟨5⟩.]

1:8270 ⟨1⟩ van Risseghem, *Bull. soc. chim. Belg.* **47,** 240 (1938). ⟨2⟩ Schmitt, Boord, *J. Am. Chem. Soc.* **54,** 754, 760 (1932). ⟨3⟩ Spiegler, Tinker, *J. Am. Chem. Soc.* **61,** 940–942 (1939). ⟨4⟩ O'Connor, Baldinger, Vogt, Hennion, *J. Am. Chem. Soc.* **61,** 1454–1456 (1939). ⟨5⟩ van Risseghem, *Bull. soc. chim. Belg.* **47,** 194–215, 221–240, 261–286 (1938). ⟨6⟩ Campbell, Eby, *J. Am. Chem. Soc.* **63,** 218 (1941).

1:8275 2-METHYLPENTENE-2 $CH_3.C(CH_3){=}CH.CH_2.CH_3$ C_6H_{12} **Beil. I-217**

B.P. 67.2-67.5° ⟨1⟩ D_4^{20} = **0.6904** ⟨1⟩ n_D^{20} = **1.4005** ⟨1⟩

C̄ adds Br_2 yielding 2,3-dibromo-2-methylpentane, b.p. 71–72° at 18 mm., D_4^{20} = 1.5849, n_D^{20} = 1.5063 ⟨1⟩.

1:8275 ⟨1⟩ Schmitt, Boord, *J. Am. Chem. Soc.* **54,** 754, 760 (1932).

1:8280 HEXENE-2 $CH_3.CH{=}CH.CH_2.CH_2.CH_3$ C_6H_{12} **Beil. I-215**

trans **B.P. 68.0-68.2°** ⟨1⟩; cf. ⟨4⟩ D_4^{15} = **0.6863** ⟨1⟩; cf. ⟨4⟩ n_D^{20} = **1.3980** ⟨1⟩; cf. ⟨4⟩
cis **B.P. 68.5-69.5°** ⟨2⟩ D_4^{25} = **0.683** ⟨2⟩ n_D^{25} = **1.3960** ⟨2⟩
mixt. **B.P. 67.9-68.1°** ⟨3⟩ D_4^{20} = **0.6813** ⟨3⟩ n_D^{20} = **1.3928** ⟨3⟩

C̄ adds Br_2 yielding 2,3-dibromohexane, b.p. 90° at 16 mm., D_4^{20} = 1.5812, n_D^{20} = 1.5025 ⟨3⟩.

1:8280 ⟨1⟩ van Risseghem, *Bull. soc. chim. Belg.* **35,** 328–364 (1926). ⟨2⟩ Gredy, *Bull. soc. chim.* (5) **2,** 1029, (1935). ⟨3⟩ Schmitt, Boord, *J. Am. Chem. Soc.* **54,** 754, 760 (1932). ⟨4⟩ van Risseghem, *Bull. soc. chim. Belg.* **47,** 51–54 (1938).

1:8285 4,4-DIMETHYLPENTENE-1 $CH_2{=}CH.CH_2.C(CH_3)_2.CH_3$ C_7H_{14} **Beil. S.N. 11**
(2,2-Dimethylpentene-4)

B.P. 72.35° ⟨1⟩ D_4^{20} = **0.6827** ⟨1⟩ n_D^{20} = **1.3911** ⟨1⟩

C̄ adds Br_2 giving (85% yield) 1,2-dibromo-4,4-dimethylpentane (4,5-dibromo-2,2-dimethylpentane), b.p. 77–78° at 9 mm., D_4^{20} = 1.5129, n_D^{20} = 1.4970 ⟨1⟩ — C̄ on ozonolysis yields formaldehyde (1:0145), *ter*-butylacetaldehyde (2,4-dinitrophenylhydrazone (T 1.14), m.p. 146–147°), and *ter*-butylacetic acid (amide, m.p. 132°) ⟨1⟩ — C̄ satd. with dry HBr at 0° yields exclusively 1-bromo-4,4-dimethylpentane (5-bromo-2,2-dimethylpentane) ⟨1⟩.

1:8285 ⟨1⟩ Whitmore, Homeyer, *J. Am. Chem. Soc.* **55,** 4557 (1933).

1:8290 **2,3-DIMETHYLBUTENE-2** $CH_3.C{=}C.CH_3$ (with CH_3 on each C) C_6H_{12} **Beil. I-218**
(Tetramethylethylene)

B.P. 72.9-73.2° ⟨1⟩ M.P. −76.4° ⟨1⟩ D_4^{20} = 0.7081 ⟨1⟩ n_D^{20} = 1.41153 ⟨1⟩

[For prepn. from dimethyl-isopropyl-carbinol (1:6187) by htg. at 100° for 8 hrs. with 3 wts. of anhydrous oxalic acid see ⟨1⟩.] [Some 2,3-dimethylbutene-1 (1:8245) is also formed (about 20%) ⟨1⟩.]

C̄ forms with MeOH a const. boilg. mixt., b.p. 52.2°_{762} ⟨2⟩.

1:8290 ⟨1⟩ Schurman, Boord, *J. Am. Chem. Soc.* **55,** 4932–4934 (1933). ⟨2⟩ Kistiakowsky, Ruhoff, Smith, Vaughan, *J. Am. Chem. Soc.* **58,** 141 (1936).

1:8292 **4,4-DIMETHYLPENTENE-2** $CH_3.CH{=}CH.C(CH_3)_2.CH_3$ C_7H_{14} **Beil. S.N. 11**
(2,2-Dimethylpentene-3)

B.P. 76.0-76.1° ⟨1⟩; cf. ⟨2⟩ D_4^{20} = 0.6881 ⟨1⟩; cf. ⟨2⟩ n_D^{20} = 1.3986 ⟨1⟩; cf. ⟨2⟩

C̄ adds Br_2 yielding 2,3-dibromo-4,4-dimethylpentane (3,4-dibromo-2,2-dimethylpentane), b.p. 92.8–93.0° at 14 mm., D_4^{20} = 1.5538, n_D^{20} = 1.5080 ⟨1⟩.

1:8292 ⟨1⟩ Schurman, Boord, *J. Am. Chem. Soc.* **55,** 4932–4933 (1933). ⟨2⟩ Cramer, Miller, *J. Am. Chem. Soc.* **62,** 1453 (1940).

1:8294 **3,3-DIMETHYLPENTENE-1** $CH_2{=}CH.C(CH_3)_2.CH_2.CH_2$ C_7H_{14} **Beil. S.N. 11**

B.P. 76.9° ⟨1⟩ D_4^{20} = 0.6961 ⟨1⟩ n_D^{20} = 1.3991 ⟨1⟩

C̄ adds Br_2 yielding 1,2-dibromo-3,3-dimethylpentane, b.p. 95.3–95.6° at 10 mm., D_4^{20} = 1.5615, n_D^{20} = 1.5109 ⟨1⟩.

1:8294 ⟨1⟩ Schurman, Boord, *J. Am. Chem. Soc.* **55,** 4932–4933 (1933).

1:8296 **2,4-DIMETHYLPENTENE-1** $CH_2{=}C(CH_3).CH_2.CH(CH_3).CH_3$ C_7H_{14} **Beil. I-220**

B.P. 80.9-81.3° ⟨1⟩ D_4^{20} = 0.6937 ⟨1⟩ n_D^{20} = 1.3970 ⟨1⟩

C̄ adds Br_2 yielding 1,2-dibromo-2,4-dimethylpentane, b.p. 65.5–66.0° at 4 mm., D_4^{20} = 1.5136, n_D^{20} = 1.5005 ⟨1⟩.

1:8296 ⟨1⟩ Soday, Boord, *J. Am. Chem. Soc.* **55,** 3295, 3300 (1933).

1:8298 **3-METHYLHEXENE-1** $CH_2{=}CH.CH(CH_3).CH_2.CH_2.CH_3$ C_7H_{14} **Beil. S.N. 11**

B.P. 83.8-84.1° ⟨1⟩ D_4^{20} = 0.6953 ⟨1⟩ n_D^{20} = 1.3970 ⟨1⟩

C̄ adds Br_2 yielding 1,2-dibromo-3-methylhexane, b.p. 84.0–84.2° at 6 mm., D_4^{20} = 1.5248, n_D^{20} = 1.5028 ⟨1⟩.

1:8298 ⟨1⟩ Soday, Boord, *J. Am. Chem. Soc.* **55,** 3295, 3300 (1933).

1:8300 2,3-DIMETHYLPENTENE-1 C_7H_{14} **Beil. S.N. 11**

$$CH_2{=}C(CH_3){-}CH(CH_3).CH_2.CH_3$$

B.P. 84.1-84.3° ⟨1⟩ D_4^{20} **= 0.7054 ⟨1⟩** n_D^{20} **= 1.4022 ⟨1⟩**

C̄ adds Br_2 yielding 1,2-dibromo-2,3-dimethylpentane, b.p. 72.5–73.0° at 3 mm., D_4^{20} = 1.5245, n_D^{20} = 1.5028 ⟨1⟩.

1:8300 ⟨1⟩ Soday, Boord, *J. Am. Chem. Soc.* **55,** 3295, 3300 (1933).

1:8302 5-METHYLHEXENE-1 C_7H_{14} **Beil. I-220**
(2-Methylhexene-5)

$$CH_2{=}CH.CH_2.CH_2.CH(CH_3).CH_3$$

B.P. 84.7° ⟨1⟩ D_4^{20} **= 0.6936 ⟨1⟩** n_D^{20} **= 1.3954 ⟨1⟩**

C̄ adds Br_2 yielding 1,2-dibromo-5-methylhexane, b.p. 142.6–143.6° at 101 mm., D_4^{20} = 1.5072, n_D^{20} = 1.4970 ⟨1⟩.

1:8302 ⟨1⟩ Soday, Boord, *J. Am. Chem. Soc.* **55,** 3295, 3300 (1933).

1:8306 4-METHYLHEXENE-2 C_7H_{14} **Beil. S.N. 11**
(3-Methylhexene-4)

$$CH_3.CH{=}CH.CH(CH_3).CH_2.CH_3$$

Higher boiling isomer
B.P. 87.1-87.6° ⟨1⟩ D_4^{20} **= 0.7007 ⟨1⟩** n_D^{20} **= 1.3980 ⟨1⟩**
Lower boiling isomer
B.P. 85.1-85.6° ⟨1⟩ D_4^{20} **= 0.6981 ⟨1⟩** n_D^{20} **= 1.4000 ⟨1⟩**

C̄ adds Br_2 yielding 2,3-dibromo-4-methylhexane, b.p. 91–92° at 11 mm., D_4^{20} = 1.5382, n_D^{20} = 1.5045 ⟨1⟩.

1:8306 ⟨1⟩ Soday, Boord, *J. Am. Chem. Soc.* **55,** 3295, 3300 (1933).

1:8308 5-METHYLHEXENE-2 $CH_3.CH{=}CH.CH_2.CH(CH_3).CH_3$ C_7H_{14} **Beil. S.N. 11**
(2-Methylhexene-4)

Higher boiling isomer
B.P. 91.1-91.6° ⟨1⟩ D_4^{20} **= 0.6990 ⟨1⟩** n_D^{20} **= 1.3990 ⟨1⟩**

C̄ adds Br_2 yielding a 2,3-dibromo-5-methylhexane, b.p. 89–90° at 11 mm., D_4^{20} = 1.5152, n_D^{20} = 1.4990 ⟨1⟩.

Lower boiling isomer
B.P. 85.6-86.1° ⟨1⟩ D_4^{20} **= 0.7020 ⟨1⟩** n_D^{20} **= 1.3995 ⟨1⟩**

C̄ adds Br_2 yielding a 2,3-dibromo-5-methylhexane, b.p. 87–88° at 10 mm., D_4^{20} = 1.5027, n_D^{20} = 1.4960 ⟨1⟩.

1:8308 ⟨1⟩ Soday, Boord, *J. Am. Chem. Soc.* **55,** 3295, 3300 (1933).

1:8310 3,4-DIMETHYLPENTENE-2 (2,3-Dimethylpentene-3) C_7H_{14} **Beil. S.N. 11**

$$CH_3.CH{=}\underset{\underset{CH_3}{|}}{C}{-}\overset{\overset{H}{|}}{\underset{\underset{CH_3}{|}}{C}}.CH_3$$

B.P. 86.2-86.4° ⟨1⟩ D_4^{20} = **0.7126 ⟨1⟩** n_D^{20} = **1.4052 ⟨1⟩**

C̄ adds Br_2 yielding 2,3-dibromo-3,4-dimethylpentane, b.p. 65.5–66.0° at 3 mm., D_4^{20} = 1.5400, n_D^{20} = 1.5104 ⟨1⟩.

[For prepn. from methyl-ethyl-isopropyl-carbinol by distn. with I_2 see ⟨2⟩; for ozonolysis of product see ⟨2⟩.]

1:8310 ⟨1⟩ Soday, Boord, *J. Am. Chem. Soc.* **55,** 3296, 3300 (1933). ⟨2⟩ Whitmore, Evers, *J. Am. Chem. Soc.* **55,** 814–815 (1933).

1:8314 2-METHYLHEXENE-3 C_7H_{14} **Beil. S.N. 11**

$$CH_3.\overset{\overset{H}{|}}{\underset{\underset{CH_3}{|}}{C}}.CH{=}CH.CH_2.CH_3$$

B.P. 86.4-86.9° ⟨1⟩ D_4^{20} = **0.6942 ⟨1⟩** n_D^{20} = **1.3991 ⟨1⟩**

C̄ adds Br_2 yielding 3,4-dibromo-2-methylhexane, b.p. 96.0° at 19 mm., D_4^{20} = 1.5310, n_D^{20} = 1.5060 ⟨1⟩.

1:8314 ⟨1⟩ Soday, Boord, *J. Am. Chem. Soc.* **55,** 3295, 3300 (1933).

1:8316 4-METHYLHEXENE-1 (3-Methylhexene-5) C_7H_{14} **Beil. S.N. 11**

$$CH_2{=}CH.CH_2.\overset{\overset{H}{|}}{\underset{\underset{CH_3}{|}}{C}}.CH_2.CH_3$$

B.P. 87.2-87.5° ⟨1⟩ D_4^{20} = **0.6969 ⟨1⟩** n_D^{20} = **1.3985 ⟨1⟩**

C̄ adds Br_2 yielding 1,2-dibromo-4-methylhexane, b.p. 94.7–95.7° at 11 mm., D_4^{20} = 1.5027, n_D^{20} = 1.4980 ⟨1⟩.

1:8316 ⟨1⟩ Soday, Boord, *J. Am. Chem. Soc.* **55,** 3295, 3300 (1933).

1:8318 2-ETHYL-3-METHYLBUTENE-1 C_7H_{14} **Beil. S.N. 11**

$$H_2C{=}\underset{\underset{CH_2.CH_3}{|}}{C}{-}\overset{\overset{CH_3}{|}}{C}H.CH_3$$

B.P. 88.7-89.1° ⟨1⟩ D_4^{20} = **0.7186 ⟨1⟩** n_D^{20} = **1.4120 ⟨1⟩**

C̄ adds Br_2 yielding 1,2-dibromo-2-ethyl-3-methylbutane, b.p. 72.5–73.5° at 3 mm., D_4^{20} = 1.5261, n_D^{20} = 1.5062 ⟨1⟩.

1:8318 ⟨1⟩ Soday, Boord, *J. Am. Chem. Soc.* **55,** 3296, 3300 (1933).

1:8320 2-METHYLHEXENE-1 C_7H_{14} **Beil. S.N. 11**

$$CH_2{=}\underset{\underset{CH_3}{|}}{C}.CH_2.CH_2.CH_2.CH_3$$

B.P. 91.1-91.5° ⟨1⟩ D_4^{20} = **0.7000 ⟨1⟩** n_D^{20} = **1.4040 ⟨1⟩**

[On dehydration of dimethyl-*n*-butyl-carbinol (2-methylhexanol-2) by refluxing with a trace of I_2, both C̄ and 2-methylhexene-2 (1:8328) are formed in ratio 55:45 ⟨2⟩.] [For ozonolysis of this mixture see ⟨3⟩.]

$\bar{C}$ adds Br_2 yielding 1,2-dibromo-2-methylhexane, b.p. 100.5–101.5° at 23 mm., 71.0–71.1° at 3 mm., D_4^{20} = 1.5066, n_D^{20} = 1.5000 ⟨1⟩.

1:8320 ⟨1⟩ Soday, Boord, *J. Am. Chem. Soc.* **55,** 3295, 3300 (1933). ⟨2⟩ Church, Whitmore, McGrew, *J. Am. Chem. Soc.* **56,** 183 (1934). ⟨3⟩ Ref. 2, page 181.

1:8322 3-METHYLHEXENE-2 $CH_3.CH{=}C(CH_3).CH_2.CH_2.CH_3$ C_7H_{14} **Beil. I-220**
(Mixt. of *cis* and *trans* isomers)

B.P. 93.1-93.3° ⟨1⟩ **D_4^{20} = 0.7120 ⟨1⟩** **n_D^{20} = 1.4080 ⟨1⟩**

$\bar{C}$ adds Br_2 yielding 2,3-dibromo-3-methylhexane, b.p. 65.0–65.1° at 2 mm., D_4^{20} = 1.5240, n_D^{20} = 1.5040 ⟨1⟩.

1:8322 ⟨1⟩ Soday, Boord, *J. Am. Chem. Soc.* **55,** 3296, 3300 (1933).

1:8324 HEPTENE-1 $CH_2{=}CH.(CH_2)_4.CH_3$ C_7H_{14} **Beil. I-219**

B.P. 93.50° ⟨1⟩; cf. ⟨2⟩ ⟨3⟩ **M.P. −119.2° ⟨2⟩**
D_4^{20} = 0.6971 ⟨1⟩ **n_D^{20} = 1.3998 ⟨1⟩;** cf. ⟨2⟩ ⟨3⟩

$\bar{C}$ forms with abs. EtOH (1:6130) a const. boilg. mixt., b.p. 70.4°_{754} contg. 57% $\bar{C}$ ⟨1⟩.

$\bar{C}$ adds Br_2 yielding 1,2-dibromoheptane, b.p. 106.2° at 13 mm., D_4^{20} = 1.5208, n_D^{20} = 1.4990 ⟨3⟩ — $\bar{C}$ adds HBr but result is influenced by solvent, e.g., with dry HBr in AcOH product is exclusively 1-bromoheptane ⟨4⟩; with aqueous HBr product is exclusively 2-bromoheptane ⟨4⟩.

[For study of polymerization of $\bar{C}$ see ⟨5⟩.]

1:8324 ⟨1⟩ Sherrill, Mayer, Walter, *J. Am. Chem. Soc.* **56,** 927 (1934). ⟨2⟩ Kistiakowsky, Ruhoff, Smith, Vaughan, *J. Am. Chem. Soc.* **58,** 140 (1936). ⟨3⟩ Soday, Boord, *J. Am. Chem. Soc.* **55,** 3295, 3300 (1933). ⟨4⟩ Ref. 1, pages 928–930, 1645. ⟨5⟩ Jostes, Bartels, *Cent.* **1938,** I, 3144; *Chem. Abs.* **32,** 3327 (1938).

1:8326 2-ETHYLPENTENE-1 $CH_2{=}C(CH_2.CH_3).CH_2.CH_2.CH_3$ C_7H_{14} **Beil. S.N. 11**

B.P. 93.9-94.3° ⟨1⟩ **D_4^{20} = 0.7079 ⟨1⟩** **n_D^{20} = 1.4050 ⟨1⟩**

$\bar{C}$ adds Br_2 yielding 1,2-dibromo-2-ethylpentane, b.p. 77–78° at 4 mm., D_4^{20} = 1.4929, n_D^{20} = 1.4990 ⟨1⟩.

1:8326 ⟨1⟩ Soday, Boord, *J. Am. Chem. Soc.* **55,** 3296, 3300 (1933).

1:8328 2-METHYLHEXENE-2 $CH_3.C(CH_3){=}CH.CH_2.CH_2.CH_3$ C_7H_{14} **Beil. S.N. 11**

B.P. 94.4-94.6° ⟨1⟩ **D_4^{20} = 0.7089 ⟨1⟩** **n_D^{20} = 1.4075 ⟨1⟩**

[On dehydration of dimethyl-*n*-butyl-carbinol (2-methylhexanol-2) by refluxing with a trace of I_2, both $\bar{C}$ and 2-methylhexene-1 (1:8320) are formed in ratio of 45:55 ⟨2⟩.] [For ozonolysis of this mixture see ⟨3⟩.]

$\bar{C}$ with Br_2 yields 2,3-dibromo-2-methylhexane, b.p. 73.0–73.1° at 8 mm., D_4^{20} = 1.5116, n_D^{20} = 1.4990 ⟨1⟩.

1:8328 ⟨1⟩ Soday, Boord, *J. Am. Chem. Soc.* **55,** 3296, 3300 (1933). ⟨2⟩ Church, Whitmore, McGrew, *J. Am. Chem. Soc.* **56,** 183 (1934). ⟨3⟩ Ref. 2, page 181.

1:8330 3-ETHYLPENTENE-2 $CH_3.CH{=}C(CH_2.CH_3).CH_2.CH_3$ C_7H_{14} Beil. I-220

B.P. 94.8-94.9° ⟨1⟩ D_4^{20} = **0.7172 ⟨1⟩** n_D^{20} = **1.4120 ⟨1⟩**

[For prepn. (84% yield) from triethylcarbinol (1:6218) by htg. with equal wt. anhydrous oxalic acid at 100° under reflux for 5 hrs. see ⟨2⟩.]

C̄ adds Br_2 yielding 2,3-dibromo-3-ethylpentane, b.p. 76.0–76.4° at 3 mm., D_4^{20} = 1.5426, n_D^{20} = 1.5090 ⟨1⟩. [C̄ in AcOH treated with HCl gas yields pure 3-chloro-3-ethylpentane ⟨2⟩.]

Ozonolysis yields product contg. 57% diethyl ketone (1:5420) and 38% acetaldehyde (1:0100) ⟨3⟩.

1:8330 ⟨1⟩ Soday, Boord, *J. Am. Chem. Soc.* **55,** 3296, 3300 (1933). ⟨2⟩ Lucas, *J. Am. Chem. Soc.* **51,** 252–253 (1929). ⟨3⟩ Church, Whitmore, McGrew, *J. Am. Chem. Soc.* **56,** 181 (1934).

1:8332 HEPTENE-3 $CH_3.CH_2.CH{=}CH.CH_2.CH_2.CH_3$ C_7H_{14} Beil. I-220

B.P. 95.8-96.1° ⟨1⟩ D_4^{20} = **0.7043 ⟨1⟩** n_D^{20} = **1.4090 ⟨1⟩**

C̄ with Br_2 yields quant. 3,4-dibromoheptane, b.p. 105.5–106.5° at 23 mm., D_4^{20} = 1.5153, n_D^{20} = 1.5010 ⟨1⟩; cf. ⟨3⟩.

C̄ on oxidn. with $KMnO_4$ gives only propionic ac. (1:1025) and *n*-butyric ac. (1:1035) ⟨2⟩.

1:8332 ⟨1⟩ Soday, Boord, *J. Am. Chem. Soc.* **55,** 3295, 3300 (1933). ⟨2⟩ Prévost, *Compt. rend.* **187,** 947 (1928). ⟨3⟩ Stewart, Dod, Stenmark, *J. Am. Chem. Soc.* **59,** 1765–1766 (1937).

1:8334 HEPTENE-2 $CH_3.CH{=}CH.(CH_2)_3.CH_3$ C_7H_{14} Beil. I-219

trans **B.P. 97.5-99.° ⟨1⟩** D_4^{26} = **0.700 ⟨1⟩** n_D^{24} = **1.4056 ⟨1⟩**
cis **B.P. 98.5-99.5° ⟨1⟩** D_4^{25} = **0.705 ⟨1⟩** n_D^{25} = **1.4052 ⟨1⟩**
mixt. **B.P. 98.1-98.4° ⟨2⟩** D_4^{20} = **0.7034 ⟨2⟩** n_D^{20} = **1.4041 ⟨2⟩**

C̄ with Br_2 yields 2,3-dibromoheptane, b.p. 96.2° at 12 mm., D_4^{20} = 1.5129, n_D^{20} = 1.5000 ⟨2⟩; cf. ⟨3⟩.

1:8334 ⟨1⟩ Gredy, *Bull. soc. chim.* (5) **2,** 1031–1032 (1935). ⟨2⟩ Soday, Boord, *J. Am. Chem. Soc.* **55,** 3295, 3300 (1933). ⟨3⟩ Stewart, Dod, Stenmark, *J. Am. Chem. Soc.* **59,** 1765–1766 (1937).

1:8340 2,4,4-TRIMETHYLPENTENE-1 $CH_2{=}C(CH_3).CH_2.C(CH_3)_2.CH_3$ C_8H_{16} Beil. S.N. 11
(" Diisobutylene ")

B.P. 101.2° ⟨1⟩ **M.P. −93.6° ⟨1⟩** D_4^{20} = **0.7151 ⟨1⟩** n_D^{20} = **1.4082 ⟨1⟩**

For ozonolysis of C̄ see ⟨2⟩ — Diisobutylene consists of a mixt. of C̄ + 2,2,4-trimethylpentene-2 (1:8345) in proportion of 4:1 ⟨2⟩.

1:8340 ⟨1⟩ Tongberg, Pickens, Fenske, Whitmore, *J. Am. Chem. Soc.* **54,** 3706 (1932). ⟨2⟩ Whitmore, Church, *J. Am. Chem. Soc.* **54,** 3710–3714 (1932).

1:8345 2,4,4-TRIMETHYLPENTENE-2 $CH_3.C(CH_3){=}CH.C(CH_3)_2.CH_3$ C_8H_{16} **Beil. S.N. 11**
(" Diisobutylene ")

B.P. 104.5° ⟨1⟩ M.P. −106.5° ⟨1⟩ D_4^{20} = 0.7211 ⟨1⟩ n_D^{20} = 1.4158 ⟨1⟩

For ozonolysis of C̄ see ⟨2⟩ — Diisobutylene consists of a mixt. of C̄ + 2,4,4-trimethylpentene-1 (1:8340) in proportion of 1:4 ⟨2⟩.

1:8345 ⟨1⟩ Tongberg, Pickens, Fenske, Whitmore, *J. Am. Chem. Soc.* **54,** 3706 (1932). ⟨2⟩ Whitmore, Church, *J. Am. Chem. Soc.* **54,** 3710–3714 (1932).

1:8360 4-METHYLHEPTENE-1 $CH_2{=}CH.CH_2.CH(CH_3).CH_2.CH_2.CH_3$ C_8H_{16} **Beil. S.N. 11**

B.P. 112.6-113.0° D_4^{20} = 0.7183 n_D^{20} = 1.4099

1:8370 2-ETHYLHEXENE-1 $CH_2{=}C(CH_2.CH_3).CH_2.CH_2.CH_2.CH_3$ C_8H_{16} **Beil. S.N. 11**

B.P. 120° D_4^{20} = 0.7274 n_D^{20} = 1.4207

1:8375 OCTENE-1 $CH_2{=}CH.(CH_2)_5.CH_3$ C_8H_{16} **Beil. I-221**

B.P. 121.85-122.15° ⟨1⟩ M.P. −104° ⟨1⟩ D_4^{20} = 0.7155 ⟨1⟩ n_D^{20} = 1.40880 ⟨1⟩

For critical survey see ⟨1⟩.

1:8375 ⟨1⟩ Waterman, de Kok, *Rec. trav. chim.* **53,** 725–729 (1934).

1:8380 OCTENE-2 $CH_3.CH{=}CH.(CH_2)_4.CH_3$ C_8H_{16} **Beil. I-221**

B.P. 124.1-124.7° ⟨1⟩ D_4^{20} = 0.722 ⟨1⟩ n_D^{20} = 1.4149 ⟨1⟩

1:8380 ⟨1⟩ Whitmore, Herndon, *J. Am. Chem. Soc.* **55,** 3430 (1933).

1:8385 NONENE-1 $CH_2{=}CH.(CH_2)_6.CH_3$ C_9H_{18} **Beil. S.N. 11**

B.P. 145.3° ⟨1⟩ ⟨2⟩ D_4^{20} = 0.7315 ⟨1⟩ n_D^{20} = 1.4163 ⟨1⟩

[For study of polymerization with H_2SO_4 see ⟨3⟩, for addn. of HBr see ⟨4⟩.]

1:8385 ⟨1⟩ Wilkinson, *J. Chem. Soc.* **1931,** 3058. ⟨2⟩ Mulliken, Wakeman, Gerry, *J. Am. Chem. Soc.* **57,** 1606 (1935). ⟨3⟩ Ipatieff, Pines, *J. Org. Chem.* **1,** 464–489 (1937). ⟨4⟩ Kharasch, Potts, *J. Org. Chem.* **2,** 195–197 (1938).

—— **HEXADECENE-1** $CH_3.(CH_2)_{13}.CH{=}CH_2$ $C_{16}H_{32}$ **Beil. I-226**
(Cetene)

B.P. 154.5-155°$_{15}$ M.P. +4.0° D_4^{20} = 0.7825 n_D^{20} = 1.4418

See 1:7000. Genus 9: Division A: Section 1.

ORDER I: SUBORDER I: GENUS 9: HYDROCARBONS

Division B, Liquids

Section 5. Naphthenes

1:8400 CYCLOPENTANE (Pentamethylene)

H_2C—CH_2, H_2C CH_2, CH_2

C_5H_{10} **Beil. V-19**

B.P. 49.30° ⟨1⟩ **M.P. −95.0° ⟨1⟩** D_4^{20} = **0.74546 ⟨1⟩** n_D^{20} = **1.4070 ⟨4⟩ ⟨5⟩**
49.20° ⟨2⟩ ⟨3⟩ D_4^{25} = **0.74059 ⟨1⟩**

1:8400 ⟨1⟩ Timmermans, Hennaut-Roland, *J. chim. phys.* **34,** 694–695 (1937). ⟨2⟩ Wibaut, Hoog, et al., *Rec. trav. chim.* **58,** 372–377 (1939). ⟨3⟩ Smittenberg, Hoog, Henkes, *J. Am. Chem. Soc.* **60,** 18 (1938). ⟨4⟩ Evans, *J. Inst. Petroleum Tech.* **24,** 328 (1938). ⟨5⟩ Garner, Evans, *J. Inst. Petroleum Tech.* **18,** 761 (1932).

1:8403 METHYLCYCLOPENTANE

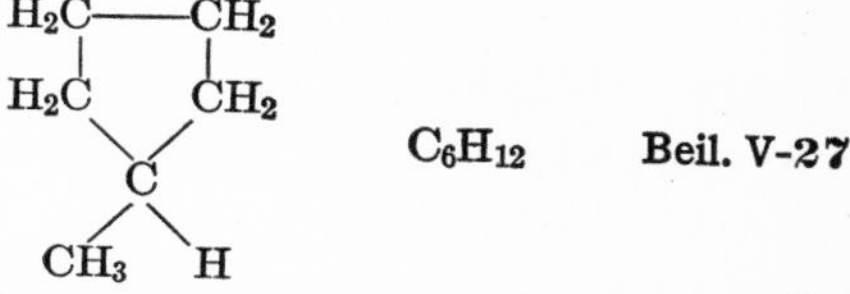

C_6H_{12} **Beil. V-27**

B.P. 72.0° ⟨1⟩ **M.P. −139.2° ⟨1⟩** D_4^{20} = **0.74878 ⟨1⟩** n_D^{20} = **1.4100 ⟨2⟩ ⟨5⟩**
71.9° ⟨2⟩ D_4^{25} = **0.74413 ⟨1⟩**
71.85 ⟨3⟩

[For study of sepn. of C̄ from *n*-hexane (1:8530) or benzene (1:7400) by distn. with phenol or aniline see ⟨4⟩.]

1:8403 ⟨1⟩ Timmermans, Hennaut-Roland, *J. chim. phys.* **34,** 696–697 (1937). ⟨2⟩ Smittenberg, Hoog, Henkes, *J. Am. Chem. Soc.* **60,** 18 (1938). ⟨3⟩ Wibaut, Hoog, et al., *Rec. trav. chim.* **58,** 372–377 (1939). ⟨4⟩ Vondraček, *Collection Czechoslov. Chem. Commun.* **9,** 521–524 (1937). ⟨5⟩ Evans, *J. Inst. Petroleum Tech.* **24,** 328 (1938).

1:8405 CYCLOHEXANE (Hexahydrobenzene)

CH_2—CH_2, H_2C CH_2, CH_2—CH_2

C_6H_{12} **Beil. V-20**

B.P. 80.80° ⟨1⟩ ⟨2⟩ **M.P. 6.47° ⟨3⟩** D_4^{20} = **0.77849 ⟨1⟩ ⟨2⟩** n_D^{20} = **1.4263 ⟨2⟩ ⟨3⟩**
D_4^{25} = **0.77388 ⟨1⟩** n_D^{25} = **1.42370 ⟨4⟩**

C̄ is only slightly attacked by $H_2SO_4 + HNO_3$, but dissolves on shaking with 27 pts. fuming H_2SO_4 (25% SO_3) at 20–25° ⟨5⟩ forming sulfonic acids of benzene.

C̄ does not decolorize Br_2 (T 1.91) — C̄ (0.5 ml.) shaken with satd. $KMnO_4$ soln. (2 ml.) + 20% H_2SO_4 (2 ml.) shows but slight reduction of $KMnO_4$ even after ½ hr. ⟨6⟩ [dif. from benzene (1:7400) which reduces $KMnO_4$ in 25 min. ⟨6⟩].

1:8405 ⟨1⟩ Timmermans, Martin, *J. chim. phys.* **23,** 759–761 (1926). ⟨2⟩ Bruun, Hicks-Bruun, *Bur. Standards J. Research* **7,** 612 (1931). ⟨3⟩ Seyer, Wright, Beil, *Ind. Eng. Chem.* **31,** 758–759 (1939). ⟨4⟩ Washburn, Spencer, *J. Am. Chem. Soc.* **56,** 361 (1934). ⟨5⟩ Menschutkin, Wolf, *Collection Czechoslov. Chem. Commun.* **2,** 396–401 (1930). ⟨6⟩ Wieland, *Ber.* **45,** 2616 (1912).

1:8410 METHYLCYCLOHEXANE C_7H_{14} **Beil. V-29**
(Hexahydrotoluene)

$CH_2—CH_2$, H_2C, C (H, CH_3), $CH_2—CH_2$

B.P. 100.80° ⟨1⟩ ⟨2⟩ M.P. −126.4° ⟨3⟩ ⟨4⟩ ⟨2⟩
D_4^{20} = **0.76944** ⟨2⟩ n_D^{20} = **1.42310** ⟨2⟩ ⟨4⟩
D_4^{25} = **0.76512** ⟨2⟩

$\bar{C}$ is insol. in $CH_3.NO_2$ (T 1.922) even at +23°; sol. in benzyl alc. (T 1.922) at +30°; $\bar{C}$ is unaffected by conc. H_2SO_4 or H_2SO_4 + HNO_3 at ord. temp. — $\bar{C}$ does not decolorize Br_2 (T 1.41).

$\bar{C}$ treated with dry Br_2 + trace $AlBr_3$ is converted to pentabromotoluene [Beil. V-310], ndls. from C_6H_6, m.p. 284° ⟨5⟩ ⟨6⟩ ⟨7⟩.

1:8410 ⟨1⟩ Cowan, Jeffery, Vogel, *J. Chem. Soc.* **1939,** 1863. ⟨2⟩ Wibaut, Hoog, et al., *Rec. trav. chim.* **58,** 372–377 (1939). ⟨3⟩ Timmermans, Martin, *J. chim. phys.* **23,** 762–763 (1926). ⟨4⟩ Smittenberg, Hoog, Henkes, *J. Am. Chem. Soc.* **60,** 18 (1938). ⟨5⟩ Kursanoff, *Ber.* **32,** 2973 (1899). ⟨6⟩ Markownikoff, *Ann.* **341,** 131 (1905). ⟨7⟩ Bodroux, Tabourg, *Bull. soc. chim.* (4) **9,** 597 (1911).

1:8415 ETHYLCYCLOPENTANE C_7H_{14} **Beil. S.N. 452**

H_2C——CH_2, H_2C, CH_2, C, $CH_3.CH_2$, H

B.P. 103.6° ⟨1⟩ M.P. −137.9° ⟨2⟩ D_4^{20} = **0.7632** ⟨1⟩ n_D^{20} = **1.4196** ⟨1⟩

$\bar{C}$ (0.2 mole) + $AlCl_3$ (0.03 mole) + 2 drops aq. sealed in 40 ml. glass tube and kept at 50° for 18 hrs. with occasional shaking yields methylcyclohexane (1:8410) ⟨1⟩.

1:8415 ⟨1⟩ Pines, Ipatieff, *J. Am. Chem. Soc.* **61,** 1077 (1939). ⟨2⟩ Chavanne, Becker, *Bull. soc. chim. Belg.* **36,** 594–595 (1927).

1:8420 *trans*-1,4-DIMETHYLCYCLOHEXANE C_8H_{16} **Beil. V-38**
(*trans*-Hexahydro-*p*-xylene)

H, $CH_2—CH_2$, CH_3, C, C, CH_3, $CH_2—CH_2$, H

B.P. 119.65° ⟨1⟩ M.P. −37.2° ⟨1⟩ D_4^{20} = **0.76264** ⟨1⟩ $n_{He\,(yellow)}^{26.4}$ = **1.41827** ⟨1⟩

1:8420 ⟨1⟩ Miller, *Bull. soc. chim. Belg.* **44,** 519–520 (1935).

1:8425 *trans*-1,3-DIMETHYLCYCLOHEXANE C_8H_{16} **Beil. V-36**
(*trans*-Hexahydro-*m*-xylene)

CH_3, H, CH_2——C, H, C, CH_2, CH_3, $CH_2—CH_2$

B.P. 120.40° ⟨1⟩ M.P. −79.4° ⟨1⟩ D_4^{20} = **0.76628** ⟨1⟩ $n_{He\,(yellow)}^{26.4}$ = **1.42047** ⟨1⟩

1:8425 ⟨1⟩ Miller, *Bull. soc. chim. Belg.* **44,** 519–520 (1935).

1:8430 ***trans*-1,2-DIMETHYLCYCLOHEXANE** C_8H_{16} **Beil. V-36**
(*trans*-Hexahydro-*o*-xylene)

```
              CH3
               |
    H          C——CH2
     \        /H    \
      C              CH2
     / \            /
  CH3   CH2——CH2
```

B.P. 123.70° ⟨1⟩ M.P. −89.4° ⟨1⟩ D_4^{20} **= 0.77601 ⟨1⟩** $n_{\text{He (yellow)}}^{26.4}$ **= 1.42443 ⟨1⟩**

1:8430 ⟨1⟩ Miller, *Bull. soc. chim. Belg.* **44,** 519–520 (1935).

1:8435 ***cis*-1,3-DIMETHYLCYCLOHEXANE** C_8H_{16} **Beil. V-36**
(*cis*-Hexahydro-*m*-xylene)

```
                        CH3
                         |
  CH3         CH2——C
     \       /      H \
      C                CH2
     / \              /
    H   CH2——CH2
```

B.P. 124.9° ⟨1⟩ M.P. −100° ⟨1⟩ D_4^{20} **= 0.78348 ⟨1⟩** $n_{\text{He (yellow)}}^{26.4}$ **= 1.42765 ⟨1⟩**

1:8435 ⟨1⟩ Miller, *Bull. soc. chim. Belg.* **44,** 519–520 (1935).

1:8440 ***cis*-1,4-DIMETHYLCYCLOHEXANE** C_8H_{16} **Beil. V-38**
(*cis*-Hexahydro-*p*-xylene)

```
   H       CH2—CH2       H
     \    /        \    /
      C              C
     /  \          /  \
  CH3    CH2—CH2       CH3
```

B.P. 124.59° ⟨1⟩ M.P. −91.6° ⟨1⟩ D_4^{20} **= 0.78271 ⟨1⟩** $n_{\text{He (yellow)}}^{26.4}$ **= 1.42700 ⟨1⟩**

1:8440 ⟨1⟩ Miller, *Bull. soc. chim. Belg.* **44,** 519–520 (1935).

1:8445 **ISOPROPYLCYCLOPENTANE** C_8H_{16} **Beil. V-39**

```
        H2C——CH2
         |     |
        H2C   CH2
           \  /
            C
           / \
   (CH3)2CH   H
```

B.P. 126.8° ⟨1⟩ M.P. −112.7° D_4^{20} **= 0.7764 ⟨1⟩** n_D^{20} **= 1.4261 ⟨1⟩**

C̄ on htg. with $AlCl_3$ isomerizes to 1,3-dimethylcyclohexane ⟨1⟩.

1:8445 ⟨1⟩ Pines, Ipatieff, *J. Am. Chem. Soc.* **61,** 1077 (1939).

1:8450 ***cis*-1,2-DIMETHYLCYCLOHEXANE** C_8H_{16} **Beil. V-36**
(*cis*-Hexahydro-*o*-xylene)

```
              CH3
               |
  CH3          C——CH2
     \        /H    \
      C              CH2
     / \            /
    H   CH2——CH2
```

B.P. 130.04° ⟨1⟩ M.P. −50.1° ⟨1⟩ D_4^{20} **= 0.79625 ⟨1⟩** $n_{\text{He (yellow)}}^{26.4}$ **= 1.43343 ⟨1⟩**

1:8450 ⟨1⟩ Miller, *Bull. soc. chim. Belg.* **44,** 519–520 (1935).

1:8455 ***n*-PROPYLCYCLOPENTANE** C_8H_{16} **Beil. S.N. 452**

H_2C—CH_2 / H_2C CH_2 / C / $CH_3CH_2CH_2$ H

B.P. 130.7° ⟨1⟩ **M.P. −120.3° ⟨2⟩** D_4^{20} **= 0.7756 ⟨1⟩** n_D^{20} **= 1.4269 ⟨1⟩ ⟨3⟩**

1:8455 ⟨1⟩ Pines, Ipatieff, *J. Am. Chem. Soc.* **61,** 1077 (1939). ⟨2⟩ Chavanne, Becker, *Bull. soc. chim. Belg.* **36,** 600 (1927). ⟨3⟩ Evans, *J. Inst. Petroleum Tech.* **24,** 328 (1938).

1:8460 **ETHYLCYCLOHEXANE** C_8H_{16} **Beil. V-35**
(Hexahydroethylbenzene)

CH_2—CH_2 CH_2CH_3 / H_2C C / CH_2—CH_2 H

B.P. 131.89° ⟨1⟩ **M.P. −111.4° ⟨1⟩** D_4^{20} **= 0.78804 ⟨1⟩** n_D^{20} **= 1.4332 ⟨2⟩**
n_D^{25} **= 1.43079 ⟨1⟩**

1:8460 ⟨1⟩ Rose, White, *J. Research Natl. Bur. Standards* **15,** 160 (1935). ⟨2⟩ Signaigo, Cramer, *J. Am. Chem. Soc.* **55,** 3331 (1933).

1:8464 **ISOPROPYLCYCLOHEXANE** C_9H_{18} **Beil. V-41**
(Hexahydrocumene)

CH_2—CH_2 H / H_2C C / CH_2—CH_2 $CH(CH_3)_2$

B.P. 154.5° ⟨1⟩ ⟨2⟩ **M.P. −89.8° ⟨1⟩ ⟨2⟩** D_4^{20} **= 0.80232 ⟨2⟩** n_D^{20} **= 1.4410 ⟨1⟩**
D_4^{25} **= 0.79840 ⟨2⟩**

1:8464 ⟨1⟩ Smittenberg, Hoog, Henkes, *J. Am. Chem. Soc.* **60,** 18 (1938). ⟨2⟩ Wibaut, Hoog, et al., *Rec. trav. chim.* **58,** 372–377 (1939).

1:8468 ***n*-PROPYLCYCLOHEXANE** C_9H_{18} **Beil. V-41**
(Hexahydro-*n*-propylbenzene)

$CH_2.CH_2$ H / H_2C C / $CH_2.CH_2$ $CH_2.CH_2.CH_3$

B.P. 155.0° ⟨1⟩ D_4^{20} **= 0.7929 ⟨2⟩** n_D^{20} **= 1.4370 ⟨1⟩**

1:8468 ⟨1⟩ Signaigo, Cramer, *J. Am. Chem. Soc.* **55,** 3331 (1933). ⟨2⟩ Evans, *J. Inst. Petroleum Tech.* **24,** 328 (1938).

1:8472 ***n*-BUTYLCYCLOHEXANE** $C_{10}H_{20}$ **Beil. S.N. 452**
(Hexahydro-*n*-butylbenzene)

CH_2—CH_2 H / H_2C C / CH_2—CH_2 $CH_2.CH_2.CH_2.CH_3$

B.P. 180.2° ⟨1⟩ **M.P. −78.6° ⟨2⟩** D_4^{20} **= 0.7996 ⟨3⟩** n_D^{20} **= 1.4408 ⟨1⟩**

1:8472 ⟨1⟩ Signaigo, Cramer, *J. Am. Chem. Soc.* **55,** 3332 (1933). ⟨2⟩ Timmermans, *Bull. soc. chim. Belg.* **36,** 503 (1927). ⟨3⟩ D'yakova, Lozovoĭ, *Chem. Abs.* **33,** 6255 (1939).

1:8476 ***trans*-DECAHYDRONAPHTHALENE** $C_{10}H_{18}$ **Beil. V-92**

```
          H2    H2
          C     C
        /   \ /   \
    H2C  H—C       CH2
     |      |       |
    H2C     C—H    CH2
        \ /   \   /
          C     C
          H2    H2
```

B.P. 185.5° ⟨1⟩ **M.P. −31.47° ⟨1⟩** D_4^{20} **= 0.8699 ⟨1⟩** n_D^{20} **= 1.46968 ⟨1⟩**

Commercial " decalin " is a mixt. of C̄ + *cis*-decahydronaphthalene (1:8480) ⟨2⟩.

1:8476 ⟨1⟩ Seyer, Walker, *J. Am. Chem. Soc.* **60,** 2125–2128 (1938). ⟨2⟩ Hückel, *Ann.* **441,** 1–48 (1924).

1:8480 ***cis*-DECAHYDRONAPHTHALENE** $C_{10}H_{18}$ **Beil. V-92**

```
          H2    H2
          C     C
        /   \ /   \
    H2C  H—C       CH2
     |      |       |
    H2C  H—C       CH2
        \ /   \   /
          C     C
          H2    H2
```

B.P. 194.6° ⟨1⟩ **M.P. −43.26° ⟨1⟩** D_4^{20} **= 0.8963 ⟨1⟩** n_D^{20} **= 1.48113 ⟨1⟩**

Commercial " decalin " is a mixt. of C̄ + *trans*-decahydronaphthalene (1:8476) ⟨2⟩.

1:8480 ⟨1⟩ Seyer, Walker, *J. Am. Chem. Soc.* **60,** 2125–2128 (1938). ⟨2⟩ Hückel, *Ann.* **441,** 1–48 (1924).

1:8484 **ISOAMYLCYCLOHEXANE** (Hexahydroisoamylbenzene) $C_{11}H_{22}$ **Beil. S.N. 452**

```
        CH2—CH2   H
       /         \|
    H2C           C—CH2.CH2.CH(CH3)2
       \         /
        CH2—CH2
```

B.P. 193° ⟨1⟩ D_4^{20} **= 0.8023 ⟨1⟩** n_D^{20} **= 1.4423 ⟨1⟩**

1:8484 ⟨1⟩ D'yakova, Lozovoĭ, *Chem. Abs.* **33,** 6255 (1939).

1:8488 ***n*-AMYLCYCLOHEXANE** (Hexahydro-*n*-amylbenzene) $C_{11}H_{22}$ **Beil. S.N. 452**

```
        CH2.CH2   H
       /         \|
    H2C           C.CH2.CH2.CH2.CH2.CH3
       \         /
        CH2.CH2
```

B.P. 201.4-201.9° ⟨1⟩ D_4^{20} **= 0.8044 ⟨2⟩** n_D^{20} **= 1.4442 ⟨2⟩**

1:8488 ⟨1⟩ Signaigo, Cramer, *J. Am. Chem. Soc.* **55,** 3332 (1933). ⟨2⟩ D'yakova, Lozovoĭ, *Chem. Abs.* **33,** 6255 (1939).

1:8490 **DICYCLOHEXYL** (Cyclohexylcyclohexane; dodecahydrobiphenyl) $C_{12}H_{22}$ **Beil. V-108**

```
      CH2.CH2   H  H   CH2.CH2
     /         \|  |  /       \
    CH2         C—C            CH2
     \         /    \         /
      CH2.CH2        CH2.CH2
```

B.P. 236.5-237.5° ⟨1⟩ **M.P. 3.5-4.0°** D_4^{20} **= 0.8848 ⟨2⟩** n_D^{20} **= 1.4795 ⟨2⟩**

1:8490 ⟨1⟩ Signaigo, Cramer, *J. Am. Chem. Soc.* **55,** 3332 (1933). ⟨2⟩ Evans, *J. Inst. Petroleum Tech.* **24,** 551–552 (1938).

ORDER I: SUBORDER I: GENUS 9: HYDROCARBONS

Division B, Liquids

Section 6. Alkanes

1:8499 **2,2-DIMETHYLPROPANE** (Tetramethylmethane, neopentane)

$$CH_3.C(CH_3)_2.CH_3$$

C_5H_{12} **Beil. I-141**

B.P. +9.4° ⟨1⟩; **9.45°** ⟨2⟩ **M.P. −16.63°** ⟨2⟩ D^0 = **1.613** ⟨1⟩ n_D^0 = **1.3513** ⟨1⟩

1:8499 ⟨1⟩ Whitmore, Fleming, *J. Am. Chem. Soc.* **55,** 3805 (1933). ⟨2⟩ Aston, Messerly, *J. Am. Chem. Soc.* **58,** 236 (1936).

1:8500 **2-METHYLBUTANE** (Isopentane)

$$CH_3.CH(CH_3).CH_2.CH_3$$

C_5H_{12} **Beil. I-134**

B.P. +27.95° ⟨1⟩ **M.P. −159.6°** ⟨1⟩ D_4^{15} = **0.62470** ⟨1⟩ n_D^{15} = **1.35796** ⟨1⟩
D_4^{20} = **0.61972** ⟨1⟩

1:8500 ⟨1⟩ Timmermans, Martin, *J. chim. phys.* **23,** 748–749 (1926). ⟨2⟩ Wibaut, Hoog, et al., *Rec. trav. chim.* **58,** 372–377 (1939).

1:8505 ***n*-PENTANE** $CH_3.CH_2.CH_2.CH_2.CH_3$ C_5H_{12} **Beil. I-130**

B.P. +36.1° ⟨1⟩ ⟨2⟩ **M.P. −129.7°** ⟨2⟩ ⟨3⟩ D_4^{15} = **0.63114** ⟨1⟩ n_D^{20} = **1.35769** ⟨4⟩
D_4^{20} = **0.62632** ⟨4⟩ n_D^{25} = **1.35495** ⟨4⟩

[For prepn. (50–53% yield) from 2-bromopentane via R.MgBr cpd. see ⟨5⟩.]

1:8505 ⟨1⟩ Timmermans, Hennaut-Roland, *J. chim. phys.* **32,** 501–503 (1935). ⟨2⟩ Mair, *J. Research Natl. Bur. Standards* **9,** 471 (1932). ⟨3⟩ Timmermans, *Bull. soc. chim. Belg.* **43,** 626 (1934). ⟨4⟩ Shepard, Henne, Midgley, *J. Am. Chem. Soc.* **53,** 1948–1958 (1931). ⟨5⟩ Noller, *Organic Syntheses* **11,** 84–86 (1931).

1:8510 **2,2-DIMETHYLBUTANE** (Neohexane)

$$CH_3.C(CH_3)_2.CH_2.CH_3$$

C_6H_{14} **Beil. I-150**

B.P. 49.7° ⟨1⟩ ⟨2⟩ **M.P. −98.7°** ⟨1⟩ D_4^{20} = **0.6494** ⟨1⟩ ⟨4⟩ n_D^{20} = **1.3689** ⟨1⟩ ⟨4⟩
D_4^{25} = **0.64475** ⟨1⟩ n_D^{25} = **1.36615** ⟨1⟩

[For prepn. (11% yield) from *ter*-butyl chloride + C_2H_5.MgBr + Cu_2I_2 see ⟨3⟩.]

1:8510 ⟨1⟩ Hicks-Bruun, Bruun, Faulconer, *J. Am. Chem. Soc.* **61,** 3100 (1939). ⟨2⟩ Wibaut, Hoog, et al., *Rec. trav. chim.* **58,** 372–373, 377 (1939). ⟨3⟩ Marker, Oakwood, *J. Am. Chem. Soc.* **60,** 2598 (1938). ⟨4⟩ Schmerling, Friedman, Ipatieff, *J. Am. Chem. Soc.* **62,** 2448 (1940).

1:8515 2,3-DIMETHYLBUTANE C_6H_{14} **Beil. I-151**
(Diisopropyl)

```
       H    H
       |    |
CH3.C—C.CH3
       |    |
      CH3  CH3
```

B.P. +58.0° ⟨1⟩ **M.P. −129.0°** ⟨2⟩ D_4^{20} = **0.6615** ⟨2⟩ n_D^{20} = **1.3750** ⟨2⟩
57.9° ⟨2⟩ n_D^{25} = **1.3722** ⟨2⟩

[For prepn. from pinacol see ⟨3⟩.]

1:8515 ⟨1⟩ Bruun, Hicks-Bruun, *J. Research Natl. Bur. Standards* **5,** 937 (1930). ⟨2⟩ Bruun, Hicks-Bruun, Faulconer, *J. Am. Chem. Soc.* **59,** 2357 (1937). ⟨3⟩ Cramer, Mulligan, *J. Am. Chem. Soc.* **58,** 373–374 (1936).

1:8520 2-METHYLPENTANE C_6H_{14} **Beil. I-148**
(Isohexane)

```
       H
       |
CH3.C.CH2.CH2.CH3
       |
      CH3
```

B.P. 60.2° ⟨1⟩ **M.P. −154.0°** ⟨1⟩ D_4^{20} = **0.6527** ⟨1⟩ n_D^{20} = **1.3716** ⟨2⟩
60.3° ⟨3⟩ n_D^{25} = **1.3684** ⟨1⟩

$\bar{C}$ with alk. $KMnO_4$ (as for *n*-hexane 1:8530) gives heavy brown ppt. after 1 min. htg. — $\bar{C}$ with Br_2 in CCl_4 (T 1.91) slightly decolorizes 0.1 ml. reagt. after 4 hrs.

[For prepn. from 2-methylpentanol-2 (1:6190) see ⟨4⟩.]

1:8520 ⟨1⟩ Bruun, Hicks-Bruun, Faulconer, *J. Am. Chem. Soc.* **59,** 2357 (1937). ⟨2⟩ Smittenberg, Hoog, Henkes, *J. Am. Chem. Soc.* **60,** 18 (1938). ⟨3⟩ Wibaut, Hoog, et al., *Rec. trav. chim.* **58,** 372–373; 377 (1939). ⟨4⟩ Cramer, Mulligan, *J. Am. Chem. Soc.* **58,** 373–374 (1936).

1:8525 3-METHYLPENTANE C_6H_{14} **Beil. I-149**

```
           H
           |
CH3.CH2.C.CH2.CH3
           |
          CH3
```

B.P. 63.3° ⟨1⟩ ⟨4⟩ **M.P. −118°** ⟨3⟩ D_4^{20} = **0.6640** ⟨2⟩ n_D^{20} = **1.3764** ⟨2⟩
63.2° ⟨2⟩ n_D^{25} = **1.3738** ⟨2⟩

$\bar{C}$ shaken with alk. $KMnO_4$ (as for *n*-hexane 1:8530) turns green immediately (dif. from *n*-hexane).

[For prepn. from 3-methylpentanol-3 (1:6189) see ⟨5⟩.]

1:8525 ⟨1⟩ Smittenberg, Hoog, Henkes, *J. Am. Chem. Soc.* **60,** 18 (1938). ⟨2⟩ Bruun, Hicks-Bruun, Faulconer, *J. Am. Chem. Soc.* **59,** 2357 (1937). ⟨3⟩ Bruun, Hicks-Bruun, *J. Research Natl. Bur. Standards* **5,** 937 (1930). ⟨4⟩ Wibaut, Hoog, et al., *Rec. trav. chim.* **58,** 372–373, 377 (1939). ⟨5⟩ Cramer, Mulligan, *J. Am. Chem. Soc.* **58,** 373–374 (1936).

1:8530 *n*-HEXANE $CH_3.CH_2.CH_2.CH_2.CH_2.CH_3$ C_6H_{14} **Beil. I-142**

B.P. 68.8° ⟨1⟩ ⟨2⟩ **M.P. −95.0°** 2⟩ D_4^{20} = **0.65945** ⟨3⟩ n_D^{20} = **1.37506** ⟨3⟩ ⟨1⟩
−95.5° ⟨1⟩

$\bar{C}$ is not visibly reactive to Br_2 in CCl_4 (T 1.91) after 4 hrs. — 0.1 ml. $\bar{C}$ shaken at 100° in stoppered tt. with 1 ml. 0.1 *N* $KMnO_4$ and 0.5 ml. *N* NaOH was still purple after 1 min., turned dull blue in 2 min., and green in 3 min.

1:8530 ⟨1⟩ Smittenberg, Hoog, Henkes, *J. Am. Chem. Soc.* **60,** 18 (1938). ⟨2⟩ Timmermans, Martin, *J. chim. phys.* **25,** 412 (1928). ⟨3⟩ Shepard, Henne, Midgley, *J. Am. Chem. Soc.* **53,** 1951–1953 (1931).

1:8534 2,2-DIMETHYLPENTANE C_7H_{16} **Beil. I-157**

$$CH_3.\overset{\displaystyle CH_3}{\underset{\displaystyle CH_3}{\overset{|}{\underset{|}{C}}}}.CH_2.CH_2.CH_3$$

B.P. 79.3° ⟨1⟩ **M.P. −124° ⟨1⟩** D_4^{20} = **0.6737** ⟨2⟩ n_D^{20} = **1.38233** ⟨2⟩
78.9° ⟨2⟩ D_4^{25} = **0.66953** ⟨3⟩

[For prepn. (21% yield) from *ter*-butyl chloride + *n*-C_3H_7.Mg.Br + Cu_2I_2 see ⟨4⟩.]

1:8534 ⟨1⟩ Smittenberg, Hoog, Henkes, *J. Am. Chem. Soc.* **60,** 18 (1938). ⟨2⟩ Edgar, Calingaert, *J. Am. Chem. Soc.* **51,** 1544–1545 (1929). ⟨3⟩ Wibaut, Hoog, et al., *Rec. trav. chim.* **58,** 372–377 (1939). ⟨4⟩ Marker, Oakwood, *J. Am. Chem. Soc.* **60,** 2598 (1938).

1:8539 2,4-DIMETHYLPENTANE C_7H_{16} **Beil. I-158**

$$CH_3.\overset{\displaystyle H}{\underset{\displaystyle CH_3}{\overset{|}{\underset{|}{C}}}}.CH_2.\overset{\displaystyle H}{\underset{\displaystyle CH_3}{\overset{|}{\underset{|}{C}}}}.CH_3$$

B.P. 80.6° ⟨1⟩ ⟨4⟩ **M.P. −119.1° ⟨1⟩** D_4^{20} = **0.6731** ⟨2⟩ n_D^{20} = **1.38233** ⟨3⟩
D_4^{25} = **0.66837** ⟨4⟩

1:8539 ⟨1⟩ Smittenberg, Hoog, Henkes, *J. Am. Chem. Soc.* **60,** 18 (1938). ⟨2⟩ Chavanne, de Graef, *Bull. soc. chim. Belg.* **33,** 375 (1924). ⟨3⟩ Edgar, Calingaert, *J. Am. Chem. Soc.* **51,** 1544–1545 (1929). ⟨4⟩ Wibaut, Hoog, et al., *Rec. trav. chim.* **58,** 372–377 (1939).

1:8544 2,2,3-TRIMETHYLBUTANE C_7H_{16} **Beil. S.N. 10**
("Triptane")

$$CH_3.\overset{\displaystyle CH_3}{\underset{\displaystyle CH_3}{\overset{|}{\underset{|}{C}}}}—\overset{\displaystyle H}{\underset{\displaystyle CH_3}{\overset{|}{\underset{|}{C}}}}.CH_3$$

B.P. 81.0° ⟨1⟩ ⟨3⟩ **M.P. −25.0° ⟨2⟩** D_4^{20} = **0.6900** ⟨2⟩ ⟨3⟩ n_D^{20} = **1.38940** ⟨2⟩
80.9° ⟨2⟩ **−26.3° ⟨1⟩** D_4^{25} = **0.68583** ⟨3⟩

1:8544 ⟨1⟩ Smittenberg, Hoog, Henkes, *J. Am. Chem. Soc.* **60,** 18 (1938). ⟨2⟩ Edgar, Calingaert, *J. Am. Chem. Soc.* **51,** 1544–1545 (1929). ⟨3⟩ Wibaut, et al., *Rec. trav. chim.* **58,** 372–377 (1939).

1:8549 3,3-DIMETHYLPENTANE C_7H_{16} **Beil. I-158**

$$CH_3.CH_2.\overset{\displaystyle CH_3}{\underset{\displaystyle CH_3}{\overset{|}{\underset{|}{C}}}}.CH_2.CH_3$$

B.P. 86.1° ⟨1⟩ ⟨3⟩ **M.P. −135.0°** D_4^{20} = **0.6934** ⟨2⟩ n_D^{20} = **1.39114** ⟨2⟩ ⟨1⟩
86.0° ⟨2⟩ ⟨1⟩ ⟨2⟩ ⟨3⟩ D_4^{25} = **0.68911** ⟨3⟩

[For prepn. (11–20% yield) from *ter*-amyl chloride + C_2H_5.Mg.Br + Cu_2I_2 see ⟨4⟩.]

1:8549 ⟨1⟩ Smittenberg, Hoog, Henkes, *J. Am. Chem. Soc.* **60,** 18 (1938). ⟨2⟩ Edgar, Calingaert, *J. Am. Chem. Soc.* **51,** 1544–1546 (1929). ⟨3⟩ Wibaut, Hoog, et al., *Rec. trav. chim.* **58,** 372–377 (1939). ⟨4⟩ Marker, Oakwood, *J. Am. Chem. Soc.* **60,** 2598 (1938).

1:8554 2,3-DIMETHYLPENTANE $CH_3.\overset{\displaystyle H}{\underset{\displaystyle CH_3}{\overset{|}{\underset{|}{C}}}}—\overset{\displaystyle H}{\underset{\displaystyle CH_3}{\overset{|}{\underset{|}{C}}}}.CH_2.CH_3$ C_7H_{16} **Beil. I-157**

B.P. 89.7° ⟨1⟩ **M.P.** (glass) D_4^{20} = **0.6952** ⟨1⟩ n_D^{20} = **1.39201** ⟨1⟩ ⟨2⟩
89.8° ⟨2⟩ ⟨3⟩ D_4^{25} = **0.69087** ⟨3⟩

1:8554 ⟨1⟩ Edgar, Calingaert, *J. Am. Chem. Soc.* **51,** 1544–1545 (1929). ⟨2⟩ Smittenberg, Hoog, Henkes, *J. Am. Chem. Soc.* **60,** 18 (1938). ⟨3⟩ Wibaut, Hoog, et al., *Rec. trav. chim.* **58,** 372–377 (1939).

1:8559 2-METHYLHEXANE (Isoheptane) C_7H_{16} **Beil. I-156**

$$CH_3.\overset{H}{\underset{CH_3}{C}}.CH_2.CH_2.CH_2.CH_3$$

B.P. 90.0° ⟨1⟩ **90.1°** ⟨2⟩ ⟨4⟩ **90.3°** ⟨3⟩ **M.P. −119.1°** ⟨1⟩ **−118.2°** ⟨2⟩ **−120.3°** ⟨3⟩ D_4^{20} = **0.6789** ⟨1⟩ D_4^{25} = **0.67437** ⟨4⟩ n_D^{20} = **1.38509** ⟨1⟩ ⟨3⟩

1:8559 ⟨1⟩ Edgar, Calingaert, *J. Am. Chem. Soc.* **51,** 1544–1545 (1929). ⟨2⟩ Smittenberg, Hoog, Henkes, *J. Am. Chem. Soc.* **60,** 18 (1938). ⟨3⟩ Whitmore, Orem, *J. Am. Chem. Soc.* **60,** 2574 (1938). ⟨4⟩ Wibaut, Hoog, et al., *Rec. trav. chim.* **58,** 372–377 (1939).

1:8564 3-METHYLHEXANE $CH_3.CH_2.\overset{H}{\underset{CH_3}{C}}.CH_2.CH_3$ C_7H_{16} **Beil. I-157**

B.P. 91.8° ⟨1⟩ **M.P. −119.4°** ⟨2⟩ D_4^{20} = **0.6870** ⟨1⟩ n_D^{20} = **1.38873** ⟨1⟩

1:8564 ⟨1⟩ Edgar, Calingaert, *J. Am. Chem. Soc.* **51,** 1544–1545 (1929). ⟨2⟩ Timmermans, *Bull. soc. chim. Belg.* **30,** 64 (1921).

1:8569 3-ETHYLPENTANE $CH_3.CH_2.\overset{H}{\underset{CH_2.CH_3}{C}}.CH_2.CH_3$ C_7H_{16} **Beil. I-157**

B.P. 93.3° ⟨1⟩ **M.P. −118.8°** ⟨2⟩ D_4^{20} = **0.6984** ⟨1⟩ n_D^{20} = **1.39366** ⟨1⟩

1:8569 ⟨1⟩ Edgar, Calingaert, *J. Am. Chem. Soc.* **51,** 1544–1545 (1929). ⟨2⟩ Huffman, Parks, Thomas, *J. Am. Chem. Soc.* **52,** 3242 (1930).

1:8575 *n*-HEPTANE $CH_3.(CH_2)_5.CH_3$ C_7H_{16} **Beil. I-154**

B.P. 98.4° ⟨1⟩ ⟨2⟩ ⟨3⟩ ⟨4⟩ ⟨5⟩ **M.P. −90.66°** ⟨2⟩ ⟨3⟩ **−90.5°** ⟨1⟩

D_4^{20} = **0.68376** ⟨3⟩ ⟨2⟩ n_D^{20} = **1.3877** ⟨3⟩ ⟨2⟩ ⟨1⟩
D_4^{25} = **0.67963** ⟨2⟩ n_D^{25} = **1.38553** ⟨2⟩

1:8575 ⟨1⟩ Edgar, Calingaert, *J. Am. Chem. Soc.* **51,** 1544–1545 (1929). ⟨2⟩ Shepard, Henne, Midgley, *J. Am. Chem. Soc.* **53,** 1951–1953 (1931). ⟨3⟩ Hicks-Bruun, Bruun, *J. Research Natl. Bur. Standards* **8,** 534 (1932). ⟨4⟩ Smittenberg, Hoog, Henkes, *J. Am. Chem. Soc.* **60,** 18 (1938). ⟨5⟩ Brooks, *J. Research Natl. Bur. Standards* **21,** 850 (1938).

1:8580 2,2,4-TRIMETHYLPENTANE (" Isooctane ") C_8H_{18} **Beil. I-164**

$$CH_3.\overset{CH_3}{\underset{CH_3}{C}}.CH_2.\overset{CH_3}{\underset{H}{C}}.CH_3$$

B.P. 99.234° ⟨1⟩ **M.P. −107.311°** ⟨1⟩ D_4^{20} = **0.69182** ⟨1⟩ n_D^{20} = **1.39146** ⟨1⟩
D_4^{25} = **0.68786** ⟨2⟩ n_D^{25} = **1.38899** ⟨1⟩

$\bar{C}$ is used as a standard fuel in detn. of anti-knock value of gasoline. [For study of impurities in crude synthetic $\bar{C}$ see ⟨3⟩.]

1:8580 ⟨1⟩ Brooks, *J. Research Natl. Bur. Standards* **21,** 850 (1938). ⟨2⟩ Wibaut, Hoog, et al., *Rec. trav. chim.* **58,** 372–377 (1939). ⟨3⟩ Brooks, Cleaton, Carter, *J. Research Natl. Bur. Standards* **19,** 319–337 (1937).

1:8585 2,2-DIMETHYLHEXANE C_8H_{18} **Beil. S.N. 10**

$$\begin{array}{c} CH_3 \\ | \\ CH_3.C.CH_2.CH_2.CH_2.CH_3 \\ | \\ CH_3 \end{array}$$

B.P. 106.8-107.1° ⟨1⟩ D_4^{20} = **0.6953** ⟨1⟩ n_D^{20} = **1.3930** ⟨1⟩ ⟨2⟩
106-107° ⟨2⟩

[For prepn. (14% yield) from *ter*-butyl chloride + *n*-C_4H_9.Mg.Br + Cu_2I_2 see ⟨3⟩.]

1:8585 ⟨1⟩ Schurman, Boord, *J. Am. Chem. Soc.* **55,** 4933 (1933). ⟨2⟩ Noller, *J. Am. Chem. Soc.* **51,** 598 (1929). ⟨3⟩ Marker, Oakwood, *J. Am. Chem. Soc.* **60,** 2598 (1938).

1:8590 2,5-DIMETHYLHEXANE C_8H_{18} **Beil. I-162**
(Diisobutyl)

$$\begin{array}{c} H \qquad\qquad H \\ | \qquad\qquad | \\ CH_3.C.CH_2.CH_2.C.CH_3 \\ | \qquad\qquad | \\ CH_3 \qquad\quad CH_3 \end{array}$$

B.P. 109.3° ⟨1⟩ ⟨3⟩ M.P. −94.0° ⟨1⟩ ⟨3⟩ D_4^{20} = **0.69376** ⟨2⟩ n_D^{20} = **1.39297** ⟨1⟩
109.4° ⟨2⟩ D_4^{25} = **0.69015** ⟨3⟩

1:8590 ⟨1⟩ Smittenberg, Hoog, Henkes, *J. Am. Chem. Soc.* **60,** 18 (1938). ⟨2⟩ Timmermans, Hennaut-Roland, *J. chim. phys.* **29,** 530–531 (1932). ⟨3⟩ Wibaut, Hoog, et al., *Rec. trav. chim.* **58,** 372–377 (1939).

1:8593 2,2,3-TRIMETHYLPENTANE C_8H_{18} **Beil. S.N. 10**

$$\begin{array}{c} CH_3\ H \\ |\quad\ \ | \\ CH_3.C—C.CH_2.CH_3 \\ |\quad\ \ | \\ CH_3\ CH_3 \end{array}$$

B.P. 110.2° ⟨1⟩ D_4^{20} = **0.7173** ⟨1⟩ n_D^{20} = **1.4030** ⟨1⟩; cf. ⟨2⟩
110.1° ⟨2⟩ ⟨3⟩ D_4^{25} = **0.71212** ⟨3⟩

1:8593 ⟨1⟩ Laughlin, Whitmore, *J. Am. Chem. Soc.* **55,** 2608 (1933). ⟨2⟩ Smittenberg, Hoog, Henkes, *J. Am. Chem. Soc.* **60,** 18 (1938). ⟨3⟩ Wibaut, Hoog, et al., *Rec. trav. chim.* **58,** 372–377 (1939).

1:8595 3,3-DIMETHYLHEXANE C_8H_{18} **Beil. S.N. 10**

$$\begin{array}{c} CH_3 \\ | \\ CH_3.CH_2.C.CH_2.CH_2.CH_3 \\ | \\ CH_3 \end{array}$$

B.P. 110.7-111.2° ⟨1⟩ D_4^{20} = **0.7078** ⟨1⟩ D_4^{20} = **1.3992** ⟨1⟩
111-112° ⟨2⟩

[For prepn. (23% yield) from *ter*-amyl chloride + *n*-C_3H_7.Mg.Br + Cu_2I_2 see ⟨3⟩.]

1:8595 ⟨1⟩ Schurman, Boord, *J. Am. Chem. Soc.* **55,** 4933 (1933). ⟨2⟩ Noller, *J. Am. Chem. Soc.* **51,** 598 (1929). ⟨3⟩ Marker, Oakwood, *J. Chem. Am. Soc.* **60,** 2598 (1938).

1:8600 2,3,4-TRIMETHYLPENTANE

```
        H    H    H
        |    |    |
CH3.C——C——C.CH3
        |    |    |
       CH3  CH3  CH3
```

C_8H_{18} **Beil. S.N. 10**

B.P. 112.8° ⟨1⟩ D_4^{20} = **0.7197 ⟨1⟩** n_D^{20} = **1.4045 ⟨1⟩**

1:8600 ⟨1⟩ Laughlin, Whitmore, *J. Am. Chem. Soc.* **55,** 2608 (1933).

1:8605 2,3,3-TRIMETHYLPENTANE

```
       H    CH3
       |    |
CH3.C——C.CH2.CH3
       |    |
      CH3  CH3
```

C_8H_{18} **Beil. S.N. 10**

B.P. 113.6° ⟨1⟩ D_4^{20} = **0.7258 ⟨1⟩** n_D^{20} = **1.4074 ⟨1⟩**

1:8605 ⟨1⟩ Laughlin, Whitmore, *J. Am. Chem. Soc.* **55,** 2608 (1933).

1:8610 2,3-DIMETHYLHEXANE

```
       H    H
       |    |
CH3.C——C.CH2.CH2.CH3
       |    |
      CH3  CH3
```

C_8H_{18} **Beil. S.N. 10**

B.P. 115.8° ⟨1⟩ ⟨2⟩ D_4^{20} = **0.71234 ⟨2⟩** n_D^{20} = **1.4015 ⟨1⟩**
D_4^{25} = **0.70829 ⟨2⟩**

1:8610 ⟨1⟩ Smittenberg, Hoog, Henkes, *J. Am. Chem. Soc.* **60,** 18 (1938). ⟨2⟩ Wibaut, Hoog, et al., *Rec. trav. chim.* **58,** 372–377 (1939).

1:8615 2-METHYLHEPTANE

```
       H
       |
CH3.C.CH2.CH2.CH2.CH2.CH3
       |
      CH3
```

C_8H_{18} **Beil. I-161**

B.P. 117.2° ⟨1⟩ **M.P. −111.3° ⟨1⟩** D_{20}^{20} = **0.6985 ⟨1⟩** n_D^{20} = **1.3949 ⟨1⟩**

1:8615 ⟨1⟩ Leslie, *J. Research Natl. Bur. Standards* **10,** 617 (1933).

1:8620 3,4-DIMETHYLHEXANE
(Di-*sec*-butyl)

```
               H    H
               |    |
CH3.CH2.C——C.CH2.CH3
               |    |
              CH3  CH3
```

C_8H_{18} **Beil. I-163**

B.P. 117.8° ⟨1⟩ ⟨2⟩ D_4^{20} = **0.71951 ⟨2⟩** n_D^{20} = **1.4044 ⟨1⟩**
D_4^{25} = **0.71548 ⟨2⟩**

1:8620 ⟨1⟩ Smittenberg, Hoog, Henkes, *J. Am. Chem. Soc.* **60,** 18 (1938). ⟨2⟩ Wibaut, Hoog, et al., *Rec. trav. chim.* **58** 372–377 (1939).

1:8625 4-METHYLHEPTANE

```
                   H
                   |
CH3.CH2.CH2.C.CH2.CH2.CH3
                   |
                  CH3
```

C_8H_{18} **Beil. I-162**

B.P. 118.0° ⟨1⟩ $D_{15.5}^{20}$ = **0.7166 ⟨1⟩** n_D^{20} = **1.39814 ⟨2⟩**
n_D^{25} = **1.40063 ⟨1⟩**

1:8625 ⟨1⟩ Brown, Carr, *Ind. Eng. Chem.* **18,** 721 (1926). ⟨2⟩ Maman, *Compt. rend.* **205,** 320 (1937).

1:8630 3-ETHYL-3-METHYLPENTANE C_8H_{18} **Beil. S.N. 10**

```
              CH3
              |
     CH3.CH2.C.CH2.CH3
              |
              CH2.CH3
```

B.P. 118.4° ⟨1⟩ ⟨2⟩ **M.P. −90.9°** ⟨1⟩ ⟨2⟩ D_4^{20} = **0.72742** ⟨2⟩ n_D^{20} = **1.4081** ⟨1⟩
D_4^{25} = **0.72358** ⟨2⟩

1:8630 ⟨1⟩ Smittenberg, Hoog, Henkes, *J. Am. Chem. Soc.* **60,** 18 (1938). ⟨2⟩ Wibaut, Hoog, et al., *Rec. trav. chim.* **58,** 372–377 (1939).

1:8635 3-ETHYLHEXANE C_8H_{18} **Beil. I-162**

```
              H
              |
     CH3.CH2.C.CH2.CH2.CH3
              |
              CH2.CH3
```

B.P. 118.9° ⟨1⟩ D_{15}^{15} = **0.7127** ⟨2⟩ n_D^{20} = **1.40128** ⟨3⟩
n_D^{25} = **1.3993** ⟨1⟩ ⟨2⟩

1:8635 ⟨1⟩ Zelinsky, Kasansky, Plate, *Ber.* **68,** 1872 (1935). ⟨2⟩ Clark, Riegel, *J. Am. Chem. Soc.* **34,** 678 (1912). ⟨3⟩ Maman, *Compt. rend.* **205,** 320 (1937).

1:8640 3-METHYLHEPTANE C_8H_{18} **Beil. I-162**

```
              H
              |
     CH3.CH2.C.CH2.CH2.CH2.CH3
              |
              CH3
```

B.P. 119.1° ⟨1⟩ ⟨2⟩ D_4^{20} = **0.7095** ⟨1⟩ n_D^{20} = **1.3988** ⟨1⟩
D_4^{25} = **0.70178** ⟨2⟩

1:8640 ⟨1⟩ Smittenberg, Hoog, Henkes, *J. Am. Chem. Soc.* **60,** 18 (1938). ⟨2⟩ Wibaut, Hoog, *Rec. trav. chim.* **58,** 372–377 (1939).

1:8645 2,2,4,4-TETRAMETHYLPENTANE C_9H_{20} **Beil. S.N. 10**

```
         CH3    CH3
         |      |
     CH3.C.CH2.C.CH3
         |      |
         CH3    CH3
```

B.P. 122.30° ⟨1⟩ **M.P. −67.0°** ⟨1⟩ $D_4^{20.1}$ = **0.7185** ⟨1⟩ n_D^{20} = **1.40695** ⟨1⟩

1:8645 ⟨1⟩ Whitmore, Southgate, *J. Am. Chem. Soc.* **60,** 2573 (1938).

1:8650 2,2,5-TRIMETHYLHEXANE C_9H_{20} **Beil. S.N. 10**

```
         CH3          H
         |            |
     CH3.C.CH2.CH2.C.CH3
         |            |
         CH3          CH3
```

B.P. 124.09° ⟨1⟩ **M.P. −106.35°** ⟨1⟩ D_4^{20} = **0.70755** ⟨1⟩ n_D^{20} = **1.39967** ⟨1⟩
n_D^{25} = **1.39736** ⟨1⟩

1:8650 ⟨1⟩ Brooks, Cleaton, Carter, *J. Research Natl. Bur. Standards* **19,** 331 (1937).

1:8655 **n-OCTANE** $CH_3.(CH_2)_6.CH_3$ C_8H_{18} **Beil. I-159**

B.P. 125.59° ⟨1⟩ ⟨2⟩ M.P. −56.90° ⟨1⟩ D_4^{20} **= 0.70279 ⟨1⟩** n_D^{20} **= 1.39760 ⟨1⟩**
−56.82° ⟨2⟩ ⟨3⟩ D_4^{25} **= 0.69882 ⟨1⟩** n_D^{25} **= 1.39534 ⟨1⟩**

1:8655 ⟨1⟩ Shepard, Henne, Midgley, *J. Am. Chem. Soc.* **53,** 1951, 1953, 1958 (1931). ⟨2⟩ Mair, *J. Research Natl. Bur. Standards* **9,** 471 (1932). ⟨3⟩ Smittenberg, Hoog, Henkes, *J. Am. Chem. Soc.* **60,** 18 (1938).

1:8660 **2,4-DIMETHYLHEPTANE** C_9H_{20} **Beil. S.N. 10**

$$CH_3.\underset{CH_3}{\overset{H}{C}}.CH_2.\underset{CH_3}{\overset{H}{C}}.CH_2.CH_2.CH_3$$

B.P. 133.0° ⟨1⟩ D_4^{20} **= 0.7158 ⟨1⟩** n_D^{20} **= 1.4023 ⟨2⟩**
n_D^{25} **= 1.4014 ⟨3⟩**

1:8660 ⟨1⟩ Richards, Shipley, *J. Am. Chem. Soc.* **38,** 996 (1916). ⟨2⟩ Tuot, *Compt. rend.* **197,** 1436 (1933). ⟨3⟩ Clarke, Beggs, *J. Am. Chem. Soc.* **34,** 62 (1912).

1:8665 **2,6-DIMETHYLHEPTANE** C_9H_{20} **Beil. I-167**

$$CH_3.\underset{CH_3}{\overset{H}{C}}.CH_2.CH_2.CH_2.\underset{CH_3}{\overset{H}{C}}.CH_3$$

B.P. 135.21° ⟨1⟩ M.P. −102.95° ⟨1⟩ D_4^{20} **= 0.70891 ⟨1⟩** n_D^{20} **= 1.40073 ⟨1⟩**

1:8665 ⟨1⟩ White, Rose, Calingaert, Soroos, *J. Research Natl. Bur. Standards* **22,** 315–319 (1939).

1:8670 **2,5-DIMETHYLHEPTANE** C_9H_{20} **Beil. I-167**

$$CH_3.\underset{CH_3}{\overset{H}{C}}.CH_2.CH_2.\underset{CH_3}{\overset{H}{C}}.CH_2.CH_3$$

B.P. 135.8° ⟨1⟩ D_4^{20} **= 0.7198 ⟨1⟩** n_D^{20} **= 1.4033 ⟨2⟩**
n_D^{25} **= 1.4020 ⟨3⟩**

1:8670 ⟨1⟩ Richards, Shipley, *J. Am. Chem. Soc.* **38,** 996 (1916). ⟨2⟩ Tuot, *Compt. rend.* **197,** 1436 (1933). ⟨3⟩ Clarke, Beggs, *J. Am. Chem. Soc.* **34,** 60 (1912).

1:8675 **3,3-DIMETHYLHEPTANE** C_9H_{20} **Beil. S.N. 10**

$$CH_3.CH_2.\underset{CH_3}{\overset{CH_3}{C}}.CH_2.CH_2.CH_2.CH_3$$

B.P. 137-138° ⟨1⟩ D_4^{20} **= 0.7304 ⟨1⟩** n_D^{20} **= 1.4095 ⟨1⟩**

1:8675 ⟨1⟩ Noller, *J. Am. Chem. Soc.* **51,** 598 (1929).

1:8680 **3,3-DIETHYLPENTANE** C_9H_{20} **Beil. S.N. 10**

$$CH_3.CH_2.\underset{CH_2.CH_3}{\overset{CH_2.CH_3}{C}}.CH_2.CH_3$$

B.P. 138.2° ⟨1⟩ D_4^{20} **= 0.75222 ⟨1⟩** n_D^{18} **= 1.42057 ⟨1⟩**

1:8680 ⟨1⟩ Morgan, Carter, Duck, *J. Chem. Soc.* **127,** 1252–1259 (1925).

1:8685 2,3-DIMETHYLHEPTANE C_9H_{20} **Beil. S.N. 1(**

$$CH_3.\overset{H}{\underset{CH_3}{C}}—\overset{H}{\underset{CH_3}{C}}.CH_2.CH_2.CH_2.CH_3$$

B.P. 140.65° ⟨1⟩ $D_4^{20.1}$ = **0.7235 ⟨1⟩** n_D^{20} = **1.40850 ⟨1**

1:8685 ⟨1⟩ Whitmore, Southgate, *J. Am. Chem. Soc.* **60,** 2573 (1938).

1:8690 4-METHYLOCTANE C_9H_{20} **Beil. S.N. 1(**

$$CH_3.CH_2.CH_2.\overset{H}{\underset{CH_3}{C}}.CH_2.CH_2.CH_2.CH_3$$

B.P. 142.433° ⟨1⟩ M.P. −119.1° ⟨1⟩ D_4^{20} = **0.7245 ⟨1⟩** n_D^{20} = **1.4078 ⟨1**

1:8690 ⟨1⟩ White, Glasgow, *J. Research Natl. Bur. Standards* **19,** 432 (1937).

1:8695 3-ETHYLHEPTANE C_9H_{20} **Beil. S.N. 10**

$$CH_3.CH_2.\overset{H}{\underset{CH_2.CH_3}{C}}.CH_2.CH_2.CH_2.CH_3$$

B.P. 143.1° ⟨1⟩ ⟨2⟩ D_4^{20} = **0.7272 ⟨1⟩** n_D^{20} = **1.4090 ⟨1⟩ ⟨2⟩**

1:8695 ⟨1⟩ Whitmore, Orem, *J. Am. Chem. Soc.* **60,** 2574 (1938). ⟨2⟩ Whitmore, Southgate, *J. Am. Chem. Soc.* **60,** 2573 (1938).

1:8700 2-METHYLOCTANE C_9H_{20} **Beil. I-166**

$$CH_3.\overset{H}{\underset{CH_3}{C}}.(CH_2)_5.CH_3$$

B.P. 143.255° ⟨1⟩ M.P. −80.5° ⟨1⟩ D_4^{20} = **0.7134 ⟨1⟩ ⟨2⟩** n_D^{20} = **1.4032 ⟨1⟩ ⟨2⟩**
142.80° ⟨2⟩

1:8700 ⟨1⟩ White, Glasgow, *J. Research Natl. Bur. Standards* **19,** 426 (1937). ⟨2⟩ Whitmore, Orem, *J. Am. Chem. Soc.* **60,** 2574 (1938).

1:8705 3-METHYLOCTANE C_9H_{20} **Beil. S.N. 10**

$$CH_3.CH_2.\overset{H}{\underset{CH_3}{C}}.(CH_2)_4.CH_3$$

B.P. 144.18° ⟨1⟩ M.P. −108° ⟨1⟩ D_4^{20} = **0.7210 ⟨1⟩** n_D^{20} = **1.4065 ⟨1⟩**

1:8705 ⟨1⟩ White, Glasgow, *J. Research Natl. Bur. Standards* **19,** 429 (1937).

1:8710 *n*-NONANE $CH_3.(CH_2)_7.CH_3$ C_9H_{20} **Beil. I-165**

B.P. 150.71° ⟨1⟩ M.P. −53.68° ⟨1⟩ D_4^{20} = **0.71780 ⟨1⟩** n_D^{20} = **1.40563 ⟨1⟩**
150.72° ⟨2⟩ −53.70° ⟨2⟩ ⟨3⟩ D_4^{25} = **0.71398 ⟨1⟩** n_D^{25} = **1.40318 ⟨2⟩**

1:8710 ⟨1⟩ Shepard, Henne, Midgley, *J. Am. Chem. Soc.* **53,** 1951, 1958 (1931). ⟨2⟩ Mair, *J. Research Natl. Bur. Standards* **9,** 471 (1932). ⟨3⟩ Smittenberg, Hoog, Henkes, *J. Am. Chem. Soc.* **60,** 18 (1938).

1:8720 **2,7-DIMETHYLOCTANE** (Diisoamyl) $CH_3.CH(CH_3).(CH_2)_4.CH(CH_3).CH_3$ $C_{10}H_{22}$ **Beil. I-169**

B.P. 160.0° ⟨1⟩ **M.P. −49.2° ⟨1⟩** D_4^{20} = **0.72258 ⟨1⟩** n_D^{15} = **1.41049 ⟨1⟩**
D_4^{25} = **0.71876 ⟨1⟩**

1:8720 ⟨1⟩ Timmermans, Hennaut-Roland, *Cent.* **1930,** I, 1613.

1:8800 ***n*-DECANE** $CH_3.(CH_2)_8.CH_3$ $C_{10}H_{22}$ **Beil. I-168**

B.P. 174.06° ⟨1⟩ **M.P. −29.68° ⟨2⟩** D_4^{20} = **0.72994 ⟨3⟩** n_D^{20} = **1.41203 ⟨1⟩**
174.02° ⟨2⟩ **−29.76° ⟨1⟩** D_4^{25} = **0.72643 ⟨1⟩** n_D^{25} = **1.40961 ⟨2⟩ ⟨3⟩**

1:8800 ⟨1⟩ Shepard, Henne, Midgley, *J. Am. Chem. Soc.* **53,** 1951, 1953, 1958 (1931). ⟨2⟩ Mair, *J. Research Natl. Bur. Standards* **9,** 471 (1932). ⟨3⟩ Bruun, Hicks-Bruun, *J. Research Natl. Bur. Standards* **8,** 587 (1932).

1:8820 ***n*-UNDECANE** (*n*-Hendecane) $CH_3.(CH_2)_9.CH_3$ $C_{11}H_{24}$ **Beil. I-170**

B.P. 195.84° ⟨1⟩ **M.P. −25.65° ⟨1⟩** D_4^{20} = **0.74025 ⟨1⟩** n_D^{20} = **1.41727 ⟨1⟩**
−25.61° ⟨2⟩ D_4^{25} = **0.73667 ⟨1⟩** n_D^{25} = **1.41495 ⟨2⟩**

1:8820 ⟨1⟩ Shepard, Henne, Midgley, *J. Am. Chem. Soc.* **53,** 1951, 1953, 1958 (1931). ⟨2⟩ Mair, *J. Research Natl. Bur. Standards* **9,** 471 (1932).

1:8840 ***n*-DODECANE** $CH_3.(CH_2)_{10}.CH_3$ $C_{12}H_{26}$ **Beil. I-171**

B.P. 216.23° ⟨1⟩ **M.P. −9.73° ⟨1⟩** n_D^{20} = **1.42188 ⟨1⟩**
−9.61° ⟨2⟩ D_4^{25} = **0.74542 ⟨1⟩** n_D^{25} = **1.41952 ⟨2⟩**

1:8840 ⟨1⟩ Shepard, Henne, Midgley, *J. Am. Chem. Soc.* **53,** 1951, 1953, 1958 (1931). ⟨2⟩ Mair, *J. Research Natl. Bur. Standards* **9,** 471 (1932).

1:8860 ***n*-TETRADECANE** $CH_3.(CH_2)_{12}.CH_3$ $C_{14}H_{30}$ **Beil. I-171**

B.P. 252.5° ⟨1⟩ **M.P. +5.5° ⟨2⟩** D_4^{20} = **0.7636 ⟨3⟩**

1:8860 ⟨1⟩ Krafft, *Ber.* **15,** 1700 (1882). ⟨2⟩ Parks, Light, *J. Am. Chem. Soc.* **56,** 1511 (1934). ⟨3⟩ Egloff, " Physical Constants of Hydrocarbons " I, 88 (1939).

1:8880 ***n*-PENTADECANE** $CH_3.(CH_2)_{13}.CH_3$ $C_{15}H_{32}$ **Beil. I-172**

B.P. 270.5° ⟨1⟩ **M.P. +10° ⟨1⟩** D_4^{20} = **0.7689 ⟨1⟩** n_D^{25} = **1.431**

1:8880 ⟨1⟩ Krafft, *Ber.* **15,** 1700–1701 (1882).

1:8900 ***n*-HEXADECANE** $CH_3.(CH_2)_{14}.CH_3$ $C_{16}H_{34}$ **Beil. I-17:**
(Cetane)

B.P. 288.6°$_{765}$ cor. ⟨1⟩ **M.P. +18.1°** ⟨2⟩ ⟨3⟩ D_4^{20} = **0.7751** ⟨4⟩ n_D^{20} = **1.4352** ⟨4

Cryst. from *n*-propyl alc. contg. a little MeOH ⟨3⟩.

[For prepn. from cetyl iodide by reduction with Zn dust + AcOH (85% yield ⟨5⟩; 90% yield ⟨6⟩) see ⟨5⟩ ⟨6⟩; with Zn/Cu couple (90% yield) see ⟨6⟩; or with H_2 + $BaCO_3$–Pd catalyst see ⟨6⟩; for prepn. by hydrogenation of hexadecene-1 (1:7000) see ⟨3⟩ ⟨7⟩.]

[For f.p.-compn. curves of systems: C̄ + *n*-heptadecane (1:7035) see ⟨2⟩; C̄ + *n*-octadecane (1:7040) see ⟨3⟩; C̄ + *n*-hexadecene-1 (1:7000) see ⟨7⟩.]

1:8900 ⟨1⟩ Francis, Wood, *J. Chem. Soc.* **1926,** 1423. ⟨2⟩ Carey, Smith, *J. Chem. Soc.* **1933** 1348–1351. ⟨3⟩ Smith, *J. Chem. Soc.* **1932,** 739–741. ⟨4⟩ Waterman, van't Spijker, Va Westen, *Rec. trav. chim.* **48,** 1110 (1929). ⟨5⟩ Levene, *Organic Syntheses* **15,** 27–28 (1935) ⟨6⟩ Carey, Smith, *J. Chem. Soc.* **1933,** 346–347. ⟨7⟩ Langedijk, Brezesinska Smithuysen *Rec. trav. chim.* **57,** 1050–1054 (1938).

CHAPTER XII

ORDER I: SUBORDER II: COLORED COMPOUNDS

1. Alphabetical Name Index*

2. Chemical Type Index

(Names used here are not necessarily same as subject index names)

*For complete alphabetical name index covering all listed names of numbered compounds in this book see the main alphabetical index.

Biacetyl.................. **1:9500**
Furil..................... **1:9065**

III. Triketones

Diphenyltriketone........ **1:9009**

IV. Quinones

A. *With no other functional group*

Acenaphthenequinone..... **1:9090**
Anthraquinone........... **1:9095**
Camphorquinone......... **1:9083**
Duroquinone............ **1:9023**
2-Methylanthraquinone... **1:9075**
2-Methylnaphthoquinone-1,4.................. **1:9021**
α-Naphthoquinone....... **1:9040**
β-Naphthoquinone........ **1:9062**
Phenanthraquinone....... **1:9086**
Quinone................. **1:9025**
Retenequinone........... **1:908**
Thymoquinone........... **1:900**
p-Toluquinone........... **1:900**

B. *Phenolic quinones*

1-Hydroxyanthraquinone.. **1:908**
2-Hydroxyanthraquinone.. **1:911**

1,2-Dihydroxyanthraquinone.............. **1:910**
1,4-Dihydroxyanthraquinone.............. **1:908**
1,5-Dihydroxyanthraquinone.............. **1:910**

1,2,3-Trihydroxyanthraquinone.............. **1:911**

V. Miscellaneous

Quinhydrone............ **1:907**

ORDER I: SUBORDER II: COLORED COMPOUNDS

Division A, Solids

—— **PHORONE** $(CH_3)_2C{=}CH.CO.CH{=}C(CH_3)_2$ $C_9H_{14}O$ **Beil. I-751**

M.P. 28° **B.P. 198.5°**

See 1:5120. Genus 7: Ketones.

1:9000 FURFURALACETOPHENONE $C_{13}H_{10}O_2$ **Beil. XVII-353**

(furyl)—CH=CH—CO—(phenyl)

M.P. 29° (see text) **B.P. 317°** dec.

Yellow cryst. which turn red on stdg. and rapidly darken in sunlight ⟨1⟩.

C̄ exists in three polymorphic forms ⟨2⟩; that from solidification of vac. distd. product shows m.p. 29°; on recrystn. from pet. ether this yields a " stable " form, m.p. 46°. By suitable inoculation a third form, m.p. 36°, has also been reported ⟨2⟩.

[For prepn. of C̄ from furfural + acetophenone in alc. NaOH see ⟨1⟩.]

C̄ gives in very poor yield an oxime, m.p. 82–83° ⟨3⟩.

Ⓓ **Furfuralacetophenone 2,4-dinitrophenylhydrazone:** scarlet cryst., m.p. 169° ⟨4⟩.

1:9000 ⟨1⟩ Drake, Gilbert, *J. Am. Chem. Soc.* 4965–4966 (1930). ⟨2⟩ Weygand, Strobelt, *Ber.* **68,** 1844, 1846 (1935). ⟨3⟩ Asahina, Mayeda, *Chem. Abs.* **27,** 4229 (1933). ⟨4⟩ Ferrante, Bloom, *Am. J. Pharm.* **105,** 383 (1933).

1:9001 FURFURALACETONE $C_8H_8O_2$ **Beil. XVII-306**

HC——CH
HC C—CH=CH.CO.CH₃
O

M.P. 39°

Eas. sol. alc., ether, $CHCl_3$; dif. sol. pet. ether — Cryst. become reddish on stdg., even in dark — [For prepn. in 60–66% yield by alk. condens. of furfural and acetone see ⟨1⟩.]

C̄ is sol. in conc. H_2SO_4 with pale br.-yel. color which on warm. becomes intense dark wine-red.

C̄ oxidized with bleaching powder suspension gives $CHCl_3$ and, on filtration and acidifn., 89% yield of furanacrylic ac. (1:0760), cryst. from aq., m.p. 139° ⟨2⟩ — Reacts. alm. explosively with cold conc. HNO_3 giving oxalic ac. ⟨2⟩.

C̄ + furfural in alc. + aq. NaOH yields difurfuralacetone, m.p. 60° (1:9005), q.v.

Ⓓ **Furfuralacetone phenylhydrazone:** from C̄ in alc. treated with phenylhydrazine in alc. + AcOH; ndls. from alc.; m.p. 131–132° ⟨3⟩. [On warming with AcOH this prod. is converted to 3-methyl-1-phenyl-5-α-furylpyrazoline [Beil. XXVII-567]; cryst. from alc., m.p. 102–103° ⟨3⟩.]

Ⓓ **Furfuralacetone 2,4-dinitrophenylhydrazone:** m.p. 241.0° cor. ⟨4⟩ [cf. T 1.14].

1:9001 ⟨1⟩ Leuck, Cejka, *Organic Syntheses, Coll. Vol.* I, 278–279 (1932). ⟨2⟩ Hurd, Thomas, *J. Am. Chem. Soc.* **55,** 1648 (1933). ⟨3⟩ von Auwers, Voss, *Ber.* **42,** 4416–4426 (1909). ⟨4⟩ Ferrante, Bloom, *Am. J. Pharm.* **105,** 383 (1933).

— **BENZALACETONE** (Benzylideneacetone; methyl styryl ketone) C_6H_5—CH=CH.CO.CH_3 $C_{10}H_{10}O$ **Beil. VII-364**

M.P. 42° **B.P. 262°** cor.

See 1:5145. Genus 7: Ketones.

1:9003 THYMOQUINONE (2-Methyl-5-isopropyl-benzoquinone-1,4) $C_{10}H_{12}O_2$ **Beil. VII-66?**

O
CH₃
(CH₃)₂CH
O

M.P. 45.5° **B.P. 232°**

Or.-yel. (OY) tbls. — Odor sharp like quinone, but also like thymol — Very dif. sol. aq. eas. sol. alc. or ether; sol. $CHCl_3$, C_6H_6, or hexane — Volat. with steam [use in purifn.] — Sol. unchanged in cold conc. H_2SO_4 or cold fumg. HNO_3 — [For prepn. (73–80% yield) from thymol see ⟨1⟩.]

Act. of light (on thin layers) converts to dithymoquinone, pale yel. ndls. (from alc.) m.p. 200–201° ⟨2⟩ ⟨3⟩ — C̄ warmed with dil. alk. gives (like many quinones) dark soln contg. unknown decn. prods.

C̄ treated with $SnCl_2$ gives 88% yield ⟨4⟩ thymohydroquinone, white ndls., m.p. 141.5° — This prod. also obtd. from C̄ by actn. of SO_2 for several days on hot aq. suspension of C̄ ⟨4⟩ ⟨5⟩; also from C̄ in warm C_6H_6 soln. on treatment with phenylhydrazine ⟨6⟩, N_2 being evolved — Slow evapn. of ether soln. of equal moles C̄ + thymohydroquinone yields thymoquinhydrone, dark green cryst., m.p. 78° dec. ⟨4⟩; dark violet alm. black cryst., m.p. 64 ⟨7⟩.

Ⓓ **3,6-Dibromothymoquinone:** Heat 0.1 g. C̄ with 5 ml. aq. and 0.2 g. Br_2 for ½ hr. on boilg. aq. bath; wash the red oil with cold aq. until it becomes yel. cryst. Recryst twice from 2 ml. hot alc. (adding a little ether if oil fails to cryst. readily, m.p. 73° ⟨8⟩ ⟨9⟩ ⟨10⟩.

Ⓓ **Thymoquinone oxime-1 (4-nitrosothymol):** from C̄ in alc. warmed with NH_2OH.HCl + a little HCl; pale yel. ndls. from $CHCl_3$, m.p. 160–162° rap. htg. ⟨11⟩. [C̄ with free NH_2OH reduces to thymohydroquinone ⟨11⟩ (see above), with evolution of N_2.]

Ⓓ **Thymoquinone (mono)-2,4-dinitrophenylhydrazone** (2′,4′-dinitro-4-hydroxy-2-methyl-5-isopropylazobenzene) [Beil. XVI-148]: from warm alc. soln. of C̄ with equimolar quant. 2,4-dinitrophenylhydrazine; dark red ndls. (from alc.), m.p. 179–180° [sol. in dil. NaOH with violet blue color] ⟨12⟩.

Ⓓ **Thymoquinone (mono)semicarbazone:** from C̄ in alc. soln., stood in cold with ½ its wt. semicarbazide.HCl; yel. ndls. (from alc.), m.p. 201–202° dec. ⟨13⟩. [From AcOH this prod. seps. in bright red cryst. contg. 2 AcOH, rap. lost at room temp yielding yel. cryst., m.p. 204° ⟨14⟩.]

Ⓓ **Thymoquinone bis-semicarbazone:** from C̄ in alc. on prolonged boiling with excess semicarbazide.HCl; yel. cryst., m.p. 237°, sometimes also as white modif. with same m.p. ⟨14⟩.

1:9003 ⟨1⟩ Kremers, Wakeman, *Organic Syntheses, Coll. Vol.* I, 498–500 (1932). ⟨2⟩ Liebermann, *Ber.* **10,** 2177 (1877). ⟨3⟩ Liebermann, Ilinski, *Ber.* **18,** 3193 (1885). ⟨4⟩ Conant, Fieser, *J. Am. Chem. Soc.* **45,** 2201 (1923). ⟨5⟩ Bargellini, *Gazz. chim. ital.* **53,** 238 (1923). ⟨6⟩ Giac

lone, *Gazz. chim. ital.* **58,** 411 (1928). ⟨7⟩ Siegmund, *J. prakt. Chem.* (2) **92,** 359 (1915). ⟨8⟩ Mulliken, " Method " I, 205 (1904). ⟨9⟩ Carstanjen, *J. prakt. Chem.* (2) **3,** 55 (1871). ⟨10⟩ Chechik, *J. Am. Pharm. Assoc.* **22,** 506–510; *Cent.* **1933,** II, 3121.
⟨11⟩ Goldschmidt, Schmid, *Ber.* **17,** 2061–2062 (1884). ⟨12⟩ Borsche, *Ann.* **357,** 181 (1907). ⟨13⟩ Heilbron, Henderson, *J. Chem. Soc.* **103,** 1419 (1913). ⟨14⟩ Henry, Paget, *J. Chem. Soc.* **1928,** 80.

—— **FURFURALACETOPHENONE** $C_{13}H_{10}O_2$ **Beil. XVII-353**

(furyl)—CH=CH.CO—(phenyl)

M.P. 46° **B.P. 217°**

See 1:9000. M.P. 29°.

—— **BENZALACETOPHENONE** $C_{15}H_{12}O$ **Beil. VII-478**

(phenyl)—CH=CH.CO—(phenyl)

M.P. 58° **B.P. 345-348°** u.c.

See 1:5155. Genus 7. Ketones.

1:9005 DIFURFURALACETONE $C_{13}H_{10}O_3$ **Beil. XIX-140**

(furyl)—CH=CH.CO.CH=CH—(furyl)

M.P. 60°

Citron-yellow pr. — Changes to tar on stdg. in air — Eas. sol. alc., ether, $CHCl_3$; dif. sol. in boilg. pet. ether.

[For prepn. from acetone + excess furfural in dil. aq. alc. NaOH see ⟨1⟩.] [Use in quant. detn. of acetone, even in 0.0001% solns., see ⟨2⟩.]

$\bar{C}$ dis. in conc. or even 40–60% H_2SO_4 or conc. HCl yielding dark violet-red solns.

Ⓓ **Difurfuralacetone phenylhydrazone:** m.p. 121–122° ⟨3⟩.

1:9005 ⟨1⟩ Claisen, Ponder, *Ann.* **223,** 146 (1884). ⟨2⟩ Tschelinzeff, Nitkin, *Bull. soc. chim.* (4) **53,** 1130–1139 (1933). ⟨3⟩ Ssurmin, *Chem. Abs.* **30,** 3430 (1936); *Cent.* **1936,** I, 4432.

—— **CINNAMALACETONE** $C_{12}H_{12}O$ **Beil. VII-390**

(phenyl)—CH=CH.CH=CH.CO.CH_3

M.P. 68°

See 1:5174. Genus 7: Ketones.

1:9007 *p*-TOLUQUINONE $C_7H_6O_2$ **Beil. VII-645**
(2-Methylbenzoquinone-1,4)

O, O, CH_3 (structure)

M.P. 69°

Golden-yel. ndls. or pl. — Spar. sol. cold aq., sol. alc., ether — Volatile with steam; subl. in lfts.

[For prepn. by oxidn. of *o*-toluidine with $K_2Cr_2O_7$ (or MnO_2) + H_2SO_4 see ⟨1⟩.]

C̄ with mixt. of equal vols. conc. H_2SO_4 + aq. yields polymer, m.p. above 300° [for structure see ⟨2⟩] — C̄ + aq. NaOH gives brown-red color and decomposes — C̄ in Ac_2O (3 pts.) + trace conc. H_2SO_4 at 50–60° stood overnight yields 2,4,5-triacetoxytoluene; cryst. from alc., m.p. 114–115° ⟨3⟩.

C̄ with SO_2 + H_2O readily reduces ⟨4⟩ to *p*-toluhydroquinone (1:1545) but yield is diminished by formn. of sulfonic acids [cf. ⟨5⟩] — C̄ with $SnCl_2$ (2 pts.) in boilg. aq. (10 pts.) instantly reduces (73% yield ⟨4⟩) to *p*-toluhydroquinone (1:1545).

Ⓓ ***p*-Toluquinone oxime** (5-nitroso-2-hydroxy-1-methylbenzene) [Beil. VII-647]: from C̄ in aq. + $NH_2OH.HCl$ ⟨6⟩; ndls. from aq., m.p. 134–135° dec. [This product with calcd. amt. NH_2OH at 60–70° yields *p*-toluquinonedioxime [Beil. VII-649], yel. ndls. becoming colorless on drying, rapidly decomposing without melting at 220° ⟨7⟩.]

Ⓓ ***p*-Toluquinone bis-(2,4-dinitrophenylhydrazone)**: ndls. from nitrobenzene, m.p. 269°.

Ⓓ ***p*-Toluquinone semicarbazone-4**: from C̄ + semicarbazide.HCl in dil. alc. at 0°; yel. ndls. from alc., m.p. 178–179° ⟨8⟩. [This product with more semicarbazide.HCl yields *p*-toluquinone bis-semicarbazone, or.-red. cryst., m.p. 240° dec. ⟨8⟩.]

1:9007 ⟨1⟩ Chattaway, Parkes, *J. Chem. Soc.* **127,** 1309 (1925). ⟨2⟩ Erdtmann, *Proc. Roy. Soc.* **A-143,** 237–239 (1933). ⟨3⟩ Thiele, Winter, *Ann.* **311,** 349 (1900). ⟨4⟩ Erdtmann, *Proc. Roy. Soc.* **A-143,** 218 (1933). ⟨5⟩ Dodgson, *J. Chem. Soc.* **1930,** 2500. ⟨6⟩ Goldschmidt, Schmid, *Ber.* **17,** 2063 (1884). ⟨7⟩ Nietzki, Guiterman, *Ber.* **21,** 431 (1888). ⟨8⟩ Heilbron, Henderson, *J. Chem. Soc.* **103,** 1417 (1913).

1:9009 DIPHENYL TRIKETONE $C_{15}H_{10}O_3$ Beil. VII-871

C_6H_5—CO—CO—CO—C_6H_5

M.P. 69°

Golden-yel. ndls. from lgr. — C̄ is exceedingly hygroscopic; readily sol. in aq.; yields monohydrate, m.p. 90° ⟨1⟩.

[For prepn. in 59% yield from dibenzoylmethane (1:1480) via bromination and hydrolysis see ⟨2⟩.]

C̄ with excess phenylhydrazine gives on warming 4-benzeneazo-1,3,5-triphenylpyrazole [Beil. XXV-546]; yel.-red pr. from alc., m.p. 156–157° ⟨3⟩ — C̄ on warming with *o*-phenylenediamine in alc. yields 2-phenyl-3-benzoylquinoxaline [Beil. XXIV_1-(285)]; yellowish pl. from alc., m.p. 153° ⟨4⟩.

1:9009 ⟨1⟩ de Neufville, von Pechmann, *Ber.* **23,** 3379–3380 (1890). ⟨2⟩ Bigelow, Hanslick, *Organic Syntheses* **13,** 38–40 (1933). ⟨3⟩ Ref. 1, pages 3383–3384. ⟨4⟩ Gastaldi, Cherchi, *Gazz. chim. ital.* **43,** I, 301 (1913).

1:9011 ANISALACETOPHENONE $C_{16}H_{14}O_2$ Beil. VIII-192

(*p*-Methoxybenzal-acetophenone; 4-methoxychalcone)

CH_3O—C_6H_4—CH=CH.CO—C_6H_5

M.P. 77°

Yellow ndls. from alc.; sol. hot. alc., ether, $CHCl_3$ — On rap. htg. distils partly undecomposed.

[For prepn. (95% yield) from anisaldehyde + acetophenone + NaOEt in alc. see ⟨1⟩ ⟨6⟩.]

C̄ with $AlBr_3$ in dry C_6H_6 yields red mol. cpd. (C̄.$AlBr_3$) or yel. mol. cpd. (C̄.$2AlBr_3$) acc. to conditions; latter on warming with C_6H_6 smoothly demethylates and yields an intermediate oil from which hydrolysis gives *p*-hydroxybenzalacetophenone, m.p. 183° ⟨2⟩.

For act. of C̄ with NH_2OH in either ac. or alk. soln. see ⟨3⟩.

C̄ in abs. alc. + PkOH (in abs. alc.) yields a picrate, C̄.2PkOH; or. ndls., m.p. 87° ⟨4⟩.

Ⓓ **Anisalacetophenone α-semicarbazone:** from C̄ + 2.5 moles semicarbazide.HCl + 2.5 moles KOAc in hot alc.; cryst. from alc., m.p. 168° ⟨5⟩. [From mother liquor, a β form, cryst. from alc., m.p. 190° can be isolated ⟨5⟩.]

1:9011 ⟨1⟩ Dippy, Lewis, *Rec. trav. chim.* **66,** 1003 (1937). ⟨2⟩ Pfeiffer, Haack, *Ann.* **460,** 176–177 (1928). ⟨3⟩ von Auwers, Brink, *Ann.* **493,** 223, 233–235 (1932). ⟨4⟩ Vorländer, *Ann.* **341,** 33 (1905). ⟨5⟩ Stobbé, Bremer, *J. prakt. Chem.* (2) **123,** 254–255 (1929). ⟨6⟩ Kohler, Conant, *J. Am. Chem. Soc.* **39,** 1702 (1917).

—— BENZALACETOPHENONE $C_{15}H_{12}O$ **Beil. VII-478**

(Chalcone) $C_6H_5.CH{=}CH.CO.C_6H_5$

M.P. 58° **B.P. 345-348°** u.c.

See 1:5155. Genus 7: Ketones.

1:9013 ANISALACETONE $C_{11}H_{12}O_2$ **Beil. VIII-131**

(*p*-Methoxybenzalacetone) *p*-CH_3O—C_6H_4—$CH{=}CH.CO.CH_3$

M.P. 73°

Lfts. (from MeOH, ether, or AcOEt) — [For prepn. (in 83% yield) from *p*-anisaldehyde and acetone see ⟨1⟩.] — Sol. in conc. H_2SO_4 with pale yel. color.

Oxid. by NaOCl ⟨2⟩ to $CHCl_3$ and *p*-methoxycinnamic acid [Beil. X-298], ndls. (from alc.), m.p. 170° to turbid liq. becoming clear at 185°.

Sol. in H_2SO_3 (6% SO_3) or in $KHSO_3$ soln. ⟨3⟩.

With $AlBr_3$ in dry C_6H_6 yields red mol. cpd. (C̄.$AlBr_3$) or yellow mol. cpd. (C̄.$2AlBr_3$) acc. to conditions; latter *boiled* with C_6H_6 yields a half solid ppt. whose alkali sol. portion, after pptn. with acid and recrystn. (from dil. MeOH) yields *p*-hydroxybenzalacetone [Beil. VIII-131], cryst. from MeOH, m.p. 101–102° ⟨4⟩.

Ⓓ **Anisalacetone 2,4-dinitrophenylhydrazone:** red ndls. from AcOH; m.p. 229° cor. ⟨2⟩ [cf. T 1.14].

1:9013 ⟨1⟩ Drake, Allen, *Organic Syntheses, Coll. Vol.* I, 71 (1932). ⟨2⟩ Einhorn, Grabfield, *Ann.* **243,** 364 (1888). ⟨3⟩ Knoevenagel, *Ber.* **37,** 4051 (1904). ⟨4⟩ Pfeiffer, Haack, *Ann.* **460,** 175 (1928). ⟨5⟩ Friedmann, *J. prakt. Chem.* (2), **145,** 325 (1936).

1:9014 FLUORENONE $C_{13}H_8O$ **Beil. VII-465**

(Diphenylene ketone)

C=O

M.P. 83° **B.P. 341.5°**

Bright yel. pr. or tbls. from C_6H_6 on addn. of pet. ether — Very sol. C_6H_6, alc., ether, insol. pet. ether — Sol. in conc. H_2SO_4 to deep reddish-violet soln. — Slowly volat. with steam [dif. from phenanthraquinone (1:9086) and anthraquinone (1:9095)].

$\bar{C}$ on fusion with KOH readily gives nearly quant. yield of *o*-**phenylbenzoic acid**, cryst. from aq., or 40% alc., m.p. 111° ⟨1⟩ — $\bar{C}$ on reductn. with Al isopropylate in isopropyl alc. gives 89% yield fluorenol [Beil. VI-691] ⟨7⟩.

Ⓓ **Fluorenone oxime:** m.p. 192–193° (195–196° cor.) ⟨2⟩ ⟨3⟩.

Ⓓ **Fluorenone phenylhydrazone:** alc. soln. of $\bar{C}$ warmed with 1 equiv. phenylhydrazine, then acidified with AcOH gives prod. recryst. from alc., yellow pr., m.p. 151–152° ⟨4⟩.

Ⓓ **Fluorenone *p*-nitrophenylhydrazone:** m.p. 269° ⟨5⟩.

Ⓓ **Fluorenone 2,4-dinitrophenylhydrazone:** m.p. 283–284° u.c. ⟨6⟩.

1:9014 ⟨1⟩ Graebe, Rateneau, *Ann.* **279,** 260 (1894). ⟨2⟩ Moore, Huntress, *J. Am. Chem. Soc.* **49,** 2621 (1927). ⟨3⟩ Spiegler, *Monatsh.* **5,** 195 (1884). ⟨4⟩ Goldschmiedt, Schranzhofer, *Monatsh.* **16,** 808 (1895). ⟨5⟩ Schmidt, Wagner, *Ber.* **43,** 1801 (1910). ⟨6⟩ Cliff, *M.I.T. Ph.D. Thesis* 1933. ⟨7⟩ Lund, *Ber.* **70,** 1524 (1937).

1:9015 BENZIL (Bibenzoyl) C_6H_5—C(=O)—C(=O)—C_6H_5 $C_{14}H_{10}O_2$ **Beil. VII-747**

M.P. 95° **B.P. 346-348°** sl. dec.

Fine pale yel. (Y-T$_2$) ndls. — Insol. aq.; eas. sol. alc., ether — [For prepn. in 86% yield by oxidn. of benzoin with $CuSO_4$ in pyridine see ⟨1⟩; for improvements raising yield to 90–95% see ⟨18⟩.]

$\bar{C}$ with Na in ether soln. gives deep violet pdr. of "sodium benzil," decomp. by aq. ⟨2⟩ or dil. H_2SO_4 ⟨3⟩ into equal parts benzil and benzoin (1:5210) — $\bar{C}$ reduced with Al isopropylate in isopropyl alc. gives 90% yield *meso*-hydrobenzoin [Beil. VI-1003] ⟨4⟩.

Ⓟ **Color reaction with alkali:** Pure benzil in alc. gives on addn. of KOH no color in cold, but on htg. a purple-red color stable in the air; if any benzoin is present, however, the color appears in the cold and disappears on shaking in the air ⟨5⟩ [cf. ⟨6⟩].

Ⓓ **Benzilic acid:** To 1 pt. $\bar{C}$ is added 1 pt. KOH and 2 pts. aq., and after soln. of KOH 2 pts. alc.; mixt. is heated on aq. bath not more than 10–12 min. after commencement of boiling. After cooling, solid is filtered, washed with alc., dislvd. in 20 pts. aq., and dil. H_2SO_4 added to boiling soln. Cryst. from aq., m.p. 150° ⟨7⟩.

Ⓓ **Benzil α-monoxime:** alc. paste of pure $\bar{C}$ + conc. aq. soln. of 1 equiv. $NH_2OH.HCl$ at −5° treated with 3 equiv. of 20% aq. NaOH dropwise with stirring. After stdg. 1½ hrs. diluted with aq., filtered, and acid. with min. quant. AcOH. α-Oxime recrystd. from 60% alc., then from C_6H_6, m.p. 140° ⟨8⟩ — [On boiling pure α-oxime for 15 min. with 1/10 wt. dried animal charcoal in just enough C_6H_6 to dissolve oxime at b.p., filtering, and evapg., gives β-oxime + ½ C_6H_6 cryst.; m.p. β-oxime = 112° ⟨8⟩ ⟨9⟩.]

Ⓓ **Benzil monophenylhydrazone:** from $\bar{C}$ + phenylhydrazine (1 mole) at 100° ⟨10⟩ or from $\bar{C}$ + phenylhydrazine.HCl in alc. ⟨11⟩; yel. ndls. from alc.; m.p. 134°.

Ⓓ **Benzil bis-phenylhydrazone** (benzilphenylosazone): from $\bar{C}$ + 2 moles phenylhydrazone in AcOH at 100°; ndls. from $CHCl_3$, m.p. 235° rap. htg. ⟨11⟩ ⟨12⟩.

Ⓓ **Benzil mono-*p*-nitrophenylhydrazone:** from $\bar{C}$ + 1 mole *p*-nitrophenylhydrazine in AcOH; dk. or. pr. from AcOH, m.p. 192–193° ⟨13⟩.

Ⓓ **Benzil bis-[*p*-nitrophenylhydrazone]:** from $\bar{C}$ + excess *p*-nitrophenylhydrazine in AcOH; yel. pdr. from pyridine + ether; m.p. 290° ⟨14⟩.

Ⓓ **Benzil mono-semicarbazone:** tbls. from alc.; m.p. unsharp abt. 174–175° dec. ⟨15⟩.

Ⓓ **Benzil bis-semicarbazone:** from $\bar{C}$ + 2 moles semicarbazide.HCl + KOAc in dil. alc.; lfts. from alc.; m.p. 243–244° dec. ⟨15⟩.

Ⓓ **Benzil 2,4-dinitrophenylhydrazone:** yel. cryst. from alc.; m.p. 189° ⟨16⟩; 185° ⟨17⟩ [cf. T 1.14]. [Use in detn. of $\bar{C}$ ⟨19⟩.]

1:9015 ⟨1⟩ Clarke, Dreger, *Organic Syntheses, Coll. Vol.* I, 80–82 (1932). ⟨2⟩ Beckmann, Paul, *Ann.* **266,** 23–24 (1891). ⟨3⟩ Nef, *Ann.* **308,** 287 (1899). ⟨4⟩ Lund, *Ber.* **70,** 1524 (1937). ⟨5⟩ Hantzsch, Glover, *Ber.* **40,** 1519–1523 (1907). ⟨6⟩ Corson, McAllister, *J. Am. Chem. Soc.* **51,** 2824 (1929). ⟨7⟩ von Liebig, *Ber.* **41,** 1644–1645 (1908). ⟨8⟩ Taylor, Marks, *J. Chem. Soc.* **1930,** 2305. ⟨9⟩ Taylor, Marks, *Nature* **125,** 636 (1930). ⟨10⟩ Bülow, *Ann.* **236,** 197 (1886).

⟨11⟩ Bamberger, Grob, *Ber.* **34,** 531, Note (1901). ⟨12⟩ Pickel, *Ann.* **232,** 230 (1885). ⟨13⟩ Biltz, Weiss, *Ber.* **35,** 3521 (1902). ⟨14⟩ Hyde, *Ber.* **32,** 1815 (1899). ⟨15⟩ Biltz, Arnd, *Ber.* **35,** 345–346 (1902); *Ann.* **339,** 256–257 (1905). ⟨16⟩ Campbell, *Analyst* **61,** 393 (1936). ⟨17⟩ Allen, *J. Am. Chem. Soc.* **52,** 2958 (1930). ⟨18⟩ Pearl, Dehn, *J. Am. Chem. Soc.* **60,** 57–58 (1938). ⟨19⟩ Iddles, Low, Rosen, Hart, *Ind. Eng. Chem., Anal. Ed.* **11,** 102–103 (1939).

1:9020 CINNAMALACETOPHENONE $C_{17}H_{14}O$ Beil. VII-499

C_6H_5—CH=CH—CH=CH.CO—C_6H_5

M.P. 102°

Gold.-yel. ndls. (from alc.) — Act. of sunlight on soln. in $CHCl_3$ or C_6H_6 yields colorless dimer, m.p. 192° ⟨1⟩; vac. distn. of dimer yields isocinnamalacetophenone, yel. cryst. (from $CHCl_3$), m.p. 235° ⟨1⟩.

Sol. in cold conc. H_2SO_4 with cherry-red color.

C̄ does not dis. in aq. H_2SO_3 but on boilg. with $KHSO_3$ soln. gives addn. prod. ⟨2⟩ — C̄ with 15% H_2O_2 + NaOH in MeOH yields oxide, pptd. by aq., recrystd. from MeOH, colorless ndls., m.p. 89° ⟨3⟩ — C̄ (in alc.) treated with alc. PkOH yields C̄.2PkOH, yel. ndls., m.p. 115–117° ⟨4⟩.

Ⓓ **Cinnamalacetophenone oxime** (**α-form**): from C̄ on boilg. with $NH_2OH.HCl$ + NaOAc in alc. (together with some β-oxime, and oxaminooxime); m.p. 135° ⟨5⟩.

Ⓓ **Cinnamalacetophenone phenylhydrazone:** from C̄ + phenylhydrazine in alc. soln.; yel. ndls. (from lgr.), m.p. 156–158° after prelim. softening ⟨6⟩. [On boilg. with AcOH this is conv. to an isomeric compd., colorless cryst. (from AcOH), m.p. 124° ⟨7⟩ ⟨8⟩.]

Ⓓ **Cinnamalacetophenone 2,4-dinitrophenylhydrazone:** red cryst. from AcOH, m.p. 222° ⟨9⟩; 218–219° dec. ⟨10⟩ [cf. T 1.14].

Ⓓ **Cinnamalacetophenone semicarbazone:** from C̄ + semicarbazide (from B̄.HCl + KOAc), refluxed several hrs. in alc. soln., cryst. (from dil. alc. or ether), m.p. (not given) ⟨8⟩.

1:9020 ⟨1⟩ Stobbé, Rücker, *Ber.* **44,** 870–872 (1911). ⟨2⟩ Knoevenagel, Morisse, *Ber.* **37,** 4053 (1904). ⟨3⟩ Weitz, Scheffer, *Ber.* **54,** 2340 (1921). ⟨4⟩ Vorländer, *Ann.* **341,** 34 (1905). ⟨5⟩ Ciusa, Terni, *Gazz. chim. ital.* **39,** I, 233 (1909). ⟨6⟩ von Auwers, Voss, *Ber.* **42,** 4427 (1909). ⟨7⟩ Straus, *Ber.* **51,** 1475 (1918). ⟨8⟩ Sorge, *Ber.* **35,** 1065–1066 (1902). ⟨9⟩ Ferrante, Bloom, *Am. J. Pharm.* **105,** 383 (1933). ⟨10⟩ Campbell, *Analyst* **61,** 393 (1936).

1:9021 2-METHYLNAPHTHOQUINONE-1,4 $C_{11}H_8O_2$ Beil. S.N. 751

(structure: naphthoquinone with O at 1 and 4, CH_3 at 2)

M.P. 106° ⟨6⟩

Yellow ndls. from MeOH, EtOH, AcOH or pet. ether — Spar. sol. aq.; pet. ether; mod. sol. alc., AcOH; sol. C_6H_6, ether — Volatile with steam.

[For prepn. by oxidn. of β-methylnaphthalene (1:7605) with CrO_3 see ⟨1⟩ ⟨2⟩.]

C̄ is unstable in light, turning dull tan color ⟨2⟩; long exposure to sunlight yields an ether sol. dimer, m.p. 235° which on fusion reverts to orig. monomeric C̄ ⟨3⟩.

C̄ is sol. in cold conc. H_2SO_4 yielding red soln.; with aq. alk. it yields dark brown decomp. products; with NH_4OH it gives blue-red color.

C̄ in MeOH treated with 30% H_2O_2 + 2 N NaOH, diluted, neutralized with dil. H_2SO_4 yields 2-methylnaphthoquinone-1,4-oxide; colorless ndls. from alc.; m.p. 102° ⟨4⟩ ⟨3⟩; yield 65%, m.p. 94.5–95.5° ⟨1⟩. [This oxide treated with 25% H_2SO_4 at 95° for 2 hrs. yields 2-methyl-3-hydroxynaphthoquinone-1,4, yel. ndls. from alc., m.p. 172–173° ⟨3⟩.]

C̄ in alc. reduced with $SnCl_2$ + HCl (yield 92–95% ⟨1⟩) or with $Na_2S_2O_4$ (yield 97% ⟨1⟩) gives 2-methylnaphthohydroquinone-1,4; white powder without sharp m.p.; darkens on keeping — C̄ in AcOH + Ac_2O + NaOAc refluxed with Zn dust gives (82% yield ⟨2⟩) 1,4-diacetoxy-2-methylnaphthalene; colorless cryst. from MeOH, or ether, m.p. 112.5–113° ⟨1⟩ — C̄ in pyridine treated with BzCl + Zn dust with cooling yields 54% 1,4-dibenzoxy-2-methylnaphthalene; colorless ndls. from alc., m.p. 180–180.5° ⟨1⟩.

C̄ yields a dioxime, m.p. 166–168° ⟨5⟩.

1:9021 ⟨1⟩ Fieser, Campbell, Fry, Gates, *J. Am. Chem. Soc.* **61,** 3218–3219 (1939). ⟨2⟩ Smith, Webster, *J. Am. Chem. Soc.* **59,** 666 (1937). ⟨3⟩ Madinaveita, *Cent.* **1934,** II, 940; *Chem. Abs.* **28,** 2708 (1934). ⟨4⟩ Lugg, Macbeth, Winzor, *J. Chem. Soc.* **1937,** 1600. ⟨5⟩ Anderson, Newman, *J. Biol. Chem.* **103,** 405–412 (1933). ⟨6⟩ Pinder, Singer, *Analyst* **65,** 7–13 (1940).

1:9022 PIPERONALACETONE $C_{11}H_{10}O_3$ Beil. XIX-37

O—C₆H₃(—O—CH₂ ring)—CH=CH.CO.CH₃

M.P. 110–111°

Pale yel. cryst. — Alleged ⟨1⟩ to exist also in a colorless form with same m.p. and derivs. but this has been denied ⟨2⟩ — Volatile with steam.

C̄ in CCl_4 treated with 1 mole Br_2 in CCl_4 yields piperonalacetone dibromide, white cryst. from CCl_4, m.p. 122° (block) ⟨3⟩ — C̄ in alc. treated with 1 mole piperonal + aq. alk. yields dipiperonalacetone (1:9080), m.p. 185° ⟨3⟩.

Ⓓ **Piperonalacetonoxime:** cryst. from alc., m.p. abt. 186° ⟨1⟩.

Ⓓ **Piperonalacetone phenylhydrazone:** m.p. abt. 163° ⟨1⟩.

Ⓓ **Piperonalacetone semicarbazone** (α-form): cryst. from alc. or $CHCl_3$; m.p. 217° ⟨4⟩. [This product in alc. on exposure to u.v. light yields β-form, cryst. from C_6H_6, m.p. 168° ⟨4⟩.] [Both semicarbazones on hydrolysis with HCl or AcOH yield yellow C̄ ⟨4⟩.]

1:9022 ⟨1⟩ Haber, *Ber.* **24,** 618–621 (1891). ⟨2⟩ Faillebin, *Ann. chim.* (10) **4,** 459 (1925). ⟨3⟩ Ref. 2, page 455. ⟨4⟩ Wilson, Heilbron, Sutherland, *J. Chem. Soc.* **105,** 2894–2895 (1914).

1:9023 DUROQUINONE (2,3,5,6-Tetramethylbenzoquinone) $C_{10}H_{12}O_2$ Beil. VII-669

CH_3 CH_3 / O=C₆=O / CH_3 CH_3

M.P. 112°

Golden-yel. ndls. from lgr. or alc. — Readily sol. C_6H_6, $CHCl_3$, ether, acetone, eas. sol. hot but dif. sol. cold lgr. — Volatile with steam; subl. below m.p.; has weak but characteristic quinone odor.

[For prepn. from durene (1:7195) via nitration, reduction and $FeCl_3$ oxidn. of diaminodurene see ⟨1⟩; for improvements see ⟨2⟩.]

C̄ is sol. in conc. H_2SO_4 with deep bluish red color; in conc. HNO_3 it is not attacked even on long warming.

C̄ in hot AcOH reduced with Zn dust gives (73% yield ⟨3⟩) or C̄ with phenylhydrazine ⟨4⟩ ⟨5⟩ gives durohydroquinone [Beil. VI-948], m.p. 239–240° [diacetyl deriv.; cryst. from alc., m.p. 207° ⟨6⟩].

C̄ on stdg. 12 hrs. with 20 pts. 5–10% alc. KOH yields diduroquinone [Beil. VIII-427], yel. ndls. from alc. or C_6H_6, m.p. 202–203° ⟨7⟩.

1:9023 ⟨1⟩ Smith, Dobrovolny, *Organic Syntheses* **10,** 40–42 (1930). ⟨2⟩ Smith, Denyes, *J. Am. Chem. Soc.* **58,** 306 (1936). ⟨3⟩ James, Weissberger, *J. Am. Chem. Soc.* **60,** 99 (1938). ⟨4⟩ Otte, von Pechmann, *Ber.* **22,** 2116, Note (1889). ⟨5⟩ von Pechmann, *Ber.* **21,** 1421 (1888). ⟨6⟩ Smith, Dobrovolny, *J. Am. Chem. Soc.* **48,** 1423 (1926). ⟨7⟩ Rugheimer, Hankel, *Ber.* **29,** 2180–2181 (1896).

1:9024 DIBENZALACETONE $C_{17}H_{14}O$ Beil. VII-500

C_6H_5—CH=CH.CO.CH=CH—C_6H_5

M.P. 112°

Pale yellowish tbls. or lfts. from ether or AcOEt — Eas. sol. $CHCl_3$, acetone; fairly eas. sol. hot alc., much more dif. sol. ether, still more so in cold alc. — Decomposes on attempted distn.

[For prepn. in 90–94% yield from BzH + acetone + alk. see ⟨1⟩.]

C̄ is sol. in conc. H_2SO_4 with or.-red color (emerald green?) ⟨2⟩.

C̄ in $CHCl_3$ + 2 Br_2 yields dibenzalacetone tetrabromide, colorless ndls., m.p. 208–211° dec. ⟨3⟩. [With only 1 mole Br_2 yields dibenzalacetone dibromide, m.p. abt. 163° dec. ⟨4⟩.]

C̄ with PkOH in hot alc. or C_6H_6 yields mol. cpd. C̄.PkOH; or. rhombs, m.p. 113–114° ⟨5⟩.

Ⓓ **Dibenzalacetonoxime:** from 2 pts. C̄ + 1 pt. $NH_2OH.HCl$ in 20 pts. alc., stood 20 days with shaking; cryst. from boilg. alc., m.p. 142–144° ⟨6⟩ ⟨7⟩.

Ⓓ **1,5-Diphenyl-3-styrylpyrazoline** [Beil. XXIII-264]: from C̄ in abs. alc. refluxed 1 hr. with phenylhydrazine; yel. ndls. from alc., m.p. 147–148° ⟨8⟩ ⟨9⟩; 152–153° ⟨10⟩.

Ⓓ **Dibenzalacetone *p*-nitrophenylhydrazone:** from C̄ + *p*-nitrophenylhydrazine in alc. + trace of AcOH refluxed 3 hrs.; yel. lfts. from C_6H_6; m.p. 173° ⟨11⟩. [This prod., boiled 1 hr. with 20 pts. AcOH, yields 1-*p*-nitrophenyl-3-styryl-5-phenylpyrazoline; yel.-red ndls. from AcOEt, m.p. 204–205° ⟨11⟩.]

Ⓓ **Dibenzalacetone 2,4-dinitrophenylhydrazone:** red cryst. from AcOH, m.p. 180° ⟨12⟩ [cf. T 1.14].

Ⓓ **Dibenzalacetone semicarbazone:** from C̄ + semicarbazide.HCl + NaOAc in dil. AcOH; ndls. from alc., m.p. 187–190° ⟨13⟩.

1:9024 ⟨1⟩ Conrad, Dolliver, *Organic Syntheses* **12,** 22–24 (1932). ⟨2⟩ Tschelinzeff, *Bull. soc. chim.* (5) **3,** 1040 (1936). ⟨3⟩ Claisen, Ponder, *Ann.* **223,** 142–143, (1884). ⟨4⟩ Groebel, *Ber.* **36,** 1497–1499 (1903). ⟨5⟩ Reddelien, *J. prakt. Chem.* (2) **91,** 240 (1915). ⟨6⟩ Minunni, *Gazz. chim. ital.* **29,** II, 394 (1899). ⟨7⟩ von Auwers, Brink, *J. prakt. Chem.* (2) **133,** 161 (1932). ⟨8⟩ Straus, *Ber.* **51,** 1457, Note 4 (1918). ⟨9⟩ Ref. 6, page 398. ⟨10⟩ Ruhemann, Watson, *J. Chem. Soc.* **85,** 1179 (1904).

⟨11⟩ Ref. 8, pages 1469–1470. ⟨12⟩ Campbell, *Analyst* **61,** 393 (1936). ⟨13⟩ Knöpfer, *Monatsh.* **32,** 764 (1911).

1:9025 QUINONE (*p*-Benzoquinone) $C_6H_4O_2$ **Beil. VII-609**

M.P. 116°

Golden-yel. pr. with peculiar characteristic irritating odor suggesting chlorine. Sublimes readily; volatile with steam and even with ether — Eas. sol. hot aq.; dif. sol. cold aq.; eas. sol. alc., ether, boilg. pet. ether or lgr.

[For prepn. in 86–92% yield by oxidn. of hydroquinone (1:1590) with $Na_2Cr_2O_7$ + H_2SO_4 see ⟨1⟩; in 92–96% yield using $NaClO_3$ + V_2O_5 + dil. H_2SO_4 see ⟨2⟩.]

C̄ liberates I_2 from slightly ac. aq. KI soln. [use in quant. detn. of C̄ ⟨3⟩].

C̄ with warm NH_4OH + $AgNO_3$ gives silver mirror; in cold, black ppt. of Ag ⟨4⟩.

C̄ in alk. soln. absorbs oxygen from air with darkening and decomposition. [For study see ⟨5⟩.]

C̄ in aq. soln. reduced by SO_2 in 80% yield to hydroquinone (1:1590) + hydroquinonesulfonic ac. ⟨6⟩ — C̄ in aq. or ether soln. mixed with similar solns. of hydroquinone (1:1590) ppts. green-black ndls. of quinhydrone, m.p. 171° (1:9070) — C̄ in 5% $CHCl_3$ soln. treated through wide tube with dry HCl gas gives in 2 min. much quinhydrone, but after 20 min. gives quant. ppt. of chlorohydroquinone, m.p. 104° ⟨7⟩ — C̄, added to 3 pts. Ac_2O contg. few drops of conc. H_2SO_4, evolves much ht. and on pouring into aq. yields hydroxyhydroquinone triacetate, cryst. from MeOH, m.p. 96° ⟨8⟩.

Ⓓ **Benzoquinone dioxime:** from C̄ in least possible aq. on stdg. 12 hrs. with 2 pts. $NH_2OH.HCl$ + $\frac{1}{2}$ pt. conc. HCl; pale yel. ndls. from aq., dec. abt. 140° ⟨9⟩. [The monoxime decomposes over wide range.] [C̄ with alk. NH_2OH evolves N_2 gas.]

Ⓓ **Benzoquinone mono-2,4-dinitrophenylhydrazone** (2,′4′-dinitrobenzeneazophenol-4) [Beil. XVI-100]: from C̄ + 2,4-dinitrophenylhydrazine.HCl in alc., br. ndls. from alc., m.p. 185–186° ⟨10⟩ [cf. T 1.14].

Ⓓ **Benzoquinone monosemicarbazone:** from C̄ in alc. stood 24 hrs. at 0° with aq. semicarbazide.HCl; either yel. or red ndls., m.p. 165–166° dec. ⟨11⟩.

Ⓓ **Benzoquinone bis-semicarbazone:** from C̄ + 2 moles semicarbazide.HCl; red pdr., m.p. abt. 243° dec. ⟨12⟩.

1:9025 ⟨1⟩ Vliet, *Organic Syntheses, Coll. Vol.* I, 469–471 (1932). ⟨2⟩ Underwood, Walsh, *Organic Syntheses* **16,** 73–74 (1936). ⟨3⟩ Willstätter, Dorogi, *Ber.* **42,** 2165 (1909). ⟨4⟩ Morgan, Micklethwaite, *J. Soc. Chem. Ind.* **21,** 1373–1375 (1902). ⟨5⟩ Erdtmann, *Proc. Roy. Soc.* **A-143,** 236–237 (1933). ⟨6⟩ Dodgson, *J. Chem. Soc.* **105,** 2435–2443 (1914). ⟨7⟩ Clark, *Am. Chem. J.* **14,** 571 (1892). ⟨8⟩ Thiele, *Ber.* **31,** 1247 (1898). ⟨9⟩ Nietzke, Kehrmann, *Ber.* **20,** 614 (1887). ⟨10⟩ Borsche, *Ann.* **357,** 180–181 (1907).
⟨11⟩ Heilbron, Henderson, *J. Chem. Soc.* **103,** 1414 (1913). ⟨12⟩ Thiele, Barlow, *Ann.* **302,** 329 (1898).

1:9035 PIPERONALACETOPHENONE (3,4-Methylenedioxychalcone) $C_{16}H_{12}O_3$ **Beil. XIX-141**

M.P. 122°

Yel. ndls. (from alc.) — Sol. in conc. H_2SO_4 with or.-yel. color.

Nitration with HNO_3 ($D = 1.395$) at 0° in AcOH yields 6-nitro-3,4-methylenedioxychalcone, cryst. from $CHCl_3$, AcOH, or acetone, yel. ndls., m.p. 165–166° ⟨1⟩.

C̄ in alc. soln. treated with alc. soln. of PkOH yields C̄.2PkOH, orange ndls., m.p. 126–128° ⟨2⟩.

Ⓓ **3,4-Methylenedioxychalcone dibromide:** from 3 g. C̄ dislvd. in CCl_4 and treated dropwise with 1.1 ml. Br_2; colorless lfts. (from 1:1 C_6H_6 + lgr.), m.p. 152° ⟨3⟩.

Ⓓ **3,4-Methylenedioxychalcone α-semicarbazone:** cryst. from abs. alc. (small yield), m.p. 203–205° ⟨4⟩.

1:9035 ⟨1⟩ Borsche, Quast, *Ber.* **52,** 436–437 (1919). ⟨2⟩ Vorländer, *Ann.* **341,** 33 (1905). ⟨3⟩ Bauer, Werner, *Ber.* **55,** 2497 (1922). ⟨4⟩ Stobbé, Bremer, *J. prakt. Chem.* (2) **123,** 256 (1929).

1:9040 α-NAPHTHOQUINONE 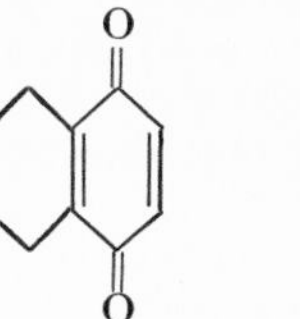 $C_{10}H_6O_2$ **Beil. VII-724**

M.P. 125°

Yel. ndls. (from alc. or pet. ether) with odor like benzoquinone — Dif. sol. cold aq., eas. sol. hot alc., or in ether, C_6H_6, $CHCl_3$, CS_2 — C̄ begins to sublime below 100°; eas. volatile with steam [dif. from β-naphthoquinone (1:9062)].

C̄ is sol. in cold conc. H_2SO_4 and repptd. unchanged on diln. with aq. — C̄ is sol. in aq. alk. with red-brown color and decompn.

[For prepn. in 50–58% yield by chromate oxidn. of 1,4-aminonaphthol.HCl see ⟨1⟩ ⟨2⟩ ⟨3⟩.]

C̄ on oxidn. with acid $KMnO_4$ at 40° gives alm. quant. yield phthalic ac. (1:0820) ⟨4⟩ — C̄ (3.2 g.) in MeOH treated with 30% H_2O_2 (15 ml.) + 2 N NaOH (20 ml.) with cooling turns brown red, then colorless in $\frac{1}{2}$ hr., and on acidif. with dil. H_2SO_4 and ether extractn. yields α-naphthoquinone oxide, ndls. from alc. or AcOH, m.p. 136° ⟨5⟩, 134.5–135.5° ⟨6⟩.

C̄ is scarcely affected by SO_2 in cold but with Sn + HCl ⟨7⟩, $SnCl_2$ + very dil. HCl ⟨8⟩, or phenylhydrazine in C_6H_6 ⟨9⟩ is reduced to 1,4-dihydroxynaphthalene (1:1592), cryst. from aq., m.p. 176°.

C̄ in Ac_2O + H_2SO_4 or $ZnCl_2$ at 40–60° yields 1,2,4-triacetoxynaphthalene, cryst. from C_6H_6, m.p. 154° ⟨10⟩.

Ⓓ **2-Anilinonaphthoquinone-1,4** [Beil. XIV-162]: Boil for 1 min. a soln. of 50 mg. C̄ + 5 drops aniline in 2 ml. alc. Cool, add 10 ml. aq. + 1 ml. AcOH and shake. Filter off ppt., wash with cold aq. and recryst. from 10 ml. 50% alc.; fluffy dark red micro-cryst. ndls., m.p. 190° u.c. ⟨12⟩ ⟨11⟩ ⟨7⟩.

Ⓓ **α-Naphthoquinone monoxime** (4-nitrosonaphthol-1) [Beil. VII-727]: from C̄ in alc. on boilg. with 1 mole $NH_2OH.HCl$ + HCl; pale yel. ndls. from C_6H_6; m.p. 198° ⟨13⟩.

Ⓓ **α-Naphthoquinone (mono)phenylhydrazone** (4-benzeneazonaphthol-1) [Beil. XVI-154] — From C̄ in AcOH susp. + sl. more than calc. quant. of phenylhydrazine.HCl in aq.; dark violet-brown lfts. from C_6H_6, m.p. 205–206° dec. ⟨14⟩.

Ⓓ **α-Naphthoquinone (mono)*p*-nitrophenylhydrazone** (*p*-nitrobenzeneazonaphthol-1) [Beil. XVI-155]: or.-red. ndls. from nitrobenzene; m.p. 277–279° dec.

Ⓓ **α-Naphthoquinone (mono)2,4-dinitrophenylhydrazone** (2,4-dinitrobenzeneazonaphthol-1) [Beil. XVI_1-(252)]: yel. cryst. from pyridine, m.p. 278°.

Ⓓ **α-Naphthoquinone (mono)semicarbazone:** from C̄ + semicarbazide.HCl; green.-yel. cryst. (from AcOH), m.p. 247° after prelim. dec. ⟨15⟩. [No bis-semicarbazone could be obtained.]

1:9040 ⟨1⟩ Fieser, *Organic Syntheses* **17,** 68–72 (1937). ⟨2⟩ Fieser, Fieser, *J. Am. Chem. Soc.* **57,** 493 (1935). ⟨3⟩ Conant, Freeman, *Organic Syntheses, Coll. Vol.* I, 375–378 (1932). ⟨4⟩ Miller, *Cent.* **1914,** I, 790. ⟨5⟩ Weitz, Schobbert, Seibert, *Ber.* **68,** 1165–1166 (1935). ⟨6⟩ Fieser,

Campbell, Fry, Gates, *J. Am. Chem. Soc.* **61**, 3219 (1939). ⟨7⟩ Plimpton, *J. Chem. Soc.* **37**, 635 (1880). ⟨8⟩ Russig, *J. prakt. Chem.* (2) **62**, 32 (1900). ⟨9⟩ Giacolone, *Gazz. chim. ital.* **58**, 411 (1928). ⟨9⟩ Thiele, Winter, *Ann.* **311**, 345–346 (1900). ⟨10⟩ Mulliken, "Method" I, 216 (1904).
⟨11⟩ Zincke, *Ber.* **12**, 1645 (1878). ⟨12⟩ Goldschmidt, Schmid, *Ber.* **17**, 2064 (1884). ⟨13⟩ Zincke, Bindewald, *Ber.* **17**, 3026 (1884). ⟨14⟩ Thiele, Barlow, *Ann.* **302**, 330 (1898).

1:9045 DIANISALACETONE $C_{19}H_{18}O_3$ Beil. VIII-354

$(CH_3O—C_6H_4—CH{=}CH)_2C{=}O$

M.P. 129°

Yel. lfts. (from AcOEt or C_6H_6 + pet. ether) — Color of product varies with nature of solvent ⟨1⟩ — Eas. sol. with yel. color in $CHCl_3$; sol. in AcOH with intense yel. color + red fluores., addn. of conc. H_2SO_4 causing change to blood-red — Soln. in fumg. H_2SO_4 is green, becoming red on diln. with conc. H_2SO_4 ⟨2⟩ — Spar. sol. alc. or ether.

$\bar{C}$ with $AlBr_3$ in dry C_6H_6 yields red mol. cpd. ($\bar{C}.AlBr_3$) or yel. mol. cpd. ($\bar{C}.3AlBr_3$) acc. to conditions; latter on boilg. with C_6H_6 gives resinous ppt. from which (after decompn. with alc. and recrystn. of the crude from ether and alc.) *p,p'*-dihydroxydibenzalacetone [Beil. VIII-353], m.p. 235° has been obtd. ⟨3⟩.

$\bar{C}$ htd. with equal amt. phenylhydrazine in 10 pts. AcOH for 5 min. at 100° yields 1-phenyl 3-(*p*-methoxystyryl)-5-(*p*-methoxyphenyl)pyrazoline, lfts. from AcOEt (soln. shows green fluorescence), m.p. 159° ⟨5⟩.

Ⓓ **Dianisalacetone 2,4-dinitrophenylhydrazone:** m.p. 82–83° ⟨4⟩.

1:9045 ⟨1⟩ Straus, Lutz, *Ann.* **374**, 59 (1910). ⟨2⟩ Baeyer, Villiger, *Ber.* **35**, 1193 (1902). ⟨3⟩ Pfeiffer, Haack, *Ann.* **460**, 178–179 (1928). ⟨4⟩ Ferrante, Bloom, *Am. J. Pharm.* **105**, 383 (1933). ⟨5⟩ Straus, *Ber.* **51**, 1471 (1918).

1:9050 VANILLALACETONE $C_{11}H_{12}O_3$ Beil. VIII-291

(3-Methoxy-4-hydroxystyryl) methyl ketone

$HO—C_6H_3(OCH_3)—CH{=}CH.CO.CH_3$

M.P. 129°

Yel. ndls. (from alc.) — Dif. sol. aq.; eas. sol. alc., ether, C_6H_6 — Sol. in conc. H_2SO_4 with or.-yel. color.

On fusion yel. form is conv. to colorless modifn. with same m.p. — Mixts. of yel. and white forms also melt 129° — The yel. isomer yields red alk. soln. (from which conc. alk. ppts. yel. salt of the *colorless* form; the colorless isomer gives yel. alk. solns. becoming red on stdg. [Red color is due to sodium salt of 3,3'-dimethoxy-4,4'-dihydroxydistyryl ketone ⟨1⟩.]

$\bar{C}$ yields benzoyl deriv., colorless ndls., m.p. 121–122° ⟨2⟩ and oxime.HCl, fine yel. ndls., m.p. 128–129° ⟨2⟩.

Ⓓ **3,4-Dimethoxystyryl methyl ketone:** $\bar{C}$, treated alternately with small amts. $(CH_3)_2SO_4$ and 8% KOH at 30–40° with const. shak. until further addn. of alk. fails to prod. yel. color, gives 100% yield alk. insol. pale yel. ppt., cryst. (from lgr. or dil. alc.), m.p. 85–86° ⟨3⟩.

Ⓓ **Vanillalacetone phenylhydrazone** (?): yel. ndls., m.p. 127–128° ⟨2⟩. [Corresp. pyrazoline obtd. by htg. $\bar{C}$ with phenylhydrazine in AcOH, yel. ndls. (from dil. alc.), m.p. 136° ⟨4⟩.]

Ⓓ **Vanillalacetone 2,4-dinitrophenylhydrazone:** carmine cryst.; m.p. 230° cor. ⟨5⟩ ⟨6⟩.

1:9050 ⟨1⟩ McGookin, Sinclair, *J. Chem. Soc.* **1926,** 1579, 1581. ⟨2⟩ Mannich, Merz, *Arch. Pharm.* **265,** 25 (1927). ⟨3⟩ Dickinson, Heilbron, Irving, *J. Chem. Soc.* **1927,** 1891. ⟨4⟩ Murakami, *Science Repts., Tohoku Imp. Univ.* (1) **18,** 651–660 (1929); *Chem. Abs.* **24,** 2445 (1930). ⟨5⟩ Allen, Richmond, *J. Org. Chem.* **2,** 224 (1937). ⟨6⟩ Ferrante, Bloom, *Am. J. Pharm.* **105,** 383 (1933).

1:9055 α-ANISAL-α'-CINNAMALACETONE $C_{20}H_{18}O_2$ Beil. VIII-208

$CH_3O-C_6H_4-CH{=}CH-C({=}O)-CH{=}CH-CH{=}CH-C_6H_5$

M.P. 139°

Yel. lfts. (from alc., CS_2, or ether + AcOEt) — Fairly sol. $CHCl_3$, C_6H_6; fairly dif. sol. alc., ether, CCl_4, lgr. — Conc. HCl colors dark red; conc. H_2SO_4 yel. ⟨1⟩.

Ⓓ **Anisalcinnamalacetone dibromide:** colorless ndls. (from CS_2), m.p. 139–140° ⟨1⟩.

Ⓓ **Anisalcinnamalacetone tetrabromide:** colorless ndls. (from CS_2), m.p. 155–156° ⟨1⟩.

Ⓓ **1-Phenyl-3-(β-styrylvinyl)-5-(p-methoxyphenyl)pyrazoline:** from $\bar{C}$ + phenylhydrazine in AcOH, yel. cryst. (from alc.), m.p. 155–156° ⟨2⟩. [The intermediate phenylhydrazone could not be obtd.]

1:9055 ⟨1⟩ Bauer, Dieterle, *Ber.* **44,** 2693–2694 (1911). ⟨2⟩ Bauer, Dieterle, *Ber.* **44,** 2699 (1911).

1:9060 DICINNAMALACETONE $C_{21}H_{18}O$ Beil. VII-524

$(C_6H_5-CH{=}CH-CH{=}CH)_2C{=}O$

M.P. 144°

Gold.-yel. ndls. (from abs. alc.) — Dif. sol. cold alc., ether; easier in hot alc., AcOH, AcOEt — Soln. in conc. H_2SO_4 is violet, becoming colorless on diln. with aq.; yellow on diln. with conc. HNO_3.

Readily decomp. by exposure to light ⟨1⟩.

Ⓓ **Dicinnamalacetone phenylhydrazone:** 3 pts. $\bar{C}$ dislvd. in 10 pts. AcOH, warmed with 1.2 pts. phenylhydrazine, cooled and diluted with 2–3 vols. alc., yields yel. prod., recryst. from hot alc., m.p. 166° ⟨2⟩. [Later workers could obt. only an isomer, m.p. 142° ⟨3⟩.]

Ⓓ **Dicinnamalacetone 2,4-dinitrophenylhydrazone:** dark red cryst., m.p. 195.7° cor. ⟨4⟩; 208° ⟨5⟩ [cf. T 1.14].

1:9060 ⟨1⟩ Straus, *Ann.* **374,** 79 (1910). ⟨2⟩ Diehl, Einhorn, *Ber.* **18,** 2325 (1885). ⟨3⟩ Straus, *Ber.* **51,** 1476 (1918). ⟨4⟩ Ferrante, Bloom, *Am. J. Pharm.* **105,** 383 (1933). ⟨5⟩ Campbell, *Analyst* **61,** 393 (1936).

1:9062 β-NAPHTHOQUINONE $C_{10}H_6O_2$ Beil. VII-709

M.P. 145-147° dec. (after softening at 140°) ⟨2⟩

Small odorless red ndls. from ether, or orange lfts. from C_6H_6; stable on storage. [For prepn. in 93–94% yield from 1-amino-2-naphthol.HCl by oxidn. with $FeCl_3$ see ⟨1⟩ ⟨2⟩.]

C̄ is not volatile with steam [dif. from α-naphthoquinone (1:9040)] — C̄ dis. in conc. H_2SO_4 with green color; sol. in dil. alk. with yel. color, absorption of oxygen from air, and decomposition.

C̄, in hot aq. soln., on reduction with SO_2 or better $Na_2S_2O_4$ ⟨12⟩ yields 1,2-dihydroxynaphthalene monohydrate (1:1524), m.p. 60° ⟨3⟩ — C̄, dislvd at 30–40° in 2 pts. Ac_2O contg. 10–20% conc. H_2SO_4, poured into aq. yields 1,2,4-triacetoxynaphthalene, cryst. from alc., m.p. 134–135° ⟨4⟩ — C̄ + *o*-phenylenediamine in dry ether over anhyd. Na_2SO_4 gives 88% yield " naphthophenazine " (1,2-benzophenazine) [Beil. XXIII-276]; clear yel. ndls., m.p. 142° ⟨5⟩.

Ⓓ **Naphthoquinone-1,2 oxime-2** (β-nitroso-α-naphthol) [Beil. VII-715]: from C̄ + $NH_2OH.HCl$ in alc. ⟨6⟩; m.p. 162–164° dec. [β-Naphthoquinone dioxime: yel. ndls. from alc., m.p. 169° ⟨7⟩].

Ⓓ **Naphthoquinone-1,2-phenylhydrazone-2** (2-benzeneazonaphthol-1) [Beil. XVI-151]: from C̄ in AcOH + phenylhydrazine.HCl; deep red ndls. from alc., m.p. 138° ⟨8⟩ ⟨9⟩.

Ⓓ **Naphthoquinone-1,2-*p*-nitrophenylhydrazone** (2-*p*-nitrobenzeneazonaphthol-1) [Beil. XVI-151]: from C̄ + *p*-nitrophenylhydrazine in cold AcOH; deep red ndls., m.p. 235–236° ⟨10⟩.

Ⓓ **Naphthoquinone-1,2 semicarbazone-2** [Beil. VII-720]: from C̄ + semicarbazide.HCl; golden-yel. lfts. from alc., dec. at 184° ⟨11⟩.

1:9062 ⟨1⟩ Fieser, *Organic Syntheses* **17,** 68–72 (1937). ⟨2⟩ Fieser, Fieser, *J. Am. Chem. Soc.* **57,** 493 (1935). ⟨3⟩ Fieser, Hartwell, *J. Am. Chem. Soc.* **57,** 1485 (1935). ⟨4⟩ Thiele, Winter, *Ann.* **311,** 345 (1900). ⟨5⟩ Kehrmann, Mermod, *Helv. Chim. Acta* **10,** 64 (1927). ⟨6⟩ Goldschmidt, *Ber.* **17,** 216 (1884). ⟨7⟩ Green, Rowe, *J. Chem. Soc.* **111,** 617 (1917). ⟨8⟩ Zincke, *Ber.* **16,** 1563 (1883). ⟨9⟩ Zincke, Bindewald, *Ber.* **17,** 3030 (1884). ⟨10⟩ Bamberger, *Ber.* **30,** 515 (1897).
⟨11⟩ Thiele, Barlow, *Ann.* **302,** 330 (1898). ⟨12⟩ Fieser, Fieser, *J. Am. Chem. Soc.* **61,** 602 (1939).

1:9065 FURIL (2,2′-Bifuroyl) $C_{10}H_6O_4$ **Beil. XIX-166**

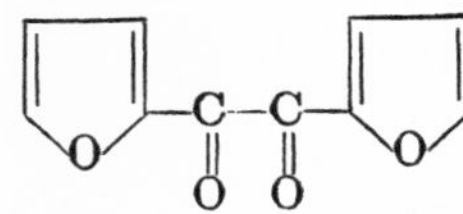

M.P. 165°

Yel. ndls. (from C_6H_6) — Alm. insol. aq., dif. sol. cold alc. or ether; very eas. sol. $CHCl_3$. [For prepn. from furoin (1:1565) in 63% yield by oxidn. with $CuSO_4$ and pyridine see ⟨1⟩; in 90% yield using nitrobenzene and alc. $NaOC_2H_5$ ⟨2⟩.]

C̄ shaken 24 hrs. with 1/5 wt. solid NaOH in dry ether gave 88% dark powd. addn. prod. ($C_{10}H_6O_4.NaOH$) which upon acidifn. and ether extn. yielded white ndls. furilic ac. ⟨3⟩ [Beil. XIX-299].

Ⓓ **α-Furildioxime:** C̄, htd. on aq. bath with alc. and excess $NH_2OH.HCl$, poured into water, recrystd. from hot aq. (decolorizing carbon) yields monohydrate, melting 90–100°, solidifying and remelting 166° ⟨4⟩. Htg. anhyd. α-dioxime with abs. alc. for 5 hrs. in s.t. at 150–160° converts to β isomer, m.p. 188–190° ⟨4⟩. [α-Furil*mono*oxime: m.p. 106°; β-furil*mono*oxime, m.p. 97–98° ⟨4⟩.]

Ⓓ **Furil (bis)phenylhydrazone** (furil phenylosazone): C̄, htd. with two moles phenylhydrazine in 4 vols. alc. (contg. a few drops AcOH) in a s.t. at 100° for 5 hrs., pptd. with aq., yel. cryst. (from lgr.), m.p. 184° ⟨4⟩. [Furil monophenylhydrazone: or.-yel. ndls., m.p. 82–83° ⟨4⟩.]

1:9065 ⟨1⟩ Hartmann, Dickey, *J. Am. Chem. Soc.* **55,** 1228–1229 (1933). ⟨2⟩ Nisbet, *J. Chem. Soc.* **1928,** 3184. ⟨4⟩ Macnair, *Ann.* **258,** 225–229 (1890). ⟨3⟩ Evans, Dehn, *J. Am. Chem. Soc.* **52,** 254 (1930).

1:9069 BENZANTHRONE $C_{17}H_{10}O$ **Beil. VII-518**

M.P. 170°

Pale yel. ndls. (from alc. or xylene) — Soln. in conc. H_2SO_4 bril. orange-red with olive-green fluores.; repptd. unchanged on diln. Volat. with superheated steam [dif. and sepn. from anthraquinone (1:9095) ⟨1⟩] — [For prepn. from anthraquinone see ⟨2⟩.]

C̄ when pure does not give red color on boilg. with Zn dust and alk. [means of detecting anthraquinone (1:9095) in pres. of C̄ ⟨1⟩] — C̄ on htg. with alk. $Na_2S_2O_4$ soln. or with Zn dust + NaOH (or NH_4OH) slowly gives a greenish yel. soln. (contg. dihydrobenzanthrone), readily reoxidizing and pptg. C̄ on exposure to air ⟨3⟩ — C̄ on fusion with alk. gives dibenzanthrone (violanthrone) [Beil. VII_1-(466)].

C̄ on careful oxidn. with CrO_3 in AcOH + dil. H_2SO_4 at 80° ⟨1⟩ ⟨4⟩ or finely divided (repptd. from H_2SO_4) C̄ with CrO_3 + H_2O ⟨5⟩ yields anthraquinone-1-carboxylic ac. [Beil. X-834], pale yel. ndls., m.p. 291–292° ⟨4⟩.

C̄ treated with 3 moles C_6H_5MgBr gave 42% yield 4-phenylbenzanthrone, pr. (from AcOH), m.p. 186° ⟨6⟩.

1:9069 ⟨1⟩ Liebermann, Roka, *Ber.* **41,** 1425 (1908). ⟨2⟩ MacLeod, Allen, *Organic Syntheses* **14,** 4–6 (1934). ⟨3⟩ Bally, Scholl, *Ber.* **44,** 1666 (1911). ⟨4⟩ Perkin, *J. Chem. Soc.* **117,** 706 (1920). ⟨5⟩ Barnett, Cook, Grainger, *Ber.* **57,** 1777 (1924). ⟨6⟩ Allen, Overbaugh, *J. Am. Chem. Soc.* **57,** 742 (1935).

1:9070 QUINHYDRONE

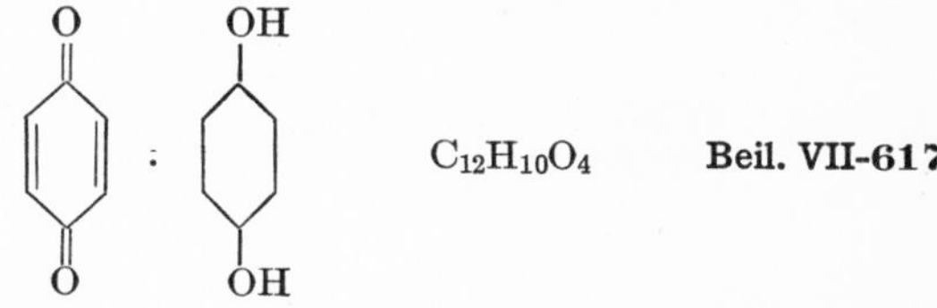

$C_{12}H_{10}O_4$ **Beil. VII-617**

M.P. 171°

Dark green pr. with metallic lustre — red-brown by transmitted light — Subl. with sl. dec. — sol. hot aq., sol. cold aq. with brown-red color — Eas. sol. in alc. or ether with yel. color — Insol. pet. ether, lgr.

Boiling with aq. dec. to quinone (1:9025) and hydroquinone (1:1590) — Oxidn. yields quinone; reduction (e.g., with SO_2), hydroquinone — Reduces ammon. $AgNO_3$.

1:9075 2-METHYLANTHRAQUINONE $C_{15}H_{10}O_2$ **Beil. VII-809**

M.P. 177°

Pale yel. ndls. pract. colorless after sublimation. Very eas. sol. AcOH or C_6H_6; eas. sol. alc., ether.

$\bar{C}$ dis. in conc. H_2SO_4 with pale yel. color ⟨1⟩. [For prepn. (81–90% yield) via ring closure of *o*-(*p*-toluyl)benzoic acid (1:0750) with fumg. H_2SO_4 see ⟨3⟩.]

Ⓓ **2-Methylanthrahydroquinone diacetate:** $\bar{C}$, on boiling with 10–15 pts. Ac_2O, 2 pts. AcONa, and 3 pts. Zn dust, filtering through glass wool, adding aq. to filtrate, gives pale yel. ppt., recryst. from AcOH, lfts. m.p. 217° ⟨2⟩.

1:9075 ⟨1⟩ Fischer, *J. prakt. Chem.* (2) **79,** 560 (1909). ⟨2⟩ Liebermann, *Ber.* **21,** 1172 (1883). ⟨3⟩ Fieser, *Organic Syntheses, Coll. Vol.* I, 345–347 (1932).

1:9080 DIPIPERONALACETONE $C_{19}H_{14}O_5$ Beil. XIX-446

$(CH_2O_2{=}C_6H_3{-}CH{=}CH)_2C{=}O$

M.P. 185°

Yel. ndls. (from C_6H_6 or AcOEt) — Insol. aq., lgr.; dif. sol. alc., eas. sol. $CHCl_3$, acetone — Sol. in conc. H_2SO_4 with deep blue col. changing to violet-red ⟨1⟩ ⟨2⟩; diln. with aq. gives dirty green ppt. ⟨3⟩.

$\bar{C}$ with $NH_2OH.HCl$ + AcONa in alc. oximates 1 ketone group and also *adds* NH_2OH to 1 unsatd. link. giving prod. [Beil. XIX-458], yel. cryst. (from alc.), m.p. 177–179° ⟨4⟩.

Ⓓ **Dipiperonalacetone 2,4-dinitrophenylhydrazone:** red cryst., m.p. 238.2° cor. ⟨5⟩.

1:9080 ⟨1⟩ Haber, *Ber.* **24,** 617 (1891). ⟨2⟩ Faillebin, *Ann. chim.* (10) **4,** 456 (1925). ⟨3⟩ von Kostanecki, Mason, *Ber.* **31,** 727 (1898). ⟨4⟩ Minunni, Carta-Satta, *Gazz. chim. ital.* **29,** II, 418 (1899). ⟨5⟩ Ferrante, Bloom, *Am. J. Pharm.* **105,** 383 (1933).

1:9082 RETENEQUINONE $C_{18}H_{16}O_2$ Beil. VII-819

(7-Isopropyl-1-methylphenanthraquinone)

M.P. 197°

Or. ndls. from alc.; sl. sol. hot ether or pet. ether; fairly eas. sol. C_6H_6, AcOH; very eas. sol. boilg. CS_2 — $\bar{C}$ sublimes partly undec.

$\bar{C}$ is sol. in hot satd. aq. $NaHSO_3$ soln. only with great difficulty; however, if $\bar{C}$ suspended in hot alc. is treated with satd. aq. $NaHSO_3$ soln. and then diluted with aq. soln. occurs; on acidification $\bar{C}$ is repptd. ⟨4⟩.

$\bar{C}$ is not attacked by CrO_3, but $\bar{C}$ in AcOH on refluxing with 30% H_2O_2 gives 65% yield retenediphenic ac., cryst. from C_6H_6, m.p. 191.0–191.5° cor. ⟨1⟩.

$\bar{C}$ with SO_2 in dil. alc. at 60–70° in s.t. reduces to retenehydroquinone [Beil. VI-1039].

$\bar{C}$ in AcOH treated with *o*-phenylenediamine yields retenequinoxaline [Beil. XXIII-333]; white ndls. pptd. from $CHCl_3$ by alc., m.p. 164° ⟨2⟩.

Ⓟ **Color reaction with alc. KOH:** $\bar{C}$ + dil. alc. KOH gives pale yel. color in cold; on htg. and shaking in air color becomes deep red, but is lost on cooling ⟨7⟩ ⟨8⟩.

Ⓓ **Retenquinone monoxime:** from $\bar{C}$ in alc. + 2 moles $NH_2OH.HCl$ + 1 mole NaOH, allowed to stand 1–2 days at 30–40°; gold.-yel. ndls. from alc., m.p. 128.5° ⟨2⟩; 130–131° cor. ⟨3⟩.

Ⓓ **Retene (mono)phenylhydrazone** (9-benzeneazo-10-hydroxyretene) [Beil. XVI-175]: from $\bar{C}$ in ether + equal wt. phenylhydrazine; ether evapd. and residue htd. 130–140° 1 hr.; or. ndls. from hot lgr. or from C_6H_6 + alc., m.p. 160° ⟨6⟩.

Ⓓ **Retenequinone mono-*p*-nitrophenylhydrazone** (9-*p*-nitrobenzeneazo-10-hydroxy-retene): red pr. from AcOH, m.p. 222–223° ⟨4⟩.

Ⓓ **Retenequinone monosemicarbazone:** yel. ndls. from pyridine, m.p. 200° ⟨5⟩.

1:9082 ⟨1⟩ Adelson, Hasselstrom, Bogert, *J. Am. Chem. Soc.* **58,** 871 (1935). ⟨2⟩ Bamberger, Hooker, *Ann.* **229,** 122–123 (1885). ⟨3⟩ Lux, *Monatsh.* **31,** 942 (1910). ⟨4⟩ Fieser, Young, *J. Am. Chem. Soc.* **53,** 4127–4128 (1931). ⟨5⟩ Heiduschka, Scheller, *Arch. pharm.* **248,** 98 (1910). ⟨6⟩ Bamberger, Grob, *Ber.* **34,** 539 (1901). ⟨7⟩ Ref. 4, page 4126. ⟨8⟩ Ref. 2, pages 119–120.

1:9083 CAMPHORQUINONE $C_{10}H_{14}O_2$ Beil. VII-581

```
                CH3
                 |
H2C-------------C-------------C=O
 |               |              |
 |       CH3—C—CH3              |
 |               |              |
H2C-------------C-------------C=O
                 H
```

M.P. 199°

Yel. ndls. from dil. alc., aq. or from sublimation; compact pr. from slow evapn. of ether soln. — Mod. sol. hot aq.; sol. alc. — Easily volatile with steam — Strongly laevorotatory.

[For prepn. from *d*-camphor (1:5215) in 90–95% yield by boiling in Ac_2O with SeO_2 see ⟨1⟩ ⟨11⟩.]

C̄ treated for 36 hrs. with 5 pts. 30% H_2O_2 ⟨2⟩ or boiled several days in AcOH soln. with 30% H_2O_2 ⟨3⟩ yields camphoric anhydride (1:0860) [60% yield].

For information on prepn. + props. of the 4-stereoisomeric dioximes of C̄ see ⟨5⟩.

C̄ in alc. warmed with 1 mole *o*-phenylenediamine.HCl yields quant. camphorquinoxaline; cryst. from pet. ether, m.p. 77–78° ⟨6⟩; 74° ⟨7⟩.

Ⓓ **Camphorquinone phenylhydrazone-3** [Beil. XV-105]: from C̄ + 1 mole phenylhydrazine ⟨8⟩; pale yel. cryst. from alc. or pet. ether, m.p. 183–190° acc. to rate of htg. [a stereoisomeric (?) lower melting form, m.p. 36° has been obtained also ⟨8⟩].

Ⓓ **Camphorquinone monosemicarbazone:** from C̄ dislvd. in aq. $NaHSO_3$ and treated with 1 mole semicarbazide acetate; pr. from alc., m.p. 236° dec. ⟨9⟩; 228–229° dec. ⟨10⟩ ⟨11⟩. [A second form, yel. pr. from C_6H_6 + pet. ether, m.p. 147° has also been reported ⟨9⟩.]

1:9083 ⟨1⟩ Rupe, Tommasi di Vignato, *Helv. Chim. Acta* **20,** 1081 (1937). ⟨2⟩ Forster, Holmes, *J. Chem. Soc.* **93,** 252 (1908). ⟨3⟩ Holleman, *Rec. trav. chim.* **23,** 171 (1904). ⟨5⟩ Meisenheimer, Theilacker, *Ann.* **493,** 33–56 (1932); *Ann.* **496,** 303 (1932). ⟨6⟩ Singh, Mazumda, *J. Chem. Soc.* **115,** 574 (1919). ⟨7⟩ Heckendorn, *Helv. Chim. Acta* **12,** 51 (1929). ⟨8⟩ Forster, Zimmerli, *J. Chem. Soc.* **99,** 483–487 (1911). ⟨9⟩ Forster, Zimmerli, *J. Chem. Soc.* **97,** 2172–2173 (1910). ⟨10⟩ Asahina, Ishidate, Momose, *Ber.* **67,** 1433 (1934).
⟨11⟩ Evans, Ridgion, Simonsen, *J. Chem. Soc.* **1934,** 157.

1:9084 1-HYDROXYANTHRAQUINONE $C_{14}H_8O_3$ Beil. VIII-338

(Structure: anthraquinone with C=O groups and OH at position 1; labels: O, OH, C, C, O)

M.P. 200° ⟨1⟩ (193°) ⟨4⟩

Orange-red ndls. from alc.; eas. sol. ether, C_6H_6 — Somewhat volatile with steam. [For prepn. in 95% yield from 1-aminoanthraquinone see ⟨4⟩.]

C̄ is insol. cold NH_4OH but completely sol. hot; does not dissolve readily in 10% aq. NaOH [dif. from 2-hydroxyanthraquinone (1:9110) ⟨1⟩], but sol. in KOH.

C̄ does *not* decompose hot aq. susp. of $BaCO_3$ [dif. from 2-hydroxyanthraquinone (1:9110)].

Ⓓ **1-Acetoxyanthraquinone:** from C̄ on protracted boilg. (6 hrs.) with Ac_2O ⟨3⟩; yel. ndls. from alc., m.p. 176–179° ⟨2⟩.

1:9084 ⟨1⟩ Blicke, Weinkauff, *J. Am. Chem. Soc.* **54,** 333 (1932). ⟨2⟩ Liebermann, Hagen, *Ber.* **15,** 1804 (1882). ⟨3⟩ Dimroth, Friedemann, Kämmerer, *Ber.* **53,** 482 (1920). ⟨4⟩ Ullmann, Conzetti, *Ber.* **53,** 829 (1920).

1:9085 1,4-DIHYDROXYANTHRAQUINONE $C_{14}H_8O_4$ Beil. VIII-450

(Quinizarin)

M.P. 200–202° cor. (**195°**)

Red cryst. from AcOH, toluene, alc. + pet. ether — Subl. in ndls. with partial dec. ⟨1⟩ — Sol. in 12–13 pts. boilg. AcOH; sol. in ether with brown-red color and greenish-yel. fluorescence.

[For prepn. in 68–74% yield from *p*-chlorophenol, phthalic anhyd. + H_3BO_3 + H_2SO_4 see ⟨2⟩.]

C̄ is sol. in conc. H_2SO_4 with violet-red color and greenish-yel. fluorescence.

C̄ is sol. in alk. with violet-blue color, but is repptd. by CO_2.

C̄ is insol. in hot 10% Na_2CO_3 soln. [dif. and sepn. from 1,2,4-trihydroxyanthraquinone (purpurin)].

C̄ is reduced by hot alk. $Na_2S_2O_4$ or Zn dust + NaOH to leucoquinizarin, reoxidized by air to original C̄. — C̄ gives no oxime but with alk. NH_2OH yields 1,4-dihydroxy-2-aminoanthraquinone, m.p. 313–314° ⟨3⟩.

Ⓓ **1,4-Diacetoxyanthraquinone:** from C̄ boiled 15 min. with Ac_2O + a few drops conc. H_2SO_4; occurs in two polymorphic forms: A, m.p. 207–208°; B, m.p. 200–201° ⟨4⟩. [A forms small six-sided yel. pr. from quickly chilled solns. in hot pyridine, yel. pl. from Ac_2O, pale yel. ndls. from alc. all melting 207–208°. B forms yel. ndls. or fine rods, m.p. 200–201°. B was converted to A by recrystn. from pyridine, Ac_2O or alc., but hot solns. of A in Ac_2O + a few drops H_2SO_4 always deposited B only ⟨4⟩.]

1:9085 ⟨1⟩ Brass, Heide, *Ber.* **57,** 113 (1924). ⟨2⟩ Bigelow, Reynolds, *Organic Syntheses, Coll. Vol.* I, 464–465 (1932). ⟨3⟩ Marschalk, *Bull. soc. chim.* (5) **4,** 632 (1937). ⟨4⟩ Green, *J. Chem. Soc.* **1926,** 1435.

1:9086 PHENANTHRAQUINONE $C_{14}H_8O_2$ Beil. VII-796

M.P. 208° (**202°**)

Orange ndls. or pdr.; insol. aq.; spar. sol. alc., C_6H_6, AcOEt; sol. ether, hot AcOH.

Sublimes in pract. odorless orange tbls. — Dif. sol. hot aq., but easily sol. in warm 40% (satd.) aq. $NaHSO_3$ soln. [dif. from anthraquinone (1:9095)], and repptd. on acidification *in cold.*

C̄ dis. in cold conc. H_2SO_4 with green color — C̄ in 7 pts. Ac_2O + 8.5 pts. pyridine stood in open flask 5–7 days *in dark* turns deep blue and ppts. dark blue cryst.; for structure see ⟨14⟩.

C̄ on oxidn. with CrO_3 + H_2SO_4 (T 1.72) yields diphenic ac. (1:0870) — C̄ (5.5 g.) in AcOH + 30% H_2O_2 (10 ml.) boiled for a day gives colorless liq., evapd., residue dislvd. in Na_2CO_3, filtered, acidified yields diphenic ac. (1:0870) ⟨1⟩.

C̄ treated with soln. of $SbCl_5$ in CCl_4 (1:4 by vol.) gives deep red color [dif. from anthraquinone (1:9095)] ⟨2⟩. [For similar result using $SbCl_3$ in $CHCl_3$ see ⟨3⟩.] — C̄ in warm soln. in AcOH treated with an alc. soln. of *o*-phenylenediamine yields immed. ppt. of phenanthrophenazine (phenanthrazine) [Beil. XXIII-326]; pale yel. ndls., m.p. 217° ⟨4⟩; 219–220° ⟨5⟩.

Ⓟ **Color effect on reduction + oxidation:** Boil together in a tt. for half a minute 5 ml. 5% aq. NaOH, 0.01 g. finely powdered C̄, and 0.2 g. Zn dust. Filter quickly while hot through a fluted filter. With phenanthraquinone the filtrate is pure intense green (also seen to advantage on edges of filter) and when vigorously shaken absorbs oxygen from the air becoming yellowish ⟨6⟩.

Ⓓ **Phenanthraquinone monoxime:** from C̄ + $NH_2OH.HCl$ in alc. + $CHCl_3$ on boilg. 1 hr. ⟨7⟩; greenish yel. lfts. from alc. or orange lfts. from C_6H_6; m.p. 158° ⟨8⟩. [This monoxime on hydrolysis with conc. HCl in presence of formalin gives 92% yield pure phenanthraquinone ⟨9⟩; use of oxime in sepn. of C̄ from anthraquinone ⟨10⟩.]

Ⓓ **Phenanthraquinone (mono)phenylhydrazone** (10-benzeneazophenanthrol-9) [Beil. XVI-174]: from C̄ in AcOH on warm. with aq. phenylhydrazine.HCl (69% yield); dark red lfts. or ndls. from alc. or AcOH, m.p. 164–165° ⟨11⟩.

Ⓓ **Phenanthraquinone (mono)-*p*-nitrophenylhydrazone** (10-*p*-nitrobenzeneazophenanthrol-9) [Beil. XVI-174]: from C̄ on warming with *p*-nitrophenylhydrazine in AcOH; red ndls. from xylene; m.p. 245° ⟨12⟩.

Ⓓ **Phenanthraquinone mono(?)-2,4-dinitrophenylhydrazone:** dark red cryst.; m.p. 312–313° dec. ⟨13⟩ [cf. T 1.14].

1:9086 ⟨1⟩ Holleman, *Rec. trav. chim.* **23,** 171–172 (1904). ⟨2⟩ Hilpert, Wolf, *Ber.* **46,** 2217 (1913). ⟨3⟩ Delaby, Sabetay, Janot, *Compt. rend.* **198,** 276–278 (1934). ⟨4⟩ Hinsberg, *Ann.* **237,** 340 (1887). ⟨5⟩ Willgerodt, Albert, *J. prakt. Chem.* (2) **84,** 386 (1911). ⟨6⟩ Mulliken, "Method" I, 216 (1904). ⟨9⟩ Tseng, Hu, Chu, *J. Chinese Chem. Soc.* **2,** 47–56 (1934). ⟨10⟩ Il'inskii, Roshal, *Chem. Abs.* **32,** 5336 (1938); *Cent.* **1938,** II, 901.

⟨11⟩ von Auwers, *Ann.* **378,** 214 (1910). ⟨12⟩ Hyde, *Ber.* **32,** 1815 (1899). ⟨13⟩ Campbell, *Analyst* **61,** 393 (1936). ⟨14⟩ Diels, Kassehart, *Ann.* **536,** 78–88 (1938).

1:9087 FLUORENONE-4-CARBOXYLIC ACID $C_{14}H_8O_3$ Beil. X-774

(Diphenyleneketonecarboxylic acid-4)

CO

HOOC

M.P. 227° cor. **Neut. Eq. 224**

Yellow ndls. from alc.; insol. aq., abundantly sol. alc., fairly sol. ether — Sol. in conc. H_2SO_4 with red color.

[For prepn. in 86% yield by htg. diphenic ac. (1:0870) with conc. H_2SO_4 at 140° see ⟨1⟩.]

C̄ on htg. at 360° loses CO_2 and gives fluorenone (1:9014) ⟨2⟩ — C̄ htd. with 1 mole PCl_5 ⟨3⟩ or with $SOCl_2$ (100% yield) ⟨4⟩ gives fluorenone-4-carboxylic ac. chloride, yel. cryst. from lgr.; yel. ndls. from C_6H_6, m.p. 128°. [This ac. chloride in dry C_6H_6 treated with NH_3 gas yields fluorenone-4-carboxylic acid amide; yel. ndls. contg. ½ mole EtOH from alc., m.p. 225° ⟨5⟩; 230° cor. ⟨6⟩.]

C̄, in MeOH htd. with dry HCl ⟨3⟩, or refluxed with a little conc. H_2SO_4 ⟨7⟩ yields methyl fluorenone-4-carboxylate, m.p. 132° ⟨3⟩; 139° ⟨7⟩ — C̄ in EtOH treated with dry HCl ⟨3⟩ or refluxed with a little conc. H_2SO_4 ⟨7⟩ yields ethyl fluorenone-4-carboxylate, m.p. 102–103°.

Ⓓ **Fluorenone-4-carboxylic acid oxime:** from Na salt of C̄ boiled with $NH_2OH.HCl$ in alc.; m.p. 263° ⟨3⟩.

Ⓓ **Fluorenone-4-carboxylic acid phenylhydrazone:** from aq. soln. of salt of C̄ + aq. phenylhydrazine.HCl in cold; yel. ndls. from alc., m.p. 205° ⟨3⟩.

1:9087 ⟨1⟩ Moore, Huntress, *J. Am. Chem. Soc.* **49**, 1329–1330 (1927). ⟨2⟩ Huntress, Hershberg, Cliff, *J. Am. Chem. Soc.* **53**, 2723 (1931). ⟨3⟩ Graebe, Aubin, *Ann.* **247**, 278–282 (1888). ⟨4⟩ Götz, *Monatsh.* **23**, 32 (1902). ⟨5⟩ Wegerhoff, *Ann.* **252**, 30 (1889). ⟨6⟩ Graebe, Schestakow, *Ann.* **284**, 311 (1895). ⟨7⟩ Underwood, Kochmann, *J. Am. Chem. Soc.* **46**, 2074 (1924).

1:9090 ACENAPHTHENEQUINONE

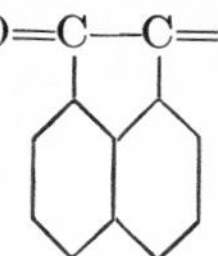

$C_{12}H_6O_2$ **Beil. VII-744**

M.P. 261° cor.

Yel. ndls. — Sl. sol. AcOH, less so in alc.; sol. hot C_6H_6, toluene — Sol. in warm 40% $NaHSO_3$ soln. [dif. from anthraquinone (1:9095)] and pptd. by acidif. in cold.

C̄, dislvd. in AcOH, refluxed 3 hrs. with *o*-phenylenediamine.HCl, gives on addn. of aq., α,α-naphthaquinoxaline [Beil. XXIII-313]; white ndls., 234° ⟨1⟩.

Ⓓ **Acenaphthenequinone dioxime:** from C̄ + 2 moles $NH_2OH.HCl$ + equiv. Na_2CO_3 in warm alc.; cryst. from alc., m.p. 222° dec. ⟨2⟩ [monoxime: pr. from dil. alc., m.p. 230° ⟨3⟩].

Ⓓ **Acenaphthenone** (**mono**)**phenylhydrazone** [Beil. XV-172]: from C̄ + equiv. phenylhydrazine on warming in alc. and evapg. ⟨2⟩ or from C̄ + phenylhydrazine.HCl on warmg. in AcOH ⟨4⟩; orange-red ndls. from alc. or acetone; m.p. 179°.

Ⓓ **Acenaphthenone** (**bis**)**-phenylhydrazone** [Beil. XV-172]: from C̄ with excess phenylhydrazine on warmg. ½ hr. at 130–140°, extg. with dil. HCl, and recrystg. from alc. or AcOH; dark yel. ndls., m.p. 219° ⟨2⟩.

Ⓓ **Acenaphthenone** (**mono**)**semicarbazone:** cryst. from AcOH or C_6H_6; m.p. 192–193° ⟨3⟩.

Ⓓ **Acenaphthenone** (**bis**)**-semicarbazone:** pr. or lfts. from alc. or AcOH; m.p. 271° ⟨3⟩.

1:9090 ⟨1⟩ Ampola, Recchi, *Atti accad. Lincei* (5) **8**, 209–218 (1899); *Cent.* **1899**, II, 338. ⟨2⟩ Graebe, Gfeller, *Ann.* **276**, 10 (1893). ⟨3⟩ Francesconi, Pirazzoli, *Gazz. chim. ital.* **33**, I, 46–47 (1903). ⟨4⟩ von Auwers, *Ann.* **378**, 251–252 (1910).

1:9095 ANTHRAQUINONE

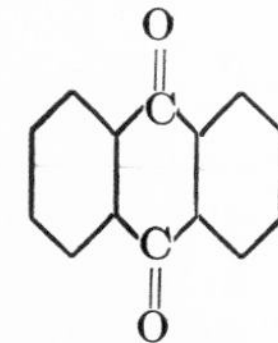

$C_{14}H_8O_2$ **Beil. VII-780**

M.P. 275° (**285°** cor. ⟨1⟩) **B.P. 376.8°** cor. ⟨1⟩

Subl. in yel. ndls. — Sol. in 44 pts. hot alc., very dif. sol. cold alc., ether, C_6H_6 — Unattacked by boiling NaOH or oxid. agts. — Can be recrystd. from 6 parts hot nitrobenzene — Sol. hot C_6H_6, toluene, nitrobenzene, aniline.

$\bar{C}$ is insol. in warm 40% $NaHSO_3$ soln. [dif. from phenanthraquinone (1:9086) and acenaphthenequinone (1:9090)].

$\bar{C}$ is not reduced by SO_2; gives no phenylhydrazone and only a monoxime (from $\bar{C}$ + $NH_2OH.HCl$ in alc. heated in s.t. at 180°; pale yel. ndls., m.p. 224° dec.; rapid htg. ⟨2⟩).

Ⓟ **Oxanthranol reaction:** Boil together in a tt. for a half a minute, a mixt. of 5 ml. 5% aq. NaOH, 0.01 g. $\bar{C}$, and 0.2 g. Zn dust. Filter quickly while hot through a fluted filter. Anthraquinone gives deep red (OR) colored filtrate, which on shaking in the air absorbs oxygen and rapidly decolorizes with ppt. of anthraquinone ⟨3⟩. [For application to quant. detn. see ⟨4⟩.]

Ⓓ **Anthrahydroquinone diacetate:** from $\bar{C}$ on boiling with 10–15 pts. Ac_2O, 2 pts. AcONa, and 2 pts. Zn dust, filtering hot through glass wool, and adding aq.; colorless ndls. from AcOH, m.p. 260° ⟨5⟩.

1:9095 ⟨1⟩ Timmermans, Burriel, *Chimie & Industrie, Spec. No.* **1931,** 196–197. ⟨2⟩ Goldschmidt, *Ber.* **16,** 2179 (1883). ⟨3⟩ Mulliken, " Method " I, 216 (1904). ⟨4⟩ Nelson, Senseman, *Ind. Eng. Chem.* **14,** 956–957 (1922). ⟨5⟩ Liebermann, *Ber.* **21,** 1172 (1888).

1:9100 ANTHRARUFIN (1,5-Dihydroxyanthraquinone) $C_{14}H_8O_4$ **Beil. VIII-453**

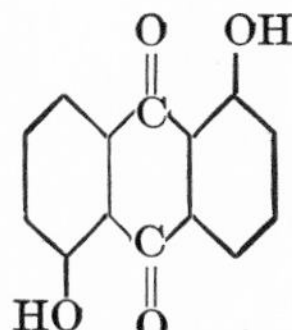

M.P. 280°

Subl. easily in pale yel. toothed lfts. — Alm. insol. aq., NH_4OH, Na_2CO_3 or $Ba(OH)_2$; eas. sol. dil. KOH with violet-red color — Dif. sol. alc., AcOH, sl. sol. ether, C_6H_6.

Sol. in conc. H_2SO_4 with intense red color and fluorescence, distinguishable even at diln. of $1:10^7$.

Ⓓ **Anthrarufin diacetate:** Although the other dihydroxyanthraquinones are converted to acetates by refluxing with Ac_2O, anthrarufin requires htg. at 200° in sealed tube. Prod. consists of pale yel. ndls. insol. in dil. KOH and recrystd. from AcOH, m.p. 245° dec. ⟨1⟩.

1:9100 ⟨1⟩ Shunck, Römer, *Ber.* **11,** 1178 (1878).

1:9105 ALIZARIN (1,2-Dihydroxyanthraquinone) $C_{14}H_8O_4$ **Beil. VIII-439**

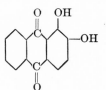

M.P. 290° cor.

Ocher-yel. powder or or. red ndls. (from alc. or by subl.) — Subl. above 110° [dif. from 1,2,6-trihydroxyanthraquinone, i.e., flavopurpurin: and 1,2,7-trihydroxyanthraquinone, i.e., anthrapurpurin, which sublime beginning at 160° and 170° respectively] ⟨2⟩.

Comml. $\bar{C}$ always conts. anthraquinone (1:9095), 1-hydroxyanthraquinone (1:9084), and isopurpurin; for purifn. from these see ⟨3⟩.

Dif. sol. aq., alc., ether — Sol. in very dil. NaOH with red-violet color. [More concd. solns. intensify color but hue is same] — Alk. soln. pptd. by CO_2. [Dif. from 1,2,7-trihydroxyanthraquinone (isopurpurin).]

Ⓓ **Alizarin diacetate:** $\bar{C}$ + Ac_2O + H_2SO_4 in cold rapidly give diacetate, pptd. on diln., recrystd. from alc., m.p. 182° ⟨1⟩.

1:9105 ⟨1⟩ Herzig, Klimosch, *Monatsh.* **30,** 535 (1909). ⟨2⟩ Shunck, Römer, *Ber.* **13,** 42 (1880). ⟨3⟩ Böeseken, *Rec. trav. chim.* **41,** 782 (1921).

1:9110 2-HYDROXYANTHRAQUINONE $C_{14}H_8O_3$ Beil. VIII-343

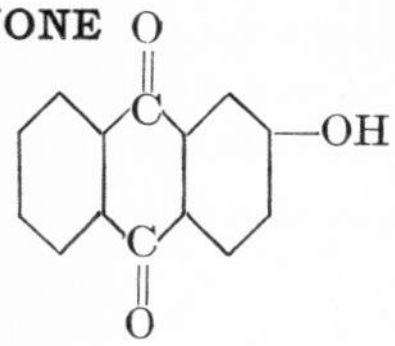

M.P. 305°

Yel. ndls. or pl. (from alc.), yel. ndls. (from AcOH) — Insol. cold aq., sol. alc., ether — Sol. in conc. H_2SO_4 yielding red.-br. soln. — Sol. in alk. or NH_4OH to red.-yel. solns. — Dec. boilg. aq. susp. of $BaCO_3$ forming sol. $Ba\bar{A}_2$ [dif. from 1-hydroxyanthraquinone (1:9084)] — $K\bar{A}$, sol. alc. [sepn. from alizarin (1:9105)].

For prepn. in 100% yield from 2-aminoanthraquinone + HNO_2 see ⟨2⟩.

Warm. with fumg. HNO_3 oxid. to phthalic ac. (1:0820) — Distn. with Zn dust yields anthracene (1:7285) — Does not react with $SOCl_2$ ⟨1⟩ — $\bar{C}$, warm. with excess Al pdr., in 10 pts. 50% alc. + 9 pts. conc. NH_4OH for 2 hrs., filtd., neutd. with HCl, gives good yield 2-hydroxyanthracene (2-anthrol) [Beil. VI-702] ⟨3⟩ — Same prod. also obtd. in 90% yield by redn. of $\bar{C}$ with Al/Hg couple ⟨4⟩.

$\bar{C}$, susp. in 10 pts. pyridine treated with Br_2, stood overnight, gives red cryst. ppt., decomp. by HCl yielding 90% yel. ppt. of 1,3-dibromo-2-hydroxyanthraquinone, cryst. (from xylene), m.p. 214–215° ⟨5⟩.

Ⓓ **2-Methoxyanthraquinone:** from $\bar{C}$ by warm. with 10% NaOH + $(CH_3)_2SO_4$, yel. ndls. (from alc.), m.p. 195–196° ⟨6⟩ ⟨7⟩.

Ⓓ **2-Acetoxyanthraquinone:** from $\bar{C}$, boiled 10 min. with 10 pts. Ac_2O, cooled, cryst. (from alc. or pyridine), m.p. 159–160° ⟨8⟩ ⟨9⟩.

Ⓓ **2-Benzoxyanthraquinone:** by htg. $\bar{C}$ with 10 pts. BzOH, cryst. (from AcOH), m.p. 202–204° ⟨10⟩.

1:9110 ⟨1⟩ Green, *J. Chem. Soc.* **1926,** 2199. ⟨2⟩ Perkin, Whattam, *J. Chem. Soc.* **121,** 289 (1922). ⟨3⟩ Perkin, Whattam, *J. Chem. Soc.* **121,** 298 (1922). ⟨4⟩ Hall, Perkin, *J. Chem. Soc.* **123,** 2035 (1923). ⟨5⟩ Barnett, Cook, *J. Chem. Soc.* **121,** 1389–1390 (1922). ⟨6⟩ Graebe, Bernhard, *Ann.* **349,** 222 (1906). ⟨7⟩ Benesch, *Monatsh.* **32,** 449 (1911). ⟨8⟩ Dimroth, Friedemann, Kämmerer, *Ber.* **53,** 482 (1920). ⟨9⟩ Green, *J. Chem. Soc.* **1926,** 2203. ⟨10⟩ D.R.P. 297,261; *Cent.* **1917,** I, 834.

1:9115 ANTHRAGALLOL (1,2,3-Trihydroxyanthraquinone) $C_{14}H_8O_5$ **Beil. VIII-505**

M.P. 313-314° dec.

Fine br.-or. ndls. — Subl. abt. 290° — Scarcely sol. aq., $CHCl_3$, CS_2; sol. alc., ether, AcOH — Sol. in conc. H_2SO_4 with br.-red color, pptd. unchanged on diln. — Sol. in alk. formg. green soln. changing to brown in air — Sol. in NH_4OH yielding dirty green soln. becoming blue on stdg. or htg.

For purifn. of comml. $\bar{C}$, recryst. from nitrobenzene, conv. to triacetyl deriv. with Ac_2O + few drops H_2SO_4, purify prod. by recrystn. from AcOH and hydrolyze by warmg. with 30 pts. 5% alc. HCl from which $\bar{C}$ seps. in pure cond. ⟨1⟩.

Ⓓ **1,2,3-Triacetoxyanthraquinone:** from $\bar{C}$ + Ac_2O, lemon yel. ndls. (cryst. from alc. or AcOH contg. Ac_2O), m.p. 181–182° ⟨2⟩, cryst. (from pyridine), m.p. 188–189° ⟨3⟩.

Ⓓ **1,2,3-Tribenzoxyanthraquinone:** from dibenzoylanthragallol ⟨4⟩, dislvd. in pyridine, and treated with BzCl; recrystd. from C_6H_6-alc., pale yel. pr., m.p. 213–215° ⟨4⟩.

Ⓓ **2,3-Di-*p*-toluenesulfonylanthragallol:** $\bar{C}$, in 10 pts. pyridine at 0° stirred with 2 pts. *p*-toluenesulfonyl chloride ½ hr., then ½ hr. at 20°; addn. of alc. ppts. prod., recryst. (from pyridine) in yel. pl., m.p. 196–198° ⟨5⟩.

Ⓓ **2,3-Thionylanthragallol:** $\bar{C}$ boiled with 20 pts. $SOCl_2$ suddenly forms green soln. after 1½ hrs.; after boilg. 5 more hrs. soln. was concd. to 3/8 vol. and on stdg. (12 hrs.) pptd. green-yel. rods, m.p. 218–220° with prelim. sintg. ⟨3⟩.

Ⓓ **2,3-Diacetoxy-1-hydroxyanthraquinone:** from 2,3-thionylanthragallol by boilg. 10 min. with 30 pts. Ac_2O, pouring into ice-water, recrystg. (from acetone), m.p. 223–224° ⟨3⟩; [for direct prepn. from $\bar{C}$ with Ac_2O or Ac_2O + pyridine, cryst. (from AcOH), m.p. 214°, see ⟨1⟩].

1:9115 ⟨1⟩ Dimroth, *Ann.* **446,** 110–111 (1926). ⟨2⟩ Perkin, Hummel, *J. Chem. Soc.* **63,** 1170 (1893). ⟨3⟩ Green, *J. Chem. Soc.* **1926,** 2202–2203. ⟨4⟩ Cross, Perkin, *J. Chem. Soc.* **1930,** 302–303. ⟨5⟩ Perkin, Story, *J. Chem. Soc.* **1929,** 1417.

ORDER I: SUBORDER II: COLORED COMPOUNDS

Division B, Liquids

1:9500 BIACETYL $CH_3.CO.CO.CH_3$ $C_4H_6O_2$ **Beil. I-769**
(Dimethylglyoxal; diacetyl)

F.P. = −2.4° ⟨1⟩ B.P. 88° D_4^{20} **= 0.975** n_D^{20} **= 1.3927**

Yel.-green liq. with odor like quinone; vapor has color of chlorine. Sol. in 4 pts. aq. at ord. temp.; misc. with alc., ether — For study of prepn. see ⟨1⟩.

With 2 moles H_3PO_4 yields cryst. addn. prod. ($C_4H_6O_2.2H_3PO_4$), decompd. by water. [Useful in purifn. ⟨1⟩.] [Excess H_3PO_4 yields liq. prods.!] — Readily adds $NaHSO_3$.

$\bar{C}$ stood with conc. HCl at 0° several days yields ppt. of a *trimer* $(C_4H_6O_2)_3$, white cryst. (from boilg. aq.), m.p. 105° ⟨2⟩ which yields an acetyl deriv., m.p. 93° ⟨2⟩, a phenylurethane, m.p. 86° ⟨2⟩, an oxime, m.p. 174–175° cor. ⟨2⟩, a *p*-nitrophenylhydrazone, m.p. 200° cor. ⟨2⟩ and a semicarbazone, m.p. 238° cor. ⟨2⟩.

Ⓓ **Biacetyldioxime** (dimethylglyoxime): from $\bar{C}$ (1 mole) + $NH_2OH.HCl$ (2 moles) + Na_2CO_3 (1 mole) in aq. soln.; cryst. (from dil. alc.), m.p. 234–235° subl. ⟨3⟩. [The sublimed prod. has been reported, m.p. 245–246° cor. ⟨4⟩.] [Biacetylmonoxime, not usually prepd. directly, but sometimes obtd. by partial hydrol. of dioxime, cryst. (from aq. or $CHCl_3$), m.p. 74°.]

Ⓓ **Biacetyl bis-phenylhydrazone** ("biacetyl phenylosazone") [Beil. XV-159]: from $\bar{C}$ + excess phenylhydrazine acetate in aq. soln. at 100°; yel. cryst. (from AcOH or C_6H_6), m.p. 243° ⟨5⟩. [Biacetyl monophenylhydrazone forms yel. ndls. (from dil. alc. or dil. AcOH), m.p. 134°.]

Ⓓ **Biacetyl mono-*p*-nitrophenylhydrazone:** from aq. soln. of $\bar{C}$ (1 mole) + dil. aq. soln. of *p*-nitrophenylhydrazine.HCl (1 mole); or.-yel. ndls., m.p. 230° ⟨6⟩.

Ⓓ **Biacetyl bis-2,4-dinitrophenylhydrazone:** from $\bar{C}$ + 2,4-dinitrophenylhydrazine HCl; red-or. cryst. from nitrobenzene, m.p. 314–315° cor. ⟨9⟩ [cf. T 1.14].

Ⓓ **Biacetyl bis-semicarbazone:** from $\bar{C}$ + semicarbazide.HCl in dil. alc. + AcONa; cryst. (from AcOH), m.p. 278–279° ⟨7⟩. [Biacetyl monosemicarbazone, cryst. (from aq. or AcOH), m.p. 235° cor. ⟨8⟩ ⟨4⟩.]

1:9500 ⟨1⟩ Olivier, *Bull. soc. chim.* (4) **51,** 100, 105 (1932). ⟨2⟩ Diels, Jost, *Ber.* **35,** 3293–3297 (1902). ⟨3⟩ Fittig, Daimler, Keller, *Ann.* **249,** 204 (1888). ⟨4⟩ Biltz, *Ber.* **41,** 1881–1882 (1908). ⟨5⟩ von Pechmann, *Ber.* **21,** 1413 (1888). ⟨6⟩ Bamberger, Djierdjian, *Ber.* **33,** 541 (Note) (1900). ⟨7⟩ Posner, *Ber.* **34,** 3977 (1901). ⟨8⟩ Diels, *Ber.* **35,** 348–349 (1902). ⟨9⟩ Strain, *J. Am. Chem. Soc.* **57,** 760 (1935).

CHAPTER XIII

TABLES OF MELTING POINTS OF SERIES OF DERIVATIVES OF COMPOUNDS OF ORDER I

A. *Carbonyl compounds*
1. Oximes
2. Phenylhydrazones
3. *p*-Nitrophenylhydrazones
4. 2,4-Dinitrophenylhydrazones
5. Semicarbazones

B. *Phenolic compounds*
1. Esters
   a. Acetates
   b. Benzoates
   c. *p*-Nitrobenzoates
   d. 3,5-Dinitrobenzoates
   e. Benzenesulfonates
   f. *p*-Toluenesulfonates
2. Ethers
   a. *p*-Nitrobenzyl ethers
   b. 2,4-Dinitrophenyl ethers
   c. Aryloxyacetic acids
3. *N*-substituted carbamates
   a. *N*-Phenylcarbamates
   b. *N*-(α-Naphthyl) carbamates
   c. *N,N*-Diphenylcarbamates
   d. *N*-(*p*-Xenyl) carbamates

C. *Alcohols*
1. Esters
   a. *p*-Nitrobenzoates
   b. 3,5-Dinitrobenzoates
   c. Acid phthalates
   d. Acid 3-nitrophthalates
2. *N*-Substituted carbamates
   a. *N*-Phenylcarbamates
   b. *N*-(α-Naphthyl) carbamates
   c. *N*-(*p*-Nitrophenyl) carbamates
   d. *N*-(*p*-Xenyl) carbamates

D. *Acids*
1. Esters
   a. *p*-Nitrobenzyl esters
   b. Phenacyl esters
   c. *p*-Chlorophenacyl esters
   d. *p*-Bromophenacyl esters
   e. *p*-Iodophenacyl esters
   f. *p*-Phenylphenacyl esters
2. Amides or *N*-substituted amides
   a. Amides
   b. Anilides (*N*-phenylamides)
   c. *p*-Toluidides (*N*-*p*-tolylamides)

A. CARBONYL COMPOUNDS

TABLE OF MELTING POINTS OF OXIMES OF CARBONYL COMPOUNDS OF ORDER I

These melting points are arranged in order of increasing magnitude. The values, however, are only approximate and in every instance the more precise information given in the Huntress-Mulliken " Tables " should be consulted. For this reason the location number of the corresponding parent compound is given.

1:0195	Benzaldehyde.....(α form)	35
1:5485	4-Methylcyclohexanone....	38
1:0232	*m*-Methoxybenzaldehyde...	39
1:5175	Di-*n*-undecyl ketone.......	39
1:5134	Ethyl *n*-undecyl ketone....	40
1:0133	Trimethylacetaldehyde.....	41
1:5470	2-Methylcyclohexanone....	43
1:5531	Methyl *n*-nonyl ketone.....	44
1:0179	β-Ethyl-α-methylacrolein...	48
1:0210	*o*-Tolualdehyde...........	48
1:5445	Mesityl oxide......(β form)	48
1:0140	Isovaleraldehyde..........	48.5
1:5535	Butyrophenone............	49
1:0176	*n*-Caproaldehyde..........	51
1:0198	5-Methylfurfural.....(*anti*)	51
1:0155	*n*-Valeraldehyde...........	52
1:5555	Valerophenone............	52
1:5525	Propiophenone............	53
1:0183	Enanthaldehyde..........	54
1:5590	*n*-Hexyl phenyl ketone.....	55
1:5130	Methyl undecyl ketone	56
1:5446	Cyclopentanone...........	56
1:0205	Salicylaldehyde...........	57
1:5527	*m*-Methylacetophenone.....	57

1:0242	*o*-Ethoxybenzaldehyde.....	58
1:5515	Acetophenone.............	58
1:5520	*l*-Menthone..............	59
1:5523	Isophorone..............	59 79
1:0192	*n*-Caprylaldehyde.........	60
1:0208	*m*-Tolualdehyde...........	60
1:5528	Isopropyl phenyl ketone....	60 94
1:0234	Cumaldehyde.....(α form)	61
1:5524	*o*-Methylacetophenone.....	61
1:0197	Pelargonaldehyde.........	64
1:0240	*p*-Anisaldehyde....(α form)	64
1:0245	Cinnamaldehyde.....(*anti*)	64
1:0222	*n*-Decylaldehyde..........	69
1:5118	Benzyl methyl ketone......	69
1:5180	α-Hydroxyacetophenone....	70
1:0002	*n*-Undecylaldehyde........	72
1:5540	*d*-Carvone...............	72
1:0285	α-*n*-Amylcinnamaldehyde...	74
1:9500	Biacetyl...........(mono)	74
1:0185	Furfural..........(α form)	75
1:1535	*m*-Hydroxybenzophenone ....(*anti*)	76
1:0017	Lauraldehyde.............	77
1:0298	5-Hydroxymethylfurfural (α?)	77
1:5425	Methyl *ter*-butyl ketone....	77
1:0215	*p*-Tolualdehyde...........	79
1:5523	Isophorone..............	79 59
1:5547	*o*-Methoxyacetophenone....	80 96
1:0003	*n*-Tridecylaldehyde........	80.5
1:1560	*p*-Hydroxybenzophenone...	81 152
1:9000	Furfuralacetophenone......	82
1:0004	*n*-Myristaldehyde.........	83
1:0251	*p*-Ethoxybenzaldehyde.....	83
1:0005	*n*-Pentadecylaldehyde......	86
1:5140	*p*-Methoxyacetophenone....	86
1:5530	*p*-Methylacetophenone.....	87
1:0007	Palmitaldehyde...........	88
1:0012	Stearaldehyde............	89
1:0009	Margaraldehyde...........	89.5
1:0186	Hexahydrobenzaldehyde....	90
1:0185	Furfural..........(β form)	91
1:5465	Cyclohexanone............	91
1:5550	2-Acetyl-*p*-cymene.........	91
1:0235	*o*-Methoxybenzaldehyde....	92
1:0015	Veratraldehyde...........	94
1:5528	Isopropyl phenyl ketone....	94 60
1:0224	Phenoxyacetaldehyde......	95
1:0225	Hydrocinnamaldehyde......	95
1:5547	*o*-Methoxyacetophenone....	96 80
1:9065	Furil........(β-monoxime)	97
1:0261	3,4-Dimethoxybenzaldehyde	98
1:5165	Desoxybenzoin............	98
1:0200	Phenylacetaldehyde........	99
1:5210	Benzoin..........(β oxime)	99
1:1565	Furoin...........(β oxime)	102
1:0030	*p*-Homosalicylaldehyde.....	105
1:0040	2,4-Dimethoxybenzaldehyde	106
1:9065	Furil........(α-monoxime)	106
1:0298	5-Hydroxymethylfurfural ....(β?)	108
1:0010	Piperonal...........(*anti*)	110
1:0025	β-(α-Furyl) acrolein........	110
1:0234	Cumaldehyde......(β form)	112
1:9015	Benzil.......(β-monoxime)	112
1:5145	Benzalacetone............	115
1:5160	Phenyl *p*-tolyl ketone......	115 154
1:5170	*p*-Methoxybenzophenone ....(β form)	115
1:1746	*o*-Hydroxyacetophenone....	116
1:0050	Vanillin.................	117
1:5215	*d*-Camphor..............	118
1:1414	*o*-Hydroxybenzophenone (mixt. of isomers).....	115–120
1:7547	*d*-Fenchone ....(β-oxime)	123
1:1800	Methyl furoylacetate......	124
1:5135	Dibenzyl ketone...........	124
1:1535	*m*-Hydroxybenzophenone ....(*syn*)	126
1:9082	Retenequinone (monoxime)	129
1:5142	*o*-Methoxybenzophenone....	130 145
1:1820	Ethyl furoylacetate	131
1:0195	Benzaldehyde..... (β-oxime)	132
1:0240	*p*-Anisaldehyde ..(β-oxime)	133
1:9007	*p*-Toluquinone..(monoxime)	134
1:9020	Cinnamalacetophenone.....	135
1:5170	*p*-Methoxybenzophenone ....(α-form)	137
1:5495	Acetonylacetone (*bis*-oxime)	137
1:0245	Cinnamaldehyde (*syn*-oxime)	138.5
1:9025	Benzoquinone ......(dioxime) dec. abt.	140
1:5600	Methyl α-naphthyl ketone..	140
1:9015	Benzil.......(α-monoxime)	140
1:1414	*o*-Hydroxybenzophenone ....(*n*-isomer)	141
1:1414	*o*-Hydroxybenzophenone ....(*h*-isomer)	142
1:5150	Benzophenone............	142
1:9024	Dibenzalacetone..........	142
1:1527	*p*-Hydroxyacetophenone....	144
1:5144	Indanone-1..............	144
1:5142	*o*-Methoxybenzophenone....	145 130
1:1700	Acetylacetone...(*bis*-oxime)	149
1:5210	Benzoin.........(α-oxime)	151
1:1560	*p*-Hydroxybenzophenone...	152 81
1:5174	Cinnamalacetone..........	152
1:5160	Phenyl *p*-tolyl ketone......	154 115
1:0036	β-Naphthaldehyde.........	156
1:0073	Protocatechualdehyde......	157
1:9086	Phenanthraquinone .... (monoxime)	158
1:7547	*d*-Fenchone..............	159
1:1565	Furoin............(α form)	160
1:9003	Thymoquinone (monoxime)	160

:9062	β-Naphthoquinone .... (monoxime)	162
:5185	Di-p-tolyl ketone	163
:1480	Dibenzoylmethane .... (monoxime)	165
:7547	d-Fenchone ...... (α-oxime)	165
:9065	Furil .... (α-dioxime)	166
:9021	2-Methylnaphthoquin-one-1,4	167
:1515	2-Aceto-1-naphthol	168
:9062	β-Naphthoquinone (dioxime)	169
:5200	Acenaphthenone	183
:5201	p-Phenylacetophenone	186
:9022	Piperonalacetone	186
1:9065	Furil .... (β-dioxime)	188
1:1443	n-Caproylresorcinol	190
1:0065	2,4-Dihydroxybenzaldehyde	191
1:9014	Fluorenone	192
1:9040	α-Naphthoquinone .. (mono)	198
1:9007	p-Toluquinone .... (dioxime) dec.	220
1:9090	Acenaphthenequinone .... (dioxime)	222
1:9090	Acenaphthenequinone .... (monoxime)	230
1:9500	Biacetyl .... (dioxime)	234
1:9087	Fluorenone-4-carboxylic acid	263

TABLE OF MELTING POINTS OF PHENYLHYDRAZONES OF CARBONYL COMPOUNDS OF ORDER I

These melting points are arranged in order of increasing magnitude. The values, how-ver, are only approximate and in every instance the more precise information given in the untress-Mulliken " Tables " should be consulted. For this reason the location number of he corresponding parent compound is given.

:5520	l-Menthone	53
:5446	Cyclopentanone	55
:0179	β-Ethyl-α-methylacrolein	59
:0200	Phenylacetaldehyde	60
:5523	Isophorone	68
:4096	Isoamyl levulinate	71
:5528	Isopropyl phenyl ketone	73
:3972	n-Butyl levulinate	79
:1565	Furoin	80
:5465	Cyclohexanone	81
:9065	Furil .... (mono)	82
:3907	Isobutyl levulinate	84
:0224	Phenoxyacetaldehyde	86
:5118	Benzyl methyl ketone	86
:3786	n-Propyl levulinate	88
:0208	m-Tolualdehyde	89
:5200	Acenaphthenone	90
:3561	Methyl levulinate	94
:5530	p-Methylacetophenone	96
:0185	Furfural	97
:5185	Di-p-tolyl ketone	100
:0010	Piperonal	102
:3616	Ethyl levulinate	103
:0050	Vanillin	105
:0210	o-Tolualdehyde	105
:5515	Acetophenone	105
:5210	Benzoin .... (β-mono)	106
:0405	Levulinic acid	108
:3666	Isopropyl levulinate	108
:1746	o-Hydroxyacetophenone	109
:5160	Phenyl p-tolyl ketone	109
:5540	d-Carvone	109
:5180	α-Hydroxyacetophenone	112
:0215	p-Tolualdehyde	113
:5547	o-Methoxyacetophenone	114
:5165	Desoxybenzoin	116
1:3308	Ethyl pyruvate	118
1:0240	p-Anisaldehyde	120
1:5495	Acetonylacetone .... (bis)	120
1:0015	Veratraldehyde	121
1:5135	Dibenzyl ketone	121
1:9005	Difurfuralacetone	121
1:5144	Indanone-1	124
1:9050	Vanillalacetone	127
1:0234	Cumaldehyde	129
1:9001	Furfuralacetophenone	131
1:0025	β-(α-Furyl)acrolein	132
1:5170	p-Methoxybenzophenone	132
1:9015	Benzil .... (mono)	134
1:9500	Biacetyl .... (mono)	134
1:1515	2-Aceto-1-naphthol	136
1:5150	Benzophenone	137
1:9062	β-Naphthoquinone ... (mono)	138
1:0298	5-Hydroxymethylfurfural	140
1:0205	Salicylaldehyde	142
1:0278	Phenylglyoxal ..... (β-mono)	142
1:9060	Dicinnamalacetone	142, 166
1:5140	p-Methoxyacetophenone	142
1:1560	p-Hydroxybenzophenone	144
1:5600	Methyl α-naphthyl ketone ...	146
1:0055	m-Hydroxybenzaldehyde	147
1:0198	5-Methylfurfural	147
1:0030	p-Homosalicylaldehyde	149
1:1527	p-Hydroxyacetophenone	151
1:9014	Fluorenone	151
1:0278	Phenylglyoxal .... (bis)	152
1:1414	o-Hydroxybenzophenone	154
1:0195	Benzaldehyde	156
1:5145	Benzalacetone	156
1:9020	Cinnamalacetophenone	156
1:5210	Benzoin .... (α-mono)	158

No.	Compound	M.P.
1:0065	2,4-Dihydroxybenzaldehyde..	159
1:9082	Retenequinone ......(mono)	160
1:9022	Piperonalacetone	163
1:9086	Phenanthraquinone.........	164
1:9060	Dicinnamalacetone.........	{166 142
1:0245	Cinnamaldehyde...........	168
1:0073	Protocatechualdehyde ...(α)	175
1:5153	Methyl β-naphthyl ketone...	176
1:0060	p-Hydroxybenzaldehyde.....	178
1:9090	Acenaphthenequinone (mono)	179
1:5194	Cinnamalacetone...........	18
1:9065	Furil..................(bis)	18
1:1040	Pyruvic acid...............	19
1:9040	α-Naphthoquinone...(mono)	20
1:9087	Fluorenone-4-carboxylic acid	20
1:0036	β-Naphthaldehyde.........	20
1:1625	Triketohydrindene hydrate ....(bis)	20
1:9090	Acenaphthenequinone ..(bis)	21
1:9015	Benzil.............. (bis)	23
1:9500	Biacetyl ....(bis)	24

MELTING POINTS OF *p*-NITROPHENYLHYDRAZONES OF CARBONYL COMPOUNDS OF ORDER I

These are arranged in order of increasing melting points. The latter are approximat values only and in every instance the more precise information given in the Huntress-Mulli ken "Tables" should be consulted. For this reason, the location number of the corre sponding compound is given.

No.	Compound	M.P.
1:0183	Enanthaldehyde...........	73
1:0192	n-Caprylaldehyde..........	80
1:0017	Lauraldehyde..............	90
1:5531	Methyl n-nonyl ketone......	90
1:5490	n-Hexyl methyl ketone......	92
1:0130	n-Butyraldehyde...........	93
1:0005	n-Pentadecylaldehyde.......	94
1:0004	n-Myristaldehyde..........	95
1:0007	Palmitaldehyde............	96
1:5130	Methyl undecyl ketone......	101
1:0012	Stearaldehyde..............	101
1:5410	Isopropyl methyl ketone....	108
1:0270	Aldol....................	109
1:0140	Isovaleraldehyde...........	109
1:0159	Ethoxyacetaldehyde........	113
1:0138	Methoxyacetaldehyde.......	115
1:5415	Methyl n-propyl ketone.....	117
1:0133	Trimethylacetaldehyde......	119
1:0225	Hydrocinnamaldehyde......	122
1:0110	Propionaldehyde...........	124
1:5590	n-Hexyl phenyl ketone......	127
1:0100	Acetaldehyde..............	128
1:5405	Ethyl methyl ketone........	128
1:5485	4-Methylcyclohexanone.....	128
1:0120	Isobutyraldehyde...........	130
1:0198	5-Methylfurfural...........	130
1:5445	Mesityl oxide.............	133
1:5420	Diethyl ketone.............	144
1:5118	Benzyl methyl ketone.......	145
1:5465	Cyclohexanone............	146
1:5400	Acetone..................	148
1:0115	Acrolein.................	150
1:5150	Benzophenone............	154
1:0185	Furfural..................	154
1:0208	m-Tolualdehyde...........	157
1:0240	p-Anisaldehyde............	160
1:5555	Valerophenone............	162
1:5165	Desoxybenzoin............	163
1:5145	Benzalacetone.............	16
1:0232	m-Methoxybenzaldehyde....	171
1:5455	Acetol.........(mono deriv.)	17
1:9024	Dibenzalacetone...........	173
1:0405	Levulinic acid.............	174
1:5540	Carvone..................	174
1:0145	Formaldehyde.............	18
1:5515	Acetophenone.............	184
1:0150	Crotonaldehyde...........	184
1:0298	5-Hydroxymethylfurfural....	184
1:3308	Ethyl pyruvate...........	18
1:0234	Cumaldehyde.............	19
1:0195	Benzaldehyde.............	191
1:9015	Benzil ....(mono deriv.)	192
1:0245	Cinnamaldehyde...........	195
1:5140	p-Methoxyacetophenone.....	195
1:5170	p-Methoxybenzophenone....	198
1:0215	p-Tolualdehyde...........	198
1:0010	Piperonal................	199
1:0235	o-Methoxybenzaldehyde.....	204
1:1040	Pyruvic acid.............	219
1:0055	m-Hydroxybenzaldehyde....	221
1:0210	o-Tolualdehyde	22
1:9082	Retenequinone ....(mono deriv.)	222
1:0050	Vanillin..................	224
1:0205	Salicylaldehyde...........	227
1:0036	β-Naphthaldehyde..........	230
1:5144	Indanone-1...............	234
1:9062	β-Naphthoquinone ....(mono deriv.)	235
1:9086	Phenanthraquinone ....(mono deriv.)	245
1:9040	α-Naphthoquinone ....(mono deriv.)	278
1:9015	Benzil...........(bis deriv.)	29
1:5455	Acetol...........(bis deriv.)	30
1:0278	Phenylglyoxal....(bis deriv.)	31

MELTING POINTS OF 2,4-DINITROPHENYLHYDRAZONES OF CARBONYL COMPOUNDS OF ORDER I

These are arranged in order of increasing melting points. The latter are approximate values only and in every instance the more precise information given in the Huntress-Mulliken " Tables " should be consulted. For this reason, the location number of the corresponding compound is given. Many 2,4-dinitrophenylhydrazones occur in stereoisomeric forms of different melting points and are listed both ways.

For general directions and comments on the preparation of 2,4-dinitrophenylhydrazones see T 1.14 in the Mulliken-Huntress " Manual."

No.	Compound	M.p.
1:4096	Isoamyl levulinate	50
1:3907	Isobutyl levulinate	55
1:1712	Ethyl methylacetoacetate	56
1:5490	*n*-Hexyl methyl ketone	58
1:5531	Methyl *n*-nonyl ketone	63
1:3972	*n*-Butyl levulinate	65
1:5472	Diisobutyl ketone	66 92
1:3786	*n*-Propyl levulinate	67
1:5130	Methyl undecyl ketone	69
1:5431	*sec*-Butyl methyl ketone	71
1:5447	Di-*n*-propyl ketone	75
1:0220	Citronellal	77
1:9045	Dianisalacetone	82
1:4121	*n*-Amyl levulinate	84
1:5433	Diisopropyl ketone	86
1:3666	Isopropyl levulinate	89
1:5460	*n*-Amyl methyl ketone	89
1:5472	Diisobutyl ketone	92 66
1:1710	Ethyl acetoacetate	93
1:0163	α-Ethyl-*n*-butyraldehyde	95 129
1:5430	Isobutyl methyl ketone	95
1:0230	Citral-*b* (neral)	96
1:0155	*n*-Valeraldehyde	98
1:5135	Dibenzyl ketone	100
1:0197	Pelargonaldehyde	100
1:3616	Ethyl levulinate	101
1:0166	Methyl-*n*-propyl-acetaldehyde	103
1:0176	*n*-Caproaldehyde	104
1:0222	*n*-Decylaldehyde	104
1:0002	*n*-Undecylaldehyde	104
1:5435	*n*-Butyl methyl ketone	106
1:0192	*n*-Caprylaldehyde	106
1:0183	Enanthaldehyde	106
1:0017	Lauraldehyde	106
1:0005	*n*-Pentadecylaldehyde	107
1:0230	Citral-*a* (geranial)	109
1:0200	Phenylacetaldehyde	110 121
1:0184	*n*-Butyl-ethyl-acetaldehyde	114 120
1:5405	Ethyl methyl ketone	115
1:0159	Ethoxyacetaldehyde	116
1:5410	Isopropyl methyl ketone	119
1:0184	*n*-Butyl-ethyl-acetaldehyde	120 114
1:0142	α-Methyl-*n*-butyraldehyde	120
1:0200	Phenylacetaldehyde	121 110
1:0130	*n*-Butyraldehyde	122
1:0140	Isobutyraldehyde	123
1:0193	α-Ethyl-β-*n*-propylacrolein	124
1:0138	Methoxyacetaldehyde	124
1:5425	Pinacolone	125
1:5400	Acetone	127
1:5455	Acetol	128
1:0163	α-Ethyl-*n*-butyraldehyde	129 95
1:5425	Pinacolone	131 125
1:5470	2-Methylcyclohexanone	136
1:5550	2-Acetyl-*p*-cymeme	140 160
1:7547	*d*-Fenchone	140
1:5446	Cyclopentanone	142
1:3561	Methyl levulinate	142
1:5415	Methyl *n*-propyl ketone	143
1:5520	*l*-Menthone	145
1:0225	Hydrocinnamaldehyde	149
1:3308	Ethyl pyruvate	155
1:5480	*d,l*-3-Methylcyclohexanone	155
1:0110	Propionaldehyde	155
1:5420	Diethyl ketone	156
1:0100	Acetaldehyde	157 168.5
1:5524	*o*-Methylacetophenone	159
1:5550	2-Acetyl-*p*-cymene	160 140
1:0179	β-Ethyl-α-methylacrolein	160
1:5465	Cyclohexanone	161
1:5528	Isopropyl phenyl ketone	163
1:0285	α-*n*-Amylcinnamaldehyde	164
1:0115	Acrolein	165
1:0145	Formaldehyde	166
1:0070	*d,l*-Glyceraldehyde	166
1:5555	Valerophenone	166
1:5111	*n*-Amyl phenyl ketone	168
1:0100	Acetaldehyde	168.5 157
1:9000	Furfuralacetophenone	169
1:5215	*d*-Camphor	176
1:9003	Thymoquinone (mono-deriv.)	179
1:5170	*p*-Methoxybenzophenone	180
1:9024	Dibenzalacetone	180
1:0298	5-Hydroxymethylfurfural	184
1:9025	Quinone..... (mono-deriv.)	186

1:0120	Isobutyraldehyde	187
1:3201	Methyl pyruvate	187
1:9015	Benzil ...... (mono-deriv.)	187
1:5535	Butyrophenone	189
1:5540	*d*-Carvone	190
1:0150	Crotonaldehyde	190
1:5525	Propiophenone	190
1:0210	*o*-Tolualdehyde	193
1:9060	Dicinnamalacetone	195
1:5160	Phenyl *p*-tolyl ketone	200
1:5445	Mesityl oxide	203
1:5165	Desoxybenzoin	204
1:0405	Levulinic acid	206
1:1700	Acetylacetone	209
1:0133	Trimethylacetaldehyde	209
1:0198	5-Methylfurfural	212
1:0185	Furfural	{213, 230}
1:1565	Furoin	216
1:1040	Pyruvic acid	218
1:5140	*p*-Methoxyacetophenone	{220, 231}
1:9020	Cinnamalacetophenone	220
1:5174	Cinnamalacetone	222
1:5145	Benzalacetone	227
1:9013	Anisalacetone	229
1:5185	Di-*p*-tolyl ketone	229
1:9050	Vanillalacetone	230
1:0185	Furfural	{230, 213}
1:5140	*p*-Methoxyacetophenone	{231, 220}
1:0215	*p*-Tolualdehyde	233
1:5210	*d,l*-Benzoin	{234, 245}
1:5515	Acetophenone	{237, 249}
1:0195	Benzaldehyde	237
1:9080	Dipiperonalacetone	238
1:5150	Benzophenone	238
1:9001	Furfuralacetone	241
1:1560	*p*-Hydroxybenzophenone	242
1:0234	Cumaldehyde	243
1:5155	Benzalacetophenone	244
1:5210	*d,l*-Benzoin	{245, 234}
1:0205	Salicylaldehyde	248
1:5515	Acetophenone	{249, 237}
1:0240	*p*-Anisaldehyde	253
1:0235	*o*-Methoxybenzaldehyde	253
1:0245	Cinnamaldehyde	255
1:5495	Acetonylacetone ..... (bis)	257
1:5144	Indanone-1	258
1:0055	*m*-Hydroxybenzaldehyde	260
1:5530	*p*-Methylacetophenone	260
1:1527	*p*-Hydroxyacetophenone	261
1:5153	Methyl β-naphthyl ketone	262
1:0015	Veratraldehyde	262
1:0010	Piperonal	266
1:9007	*p*-Toluquinone .... (bis)	269
1:0036	β-Naphthaldehyde	270
1:0050	Vanillin	271
1:0073	Protocatechualdehyde	275
1:9040	α-Naphthoquinone .... (mono deriv.)	278
1:0060	*p*-Hydroxybenzaldehyde	280
1:9014	Fluorenone	283
1:0065	β-Resorcylaldehyde	286
1:9500	Biacetyl .... (bis)	314
1:9086	Phenanthraquinone	312
1:5448	*d,l*-Acetoin .... (bis)	318

TABLE OF MELTING POINTS OF SEMICARBAZONES OF CARBONYL COMPOUNDS OF ORDER I

These melting points are arranged in order of increasing magnitude. The values, however, are only approximate and in every instance the more precise information given in the Huntress-Mulliken " Tables " should be consulted. For this reason the location number of the corresponding parent compound is given.

Although the semicarbazones have been more frequently reported than almost any other type of carbonyl derivative, their melting points are somewhat less reproducible than those of other derivatives and are likely to vary considerably according to the rate of heating.

1:1723	Ethyl ethylacetoacetate	80
1:0220	*d*-Citronellal	83
1:0197	Pelargonaldehyde	{84, 100}
1:4121	*n*-Amyl levulinate	84
1:1712	Ethyl methylacetoacetate	86
1:5493	Di-*n*-butyl ketone	90
1:4096	Isoamyl levulinate	91
1:5134	Ethyl *n*-undecyl ketone	92
1:1772	Diethyl acetonedicarboxylate	94
1:5431	*sec*-Butyl methyl ketone	95
1:0130	*n*-Butyraldehyde	{95.5, 106}
1:0163	α-Ethyl-*n*-butyraldehyde	98
1:1718	Methyl ethylacetoacetate	98
1:0192	*n*-Caprylaldehyde	100
1:0197	Pelargonaldehyde	{100, 84}
1:0166	Methyl-*n*-propyl-acetaldehyde	101
1:3972	*n*-Butyl levulinate	102

No.	Compound	M.P.
1:0222	*n*-Decylaldehyde	102
1:0002	*n*-Undecylaldehyde	103
1:0017	Lauraldehyde	104
1:0142	α-Methyl-*n*-butyraldehyde.	104
1:5415	Methyl *n*-propyl ketone	105 112
1:0003	*n*-Tridecylaldehyde	106
1:0130	*n*-Butyraldehyde	106 95.5
1:0176	*n*-Caproaldehyde	106
1:0004	*n*-Myristaldehyde	106.5
1:0005	*n*-Pentadecylaldehyde	106.5
1:0009	Margaraldehyde	107
1:0007	Palmitaldehyde	108
1:0012	Stearaldehyde	108
1:0183	Enanthaldehyde	108
1:3907	Isobutyl levulinate	112
1:5415	Methyl *n*-propyl ketone	112 105
1:5410	Isopropyl methyl ketone	113
1:5133	*n*-Dodecyl methyl ketone	115
1:0285	α-*n*-Amylcinnamaldehyde	118
1:5501	*n*-Heptyl methyl ketone	118
1:5590	*n*-Hexyl phenyl ketone	119
1:5160	Phenyl *p*-tolyl ketone	121
1:5435	*n*-Butyl methyl ketone	121
1:5472	Diisobutyl ketone	121
1:5490	*n*-Hexyl methyl ketone	122
1:5531	Methyl *n*-nonyl ketone	122
1:5552	*n*-Decyl methyl ketone	122
1:5130	Methyl undecyl ketone	123
1:5460	*n*-Amyl methyl ketone	123
1:0120	Isobutyraldehyde	125
1:1738	Ethyl allylacetoacetate	125
1:5135	Dibenzyl ketone	125 145
1:5522	Methyl *n*-octyl ketone	125
1:0225	Hydrocinnamaldehyde	127
1:1710	Ethyl acetoacetate	129
1:3786	*n*-Propyl levulinate	129
1:0140	Isovaleraldehyde	131
1:5111	*n*-Amyl phenyl ketone	132
1:5430	Isobutyl methyl ketone	132
1:5447	Di-*n*-propyl ketone	132
1:5445	Mesityl oxide . . . (β-form)	133
1:5405	Ethyl methyl ketone	135
1:1708	Methyl ethylacetoacetate	138
1:5420	Diethyl ketone	138
1:1800	Methyl furoylacetate	141
1:3666	Isopropyl levulinate	141
1:3561	Methyl levulinate	142
1:5540	*d*-Carvone . . . . (low melt.)	142
1:0224	Phenoxyacetaldehyde	145
1:5135	Dibenzyl ketone	145 125
1:5180	α-Hydroxyacetophenone	146
1:3616	Ethyl levulinate	147
1:5550	2-Acetyl-*p*-cymene	147
1:9083	Camphorquinone . . (mono)	147 230
1:5165	Desoxybenzoin	148
1:5433	Diisopropyl ketone	149 160
1:0193	α-Ethyl-β-*n*-propylacrolein.	151
1:1705	Methyl acetoacetate	152
1:0200	Phenylacetaldehyde	153
1:5425	Pinacolone	157
1:5433	Diisopropyl ketone	160 149
1:5540	*d*-Carvone . . . . . (high melt.)	162
1:0230	Citral-*a* (geranial)	164
1:5150	Benzophenone	164
1:5445	Mesityl oxide . . . . . (α form)	164
1:9025	Benzoquinone . . . . . . (mono)	165
1:0182	Tetrahydrofurfural	166
1:5465	Cyclohexanone	166
1:5555	Valerophenone	166
1:5528	Isopropyl phenyl ketone	167 181
1:5155	Benzalacetophenone . . . . (α)	168
1:9011	Anisalacetophenone . . . (α)	168
1:9022	Piperonalacetone . . . . . (β)	168
1:0115	Acrolein	171
1:0230	Citral-*b* (neral)	171
1:5525	Propiophenone	173
1:0186	Hexahydrobenzaldehyde	174
1:9015	Benzil . . . . (mono)	174
1:5534	Phenoxyacetone	176
1:9007	*p*-Toluquinone . . . (mono)	178
1:5480	*d,l*-3-Methylcyclohexanone.	179 191
1:5528	Isopropyl phenyl ketone	181 167
1:5547	*o*-Methoxyacetophenone	182
1:7547	*d*-Fenchone	183
1:9062	β-Naphthoquinone . . . . (mono) dec.	184
1:5195	Anisoin . . . . abt.	185
1:5448	Acetoin	185
1:5145	Benzalacetone	186
1:5174	Cinnamalacetone	186
1:9024	Dibenzalacetone	187
1:5118	Benzyl methyl ketone	187–190
1:5535	Butyrophenone	188
1:5520	*l*-Menthone	189
1:0133	Trimethylacetaldehyde	190
1:5400	Acetone	190
1:5523	Isophorone	190
1:9011	Anisalacetophenone . . . (β)	190
1:5480	*d,l*,3-Methylcyclohexanone.	191 179
1:9090	Acenaphthenequinone . . . . (mono)	192
1:0298	5-Hydroxymethylfurfural	194
1:1560	*p*-Hydroxybenzophenone	194
1:1506	*m*-Hydroxyacetophenone	195
1:5455	Acetol	196
1:5548	*m*-Methoxyacetophenone	196
1:5140	*p*-Methoxyacetophenone	197
1:5470	2-Methylcyclohexanone	197
1:5515	Acetophenone	198
1:5527	*m*-Methylacetophenone	198
1:1527	*p*-Hydroxyacetophenone	199
1:5485	4-Methylcyclohexanone	199
1:9082	Retenequinone . . . . (mono)	200
1:9003	Thymoquinone . . . (mono)	201

1:0185	Furfural.................	202
1:0251	*p*-Ethoxybenzaldehyde....	202
1:9035	Piperonalacetophenone (α)	203
1:5530	*p*-Methylacetophenone....	204
1:5210	Benzoin...............(α)	205
1:5524	*o*-Methylacetophenone....	205
1:0179	β-Ethyl-α-methylacrolein..	207
1:0278	Phenylglyoxal..... (mono)	208
1:1746	*o*-Hydroxyacetophenone...	209
1:0198	5-Methylfurfural.........	210
1:0210	*o*-Tolualdehyde...........	210
1:0240	*p*-Anisaldehyde...........	210
1:5446	Cyclopentanone ...... abt.	210
1:0234	Cumaldehyde............	212
1:0235	*o*-Methoxybenzaldehyde...	215
1:0245	Cinnamaldehyde.........	216
1:0195	Benzaldehyde............	217
1:9022	Piperonalacetone .....(α)	217
1:0242	*o*-Ethoxybenzaldehyde....	219
1:0025	β-(α-Furyl)acrolein.......	219.5
1:5120	Phorone..................	221
1:0278	Phenylglyoxal........(bis)	229
1:0050	Vanillin.................	230
1:0205	Salicylaldehyde..........	230
1:5600	Methyl α-naphthyl ketone.	230
1:9083	Camphorquinone ..(mono)	{230 147
1:5144	Indanone-1..............	233
1:0010	Piperonal................	234
1:0215	*p*-Tolualdehyde..........	234
1:5153	Methyl β-naphthyl ketone.	235
1:9500	Biacetyl ....(mono)	235
1:5215	*d*-Camphor..............	237
1:9003	Thymoquinone.......(bis)	237
1:9007	*p*-Toluquinone ....(bis)	240
1:9015	Benzil..............(bis)	243
1:9025	Benzoquinone........(bis)	243
1:0036	β-Naphthaldehyde........	245
1:9040	α-Naphthoquinone. (mono)	247
1:9090	Acenaphthenequinone (bis)	271
1:9500	Biacetyl.............(bis)	278

B. PHENOLIC COMPOUNDS

TABLE OF MELTING POINTS OF ACETATES OF PHENOLIC COMPOUNDS OF ORDER I

These are arranged in order of increasing melting points. The latter are approximate values only and in every instance the more precise information given in the Huntress-Mulliken " Tables " should be consulted. For this reason, the location number of the corresponding original compound is given.

For general directions and comments on the preparation of acetates of organic hydroxyl compounds see the Mulliken-Huntress " Manual," T 2.26.

1:1525	3,5 Dihydroxytoluene . . . (di)	25
1:1775	Eugenol	29
1:1435	*p*-Methoxyphenol	31
1:1469	Pseudocumenol	34
1:1471	Ethyl *m*-hydroxybenzoate	35
1:1550	*p*-Cyclohexylphenol	35
1:0205	Salicylaldehyde	38
1:1500	α-Naphthol	48
1:1545	2,5-Dihydroxytoluene . . . (di)	49
1:1750	Methyl salicylate	52
1:1527	*p*-Hydroxyacetophenone	54
1:1544	1,3-Dihydroxy-naphthalene . . . (di)	55
1:1460	3,4-Dihydroxytoluene . . . (di)	57
1:1590	Hydroquinone . . . (mono)	62
1:1440	*o*-Phenylphenol	63
1:1520	Pyrocatechol . . . (di)	64
1:0065	2,4-Dihydroxy-benzaldehyde . . . (di)	69
1:1540	β-Naphthol	71
1:1532	4,4′-Dihydroxy-2,2′-dimethyl-biphenyl . . . (di)	75
1:1565	Furoin	76
1:0050	Vanillin	78
1:1576	3,4-Dihydroxybiphenyl . . . (di)	78
1:1785	Isoeugenol . . . (*trans*)	79
1:1560	*p*-Benzoylphenol	81
1:1541	3,3′-Dihydroxybiphenyl (di)	82
1:1549	Methyl *p*-hydroxybenzoate	85
1:1583	2,2′-Dihydroxy-6,6′-dimethyl-biphenyl . . . (di)	87
1:1585	*p*-Phenylphenol	87
1:1579	2,2′-Dihydroxy-5,5′-dimethyl-biphenyl . . . (di)	88
1:1746	*o*-Acetylphenol	89
1:1545	2,5-Dihydroxytoluene (mono)	92
1:1581	2,4′-Dihydroxybiphenyl . (di)	94
1:1529	2,2′-Dihydroxybiphenyl . (di)	95
1:1570	Hydroxyhydroquinone . . (tri)	96
1:1415	Phenyl salicylate	99
1:1620	Phloroglucinol . . . (di)	104
1:1620	Phloroglucinol . . . (tri)	104
1:1515	2-Aceto-1-naphthol	107
1:1524	1,2-Dihydroxy-naphthalene . . . (di)	109
1:1621	Bi-β-naphthol . . . (di)	109
1:1605	Methyl gallate . . . (tri)	121
1:1590	Hydroquinone . . . (di)	123
1:1592	1,4-Dihydroxy-naphthalene . . . (di)	128
1:0825	*m*-Hydroxybenzoic acid	131
1:1580	4,4′-Dihydroxy-3,3′-dimethyl-biphenyl . . . (di)	134
1:0780	Salicylic acid	135
1:1594	2,7-Dihydroxy-naphthalene . . . (di)	136
1:1505	β-Naphthyl salicylate	136
1:0843	2,4-Dihydroxybenzoic acid . . . (di)	140
1:1635	Phenolphthalein . . . (di)	143
1:0873	Phenolphthalin . . . (di)	146
1:0835	*o*-Coumaric acid	154
1:1572	1,8-Dihydroxy-naphthalene . . . (di)	155
1:0545	3,4-Dihydroxybenzoic acid . . . (di)	157
1:1630	1,5-Dihydroxy-naphthalene . . . (di)	159
1:1640	4,4′-Dihydroxybiphenyl . . (di)	162
1:0875	Gallic acid . . . (tri)	171
1:1594	2,7-Dihydroxy-naphthalene . . . (mono)	171
1:1555	Pyrogallol . . . (tri)	172
1:9084	1-Hydroxyanthraquinone	176
1:0850	2-Hydroxy-3-naphthoic acid	184
1:0830	Syringic acid	187
1:0840	*p*-Hydroxybenzoic acid	191
1:9085	1,4-Dihydroxyanthra-quinone	{200 / 207
1:0545	3,4-Dihydroxybenzoic acid . . . (4-mono)	202

TABLE OF MELTING POINTS OF BENZOATES OF PHENOLIC COMPOUNDS OF ORDER I

These are arranged in order of increasing melting points. The latter are approximate values only and in every instance the more precise information given in the Huntress-Mulliken "Tables" should be consulted. For this reason, the location number of the corresponding original compound is given.

For general directions and comments on the preparation of benzoates and substituted benzoates of phenols see the Mulliken-Huntress "Manual," T 1.47, T 1.82, and T 2.26.

1:1455	3,5-Dimethylphenol	24
1:1771	*p-n*-Butylphenol	27
1:1745	*o*-Ethoxyphenol	31
1:1430	Thymol	33
1:0055	*m*-Hydroxybenzaldehyde	37
1:1740	2,4-Dimethylphenol	37
1:1739	*o*-Ethylphenol	38
1:1490	*o*-Hydroxybenzyl alcohol (di)	51
1:1773	*p-n*-Amylphenol	51
1:1744	*m*-Ethylphenol	52
1:1730	*m*-Cresol	55
1:1500	α-Naphthol	56
1:1405	Guaiacol	57
1:1453	3,4-Dimethylphenol	58
1:1460	3,4-Dihydroxytoluene (di)	58
1:1471	Ethyl *m*-hydroxybenzoate	58
1:1424	*p*-Ethylphenol	59
1:1475	*m*-Phenylphenol	60
1:1495	*p-ter*-Amylphenol	60
1:1473	2,5-Dimethylphenol	61
1:1467	Mesitol	62
1:1469	Pseudocumenol	63
1:1785	Isoeugenol (*cis*)	68
1:1420	Phenol	69
1:1410	*p*-Cresol	70
1:1775	Eugenol	70
1:1481	Isodurenol	71
1:1440	*o*-Phenylphenol	75
1:0050	Vanillin	78
1:1415	Phenyl salicylate	81
1:1510	*p-ter*-Butylphenol	81
1:1520	Pyrocatechol (di)	84
1:1459	1-Aceto-2-naphthol	85
1:1485	*p*-Benzylphenol	87
1:1435	*p*-Methoxyphenol	87
1:1525	3,5-Dihydroxytoluene (di)	87
1:1746	*o*-Acetylphenol	87
1:1755	Ethyl salicylate	87
1:0060	*p*-Hydroxybenzaldehyde	89
1:1555	Pyrogallol (tri)	89
1:1533	Vanillyl alcohol (mono)	90 99
1:1541	3,3′-Dihydroxybiphenyl (di)	92
1:1565	Furoin	92
1:1750	Methyl salicylate	92
1:1534	Ethyl *p*-hydroxybenzoate	94
1:0073	3,4-Dihydroxybenzaldehyde (di)	96
1:0065	2,4-Dihydroxybenzaldehyde (di)	98
1:1533	Vanillyl alcohol (mono)	99 90
1:1785	Isoeugenol (*trans*)	104
1:1536	2,6-Dihydroxytoluene (di)	105
1:1540	β-Naphthol	106
1:1555	Pyrogallol (di)	108
1:1560	*p*-Benzoylphenol	114
1:1530	Resorcinol (di)	117
1:1550	*p*-Cyclohexylphenol	118.5
1:1570	Hydroxyhydroquinone (tri)	120
1:1533	Vanillyl alcohol (di)	121
1:1532	4,4′-Dihydroxy-2,2′-dimethylbiphenyl (di)	127
1:1515	2-Aceto-1-naphthol	128
1:9050	Vanillalacetone	128
1:1520	Pyrocatechol (mono)	130
1:0780	Salicylic acid	132
1:1527	*p*-Hydroxyacetophenone	134
1:1530	Resorcinol (mono)	135
1:1549	Methyl *p*-hydroxybenzoate	135
1:1583	2,2′-Dihydroxy-6,6′-dimethylbiphenyl (di)	136
1:1594	2,7-Dihydroxynaphthalene (di)	139
1:1605	Methyl gallate (tri)	139
1:1555	Pyrogallol (mono)	140
1:1531	2,2′-Dihydroxy-3,3′-dimethylbiphenyl (di)	147
1:1538	2,2′-Dihydroxy-4,4′-dimethylbiphenyl (di)	148
1:1585	*p*-Phenylphenol	149
1:1621	Bi-β-naphthol	160
1:1590	Hydroquinone (mono)	163
1:1592	1,4-Dihydroxynaphthalene (di)	169
1:1635	Phenolphthalein (di)	169
1:1620	Phloroglucinol (tri)	173
1:1572	1,8-Dihydroxynaphthalene (di)	174
1:1580	4,4′-Dihydroxy-3,3′-dimethylbiphenyl (di)	185
1:0875	Gallic acid (tri)	191
1:0545	3,4-Dihydroxybenzoic acid (di)	198
1:1590	Hydroquinone (di)	199
1:1594	2,7-Dihydroxynaphthalene (mono)	199
1:1621	Bi-β-naphthol (mono)	204
1:0825	2-Hydroxy-3-naphthoic acid	208
1:0830	Syringic acid	230
1:1630	1,5-Dihydroxynaphthalene (di)	235
1:1640	4,4′-Dihydroxybiphenyl	241

TABLE OF MELTING POINTS OF

p-Nitrobenzoates of Phenolic Compounds of Order I

3,5-Dinitrobenzoates of Phenolic Compounds of Order I

These are arranged in order of increasing melting points. The latter are approximate values only and in every instance the more precise information given in the Huntress-Mulliken " Tables " should be consulted. For this reason, location number of the corresponding original compound is given.

For general directions and comments on the preparation of benzoates and substituted benzoates of phenols see the Mulliken-Huntress " Manual," T 1.47, T 1.82, and T 2.26.

p-Nitrobenzoates

1:1760	Carvacrol	51
1:1739	*o*-Ethylphenol	56
1:1771	*p-n*-Butylphenol	67
1:1744	*m*-Ethylphenol	68
1:1430	Thymol	70
1:1424	*p*-Ethylphenol	80
1:1775	Eugenol	81
1:1473	2,5-Dimethylphenol	87
1:1443	*n*-Caproylresorcinol.. (mono)	90
1:1730	*m*-Cresol	90
1:1405	*o*-Methoxyphenol	93
1:1400	*o*-Cresol	94
1:1410	*p*-Cresol	98
1:1740	2,4-Dimethylphenol	105
1:1755	Ethyl salicylate	107
1:1785	Isoeugenol	109
1:1415	Phenyl salicylate	111
1:0205	Salicylaldehyde	123
1:1420	Phenol	127
1:1550	*p*-Cyclohexylphenol	137
1:1500	α-Naphthol	143
1:1540	β-Naphthol	169
1:1520	Pyrocatechol (di)	169
1:1530	Resorcinol (di)	182
1:0780	Salicylic acid	205
1:1525	3,5-Dihydroxytoluene (di)	214
1:1555	Pyrogallol (tri)	230
1:1590	Hydroquinone (di)	258
1:1620	Phloroglucinol (tri)	283

3,5-Dinitrobenzoates

1:1760	Carvacrol	83
1:1430	Thymol	103
1:1739	*o*-Ethylphenol	108
1:1775	Eugenol	130
1:1424	*p*-Ethylphenol	132
1:1473	2,5-Dimethylphenol	137
1:1400	*o*-Cresol	138
1:1405	Guaiacol	141
1:1420	Phenol	145
1:1520	Pyrocatechol (di)	152
1:1785	Isoeugenol	158
1:1425	2,6-Dimethylphenol	158
1:1620	Phloroglucinol (tri)	162
1:1740	2,4-Dimethylphenol	164
1:1730	*m*-Cresol	165
1:1550	Cyclohexylphenol	168
1:1453	3,4-Dimethylphenol	181
1:1410	*p*-Cresol	188
1:1525	3,5-Dihydroxytoluene (di)	190
1:1455	3,5-Dimethylphenol	195
1:1530	Resorcinol (di)	201
1:1555	Pyrogallol (tri)	205
1:1540	β-Naphthol	210
1:1500	α-Naphthol	217
1:1590	Hydroquinone (di)	317

TABLE OF MELTING POINTS OF

Benzenesulfonyl Esters of Phenolic Compounds of Order I

p-Toluenesulfonyl Esters of Phenolic Compounds of Order I

These are arranged in order of increasing melting points. The latter are approximate values only and in every instance the more precise information given in the Huntress-Mulliken " Tables " should be consulted. For this reason, the location number of the corresponding original compound is given.

For general directions and comment on the preparation of benzenesulfonyl and *p*-toluenesulfonyl derivatives of organic hydroxyl compounds see the Mulliken-Huntress " Manual," T 2.26.

Benzenesulfonyl Esters

1:1730	*m*-Cresol	45
1:1405	*o*-Methoxyphenol	51
1:1440	*o*-Phenylphenol	67
1:1530	Resorcinol (di)	69
1:1510	*p-ter*-Butylphenol	70

(*Continued*)

***p*-Toluenesulfonyl Esters**

1:1730	*m*-Cresol	51
1:1400	*o*-Cresol	54
1:1495	*p-ter*-Amylphenol	54
1:0205	Salicylaldehyde	63
1:1440	*o*-Phenylphenol	65

(*Continued*)

Benzenesulfonyl Esters of Phenolic Compounds of Order I

(Continued)

1:1585	*p*-Phenylphenol	104
1:1540	β-Naphthol	106
1:1635	Phenolphthalein (di)	112
1:1620	Phloroglucinol (tri)	116
1:1590	Hydroquinone (di)	120
1:1555	Pyrogallol (tri)	142
1:1640	4,4′-Dihydroxybiphenyl (di)	148

p-Toluenesulfonyl Esters of Phenolic Compounds of Order I

(Continued)

1:1410	*p*-Cresol	69
1:1430	Thymol	71
1:1530	Resorcinol (di)	80
1:1455	3,5-Dimethylphenol	83
1:1405	*o*-Methoxyphenol	85
1:1500	α-Naphthol	89
1:1420	Phenol	95
1:1590	Hydroquinone (mono)	98
1:1510	*p-ter*-Butylphenol	109
1:1540	β-Naphthol	125
1:1594	2,7-Dihydroxy-naphthalene (di)	150
1:1590	Hydroquinone (di)	159
1:1585	*p*-Phenylphenol	177
1:1640	4,4′-Dihydroxybiphenyl (di)	189

TABLE OF MELTING POINTS OF *p*-NITROBENZYL AND OF 2,4-DINITROPHENYL ETHERS OF PHENOLIC COMPOUNDS OF ORDER I

These melting points are arranged in order of increasing magnitude. The values are, however, only approximate and in every instance the more precise information given in the Huntress-Mull'ken " Tables " should be consulted. For this reason, the location numbers of the corresponding parent compound is given.

For general directions on the preparation of *p*-nitrobenzyl ethers see T 1.44 in the Mulliken-Huntress " Manual."

p-Nitrobenzyl ethers

1:1730	*m*-Cresol	51
1:1775	Eugenol	53.5
1:1405	Guaiacol	64
1:1430	Thymol	85.5
1:1415	Phenyl salicylate	87
1:1410	*p*-Cresol	88
1:1400	*o*-Cresol	90
1:1420	Phenol	91
1:1780	*n*-Butyl salicylate	92
1:1540	β-Naphthol	106
1:1414	*o*-Benzoylphenol	124
1:0050	Vanillin	124.5
1:1755	Ethyl salicylate	125
1:1750	Methyl salicylate	128
1:0780	Salicylic acid (ether-ester)	138
1:1500	α-Naphthol	140
1:0825	*m*-Hydroxybenzoic acid) (ether-ester)	143
1:0835	*o*-Coumaric acid	152
1:0780	Salicylic acid (ether-acid)	167
1:0825	*m*-Hydroxybenzoic acid (ether-acid)	194
1:0840	*p*-Hydroxybenzoic acid (ether-ester)	196
1:0840	*p*-Hydroxybenzoic acid (ether-acid)	260

2,4-Dinitrophenyl ethers

1:1420	Phenol	69
1:1430	Thymol	67
1:1730	*m*-Cresol	74
1:1400	*o*-Cresol	90
1:1410	*p*-Cresol	93.5
1:1540	β-Naphthol	95
1:1405	Guaiacol	97
1:1475	*m*-Phenylphenol	100
1:1775	Eugenol	114
1:1585	*p*-Phenylphenol	118
1:1500	α-Naphthol	128
1:1785	Isoeugenol	129
1:1530	Resorcinol (bis)	194

TABLE OF MELTING POINTS OF ARYLOXYACETIC ACIDS DERIVED FROM PHENOLIC COMPOUNDS OF ORDER I

These are arranged in order of increasing melting points. The latter are approximate values only and in every instance the more precise information given in the Huntress-Mulliken "Tables" should be consulted. For this reason the location number of the corresponding compound is given. For general directions and comments on the preparation of aryloxyacetic acids see T 1.46 in the Mulliken-Huntress "Manual."

No.	Compound	M.p.
1:1744	*m*-Ethylphenol	76
1:1775	Eugenol	81*
1:1771	*p*-*n*-Butylphenol	81
1:1510	*p*-*ter*-Butylphenol	86.5
1:1420	Phenol	88
1:1773	*p*-*n*-Amylphenol	90
1:1785	Isoeugenol	93
1:1424	*p*-Ethylphenol	96
1:1775	Eugenol	100
1:1730	*m*-Cresol	102
1:1435	*p*-Methoxyphenol	111
1:1455	3,5-Dimethylphenol	111
1:1405	Guaiacol	116
1:1765	*m*-Methoxyphenol	116
1:1473	2,5-Dimethylphenol	118
1:1490	*o*-Hydroxybenzyl alcohol	120
1:1759	*p*-Isobutylphenol	124
1:1515	2-Aceto-1-naphthol	130
1:0205	Salicylaldehyde	132
1:1469	Pseudocumenol	132
1:1410	*p*-Cresol	135
1:1467	Mesitol	139.5
1:1425	2,6-Dimethylphenol	139.5
1:1739	*o*-Ethylphenol	140
1:1740	2,4-Dimethylphenol	141
1:1459	1-Aceto-2-naphthol	145
1:0055	*m*-Hydroxybenzaldehyde	148
1:1430	Thymol	148
1:1760	Carvacrol	150
1:1400	*o*-Cresol	151
1:1540	β-Naphthol	154
1:1530	Resorcinol (mono)	158
1:1453	3,4-Dimethylphenol	162.5
1:0030	2-Hydroxy-5-methylbenzaldehyde	182
1:0050	Vanillin	189
1:0780	Salicylic acid	191
1:1500	α-Naphthol	192
1:1530	Resorcinol (bis)	195
1:0060	*p*-Hydroxybenzaldehyde	198
1:1555	Pyrogallol (tris)	198
1:0825	*m*-Hydroxybenzoic acid	206
1:1525	3,5-Dihydroxytoluene (bis)	216
1:1590	Hydroquinone (bis)	250
1:1640	4,4′-Dihydroxybiphenyl (bis)	274

* Monohydrate of derivative.

TABLE OF MELTING POINTS OF *N*-SUBSTITUTED CARBAMATES OF PHENOLIC COMPOUNDS OF ORDER I

These are arranged in order of increasing melting points. The latter are approximate values only and in every instance the more precise information given in the Huntress-Mulliken "Tables" should be consulted. For this reason, the location number of the corresponding original compound is given.

For general directions and comments on the preparation of *N*-substituted carbamates as derivatives of organic hydroxyl compounds see the Mulliken-Huntress "Manual," T 1.45, T 1.43, and T 1.86.

N-Phenylcarbamates

No.	Compound	M.p.
1:1775	Eugenol	95
1:1755	Ethyl salicylate	99
1:1430	Thymol	107
1:1469	Pseudocumenol	110
1:1415	Phenyl salicylate	111
1:1740	2,4-Dimethylphenol	112
1:1771	*p*-*n*-Butylphenol	114
1:1468	Methyl *m*-hydroxybenzoate	115
1:1410	*p*-Cresol	115
1:1750	Methyl salicylate	117

(Continued)

N-α-Naphthylcarbamates

No.	Compound	M.p.
1:1760	Carvacrol	116
1:1405	Guaiacol	118
1:1775	Eugenol	122
1:1730	*m*-Cresol	127
1:1424	*p*-Ethylphenol	128
1:1765	*m*-Methoxyphenol	128
1:1420	Phenol	132
1:1740	2,4-Dimethylphenol	135
1:1400	*o*-Cresol	141
1:1453	3,4-Dimethylphenol	141

(Continued)

N-Phenylcarbamates

(*Continued*)

1:1431	*o*-Benzylphenol	118
1:1785	Isoeugenol (*cis*)	118
1:1424	*p*-Ethylphenol	120
1:1453	3,4-Dimethylphenol	120
1:1730	*m*-Cresol	122
1:1420	Phenol	126
1:0205	Salicylaldehyde	133
1:1425	2,6-Dimethylphenol	133
1:1760	Carvacrol	134
1:1549	Methyl *p*-hydroxybenzoate	134
1:1635	Phenolphthalein (bis)	135
1:0060	*p*-Hydroxybenzaldehyde	136
1:1405	Guaiacol	136
1:1744	*m*-Ethylphenol	139
1:1400	*o*-Cresol	141
1:1739	*o*-Ethylphenol	141
1:1467	Mesitol	141
1:1529	2,2′-Dihydroxybiphenyl (bis)	144
1:1455	3,5-Dimethylphenol	148
1:1785	Isoeugenol (*trans*)	152
1:1525	Orcinol (bis)	154
1:1540	β-Naphthol	155
1:0055	*m*-Hydroxybenzaldehyde	159
1:1473	2,5-Dimethylphenol	160
1:1530	Resorcinol (bis)	164
1:1460	3,4-Dihydroxytoluene (bis)	166
1:1520	Pyrocatechol (bis)	169
1:1555	Pyrogallol (tris)	173
1:1500	α-Naphthol	177
1:1481	Isodurenol	178
1:1620	Phloroglucinol (tris)	190
1:1590	Hydroquinone (bis)	206
1:1505	β-Naphthyl salicylate	268

N-α-Naphthylcarbamates

(*Continued*)

1:1410	*p*-Cresol	146
1:1785	Isoeugenol	149
1:1500	α-Naphthol	152
1:1540	β-Naphthol	156
1:1430	Thymol	160
1:1525	Orcinol (bis)	160
1:1473	2,5-Dimethylphenol	172
1:1425	2,6-Dimethylphenol	176

TABLE OF MELTING POINTS OF

N,N-Diphenylcarbamates of phenols

1:1400	*o*-Cresol	72
1:1410	*p*-Cresol	93
1:1730	*m*-Cresol	101
1:1420	Phenol	104
1:1775	Eugenol	107
1:1530	Resorcinol (bis)	129
1:1540	β-Naphthol	141
1:1415	Phenyl salicylate	144
1:1594	2,7-Dihydroxynaphthalene (bis)	176
1:1555	Pyrogallol (tris)	212
1:1594	2,7-Dihydroxynaphthalene (mono)	261

N-p-Xenylcarbamates of phenols

1:1455	3,5-Dimethylphenol	150
1:1400	*o*-Cresol	151
1:1473	2,5-Dimethylphenol	162
1:1730	*m*-Cresol	164
1:1760	Carvacrol	166
1:1420	Phenol	173
1:1453	3,4-Dimethylphenol	183
1:1740	2,4-Dimethylphenol	184
1:1500	α-Naphthol	190
1:1460	3,4-Dihydroxytoluene	193
1:1430	Thymol	194
1:1469	Pseudocumenol	196
1:1525	Orcinol (bis)	196
1:1410	*p*-Cresol	198
1:1425	2,6-Dimethylphenol	198

C. ALCOHOLS

TABLE OF MELTING POINTS OF *p*-NITROBENZOATES OF ALCOHOLS OF ORDER I

These are arranged in order of increasing melting points. The latter are approximate alues only and in every instance the more precise information given in the Huntress-Mulliken "Tables" should be consulted. For this reason, the location number of the corre-onding parent compound is given.

For general directions and comments on the preparation of *p*-nitrobenzoates and 3,5-di-itrobenzoates of alcohols see the Mulliken-Huntress "Manual," T 1.82, also T 2.26 A, B, nd C.

:6255	Octanol-1	12
:6155	Butanol-2 . . . . (*d* or *l*)	17.5
:6155	Butanol-2 . . . . (*d,l* form)	25
:6199	2-Methylpentanol-4	25
:6145	Allyl alcohol	28
:6245	Octanol-2	28
:6275	Decanol-1	30
:6150	Propanol-1	35
:6180	Butanol-1	35
:6228	Heptanol-4	35
:6270	Geraniol	35
:6210	Hexanol-2	40
:5900	Dodecanol-1 (lauryl alcohol)	45
:6520	Hydrocinnamyl alcohol	45
:6445	Tetrahydrofurfuryl alcohol	47
:6475	Methyl-phenyl-carbinol . . .	47
:6490	Trimethylene glycol (mono)	49
:6415	Cyclohexanol	50
:6405	*β*-Methoxyethanol	50.5
:5945	Hexadecanol-1 (cetyl alcohol)	52
:6420	2-Methylcyclohexanol-1 . . . . (*cis* form)	55
:6130	Ethyl alcohol	57
:6435	3-Methylcyclohexanol-1 . . . . (*trans* form)	58
:6700	Phenyl-*n*-propyl-carbinol . .	58
:6504	Ethyl-phenyl-carbinol	59
:5940	*l*-Menthol	61
:6505	*β*-Phenylethyl alcohol	62
:6420	2-Methylcyclohexanol-1 . . . . (*trans* form)	65
:6435	3-Methylcyclohexanol-1 . . . . (*cis* form)	65
1:6440	4-Methylcyclohexanol-1 . . . . (*trans* form)	67
1:6165	Isobutyl alcohol	69
1:6260	*l*-Linalyl alcohol	70
1:6425	Furfuryl alcohol	76
1:5920	Cinnamyl alcohol	78
1:6160	*ter*-Amyl alcohol	85
1:6480	Benzyl alcohol	85
1:5940	*d,l*-Menthol	91
1:5930	*d,l*-Fenchyl alcohol *α*-form	94
	d,l-Fenchyl alcohol *β*-form	108
1:6440	4-Methylcyclohexanol-1 . . . . (*cis* form)	94
1:6120	Methyl alcohol	96
1:6519	Pentamethylene glycol (*bis*)	104
1:6540	Glycerol . . . . (*α*-mono)	107
1:5930	*d,l*-Fenchyl alcohol *β*-form	108
	d,l-Fenchyl alcohol *α*-form	94
1:6135	Isopropyl alcohol	110.5
1:6140	*ter*-Butyl alcohol	116
1:6490	Trimethylene glycol . . (bis)	119
1:6540	Glycerol . . . . (*β*-mono)	120
1:5210	Benzoin	123
1:5180	Phenacyl alcohol	128
1:5960	Diphenylcarbinol	131
1:5990	*d,l*-Borneol	134
1:6507	*d,l*-*α*-Terpineol	139
1:6465	Ethylene glycol . . . . . . (bis)	140
1:5990	*d*-Borneol	153
1:6516	Tetramethylene glycol (bis)	175
1:6540	Glycerol . . . . (tri)	188
1:5975	Cholesterol	190
1:0070	*d,l*-Glyceraldehyde . . . . . (di)	247

TABLE OF MELTING POINTS OF 3,5-DINITROBENZOATES OF ALCOHOLS OF ORDER I

These are arranged in order of increasing melting points. The latter are approximate values only and in every instance the more precise information given in the Huntress-Mulliken "Tables" should be consulted. For this reason the location number of the corresponding parent compound is given.

For general directions and comments on the preparation of *p*-nitrobenzoates and 3,5-dinitrobenzoates of alcohols see the Mulliken-Huntress "Manual," T 1.82, also T 2.26 A, B, and C.

1:6245	Octanol-2	32
1:6210	Hexanol-2	38
1:6226	3-Methylpentanol-1	38
1:6202	3-Methylpentanol-2	43
1:6259	Nonanol-2	43
1:6205	Pentanol-1	46.5
1:6240	Heptanol-1	47
1:6145	Allyl alcohol	49
1:6235	Heptanol-2	49
1:6222	2-Methylpentanol-1	50
1:6204	2,2-Dimethylbutanol-1	51
1:6221	2,3-Dimethylbutanol-1	51.5
1:6223	2-Ethylbutanol-1	51.5
1:6265	Nonanol-1	52
1:6275	Decanol-1	56.5
1:6230	Hexanol-1	59
1:5900	Dodecanol-1 (lauryl alcohol)	60
1:6200	Isoamyl alcohol	61
1:6255	Octanol-1	61
1:6185	Pentanol-2	62
1:6270	Geraniol	62
1:6180	Butanol-1	64
1:6228	Heptanol-4	64
1:6199	2-Methylpentanol-4	65
1:5945	Hexadecanol-1 (cetyl alcohol)	66
1:6195	*act.*-Amyl alcohol	70
1:6224	2-Methylpentanol-5	70
1:6190	2-Methylpentanol-2	72
1:6150	*n*-Propyl alcohol	74
1:6410	β-Ethoxyethanol	75
1:6155	Butanol-2	76
1:6203	Hexanol-3	77
1:6507	*d,l*-α-Terpineol	78
1:6425	Furfuryl alcohol	80
1:6445	Tetrahydrofurfuryl alcohol	83
1:6219	2,2-Dimethylbutanol-4	83.5
1:6194	2-Methylpentanol-3	85
1:5840	*meso*-Inositol (hexa)	86
1:6165	Isobutyl alcohol	87
1:6435	3-Methylcyclohexanol-1 (*cis* form)	91
1:6520	Hydrocinnamyl alcohol	92
1:6130	Ethyl alcohol	93
1:6475	Methyl-phenyl-carbinol	94
1:6189	3-Methylpentanol-3	96.5
1:6435	3-Methylcyclohexanol-1 (*trans* form)	97
1:6420	2-Methylcyclohexanol-1 (*cis* form)	98
1:6175	Pentanol-3	99
1:6186	2,2-Dimethylbutanol-3	107
1:6120	Methyl alcohol	108
1:6505	β-Phenylethyl alcohol	108
1:6187	2,3-Dimethylbutanol-2	111
1:6415	Cyclohexanol	112
1:6480	Benzyl alcohol	113
1:6420	2-Methylcyclohexanol-1 (*trans* form)	114
1:6160	*ter*-Amyl alcohol	117
1:5920	Cinnamyl alcohol	121
1:5940	*d,l*-Menthol	121
1:6135	Propanol-2	122
1:6440	4-Methylcyclohexanol-1 (*cis* form)	134
1:6440	4-Methylcyclohexanol-1 (*trans* form)	139
1:5960	Diphenylcarbinol	141
1:6140	*ter*-Butyl alcohol	142
1:6525	Diethylene glycol (bis)	149
1:5940	*l*-Menthol	153
1:5990	*d*-Borneol	154
1:6465	Ethylene glycol (bis)	169
1:6490	Trimethylene glycol (bis)	178
1:5980	Ergosterol	202

TABLE OF MELTING POINTS OF ACID PHTHALATES OF ALCOHOLS OF ORDER I

These are arranged in order of increasing melting points. The latter are approximate values only and in every instance the more precise information given in the Huntress-Mulliken "Tables" should be consulted. For this reason the location number of the corresponding parent compound is given.

No.	Alcohol	M.P.
1:6240	Heptanol-1	17
1:6255	Octanol-1	22
1:6230	Hexanol-1	25
1:6210	Hexanol-2 (*d* form)	29
1:6268	Undecanol-2 (*d* or *l* form)	31
1:6185	Pentanol-2 (*d* or *l* form)	34
1:6263	Decanol-2 (*d* form)	38
1:6275	Decanol-1	38
1:6170	2-Methylbutanol-3 (*d,l* form)	39
1:6265	Nonanol-1	42.5
1:6259	Nonanol-2 (*d,l* form)	43
1:5890	Undecanol-1	44
1:6250	Nonanol-5	45
1:6130	Ethyl alcohol	47
1:6270	Geraniol	47
1:6263	Decanol-2	48
1:6268	Undecanol-2 (*d,l* form)	49
1:5900	Dodecanol-1	50
1:5917	Tridecanol-1	52.5
1:6150	Propanol-1	54
1:6223	2-Ethylbutanol-1	54
1:6245	Octanol-2 (*d,l* form)	55
1:6235	Heptanol-2 (*d,l* form)	57
1:6259	Nonanol-2 (*d* or *l* form)	58
1:6155	Butanol-2	59
1:5935	Tetradecanol-1	60
1:6185	Pentanol-2 (*d,l* form)	60
1:6228	Heptanol-4	60
1:5941	Pentadecanol-1	60.4
1:6165	Isobutyl alcohol	65
1:5950	Heptadecanol-1	66.7
1:5945	Hexadecanol-1	66.8
1:6204	2,2-Dimethylbutanol-1	68
1:5812	Neopentyl alcohol	70
1:6194	2-Methylpentanol-3 (*d,l* form)	70
1:6440	4-Methylcyclohexanol-1 (*cis* form)	72
1:5953	Octadecanol-1	72.5
1:6180	Butanol-1	73
1:6245	Octanol-2 (*d* or *l* form)	75
1:6205	Pentanol-1	75.5
1:6203	Hexanol-3	76
1:6235	Heptanol-2 (*d* or *l* form)	76.5
1:6435	3-Methylcyclohexanol (*cis* form)	82
1:6120	Methyl alcohol	82.5
1:6186	2,2-Dimethylbutanol-3	85
1:6425	Furfuryl alcohol	85
1:6700	Phenyl-*n*-propyl-carbinol	90
1:6435	3-Methylcyclohexanol-1 (*trans* form)	93
1:6415	Cyclohexanol	99
1:6420	2-Methylcyclohexanol-1 (*cis* form)	104
1:6480	Benzyl alcohol	105
1:6475	Methyl-phenyl-carbinol	108
1:5940	*l*-Menthol	110, 122
1:6507	*d,l*-α-Terpineol	117
1:6440	4-Methylcyclohexanol-1 (*trans* form)	119
1:5940	*l*-Menthol	122, 110
1:6420	2-Methylcyclohexanol-1 (*trans* form)	124
1:5957	Methyl-α-naphthyl-carbinol	131
1:5958	Benzyl-phenyl-carbinol	131
1:5975	Cholesterol	161
1:5960	Diphenylcarbinol	164
1:5990	*d*-Borneol	165
1:5930	*d,l*-Fenchyl alcohol	169
1:6505	β-Phenylethyl alcohol	188

TABLE OF MELTING POINTS OF 3-NITRO ACID PHTHALATES OF ALCOHOLS OF ORDER I

These are arranged in order of increasing melting points. The latter are approximate values only and in every instance the more precise information given in the Huntress-Mulliken " Tables " should be consulted. For this reason the location number of the corresponding parent compound is given.

For general directions and comments on the preparation of 3-nitro acid phthalates see the Mulliken-Huntress " Manual," T 1.83.

No.	Alcohol	M.P.
1:6458	Diethylene glycol monomethyl ether (hydrate)	87
1:6458	Diethylene glycol monomethyl ether (anhydrous)	92
1:6410	β-Ethoxyethanol (monohydrate deriv.)	94
1:6185	Pentanol-2	102
1:6248	2-Ethylhexanol-1	107
1:6518	β-Phenoxyethanol	112
1:6270	Geraniol	117
1:6520	Hydrocinnamyl alcohol	117
1:6410	β-Ethoxyethanol	118.5
1:5953	Octadecanol-1	118.8
1:6430	β-*n*-Butoxyethanol	120.5
1:5950	Heptadecanol-1	121.4
1:5945	Hexadecanol-1 (cetyl alcohol)	121.7
1:5941	Pentadecanol-1	122.5
1:5890	Undecanol-1	123
1:6275	Decanol-1	123
1:6505	β-Phenylethyl alcohol	123
1:5935	Tetradecanol-1	123.5
1:5900	Dodecanol-1	124
1:5917	Tridecanol-1	124
1:6145	Allyl alcohol	124
1:6230	Hexanol-1	124
1:6265	Nonanol-1	125
1:6239	2-Ethylpentanol-1	127
1:6240	Heptanol-1	127
1:6255	Octanol-1	128
1:6405	β-Methoxyethanol	128.5
1:6155	Butanol-2	131
1:6237	2-Methylhexanol-1	131
1:6247	4-Methylheptanol-1	133
1:6205	Pentanol-1	136.5
1:6224	2-Methylpentanol-5	139
1:6238	3-Methylhexanol-6	144
1:6150	Propanol-1	145
1:6222	2-Methylpentanol-1	145
1:6180	Butanol-1	147
1:6215	2,4-Dimethylpentanol-3	150
1:6120	Methyl alcohol	153
1:6135	Propanol-2	154
1:6236	2,4-Dimethylpentanol-1	154
1:6195	*act.*-Amyl alcohol	157
1:6130	Ethyl alcohol	158
1:6415	Cyclohexanol	160
1:6200	Isoamyl alcohol	163
1:6480	Benzyl alcohol	176
1:6165	Isobutyl alcohol	180

TABLE OF MELTING POINTS OF *N*-PHENYLCARBAMATES OF ALCOHOLS OF ORDER I

These are arranged in order of increasing melting points. The latter are approximate values only and in every instance the more precise information given in the Huntress-Mulliken " Tables " should be consulted. For this reason the location number of the corresponding parent compound is given.

No.	Alcohol	M.P.
1:6221	2,3-Dimethylbutanol-1	28
1:6248	2-Ethylhexanol-1	33
1:6160	*ter*-Amyl alcohol	42
1:6230	Hexanol-1	42
1:6189	3-Methylpentanol-3	43.5
1:6425	Furfuryl alcohol	45
1:6205	Pentanol-1	46
1:6120	Methyl alcohol	47
1:6520	Hydrocinnamyl alcohol	{47, 56
1:6175	Pentanol-3	48
1:6224	2-Methylpentanol-5	48
1:6194	2-Methylpentanol-3	50
1:6130	Ethyl alcohol	52
1:5925	Elaidyl alcohol	56
1:6200	Isoamyl alcohol	56
1:6520	Hydrocinnamyl alcohol	{56, 47
1:6150	Propanol-1	57
1:6275	Decanol-1	59.5
1:6265	Nonanol-1	60
1:6180	Butanol-1	61
1:6239A	2,6-Dimethylheptanol-4	61
1:6445	Tetrahydrofurfuryl alcohol	61
1:5890	Undecanol-1	62
1:6155	Butanol-2	64.5
1:6187	2,3-Dimethylbutanol-2	65

1:6204	2,2-Dimethylbutanol-1....	65
1:6240	Heptanol-1..............	65
1:6260	*l*-Linalyl alcohol	65
1:6170	2-Methylbutanol-3........	68
1:6145	Allyl alcohol............	70
1:5935	Tetradecanol-1...........	71
1:5941	Pentadecanol-1...........	72
1:5945	Hexadecanol-1...........	73
1:5900	Dodecanol-1............	74
1:6255	Octanol-1..............	74
1:6135	Propanol-2.............	75
1:6480	Benzyl alcohol..........	75.5
1:6535	*n*-Hexyl-phenyl-carbinol...	77
1:6186	2,2-Dimethylbutanol-3....	78
1:5922	*o*-Tolylcarbinol..........	79
1:5953	Octadecanol-1...........	79
1:5954	*p*-Tolylcarbinol..........	79
1:6505	*β*-Phenylethyl alcohol.....	79
1:6415	Cyclohexanol...........	82
1:6550	*p*-Anisyl-methyl-carbinol ..	82
1:6165	Isobutyl alcohol..........	86
1:6435	3-Methylcyclohexanol-1 ....(*cis* form)	87
1:5920	Cinnamyl alcohol.........	91
1:6475	Methyl-phenyl-carbinol...	91
1:5915	*p*-Anisyl alcohol..........	92
1:6420	2-Methylcyclohexanol-1 ....(*cis* form)	93
1:6435	3-Methylcyclohexanol-1 ....(*trans* form)	94
1:6215	2,4-Dimethylpentanol-3...	95
1:6502	Methyl-*p*-tolyl-carbinol ...	96
1:6452	*d,l*-Butylene glycol-2,3 ....(mono)	100
1:5940	*d,l*-Menthol..............	103
1:5930	*d,l*-Fenchyl alcohol.......	104
1:6420	2-Methylcyclohexanol-1 ....(*trans* form)	105
1:6538	Triethylene glycol...(bis)	108
1:5940	*l*-Menthol	111
1:6507	*d,l*-*α*-Terpineol...........	112
1:6440	4-Methylcyclohexanol-1 ....(*cis* form)	118
1:6482	*d,l*-Butylene glycol-1,3 (bis)	122
1:6440	4-Methylcyclohexanol-1 ....(*trans* form)	124
1:6412	Cyclopentanol...........	132.5
1:6140	*ter*-Butyl alcohol.........	135
1:6490	Trimethylene glycol..(bis)	137
1:5990	*d*-Borneol..............	138
1:5960	Diphenylcarbinol.........	139
1:6446	Isobutylene glycol..(bis)	140.5
1:6519	Pentamethylene glycol (bis)	142 175
1:6199	2-Methylpentanol-4.......	143
1:5812	Neopentyl alcohol........	144
1:6455	*d,l*-Propylene glycol..(bis)	144 153
1:6465	Ethylene glycol ......(bis)	157
1:6516	Tetramethylene glycol (bis)	163 180
1:5210	Benzoin	165
1:6519	Pentamethylene glycol (bis)	175 142
1:6516	Tetramethylene glycol (bis)	180 163
1:6452	*d,l*-Butylene glycol-2,3 (bis)	199.5
1:5805	Pinacol ....(bis)	215

TABLE OF MELTING POINTS OF *N*-(*α*-NAPHTHYL)CARBAMATES OF ALCOHOLS OF ORDER I

These are arranged in order of increasing melting points. The latter are approximate values only and in every instance the more precise information given in the Huntress-Mulliken " Tables " should be consulted. For this reason the location number of the corresponding parent compound is given.

For general directions and comments on the preparation of *N*-(*α*-naphthyl)carbamates of alcohols see the Mulliken-Huntress " Manual," T 1.86.

1:6300	Oleyl alcohol............	44
1:6270	Geraniol................	47
1:6238	3-Methylhexanol-6........	50
1:6260	*l*-Linalyl alcohol..........	53
1:6235	Heptanol-2.............	54
1:6259	Nonanol-2..............	55.5
1:6230	Hexanol-1..............	59
1:6248	2-Ethylhexanol-1.........	60
1:6210	Hexanol-2.......(*d,l* form)	61
1:6240	Heptanol-1..............	62
1:6245	Octanol-2..............	63
1:6265	Nonanol-1..............	65.5
1:6255	Octanol-1..............	66
1:6200	Isoamyl alcohol..........	67
1:6410	*β*-Ethoxyethyl aclohol.....	67.5
1:6205	Pentanol-1..............	68
1:6263	Decanol-2..............	69
1:6160	*ter*-Amyl alcohol.........	71
1:6180	Butanol-1..............	71
1:6202	3-Methylpentanol-2.......	72
1:6275	Decanol-1..............	72
1:6185	Pentanol-2.............	74
1:6222	2-Methylpentanol-1.......	75
1:6130	Ethyl alcohol............	79
1:6228	Heptanol-4.............	79
1:5900	Dodecanol-1............	80
1:6150	Propanol-1.............	80
1:6204	2,2-Dimethylbutanol-1....	80

1:6210	Hexanol-2. . . . . (*d* form)	81
1:5945	Hexadecanol-1.	82
1:6195	*act.*-Amyl alcohol	82
1:6189	3-Methylpentanol-3.	83.5
1:6199	2-Methylpentanol-4.	87
1:6175	Pentanol-3.	95
1:6155	Butanol-2.	97
1:6700	Phenyl-*n*-propyl-carbinol. . .	98
1:5812	Neopentyl alcohol.	99
1:6140	*ter*-Butyl alcohol.	101
1:6504	Ethyl-phenyl-carbinol.	102
1:6165	Isobutyl alcohol.	104
1:6135	Propanol-2.	105
1:6475	Methyl-phenyl-carbinol. . . .	106
1:6145	Allyl alcohol.	108
1:6170	2-Methylbutanol-3.	108
1:6405	β-Methoxyethyl alcohol. . .	113
1:5920	Cinnamyl alcohol.	114
1:6495	*m*-Tolylcarbinol.	116
1:6515	Isopropyl-phenyl-carbinol. .	116
1:6505	β-Phenylethyl alcohol.	119
1:6120	Methyl alcohol.	124
1:5490	*l*-Menthol.	126
1:5990	*d*-Borneol.	127
1:6415	Cyclohexanol.	128
1:6425	Furfuryl alcohol.	130
1:6480	Benzyl alcohol.	134
1:6530	*o*-Methoxybenzyl alcohol. .	135
1:5960	Diphenylcarbinol.	135
1:5210	Benzoin.	140
1:6519	Pentamethylene glycol (bis)	147
1:5930	*d,l*-Fenchyl alcohol.	149
1:6507	*d,l*-α-Terpineol.	151
1:6490	Trimethylene glycol . . (bis)	164
1:5975	Cholesterol.	175
1:6465	Ethylene glycol . . . . . (bis)	176
1:6540	Glycerol . . . . (tris)	191
1:6516	Tetramethylene glycol (bis)	198

TABLE OF MELTING POINTS OF *N*-(*p*-NITROPHENYL)CARBAMATES AND OF *N*-(*p*-XENYL)CARBAMATES OF ALCOHOLS OF ORDER I

These are arranged in order of increasing melting points. The latter are approximate values only and in every instance the more precise information given in the Huntress-Mulliken " Tables " should be consulted. For this reason the location number of the corresponding parent compound is given.

N-(*p*-Nitrophenyl)carbamates

1:6517	β-(β-*n*-Butoxyethoxy)ethyl alcohol.	55
1:6430	β-(*n*-Butoxy)ethyl alcohol .	59
1:6458	β-(β-Methoxyethoxy)ethyl alcohol.	73.5
1:6155	Butanol-2.	75
1:6165	Isobutyl alcohol.	80
1:6410	β-Ethoxyethyl alcohol.	80
1:6205	Pentanol-1.	86 91
1:6180	Butanol-1.	96
1:6200	Isoamyl alcohol.	97.5
1:5890	Undecanol-1.	99.5
1:6230	Hexanol-1.	103
1:6240	Heptanol-1.	103
1:6265	Nonanol-1.	104
1:6520	Hydrocinnamyl alcohol. . . .	104
1:6145	Allyl alcohol.	108
1:6255	Octanol-1.	111
1:6405	β-Methoxyethyl alcohol. . .	111
1:5953	Octadecanol-1.	115
1:6150	Propanol-1.	115
1:6135	Propanol-2.	116
1:5900	Dodecanol-1.	117
1:5945	Hexadecanol-1.	117
1:6275	Decanol-1.	117
1:6130	Ethyl alcohol.	129
1:6505	β-Phenylethyl alcohol.	135
1:6465	Ethylene glycol . . . . . . (*bis*)	136 236
1:6480	Benzyl alcohol.	157
1:6120	Methyl alcohol.	179.5
1:5210	Benzoin.	183
1:5975	Cholesterol.	204
1:6540	Glycerol . . . . (tris)	216
1:6465	Ethylene glycol.	236 136

N-(*p*-Xenyl)carbamates

1:6236	2,4-Dimethylpentanol-1. . .	74
1:6239	2-Ethylpentanol-1.	77
1:6248	2-Ethylhexanol-1.	79.5
1:6237	2-Methylhexanol-1.	88
1:6185	Pentanol-2.	94.5
1:6199	2-Methylpentanol-4.	95.5
1:6230	Hexanol-1.	97
1:6222	2-Methylpentanol-1.	98
1:6205	Pentanol-1.	99
1:6155	Butanol-2.	105.5
1:6180	Butanol-1.	109
1:6239A	2,6-Dimethylheptanol-4 . .	118
1:6130	Ethyl alcohol.	119
1:6120	Methyl alcohol.	127
1:6150	Propanol-1.	129
1:6135	Propanol-2.	138
1:6480	Benzyl alcohol.	156
1:6415	Cyclohexanol.	166

D. ACIDS

TABLE OF MELTING POINTS OF *p*-NITROBENZYL ESTERS OF ACIDS OF ORDER I

These are arranged in order of increasing melting points. The latter are approximate values only and in every instance the more precise information given in the Huntress-Mulliken " Tables " should be consulted. For this reason, the location number of the corresponding original compound is given.

For general directions and comments on the preparation of *p*-nitrobenzyl esters see the Mulliken-Huntress " Manual," T 1.39.

No.	Acid	M.p.
1:1005	Formic acid	31
1:1025	Propionic acid	31
1:1035	*n*-Butyric acid	35
1:0615	Hydrocinnamic acid	36
1:0620	Pentadecylic acid	39.5
1:0650	Palmitic acid	42.5
1:0695	Azelaic acid	43.5
1:0635	Margaric acid	48.5
1:0405	Levulinic acid	61
1:0420	Tiglic acid	63
1:0665	Phenylacetic acid	65
1:0810	*d*-Camphoric acid	66.5
1:0425	α-Crotonic acid	67
1:0440	Glutaric acid	69
1:0435	Citraconic acid	70.5
1:0730	Sebacic acid	72.5
1:1010	Acetic acid	78
1:0431	α-Hydroxyisobutyric acid	80.5
1:0745	Phenylpropiolic acid	83
1:0755	Suberic acid	85
1:0480	Malonic acid	85.5
1:0705	*m*-Toluic acid	86.5
1:0530	Succinic acid	88
1:0715	Benzoic acid	89
1:0470	Maleic acid	90
1:0515	Itaconic acid	90.5
1:0690	*o*-Toluic acid	90.5
1:0780	Salicylic acid	97
1:0770	Benzilic acid	99.5
1:0720	*o*-Benzoylbenzoic acid	100
1:0455	Citric acid	102
1:0795	*p*-Toluic acid	104.5
1:0775	Adipic acid	105.6
1:0825	*m*-Hydroxybenzoic acid	106
1:0430	Glycolic acid	106.5
1:0735	Cinnamic acid	116.5
1:0465	*d,l*-Mandelic acid	123
1:0450	*l*-Malic acid	124.5
1:0805	Anisic acid	132
1:0475	Furoic acid	133.5
1:0548	Mesaconic acid	134
1:0550	*d,l*-Tartaric acid	147.5
1:0895	Fumaric acid	150.5
1:0835	*o*-Coumaric acid	152.5
1:0820	Phthalic acid	155.5
1:0525	*d*-Tartaric acid	163
1:0840	*p*-Hydroxybenzoic acid	180
1:0870	Diphenic acid	182.6
1:0843	2,4-Dihydroxybenzoic acid	188
1:0900	Isophthalic acid	202.5
1:0445	Oxalic acid	204
1:0910	Terephthalic acid	263.5

TABLE OF MELTING POINTS OF PHENACYL ESTERS OF ACIDS OF ORDER I

These are arranged in order of increasing melting points. The latter are approximate values only and in every instance the more precise information given in the Huntress-Mulliken "Tables" should be consulted. For this reason, the location number of the corresponding original compound is given.

For general directions and comments on the preparation of phenacyl esters see the Mulliken-Huntress "Manual," T 1.391.

1:1010	Acetic acid	40	**1:0795**	*p*-Toluic acid	103
1:0615	Hydrocinnamic acid	42	**1:0455**	Citric acid	104
1:0600	Tridecylic acid	45	**1:0440**	Glutaric acid	104.5
1:0605	Lauric acid	48	**1:0740**	Acetylsalicylic acid	105
1:0665	Phenylacetic acid	50.5	**1:0450**	*l*-Malic acid	106
1:0620	Pentadecylic acid	53.6	**1:0435**	Citraconic acid	108.5
1:0630	Myristic acid	56	**1:0780**	Salicylic acid	110
1:0635	Margaric acid	60	**1:0715**	Benzoic acid	118.5
1:0650	Palmitic acid	63	**1:0770**	Benzilic acid	125.5
1:0660	Stearic acid	69	**1:0470**	Maleic acid	128
1:0695	Azelaic acid	70	**1:0525**	*d*-Tartaric acid	130
1:0456	Pimelic acid	72	**1:0805**	Anisic acid	134
1:0690	*o*-Toluic acid	74.5	**1:0735**	Cinnamic acid	140.5
1:0515	Itaconic acid	79	**1:0825**	*m*-Hydroxybenzoic acid	146.5
1:0730	Sebacic acid	80	**1:0530**	Succinic acid	148
1:0465	*d,l*-Mandelic acid	85	**1:0820**	Phthalic acid	154
1:0775	Adipic acid	88	**1:0840**	*p*-Hydroxybenzoic acid	178
1:0540	Aconitic acid	90	**1:0900**	Isophthalic acid	191
1:0400	*d,l*-Lactic acid	96	**1:0910**	Terephthalic acid	192
1:0755	Suberic acid	102	**1:0895**	Fumaric acid	204

TABLE OF MELTING POINTS OF *p*-CHLOROPHENACYL ESTERS AND OF *p*-IODOPHENACYL ESTERS OF ACIDS OF ORDER I

These are arranged in order of increasing melting points. The latter are approximate values only and in every instance the more precise information given in the Huntress-Mulliken "Tables" should be consulted. For this reason, the location number of the corresponding original compound is given.

For general directions and comments on the preparation of *p*-chlorophenacyl esters and of *p*-iodophenacyl esters see the Mulliken-Huntress "Manual," T 1.391.

p-Chlorophenacyl Esters			*p*-Iodophenacyl Esters		
1:0565	Oleic acid	40	**1:1115**	2-Ethylbutanoic acid-1	54
1:1035	*n*-Butyric acid	55	**1:1114**	2,3-Dimethylbutanoic acid-1	66
1:0590	Erucic acid	56	**1:1117**	2-Methylpentanoic acid-1	66
1:0610	Elaidic acid	56	**1:0590**	Erucic acid	74
1:0560	Pelargonic acid	59	**1:0610**	Elaidic acid	74
1:0573	*n*-Undecylic acid	60	**1:0560**	Pelargonic acid	77
1:0585	*n*-Capric acid	61	**1:1050**	Isovaleric acid	78
1:1130	*n*-Hexanoic acid	62	**1:1140**	*n*-Heptanoic acid	78
1:1145	*n*-Caprylic acid	63	**1:1145**	*n*-Caprylic acid	79
1:1140	*n*-Heptanoic acid	65	**1:0585**	*n*-Capric acid	81
1:0600	Tridecylic acid	67	**1:1035**	*n*-Butyric acid	81
1:0633	Brassidic acid	69.5	**1:1060**	*n*-Valeric acid	81
1:0605	Lauric acid	70	**1:0573**	*n*-Undecylic acid	82
1:1010	Acetic acid	72			

(*Continued*) (*Continued*)

p-Chlorophenacyl Esters

(*Continued*)

1:0620	*n*-Pentadecylic acid	74
1:0630	Myristic acid	76
1:0635	Margaric acid	79
1:0650	Palmitic acid	82
1:0660	Stearic acid	86
1:1070	Ethoxyacetic acid	94
1:1060	*n*-Valeric acid	97
1:1025	Propionic acid	98
1:0715	Benzoic acid	118.5
1:0520	Tricarballylic acid	125
1:1005	Formic acid	128
1:0540	Aconitic acid	169
1:0530	Succinic acid	197

p-Iodophenacyl Esters

(*Continued*)

1:0633	Brassidic acid	84
1:1130	*n*-Hexanoic acid	84
1:0605	Lauric acid	86
1:0600	*n*-Tridecylic acid	88.5
1:0630	Myristic acid	90
1:0635	Margaric acid	92
1:0620	*n*-Pentadecylic acid	93
1:0650	Palmitic acid	94
1:0660	Stearic acid	97
1:1025	Propionic acid	98
1:1030	Isobutyric acid	109
1:1010	Acetic acid	117
1:0715	Benzoic acid	126.5
1:0400	*d,l*-Lactic acid	140
1:1005	Formic acid	163

TABLE OF MELTING POINTS OF *p*-BROMOPHENACYL ESTERS OF ACIDS OF ORDER I

These are arranged in order of increasing melting points. The latter are approximate values only and in every instance the more precise information given in the Huntress-Mulliken " Tables " should be consulted. For this reason, the location number of the corresponding original compound is given.

For general directions and comments on the preparation of *p*-bromophenacyl esters see the Mulliken-Huntress " Manual, " T 1.391.

1:0565	Oleic acid	46
1:1105	2-Methylbutanoic acid-1	55
1:0690	*o*-Toluic acid	57
1:0590	Erucic acid	62
1:1025	Propionic acid	63
1:1035	*n*-Butyric acid	63
1:0610	Elaidic acid	65
1:1145	*n*-Caprylic acid	66
1:0585	*n*-Capric acid	67
1:0420	Tiglic acid	68
1:0560	Pelargonic acid	68
1:0573	*n*-Undecylic acid	68
1:1050	Isovaleric acid	68
1:1130	*n*-Hexanoic acid	72
1:1140	*n*-Heptanoic acid	72
1:0633	Brassidic acid	74
1:0600	*n*-Tridecylic acid	75
1:1060	*n*-Valeric acid	75
1:0410	Trimethylacetic acid	76
1:0605	Lauric acid	76
1:1030	Isobutyric acid	76
1:0620	*n*-Pentadecylic acid	77
1:1127	Isocaproic acid	77
1:0630	Myristic acid	81
1:1045	Isocrotonic acid	81
1:0635	Margaric acid	82
1:0405	Levulinic acid	84
1:0650	Palmitic acid	86
1:1010	Acetic acid	86
1:0665	Phenylacetic acid	89
1:0660	Stearic acid	90
1:0425	α-Crotonic acid	95
1:0615	Hydrocinnamic acid	104
1:1070	Ethoxyacetic acid	104
1:0705	*m*-Toluic acid	108
1:0400	*d,l*-Lactic acid	113
1:0685	*o*-Methoxybenzoic acid	113
1:0515	Itaconic acid	117
1:0715	Benzoic acid	119
1:0695	Azelaic acid	131
1:0785	α-Naphthoic acid	135.5
1:0456	Pimelic acid	136
1:0440	Glutaric acid	137
1:0430	Glycolic acid	138
1:0475	Furoic acid	138
1:0520	Tricarballylic acid	138
1:0780	Salicylic acid	140
1:1005	Formic acid	140
1:0755	Suberic acid	144
1:0735	Cinnamic acid	146
1:0730	Sebacic acid	147
1:0455	Citric acid	148
1:0680	Phenoxyacetic acid	148.5
1:0770	Benzilic acid	152
1:0805	Anisic acid	152
1:0795	*p*-Toluic acid	153
1:0820	Phthalic acid	153
1:0775	Adipic acid	154
1:0825	*m*-Hydroxybenzoic acid	176
1:0450	*l*-Malic acid	179
1:0900	Isophthalic acid	179
1:0540	Aconitic acid	186
1:0840	*p*-Hydroxybenzoic acid	191
1:0530	Succinic acid	211
1:0910	Terephthalic acid	225

TABLE OF MELTING POINTS OF *p*-PHENYLPHENACYL ESTERS OF ACIDS OF ORDER I

These are arranged in order of increasing melting points. The latter are approximate values only and in every instance the more precise information given in the Huntress-Mulliken "Tables" should be consulted. For this reason, the location number of the corresponding original compound is given.

For general directions and comments on the preparation of *p*-phenylphenacyl esters see the Mulliken-Huntress "Manual," T 1.391.

No.	Acid	M.P.
1:1125	3-Methylpentanoic acid-1..	47
1:1143	2-Ethylhexanoic acid-1....	50
1:0565	Oleic acid................	60
1:1140	*n*-Heptanoic acid.........	62
1:0665	Phenylacetic acid.....dec.	63
1:1060	*n*-Valeric acid...........	63.5
1:1117	2-Methylpentanoic acid-1..	64
1:1130	*n*-Hexanoic acid..........	65
1:1114	2,3-Dimethylbutanoic acid-1	66
1:1145	*n*-Caprylic acid...........	67
1:1105	2-Methylbutanoic acid-1...	70
1:1127	4-Methylbutanoic acid-1...	70
1:0560	Pelargonic acid...........	71
1:0593	α-Methylhydrocinnamic acid..................	73
1:0610	Elaidic acid..............	73.5
1:1114	2,3-Dimethylbutanoic acid-1.................	73.5
1:1005	Formic acid.............	74
1:0590	Erucic acid..............	76
1:1115	2-Ethylbutanoic acid-1....	77.5
1:1050	Isovaleric acid...........	78
1:0573	*n*-Undecylic acid.........	79.5
1:1035	*n*-Butyric acid...........	82
1:0605	Lauric acid..............	86
1:0633	Brassidic acid............	86
1:0600	Tridecylic acid...........	86.5
1:1113	2,2-Dimethylbutanoic acid-1.................	86.5
1:1030	Isobutyric acid...........	89
1:0630	Myristic acid............	90
1:0620	Pentadecylic acid.........	91.5
1:1112	3,3-Dimethylbutanoic acid-1.................	92
1:0650	Palmitic acid.............	94
1:0690	*o*-Toluic acid.............	94.5
1:0615	Hydrocinnamic acid......	95
1:0635	Margaric acid............	95.5
1:0660	Stearic acid..............	97
1:1025	Propionic acid...........	102
1:0765	Diphenylacetic acid.......	111
1:1010	Acetic acid..............	111
1:0770	Benzilic acid.............	122
1:0685	*o*-Methoxybenzoic acid....	131
1:0705	*m*-Toluic acid............	136.5
1:0730	Sebacic acid.............	140
1:0695	Azelaic acid..............	141
1:0400	*d,l*-Lactic acid............	145
1:0456	Pimelic acid.........dec.	145–148
1:0455	Citric acid...............	146
1:0775	Adipic acid..............	148
1:0780	Salicylic acid.............	148
1:0845	Mucic acid...........dec.	149.5
1:0755	Suberic acid.............	151
1:0440	Glutaric acid.............	152
1:0805	Anisic acid..............	160
1:0445	Oxalic acid...........dec.	165
1:0795	*p*-Toluic acid............	165
1:0715	Benzoic acid.............	167
1:0820	Phthalic acid............	167.5
1:0470	Maleic acid..............	168
1:0480	Malonic acid.............	175
1:0735	Cinnamic acid...........	182.5
1:0875	Gallic acid..........dec.	195–198
1:0525	*d*-Tartaric acid........dec.	203
1:0530	Succinic acid.............	208
1:0840	*p*-Hydroxybenzoic acid....	240

TABLE OF MELTING POINTS OF AMIDES OF ACIDS OF ORDER I

These melting points are arranged in order of increasing magnitude. The values, however, are only approximate and in every instance the more precise information given in the Huntress-Mulliken " Tables " should be consulted. For this reason the location number of the corresponding parent acid is given.

In this table only the neutral amides are listed; for data on monoamides of dibasic acids or on cyclic imides of dibasic acids see the detailed data of the " Tables " under the parent compound.

1:1134	2-Methylhexanoic acid-1	72
1:1042	Vinylacetic acid	73
1:0565	Oleic acid	75
1:0420	Tiglic acid	76
1:0400	*d,l*-Lactic acid	78
1:1117	2-Methylpentanoic acid-1	79
1:1025	Propionic acid	80
1:1070	Ethoxyacetic acid	81
1:1010	Acetic acid	81.5
1:0590	Erucic acid	84
1:1020	Acrylic acid	84
1:0594	*d,l*-α-Ethylphenylacetic acid	86
1:0570	Undecylenic acid	87
1:0610	Elaidic acid	89
1:0633	Brassidic acid	94
1:0705	*m*-Toluic acid	94
1:1065	Methoxyacetic acid	94
1:1140	*n*-Heptanoic acid	96
1:0431	α-Hydroxyisobutyric acid	98
1:1136	4-Methylhexanoic acid-1	98
1:0560	Pelargonic acid	99
1:0573	*n*-Undecylic acid	99
1:0585	*n*-Capric acid	99
1:0605	Lauric acid	99
1:0745	Phenylpropiolic acid	99
1:0600	Tridecylic acid	100
1:1045	Isocrotonic acid	101
1:1130	*n*-Hexanoic acid (caproic acid	101
1:1143	2-Ethylhexanoic acid	101
1:0680	Phenoxyacetic acid	101.5
1:0620	*n*-Pentadecylic acid	102.5
1:0630	Myristic acid	103
1:1113	2,2-Dimethylbutanoic acid-1	103
1:1133	2-Ethylpentanoic acid-1	104
1:0615	Hydrocinnamic acid	105
1:0655	*d*-Chaulmoogric acid	105
1:1145	*n*-Caprylic acid	105
1:0635	Margaric acid	106
1:0650	Palmitic acid	106
1:1060	*n*-Valeric acid	106
1:0405	Levulinic acid	107
1:0660	Stearic acid	108
1:0593	*d,l*-α-Methylhydrocinnamic acid	109
1:1105	2-Methylbutanoic acid-1	111
1:0634	*d*-Hydnocarpic acid	112
1:1115	2-Ethylbutanoic acid-1	112
1:1035	*n*-Butyric acid	115
1:1127	4-Methylpentanoic acid-1	119
1:0430	Glycolic acid	120
1:1040	Pyruvic acid	124
1:1125	3-Methylpentanoic acid-1	125
1:0612	Angelic acid	127
1:1030	Isobutyric acid	127
1:0668	Dibenzylacetic acid	128
1:0685	*o*-Methoxybenzoic acid	129
1:0715	Benzoic acid	130
1:1114	2,3-Dimethylbutanoic acid-1	131
1:0571	*o*-Ethoxybenzoic acid	132
1:1112	3,3-Dimethylbutanoic acid-1	132
1:0465	*d,l*-Mandelic acid	133
1:1050	Isovaleric acid	136
1:0746	*m*-Ethoxybenzoic acid	139
1:0780	Salicylic acid	139
1:0690	*o*-Toluic acid	141
1:0475	Furoic acid	142
1:0735	Cinnamic acid	147
1:0410	Trimethylacetic acid	154
1:0770	Benzilic acid	154
1:0665	Phenylacetic acid	156
1:0450	*l*-Malic acid	157
1:0425	α-Crotonic acid	159
1:0795	*p*-Toluic acid	160
1:0720	*o*-Benzoylbenzoic acid	162
1:0805	Anisic acid	162
1:0840	*p*-Hydroxybenzoic acid	162
1:0825	*m*-Hydroxybenzoic acid	167
1:0765	Diphenylacetic acid	167.5
1:0760	Furanacrylic acid	168
1:0865	Piperonylic acid	169
1:0480	Malonic acid	170
1:0695	Azelaic acid	172
1:0440	Glutaric acid	175
1:0548	Mesaconic acid	177
1:0470	Maleic acid	180
1:0728	α-Naphthylacetic acid	180
1:0435	Citraconic acid......dec.	185–191
1:0575	Hexahydrobenzoic acid	185
1:0490	*meso*-Tartaric acid	189
1:0515	Itaconic acid	191
1:0800	β-Naphthoic acid	192
1:0810	*d*-Camphoric acid	192
1:0510	Tartronic acid	196
1:0525	*d*-Tartaric acid	196
1:0761	β-Naphthylacetic acid	200

1:0785	α-Naphthoic acid.........	202
1:0817	*p*-Ethoxybenzoic acid.....	202
1:0520	Tricarballylic acid.....dec.	206
1:0730	Sebacic acid.............	209
1:0455	Citric acid...........dec.	210–215
1:0790	Phenylsuccinic acid.......	211
1:0870	Diphenic acid............	212
1:0755	Suberic acid.............	216
1:0850	2-Hydroxy-3-naphthoic acid..................	217
1:0775	Adipic acid..............	220
1:0550	*d,l*-Tartaric acid (racemic acid).................	226
1:0530	Succinic acid.............	260
1:0894	Fumaric acid.........dec.	266
1:0900	Isophthalic acid..........	280

TABLE OF MELTING POINTS OF ANILIDES OF ACIDS OF ORDER I

These melting points are arranged in order of increasing magnitude. The values, however, are only approximate and in every case the more precise information given in the Huntress-Mulliken " Tables " should be consulted. For this reason the location number of the corresponding parent acid is given.

In this table only neutral anilides are listed; for data on monoanilides of dibasic acids, or on anils of dibasic acids see the detailed " Tables " under the parent compound.

1:0565	Oleic acid...............	41
1:1005	Formic acid.............	50
1:0590	Erucic acid..............	55
1:1145	*n*-Caprylic acid..........	56
1:0560	Pelargonic acid..........	57
1:0400	*d,l*-Lactic acid...........	58
1:1042	Vinylacetic acid..........	58
1:1065	Methoxyacetic acid.......	58
1:0685	*o*-Methoxybenzoic acid....	62
1:1060	*n*-Valeric acid...........	62
1:1140	*n*-Heptanoic acid.........	65
1:0585	*n*-Capric acid............	70
1:0573	*n*-Undecylic acid.........	71
1:1136	4-Methylhexanoic acid-1...	76
1:0420	Tiglic acid..............	77
1:0605	Lauric acid.............	77
1:0620	*n*-Pentadecylic acid.......	78
1:0633	Brassidic acid...........	78
1:1114	2,3-Dimethylbutanoic acid-1................	78
1:0600	*n*-Tridecylic acid.........	80
1:0630	Myristic acid............	82
1:1125	3-Methylpentanoic acid-1..	87
1:0655	*d*-Chaulmoogric acid......	89
1:0650	Palmitic acid............	90.5
1:1113	2,2-Dimethylbutanoic acid-1................	92
1:1117	2-Methylpentanoic acid-1..	93
1:1133	2-Ethylpentanoic acid-1...	94
1:0660	Stearic acid.............	95
1:1130	*n*-Hexanoic acid (*n*-caproic acid).................	95
1:0615	Hydrocinnamic acid......	96
1:1035	*n*-Butyric acid..........	96
1:0430	Glycolic acid............	97
1:1134	2-Methylhexanoic acid-1...	98
1:0680	Phenoxyacetic acid.......	99
1:1045	Isocrotonic acid..........	101
1:0405	Levulinic acid...........	102
1:1020	Acrylic acid.............	104
1:1040	Pyruvic acid.............	104
1:1025	Propionic acid...........	105
1:1030	Isobutyric acid...........	105
1:1050	Isovaleric acid...........	109
1:1105	2-Methylbutanoic acid-1...	110
1:1127	Isocaproic acid...........	111
1:1010	Acetic acid..............	114
1:0665	Phenylacetic acid.........	117
1:0425	α-Crotonic acid..........	118
1:0475	Furoic acid..............	123
1:0690	*o*-Toluic acid............	125
1:1115	2-Ethylbutanoic acid-1....	125
1:0612	Angelic acid.............	126
1:0705	*m*-Toluic acid...........	126
1:0745	Phenylpropiolic acid......	126
1:1112	3,3-Dimethylbutanoic acid-1................	131
1:0410	Trimethylacetic acid......	132
1:0780	Salicylic acid............	135
1:0431	α-Hydroxyisobutyric acid..	136
1:0575	Hexahydrobenzoic acid....	144
1:0795	*p*-Toluic acid............	144
1:0465	*d,l*-Mandelic acid.........	151
1:0735	Cinnamic acid...........	151
1:0495	Diglycolic acid...........	152
1:0456	Pimelic acid.............	155
1:0485	Acetonedicarboxylic acid..	155
1:0668	Dibenzylacetic acid.......	155
1:0728	α-Naphthylacetic acid.....	156
1:0825	*m*-Hydroxybenzoic acid...	156
1:0715	Benzoic acid.............	160
1:0785	α-Naphthoic acid.........	162
1:0805	Anisic acid..............	169
1:0800	β-Naphthoic acid.........	171
1:0817	*p*-Ethoxybenzoic acid.....	171
1:0770	Benzilic acid............	174
1:0435	Citraconic acid...........	175
1:0765	Diphenylacetic acid.......	180
1:0548	Mesaconic acid...........	186
1:0695	Azelaic acid.............	186
1:0755	Suberic acid.............	186
1:0470	Maleic acid..............	187

1:0720	*o*-Benzoylbenzoic acid	195
1:0840	*p*-Hydroxybenzoic acid	196
1:0450	*l*-Malic acid	197
1:0455	Citric acid	199
1:0730	Sebacic acid	201
1:0790	Phenylsuccinic acid	222
1:0440	Glutaric acid	223
1:0480	Malonic acid	225
1:0810	*d*-Camphoric acid	226
1:0530	Succinic acid	228
1:0870	Diphenic acid	229
1:0775	Adipic acid	240
1:0850	2-Hydroxy-3-naphthoic acid	243
1:0445	Oxalic acid	246
1:0520	Tricarballylic acid	252
1:0820	Phthalic acid	254
1:0525	*d*-Tartaric acid	264
1:0895	Fumaric acid	313

TABLE OF MELTING POINTS OF *p*-TOLUIDIDES OF ACIDS OF ORDER I

These melting points are arranged in order of increasing magnitude. The values, however, are only approximate and in every instance the more precise information given in the Huntress-Mulliken " Tables " should be consulted. For this reason the location number of the corresponding parent acid is given.

In this table only neutral *p*-toluidides are listed; for data on mono-*p*-toluidides of dibasic acids, or on *N*-*p*-tolylimides (tolils) of dibasic acids see the detailed " Tables " under the parent compound.

1:1070	Ethoxyacetic acid	32
1:0565	Oleic acid	42
1:1005	Formic acid	53
1:0590	Erucic acid	57
1:1127	Isocaproic acid	62
1:1145	*n*-Caprylic acid	70
1:0420	Tiglic acid	71
1:1060	*n*-Valeric acid	73
1:1130	*n*-Caproic acid	74
1:1035	*n*-Butyric acid	75
1:1125	3-Methylpentanoic acid-1	75
1:0585	*n*-Capric acid	79
1:0573	*n*-Undecylic acid	80
1:1117	2-Methylpentanoic acid-1	80
1:1140	*n*-Heptanoic acid	81
1:1113	2,2-Dimethylbutanoic acid-1	83
1:0560	Pelargonic acid	84
1:1134	2-Methylhexanoic acid-1	85
1:0605	Lauric acid	87
1:0600	*n*-Tridecylic acid	88
1:0630	Myristic acid	93
1:1105	2-Methylbutanoic acid-1	93
1:0650	Palmitic acid	98
1:0655	*d*-Chaulmoogric acid	100
1:0660	Stearic acid	102
1:1050	Isovaleric acid	106
1:0400	*d,l*-Lactic acid	107
1:0475	Furoic acid	107
1:1030	Isobutyric acid	107
1:0405	Levulinic acid	108
1:1114	2,3-Dimethylbutanoic acid-1	112
1:1115	2-Ethylbutanoic acid-1	116
1:0705	*m*-Toluic acid	118
1:0410	Trimethylacetic acid	119
1:1025	Propionic acid	123
1:1133	2-Ethylpentanoic acid-1	129
1:0593	*d,l*-α-Methylhydrocinnamic acid	130
1:1040	Pyruvic acid	130
1:0425	α-Crotonic acid	132
1:0431	α-Hydroxyisobutyric acid	132
1:1112	3,3-Dimethylbutanoic acid-1	134
1:0615	Hydrocinnamic acid	135
1:0665	Phenylacetic acid	135
1:1020	Acrylic acid	141
1:0470	Maleic acid	142
1:0745	Phenylpropiolic acid	142
1:0430	Glycolic acid	143
1:0690	*o*-Toluic acid	144
1:1010	Acetic acid	153
1:0715	Benzoic acid	158
1:0795	*p*-Toluic acid	160
1:0825	*m*-Hydroxybenzoic acid	163
1:0735	Cinnamic acid	168
1:0465	*d,l*-Mandelic acid	172
1:0765	Diphenylacetic acid	172
1:0668	Dibenzylacetic acid	175
1:0805	Anisic acid	186
1:0455	Citric acid	189
1:0770	Benzilic acid	189
1:0800	β-Naphthoic acid	192
1:0695	Azelaic acid	201
1:0730	Sebacic acid	201
1:0840	*p*-Hydroxybenzoic acid	203
1:0450	*l*-Malic acid	206
1:0456	Pimelic acid	206
1:0548	Mesaconic acid	212
1:0440	Glutaric acid	218
1:0755	Suberic acid	218
1:0850	2-Hydroxy-3-naphthoic acid	221
1:0775	Adipic acid	241
1:0480	Malonic acid	252
1:0530	Succinic acid	255
1:0445	Oxalic acid	268

CHAPTER XIV

A. INDEX OF COMPOUNDS ACCORDING TO EMPIRICAL FORMULA

Formula	*Name*	*Location*
	C_1 GROUP	
CH_2O	Formaldehyde........	**1:0145**
$(CH_2O)_n$	Paraformaldehyde.....	**1:0080**
CH_2O_2	Formic acid...........	**1:1005**
CH_4O	Methyl alcohol........	**1:6120**
	C_2 GROUP	
$C_2H_2O_4$	Oxalic acid (anhydrous)	**1:0535**
	Oxalic acid (hydrated)..	**1:0445**
C_2H_4O	Acetaldehyde.........	**1:0100**
	Ethylene oxide........	**1:6105**
$(C_2H_4O)_n$	Metaldehyde.........	**1:0075**
$C_2H_4O_2$	Methyl formate.......	**1:1000**
	Acetic acid...........	**1:1010**
$C_2H_4O_3$	Glycolic acid..........	**1:0430**
C_2H_6O	Ethyl alcohol.........	**1:6130**
$C_2H_6O_2$	Ethylene glycol.......	**1:6465**
	C_3 GROUP	
C_3H_4O	Acrolein..............	**1:0115**
$C_3H_4O_2$	Acrylic acid...........	**1:1020**
$C_3H_4O_3$	Pyruvic acid..........	**1:1040**
$C_3H_4O_4$	Malonic acid..........	**1:0480**
$C_3H_4O_5$	Tartronic acid........	**1:0510**
C_3H_6O	Acetone..............	**1:5400**
	Allyl alcohol..........	**1:6145**
	Propionaldehyde......	**1:0110**
	Propylene oxide.......	**1:6115**
$C_3H_6O_2$	Acetol...............	**1:5455**
	Ethyl formate........	**1:3000**
	Methoxyacetaldehyde..	**1:0138**
	Methyl acetate........	**1:3005**
	Propionic acid........	**1:1025**
$C_3H_6O_3$	Dimethyl carbonate....	**1:3046**
	Ethylene glycol monoformate............	**1:3447**
	Glyceraldehyde.......	**1:0070**
	Lactic acid...........	**1:0400**
	Methoxyacetic acid....	**1:1065**
	Methyl glycolate......	**1:3286**
C_3H_8O	Ethyl methyl ether.....	**1:6100**
	Isopropyl alcohol......	**1:6135**
	n-Propyl alcohol.......	**1:6150**
$C_3H_8O_2$	Ethylene glycol monomethyl ether........	**1:6405**
	Methylal.............	**1:0105**
	Propylene glycol.......	**1:6455**
	Trimethylene glycol....	**1:6490**
$C_3H_8O_3$	Glycerol..............	**1:6540**
	C_4 GROUP	
$C_4H_2O_3$	Maleic anhydride......	**1:0625**
C_4H_4O	Furan................	**1:8015**
$C_4H_4O_3$	Succinic anhydride.....	**1:0710**
$C_4H_4O_4$	Fumaric acid..........	**1:0895**
	Glycolid..............	**1:0667**
	Maleic acid...........	**1:0470**
$(C_4H_4O_4)_x$	Polyglycolid...........	**1:4970**
C_4H_6	Butyne-1.............	**1:8000**
	Butyne-2.............	**1:8005**
C_4H_6O	Crotonaldehyde.......	**1:0150**
	Divinyl ether.........	**1:7800**
$C_4H_6O_2$	Allyl formate..........	**1:3035**
	Biacetyl..............	**1:9500**
	γ-Butyrolactone.......	**1:5070**
	α-Crotonic acid........	**1:0425**
	Isocrotonic acid.......	**1:1045**
	Methyl acrylate.......	**1:3025**
	Vinylacetic acid.......	**1:1042**
$C_4H_6O_3$	Acetic anhydride......	**1:1015**
	Methyl pyruvate......	**1:3201**

C_6 GROUP

C_7 GROUP

C_8 GROUP

C_{10} GROUP

C_{13} GROUP

C_{14} GROUP

C_{15} GROUP

C_{16} GROUP

B. ALPHABETICAL INDEX OF SPECIES OF ORDER I

C

D

E

F

G

I

N

O

P

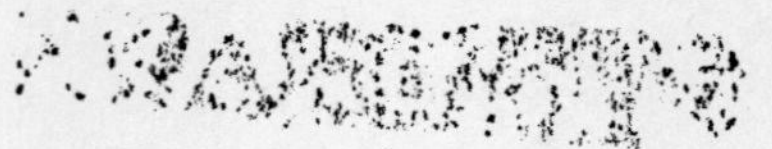